Electrical Costs with RSMeans Data

Chris Morris, Senior Editor

2017
40th annual edition

Engineering Director
Bob Mewis, CCP

Contributing Editors
Christopher Babbitt
Adrian C. Charest, PE
Cheryl Elsmore
John Gomes *(13, 41)*
Derrick Hale *(2, 31, 32, 33, 34, 35, 44, 46)*
Wafaa Hamitou *(11, 12)*
Joseph Kelble *(14, 23)*
Charles Kibbee *(1, 4)*
Robert J. Kuchta *(8)*
Gerard Lafond, PE
Michael Landry

Thomas Lane *(6, 7)*
Genevieve Medeiros
Elisa Mello
Ken Monty
Chris Morris *(26, 27, 28, 48)*
Dale Morris *(21, 22)*
Marilyn Phelan, AIA *(9, 10)*
Stephen C. Plotner *(3, 5)*
Stephen Rosenberg
Matthew Sorrentino
Kevin Souza
Tim Tonello
David Yazbek

Product Manager
Andrea Sillah

Production Manager
Debbie Panarelli

Production
Jonathan Forgit
Mary Lou Geary
Sharon Larsen
Sheryl Rose

Technical Support
Judy Abbruzzese
Gary L. Hoitt

Cover Design
Blaire Gaddis

Numbers in italics are the divisional responsibilities for each editor. Please contact the designated editor directly with any questions.

Gordian RSMeans Data
Construction Publishers & Consultants
1099 Hingham Street, Suite 201
Rockland, MA 02370
United States of America
1-800-448-8182
www.RSMeans.com

Printed in the United States of America
ISSN 1540-6318
ISBN 978-1-943215-52-2

0037 $241.99 per copy (in United States)
Price is subject to change without prior notice.

Related Data and Services

For procurement and construction cost data, such as Job Order Contracting and Change Order Management, please refer to Gordian's other offerings.

Our engineers, who are experts in RSMeans data, suggest the following products and services as companion information resources to *Electrical Costs with RSMeans Data:*

Construction Cost Data

Electric Change Order Costs with RSMeans Data 2017
Building Construction Costs with RSMeans Data 2017
Mechanical Costs with RSMeans Data 2017

Reference Books

Electrical Estimating Methods
Estimating Building Costs
RSMeans Estimating Handbook
Green Building: Project Planning & Estimating
How to Estimate with RSMeans Data
Plan Reading & Material Takeoff
Project Scheduling & Management for Construction

Seminars and In-House Training

Unit Price Estimating
Training for our online estimation solution
Practical Project Management for Construction Professionals
Scheduling with MSProject for Construction Professionals
Mechanical & Electrical Estimating

Online Store

Visit www.RSMeans.com for the most reliable and current resources available on the market. Learn more about our more than 20 data sets available in Online, Book, eBook, and CD formats. Our library of reference books is also available, along with professional development seminars aimed at improving cost estimating, project management, administration, and facilities management skills.

RSMeans Electronic Data

Receive the most up-to-date cost information with our online estimating solution. This web-based service is quick, intuitive, and easy to use, giving you instant access to our comprehensive database. Learn more at: **www.RSMeans.com/Online**.

Custom Solutions

Building owners, facility managers, building product manufacturers, attorneys, and even insurance firms across the public and private sectors have engaged in custom solutions to solve their estimating needs including:

Custom Cost Engineering Solutions

Knowing the lifetime maintenance cost of your building, how much it will cost to build a specific building type in different locations across the country and globe, and if the estimate from which you are basing a major decision is accurate are all imperative for building owners and their facility managers.

Market & Custom Analytics

Taking a construction product to market requires accurate market research in order to make critical business development decisions. Once the product goes to market, one way to differentiate your product from the competition is to make any cost saving claims you have to offer.

Third-Party Legal Resources

Natural disasters can lead to reconstruction and repairs just as new developments and expansions can lead to issues of eminent domain. In these cases where one party must pay, it is plausible for legal disputes over costs and estimates to arise.

Construction Costs for Software Applications

More than 25 unit price and assemblies cost databases are available through a number of leading estimating and facilities management software partners.

RSMeans data is also available to federal, state, and local government agencies as multi-year, multi-seat licenses.

For information on our current partners, call 1-800-448-8182.

Table of Contents

Foreword

Who We Are

Gordian was founded in the spirit of innovation and a strong commitment to help our clients reach and exceed their construction goals. In 1982, Gordian's Chairman and Founder, Harry H. Mellon, invented the family of contracting systems known as Job Order Contracting while serving as Chief Engineer at the Supreme Headquarters Allied Powers Europe in Mons, Belgium. Mr. Mellon realized facility and infrastructure owners could greatly benefit from the time and cost saving advantages of this cutting-edge construction procurement solution, and, in 1990, he started Gordian to provide these products and services for that purpose.

Since 1942, RSMeans data has been available for construction cost estimating information and consulting throughout North America, and is the industry standard for estimating. In 2014, Gordian combined two industry-leading construction cost data companies, enhancing the fortitude of its data with the addition of RSMeans. Today, Gordian draws on its highly specialized engineers, software and unique proprietary data sets to solve the construction information, planning and management needs of people in building construction, building products manufacturing, education, healthcare, retail, insurance, legal and government.

Our Offerings

Gordian is the leading provider of construction cost data, software and services to organizations pursuing efficiency and effectiveness throughout all phases of the construction lifecycle. From Planning, Design, and Procurement through Construction and, finally, Operations, Gordian's portfolio of solutions delivers accurate and up-to-date data to meet the needs of contractors, architects, engineers, facility owners, managers and others in the construction industry. Our products and services include Sightlines planning solutions, estimating solutions with RSMeans data and Job Order Contracting offerings from basic online services to enterprise solutions.

Our Commitment

Today at Gordian, we do more than talk about the quality of our data and the usefulness of its application. We stand behind all of our RSMeans data—from historical cost indexes to construction materials and techniques—to craft current costs and predict future trends.

If you have any questions about our products or services, please call us toll-free at 800-448-8182 or visit our website at: www.TheGordianGroup.com.

How the Cost Data Is Built: An Overview

A Powerful Construction Tool

You now have one of the most powerful construction tools available today. A successful project is built on the foundation of an accurate and dependable estimate. This tool will enable you to construct such an estimate.

For the casual user the information is designed to be:

- quickly and easily understood so you can get right to your estimate.
- filled with valuable information so you can understand the necessary factors that go into a cost estimate.

For the professional user, the information is designed to be:

- a handy reference that can be quickly referred to for key costs.
- a comprehensive, fully reliable source of current construction costs and productivity rates so you'll be prepared to estimate any project.
- a source for preliminary project costs, product selections, and alternate materials and methods.

To meet all of these requirements, we have organized the information into the following clearly defined sections.

Estimating with RSMeans Unit Price Cost Data*

Please refer to these steps for guidance on completing an estimate using RSMeans unit price cost data.

How to Use the Cost Data: The Details

This section contains an in-depth explanation of how the information is arranged and how you can use it to determine a reliable construction cost estimate. It includes how we develop our cost figures and how to prepare your estimate.

Unit Prices*

All cost data has been divided into 50 divisions according to the MasterFormat system of classification and numbering.

Assemblies*

The cost data in this section has been organized in an "Assemblies" format. These assemblies are the functional elements of a building and are arranged according to the 7 elements of the UNIFORMAT II classification system. For a complete explanation of a typical "Assembly", see "How RSMeans Assemblies Data Works."

Residential Models*

Model buildings for four classes of construction—economy, average, custom, and luxury—are developed and shown with complete costs per square foot.

Commercial/Industrial/Institutional Models*

This section contains complete costs for 77 typical model buildings expressed as costs per square foot.

Green Commercial/Industrial/Institutional Models*

This section contains complete costs for 25 green model buildings expressed as costs per square foot.

References*

This section includes information on Equipment Rental Costs, Crew Listings, Historical Cost Indexes, City Cost Indexes, Location Factors, Reference Tables, and Change Orders, as well as a listing of abbreviations.

- **Equipment Rental Costs:** Included are the average costs to rent and operate hundreds of pieces of construction equipment.
- **Crew Listings:** This section lists all the crews referenced in the cost data. A crew is composed of more than one trade classification and/or the addition of power equipment to any trade classification. Power equipment is included in the cost of the crew. Costs are shown both with bare labor rates and with the installing contractor's overhead and profit added. For each, the total crew cost per eight-hour day and the composite cost per labor-hour are listed.

- **Historical Cost Indexes:** These indexes provide you with data to adjust construction costs over time.
- **City Cost Indexes:** All costs in this data set are U.S. national averages. Costs vary by region. You can adjust for this by CSI Division to over 900 locations throughout the U.S. and Canada by using this data.
- **Location Factors:** You can adjust total project costs to over 900 locations throughout the U.S. and Canada by using the weighted number, which applies across all divisions.
- **Reference Tables:** At the beginning of selected major classifications in the Unit Prices are reference numbers indicators. These numbers refer you to related information in the Reference Section. In this section, you'll find reference tables, explanations, and estimating information that support how we develop the unit price data, technical data, and estimating procedures.
- **Change Orders:** This section includes information on the factors that influence the pricing of change orders.
- **Abbreviations:** A listing of abbreviations used throughout this information, along with the terms they represent, is included.

Index (printed versions only)

A comprehensive listing of all terms and subjects will help you quickly find what you need when you are not sure where it occurs in MasterFormat.

Conclusion

This information is designed to be as comprehensive and easy to use as possible.

The Construction Specifications Institute (CSI) and Construction Specifications Canada (CSC) have produced the 2014 edition of MasterFormat®, a system of titles and numbers used extensively to organize construction information.

All unit prices in the RSMeans cost data are now arranged in the 50-division MasterFormat® 2014 system.

---

* Not all information is available in all data sets

Note: The material prices in RSMeans cost data are "contractor's prices." They are the prices that contractors can expect to pay at the lumberyards, suppliers'/distributors' warehouses, etc. Small orders of specialty items would be higher than the costs shown, while very large orders, such as truckload lots, would be less. The variation would depend on the size, timing, and negotiating power of the contractor. The labor costs are primarily for new construction or major renovation rather than repairs or minor alterations. With reasonable exercise of judgment, the figures can be used for any building work.

Estimating with RSMeans Unit Price Cost Data

Following these steps will allow you to complete an accurate estimate using RSMeans Unit Price cost data.

1. Scope Out the Project
- Think through the project and identify the CSI Divisions needed in your estimate.
- Identify the individual work tasks that will need to be covered in your estimate.
- The Unit Price data has been divided into 50 Divisions according to the CSI MasterFormat® 2014.
- In printed versions, the Unit Price Section Table of Contents on page 1 may also be helpful when scoping out your project.
- Experienced estimators find it helpful to begin with Division 2 and continue through completion. Division 1 can be estimated after the full project scope is known.

2. Quantify
- Determine the number of units required for each work task that you identified.
- Experienced estimators include an allowance for waste in their quantities. (Waste is not included in our Unit Price line items unless otherwise stated.)

3. Price the Quantities
- Use the search tools available to locate individual Unit Price line items for your estimate.
- Reference Numbers indicated within a Unit Price section refer to additional information that you may find useful.
- The crew indicates who is performing the work for that task. Crew codes are expanded in the Crew Listings in the Reference Section to include all trades and equipment that comprise the crew.
- The Daily Output is the amount of work the crew is expected to complete in one day.
- The Labor-Hours value is the amount of time it will take for the crew to install one unit of work.
- The abbreviated Unit designation indicates the unit of measure upon which the crew, productivity, and prices are based.
- Bare Costs are shown for materials, labor, and equipment needed to complete the Unit Price line item. Bare costs do not include waste, project overhead, payroll insurance, payroll taxes, main office overhead, or profit.
- The Total Incl O&P cost is the billing rate or invoice amount of the installing contractor or subcontractor who performs the work for the Unit Price line item.

4. Multiply
- Multiply the total number of units needed for your project by the Total Incl O&P cost for each Unit Price line item.
- Be careful that your take off unit of measure matches the unit of measure in the Unit column.
- The price you calculate is an estimate for a completed item of work.
- Keep scoping individual tasks, determining the number of units required for those tasks, matching each task with individual Unit Price line items, and multiplying quantities by Total Incl O&P costs.
- An estimate completed in this manner is priced as if a subcontractor, or set of subcontractors, is performing the work. The estimate does not yet include Project Overhead or Estimate Summary components such as general contractor markups on subcontracted work, general contractor office overhead and profit, contingency, and location factors.

5. Project Overhead
- Include project overhead items from Division 1-General Requirements.
- These items are needed to make the job run. They are typically, but not always, provided by the general contractor. Items include, but are not limited to, field personnel, insurance, performance bond, permits, testing, temporary utilities, field office and storage facilities, temporary scaffolding and platforms, equipment mobilization and demobilization, temporary roads and sidewalks, winter protection, temporary barricades and fencing, temporary security, temporary signs, field engineering and layout, final cleaning, and commissioning.
- Each item should be quantified and matched to individual Unit Price line items in Division 1, then priced and added to your estimate.
- An alternate method of estimating project overhead costs is to apply a percentage of the total project cost, usually 5% to 15% with an average of 10% (see General Conditions).
- Include other project related expenses in your estimate such as:
  - Rented equipment not itemized in the Crew Listings
  - Rubbish handling throughout the project (see section 02 41 19.19)

6. Estimate Summary
- Include sales tax as required by laws of your state or county.
- Include the general contractor's markup on self-performed work, usually 5% to 15% with an average of 10%.
- Include the general contractor's markup on subcontracted work, usually 5% to 15% with an average of 10%.
- Include the general contractor's main office overhead and profit:
  - RSMeans data provides general guidelines on the general contractor's main office overhead (see section 01 31 13.60 and Reference Number R013113-50).
  - Markups will depend on the size of the general contractor's operations, projected annual revenue, the level of risk, and the level of competition in the local area and for this project in particular.
- Include a contingency, usually 3% to 5%, if appropriate.
- Adjust your estimate to the project's location by using the City Cost Indexes or the Location Factors in the Reference Section:
  - Look at the rules in "How to Use the City Cost Indexes" to see how to apply the Indexes for your location.
  - When the proper Index or Factor has been identified for the project's location, convert it to a multiplier by dividing it by 100, then multiply that multiplier by your estimated total cost. The original estimated total cost will now be adjusted up or down from the national average to a total that is appropriate for your location.

Editors' Note:
We urge you to spend time reading and
understanding the supporting material. An
accurate estimate requires experience, knowledge,
and careful calculation. The more you know about
how we at RSMeans developed the data, the more
accurate your estimate will be. In addition, it is
important to take into consideration the reference
material such as Equipment Listings, Crew
Listings, City Cost Indexes, Location Factors, and
Reference Tables.

How to Use the Cost Data: The Details

What's Behind the Numbers? The Development of Cost Data

Gordian's RSMeans staff continually monitors developments in the construction industry in order to ensure reliable, thorough, and up-to-date cost information. While overall construction costs may vary relative to general economic conditions, price fluctuations within the industry are dependent upon many factors. Individual price variations may, in fact, be opposite to overall economic trends. Therefore, costs are constantly tracked, and complete updates are performed yearly. Also, new items are frequently added in response to changes in materials and methods.

Costs—$ (U.S.)

All costs represent U.S. national averages and are given in U.S. dollars. The City Cost Index (CCI) with RSMeans data can be used to adjust costs to a particular location. The CCI for Canada can be used to adjust U.S. national averages to local costs in Canadian dollars. No exchange rate conversion is necessary because it has already been factored in.

G   The processes or products identified by the green symbol in our publications have been determined to be environmentally responsible and/or resource-efficient solely by Gordian's RSMeans engineering staff. The inclusion of the green symbol does not represent compliance with any specific industry association or standard.

Material Costs

Gordian's RSMeans staff contacts manufacturers, dealers, distributors, and contractors all across the U.S. and Canada to determine national average material costs. If you have access to current material costs for your specific location, you may wish to make adjustments to reflect differences from the national average. Included within material costs are fasteners for a normal installation. Gordian's RSMeans engineers use manufacturers' recommendations, written specifications, and/or standard construction practices for the sizing and spacing of fasteners. Adjustments to material costs may be required for your specific application or location. The manufacturer's warranty is assumed. Extended warranties are not included in the material costs. **Material costs do not include sales tax.**

Labor Costs

Labor costs are based upon a mathematical average of trade-specific wages in 30 major U.S. cities. The type of wage (union, open shop, or residential) is identified on the inside back cover of printed publications or is selected by the estimator when using the electronic products. Markups for the wages can also be found on the inside back cover of printed publications and/or under the labor references found in the electronic products.

- If wage rates in your area vary from those used, or if rate increases are expected within a given year, labor costs should be adjusted accordingly.

Labor costs reflect productivity based on actual working conditions. In addition to actual installation, these figures include time spent during a normal weekday on tasks, such as material receiving and handling, mobilization at site, site movement, breaks, and cleanup.

Productivity data is developed over an extended period so as not to be influenced by abnormal variations and reflects a typical average.

Equipment Costs

Equipment costs include not only rental, but also operating costs for equipment under normal use. The operating costs include parts and labor for routine servicing, such as repair and replacement of pumps, filters, and worn lines. Normal operating expendables, such as fuel, lubricants, tires, and electricity (where applicable), are also included. Extraordinary operating expendables with highly variable wear patterns, such as diamond bits and blades, are excluded. These costs are included under materials. Equipment rental rates are obtained from industry sources throughout North America—contractors, suppliers, dealers, manufacturers, and distributors.

Rental rates can also be treated as reimbursement costs for contractor-owned equipment. Owned equipment costs include depreciation, loan payments, interest, taxes, insurance, storage, and major repairs.

Equipment costs do not include operators' wages.

Equipment Cost/Day—The cost of equipment required for each crew is included in the Crew Listings in the Reference Section (small tools that are considered essential everyday tools are not listed out separately). The Crew Listings itemize specialized tools and heavy equipment along with labor trades. The daily cost of itemized equipment included in a crew is based on dividing the weekly bare rental rate by 5 (number of working days per week), then adding the hourly operating cost times 8 (the number of hours per day). This Equipment Cost/Day is shown in the last column of the Equipment Rental Costs in the Reference Section.

Mobilization, Demobilization—The cost to move construction equipment from an equipment yard or rental company to the job site and back again is not included in equipment costs. Mobilization (to the site) and demobilization (from the site) costs can be found in the Unit Price Section. If a piece of equipment is already at the job site, it is not appropriate to utilize mobilization or demobilization costs again in an estimate.

Overhead and Profit

Total Cost including O&P for the installing contractor is shown in the last column of the Unit Price and/or Assemblies. This figure is the sum of the bare material cost plus 10% for profit, the bare labor cost plus total overhead and profit, and the bare equipment cost plus 10% for profit. Details for the calculation of overhead and profit on labor are shown on the inside back cover of the printed product and in the Reference Section of the electronic product.

General Conditions

Cost data in this data set is presented in two ways: Bare Costs and Total Cost including O&P (Overhead and Profit). General Conditions, or General Requirements, of the contract should also be added to the Total Cost including O&P when applicable. Costs for General Conditions are listed in Division 1 of the Unit Price Section and in the Reference Section.

General Conditions for the installing contractor may range from 0% to 10% of the Total Cost including O&P. For the general or prime contractor, costs for General Conditions may range from 5% to 15% of the Total Cost including O&P, with a figure of 10% as the most typical allowance. If applicable, the Assemblies and Models sections use costs that include the installing contractor's overhead and profit (O&P).

Factors Affecting Costs

Costs can vary depending upon a number of variables. Here's a listing of some factors that affect costs and points to consider.

Quality—The prices for materials and the workmanship upon which productivity is based represent sound construction work. They are also in line with industry standard and manufacturer specifications and are frequently used by federal, state, and local governments.

Overtime—We have made no allowance for overtime. If you anticipate premium time or work beyond normal working hours, be sure to make an appropriate adjustment to your labor costs.

Productivity—The productivity, daily output, and labor-hour figures for each line item are based on working an eight-hour day in daylight hours in moderate temperatures, and up to a 14 foot working height unless otherwise indicated. For work that extends beyond normal work hours or is performed under adverse conditions, productivity may decrease.

Size of Project—The size, scope of work, and type of construction project will have a significant impact on cost. Economies of scale can reduce costs for large projects. Unit costs can often run higher for small projects.

Location—Material prices are for metropolitan areas. However, in dense urban areas, traffic and site storage limitations may increase costs. Beyond a 20-mile radius of metropolitan areas, extra trucking or transportation charges may also increase the material costs slightly. On the other hand, lower wage rates may be in effect. Be sure to consider both of these factors when preparing an estimate, particularly if the job site is located in a central city or remote rural location. In addition, highly specialized subcontract items may require travel and per-diem expenses for mechanics.

Other Factors—

- season of year
- contractor management
- weather conditions
- local union restrictions
- building code requirements
- availability of:
  - adequate energy
  - skilled labor
  - building materials
- owner's special requirements/restrictions
- safety requirements
- environmental considerations
- access

Unpredictable Factors—General business conditions influence "in-place" costs of all items. Substitute materials and construction methods may have to be employed. These may affect the installed cost and/or life cycle costs. Such factors may be difficult to evaluate and cannot necessarily be predicted on the basis of the job's location in a particular section of the country. Thus, where these factors apply, you may find significant but unavoidable cost variations for which you will have to apply a measure of judgment to your estimate.

Rounding of Costs

In printed publications only, all unit prices in excess of $5.00 have been rounded to make them easier to use and still maintain adequate precision of the results.

How Subcontracted Items Affect Costs

A considerable portion of all large construction jobs is usually subcontracted. In fact, the percentage done by subcontractors is constantly increasing and may run over 90%. Since the workers employed by these companies do nothing else but install their particular product, they soon become experts in that line. The result is, installation by these firms is accomplished so efficiently that the total in-place cost, even adding the general contractor's overhead and profit, is no more, and often less, than if the principal contractor had handled the installation. Companies that deal with construction specialties are anxious to have their product perform well and, consequently, the installation will be the best possible.

Contingencies

The allowance for contingencies generally provides for unforeseen construction difficulties. On alterations or repair jobs, 20% is not too much. If drawings are final and only field contingencies are being considered, 2% or 3% is probably sufficient, and often nothing needs to be added. Contractually, changes in plans will be covered by extras. The contractor should consider inflationary price trends and possible material shortages during the course of the job. These escalation factors are dependent upon both economic conditions and the anticipated time between the estimate and actual construction. If drawings are not complete or approved, or a budget cost is wanted, it is wise to add 5% to 10%. Contingencies, then, are a matter of judgment.

Important Estimating Considerations

The productivity, or daily output, of each craftsman or crew assumes a well-managed job where tradesmen with the proper tools and equipment, along with the appropriate construction materials, are present. Included are daily set-up and cleanup time, break time, and plan layout time. Unless otherwise indicated, time for material movement on site (for items that can be transported by hand) of up to 200' into the building and to the first or second floor is also included. If material has to be transported by other means, over greater distances, or to higher floors, an additional allowance should be considered by the estimator.

While horizontal movement is typically a sole function of distances, vertical transport introduces other variables that can significantly impact productivity. In an occupied building, the use of elevators (assuming access, size, and required protective measures are acceptable) must be understood at the time of the estimate. For new construction, hoist wait and cycle times can easily be 15 minutes and may result in scheduled access extending beyond the normal work day. Finally, all vertical transport will impose strict weight limits likely to preclude the use of any motorized material handling.

The productivity, or daily output, also assumes installation that meets manufacturer/designer/ standard specifications. A time allowance for quality control checks, minor adjustments, and any task required to ensure the proper function or operation is also included. For items that require connections to services, time is included for positioning, leveling, securing the unit, and for making all the necessary connections (and start up where applicable), ensuring a complete installation. Estimating of the services themselves (electrical, plumbing, water, steam, hydraulics, dust collection, etc.) is separate.

In some cases, the estimator must consider the use of a crane and an appropriate crew for the installation of large or heavy items. For those situations where a crane is not included in the assigned crew and as part of the line item

cost, equipment rental costs, mobilization and demobilization costs, and operator and support personnel costs must be considered.

Labor-Hours

The labor-hours expressed in this publication are derived by dividing the total daily labor-hours for the crew by the daily output. Based on average installation time and the assumptions listed above, the labor-hours include: direct labor, indirect labor, and nonproductive time. A typical day for a craftsman might include, but is not limited to:

- Direct Work
  - □ Measuring and layout
  - □ Preparing materials
  - □ Actual installation
  - □ Quality assurance/quality control
- Indirect Work
  - □ Reading plans or specifications
  - □ Preparing space
  - □ Receiving materials
  - □ Material movement
  - □ Giving or receiving instruction
  - □ Miscellaneous
- Non-Work
  - □ Chatting
  - □ Personal issues
  - □ Breaks
  - □ Interruptions (i.e., sickness, weather, material or equipment shortages, etc.)

If any of the items for a typical day do not apply to the particular work or project situation, the estimator should make any necessary adjustments.

Final Checklist

Estimating can be a straightforward process provided you remember the basics. Here's a checklist of some of the steps you should remember to complete before finalizing your estimate.

Did you remember to:

- factor in the City Cost Index for your locale?
- take into consideration which items have been marked up and by how much?
- mark up the entire estimate sufficiently for your purposes?
- read the background information on techniques and technical matters that could impact your project time span and cost?
- include all components of your project in the final estimate?
- double check your figures for accuracy?
- call Gordian's RSMeans staff if you have any questions about your estimate or the data you've used? Remember, Gordian stands behind all of our products, including our extensive RSMeans data solutions. If you have any questions about your estimate, about the costs you've used from our data, or even about the technical aspects of the job that may affect your estimate, feel free to call the Gordian RSMeans editors at 1-800-448-8182.

Free Quarterly Updates

Stay up-to-date throughout the year with free RSMeans cost data updates four times a year. Sign up online to make sure you have access to the newest data. Every quarter we provide the city cost adjustment factors for hundreds of cities and updated national average pricing for key materials.

Register at: **http://info.TheGordianGroup.com/ 2017-quarterly-updates.html**.

Unit Price Section

Table of Contents

How RSMeans Unit Price Data Works

All RSMeans unit price data is organized in the same way.

03 30 Cast-In-Place Concrete

03 30 53 – Miscellaneous Cast-In-Place Concrete

03 30 53.40 Concrete In Place	Crew	Daily Output	Labor-Hours	Unit	Material	2017 Bare Costs Labor	Equipment	Total	Total Incl O&P
0010 **CONCRETE IN PLACE**									
0020 Including forms (4 uses), Grade 60 rebar, concrete (Portland cement									
0050 Type I), placement and finishing unless otherwise indicated									
3540 Equipment pad (3000 psi), 3' x 3' x 6" thick	C-14H	45	1.067	Ea.	49	51.50	.63	101.13	133
3550 4' x 4' x 6" thick		30	1.600		73.50	77.50	.94	151.94	200
3560 5' x 5' x 8" thick		18	2.667		131	129	1.57	261.57	345
3570 6' x 6' x 8" thick		14	3.429		177	166	2.02	345.02	450
3580 8' x 8' x 10" thick		8	6		380	290	3.54	673.54	870
3590 10' x 10' x 12" thick		5	9.600		655	465	5.65	1,125.65	1,425
3800 Footings (3000 psi), spread under 1 C.Y.	C-14C	28	4	C.Y.	181	188	1	370	490
3825 1 C.Y. to 5 C.Y.		43	2.605		218	123	.65	341.65	430
3850 Over 5 C.Y.		75	1.493		201	70.50	.37	271.87	330
3900 Footings, strip (3000 psi), 18" x 9", unreinforced	C-14L	40	2.400		143	110	.70	253.70	325
3920 18" x 9", reinforced	C-14C	35	3.200		165	151	.80	316.80	415

It is important to understand the structure of RSMeans Unit Price data, so that you can find information easily and use it correctly.

① Line Numbers

Line Numbers consist of 12 characters, which identify a unique location in the database for each task. The first 6 or 8 digits conform to the Construction Specifications Institute MasterFormat® 2014. The remainder of the digits are a further breakdown in order to arrange items in understandable groups of similar tasks. Line numbers are consistent across all all of our publications, so a line number in any of our products will always refer to the same item of work.

② Descriptions

Descriptions are shown in a hierarchical structure to make them readable. In order to read a complete description, read up through the indents to the top of the section. Include everything that is above and to the left that is not contradicted by information below. For instance, the complete description for line 03 30 53.40 3550 is "Concrete in place, including forms (4 uses), Grade 60 rebar, concrete (Portland cement Type 1), placement and finishing unless otherwise indicated; Equipment pad (3000 psi), 4' × 4' × 6" thick."

③ RSMeans Data

When using **RSMeans data**, it is important to read through an entire section to ensure that you use the data that most closely matches your work. Note that sometimes there is additional information shown in the section that may improve your price. There are frequently lines that further describe, add to, or adjust data for specific situations.

④ Reference Information

Gordian's RSMeans engineers have created **reference** information to assist you in your estimate. **If** there is information that applies to a section, it will be indicated at the start of the section.

⑤ Crews

Crews include labor and/or equipment necessary to accomplish each task. In this case, Crew C-14H is used. Gordian's RSMeans staff selects a crew to represent the workers and equipment that are typically used for that task. In this case, Crew C-14H consists of one carpenter foreman (outside), two carpenters, one rodman, one laborer, one cement finisher, and one gas engine vibrator. Details of all crews can be found in the reference section.

Crews - Standard

Crew No.	Bare Costs		Incl. Subs O&P		Cost Per Labor-Hour	
Crew C-14H	Hr.	Daily	Hr.	Daily	Bare Costs	Incl. O&P
1 Carpenter Foreman (outside)	$51.25	$410.00	$78.50	$628.00	$48.33	$73.78
2 Carpenters	49.25	788.00	75.45	1207.20		
1 Rodman (reinf.)	54.30	434.40	83.70	669.60		
1 Laborer	39.15	313.20	60.00	480.00		
1 Cement Finisher	46.80	374.40	69.60	556.80		
1 Gas Engine Vibrator		28.25		31.07	.59	.65
48 L.H., Daily Totals		$2348.25		$3572.68	$48.92	$74.43

6 Daily Output

The **Daily Output** is the amount of work that the crew can do in a normal 8-hour workday, including mobilization, layout, movement of materials, and cleanup. In this case, crew C-14H can install thirty 4' × 4' × 6" thick concrete pads in a day. Daily output is variable and based on many factors, including the size of the job, location, and environmental conditions. RSMeans data represents work done in daylight (or adequate lighting) and temperate conditions.

7 Labor-Hours

The figure in the **Labor-Hours** column is the amount of labor required to perform one unit of work—in this case the amount of labor required to construct one 4' × 4' equipment pad. This figure is calculated by dividing the number of hours of labor in the crew by the daily output (48 labor-hours divided by 30 pads = 1.6 hours of labor per pad). Multiply 1.600 times 60 to see the value in minutes: 60 × 1.6 = 96

minutes. Note: the labor-hour figure is not dependent on the crew size. A change in crew size will result in a corresponding change in daily output, but the labor-hours per unit of work will not change.

8 Unit of Measure

All RSMeans unit cost data includes the typical **Unit of Measure** used for estimating that item. For concrete-in-place the typical unit is cubic yards (C.Y.) or each (Ea.). For installing broadloom carpet it is square yard, and for gypsum board it is square foot. The estimator needs to take special care that the unit in the data matches the unit in the take-off. Unit conversions may be found in the Reference Section.

9 Bare Costs

Bare Costs are the costs of materials, labor, and equipment that the installing contractor pays. They represent the cost, in U.S. dollars, for one unit of work. They do not include any markups for profit or labor burden.

10 Bare Total

The **Total column** represents the total bare cost for the installing contractor, in U.S. dollars. In this case, the sum of $73.50 for material + $77.50 for labor + $.94 for equipment is $151.94.

11 Total Incl O&P

The **Total Incl O&P column** is the total cost, including overhead and profit, that the installing contractor will charge the customer. This represents the cost of materials plus 10% profit, the cost of labor plus labor burden and 10% profit, and the cost of equipment plus 10% profit. It does not include the general contractor's overhead and profit. Note: See the inside back cover of the printed product or the reference section of the electronic product for details of how the labor burden is calculated.

National Average

*The RSMeans data in our print publications represents a "national average" cost. This data should be modified to the project location using the **City Cost Indexes** or **Location Factors** tables found in the Reference Section. Use the location factors to adjust estimate totals if the project covers multiple trades. Use the city cost indexes (CCI) for single trade*

projects or projects where a more detailed analysis is required. All figures in the two tables are derived from the same research. The last row of data in the CCI, the weighted average, is the same as the numbers reported for each location in the location factor table.

How RSMeans Unit Price Data Works (Continued)

①

Line Number	Description	Qty	Unit	Material	Labor	Equipment	SubContract	Estimate Total
	Project Name: Pre-Engineered Steel Building			**Architect: As Shown**				
	Location:	**Anywhere, USA**					**01/01/17**	**STD**
03 30 53.40 3940	Strip footing, 12" x 24", reinforced	34	C.Y.	$5,304.00	$3,740.00	$19.72	$0.00	
03 30 53.40 3950	Strip footing, 12" x 36", reinforced	15	C.Y.	$2,250.00	$1,320.00	$7.05	$0.00	
03 11 13.65 3000	Concrete slab edge forms	500	L.F.	$120.00	$1,245.00	$0.00	$0.00	
03 22 11.10 0200	Welded wire fabric reinforcing	150	C.S.F.	$2,820.00	$4,200.00	$0.00	$0.00	
03 31 13.35 0300	Ready mix concrete, 4000 psi for slab on grade	278	C.Y.	$34,750.00	$0.00	$0.00	$0.00	
03 31 13.70 4300	Place, strike off & consolidate concrete slab	278	C.Y.	$0.00	$4,948.40	$141.78	$0.00	
03 35 13.30 0250	Machine float & trowel concrete slab	15,000	S.F.	$0.00	$9,300.00	$450.00	$0.00	
03 15 16.20 0140	Cut control joints in concrete slab	950	L.F.	$47.50	$399.00	$85.50	$0.00	
03 39 23.13 0300	Sprayed concrete curing membrane	150	C.S.F.	$1,905.00	$990.00	$0.00	$0.00	
Division 03	**Subtotal**			**$47,196.50**	**$26,142.40**	**$704.05**	**$0.00**	**$74,042.95**
08 36 13.10 2650	Manual 10' x 10' steel sectional overhead door	8	Ea.	$10,000.00	$3,520.00	$0.00	$0.00	
08 36 13.10 2860	Insulation and steel back panel for OH door	800	S.F.	$3,800.00	$0.00	$0.00	$0.00	
Division 08	**Subtotal**			**$13,800.00**	**$3,520.00**	**$0.00**	**$0.00**	**$17,320.00**
13 34 19.50 1100	Pre-Engineered Steel Building, 100' x 150' x 24'	15,000	SF Flr.	$0.00	$0.00	$0.00	$367,500.00	
13 34 19.50 6050	Framing for PESB door opening, 3' x 7'	4	Opng.	$0.00	$0.00	$0.00	$2,240.00	
13 34 19.50 6100	Framing for PESB door opening, 10' x 10'	8	Opng.	$0.00	$0.00	$0.00	$9,200.00	
13 34 19.50 6200	Framing for PESB window opening, 4' x 3'	6	Opng.	$0.00	$0.00	$0.00	$3,300.00	
13 34 19.50 5750	PESB door, 3' x 7', single leaf	4	Opng.	$2,460.00	$696.00	$0.00	$0.00	
13 34 19.50 7750	PESB sliding window, 4' x 3' with screen	6	Opng.	$2,490.00	$597.00	$66.00	$0.00	
13 34 19.50 6550	PESB gutter, eave type, 26 ga., painted	300	L.F.	$2,190.00	$816.00	$0.00	$0.00	
13 34 19.50 8650	PESB roof vent, 12" wide x 10' long	15	Ea.	$547.50	$3,255.00	$0.00	$0.00	
13 34 19.50 6900	PESB insulation, vinyl faced, 4" thick	27,400	S.F.	$12,878.00	$9,316.00	$0.00	$0.00	
Division 13	**Subtotal**			**$20,565.50**	**$14,680.00**	**$66.00**	**$382,240.00**	**$417,551.50**
			Subtotal	**$81,562.00**	**$44,342.40**	**$770.05**	**$382,240.00**	**$508,914.45**
Division 01 **②**	General Requirements @ 7%			5,709.34	3,103.97	53.90	26,756.80	
			Estimate Subtotal	$87,271.34	$47,446.37	$823.95	$408,996.80	$508,914.45
	③		Sales Tax @ 5%	4,363.57		41.20	10,224.92	
			Subtotal A	91,634.91	47,446.37	865.15	419,221.72	
	④		GC O & P	9,163.49	25,573.59	86.52	41,922.17	
			Subtotal B	100,798.40	73,019.96	951.67	461,143.89	$635,913.92
	⑤		Contingency @ 5%					31,795.70
			Subtotal C					$667,709.61
	⑥		Bond @ $12/1000 +10% O&P					8,813.77
			Subtotal D					$676,523.38
	⑦		Location Adjustment Factor	102.30				15,560.04
			Grand Total					$692,083.42

This estimate is based on an interactive spreadsheet. A copy of this spreadsheet is located at
www.RSMeans.com/2017samples. You are free to download it and adjust it to your methodology.

Sample Estimate

This sample demonstrates the elements of an estimate, including a tally of the RSMeans data lines and a summary of the markups on a contractor's work to arrive at a total cost to the owner. The Location Factor with RSMeans data is added at the bottom of the estimate to adjust the cost of the work to a specific location.

---

① Work Performed

The body of the estimate shows the RSMeans data selected, including the line number, a brief description of each item, its take-off unit and quantity, and the bare costs of materials, labor, and equipment. This estimate also includes a column titled "SubContract." This data is taken from the column "Total Incl O&P" and represents the total that a subcontractor would charge a general contractor for the work, including the sub's markup for overhead and profit.

② Division 1, General Requirements

This is the first division numerically but the last division estimated. Division 1 includes project-wide needs provided by the general contractor. These requirements vary by project but may include temporary facilities and utilities, security, testing, project cleanup, etc. For small projects a percentage can be used, typically between 5% and 15% of project cost. For large projects the costs may be itemized and priced individually.

③ Sales Tax

If the work is subject to state or local sales taxes, the amount must be added to the estimate. Sales tax may be added to material costs, equipment costs, and subcontracted work. In this case, sales tax was added in all three categories. It was assumed that approximately half the subcontracted work would be material cost, so the tax was applied to 50% of the subcontract total.

④ GC O&P

This entry represents the general contractor's markup on material, labor, equipment, and subcontractor costs. Our standard markup on materials, equipment, and subcontracted work is 10%. In this estimate, the markup on the labor performed by the GC's workers uses "Skilled Workers Average" shown in Column F on the table "Installing Contractor's Overhead & Profit," which can be found on the inside-back cover of the printed product or in the Reference Section of the electronic product.

⑤ Contingency

A factor for contingency may be added to any estimate to represent the cost of unknowns that may occur between the time that the estimate is performed and the time the project is constructed. The amount of the allowance will depend on the stage of design at which the estimate is done and the contractor's assessment of the risk involved. Refer to section 01 21 16.50 for contingency allowances.

⑥ Bonds

Bond costs should be added to the estimate. The figures here represent a typical performance bond, ensuring the owner that if the general contractor does not complete the obligations in the construction contract the bonding company will pay the cost for completion of the work.

⑦ Location Adjustment

RSMeans published data is based on national average costs. If necessary, adjust the total cost of the project using a location factor from the "Location Factor" table or the "City Cost Index" table. Use location factors if the work is general, covering multiple trades. If the work is by a single trade (e.g., masonry) use the more specific data found in the "City Cost Indexes."

Estimating Tips
01 20 00 Price and Payment Procedures

- Allowances that should be added to estimates to cover contingencies and job conditions that are not included in the national average material and labor costs are shown in Section 01 21.

- When estimating historic preservation projects (depending on the condition of the existing structure and the owner's requirements), a 15%–20% contingency or allowance is recommended, regardless of the stage of the drawings.

01 30 00 Administrative Requirements

- Before determining a final cost estimate, it is a good practice to review all the items listed in Subdivisions 01 31 and 01 32 to make final adjustments for items that may need customizing to specific job conditions.

- Requirements for initial and periodic submittals can represent a significant cost to the General Requirements of a job. Thoroughly check the submittal specifications when estimating a project to determine any costs that should be included.

01 40 00 Quality Requirements

- All projects will require some degree of quality control. This cost is not included in the unit cost of construction listed in each division. Depending upon the terms of the contract, the various costs of inspection and testing can be the responsibility of either the owner or the contractor. Be sure to include the required costs in your estimate.

01 50 00 Temporary Facilities and Controls

- Barricades, access roads, safety nets, scaffolding, security, and many more requirements for the execution of a safe project are elements of direct cost. These costs can easily be overlooked when preparing an estimate. When looking through the major classifications of this subdivision, determine which items apply to each division in your estimate.

- Construction equipment rental costs can be found in the Reference Section in Section 01 54 33. Operators' wages are not included in equipment rental costs.

- Equipment mobilization and demobilization costs are not included in equipment rental costs and must be considered separately.

- The cost of small tools provided by the installing contractor for his workers is covered in the "Overhead" column on the "Installing Contractor's Overhead and Profit" table that lists labor trades, base rates, and markups and, therefore, is included in the "Total Incl. O&P" cost of any unit price line item.

01 70 00 Execution and Closeout Requirements

- When preparing an estimate, thoroughly read the specifications to determine the requirements for Contract Closeout. Final cleaning, record documentation, operation and maintenance data, warranties and bonds, and spare parts and maintenance materials can all be elements of cost for the completion of a contract. Do not overlook these in your estimate.

Reference Numbers

Reference numbers are shown at the beginning of some major classifications. These numbers refer to related items in the Reference Section. The reference information may be an estimating procedure, an alternate pricing method, or technical information.

Note: Not all subdivisions listed here necessarily appear. ∎

Did you know?

Our online estimating solution gives you the same access to RSMeans' data with 24/7 access:

- Quickly locate costs in the searchable database.

- Build cost lists, estimates, and reports in minutes.

- Adjust costs to any location in the U.S. and Canada with the click of a button.

Start your free trial today at
www.RSMeansOnline.com

01 11 Summary of Work

01 11 31 – Professional Consultants

01 11 31.20 Construction Management Fees	Crew	Daily Output	Labor-Hours	Unit	Material	2017 Bare Costs Labor	Equipment	Total	Total Incl O&P
0010 **CONSTRUCTION MANAGEMENT FEES**									
0020 $1,000,000 job, minimum				Project				4.50%	4.50%
0050 Maximum								7.50%	7.50%
0060 For work to $100,000								10%	10%
0300 $50,000,000 job, minimum								2.50%	2.50%
0350 Maximum								4%	4%

01 11 31.30 Engineering Fees

	Crew	Daily Output	Labor-Hours	Unit	Material	2017 Bare Costs Labor	Equipment	Total	Total Incl O&P
0010 **ENGINEERING FEES** R011110-30									
0020 Educational planning consultant, minimum				Project				.50%	.50%
0100 Maximum				"				2.50%	2.50%
0200 Electrical, minimum				Contrct				4.10%	4.10%
0300 Maximum								10.10%	10.10%
0400 Elevator & conveying systems, minimum								2.50%	2.50%
0500 Maximum								5%	5%
0600 Food service & kitchen equipment, minimum								8%	8%
0700 Maximum								12%	12%
1000 Mechanical (plumbing & HVAC), minimum								4.10%	4.10%
1100 Maximum								10.10%	10.10%

01 21 Allowances

01 21 16 – Contingency Allowances

01 21 16.50 Contingencies

	Crew	Daily Output	Labor-Hours	Unit	Material	2017 Bare Costs Labor	Equipment	Total	Total Incl O&P
0010 **CONTINGENCIES**, Add to estimate									
0020 Conceptual stage				Project				20%	20%
0050 Schematic stage								15%	15%
0100 Preliminary working drawing stage (Design Dev.)								10%	10%
0150 Final working drawing stage								3%	3%

01 21 53 – Factors Allowance

01 21 53.50 Factors

	Crew	Daily Output	Labor-Hours	Unit	Material	2017 Bare Costs Labor	Equipment	Total	Total Incl O&P
0010 **FACTORS** Cost adjustments									
0100 Add to construction costs for particular job requirements									
0500 Cut & patch to match existing construction, add, minimum				Costs	2%	3%			
0550 Maximum					5%	9%			
0800 Dust protection, add, minimum					1%	2%			
0850 Maximum					4%	11%			
1100 Equipment usage curtailment, add, minimum					1%	1%			
1150 Maximum					3%	10%			
1400 Material handling & storage limitation, add, minimum					1%	1%			
1450 Maximum					6%	7%			
1700 Protection of existing work, add, minimum					2%	2%			
1750 Maximum					5%	7%			
2000 Shift work requirements, add, minimum						5%			
2050 Maximum						30%			
2300 Temporary shoring and bracing, add, minimum					2%	5%			
2350 Maximum					5%	12%			

01 21 53.60 Security Factors

	Crew	Daily Output	Labor-Hours	Unit	Material	2017 Bare Costs Labor	Equipment	Total	Total Incl O&P
0010 **SECURITY FACTORS**									
0100 Additional costs due to security requirements									
0110 Daily search of personnel, supplies, equipment and vehicles									
0120 Physical search, inventory and doc of assets, at entry				Costs		30%			

01 21 Allowances

01 21 53 – Factors Allowance

01 21 53.60 Security Factors

		Crew	Daily Output	Labor-Hours	Unit	Material	2017 Bare Costs Labor	Equipment	Total	Total Incl O&P
0130	At entry and exit				Costs		50%			
0140	Physical search, at entry						6.25%			
0150	At entry and exit						12.50%			
0160	Electronic scan search, at entry						2%			
0170	At entry and exit						4%			
0180	Visual inspection only, at entry						.25%			
0190	At entry and exit						.50%			
0200	ID card or display sticker only, at entry						.12%			
0210	At entry and exit				↓		.25%			
0220	Day 1 as described below, then visual only for up to 5 day job duration									
0230	Physical search, inventory and doc of assets, at entry				Costs		5%			
0240	At entry and exit						10%			
0250	Physical search, at entry						1.25%			
0260	At entry and exit						2.50%			
0270	Electronic scan search, at entry						.42%			
0280	At entry and exit				↓		.83%			
0290	Day 1 as described below, then visual only for 6-10 day job duration									
0300	Physical search, inventory and doc of assets, at entry				Costs		2.50%			
0310	At entry and exit						5%			
0320	Physical search, at entry						.63%			
0330	At entry and exit						1.25%			
0340	Electronic scan search, at entry						.21%			
0350	At entry and exit				↓		.42%			
0360	Day 1 as described below, then visual only for 11-20 day job duration									
0370	Physical search, inventory and doc of assets, at entry				Costs		1.25%			
0380	At entry and exit						2.50%			
0390	Physical search, at entry						.31%			
0400	At entry and exit						.63%			
0410	Electronic scan search, at entry						.10%			
0420	At entry and exit				↓		.21%			
0430	Beyond 20 days, costs are negligible									
0440	Escort required to be with tradesperson during work effort				Costs		6.25%			

01 21 55 – Job Conditions Allowance

01 21 55.50 Job Conditions

		Crew	Daily Output	Labor-Hours	Unit	Material	2017 Bare Costs Labor	Equipment	Total	Total Incl O&P
0010	**JOB CONDITIONS** Modifications to applicable									
0020	cost summaries									
0100	Economic conditions, favorable, deduct				Project				2%	2%
0200	Unfavorable, add								5%	5%
0300	Hoisting conditions, favorable, deduct								2%	2%
0400	Unfavorable, add								5%	5%
0700	Labor availability, surplus, deduct								1%	1%
0800	Shortage, add								10%	10%
0900	Material storage area, available, deduct								1%	1%
1000	Not available, add								2%	2%
1100	Subcontractor availability, surplus, deduct								5%	5%
1200	Shortage, add								12%	12%
1300	Work space, available, deduct								2%	2%
1400	Not available, add				↓				5%	5%

01 21 Allowances

01 21 57 – Overtime Allowance

01 21 57.50 Overtime		Crew	Daily Output	Labor-Hours	Unit	Material	2017 Bare Costs Labor	Equipment	Total	Total Incl O&P
0010	**OVERTIME** for early completion of projects or where	R012909-90								
0020	labor shortages exist, add to usual labor, up to					Costs		100%			

01 21 63 – Taxes

01 21 63.10 Taxes

0010	**TAXES**	R012909-80								
0020	Sales tax, State, average					%	5.08%			
0050	Maximum	R012909-85					7.50%			
0200	Social Security, on first $118,500 of wages							7.65%		
0300	Unemployment, combined Federal and State, minimum							.60%		
0350	Average							9.60%		
0400	Maximum							12%		

01 31 Project Management and Coordination

01 31 13 – Project Coordination

01 31 13.20 Field Personnel

		Crew	Daily Output	Labor-Hours	Unit	Material	Labor	Equipment	Total	Total Incl O&P
0010	**FIELD PERSONNEL**									
0020	Clerk, average				Week		475		475	730
0100	Field engineer, minimum						1,125		1,125	1,725
0120	Average						1,475		1,475	2,275
0140	Maximum						1,675		1,675	2,575
0160	General purpose laborer, average						1,575		1,575	2,400
0180	Project manager, minimum						2,100		2,100	3,225
0200	Average						2,400		2,400	3,700
0220	Maximum						2,750		2,750	4,225
0240	Superintendent, minimum						2,050		2,050	3,150
0260	Average						2,250		2,250	3,450
0280	Maximum						2,550		2,550	3,925
0290	Timekeeper, average						1,300		1,300	2,000

01 31 13.30 Insurance

0010	**INSURANCE**	R013113-40								
0020	Builders risk, standard, minimum					Job				.24%	.24%
0050	Maximum	R013113-60							.64%	.64%
0200	All-risk type, minimum									.25%	.25%
0250	Maximum									.62%	.62%
0400	Contractor's equipment floater, minimum					Value				.50%	.50%
0450	Maximum					"				1.50%	1.50%
0600	Public liability, average					Job				2.02%	2.02%
0800	Workers' compensation & employer's liability, average										
0850	by trade, carpentry, general					Payroll	13.93%			
1000	Electrical						5.52%			
1150	Insulation						11.13%			
1450	Plumbing						6.94%			
1550	Sheet metal work (HVAC)						8.82%			

01 31 13.50 General Contractor's Mark-Up

0010	**GENERAL CONTRACTOR'S MARK-UP** on Change Orders									
0200	Extra work, by subcontractors, add					%				10%	10%
0250	By General Contractor, add									15%	15%
0400	Omitted work, by subcontractors, deduct all but									5%	5%
0450	By General Contractor, deduct all but									7.50%	7.50%

10

01 31 Project Management and Coordination

01 31 13 – Project Coordination

01 31 13.50 General Contractor's Mark-Up

	Crew	Daily Output	Labor-Hours	Unit	Material	2017 Bare Costs Labor	Equipment	Total	Total Incl O&P
0600	Overtime work, by subcontractors, add				%				15%	15%
0650	By General Contractor, add								10%	10%

01 31 13.60 General Contractor's Main Office Overhead

0010	**GENERAL CONTRACTOR'S MAIN OFFICE OVERHEAD**								
0020	As percent of direct costs, minimum				%				5%	
0050	Average								13%	
0100	Maximum								30%	

01 31 13.80 Overhead and Profit

0010	**OVERHEAD & PROFIT** Allowance to add to items in this								
0020	book that do not include Subs O&P, average				%				25%	
0100	Allowance to add to items in this book that								
0110	do include Subs O&P, minimum				%				5%	5%
0150	Average								10%	10%
0200	Maximum								15%	15%
0300	Typical, by size of project, under $100,000								30%	
0350	$500,000 project								25%	
0400	$2,000,000 project								20%	
0450	Over $10,000,000 project								15%	

01 31 13.90 Performance Bond

0010	**PERFORMANCE BOND** R013113-80								
0020	For buildings, minimum				Job				.60%	.60%
0100	Maximum				"				2.50%	2.50%

01 32 Construction Progress Documentation

01 32 33 – Photographic Documentation

01 32 33.50 Photographs

	Crew	Daily Output	Labor-Hours	Unit	Material	2017 Bare Costs Labor	Equipment	Total	Total Incl O&P
0010	**PHOTOGRAPHS**									
0020	8" x 10", 4 shots, 2 prints ea., std. mounting				Set	535			535	590
0100	Hinged linen mounts					540			540	595
0200	8" x 10", 4 shots, 2 prints each, in color					495			495	545
0300	For I.D. slugs, add to all above					5			5	5.50
1500	Time lapse equipment, camera and projector, buy				Ea.	2,700			2,700	2,975
1550	Rent per month				"	1,275			1,275	1,400
1700	Cameraman and processing, black & white				Day	1,250			1,250	1,375
1720	Color				"	1,450			1,450	1,600

01 41 Regulatory Requirements

01 41 26 – Permit Requirements

01 41 26.50 Permits

0010	**PERMITS**								
0020	Rule of thumb, most cities, minimum				Job				.50%	.50%
0100	Maximum				"				2%	2%

For customer support on your Electrical Costs with RSMeans Data, call 800.448.8182.

11

01 51 Temporary Utilities

01 51 13 – Temporary Electricity

01 51 13.50 Temporary Power Equip (Pro-Rated Per Job)	Crew	Daily Output	Labor-Hours	Unit	Material	2017 Bare Costs Labor	Equipment	Total	Total Incl O&P
0010 **TEMPORARY POWER EQUIP (PRO-RATED PER JOB)** R015113-65									
0020 Service, overhead feed, 3 use									
0030 100 Amp	1 Elec	1.25	6.400	Ea.	415	360		775	1,000
0040 200 Amp		1	8		515	455		970	1,250
0050 400 Amp		.75	10.667		905	605		1,510	1,900
0060 600 Amp		.50	16		1,300	905		2,205	2,775
0100 Underground feed, 3 use									
0110 100 Amp	1 Elec	2	4	Ea.	405	226		631	785
0120 200 Amp		1.15	6.957		540	395		935	1,175
0130 400 Amp		1	8		930	455		1,385	1,700
0140 600 Amp		.75	10.667		1,150	605		1,755	2,175
0150 800 Amp		.50	16		1,675	905		2,580	3,200
0160 1000 Amp		.35	22.857		1,900	1,300		3,200	4,025
0170 1200 Amp		.25	32		2,100	1,800		3,900	5,025
0180 2000 Amp		.20	40		2,575	2,275		4,850	6,225
0200 Transformers, 3 use									
0210 30 kVA	1 Elec	1	8	Ea.	1,750	455		2,205	2,600
0220 45 kVA		.75	10.667		2,075	605		2,680	3,200
0230 75 kVA		.50	16		3,525	905		4,430	5,250
0240 112.5 kVA		.40	20		3,800	1,125		4,925	5,875
0250 Feeder, PVC, CU wire in trench									
0260 60 Amp	1 Elec	96	.083	L.F.	3.24	4.72		7.96	10.60
0270 100 Amp		85	.094		5.70	5.35		11.05	14.25
0280 200 Amp		59	.136		13.30	7.65		20.95	26
0290 400 Amp		42	.190		33	10.80		43.80	52.50
0300 Feeder, PVC, aluminum wire in trench									
0310 60 Amp	1 Elec	96	.083	L.F.	4.11	4.72		8.83	11.60
0320 100 Amp		85	.094		4.63	5.35		9.98	13.10
0330 200 Amp		59	.136		10.10	7.65		17.75	22.50
0340 400 Amp		42	.190		20.50	10.80		31.30	38.50
0350 Feeder, EMT, CU wire									
0360 60 Amp	1 Elec	90	.089	L.F.	3.01	5.05		8.06	10.85
0370 100 Amp		80	.100		5.75	5.65		11.40	14.85
0380 200 Amp		60	.133		13.40	7.55		20.95	26
0390 400 Amp		35	.229		38.50	12.95		51.45	62
0400 Feeder, EMT, aluminum wire									
0410 60 Amp	1 Elec	90	.089	L.F.	4.88	5.05		9.93	12.90
0420 100 Amp		80	.100		6.10	5.65		11.75	15.20
0430 200 Amp		60	.133		15.30	7.55		22.85	28
0440 400 Amp		35	.229		27.50	12.95		40.45	49.50
0500 Equipment, 3 use									
0510 Spider box, 50 Amp	1 Elec	8	1	Ea.	975	56.50		1,031.50	1,150
0520 Lighting cord, 100'		8	1		121	56.50		177.50	218
0530 Light stanchion		8	1		73.50	56.50		130	166
0540 Temporary cords, 100', 3 use									
0550 Feeder cord, 50 Amp	1 Elec	16	.500	Ea.	515	28.50		543.50	610
0560 Feeder cord, 100 Amp		12	.667		1,175	37.50		1,212.50	1,350
0570 Tap cord, 50 Amp		12	.667		233	37.50		270.50	315
0580 Tap cord, 100 Amp		6	1.333		1,175	75.50		1,250.50	1,425
0590 Temporary cords, 50', 3 use									
0600 Feeder cord, 50 Amp	1 Elec	16	.500	Ea.	230	28.50		258.50	296
0610 Feeder cord, 100 Amp		12	.667		685	37.50		722.50	805
0620 Tap cord, 50 Amp		12	.667		124	37.50		161.50	193

01 51 Temporary Utilities

01 51 13 – Temporary Electricity

01 51 13.50 Temporary Power Equip (Pro-Rated Per Job)

		Crew	Daily Output	Labor-Hours	Unit	Material	2017 Bare Costs Labor	Equipment	Total	Total Incl O&P
0630	Tap cord, 100 Amp	1 Elec	6	1.333	Ea.	685	75.50		760.50	865
0700	Connections									
0710	Compressor or pump									
0720	30 Amp	1 Elec	7	1.143	Ea.	18.55	64.50		83.05	118
0730	60 Amp		5.30	1.509		23	85.50		108.50	154
0740	100 Amp		4	2		53	113		166	229
0750	Tower crane									
0760	60 Amp	1 Elec	4.50	1.778	Ea.	23	101		124	177
0770	100 Amp	"	3	2.667	"	53	151		204	285
0780	Manlift									
0790	Single	1 Elec	3	2.667	Ea.	37	151		188	267
0800	Double	"	2	4	"	71	226		297	420
0810	Welder with disconnect									
0820	50 Amp	1 Elec	5	1.600	Ea.	209	90.50		299.50	365
0830	100 Amp		3.80	2.105		360	119		479	575
0840	200 Amp		2.50	3.200		670	181		851	1,000
0850	400 Amp		1	8		1,550	455		2,005	2,375
0860	Office trailer									
0870	60 Amp	1 Elec	4.50	1.778	Ea.	61	101		162	219
0880	100 Amp		3	2.667		97.50	151		248.50	335
0890	200 Amp		2	4		325	226		551	700
0900	Lamping, add per floor				Total				625	690
0910	Maintenance, total temp. power cost				Job				5%	5%

01 51 13.80 Temporary Utilities

		Crew	Daily Output	Labor-Hours	Unit	Material	2017 Bare Costs Labor	Equipment	Total	Total Incl O&P
0010	**TEMPORARY UTILITIES**									
0350	Lighting, lamps, wiring, outlets, 40,000 S.F. building, 8 strings	1 Elec	34	.235	CSF Flr	5	13.30		18.30	25.50
0360	16 strings	"	17	.471		10	26.50		36.50	51
0400	Power for temp lighting only, 6.6 KWH, per month								.92	1.01
0430	11.8 KWH, per month								1.65	1.82
0450	23.6 KWH, per month								3.30	3.63
0600	Power for job duration incl. elevator, etc., minimum								47	51.50
0650	Maximum								110	121
1000	Toilet, portable, see Equip. Rental 01 54 33 in Reference Section									

01 52 Construction Facilities

01 52 13 – Field Offices and Sheds

01 52 13.20 Office and Storage Space

		Crew	Daily Output	Labor-Hours	Unit	Material	2017 Bare Costs Labor	Equipment	Total	Total Incl O&P
0010	**OFFICE AND STORAGE SPACE**									
0020	Office trailer, furnished, no hookups, 20' x 8', buy	2 Skwk	1	16	Ea.	10,800	825		11,625	13,100
0250	Rent per month					195			195	214
0300	32' x 8', buy	2 Skwk	.70	22.857		16,000	1,175		17,175	19,400
0350	Rent per month					250			250	275
0400	50' x 10', buy	2 Skwk	.60	26.667		24,700	1,375		26,075	29,300
0450	Rent per month					355			355	390
0500	50' x 12', buy	2 Skwk	.50	32		30,200	1,650		31,850	35,700
0550	Rent per month					440			440	485
0700	For air conditioning, rent per month, add					49			49	54
0800	For delivery, add per mile				Mile	11			11	12.10
0890	Delivery each way				Ea.	1,650			1,650	1,800
0900	Bunk house trailer, 8' x 40' duplex dorm with kitchen, no hookups, buy	2 Carp	1	16		86,000	790		86,790	95,500
0910	9 man with kitchen and bath, no hookups, buy		1	16		90,500	790		91,290	100,500

For customer support on your Electrical Costs with RSMeans Data, call 800.448.8182.

13

01 52 Construction Facilities

01 52 13 – Field Offices and Sheds

01 52 13.20 Office and Storage Space

01 52 13.20 Office and Storage Space	Crew	Daily Output	Labor-Hours	Unit	Material	2017 Bare Costs Labor	2017 Bare Costs Equipment	Total	Total Incl O&P
0920	18 man sleeper with bath, no hookups, buy	2 Carp	1	16	Ea.	95,000	790		95,790	105,500
1000	Portable buildings, prefab, on skids, economy, 8' x 8'		265	.060	S.F.	24	2.97		26.97	31
1100	Deluxe, 8' x 12'		150	.107	"	19.60	5.25		24.85	29.50
1200	Storage boxes, 20' x 8', buy	2 Skwk	1.80	8.889	Ea.	3,025	455		3,480	4,025
1250	Rent per month					81			81	89
1300	40' x 8', buy	2 Skwk	1.40	11.429		3,900	590		4,490	5,175
1350	Rent per month					110			110	121

01 52 13.40 Field Office Expense

01 52 13.40 Field Office Expense	Crew	Daily Output	Labor-Hours	Unit	Material	2017 Bare Costs Labor	2017 Bare Costs Equipment	Total	Total Incl O&P
0010	**FIELD OFFICE EXPENSE**									
0100	Office equipment rental average				Month	205			205	226
0120	Office supplies, average				"	82			82	90
0125	Office trailer rental, see Section 01 52 13.20									
0140	Telephone bill; avg. bill/month incl. long dist.				Month	86			86	94.50
0160	Lights & HVAC				"	161			161	177

01 54 Construction Aids

01 54 16 – Temporary Hoists

01 54 16.50 Weekly Forklift Crew

01 54 16.50 Weekly Forklift Crew	Crew	Daily Output	Labor-Hours	Unit	Material	2017 Bare Costs Labor	2017 Bare Costs Equipment	Total	Total Incl O&P
0010	**WEEKLY FORKLIFT CREW**									
0100	All-terrain forklift, 45' lift, 35' reach, 9000 lb. capacity	A-3P	.20	40	Week		2,050	2,600	4,650	5,950

01 54 19 – Temporary Cranes

01 54 19.50 Daily Crane Crews

01 54 19.50 Daily Crane Crews	Crew	Daily Output	Labor-Hours	Unit	Material	2017 Bare Costs Labor	2017 Bare Costs Equipment	Total	Total Incl O&P
0010	**DAILY CRANE CREWS** for small jobs, portal to portal									
0100	12-ton truck-mounted hydraulic crane	A-3H	1	8	Day		445	770	1,215	1,525
0200	25-ton	A-3I	1	8			445	905	1,350	1,675
0300	40-ton	A-3J	1	8			445	1,350	1,795	2,175
0400	55-ton	A-3K	1	16			830	1,600	2,430	3,025
0500	80-ton	A-3L	1	16			830	2,400	3,230	3,900
0900	If crane is needed on a Saturday, Sunday or Holiday									
0910	At time-and-a-half, add				Day		50%			
0920	At double time, add				"		100%			

01 54 19.60 Monthly Tower Crane Crew

01 54 19.60 Monthly Tower Crane Crew	Crew	Daily Output	Labor-Hours	Unit	Material	2017 Bare Costs Labor	2017 Bare Costs Equipment	Total	Total Incl O&P
0010	**MONTHLY TOWER CRANE CREW**, excludes concrete footing									
0100	Static tower crane, 130' high, 106' jib, 6200 lb. capacity	A-3N	.05	176	Month		9,800	25,700	35,500	43,000

01 54 23 – Temporary Scaffolding and Platforms

01 54 23.70 Scaffolding

01 54 23.70 Scaffolding	Crew	Daily Output	Labor-Hours	Unit	Material	2017 Bare Costs Labor	2017 Bare Costs Equipment	Total	Total Incl O&P
0010	**SCAFFOLDING** R015423-10									
0015	Steel tube, regular, no plank, labor only to erect & dismantle									
0090	Building exterior, wall face, 1 to 5 stories, 6'-4" x 5' frames	3 Carp	8	3	C.S.F.		148		148	226
0200	6 to 12 stories	4 Carp	8	4			197		197	300
0301	13 to 20 stories	5 Clab	8	5			196		196	300
0460	Building interior, wall face area, up to 16' high	3 Carp	12	2			98.50		98.50	151
0560	16' to 40' high		10	2.400			118		118	181
0800	Building interior floor area, up to 30' high		150	.160	C.C.F.		7.90		7.90	12.05
0900	Over 30' high	4 Carp	160	.200	"		9.85		9.85	15.10
0906	Complete system for face of walls, no plank, material only rent/mo				C.S.F.	35			35	38.50
0908	Interior spaces, no plank, material only rent/mo				C.C.F.	4.28			4.28	4.71
0910	Steel tubular, heavy duty shoring, buy									
0920	Frames 5' high 2' wide				Ea.	88			88	97

01 54 Construction Aids

01 54 23 – Temporary Scaffolding and Platforms

01 54 23.70 Scaffolding		Crew	Daily Output	Labor-Hours	Unit	Material	2017 Bare Costs Labor	Equipment	Total	Total Incl O&P
0925	5' high 4' wide				Ea.	101			101	111
0930	6' high 2' wide					102			102	112
0935	6' high 4' wide				↓	117			117	129
0940	Accessories									
0945	Cross braces				Ea.	17			17	18.70
0950	U-head, 8" x 8"					21			21	23
0955	J-head, 4" x 8"					15.20			15.20	16.70
0960	Base plate, 8" x 8"					17			17	18.70
0965	Leveling jack				↓	36			36	39.50
1000	Steel tubular, regular, buy									
1100	Frames 3' high 5' wide				Ea.	89			89	97.50
1150	5' high 5' wide					94.50			94.50	104
1200	6'-4" high 5' wide					140			140	154
1350	7'-6" high 6' wide					170			170	187
1500	Accessories, cross braces					16.50			16.50	18.15
1550	Guardrail post					17.60			17.60	19.35
1600	Guardrail 7' section					8			8	8.80
1650	Screw jacks & plates					21.50			21.50	24
1700	Sidearm brackets					28			28	30.50
1750	8" casters					31			31	34
1800	Plank 2" x 10" x 16'-0"					59.50			59.50	65.50
1900	Stairway section					275			275	305
1910	Stairway starter bar					32			32	35
1920	Stairway inside handrail					53			53	58
1930	Stairway outside handrail					86			86	94.50
1940	Walk-thru frame guardrail				↓	41.50			41.50	46
2000	Steel tubular, regular, rent/mo.									
2100	Frames 3' high 5' wide				Ea.	5			5	5.50
2150	5' high 5' wide					5			5	5.50
2200	6'-4" high 5' wide					5.40			5.40	5.95
2250	7'-6" high 6' wide					10			10	11
2500	Accessories, cross braces					1			1	1.10
2550	Guardrail post					1			1	1.10
2600	Guardrail 7' section					1			1	1.10
2650	Screw jacks & plates					2			2	2.20
2700	Sidearm brackets					2			2	2.20
2750	8" casters					8			8	8.80
2800	Outrigger for rolling tower					3			3	3.30
2850	Plank 2" x 10" x 16'-0"					10			10	11
2900	Stairway section					33			33	36.50
2940	Walk-thru frame guardrail				↓	2.50			2.50	2.75
3000	Steel tubular, heavy duty shoring, rent/mo.									
3250	5' high 2' & 4' wide				Ea.	8.50			8.50	9.35
3300	6' high 2' & 4' wide					8.50			8.50	9.35
3500	Accessories, cross braces					1			1	1.10
3600	U-head, 8" x 8"					2.50			2.50	2.75
3650	J-head, 4" x 8"					2.50			2.50	2.75
3700	Base plate, 8" x 8"					1			1	1.10
3750	Leveling jack					2.50			2.50	2.75
5700	Planks, 2" x 10" x 16'-0", labor only to erect & remove to 50' H	3 Carp	72	.333			16.40		16.40	25
5800	Over 50' high	4 Carp	80	.400	↓		19.70		19.70	30

For customer support on your Electrical Costs with RSMeans Data, call 800.448.8182.

15

01 54 Construction Aids

01 54 23 – Temporary Scaffolding and Platforms

01 54 23.75 Scaffolding Specialties

	01 54 23.75 Scaffolding Specialties	Crew	Daily Output	Labor-Hours	Unit	Material	2017 Bare Costs Labor	2017 Bare Costs Equipment	Total	Total Incl O&P
0010	**SCAFFOLDING SPECIALTIES**									
1500	Sidewalk bridge using tubular steel scaffold frames including									
1510	planking (material cost is rent/month)	3 Carp	45	.533	L.F.	8.55	26.50		35.05	49.50
1600	For 2 uses per month, deduct from all above					50%				
1700	For 1 use every 2 months, add to all above					100%				
1900	Catwalks, 20" wide, no guardrails, 7' span, buy				Ea.	175			175	193
2000	10' span, buy					251			251	276
3720	Putlog, standard, 8' span, with hangers, buy					61			61	67
3750	12' span, buy					108			108	119
3760	Trussed type, 16' span, buy					249			249	274
3790	22' span, buy					255			255	281
3795	Rent per month					40			40	44
3800	Rolling ladders with handrails, 30" wide, buy, 2 step					280			280	305
4000	7 step					790			790	870
4050	10 step					1,125			1,125	1,225
4100	Rolling towers, buy, 5' wide, 7' long, 10' high					1,225			1,225	1,350
4200	For additional 5' high sections, to buy				▼	222			222	244
4300	Complete incl. wheels, railings, outriggers,									
4350	21' high, to buy				Ea.	2,075			2,075	2,275
4400	Rent/month = 5% of purchase cost				"	200			200	220

01 54 26 – Temporary Swing Staging

01 54 26.50 Swing Staging

	01 54 26.50 Swing Staging	Crew	Daily Output	Labor-Hours	Unit	Material	2017 Bare Costs Labor	2017 Bare Costs Equipment	Total	Total Incl O&P
0010	**SWING STAGING**, 500 lb. cap., 2' wide to 24' long, hand operated									
0020	steel cable type, with 60' cables, buy				Ea.	5,275			5,275	5,825
0030	Rent per month				"	530			530	580
2200	Move swing staging (setup and remove)	E-4	2	16	Move		875	65	940	1,525

01 54 36 – Equipment Mobilization

01 54 36.50 Mobilization

	01 54 36.50 Mobilization	Crew	Daily Output	Labor-Hours	Unit	Material	2017 Bare Costs Labor	2017 Bare Costs Equipment	Total	Total Incl O&P
0010	**MOBILIZATION** (Use line item again for demobilization) R015436-50									
0015	Up to 25 mi. haul dist. (50 mi. RT for mob/demob crew)									
1200	Small equipment, placed in rear of, or towed by pickup truck	A-3A	4	2	Ea.		102	35	137	193
1300	Equipment hauled on 3-ton capacity towed trailer	A-3Q	2.67	3			153	61.50	214.50	299
1400	20-ton capacity	B-34U	2	8			385	232	617	840
1500	40-ton capacity	B-34N	2	8			395	365	760	1,000
1600	50-ton capacity	B-34V	1	24			1,225	1,000	2,225	2,975
1700	Crane, truck-mounted, up to 75 ton (driver only)	1 Eqhv	4	2			111		111	169
1800	Over 75 ton (with chase vehicle)	A-3E	2.50	6.400			325	56	381	550
2400	Crane, large lattice boom, requiring assembly	B-34W	.50	144	▼		6,950	7,325	14,275	18,600
2500	For each additional 5 miles haul distance, add						10%	10%		
3000	For large pieces of equipment, allow for assembly/knockdown									
3100	For mob/demob of micro-tunneling equip, see Section 33 05 23.19									

01 55 Vehicular Access and Parking

01 55 23 – Temporary Roads

01 55 23.50 Roads and Sidewalks	Crew	Daily Output	Labor-Hours	Unit	Material	2017 Bare Costs Labor	Equipment	Total	Total Incl O&P
0010 **ROADS AND SIDEWALKS** Temporary									
0050 Roads, gravel fill, no surfacing, 4" gravel depth	B-14	715	.067	S.Y.	3.44	2.78	.51	6.73	8.60
0100 8" gravel depth	"	615	.078	"	6.90	3.24	.60	10.74	13.15
1000 Ramp, 3/4" plywood on 2" x 6" joists, 16" O.C.	2 Carp	300	.053	S.F.	1.56	2.63		4.19	5.75
1100 On 2" x 10" joists, 16" O.C.	"	275	.058	"	2.29	2.87		5.16	6.90

01 56 Temporary Barriers and Enclosures

01 56 13 – Temporary Air Barriers

01 56 13.90 Winter Protection

	Crew	Daily Output	Labor-Hours	Unit	Material	Labor	Equipment	Total	Total Incl O&P
0010 **WINTER PROTECTION**									
0100 Framing to close openings	2 Clab	500	.032	S.F.	.44	1.25		1.69	2.40
0200 Tarpaulins hung over scaffolding, 8 uses, not incl. scaffolding	↓	1500	.011		.25	.42		.67	.92
0300 Prefab fiberglass panels, steel frame, 8 uses	↓	1200	.013	↓	2.45	.52		2.97	3.50

01 56 16 – Temporary Dust Barriers

01 56 16.10 Dust Barriers, Temporary

	Crew	Daily Output	Labor-Hours	Unit	Material	Labor	Equipment	Total	Total Incl O&P
0010 **DUST BARRIERS, TEMPORARY**									
0020 Spring loaded telescoping pole & head, to 12', erect and dismantle	1 Clab	240	.033	Ea.		1.30		1.30	2
0025 Cost per day (based upon 250 days)				Day	.26			.26	.29
0030 To 21', erect and dismantle	1 Clab	240	.033	Ea.		1.30		1.30	2
0035 Cost per day (based upon 250 days)				Day	.58			.58	.63
0040 Accessories, caution tape reel, erect and dismantle	1 Clab	480	.017	Ea.		.65		.65	1
0045 Cost per day (based upon 250 days)				Day	.37			.37	.40
0060 Foam rail and connector, erect and dismantle	1 Clab	240	.033	Ea.		1.30		1.30	2
0065 Cost per day (based upon 250 days)				Day	.12			.12	.13
0070 Caution tape	1 Clab	384	.021	C.L.F.	3.13	.82		3.95	4.69
0080 Zipper, standard duty		60	.133	Ea.	8	5.20		13.20	16.80
0090 Heavy duty		48	.167	"	9.75	6.55		16.30	21
0100 Polyethylene sheet, 4 mil		37	.216	Sq.	2.58	8.45		11.03	15.80
0110 6 mil		37	.216	"	3.73	8.45		12.18	17.05
1000 Dust partition, 6 mil polyethylene, 1" x 3" frame	2 Carp	2000	.008	S.F.	.31	.39		.70	.94
1080 2" x 4" frame	"	2000	.008	"	.34	.39		.73	.97
1085 Negative air machine, 1800 CFM				Ea.	805			805	885
1090 Adhesive strip application, 2" width	1 Clab	192	.042	C.L.F.	7.25	1.63		8.88	10.45

01 56 23 – Temporary Barricades

01 56 23.10 Barricades

	Crew	Daily Output	Labor-Hours	Unit	Material	Labor	Equipment	Total	Total Incl O&P
0010 **BARRICADES**									
0020 5' high, 3 rail @ 2" x 8", fixed	2 Carp	20	.800	L.F.	5.90	39.50		45.40	67
0150 Movable		30	.533		4.88	26.50		31.38	45.50
1000 Guardrail, wooden, 3' high, 1" x 6", on 2" x 4" posts		200	.080		1.28	3.94		5.22	7.45
1100 2" x 6", on 4" x 4" posts	↓	165	.097		2.48	4.78		7.26	10.05
1200 Portable metal with base pads, buy					16.10			16.10	17.70
1250 Typical installation, assume 10 reuses	2 Carp	600	.027	↓	2.60	1.31		3.91	4.87
1300 Barricade tape, polyethylene, 7 mil, 3" wide x 500' long roll				Ea.	25			25	27.50
3000 Detour signs, set up and remove									
3010 Reflective aluminum, MUTCD, 24" x 24", post mounted	1 Clab	20	.400	Ea.	2.48	15.65		18.13	26.50
4000 Roof edge portable barrier stands and warning flags, 50 uses	1 Rohe	9100	.001	L.F.	.07	.03		.10	.13
4010 100 uses	"	9100	.001	"	.04	.03		.07	.09

For customer support on your Electrical Costs with RSMeans Data, call 800.448.8182.

17

01 56 Temporary Barriers and Enclosures

01 56 26 – Temporary Fencing

01 56 26.50 Temporary Fencing	Crew	Daily Output	Labor-Hours	Unit	Material	2017 Bare Costs Labor	Equipment	Total	Total Incl O&P
0010 **TEMPORARY FENCING**									
0020 Chain link, 11 ga., 4' high	2 Clab	400	.040	L.F.	1.64	1.57		3.21	4.20
0100 6' high		300	.053		3.80	2.09		5.89	7.40
0200 Rented chain link, 6' high, to 1000' (up to 12 mo.)		400	.040		2.95	1.57		4.52	5.65
0250 Over 1000' (up to 12 mo.)	↓	300	.053		3	2.09		5.09	6.50
0350 Plywood, painted, 2" x 4" frame, 4' high	A-4	135	.178		6.25	8.30		14.55	19.55
0400 4" x 4" frame, 8' high	"	110	.218		12	10.20		22.20	29
0500 Wire mesh on 4" x 4" posts, 4' high	2 Carp	100	.160		10.20	7.90		18.10	23.50
0550 8' high	"	80	.200	↓	15.40	9.85		25.25	32

01 56 29 – Temporary Protective Walkways

01 56 29.50 Protection

	Crew	Daily Output	Labor-Hours	Unit	Material	Labor	Equipment	Total	Total Incl O&P
0010 **PROTECTION**									
0020 Stair tread, 2" x 12" planks, 1 use	1 Carp	75	.107	Tread	5.20	5.25		10.45	13.75
0100 Exterior plywood, 1/2" thick, 1 use		65	.123		1.88	6.05		7.93	11.35
0200 3/4" thick, 1 use		60	.133	↓	2.81	6.55		9.36	13.15
2200 Sidewalks, 2" x 12" planks, 2 uses		350	.023	S.F.	.87	1.13		2	2.67
2300 Exterior plywood, 2 uses, 1/2" thick		750	.011		.31	.53		.84	1.15
2400 5/8" thick		650	.012		.39	.61		1	1.36
2500 3/4" thick	↓	600	.013	↓	.47	.66		1.13	1.53

01 58 Project Identification

01 58 13 – Temporary Project Signage

01 58 13.50 Signs

	Crew	Daily Output	Labor-Hours	Unit	Material	Labor	Equipment	Total	Total Incl O&P
0010 **SIGNS**									
0020 High intensity reflectorized, no posts, buy				Ea.	26			26	28.50

01 66 Product Storage and Handling Requirements

01 66 19 – Material Handling

01 66 19.10 Material Handling

	Crew	Daily Output	Labor-Hours	Unit	Material	Labor	Equipment	Total	Total Incl O&P
0010 **MATERIAL HANDLING**									
0020 Above 2nd story, via stairs, per CY of material per floor	2 Clab	145	.110	C.Y.		4.32		4.32	6.60
0030 Via elevator, per CY of material		240	.067			2.61		2.61	4
0050 Distances greater than 200', per CY of material per each addl 200'	↓	300	.053	↓		2.09		2.09	3.20

01 74 Cleaning and Waste Management

01 74 13 – Progress Cleaning

01 74 13.20 Cleaning Up

	Crew	Daily Output	Labor-Hours	Unit	Material	Labor	Equipment	Total	Total Incl O&P
0010 **CLEANING UP**									
0020 After job completion, allow, minimum				Job				.30%	.30%
0040 Maximum				"				1%	1%
0050 Cleanup of floor area, continuous, per day, during const.	A-5	24	.750	M.S.F.	2.27	30	2.27	34.54	50.50
0100 Final by GC at end of job	"	11.50	1.565	"	2.40	62	4.73	69.13	103

01 91 Commissioning

01 91 13 – General Commissioning Requirements

01 91 13.50 Building Commissioning	Crew	Daily Output	Labor-Hours	Unit	Material	2017 Bare Costs Labor	Equipment	Total	Total Incl O&P
0010 **BUILDING COMMISSIONING**									
0100 Systems operation and verification during turnover				%				.25%	.25%
0150 Including all systems subcontractors								.50%	.50%
0200 Systems design assistance, operation, verification and training								.50%	.50%
0250 Including all systems subcontractors				▼				1%	1%

01 93 Facility Maintenance

01 93 13 – Facility Maintenance Procedures

01 93 13.16 Electrical Facilities Maintenance

	Crew	Daily Output	Labor-Hours	Unit	Material	2017 Bare Costs Labor	Equipment	Total	Total Incl O&P
0010 **ELECTRICAL FACILITIES MAINTENANCE**									
0700 Cathodic protection systems									
0720 Check and adjust reading on rectifier	1 Elec	20	.400	Ea.		22.50		22.50	34
0730 Check pipe to soil potential		20	.400			22.50		22.50	34
0740 Replace lead connection		4	2			113		113	170
0800 Control device, install		5.70	1.404			79.50		79.50	119
0810 Disassemble, clean and reinstall		7	1.143			64.50		64.50	97
0820 Replace		10.70	.748			42.50		42.50	63.50
0830 Trouble shoot	▼	10	.800	▼		45.50		45.50	68
0900 Demolition, for electrical demolition see Section 26 05 05.10									
1000 Distribution systems and equipment install or repair a breaker									
1010 In power panels up to 200 amps	1 Elec	7	1.143	Ea.		64.50		64.50	97
1020 Over 200 amps		2	4			226		226	340
1030 Reset breaker or replace fuse		20	.400			22.50		22.50	34
1100 Megger test MCC (each stack)		4	2			113		113	170
1110 MCC vacuum and clean (each stack)		5.30	1.509			85.50		85.50	128
2500 Remove and replace or maint., road fixture & lamp		3	2.667		1,000	151		1,151	1,325
2510 Fluorescent fixture	▼	7	1.143		79	64.50		143.50	184
2515 Relamp (fluor.) facility area each tube, spot	1 Clab	24	.333		3.34	13.05		16.39	23.50
2516 Group		100	.080		3.34	3.13		6.47	8.50
2518 Fluorescent fixture, clean (area)	▼	44	.182		.11	7.10		7.21	11.05
2520 Incandescent fixture	1 Elec	11	.727		56	41		97	123
2530 Lamp (incandescent or fluorescent)	1 Clab	60	.133		3.34	5.20		8.54	11.70
2535 Replace cord in socket lamp	1 Elec	13	.615		1.10	35		36.10	53
2540 Ballast electronic type for two tubes		8	1		33.50	56.50		90	122
2541 Starter		30	.267		.37	15.10		15.47	23
2545 Replace other lighting parts		11	.727		14.45	41		55.45	77.50
2550 Switch		11	.727		3.35	41		44.35	65
2555 Receptacle		11	.727		7.95	41		48.95	70
2560 Floodlight	▼	4	2		231	113		344	425
2570 Christmas lighting, indoor, per string	1 Clab	16	.500			19.60		19.60	30
2580 Outdoor		13	.615			24		24	37
2590 Test battery operated emergency lights	▼	40	.200			7.85		7.85	12
2600 Repair and replace component in communication system	1 Elec	6	1.333		53	75.50		128.50	171
2700 Repair misc. appliances (incl. clocks, vent fan, blower, etc.)	"	6	1.333			75.50		75.50	113
2710 Reset clocks & timers	1 Clab	50	.160			6.25		6.25	9.60
2720 Adjust time delay relays	1 Elec	16	.500	▼		28.50		28.50	42.50
2730 Test specific gravity of lead-acid batteries	1 Clab	80	.100	▼		3.92		3.92	6
3000 Motors and generators									
3020 Disassemble, clean and reinstall motor, up to 1/4 HP	1 Elec	4	2	Ea.		113		113	170
3030 Up to 3/4 HP		3	2.667			151		151	226
3040 Up to 10 HP	▼	2	4	▼		226		226	340

For customer support on your Electrical Costs with RSMeans Data, call 800.448.8182.

19

01 93 13 – Facility Maintenance Procedures

01 93 13.16 Electrical Facilities Maintenance	Crew	Daily Output	Labor-Hours	Unit	Material	2017 Bare Costs Labor	Equipment	Total	Total Incl O&P
3050	Replace part, up to 1/4 HP	1 Elec	6	1.333	Ea.		75.50		75.50	113
3060	Up to 3/4 HP		4	2			113		113	170
3070	Up to 10 HP		3	2.667			151		151	226
3080	Megger test motor windings		5.33	1.501			85		85	127
3082	Motor vibration check		16	.500			28.50		28.50	42.50
3084	Oil motor bearings		25	.320			18.10		18.10	27
3086	Run test emergency generator for 30 minutes		11	.727			41		41	61.50
3090	Rewind motor, up to 1/4 HP		3	2.667			151		151	226
3100	Up to 3/4 HP		2	4			226		226	340
3110	Up to 10 HP		1.50	5.333			300		300	450
3150	Generator, repair or replace part		4	2			113		113	170
3160	Repair DC generator		2	4			226		226	340
4000	Stub pole, install or remove		3	2.667			151		151	226
4500	Transformer maintenance up to 15 kVA		2.70	2.963			168		168	251

Estimating Tips
02 30 00 Subsurface Investigation

In preparing estimates on structures involving earthwork or foundations, all information concerning soil characteristics should be obtained. Look particularly for hazardous waste, evidence of prior dumping of debris, and previous stream beds.

02 40 00 Demolition and Structure Moving

The costs shown for selective demolition do not include rubbish handling or disposal. These items should be estimated separately using RSMeans data or other sources.

- Historic preservation often requires that the contractor remove materials from the existing structure, rehab them, and replace them. The estimator must be aware of any related measures and precautions that must be taken when doing selective demolition and cutting and patching. Requirements may include special handling and storage, as well as security.

- In addition to Subdivision 02 41 00, you can find selective demolition items in each division. Example: Roofing demolition is in Division 7.
- Absent of any other specific reference, an approximate demolish-in-place cost can be obtained by halving the new-install labor cost. To remove for reuse, allow the entire new-install labor figure.

02 40 00 Building Deconstruction

This section provides costs for the careful dismantling and recycling of most low-rise building materials.

02 50 00 Containment of Hazardous Waste

This section addresses on-site hazardous waste disposal costs.

02 80 00 Hazardous Material Disposal/Remediation

This subdivision includes information on hazardous waste handling, asbestos remediation, lead remediation, and mold remediation. See reference numbers

R028213-20 and R028319-60 for further guidance in using these unit price lines.

02 90 00 Monitoring Chemical Sampling, Testing Analysis

This section provides costs for on-site sampling and testing hazardous waste.

Reference Numbers

Reference numbers are shown at the beginning of some major classifications. These numbers refer to related items in the Reference Section. The reference information may be an estimating procedure, an alternate pricing method, or technical information.

Note: Not all subdivisions listed here necessarily appear. ■

02 41 Demolition

02 41 13 – Selective Site Demolition

02 41 13.17 Demolish, Remove Pavement and Curb

	Crew	Daily Output	Labor-Hours	Unit	Material	2017 Bare Costs Labor	Equipment	Total	Total Incl O&P
0010 **DEMOLISH, REMOVE PAVEMENT AND CURB** R024119-10									
5010 Pavement removal, bituminous roads, up to 3" thick	B-38	690	.058	S.Y.		2.60	1.83	4.43	5.95
5050 4" to 6" thick		420	.095			4.27	3.01	7.28	9.80
5100 Bituminous driveways		640	.063			2.80	1.98	4.78	6.45
5200 Concrete to 6" thick, hydraulic hammer, mesh reinforced		255	.157			7.05	4.96	12.01	16.15
5300 Rod reinforced		200	.200			8.95	6.30	15.25	20.50
5400 Concrete, 7" to 24" thick, plain		33	1.212	C.Y.		54.50	38.50	93	125
5500 Reinforced		24	1.667	"		74.50	52.50	127	172
5600 With hand held air equipment, bituminous, to 6" thick	B-39	1900	.025	S.F.		1.05	.11	1.16	1.72
5700 Concrete to 6" thick, no reinforcing		1600	.030			1.24	.13	1.37	2.05
5800 Mesh reinforced		1400	.034			1.42	.15	1.57	2.34
5900 Rod reinforced		765	.063			2.60	.28	2.88	4.29

02 41 13.23 Utility Line Removal

	Crew	Daily Output	Labor-Hours	Unit	Material	2017 Bare Costs Labor	Equipment	Total	Total Incl O&P
0010 **UTILITY LINE REMOVAL**									
0015 No hauling, abandon catch basin or manhole	B-6	7	3.429	Ea.		148	52.50	200.50	283
0020 Remove existing catch basin or manhole, masonry		4	6			259	91.50	350.50	495
0030 Catch basin or manhole frames and covers, stored		13	1.846			79.50	28	107.50	152
0040 Remove and reset		7	3.429			148	52.50	200.50	283

02 41 13.30 Minor Site Demolition

	Crew	Daily Output	Labor-Hours	Unit	Material	2017 Bare Costs Labor	Equipment	Total	Total Incl O&P
0010 **MINOR SITE DEMOLITION** R024119-10									
4000 Sidewalk removal, bituminous, 2" thick	B-6	350	.069	S.Y.		2.96	1.05	4.01	5.65
4010 2-1/2" thick		325	.074			3.18	1.13	4.31	6.10
4050 Brick, set in mortar		185	.130			5.60	1.98	7.58	10.75
4100 Concrete, plain, 4"		160	.150			6.45	2.29	8.74	12.35
4110 Plain, 5"		140	.171			7.40	2.62	10.02	14.15
4120 Plain, 6"		120	.200			8.60	3.05	11.65	16.50
4200 Mesh reinforced, concrete, 4"		150	.160			6.90	2.44	9.34	13.20
4210 5" thick		131	.183			7.90	2.80	10.70	15.10
4220 6" thick		112	.214			9.25	3.27	12.52	17.70

02 41 19 – Selective Demolition

02 41 19.13 Selective Building Demolition

	Crew	Daily Output	Labor-Hours	Unit	Material	2017 Bare Costs Labor	Equipment	Total	Total Incl O&P
0010 **SELECTIVE BUILDING DEMOLITION**									
0020 Costs related to selective demolition of specific building components									
0025 are included under Common Work Results (XX 05)									
0030 in the component's appropriate division.									

02 41 19.16 Selective Demolition, Cutout

	Crew	Daily Output	Labor-Hours	Unit	Material	2017 Bare Costs Labor	Equipment	Total	Total Incl O&P
0010 **SELECTIVE DEMOLITION, CUTOUT** R024119-10									
0020 Concrete, elev. slab, light reinforcement, under 6 C.F.	B-9	65	.615	C.F.		24.50	3.28	27.78	41
0050 Light reinforcing, over 6 C.F.	"	75	.533	"		21	2.84	23.84	35.50
6000 Walls, interior, not including re-framing,									
6010 openings to 5 S.F.									
6100 Drywall to 5/8" thick	1 Clab	24	.333	Ea.		13.05		13.05	20
6200 Paneling to 3/4" thick		20	.400			15.65		15.65	24
6300 Plaster, on gypsum lath		20	.400			15.65		15.65	24
6340 On wire lath		14	.571			22.50		22.50	34.50

02 41 19.19 Selective Demolition

	Crew	Daily Output	Labor-Hours	Unit	Material	2017 Bare Costs Labor	Equipment	Total	Total Incl O&P
0010 **SELECTIVE DEMOLITION**, Rubbish Handling R024119-10									
0020 The following are to be added to the demolition prices									
0600 Dumpster, weekly rental, 1 dump/week, 6 C.Y. capacity (2 Tons)				Week	415			415	455
0700 10 C.Y. capacity (3 Tons)					480			480	530
0725 20 C.Y. capacity (5 Tons) R024119-20					565			565	625

02 41 Demolition

02 41 19 – Selective Demolition

02 41 19.19 Selective Demolition

		Crew	Daily Output	Labor-Hours	Unit	Material	2017 Bare Costs Labor	Equipment	Total	Total Incl O&P
0800	30 C.Y. capacity (7 Tons)				Week	730			730	800
0840	40 C.Y. capacity (10 Tons)				↓	775			775	850
2000	Load, haul, dump and return, 0 – 50' haul, hand carried	2 Clab	24	.667	C.Y.		26		26	40
2005	Wheeled		37	.432			16.95		16.95	26
2040	0 – 100' haul, hand carried		16.50	.970			38		38	58
2045	Wheeled	↓	25	.640			25		25	38.50
2050	Forklift	A-3R	25	.320			16.30	6.85	23.15	32
2080	Haul and return, add per each extra 100' haul, hand carried	2 Clab	35.50	.451			17.65		17.65	27
2085	Wheeled		54	.296			11.60		11.60	17.80
2120	For travel in elevators, up to 10 floors, add		140	.114			4.47		4.47	6.85
2130	0 – 50' haul, incl. up to 5 riser stairs, hand carried		23	.696			27		27	41.50
2135	Wheeled		35	.457			17.90		17.90	27.50
2140	6 – 10 riser stairs, hand carried		22	.727			28.50		28.50	43.50
2145	Wheeled		34	.471			18.40		18.40	28
2150	11 – 20 riser stairs, hand carried		20	.800			31.50		31.50	48
2155	Wheeled		31	.516			20		20	31
2160	21 – 40 riser stairs, hand carried		16	1			39		39	60
2165	Wheeled		24	.667			26		26	40
2170	0 – 100' haul, incl. 5 riser stairs, hand carried		15	1.067			42		42	64
2175	Wheeled		23	.696			27		27	41.50
2180	6 – 10 riser stairs, hand carried		14	1.143			44.50		44.50	68.50
2185	Wheeled		21	.762			30		30	45.50
2190	11 – 20 riser stairs, hand carried		12	1.333			52		52	80
2195	Wheeled		18	.889			35		35	53.50
2200	21 – 40 riser stairs, hand carried		8	2			78.50		78.50	120
2205	Wheeled		12	1.333			52		52	80
2210	Haul and return, add per each extra 100' haul, hand carried		35.50	.451			17.65		17.65	27
2215	Wheeled	↓	54	.296	↓		11.60		11.60	17.80
2220	For each additional flight of stairs, up to 5 risers, add		550	.029	Flight		1.14		1.14	1.75
2225	6 – 10 risers, add		275	.058			2.28		2.28	3.49
2230	11 – 20 risers, add		138	.116			4.54		4.54	6.95
2235	21 – 40 risers, add	↓	69	.232	↓		9.10		9.10	13.90
3000	Loading & trucking, including 2 mile haul, chute loaded	B-16	45	.711	C.Y.		29.50	14.30	43.80	60.50
3040	Hand loading truck, 50' haul	"	48	.667			27.50	13.40	40.90	57
3080	Machine loading truck	B-17	120	.267			11.65	6.30	17.95	24.50
5000	Haul, per mile, up to 8 C.Y. truck	B-34B	1165	.007	↓		.31	.55	.86	1.08
5100	Over 8 C.Y. truck	"	1550	.005	↓		.24	.41	.65	.81

02 41 19.20 Selective Demolition, Dump Charges

		Crew	Daily Output	Labor-Hours	Unit	Material	2017 Bare Costs Labor	Equipment	Total	Total Incl O&P
0010	SELECTIVE DEMOLITION, DUMP CHARGES	R024119-10								
0020	Dump charges, typical urban city, tipping fees only									
0100	Building construction materials				Ton	74			74	81
0200	Trees, brush, lumber					63			63	69.50
0300	Rubbish only					63			63	69.50
0500	Reclamation station, usual charge				↓	74			74	81

02 41 19.27 Selective Demolition, Torch Cutting

		Crew	Daily Output	Labor-Hours	Unit	Material	2017 Bare Costs Labor	Equipment	Total	Total Incl O&P
0010	SELECTIVE DEMOLITION, TORCH CUTTING	R024119-10								
0020	Steel, 1" thick plate	E-25	333	.024	L.F.	.84	1.35	.04	2.23	3.21
0040	1" diameter bar	"	600	.013	Ea.	.14	.75	.02	.91	1.42
1000	Oxygen lance cutting, reinforced concrete walls									
1040	12" to 16" thick walls	1 Clab	10	.800	L.F.		31.50		31.50	48
1080	24" thick walls	"	6	1.333	"		52		52	80

For customer support on your Electrical Costs with RSMeans Data, call 800.448.8182.

23

02 82 Asbestos Remediation

02 82 13 – Asbestos Abatement

02 82 13.47 Asbestos Waste Pkg., Handling, and Disp.	Crew	Daily Output	Labor-Hours	Unit	Material	2017 Bare Costs Labor	Equipment	Total	Total Incl O&P
0010 **ASBESTOS WASTE PACKAGING, HANDLING, AND DISPOSAL**									
0100 Collect and bag bulk material, 3 C.F. bags, by hand	A-9	400	.160	Ea.	.85	8.80		9.65	14.65
0200 Large production vacuum loader	A-12	880	.073		1	4.01	.84	5.85	8.25
1000 Double bag and decontaminate	A-9	960	.067		.85	3.67		4.52	6.65
2000 Containerize bagged material in drums, per 3 C.F. drum	"	800	.080		18.75	4.41		23.16	27.50
3000 Cart bags 50' to dumpster	2 Asbe	400	.040			2.20		2.20	3.42
5000 Disposal charges, not including haul, minimum				C.Y.				61	67
5020 Maximum				"				355	395
9000 For type B (supplied air) respirator equipment, add				%				10%	10%

Estimating Tips
General

- Carefully check all the plans and specifications. Concrete often appears on drawings other than structural drawings, including mechanical and electrical drawings for equipment pads. The cost of cutting and patching is often difficult to estimate. See Subdivision 03 81 for Concrete Cutting, Subdivision 02 41 19.16 for Cutout Demolition, Subdivision 03 05 05.10 for Concrete Demolition, and Subdivision 02 41 19.19 for Rubbish Handling (handling, loading, and hauling of debris).

- Always obtain concrete prices from suppliers near the job site. A volume discount can often be negotiated, depending upon competition in the area. Remember to add for waste, particularly for slabs and footings on grade.

03 10 00 Concrete Forming and Accessories

- A primary cost for concrete construction is forming. Most jobs today are constructed with prefabricated forms. The selection of the forms best suited for the job and the total square feet of forms required for efficient concrete forming and placing are key elements in estimating concrete construction. Enough forms must be available for erection to make efficient use of the concrete placing equipment and crew.

- Concrete accessories for forming and placing depend upon the systems used. Study the plans and specifications to ensure that all special accessory requirements have been included in the cost estimate, such as anchor bolts, inserts, and hangers.

- Included within costs for forms-in-place are all necessary bracing and shoring.

03 20 00 Concrete Reinforcing

- Ascertain that the reinforcing steel supplier has included all accessories, cutting, bending, and an allowance for lapping, splicing, and waste. A good rule of thumb is 10% for lapping, splicing, and waste. Also, 10% waste should be allowed for welded wire fabric.

- The unit price items in the subdivisions for Reinforcing In Place, Glass Fiber Reinforcing, and Welded Wire Fabric include the labor to install accessories such as beam and slab bolsters, high chairs, and bar ties and tie wire. The material cost for these accessories is not included; they may be obtained from the Accessories Subdivisions.

03 30 00 Cast-In-Place Concrete

- When estimating structural concrete, pay particular attention to requirements for concrete additives, curing methods, and surface treatments. Special consideration for climate, hot or cold, must be included in your estimate. Be sure to include requirements for concrete placing equipment and concrete finishing.

- For accurate concrete estimating, the estimator must consider each of the following major components individually: forms, reinforcing steel, ready-mix concrete, placement of the concrete, and finishing of the top surface. For faster estimating, Subdivision 03 30 53.40 for Concrete-In-Place can be used; here, various items of concrete work are presented that include the costs of all five major components (unless specifically stated otherwise).

03 40 00 Precast Concrete
03 50 00 Cast Decks and Underlayment

- The cost of hauling precast concrete structural members is often an important factor. For this reason, it is important to get a quote from the nearest supplier. It may become economically feasible to set up precasting beds on the site if the hauling costs are prohibitive.

Reference Numbers

Reference numbers are shown at the beginning of some major classifications. These numbers refer to related items in the Reference Section. The reference information may be an estimating procedure, an alternate pricing method, or technical information.

Note: Not all subdivisions listed here necessarily appear. ∎

03 01 Maintenance of Concrete

03 01 30 – Maintenance of Cast-In-Place Concrete

03 01 30.62 Concrete Patching

	03 01 30.62 Concrete Patching	Crew	Daily Output	Labor-Hours	Unit	Material	2017 Bare Costs Labor	Equipment	Total	Total Incl O&P
0010	**CONCRETE PATCHING**									
0100	Floors, 1/4" thick, small areas, regular grout	1 Cefi	170	.047	S.F.	1.56	2.20		3.76	5
0150	Epoxy grout	"	100	.080	"	8.30	3.74		12.04	14.65
2000	Walls, including chipping, cleaning and epoxy grout									
2100	1/4" deep	1 Cefi	65	.123	S.F.	7.25	5.75		13	16.55
2150	1/2" deep		50	.160		14.50	7.50		22	27
2200	3/4" deep		40	.200		22	9.35		31.35	38

03 11 Concrete Forming

03 11 13 – Structural Cast-In-Place Concrete Forming

03 11 13.40 Forms In Place, Equipment Foundations

	03 11 13.40 Forms In Place, Equipment Foundations	Crew	Daily Output	Labor-Hours	Unit	Material	2017 Bare Costs Labor	Equipment	Total	Total Incl O&P
0010	**FORMS IN PLACE, EQUIPMENT FOUNDATIONS**									
0020	1 use	C-2	160	.300	SFCA	3.40	14.35		17.75	25.50
0050	2 use		190	.253		1.87	12.10		13.97	20.50
0100	3 use		200	.240		1.36	11.50		12.86	19.10
0150	4 use		205	.234		1.11	11.20		12.31	18.40

03 11 13.45 Forms In Place, Footings

	03 11 13.45 Forms In Place, Footings	Crew	Daily Output	Labor-Hours	Unit	Material	2017 Bare Costs Labor	Equipment	Total	Total Incl O&P
0010	**FORMS IN PLACE, FOOTINGS**									
0020	Continuous wall, plywood, 1 use	C-1	375	.085	SFCA	6.85	3.99		10.84	13.60
0050	2 use		440	.073		3.76	3.40		7.16	9.35
0100	3 use		470	.068		2.74	3.18		5.92	7.90
0150	4 use		485	.066		2.23	3.08		5.31	7.15
5000	Spread footings, job-built lumber, 1 use		305	.105		2.20	4.90		7.10	9.90
5050	2 use		371	.086		1.22	4.03		5.25	7.50
5100	3 use		401	.080		.88	3.73		4.61	6.65
5150	4 use		414	.077		.72	3.61		4.33	6.35

03 11 13.65 Forms In Place, Slab On Grade

	03 11 13.65 Forms In Place, Slab On Grade	Crew	Daily Output	Labor-Hours	Unit	Material	2017 Bare Costs Labor	Equipment	Total	Total Incl O&P
0010	**FORMS IN PLACE, SLAB ON GRADE**									
3000	Edge forms, wood, 4 use, on grade, to 6" high	C-1	600	.053	L.F.	.34	2.49		2.83	4.19
6000	Trench forms in floor, wood, 1 use		160	.200	SFCA	1.84	9.35		11.19	16.30
6050	2 use		175	.183		1.01	8.55		9.56	14.20
6100	3 use		180	.178		.74	8.30		9.04	13.55
6150	4 use		185	.173		.60	8.10		8.70	13.05

03 15 Concrete Accessories

03 15 05 – Concrete Forming Accessories

03 15 05.75 Sleeves and Chases

	03 15 05.75 Sleeves and Chases		Crew	Daily Output	Labor-Hours	Unit	Material	2017 Bare Costs Labor	Equipment	Total	Total Incl O&P
0010	**SLEEVES AND CHASES**										
0100	Plastic, 1 use, 12" long, 2" diameter		1 Carp	100	.080	Ea.	1.62	3.94		5.56	7.85
0150	4" diameter			90	.089		4.54	4.38		8.92	11.70
0200	6" diameter			75	.107		7.80	5.25		13.05	16.60
0250	12" diameter			60	.133		23.50	6.55		30.05	36
5000	Sheet metal, 2" diameter	[G]		100	.080		1.49	3.94		5.43	7.70
5100	4" diameter	[G]		90	.089		1.86	4.38		6.24	8.75
5150	6" diameter	[G]		75	.107		1.86	5.25		7.11	10.10
5200	12" diameter	[G]		60	.133		3.72	6.55		10.27	14.15
6000	Steel pipe, 2" diameter	[G]		100	.080		3.34	3.94		7.28	9.70
6100	4" diameter	[G]		90	.089		12.15	4.38		16.53	20
6150	6" diameter	[G]		75	.107		39	5.25		44.25	51

03 15 Concrete Accessories

03 15 05 – Concrete Forming Accessories

03 15 05.75 Sleeves and Chases

		Crew	Daily Output	Labor-Hours	Unit	Material	2017 Bare Costs Labor	2017 Bare Costs Equipment	Total	Total Incl O&P
6200	12" diameter	G 1 Carp	60	.133	Ea.	93.50	6.55		100.05	113

03 15 16 – Concrete Construction Joints

03 15 16.20 Control Joints, Saw Cut

		Crew	Daily Output	Labor-Hours	Unit	Material	Labor	Equipment	Total	Total Incl O&P
0010	**CONTROL JOINTS, SAW CUT**									
0100	Sawcut control joints in green concrete									
0120	1" depth	C-27	2000	.008	L.F.	.04	.37	.08	.49	.68
0140	1-1/2" depth		1800	.009		.05	.42	.09	.56	.77
0160	2" depth	↓	1600	.010	↓	.07	.47	.10	.64	.89
0180	Sawcut joint reservoir in cured concrete									
0182	3/8" wide x 3/4" deep, with single saw blade	C-27	1000	.016	L.F.	.05	.75	.15	.95	1.34
0184	1/2" wide x 1" deep, with double saw blades		900	.018		.10	.83	.17	1.10	1.54
0186	3/4" wide x 1-1/2" deep, with double saw blades	↓	800	.020		.21	.94	.19	1.34	1.83
0190	Water blast joint to wash away laitance, 2 passes	C-29	2500	.003			.13	.03	.16	.22
0200	Air blast joint to blow out debris and air dry, 2 passes	C-28	2000	.004	↓		.19	.01	.20	.29
0300	For backer rod, see Section 07 91 23.10									
0342	For joint sealant, see Section 07 92 13.20									

03 15 19 – Cast-In Concrete Anchors

03 15 19.10 Anchor Bolts

		Crew	Daily Output	Labor-Hours	Unit	Material	Labor	Equipment	Total	Total Incl O&P
0010	**ANCHOR BOLTS**									
0015	Made from recycled materials									
0025	Single bolts installed in fresh concrete, no templates									
0030	Hooked w/nut and washer, 1/2" diameter, 8" long	G 1 Carp	132	.061	Ea.	1.38	2.99		4.37	6.10
0040	12" long	G	131	.061		1.53	3.01		4.54	6.30
0050	5/8" diameter, 8" long	G	129	.062		3.35	3.05		6.40	8.35
0060	12" long	G	127	.063		4.12	3.10		7.22	9.30
0070	3/4" diameter, 8" long	G	127	.063		4.12	3.10		7.22	9.30
0080	12" long	G	125	.064	↓	5.15	3.15		8.30	10.50

03 15 19.45 Machinery Anchors

		Crew	Daily Output	Labor-Hours	Unit	Material	Labor	Equipment	Total	Total Incl O&P
0010	**MACHINERY ANCHORS**, heavy duty, incl. sleeve, floating base nut,									
0020	lower stud & coupling nut, fiber plug, connecting stud, washer & nut.									
0030	For flush mounted embedment in poured concrete heavy equip. pads.									
0200	Stud & bolt, 1/2" diameter	G E-16	40	.400	Ea.	52.50	22	3.24	77.74	98.50
0300	5/8" diameter	G	35	.457		61	25.50	3.71	90.21	113
0500	3/4" diameter	G	30	.533		72.50	29.50	4.33	106.33	134
0600	7/8" diameter	G	25	.640		82.50	35.50	5.20	123.20	155
0800	1" diameter	G	20	.800		88.50	44	6.50	139	178
0900	1-1/4" diameter	G	15	1.067	↓	118	59	8.65	185.65	238

03 21 Reinforcement Bars

03 21 11 – Plain Steel Reinforcement Bars

03 21 11.60 Reinforcing In Place

		Crew	Daily Output	Labor-Hours	Unit	Material	Labor	Equipment	Total	Total Incl O&P
0010	**REINFORCING IN PLACE**, 50-60 ton lots, A615 Grade 60									
0020	Includes labor, but not material cost, to install accessories									
0030	Made from recycled materials									
0502	Footings, #4 to #7	G 4 Rodm	4200	.008	Lb.	.47	.41		.88	1.16
0552	#8 to #18	G	7200	.004		.47	.24		.71	.89
0602	Slab on grade, #3 to #7	G	4200	.008	↓	.47	.41		.88	1.16
0900	For other than 50 – 60 ton lots									
1000	Under 10 ton job, #3 to #7, add					25%	10%			
1010	#8 to #18, add					20%	10%			

03 21 Reinforcement Bars

03 21 11 – Plain Steel Reinforcement Bars

03 21 11.60 Reinforcing In Place	Crew	Daily Output	Labor-Hours	Unit	Material	2017 Bare Costs Labor	Equipment	Total	Total Incl O&P
1050	10 – 50 ton job, #3 to #7, add					10%				
1060	#8 to #18, add					5%				
1100	60 – 100 ton job, #3 to #7, deduct					5%				
1110	#8 to #18, deduct					10%				
1150	Over 100 ton job, #3 to #7, deduct					10%				
1160	#8 to #18, deduct					15%				

03 22 Fabric and Grid Reinforcing

03 22 11 – Plain Welded Wire Fabric Reinforcing

03 22 11.10 Plain Welded Wire Fabric

		Crew	Daily Output	Labor-Hours	Unit	Material	Labor	Equipment	Total	Total Incl O&P
0010	**PLAIN WELDED WIRE FABRIC** ASTM A185									
0020	Includes labor, but not material cost, to install accessories									
0050	Sheets									
0100	6 x 6 - W1.4 x W1.4 (10 x 10) 21 lb. per C.S.F. [G]	2 Rodm	35	.457	C.S.F.	14.45	25		39.45	54.50

03 22 13 – Galvanized Welded Wire Fabric Reinforcing

03 22 13.10 Galvanized Welded Wire Fabric

					Unit	Material			Total	Total Incl O&P
0010	**GALVANIZED WELDED WIRE FABRIC**									
0100	Add to plain welded wire pricing for galvanized welded wire				Lb.	.23			.23	.25

03 22 16 – Epoxy-Coated Welded Wire Fabric Reinforcing

03 22 16.10 Epoxy-Coated Welded Wire Fabric

					Unit	Material			Total	Total Incl O&P
0010	**EPOXY-COATED WELDED WIRE FABRIC**									
0100	Add to plain welded wire pricing for epoxy-coated welded wire				Lb.	.39			.39	.42

03 30 Cast-In-Place Concrete

03 30 53 – Miscellaneous Cast-In-Place Concrete

03 30 53.40 Concrete In Place

		Crew	Daily Output	Labor-Hours	Unit	Material	Labor	Equipment	Total	Total Incl O&P
0010	**CONCRETE IN PLACE**									
0020	Including forms (4 uses), Grade 60 rebar, concrete (Portland cement									
0050	Type I), placement and finishing unless otherwise indicated									
3540	Equipment pad (3000 psi), 3' x 3' x 6" thick	C-14H	45	1.067	Ea.	49	51.50	.63	101.13	133
3550	4' x 4' x 6" thick		30	1.600		73.50	77.50	.94	151.94	200
3560	5' x 5' x 8" thick		18	2.667		131	129	1.57	261.57	345
3570	6' x 6' x 8" thick		14	3.429		177	166	2.02	345.02	450
3580	8' x 8' x 10" thick		8	6		380	290	3.54	673.54	870
3590	10' x 10' x 12" thick		5	9.600		655	465	5.65	1,125.65	1,425
3800	Footings (3000 psi), spread under 1 C.Y.	C-14C	28	4	C.Y.	181	188	1	370	490
3825	1 C.Y. to 5 C.Y.		43	2.605		218	123	.65	341.65	430
3850	Over 5 C.Y.		75	1.493		201	70.50	.37	271.87	330
3900	Footings, strip (3000 psi), 18" x 9", unreinforced	C-14L	40	2.400		143	110	.70	253.70	325
3920	18" x 9", reinforced	C-14C	35	3.200		165	151	.80	316.80	415
3925	20" x 10", unreinforced	C-14L	45	2.133		139	98	.62	237.62	305
3930	20" x 10", reinforced	C-14C	40	2.800		157	132	.70	289.70	375
3935	24" x 12", unreinforced	C-14L	55	1.745		137	80	.51	217.51	274
3940	24" x 12", reinforced	C-14C	48	2.333		156	110	.58	266.58	340
3945	36" x 12", unreinforced	C-14L	70	1.371		133	63	.40	196.40	242
3950	36" x 12", reinforced	C-14C	60	1.867		150	88	.47	238.47	300
4000	Foundation mat (3000 psi), under 10 C.Y.		38.67	2.896		218	136	.72	354.72	450
4050	Over 20 C.Y.		56.40	1.986		193	93.50	.50	287	355

03 30 Cast-In-Place Concrete

03 30 53 – Miscellaneous Cast-In-Place Concrete

03 30 53.40 Concrete In Place

		Crew	Daily Output	Labor-Hours	Unit	Material	2017 Bare Costs Labor	Equipment	Total	Total Incl O&P
4650	Slab on grade (3500 psi), not including finish, 4" thick	C-14E	60.75	1.449	C.Y.	142	70	.46	212.46	264
4700	6" thick	"	92	.957	↓	137	46	.31	183.31	222
4701	Thickened slab edge (3500 psi), for slab on grade poured									
4702	monolithically with slab; depth is in addition to slab thickness;									
4703	formed vertical outside edge, earthen bottom and inside slope									
4705	8" deep x 8" wide bottom, unreinforced	C-14L	2190	.044	L.F.	3.85	2.01	.01	5.87	7.30
4710	8" x 8", reinforced	C-14C	1670	.067		6.05	3.16	.02	9.23	11.50
4715	12" deep x 12" wide bottom, unreinforced	C-14L	1800	.053		7.90	2.45	.02	10.37	12.45
4720	12" x 12", reinforced	C-14C	1310	.086		11.95	4.02	.02	15.99	19.30
4725	16" deep x 16" wide bottom, unreinforced	C-14L	1440	.067		13.45	3.06	.02	16.53	19.50
4730	16" x 16", reinforced	C-14C	1120	.100		18.25	4.71	.03	22.99	27
4735	20" deep x 20" wide bottom, unreinforced	C-14L	1150	.083		20.50	3.83	.02	24.35	28.50
4740	20" x 20", reinforced	C-14C	920	.122		26.50	5.75	.03	32.28	38
4745	24" deep x 24" wide bottom, unreinforced	C-14L	930	.103		29	4.73	.03	33.76	39.50
4750	24" x 24", reinforced	C-14C	740	.151	↓	37	7.10	.04	44.14	51.50

03 31 Structural Concrete

03 31 13 – Heavyweight Structural Concrete

03 31 13.35 Heavyweight Concrete, Ready Mix

		Crew	Daily Output	Labor-Hours	Unit	Material	2017 Bare Costs Labor	Equipment	Total	Total Incl O&P
0010	**HEAVYWEIGHT CONCRETE, READY MIX**, delivered									
0012	Includes local aggregate, sand, Portland cement (Type I) and water									
0015	Excludes all additives and treatments									
0020	2000 psi				C.Y.	112			112	124
0100	2500 psi					116			116	127
0150	3000 psi					118			118	130
0200	3500 psi					121			121	133
0300	4000 psi					125			125	137
1000	For high early strength (Portland cement Type III), add					10%				
1300	For winter concrete (hot water), add					4.45			4.45	4.90
1410	For mid-range water reducer, add					3.33			3.33	3.66
1420	For high-range water reducer/superplasticizer, add					6			6	6.60
1430	For retarder, add					3.23			3.23	3.55
1440	For non-Chloride accelerator, add					5.70			5.70	6.25
1450	For Chloride accelerator, per 1%, add					3			3	3.30
1460	For fiber reinforcing, synthetic (1 lb./C.Y.), add					6.70			6.70	7.35
1500	For Saturday delivery, add				↓	8.50			8.50	9.35
1510	For truck holding/waiting time past 1st hour per load, add				Hr.	96.50			96.50	106
1520	For short load (less than 4 C.Y.), add per load				Ea.	74.50			74.50	82
2000	For all lightweight aggregate, add				C.Y.	45%				

03 31 13.70 Placing Concrete

		Crew	Daily Output	Labor-Hours	Unit	Material	2017 Bare Costs Labor	Equipment	Total	Total Incl O&P
0010	**PLACING CONCRETE**									
0020	Includes labor and equipment to place, level (strike off) and consolidate									
1900	Footings, continuous, shallow, direct chute	C-6	120	.400	C.Y.		16.30	.47	16.77	25.50
1950	Pumped	C-20	150	.427			18	5.75	23.75	34
2000	With crane and bucket	C-7	90	.800			34.50	12.85	47.35	66
2100	Footings, continuous, deep, direct chute	C-6	140	.343			14	.40	14.40	22
2150	Pumped	C-20	160	.400			16.85	5.40	22.25	31.50
2200	With crane and bucket	C-7	110	.655			28	10.50	38.50	54
2400	Footings, spread, under 1 C.Y., direct chute	C-6	55	.873			35.50	1.03	36.53	55
2450	Pumped	C-20	65	.985			41.50	13.25	54.75	77.50
2500	With crane and bucket	C-7	45	1.600	↓		68.50	25.50	94	133

For customer support on your Electrical Costs with RSMeans Data, call 800.448.8182.

29

03 31 Structural Concrete

03 31 13 – Heavyweight Structural Concrete

03 31 13.70 Placing Concrete

03 31 13.70 Placing Concrete	Crew	Daily Output	Labor-Hours	Unit	Material	2017 Bare Costs Labor	Equipment	Total	Total Incl O&P
2600	Over 5 C.Y., direct chute	C-6	120	.400	C.Y.		16.30	.47	16.77	25.50
2650	Pumped	C-20	150	.427			18	5.75	23.75	34
2700	With crane and bucket	C-7	100	.720			31	11.55	42.55	59.50
2900	Foundation mats, over 20 C.Y., direct chute	C-6	350	.137			5.60	.16	5.76	8.70
2950	Pumped	C-20	400	.160			6.75	2.16	8.91	12.60
3000	With crane and bucket	C-7	300	.240	▼		10.25	3.85	14.10	19.90

03 35 Concrete Finishing

03 35 13 – High-Tolerance Concrete Floor Finishing

03 35 13.30 Finishing Floors, High Tolerance

03 35 13.30 Finishing Floors, High Tolerance	Crew	Daily Output	Labor-Hours	Unit	Material	2017 Bare Costs Labor	Equipment	Total	Total Incl O&P
0010	**FINISHING FLOORS, HIGH TOLERANCE**									
0012	Finishing of fresh concrete flatwork requires that concrete									
0013	first be placed, struck off & consolidated									
0015	Basic finishing for various unspecified flatwork									
0100	Bull float only	C-10	4000	.006	S.F.		.27		.27	.40
0125	Bull float & manual float		2000	.012			.53		.53	.80
0150	Bull float, manual float, & broom finish, w/edging & joints		1850	.013			.57		.57	.86
0200	Bull float, manual float & manual steel trowel	▼	1265	.019	▼		.84		.84	1.26
0210	For specified Random Access Floors in ACI Classes 1, 2, 3 and 4 to achieve									
0215	Composite Overall Floor Flatness and Levelness values up to FF35/FL25									
0250	Bull float, machine float & machine trowel (walk-behind)	C-10C	1715	.014	S.F.		.62	.03	.65	.96
0300	Power screed, bull float, machine float & trowel (walk-behind)	C-10D	2400	.010			.44	.05	.49	.71
0350	Power screed, bull float, machine float & trowel (ride-on)	C-10E	4000	.006	▼		.27	.06	.33	.47
0352	For specified Random Access Floors in ACI Classes 5, 6, 7 and 8 to achieve									
0354	Composite Overall Floor Flatness and Levelness values up to FF50/FL50									
0356	Add for two-dimensional restraightening after power float	C-10	6000	.004	S.F.		.18		.18	.27
0358	For specified Random or Defined Access Floors in ACI Class 9 to achieve									
0360	Composite Overall Floor Flatness and Levelness values up to FF100/FL100									
0362	Add for two-dimensional restraightening after bull float & power float	C-10	3000	.008	S.F.		.35		.35	.53
0364	For specified Superflat Defined Access Floors in ACI Class 9 to achieve									
0366	Minimum Floor Flatness and Levelness values of FF100/FL100									
0368	Add for 2-dim'l restraightening after bull float, power float, power trowel	C-10	2000	.012	S.F.		.53		.53	.80

03 54 Cast Underlayment

03 54 16 – Hydraulic Cement Underlayment

03 54 16.50 Cement Underlayment

03 54 16.50 Cement Underlayment	Crew	Daily Output	Labor-Hours	Unit	Material	2017 Bare Costs Labor	Equipment	Total	Total Incl O&P
0010	**CEMENT UNDERLAYMENT**									
2510	Underlayment, P.C. based, self-leveling, 4100 psi, pumped, 1/4" thick	C-8	20000	.003	S.F.	1.63	.12	.04	1.79	2.03
2520	1/2" thick		19000	.003		3.27	.13	.04	3.44	3.84
2530	3/4" thick		18000	.003		4.90	.14	.04	5.08	5.65
2540	1" thick		17000	.003		6.55	.14	.05	6.74	7.45
2550	1-1/2" thick	▼	15000	.004		9.80	.16	.05	10.01	11.10
2560	Hand placed, 1/2" thick	C-18	450	.020		3.27	.79	.13	4.19	4.94
2610	Topping, P.C. based, self-leveling, 6100 psi, pumped, 1/4" thick	C-8	20000	.003		2.40	.12	.04	2.56	2.87
2620	1/2" thick		19000	.003		4.81	.13	.04	4.98	5.55
2630	3/4" thick		18000	.003		7.20	.14	.04	7.38	8.20
2660	1" thick		17000	.003		9.60	.14	.05	9.79	10.80
2670	1-1/2" thick	▼	15000	.004		14.40	.16	.05	14.61	16.15
2680	Hand placed, 1/2" thick	C-18	450	.020	▼	4.81	.79	.13	5.73	6.65

03 63 Epoxy Grouting

03 63 05 – Grouting of Dowels and Fasteners

03 63 05.10 Epoxy Only

		Crew	Daily Output	Labor-Hours	Unit	Material	2017 Bare Costs Labor	Equipment	Total	Total Incl O&P
0010	**EPOXY ONLY**									
1500	Chemical anchoring, epoxy cartridge, excludes layout, drilling, fastener									
1530	For fastener 3/4" diam. x 6" embedment	2 Skwk	72	.222	Ea.	5.15	11.45		16.60	23.50
1535	1" diam. x 8" embedment		66	.242		7.75	12.45		20.20	27.50
1540	1-1/4" diam. x 10" embedment		60	.267		15.45	13.70		29.15	38
1545	1-3/4" diam. x 12" embedment		54	.296		26	15.25		41.25	52
1550	14" embedment		48	.333		31	17.15		48.15	60.50
1555	2" diam. x 12" embedment		42	.381		41	19.60		60.60	75.50
1560	18" embedment		32	.500		51.50	25.50		77	96

03 81 Concrete Cutting

03 81 13 – Flat Concrete Sawing

03 81 13.50 Concrete Floor/Slab Cutting

		Crew	Daily Output	Labor-Hours	Unit	Material	2017 Bare Costs Labor	Equipment	Total	Total Incl O&P
0010	**CONCRETE FLOOR/SLAB CUTTING**									
0050	Includes blade cost, layout and set-up time									
0300	Saw cut concrete slabs, plain, up to 3" deep	B-89	1060	.015	L.F.	.13	.72	.42	1.27	1.68
0320	Each additional inch of depth		3180	.005		.04	.24	.14	.42	.56
0400	Mesh reinforced, up to 3" deep		980	.016		.14	.78	.45	1.37	1.83
0420	Each additional inch of depth		2940	.005		.05	.26	.15	.46	.61
0500	Rod reinforced, up to 3" deep		800	.020		.18	.95	.55	1.68	2.24
0520	Each additional inch of depth		2400	.007		.06	.32	.18	.56	.74

03 81 13.75 Concrete Saw Blades

		Crew	Daily Output	Labor-Hours	Unit	Material	2017 Bare Costs Labor	Equipment	Total	Total Incl O&P
0010	**CONCRETE SAW BLADES**									
3000	Blades for saw cutting, included in cutting line items									
3020	Diamond, 12" diameter				Ea.	230			230	253
3040	18" diameter					425			425	465
3080	24" diameter					705			705	775
3120	30" diameter					995			995	1,100
3160	36" diameter					1,325			1,325	1,450
3200	42" diameter					2,350			2,350	2,600

03 82 Concrete Boring

03 82 13 – Concrete Core Drilling

03 82 13.10 Core Drilling

		Crew	Daily Output	Labor-Hours	Unit	Material	2017 Bare Costs Labor	Equipment	Total	Total Incl O&P
0010	**CORE DRILLING**									
0015	Includes bit cost, layout and set-up time									
0020	Reinforced concrete slab, up to 6" thick									
0100	1" diameter core	B-89A	17	.941	Ea.	.18	42.50	6.75	49.43	73
0150	For each additional inch of slab thickness in same hole, add		1440	.011		.03	.50	.08	.61	.89
0200	2" diameter core		16.50	.970		.29	44	6.95	51.24	75.50
0250	For each additional inch of slab thickness in same hole, add		1080	.015		.05	.67	.11	.83	1.20
0300	3" diameter core		16	1		.39	45.50	7.15	53.04	78
0350	For each additional inch of slab thickness in same hole, add		720	.022		.06	1.01	.16	1.23	1.80
0500	4" diameter core		15	1.067		.50	48.50	7.65	56.65	83
0550	For each additional inch of slab thickness in same hole, add		480	.033		.08	1.51	.24	1.83	2.67
0700	6" diameter core		14	1.143		.77	52	8.20	60.97	89.50
0750	For each additional inch of slab thickness in same hole, add		360	.044		.13	2.01	.32	2.46	3.58
0900	8" diameter core		13	1.231		1.05	56	8.80	65.85	96.50
0950	For each additional inch of slab thickness in same hole, add		288	.056		.17	2.52	.40	3.09	4.50

For customer support on your Electrical Costs with RSMeans Data, call 800.448.8182.

31

03 82 Concrete Boring

03 82 13 – Concrete Core Drilling

03 82 13.10 Core Drilling	Crew	Daily Output	Labor-Hours	Unit	Material	2017 Bare Costs Labor	Equipment	Total	Total Incl O&P
1100	10" diameter core	B-89A	12	1.333	Ea.	1.47	60.50	9.55	71.52	105
1150	For each additional inch of slab thickness in same hole, add		240	.067		.24	3.02	.48	3.74	5.45
1300	12" diameter core		11	1.455		1.78	66	10.40	78.18	114
1350	For each additional inch of slab thickness in same hole, add		206	.078		.30	3.52	.56	4.38	6.35
1500	14" diameter core		10	1.600		2.07	72.50	11.45	86.02	126
1550	For each additional inch of slab thickness in same hole, add		180	.089		.35	4.03	.64	5.02	7.30
1700	18" diameter core		9	1.778		2.80	80.50	12.75	96.05	141
1750	For each additional inch of slab thickness in same hole, add		144	.111		.47	5.05	.80	6.32	9.15
1754	24" diameter core		8	2		3.97	90.50	14.30	108.77	159
1756	For each additional inch of slab thickness in same hole, add	▼	120	.133	▼	.66	6.05	.95	7.66	11.10
1760	For horizontal holes, add to above						20%	20%		
1770	Prestressed hollow core plank, 8" thick									
1780	1" diameter core	B-89A	17.50	.914	Ea.	.24	41.50	6.55	48.29	71
1790	For each additional inch of plank thickness in same hole, add		3840	.004		.03	.19	.03	.25	.35
1794	2" diameter core		17.25	.928		.38	42	6.65	49.03	72
1796	For each additional inch of plank thickness in same hole, add		2880	.006		.05	.25	.04	.34	.48
1800	3" diameter core		17	.941		.52	42.50	6.75	49.77	73.50
1810	For each additional inch of plank thickness in same hole, add		1920	.008		.06	.38	.06	.50	.72
1820	4" diameter core		16.50	.970		.67	44	6.95	51.62	76
1830	For each additional inch of plank thickness in same hole, add		1280	.013		.08	.57	.09	.74	1.06
1840	6" diameter core		15.50	1.032		1.03	47	7.40	55.43	81.50
1850	For each additional inch of plank thickness in same hole, add		960	.017		.13	.76	.12	1.01	1.43
1860	8" diameter core		15	1.067		1.40	48.50	7.65	57.55	84
1870	For each additional inch of plank thickness in same hole, add		768	.021		.17	.94	.15	1.26	1.80
1880	10" diameter core		14	1.143		1.96	52	8.20	62.16	90.50
1890	For each additional inch of plank thickness in same hole, add		640	.025		.24	1.13	.18	1.55	2.21
1900	12" diameter core		13.50	1.185		2.37	53.50	8.50	64.37	94.50
1910	For each additional inch of plank thickness in same hole, add	▼	548	.029	▼	.30	1.32	.21	1.83	2.59

03 82 16 – Concrete Drilling

03 82 16.10 Concrete Impact Drilling	Crew	Daily Output	Labor-Hours	Unit	Material	2017 Bare Costs Labor	Equipment	Total	Total Incl O&P
0010	**CONCRETE IMPACT DRILLING**									
0020	Includes bit cost, layout and set-up time, no anchors									
0050	Up to 4" deep in concrete/brick floors/walls									
0100	Holes, 1/4" diameter	1 Carp	75	.107	Ea.	.07	5.25		5.32	8.15
0150	For each additional inch of depth in same hole, add		430	.019		.02	.92		.94	1.42
0200	3/8" diameter		63	.127		.06	6.25		6.31	9.65
0250	For each additional inch of depth in same hole, add		340	.024		.01	1.16		1.17	1.80
0300	1/2" diameter		50	.160		.06	7.90		7.96	12.10
0350	For each additional inch of depth in same hole, add		250	.032		.02	1.58		1.60	2.43
0400	5/8" diameter		48	.167		.10	8.20		8.30	12.70
0450	For each additional inch of depth in same hole, add		240	.033		.03	1.64		1.67	2.54
0500	3/4" diameter		45	.178		.13	8.75		8.88	13.55
0550	For each additional inch of depth in same hole, add		220	.036		.03	1.79		1.82	2.78
0600	7/8" diameter		43	.186		.18	9.15		9.33	14.25
0650	For each additional inch of depth in same hole, add		210	.038		.04	1.88		1.92	2.92
0700	1" diameter		40	.200		.16	9.85		10.01	15.25
0750	For each additional inch of depth in same hole, add		190	.042		.04	2.07		2.11	3.22
0800	1-1/4" diameter		38	.211		.29	10.35		10.64	16.20
0850	For each additional inch of depth in same hole, add		180	.044		.07	2.19		2.26	3.43
0900	1-1/2" diameter		35	.229		.44	11.25		11.69	17.75
0950	For each additional inch of depth in same hole, add	▼	165	.048	▼	.11	2.39		2.50	3.78
1000	For ceiling installations, add						40%			

Estimating Tips
05 05 00 Common Work Results for Metals

- Nuts, bolts, washers, connection angles, and plates can add a significant amount to both the tonnage of a structural steel job and the estimated cost. As a rule of thumb, add 10% to the total weight to account for these accessories.

- Type 2 steel construction, commonly referred to as "simple construction," consists generally of field-bolted connections with lateral bracing supplied by other elements of the building, such as masonry walls or x-bracing. The estimator should be aware, however, that shop connections may be accomplished by welding or bolting. The method may be particular to the fabrication shop and may have an impact on the estimated cost.

05 10 00 Structural Steel

- Steel items can be obtained from two sources: a fabrication shop or a metals service center. Fabrication shops can fabricate items under more controlled conditions than crews in the field can. They are also more efficient and can produce items more economically. Metal service centers serve as a source of long mill shapes to both fabrication shops and contractors.

- Most line items in this structural steel subdivision, and most items in 05 50 00 Metal Fabrications, are indicated as being shop fabricated. The bare material cost for these shop fabricated items is the "Invoice Cost" from the shop and includes the mill base price of steel plus mill extras, transportation to the shop, shop drawings and detailing where warranted, shop fabrication and handling, sandblasting and a shop coat of primer paint, all necessary structural bolts, and delivery to the job site. The bare labor cost and bare equipment cost for these shop fabricated items are for field installation or erection.

- Line items in Subdivision 05 12 23.40 Lightweight Framing, and other items scattered in Division 5, are indicated as being field fabricated. The bare material cost for these field fabricated items is the "Invoice Cost" from the metals service center and includes the mill base price of steel plus mill extras, transportation to the metals service center, material handling, and delivery of long lengths of mill shapes to the job site. Material costs for structural bolts and welding rods should be added to the estimate. The bare labor cost and bare equipment cost for these items are for both field fabrication and field installation or erection, and include time for cutting, welding, and drilling in the fabricated metal items. Drilling into concrete and fasteners to fasten field fabricated items to other work are not included and should be added to the estimate.

05 20 00 Steel Joist Framing

- In any given project the total weight of open web steel joists is determined by the loads to be supported and the design. However, economies can be realized in minimizing the amount of labor used to place the joists. This is done by maximizing the joist spacing, and therefore minimizing the number of joists required to be installed on the job. Certain spacings and locations may be required by the design, but in other cases maximizing the spacing and keeping it as uniform as possible will keep the costs down.

05 30 00 Steel Decking

- The takeoff and estimating of a metal deck involves more than the area of the floor or roof and the type of deck specified or shown on the drawings. Many different sizes and types of openings may exist. Small openings for individual pipes or conduits may be drilled after the floor/roof is installed, but larger openings may require special deck lengths as well as reinforcing or structural support. The estimator should determine who will be supplying this reinforcing. Additionally, some deck terminations are part of the deck package, such as screed angles and pour stops, and others will be part of the steel contract, such as angles attached to structural members and cast-in-place angles and plates. The estimator must ensure that all pieces are accounted for in the complete estimate.

05 50 00 Metal Fabrications

- The most economical steel stairs are those that use common materials, standard details, and most importantly, a uniform and relatively simple method of field assembly. Commonly available A36/A992 channels and plates are very good choices for the main stringers of the stairs, as are angles and tees for the carrier members. Risers and treads are usually made by specialty shops, and it is most economical to use a typical detail in as many places as possible. The stairs should be pre-assembled and shipped directly to the site. The field connections should be simple and straightforward enough to be accomplished efficiently, and with minimum equipment and labor.

Reference Numbers

Reference numbers are shown at the beginning of some major classifications. These numbers refer to related items in the Reference Section. The reference information may be an estimating procedure, an alternate pricing method, or technical information.

Note: Not all subdivisions listed here necessarily appear. ■

Did you know?

Our online estimating solution gives you the same access to RSMeans' data with 24/7 access:

- Quickly locate costs in the searchable database.

- Build cost lists, estimates, and reports in minutes.

- Adjust costs to any location in the U.S. and Canada with the click of a button.

Start your free trial today at
www.RSMeansOnline.com

05 05 19 – Post-Installed Concrete Anchors

05 05 19.10 Chemical Anchors		Crew	Daily Output	Labor-Hours	Unit	Material	2017 Bare Costs Labor	Equipment	Total	Total Incl O&P
0010	**CHEMICAL ANCHORS**									
0020	Includes layout & drilling									
1430	Chemical anchor, w/rod & epoxy cartridge, 3/4" diam. x 9-1/2" long	B-89A	27	.593	Ea.	9.80	27	4.24	41.04	56.50
1435	1" diameter x 11-3/4" long		24	.667		18.25	30	4.77	53.02	72
1440	1-1/4" diameter x 14" long		21	.762		37	34.50	5.45	76.95	100
1445	1-3/4" diameter x 15" long		20	.800		65	36	5.75	106.75	133
1450	18" long		17	.941		78	42.50	6.75	127.25	158
1455	2" diameter x 18" long		16	1		103	45.50	7.15	155.65	190
1460	24" long		15	1.067		134	48.50	7.65	190.15	229

05 05 19.20 Expansion Anchors			Crew	Daily Output	Labor-Hours	Unit	Material	2017 Bare Costs Labor	Equipment	Total	Total Incl O&P
0010	**EXPANSION ANCHORS**										
0100	Anchors for concrete, brick or stone, no layout and drilling										
0200	Expansion shields, zinc, 1/4" diameter, 1-5/16" long, single	G	1 Carp	90	.089	Ea.	.45	4.38		4.83	7.20
0300	1-3/8" long, double	G		85	.094		.55	4.64		5.19	7.70
0400	3/8" diameter, 1-1/2" long, single	G		85	.094		.68	4.64		5.32	7.85
0500	2" long, double	G		80	.100		1.22	4.93		6.15	8.90
0600	1/2" diameter, 2-1/16" long, single	G		80	.100		1.25	4.93		6.18	8.95
0700	2-1/2" long, double	G		75	.107		2.35	5.25		7.60	10.65
0800	5/8" diameter, 2-5/8" long, single	G		75	.107		2.16	5.25		7.41	10.45
0900	2-3/4" long, double	G		70	.114		3.31	5.65		8.96	12.25
1000	3/4" diameter, 2-3/4" long, single	G		70	.114		3.27	5.65		8.92	12.20
1100	3-15/16" long, double	G		65	.123		6.15	6.05		12.20	16.10
2100	Hollow wall anchors for gypsum wall board, plaster or tile										
2300	1/8" diameter, short	G	1 Carp	160	.050	Ea.	.27	2.46		2.73	4.07
2400	Long	G		150	.053		.30	2.63		2.93	4.35
2500	3/16" diameter, short	G		150	.053		.47	2.63		3.10	4.54
2600	Long	G		140	.057		.64	2.81		3.45	5
2700	1/4" diameter, short	G		140	.057		.64	2.81		3.45	5
2800	Long	G		130	.062		.70	3.03		3.73	5.40
3000	Toggle bolts, bright steel, 1/8" diameter, 2" long	G		85	.094		.22	4.64		4.86	7.35
3100	4" long	G		80	.100		.27	4.93		5.20	7.85
3400	1/4" diameter, 3" long	G		75	.107		.36	5.25		5.61	8.45
3500	6" long	G		70	.114		.54	5.65		6.19	9.20
3600	3/8" diameter, 3" long	G		70	.114		.96	5.65		6.61	9.65
3700	6" long	G		60	.133		1.38	6.55		7.93	11.55
3800	1/2" diameter, 4" long	G		60	.133		1.94	6.55		8.49	12.20
3900	6" long	G		50	.160		2.48	7.90		10.38	14.80
4000	Nailing anchors										
4100	Nylon nailing anchor, 1/4" diameter, 1" long		1 Carp	3.20	2.500	C	22	123		145	213
4200	1-1/2" long			2.80	2.857		26	141		167	245
4300	2" long			2.40	3.333		30.50	164		194.50	286
4400	Metal nailing anchor, 1/4" diameter, 1" long	G		3.20	2.500		20.50	123		143.50	212
4500	1-1/2" long	G		2.80	2.857		26	141		167	245
4600	2" long	G		2.40	3.333		31.50	164		195.50	287
5000	Screw anchors for concrete, masonry,										
5100	stone & tile, no layout or drilling included										
5700	Lag screw shields, 1/4" diameter, short	G	1 Carp	90	.089	Ea.	.37	4.38		4.75	7.10
5900	3/8" diameter, short	G		85	.094		.72	4.64		5.36	7.90
6100	1/2" diameter, short	G		80	.100		1.06	4.93		5.99	8.70
6300	5/8" diameter, short	G		70	.114		1.64	5.65		7.29	10.40
6600	Lead, #6 & #8, 3/4" long	G		260	.031		.20	1.52		1.72	2.54
6700	#10 - #14, 1-1/2" long	G		200	.040		.41	1.97		2.38	3.47

05 05 Common Work Results for Metals

05 05 19 – Post-Installed Concrete Anchors

05 05 19.20 Expansion Anchors

		Crew	Daily Output	Labor-Hours	Unit	Material	2017 Bare Costs Labor	Equipment	Total	Total Incl O&P
6800	#16 & #18, 1-1/2" long	1 Carp	160	.050	Ea.	.43	2.46		2.89	4.24
6900	Plastic, #6 & #8, 3/4" long		260	.031		.04	1.52		1.56	2.36
7100	#10 & #12, 1" long		220	.036		.05	1.79		1.84	2.80
8000	Wedge anchors, not including layout or drilling									
8050	Carbon steel, 1/4" diameter, 1-3/4" long	G 1 Carp	150	.053	Ea.	.45	2.63		3.08	4.51
8100	3-1/4" long	G	140	.057		.59	2.81		3.40	4.96
8150	3/8" diameter, 2-1/4" long	G	145	.055		.53	2.72		3.25	4.74
8200	5" long	G	140	.057		.93	2.81		3.74	5.35
8250	1/2" diameter, 2-3/4" long	G	140	.057		1.05	2.81		3.86	5.45
8300	7" long	G	125	.064		1.80	3.15		4.95	6.80
8350	5/8" diameter, 3-1/2" long	G	130	.062		2.03	3.03		5.06	6.85
8400	8-1/2" long	G	115	.070		4.32	3.43		7.75	10
8450	3/4" diameter, 4-1/4" long	G	115	.070		3.09	3.43		6.52	8.65
8500	10" long	G	95	.084		7.05	4.15		11.20	14.10
8550	1" diameter, 6" long	G	100	.080		9.70	3.94		13.64	16.75
8575	9" long	G	85	.094		12.60	4.64		17.24	21
8600	12" long	G	75	.107		13.65	5.25		18.90	23
8650	1-1/4" diameter, 9" long	G	70	.114		25.50	5.65		31.15	37
8700	12" long	G	60	.133		33	6.55		39.55	46
8750	For type 303 stainless steel, add					350%				
8800	For type 316 stainless steel, add					450%				
8950	Self-drilling concrete screw, hex washer head, 3/16" diam. x 1-3/4" long	G 1 Carp	300	.027	Ea.	.21	1.31		1.52	2.24
8960	2-1/4" long	G	250	.032		.25	1.58		1.83	2.69
8970	Phillips flat head, 3/16" diam. x 1-3/4" long	G	300	.027		.21	1.31		1.52	2.24
8980	2-1/4" long	G	250	.032		.24	1.58		1.82	2.67

05 05 21 – Fastening Methods for Metal

05 05 21.15 Drilling Steel

		Crew	Daily Output	Labor-Hours	Unit	Material	2017 Bare Costs Labor	Equipment	Total	Total Incl O&P
0010	**DRILLING STEEL**									
1910	Drilling & layout for steel, up to 1/4" deep, no anchor									
1920	Holes, 1/4" diameter	1 Sswk	112	.071	Ea.	.10	3.88		3.98	6.55
1925	For each additional 1/4" depth, add		336	.024		.10	1.29		1.39	2.26
1930	3/8" diameter		104	.077		.09	4.18		4.27	7.05
1935	For each additional 1/4" depth, add		312	.026		.09	1.39		1.48	2.42
1940	1/2" diameter		96	.083		.11	4.52		4.63	7.70
1945	For each additional 1/4" depth, add		288	.028		.11	1.51		1.62	2.64
1950	5/8" diameter		88	.091		.16	4.94		5.10	8.45
1955	For each additional 1/4" depth, add		264	.030		.16	1.65		1.81	2.92
1960	3/4" diameter		80	.100		.20	5.45		5.65	9.25
1965	For each additional 1/4" depth, add		240	.033		.20	1.81		2.01	3.24
1970	7/8" diameter		72	.111		.26	6.05		6.31	10.35
1975	For each additional 1/4" depth, add		216	.037		.26	2.01		2.27	3.64
1980	1" diameter		64	.125		.23	6.80		7.03	11.55
1985	For each additional 1/4" depth, add		192	.042		.23	2.26		2.49	4.02
1990	For drilling up, add						40%			

05 05 23 – Metal Fastenings

05 05 23.10 Bolts and Hex Nuts

		Crew	Daily Output	Labor-Hours	Unit	Material	2017 Bare Costs Labor	Equipment	Total	Total Incl O&P
0010	**BOLTS & HEX NUTS**, Steel, A307									
0100	1/4" diameter, 1/2" long	G 1 Sswk	140	.057	Ea.	.06	3.10		3.16	5.20
0200	1" long	G	140	.057		.07	3.10		3.17	5.25
0300	2" long	G	130	.062		.10	3.34		3.44	5.65
0400	3" long	G	130	.062		.15	3.34		3.49	5.70
0500	4" long	G	120	.067		.17	3.62		3.79	6.25

For customer support on your Electrical Costs with RSMeans Data, call 800.448.8182.

35

05 05 Common Work Results for Metals

05 05 23 – Metal Fastenings

05 05 23.10 Bolts and Hex Nuts

		Crew	Daily Output	Labor-Hours	Unit	Material	2017 Bare Costs Labor	Equipment	Total	Total Incl O&P
0600	3/8" diameter, 1" long	G 1 Sswk	130	.062	Ea.	.14	3.34		3.48	5.70
0700	2" long	G	130	.062		.18	3.34		3.52	5.75
0800	3" long	G	120	.067		.24	3.62		3.86	6.30
0900	4" long	G	120	.067		.30	3.62		3.92	6.40
1000	5" long	G	115	.070		.38	3.78		4.16	6.70
1100	1/2" diameter, 1-1/2" long	G	120	.067		.40	3.62		4.02	6.50
1200	2" long	G	120	.067		.46	3.62		4.08	6.55
1300	4" long	G	115	.070		.75	3.78		4.53	7.15
1400	6" long	G	110	.073		1.05	3.95		5	7.75
1500	8" long	G	105	.076		1.38	4.14		5.52	8.40
1600	5/8" diameter, 1-1/2" long	G	120	.067		.85	3.62		4.47	7
1700	2" long	G	120	.067		.94	3.62		4.56	7.10
1800	4" long	G	115	.070		1.34	3.78		5.12	7.80
1900	6" long	G	110	.073		1.72	3.95		5.67	8.50
2000	8" long	G	105	.076		2.55	4.14		6.69	9.70
2100	10" long	G	100	.080		3.20	4.34		7.54	10.75
2200	3/4" diameter, 2" long	G	120	.067		1.15	3.62		4.77	7.30
2300	4" long	G	110	.073		1.65	3.95		5.60	8.40
2400	6" long	G	105	.076		2.12	4.14		6.26	9.25
2500	8" long	G	95	.084		3.20	4.57		7.77	11.10
2600	10" long	G	85	.094		4.20	5.10		9.30	13.10
2700	12" long	G	80	.100		4.92	5.45		10.37	14.45
2800	1" diameter, 3" long	G	105	.076		2.67	4.14		6.81	9.85
2900	6" long	G	90	.089		3.92	4.83		8.75	12.35
3000	12" long	G	75	.107		7.05	5.80		12.85	17.45
3100	For galvanized, add					75%				
3200	For stainless, add					350%				

05 05 23.30 Lag Screws

		Crew	Daily Output	Labor-Hours	Unit	Material	2017 Bare Costs Labor	Equipment	Total	Total Incl O&P
0010	**LAG SCREWS**									
0020	Steel, 1/4" diameter, 2" long	G 1 Carp	200	.040	Ea.	.11	1.97		2.08	3.14
0100	3/8" diameter, 3" long	G	150	.053		.34	2.63		2.97	4.39
0200	1/2" diameter, 3" long	G	130	.062		.70	3.03		3.73	5.40
0300	5/8" diameter, 3" long	G	120	.067		1.20	3.28		4.48	6.35

05 05 23.35 Machine Screws

		Crew	Daily Output	Labor-Hours	Unit	Material	2017 Bare Costs Labor	Equipment	Total	Total Incl O&P
0010	**MACHINE SCREWS**									
0020	Steel, round head, #8 x 1" long	G 1 Carp	4.80	1.667	C	5.05	82		87.05	132
0110	#8 x 2" long	G	2.40	3.333		7.55	164		171.55	260
0200	#10 x 1" long	G	4	2		5.95	98.50		104.45	158
0300	#10 x 2" long	G	2	4		12.05	197		209.05	315

05 05 23.50 Powder Actuated Tools and Fasteners

		Crew	Daily Output	Labor-Hours	Unit	Material	2017 Bare Costs Labor	Equipment	Total	Total Incl O&P
0010	**POWDER ACTUATED TOOLS & FASTENERS**									
0020	Stud driver, .22 caliber, single shot				Ea.	151			151	166
0100	.27 caliber, semi automatic, strip				"	460			460	505
0300	Powder load, single shot, .22 cal, power level 2, brown				C	5.60			5.60	6.20
0400	Strip, .27 cal, power level 4, red					8.10			8.10	8.90
0600	Drive pin, .300 x 3/4" long	G 1 Carp	4.80	1.667		4.36	82		86.36	131
0700	.300 x 3" long with washer	G "	4	2		13.30	98.50		111.80	166

05 05 23.70 Structural Blind Bolts

		Crew	Daily Output	Labor-Hours	Unit	Material	2017 Bare Costs Labor	Equipment	Total	Total Incl O&P
0010	**STRUCTURAL BLIND BOLTS**									
0100	1/4" diameter x 1/4" grip	G 1 Sswk	240	.033	Ea.	1.73	1.81		3.54	4.92
0150	1/2" grip	G	216	.037		1.86	2.01		3.87	5.40
0200	3/8" diameter x 1/2" grip	G	232	.034		2.44	1.87		4.31	5.80

For customer support on your Electrical Costs with RSMeans Data, call 800.448.8182.

05 05 Common Work Results for Metals

05 05 23 – Metal Fastenings

05 05 23.70 Structural Blind Bolts		Crew	Daily Output	Labor-Hours	Unit	Material	2017 Bare Costs Labor	Equipment	Total	Total Incl O&P
0250	3/4" grip	G	1 Sswk	208	.038	Ea.	2.56	2.09		4.65	6.30
0300	1/2" diameter x 1/2" grip	G		224	.036		5.85	1.94		7.79	9.65
0350	3/4" grip	G		200	.040		8.20	2.17		10.37	12.60
0400	5/8" diameter x 3/4" grip	G		216	.037		10.30	2.01		12.31	14.70
0450	1" grip	G		192	.042		11.85	2.26		14.11	16.80

05 12 Structural Steel Framing

05 12 23 – Structural Steel for Buildings

05 12 23.60 Pipe Support Framing

		Crew	Daily Output	Labor-Hours	Unit	Material	2017 Bare Costs Labor	Equipment	Total	Total Incl O&P
0010	**PIPE SUPPORT FRAMING**										
0020	Under 10#/L.F., shop fabricated	G	E-4	3900	.008	Lb.	1.76	.45	.03	2.24	2.72
0200	10.1 to 15#/L.F.	G		4300	.007		1.73	.41	.03	2.17	2.61
0400	15.1 to 20#/L.F.	G		4800	.007		1.70	.37	.03	2.10	2.51
0600	Over 20#/L.F.	G		5400	.006		1.68	.33	.02	2.03	2.42

05 35 Raceway Decking Assemblies

05 35 13 – Steel Cellular Decking

05 35 13.50 Cellular Decking

		Crew	Daily Output	Labor-Hours	Unit	Material	2017 Bare Costs Labor	Equipment	Total	Total Incl O&P
0010	**CELLULAR DECKING**										
0015	Made from recycled materials										
0200	Cellular units, galv, 1-1/2" deep, Type BC, 20-20 ga., over 15 squares	G	E-4	1460	.022	S.F.	9.15	1.20	.09	10.44	12.15
0250	18-20 ga.	G		1420	.023		10.35	1.24	.09	11.68	13.55
0300	18-18 ga.	G		1390	.023		10.65	1.26	.09	12	13.90
0320	16-18 ga.	G		1360	.024		12.70	1.29	.10	14.09	16.20
0340	16-16 ga.	G		1330	.024		14.10	1.32	.10	15.52	17.80
0400	3" deep, Type NC, galvanized, 20-20 ga.	G		1375	.023		10.05	1.28	.09	11.42	13.30
0500	18-20 ga.	G		1350	.024		12.15	1.30	.10	13.55	15.60
0600	18-18 ga.	G		1290	.025		12.10	1.36	.10	13.56	15.70
0700	16-18 ga.	G		1230	.026		13.65	1.43	.11	15.19	17.50
0800	16-16 ga.	G		1150	.028		14.85	1.53	.11	16.49	19
1000	4-1/2" deep, Type JC, galvanized, 18-20 ga.	G		1100	.029		14	1.59	.12	15.71	18.20
1100	18-18 ga.	G		1040	.031		13.90	1.69	.12	15.71	18.25
1200	16-18 ga.	G		980	.033		15.65	1.79	.13	17.57	20.50
1300	16-16 ga.	G		935	.034		17.10	1.88	.14	19.12	22
1900	For multi-story or congested site, add							50%			

Division Notes

	CREW	DAILY OUTPUT	LABOR-HOURS	UNIT	BARE COSTS				TOTAL INCL O&P
					MAT.	LABOR	EQUIP.	TOTAL	

Estimating Tips
06 05 00 Common Work Results for Wood, Plastics, and Composites

- Common to any wood-framed structure are the accessory connector items such as screws, nails, adhesives, hangers, connector plates, straps, angles, and hold-downs. For typical wood-framed buildings, such as residential projects, the aggregate total for these items can be significant, especially in areas where seismic loading is a concern. For floor and wall framing, the material cost is based on 10 to 25 lbs. of accessory connectors per MBF. Hold-downs, hangers, and other connectors should be taken off by the piece.

  Included with material costs are fasteners for a normal installation. Gordian's RSMeans engineers use manufacturers' recommendations, written specifications, and/or standard construction practice for the sizing and spacing of fasteners. Prices for various fasteners are shown for informational purposes only. Adjustments should be made if unusual fastening conditions exist.

06 10 00 Carpentry

- Lumber is a traded commodity and therefore sensitive to supply and demand in the marketplace. Even with "budgetary" estimating of wood-framed projects, it is advisable to call local suppliers for the latest market pricing.

- The common quantity unit for wood-framed projects is "thousand board feet" (MBF). A board foot is a volume of wood—1" x 1' x 1' or 144 cubic inches. Board-foot quantities are generally calculated using nominal material dimensions— dressed sizes are ignored. Board foot per lineal foot of any stick of lumber can be calculated by dividing the nominal cross-sectional area by 12. As an example, 2,000 lineal feet of 2 x 12 equates to 4 MBF by dividing the nominal area, 2 x 12, by 12, which equals 2, and multiplying by 2,000 to give 4,000 board feet. This simple rule applies to all nominal dimensioned lumber.

- Waste is an issue of concern at the quantity takeoff for any area of construction. Framing lumber is sold in even foot lengths, i.e., 8', 10', 12', 14', 16' and depending on spans, wall heights, and the grade of lumber, waste is inevitable. A rule of thumb for lumber waste is 5%–10% depending on material quality and the complexity of the framing.

- Wood in various forms and shapes is used in many projects, even where the main structural framing is steel, concrete, or masonry. Plywood as a back-up partition material and 2x boards used as blocking and cant strips around roof edges are two common examples. The estimator should ensure that the costs of all wood materials are included in the final estimate.

06 20 00 Finish Carpentry

- It is necessary to consider the grade of workmanship when estimating labor costs for erecting millwork and an interior finish. In practice, there are three grades: premium, custom, and economy. The RSMeans daily output for base and case moldings is in the range of 200 to 250 L.F. per carpenter per day. This is appropriate for most average custom-grade projects. For premium projects, an adjustment to productivity of 25%–50% should be made, depending on the complexity of the job.

Reference Numbers

Reference numbers are shown at the beginning of some major classifications. These numbers refer to related items in the Reference Section. The reference information may be an estimating procedure, an alternate pricing method, or technical information.

Note: Not all subdivisions listed here necessarily appear. ■

Did you know?

Our online estimating solution gives you the same access to RSMeans' data with 24/7 access:

- Quickly locate costs in the searchable database.

- Build cost lists, estimates, and reports in minutes.

- Adjust costs to any location in the U.S. and Canada with the click of a button.

Start your free trial today at
www.RSMeansOnline.com

06 16 36 – Wood Panel Product Sheathing

06 16 36.10 Sheathing	Crew	Daily Output	Labor-Hours	Unit	Material	2017 Bare Costs Labor	Equipment	Total	Total Incl O&P
0010 **SHEATHING**									
0012 Plywood on roofs, CDX									
0030 5/16" thick	2 Carp	1600	.010	S.F.	.59	.49		1.08	1.40
0035 Pneumatic nailed		1952	.008		.59	.40		.99	1.27
0050 3/8" thick		1525	.010		.61	.52		1.13	1.46
0055 Pneumatic nailed		1860	.009		.61	.42		1.03	1.32
0100 1/2" thick		1400	.011		.63	.56		1.19	1.55
0105 Pneumatic nailed		1708	.009		.63	.46		1.09	1.40
0200 5/8" thick		1300	.012		.78	.61		1.39	1.79
0205 Pneumatic nailed		1586	.010		.78	.50		1.28	1.62
0300 3/4" thick		1200	.013		.94	.66		1.60	2.04
0305 Pneumatic nailed		1464	.011		.94	.54		1.48	1.85
0500 Plywood on walls, with exterior CDX, 3/8" thick		1200	.013		.61	.66		1.27	1.68
0505 Pneumatic nailed		1488	.011		.61	.53		1.14	1.48
0600 1/2" thick		1125	.014		.63	.70		1.33	1.76
0605 Pneumatic nailed		1395	.011		.63	.56		1.19	1.56
0700 5/8" thick		1050	.015		.78	.75		1.53	2.01
0705 Pneumatic nailed		1302	.012		.78	.61		1.39	1.79
0800 3/4" thick		975	.016		.94	.81		1.75	2.27
0805 Pneumatic nailed		1209	.013		.94	.65		1.59	2.03

Estimating Tips
07 10 00 Dampproofing and Waterproofing

- Be sure of the job specifications before pricing this subdivision. The difference in cost between waterproofing and dampproofing can be great. Waterproofing will hold back standing water. Dampproofing prevents the transmission of water vapor. Also included in this section are vapor retarding membranes.

07 20 00 Thermal Protection

- Insulation and fireproofing products are measured by area, thickness, volume or R-value. Specifications may give only what the specific R-value should be in a certain situation. The estimator may need to choose the type of insulation to meet that R-value.

07 30 00 Steep Slope Roofing
07 40 00 Roofing and Siding Panels

- Many roofing and siding products are bought and sold by the square. One square is equal to an area that measures 100 square feet.

  This simple change in unit of measure could create a large error if the estimator is not observant. Accessories necessary for a complete installation must be figured into any calculations for both material and labor.

07 50 00 Membrane Roofing
07 60 00 Flashing and Sheet Metal
07 70 00 Roofing and Wall Specialties and Accessories

- The items in these subdivisions compose a roofing system. No one component completes the installation, and all must be estimated. Built-up or single-ply membrane roofing systems are made up of many products and installation trades. Wood blocking at roof perimeters or penetrations, parapet coverings, reglets, roof drains, gutters, downspouts, sheet metal flashing, skylights, smoke vents, and roof hatches all need to be considered along with the roofing material. Several different installation trades will need to work together on the roofing system. Inherent difficulties in the scheduling and coordination of various trades must be accounted for when estimating labor costs.

07 90 00 Joint Protection

- To complete the weather-tight shell, the sealants and caulkings must be estimated. Where different materials meet—at expansion joints, at flashing penetrations, and at hundreds of other locations throughout a construction project—caulking and sealants provide another line of defense against water penetration. Often, an entire system is based on the proper location and placement of caulking or sealants. The detailed drawings that are included as part of a set of architectural plans show typical locations for these materials. When caulking or sealants are shown at typical locations, this means the estimator must include them for all the locations where this detail is applicable. Be careful to keep different types of sealants separate, and remember to consider backer rods and primers if necessary.

Reference Numbers

Reference numbers are shown at the beginning of some major classifications. These numbers refer to related items in the Reference Section. The reference information may be an estimating procedure, an alternate pricing method, or technical information.

Note: Not all subdivisions listed here necessarily appear. ■

Did you know?

Our online estimating solution gives you the same access to RSMeans' data with 24/7 access:

- Quickly locate costs in the searchable database.
- Build cost lists, estimates, and reports in minutes.
- Adjust costs to any location in the U.S. and Canada with the click of a button.

Start your free trial today at
www.RSMeansOnline.com

07 84 13 – Penetration Firestopping

07 84 13.10 Firestopping		Crew	Daily Output	Labor-Hours	Unit	Material	2017 Bare Costs Labor	Equipment	Total	Total Incl O&P
0010	**FIRESTOPPING** R078413-30									
0100	Metallic piping, non insulated									
0110	Through walls, 2" diameter	1 Carp	16	.500	Ea.	3.60	24.50		28.10	41.50
0120	4" diameter		14	.571		6.30	28		34.30	50
0130	6" diameter		12	.667		9.25	33		42.25	60.50
0140	12" diameter		10	.800		18.45	39.50		57.95	81
0150	Through floors, 2" diameter		32	.250		1.80	12.30		14.10	21
0160	4" diameter		28	.286		3.15	14.05		17.20	25
0170	6" diameter		24	.333		4.60	16.40		21	30
0180	12" diameter		20	.400		9.25	19.70		28.95	40
0190	Metallic piping, insulated									
0200	Through walls, 2" diameter	1 Carp	16	.500	Ea.	6.30	24.50		30.80	44.50
0210	4" diameter		14	.571		9.25	28		37.25	53
0220	6" diameter		12	.667		12.40	33		45.40	64
0230	12" diameter		10	.800		21	39.50		60.50	84
0240	Through floors, 2" diameter		32	.250		3.15	12.30		15.45	22.50
0250	4" diameter		28	.286		4.60	14.05		18.65	26.50
0260	6" diameter		24	.333		6.20	16.40		22.60	32
0270	12" diameter		20	.400		10.60	19.70		30.30	41.50
0280	Non metallic piping, non insulated									
0290	Through walls, 2" diameter	1 Carp	12	.667	Ea.	45.50	33		78.50	101
0300	4" diameter		10	.800		87	39.50		126.50	156
0310	6" diameter		8	1		170	49.50		219.50	263
0330	Through floors, 2" diameter		16	.500		30	24.50		54.50	70.50
0340	4" diameter		6	1.333		55.50	65.50		121	162
0350	6" diameter		6	1.333		103	65.50		168.50	214
0370	Ductwork, insulated & non insulated, round									
0380	Through walls, 6" diameter	1 Carp	12	.667	Ea.	12.40	33		45.40	64
0390	12" diameter		10	.800		21	39.50		60.50	84
0400	18" diameter		8	1		25.50	49.50		75	104
0410	Through floors, 6" diameter		16	.500		6.20	24.50		30.70	44.50
0420	12" diameter		14	.571		10.60	28		38.60	54.50
0430	18" diameter		12	.667		12.85	33		45.85	64.50
0440	Ductwork, insulated & non insulated, rectangular									
0450	With stiffener/closure angle, through walls, 6" x 12"	1 Carp	8	1	Ea.	16.20	49.50		65.70	93.50
0460	12" x 24"		6	1.333		32.50	65.50		98	137
0470	24" x 48"		4	2		65	98.50		163.50	223
0480	With stiffener/closure angle, through floors, 6" x 12"		10	.800		8.10	39.50		47.60	69.50
0490	12" x 24"		8	1		16.20	49.50		65.70	93.50
0500	24" x 48"		6	1.333		32.50	65.50		98	137
0510	Multi trade openings									
0520	Through walls, 6" x 12"	1 Carp	2	4	Ea.	45	197		242	350
0530	12" x 24"	"	1	8		147	395		542	765
0540	24" x 48"	2 Carp	1	16		525	790		1,315	1,775
0550	48" x 96"	"	.75	21.333		1,975	1,050		3,025	3,775
0560	Through floors, 6" x 12"	1 Carp	2	4		49.50	197		246.50	355
0570	12" x 24"	"	1	8		68	395		463	680
0580	24" x 48"	2 Carp	.75	21.333		138	1,050		1,188	1,750
0590	48" x 96"	"	.50	32		390	1,575		1,965	2,850
0600	Structural penetrations, through walls									
0610	Steel beams, W8 x 10	1 Carp	8	1	Ea.	68.50	49.50		118	151
0620	W12 x 14		6	1.333		99	65.50		164.50	210
0630	W21 x 44		5	1.600		138	79		217	273

For customer support on your Electrical Costs with RSMeans Data, call 800.448.8182.

07 84 Firestopping

07 84 13 – Penetration Firestopping

07 84 13.10 Firestopping

		Crew	Daily Output	Labor-Hours	Unit	Material	2017 Bare Costs Labor	Equipment	Total	Total Incl O&P
0640	W36 x 135	1 Carp	3	2.667	Ea.	219	131		350	440
0650	Bar joists, 18" deep		6	1.333		40.50	65.50		106	146
0660	24" deep		6	1.333		54	65.50		119.50	160
0670	36" deep		5	1.600		81	79		160	210
0680	48" deep	↓	4	2	↓	108	98.50		206.50	269
0690	Construction joints, floor slab at exterior wall									
0700	Precast, brick, block or drywall exterior									
0710	2" wide joint	1 Carp	125	.064	L.F.	9.50	3.15		12.65	15.30
0720	4" wide joint	"	75	.107	"	14.85	5.25		20.10	24.50
0730	Metal panel, glass or curtain wall exterior									
0740	2" wide joint	1 Carp	40	.200	L.F.	9.50	9.85		19.35	25.50
0750	4" wide joint	"	25	.320	"	14.85	15.75		30.60	40.50
0760	Floor slab to drywall partition									
0770	Flat joint	1 Carp	100	.080	L.F.	13.20	3.94		17.14	20.50
0780	Fluted joint		50	.160		15.05	7.90		22.95	28.50
0790	Etched fluted joint	↓	75	.107	↓	18.50	5.25		23.75	28.50
0800	Floor slab to concrete/masonry partition									
0810	Flat joint	1 Carp	75	.107	L.F.	13.20	5.25		18.45	22.50
0820	Fluted joint	"	50	.160	"	15.05	7.90		22.95	28.50
0830	Concrete/CMU wall joints									
0840	1" wide	1 Carp	100	.080	L.F.	18.85	3.94		22.79	26.50
0850	2" wide		75	.107		23.50	5.25		28.75	33.50
0860	4" wide	↓	50	.160	↓	33.50	7.90		41.40	48.50
0870	Concrete/CMU floor joints									
0880	1" wide	1 Carp	200	.040	L.F.	18.85	1.97		20.82	23.50
0890	2" wide		150	.053		23.50	2.63		26.13	29.50
0900	4" wide	↓	100	.080	↓	33.50	3.94		37.44	42.50

07 91 Preformed Joint Seals

07 91 13 – Compression Seals

07 91 13.10 Compression Seals

		Crew	Daily Output	Labor-Hours	Unit	Material	2017 Bare Costs Labor	Equipment	Total	Total Incl O&P
0010	**COMPRESSION SEALS**									
4900	O-ring type cord, 1/4"	1 Bric	472	.017	L.F.	.43	.81		1.24	1.72
4910	1/2"		440	.018		1.21	.87		2.08	2.67
4920	3/4"		424	.019		2.43	.90		3.33	4.06
4930	1"		408	.020		4.10	.94		5.04	5.95
4940	1-1/4"		384	.021		7.50	.99		8.49	9.80
4950	1-1/2"		368	.022		9.25	1.04		10.29	11.75
4960	1-3/4"		352	.023		18.75	1.09		19.84	22
4970	2"	↓	344	.023	↓	22.50	1.11		23.61	26.50

07 91 23 – Backer Rods

07 91 23.10 Backer Rods

		Crew	Daily Output	Labor-Hours	Unit	Material	2017 Bare Costs Labor	Equipment	Total	Total Incl O&P
0010	**BACKER RODS**									
0030	Backer rod, polyethylene, 1/4" diameter	1 Bric	4.60	1.739	C.L.F.	2.37	83		85.37	131
0050	1/2" diameter		4.60	1.739		4.28	83		87.28	133
0070	3/4" diameter		4.60	1.739		6.75	83		89.75	135
0090	1" diameter	↓	4.60	1.739	↓	12.10	83		95.10	141

For customer support on your Electrical Costs with RSMeans Data, call 800.448.8182.

43

07 91 26 – Joint Fillers

07 91 26.10 Joint Fillers	Crew	Daily Output	Labor-Hours	Unit	Material	2017 Bare Costs Labor	Equipment	Total	Total Incl O&P
0010	**JOINT FILLERS**								
4360	Butyl rubber filler, 1/4" x 1/4"	1 Bric	290	.028	L.F.	.23	1.32		1.55	2.28
4365	1/2" x 1/2"		250	.032		.90	1.53		2.43	3.34
4370	1/2" x 3/4"		210	.038		1.35	1.82		3.17	4.29
4375	3/4" x 3/4"		230	.035		2.03	1.66		3.69	4.78
4380	1" x 1"	↓	180	.044	↓	2.71	2.12		4.83	6.25
4390	For coloring, add					12%			
4980	Polyethylene joint backing, 1/4" x 2"	1 Bric	2.08	3.846	C.L.F.	13.20	184		197.20	298
4990	1/4" x 6"		1.28	6.250	"	29	298		327	490
5600	Silicone, room temp vulcanizing foam seal, 1/4" x 1/2"		1312	.006	L.F.	.46	.29		.75	.96
5610	1/2" x 1/2"		656	.012		.93	.58		1.51	1.92
5620	1/2" x 3/4"		442	.018		1.39	.86		2.25	2.86
5630	3/4" x 3/4"		328	.024		2.08	1.16		3.24	4.08
5640	1/8" x 1"		1312	.006		.46	.29		.75	.96
5650	1/8" x 3"		442	.018		1.39	.86		2.25	2.86
5670	1/4" x 3"		295	.027		2.78	1.30		4.08	5.05
5680	1/4" x 6"		148	.054		5.55	2.58		8.13	10.05
5690	1/2" x 6"		82	.098		11.10	4.66		15.76	19.35
5700	1/2" x 9"		52.50	.152		16.65	7.30		23.95	29.50
5710	1/2" x 12"	↓	33	.242	↓	22	11.60		33.60	42.50

07 92 Joint Sealants

07 92 13 – Elastomeric Joint Sealants

07 92 13.20 Caulking and Sealant Options	Crew	Daily Output	Labor-Hours	Unit	Material	2017 Bare Costs Labor	Equipment	Total	Total Incl O&P
0010	**CAULKING AND SEALANT OPTIONS**								
0050	Latex acrylic based, bulk				Gal.	27			27	29.50
0055	Bulk in place 1/4" x 1/4" bead	1 Bric	300	.027	L.F.	.08	1.27		1.35	2.05
0060	1/4" x 3/8"		294	.027		.14	1.30		1.44	2.15
0065	1/4" x 1/2"		288	.028		.19	1.33		1.52	2.25
0075	3/8" x 3/8"		284	.028		.21	1.35		1.56	2.30
0080	3/8" x 1/2"		280	.029		.28	1.36		1.64	2.41
0085	3/8" x 5/8"		276	.029		.35	1.38		1.73	2.52
0095	3/8" x 3/4"		272	.029		.42	1.40		1.82	2.62
0100	1/2" x 1/2"		275	.029		.38	1.39		1.77	2.55
0105	1/2" x 5/8"		269	.030		.47	1.42		1.89	2.70
0110	1/2" x 3/4"		263	.030		.56	1.45		2.01	2.85
0115	1/2" x 7/8"		256	.031		.66	1.49		2.15	3.02
0120	1/2" x 1"		250	.032		.75	1.53		2.28	3.18
0125	3/4" x 3/4"		244	.033		.85	1.57		2.42	3.34
0130	3/4" x 1"		225	.036		1.13	1.70		2.83	3.85
0135	1" x 1"	↓	200	.040	↓	1.50	1.91		3.41	4.59
0190	Cartridges				Gal.	33			33	36
0200	11 fl. oz. cartridge				Ea.	2.82			2.82	3.10
0600	1/2" x 1/2"	1 Bric	275	.029	L.F.	.46	1.39		1.85	2.65
3200	Polyurethane, 1 or 2 component				Gal.	53.50			53.50	58.50
3300	Cartridges				"	67			67	73.50
3500	Bulk, in place, 1/4" x 1/4"	1 Bric	300	.027	L.F.	.17	1.27		1.44	2.15
3655	1/2" x 1/4"		288	.028		.35	1.33		1.68	2.42
3800	3/4" x 3/8"		272	.029		.78	1.40		2.18	3.02
3900	1" x 1/2"	↓	250	.032		1.38	1.53		2.91	3.87

07 92 Joint Sealants

07 92 19 – Acoustical Joint Sealants

07 92 19.10 Acoustical Sealant	Crew	Daily Output	Labor-Hours	Unit	Material	2017 Bare Costs Labor	Equipment	Total	Total Incl O&P
0010 **ACOUSTICAL SEALANT**									
0020 Acoustical sealant, elastomeric, cartridges				Ea.	8.50			8.50	9.35
0025 In place, 1/4" x 1/4"	1 Bric	300	.027	L.F.	.35	1.27		1.62	2.34
0030 1/4" x 1/2"		288	.028		.69	1.33		2.02	2.80
0035 1/2" x 1/2"		275	.029		1.39	1.39		2.78	3.67
0040 1/2" x 3/4"		263	.030		2.08	1.45		3.53	4.52
0045 3/4" x 3/4"		244	.033		3.13	1.57		4.70	5.85
0050 1" x 1"		200	.040		5.55	1.91		7.46	9.05

For customer support on your Electrical Costs with RSMeans Data, call 800.448.8182.

45

Division Notes

	CREW	DAILY OUTPUT	LABOR-HOURS	UNIT	BARE COSTS				TOTAL INCL O&P
					MAT.	LABOR	EQUIP.	TOTAL	

Estimating Tips
08 10 00 Doors and Frames
All exterior doors should be addressed for their energy conservation (insulation and seals).

- Most metal doors and frames look alike, but there may be significant differences among them. When estimating these items, be sure to choose the line item that most closely compares to the specification or door schedule requirements regarding:
  - type of metal
  - metal gauge
  - door core material
  - fire rating
  - finish
- Wood and plastic doors vary considerably in price. The primary determinant is the veneer material. Lauan, birch, and oak are the most common veneers. Other variables include the following:
  - hollow or solid core
  - fire rating
  - flush or raised panel
  - finish
- Door pricing includes bore for cylindrical locksets and mortise for hinges.

08 30 00 Specialty Doors and Frames
- There are many varieties of special doors, and they are usually priced per each. Add frames, hardware, or operators required for a complete installation.

08 40 00 Entrances, Storefronts, and Curtain Walls
- Glazed curtain walls consist of the metal tube framing and the glazing material. The cost data in this subdivision is presented for the metal tube framing alone or the composite wall. If your estimate requires a detailed takeoff of the framing, be sure to add the glazing cost and any tints.

08 50 00 Windows
- Steel windows are unglazed and aluminum can be glazed or unglazed. Some metal windows are priced without glass. Refer to 08 80 00 Glazing for glass pricing. The grade C indicates commercial grade windows, usually ASTM C-35.
- All wood windows and vinyl are priced preglazed. The glazing is insulating glass. Add the cost of screens and grills if required and not already included.

08 70 00 Hardware
- Hardware costs add considerably to the cost of a door. The most efficient method to determine the hardware requirements for a project is to review the door and hardware schedule together. One type of door may have different hardware, depending on the door usage.
- Door hinges are priced by the pair, with most doors requiring 1-1/2 pairs per door. The hinge prices do not include installation labor, because it is included in door installation.

Hinges are classified according to the frequency of use, base material, and finish.

08 80 00 Glazing
- Different openings require different types of glass. The most common types are:
  - float
  - tempered
  - insulating
  - impact-resistant
  - ballistic-resistant
- Most exterior windows are glazed with insulating glass. Entrance doors and window walls, where the glass is less than 18" from the floor, are generally glazed with tempered glass. Interior windows and some residential windows are glazed with float glass.
- Coastal communities require the use of impact-resistant glass, dependent on wind speed.
- The insulation or 'u' value is a strong consideration, along with solar heat gain, to determine total energy efficiency.

Reference Numbers
Reference numbers are shown at the beginning of some major classifications. These numbers refer to related items in the Reference Section. The reference information may be an estimating procedure, an alternate pricing method, or technical information.

Note: Not all subdivisions listed here necessarily appear. ■

08 31 Access Doors and Panels

08 31 13 – Access Doors and Frames

08 31 13.10 Types of Framed Access Doors	Crew	Daily Output	Labor-Hours	Unit	Material	2017 Bare Costs Labor	Equipment	Total	Total Incl O&P
0010 **TYPES OF FRAMED ACCESS DOORS**									
4000 Recessed door for drywall									
4100 Metal 12" x 12"	1 Carp	6	1.333	Ea.	87	65.50		152.50	197
4150 12" x 24"		5.50	1.455		116	71.50		187.50	237
4200 24" x 36"		5	1.600		173	79		252	310

08 74 Access Control Hardware

08 74 13 – Card Key Access Control Hardware

08 74 13.50 Card Key Access

08 74 13.50 Card Key Access	Crew	Daily Output	Labor-Hours	Unit	Material	2017 Bare Costs Labor	Equipment	Total	Total Incl O&P
0010 **CARD KEY ACCESS**									
0020 Computerized system, processor, proximity reader and cards									
0030 Does not include door hardware, lockset or wiring									
0040 Card key system for 1 door				Ea.	1,350			1,350	1,475
0060 Card key system for 2 doors					2,175			2,175	2,400
0080 Card key system for 4 doors					2,700			2,700	2,975
0100 Processor for card key access system					940			940	1,025
0160 Magnetic lock for electric access, 600 pound holding force					205			205	226
0170 Magnetic lock for electric access, 1200 pound holding force					205			205	226
0200 Proximity card reader					140			140	154

08 74 13.60 Entrance Card Systems

08 74 13.60 Entrance Card Systems	Crew	Daily Output	Labor-Hours	Unit	Material	2017 Bare Costs Labor	Equipment	Total	Total Incl O&P
0010 **ENTRANCE CARD SYSTEMS**									
0100 Entrance card, barium ferrite				Ea.	4.78			4.78	5.25
0120 Credential					6.60			6.60	7.25
0140 Proximity					9.05			9.05	9.95
0160 Weigand					9.90			9.90	10.90
0500 Entrance card reader, barium ferrite	R-19	4	5		310	284		594	765
0520 Credential		4	5		250	284		534	700
0540 Proximity		4	5		297	284		581	750
0560 Weigand		4	5		445	284		729	910
0650 Scanner, eye retina		4	5		6,000	284		6,284	7,025
0700 Gate opener, cantilever	R-18	3	8.667		2,300	430		2,730	3,175
0710 Light duty		3	8.667		1,650	430		2,080	2,475
0712 Custom		3	8.667		2,200	430		2,630	3,075
0750 Switch, tamper	R-19	6	3.333		24.50	189		213.50	310
0900 Accessories, electric door strike/bolt		5	4		80	227		307	430
0920 Electromagnetic lock		5	4		175	227		402	535
0940 Keypad for card reader		4	5		630	284		914	1,125

08 74 16 – Keypad Access Control Hardware

08 74 16.50 Keypad Access

08 74 16.50 Keypad Access	Crew	Daily Output	Labor-Hours	Unit	Material	2017 Bare Costs Labor	Equipment	Total	Total Incl O&P
0010 **KEYPAD ACCESS**									
0340 Digital keypad, int/ext, basic, excl. striker/power/wiring	1 Elec	3	2.667	Ea.	115	151		266	355
0350 Lockset, mechanical push-button type, complete, incl hardware	1 Carp	4	2	"	380	98.50		478.50	570

08 74 19 – Biometric Identity Access Control Hardware

08 74 19.50 Biometric Identity Access

08 74 19.50 Biometric Identity Access	Crew	Daily Output	Labor-Hours	Unit	Material	2017 Bare Costs Labor	Equipment	Total	Total Incl O&P
0010 **BIOMETRIC IDENTITY ACCESS**									
0200 Fingerprint scanner unit, excl striker/power supply	1 Elec	4	2	Ea.	1,500	113		1,613	1,825
0210 Fingerprint scanner unit, for computer keyboard access		8	1		1,200	56.50		1,256.50	1,400
0220 Hand geometry scanner, mem of 512 users, excl striker/power		3	2.667		2,200	151		2,351	2,650
0230 Memory upgrade for, adds 9,700 user profiles		8	1		320	56.50		376.50	435
0240 Adds 32,500 user profiles		8	1		650	56.50		706.50	800

08 74 Access Control Hardware

08 74 19 – Biometric Identity Access Control Hardware

08 74 19.50 Biometric Identity Access	Crew	Daily Output	Labor-Hours	Unit	Material	2017 Bare Costs Labor	Equipment	Total	Total Incl O&P
0250	Prison type, memory of 256 users, excl striker/power	1 Elec	3	2.667	Ea.	2,650	151		2,801	3,150
0260	Memory upgrade for, adds 3,300 user profiles		8	1		300	56.50		356.50	415
0270	Adds 9,700 user profiles		8	1		480	56.50		536.50	615
0280	Adds 27,900 user profiles		8	1		650	56.50		706.50	800
0290	All weather, mem of 512 users, excl striker/power		3	2.667		4,000	151		4,151	4,625
0300	Facial & fingerprint scanner, combination unit, excl striker/power		3	2.667		4,300	151		4,451	4,950
0310	Access for, for initial setup, excl striker/power	↓	3	2.667	↓	1,200	151		1,351	1,550

08 74 23 – Access Control Accessories

08 74 23.50 Security Access Control Accessories

	Crew	Daily Output	Labor-Hours	Unit	Material	2017 Bare Costs Labor	Equipment	Total	Total Incl O&P
0010	**SECURITY ACCESS CONTROL ACCESSORIES**									
0360	Scanner/reader access, power supply/transf, 110V to 12/24V	1 Elec	4	2	Ea.	255	113		368	450
0370	Elec/mag strikers, 12/24V		4	2		95	113		208	275
0380	1 hour battery backup power supply	↓	4	2		110	113		223	291
0390	Deadbolt, digital, batt-operated, indoor/outdoor, complete, incl hardware	1 Carp	4	2	↓	320	98.50		418.50	500

Division Notes

	CREW	DAILY OUTPUT	LABOR-HOURS	UNIT	BARE COSTS				TOTAL INCL O&P
					MAT.	LABOR	EQUIP.	TOTAL	

Estimating Tips
General

- Room Finish Schedule: A complete set of plans should contain a room finish schedule. If one is not available, it would be well worth the time and effort to obtain one.

09 20 00 Plaster and Gypsum Board

- Lath is estimated by the square yard plus a 5% allowance for waste. Furring, channels, and accessories are measured by the linear foot. An extra foot should be allowed for each accessory miter or stop.

- Plaster is also estimated by the square yard. Deductions for openings vary by preference, from zero deduction to 50% of all openings over 2 feet in width. The estimator should allow one extra square foot for each linear foot of horizontal interior or exterior angle located below the ceiling level. Also, double the areas of small radius work.

- Drywall accessories, studs, track, and acoustical caulking are all measured by the linear foot. Drywall taping is figured by the square foot. Gypsum wallboard is estimated by the square foot. No material deductions should be made for door or window openings under 32 S.F.

09 60 00 Flooring

- Tile and terrazzo areas are taken off on a square foot basis. Trim and base materials are measured by the linear foot. Accent tiles are listed per each. Two basic methods of installation are used. Mud set is approximately 30% more expensive than thin set. The cost of grout is included with tile unit price lines unless otherwise noted. In terrazzo work, be sure to include the linear footage of embedded decorative strips, grounds, machine rubbing, and power cleanup.

- Wood flooring is available in strip, parquet, or block configuration. The latter two types are set in adhesives with quantities estimated by the square foot. The laying pattern will influence labor costs and material waste. In addition to the material and labor for laying wood floors, the estimator must make allowances for sanding and finishing these areas, unless the flooring is prefinished.

- Sheet flooring is measured by the square yard. Roll widths vary, so consideration should be given to use the most economical width, as waste must be figured into the total quantity. Consider also the installation methods available—direct glue down or stretched. Direct glue-down installation is assumed with sheet carpet unit price lines unless otherwise noted.

09 70 00 Wall Finishes

- Wall coverings are estimated by the square foot. The area to be covered is measured—length by height of the wall above the baseboards—to calculate the square footage of each wall. This figure is divided by the number of square feet in the single roll which is being used. Deduct, in full, the areas of openings such as doors and windows. Where a pattern match is required allow 25%–30% waste.

09 80 00 Acoustic Treatment

- Acoustical systems fall into several categories. The takeoff of these materials should be by the square foot of area with a 5% allowance for waste. Do not forget about scaffolding, if applicable, when estimating these systems.

09 90 00 Painting and Coating

- A major portion of the work in painting involves surface preparation. Be sure to include cleaning, sanding, filling, and masking costs in the estimate.

- Protection of adjacent surfaces is not included in painting costs. When considering the method of paint application, an important factor is the amount of protection and masking required. These must be estimated separately and may be the determining factor in choosing the method of application.

Reference Numbers

Reference numbers are shown at the beginning of some major classifications. These numbers refer to related items in the Reference Section. The reference information may be an estimating procedure, an alternate pricing method, or technical information.

Note: Not all subdivisions listed here necessarily appear. ■

Did you know?

Our online estimating solution gives you the same access to RSMeans' data with 24/7 access:

- Quickly locate costs in the searchable database.
- Build cost lists, estimates, and reports in minutes.
- Adjust costs to any location in the U.S. and Canada with the click of a button.

Start your free trial today at
www.RSMeansOnline.com

09 22 Supports for Plaster and Gypsum Board

09 22 03 – Fastening Methods for Finishes

09 22 03.20 Drilling Plaster/Drywall		Crew	Daily Output	Labor-Hours	Unit	Material	2017 Bare Costs Labor	Equipment	Total	Total Incl O&P
0010	**DRILLING PLASTER/DRYWALL**									
1100	Drilling & layout for drywall/plaster walls, up to 1" deep, no anchor									
1200	Holes, 1/4" diameter	1 Carp	150	.053	Ea.	.01	2.63		2.64	4.03
1300	3/8" diameter		140	.057		.01	2.81		2.82	4.32
1400	1/2" diameter		130	.062		.01	3.03		3.04	4.65
1500	3/4" diameter		120	.067		.02	3.28		3.30	5.05
1600	1" diameter		110	.073		.02	3.58		3.60	5.50
1700	1-1/4" diameter		100	.080		.04	3.94		3.98	6.10
1800	1-1/2" diameter		90	.089		.05	4.38		4.43	6.75
1900	For ceiling installations, add						40%			

09 57 Special Function Ceilings

09 57 53 – Security Ceiling Assemblies

09 57 53.10 Ceiling Assem., Security, Radio Freq. Shielding		Crew	Daily Output	Labor-Hours	Unit	Material	2017 Bare Costs Labor	Equipment	Total	Total Incl O&P
0010	**CEILING ASSEMBLY, SECURITY, RADIO FREQUENCY SHIELDING**									
0020	Prefabricated, galvanized steel	2 Carp	375	.043	SF Surf	5.30	2.10		7.40	9
0050	5 oz., copper ceiling panel		155	.103		4.48	5.10		9.58	12.75
0110	12 oz., copper ceiling panel		140	.114		9.05	5.65		14.70	18.55
0250	Ceiling hangers	E-1	45	.533	Ea.	32	28.50	2.89	63.39	84.50
0300	Shielding transition, 11 ga. preformed angles	"	1365	.018	L.F.	32	.95	.10	33.05	36.50

09 69 Access Flooring

09 69 13 – Rigid-Grid Access Flooring

09 69 13.10 Access Floors		Crew	Daily Output	Labor-Hours	Unit	Material	2017 Bare Costs Labor	Equipment	Total	Total Incl O&P
0010	**ACCESS FLOORS**									
0015	Access floor pkg. including panel, pedestal, & stringers 1500 lbs load									
0100	Package pricing, conc. fill panels, no fin., 6" ht.	4 Carp	750	.043	S.F.	16.05	2.10		18.15	21
0105	12" ht.		750	.043		16.65	2.10		18.75	21.50
0110	18" ht.		750	.043		16.45	2.10		18.55	21.50
0115	24" ht.		750	.043		17.30	2.10		19.40	22.50
0120	Package pricing, steel panels, no fin., 6" ht.		750	.043		12.70	2.10		14.80	17.15
0125	12" ht.		750	.043		15.55	2.10		17.65	20.50
0130	18" ht.		750	.043		15.65	2.10		17.75	20.50
0135	24" ht.		750	.043		15.75	2.10		17.85	20.50
0140	Package pricing, wood core panels, no fin., 6" ht.		750	.043		11.65	2.10		13.75	16
0145	12" ht.		750	.043		11.80	2.10		13.90	16.20
0150	18" ht.		750	.043		11.95	2.10		14.05	16.30
0155	24" ht.		750	.043		12.05	2.10		14.15	16.45
0160	Pkg. pricing, conc. fill pnls, no stringers, no fin., 6" ht, 1250 lbs load		700	.046		10.45	2.25		12.70	14.95
0165	12" ht.		700	.046		10.25	2.25		12.50	14.70
0170	18" ht.		700	.046		10.80	2.25		13.05	15.30
0175	24" ht.		700	.046		11.35	2.25		13.60	15.90
0250	Panels, 2' x 2' conc. fill, no fin.	2 Carp	500	.032		20.50	1.58		22.08	25.50
0255	With 1/8" high pressure laminate		500	.032		62	1.58		63.58	70.50
0260	Metal panels with 1/8" high pressure laminate		500	.032		73	1.58		74.58	83
0265	Wood core panels with 1/8" high pressure laminate		500	.032		48	1.58		49.58	55.50
0400	Aluminum panels, no fin.		500	.032		33.50	1.58		35.08	39
0600	For carpet covering, add					9.05			9.05	10
0700	For vinyl floor covering, add					9.35			9.35	10.30

09 69 13 – Rigid-Grid Access Flooring

09 69 13.10 Access Floors	Crew	Daily Output	Labor-Hours	Unit	Material	2017 Bare Costs Labor	Equipment	Total	Total Incl O&P
0900	For high pressure laminate covering, add				S.F.	7.70			7.70	8.45
0910	For snap on stringer system, add	2 Carp	1000	.016	↓	1.59	.79		2.38	2.96
1000	Machine cutouts after initial installation	1 Carp	50	.160	Ea.	20	7.90		27.90	34
1050	Pedestals, 6" to 12"	2 Carp	85	.188		8.65	9.25		17.90	23.50
1100	Air conditioning grilles, 4" x 12"	1 Carp	17	.471		72.50	23		95.50	116
1150	4" x 18"	"	14	.571	↓	99.50	28		127.50	153
1200	Approach ramps, steel	2 Carp	60	.267	S.F.	26	13.15		39.15	49
1300	Aluminum	"	40	.400	"	34	19.70		53.70	67.50
1500	Handrail, 2 rail, aluminum	1 Carp	15	.533	L.F.	114	26.50		140.50	165

Division Notes

	CREW	DAILY OUTPUT	LABOR-HOURS	UNIT	BARE COSTS				TOTAL INCL O&P
					MAT.	LABOR	EQUIP.	TOTAL	

Estimating Tips
General

- The items in this division are usually priced per square foot or each.

- Many items in Division 10 require some type of support system or special anchors that are not usually furnished with the item. The required anchors must be added to the estimate in the appropriate division.

- Some items in Division 10, such as lockers, may require assembly before installation. Verify the amount of assembly required. Assembly can often exceed installation time.

10 20 00 Interior Specialties

- Support angles and blocking are not included in the installation of toilet compartments, shower/ dressing compartments, or cubicles. Appropriate line items from Division 5 or 6 may need to be added to support the installations.

- Toilet partitions are priced by the stall. A stall consists of a side wall, pilaster, and door with hardware. Toilet tissue holders and grab bars are extra.

- The required acoustical rating of a folding partition can have a significant impact on costs. Verify the sound transmission coefficient rating of the panel priced against the specification requirements.

- Grab bar installation does not include supplemental blocking or backing to support the required load. When grab bars are installed at an existing facility, provisions must be made to attach the grab bars to a solid structure.

Reference Numbers

Reference numbers are shown at the beginning of some major classifications. These numbers refer to related items in the Reference Section. The reference information may be an estimating procedure, an alternate pricing method, or technical information.

Note: Not all subdivisions listed here necessarily appear. ■

Did you know?

Our online estimating solution gives you the same access to RSMeans' data with 24/7 access:

- Quickly locate costs in the searchable database.

- Build cost lists, estimates, and reports in minutes.

- Adjust costs to any location in the U.S. and Canada with the click of a button.

Start your free trial today at
www.RSMeansOnline.com

10 28 16.20 Medicine Cabinets		Crew	Daily Output	Labor-Hours	Unit	Material	2017 Bare Costs Labor	Equipment	Total	Total Incl O&P
0010	**MEDICINE CABINETS**									
0020	With mirror, sst frame, 16" x 22", unlighted	1 Carp	14	.571	Ea.	107	28		135	161
0100	Wood frame		14	.571		140	28		168	197
0300	Sliding mirror doors, 20" x 16" x 4-3/4", unlighted		7	1.143		128	56.50		184.50	226
0400	24" x 19" x 8-1/2", lighted		5	1.600		189	79		268	330
0600	Triple door, 30" x 32", unlighted, plywood body		7	1.143		350	56.50		406.50	470
0700	Steel body		7	1.143		375	56.50		431.50	495
0900	Oak door, wood body, beveled mirror, single door		7	1.143		196	56.50		252.50	300
1000	Double door		6	1.333		415	65.50		480.50	555
1200	Hotel cabinets, stainless, with lower shelf, unlighted		10	.800		200	39.50		239.50	280
1300	Lighted		5	1.600		310	79		389	465

Estimating Tips
General

- The items in this division are usually priced per square foot or each. Many of these items are purchased by the owner for installation by the contractor. Check the specifications for responsibilities and include time for receiving, storage, installation, and mechanical and electrical hookups in the appropriate divisions.

- Many items in Division 11 require some type of support system that is not usually furnished with the item. Examples of these systems include blocking for the attachment of casework and support angles for ceiling-hung projection screens. The required blocking or supports must be added to the estimate in the appropriate division.

- Some items in Division 11 may require assembly or electrical hookups. Verify the amount of assembly required or the need for a hard electrical connection and add the appropriate costs.

Reference Numbers

Reference numbers are shown at the beginning of some major classifications. These numbers refer to related items in the Reference Section. The reference information may be an estimating procedure, an alternate pricing method, or technical information.

Note: Not all subdivisions listed here necessarily appear. ■

Did you know?

Our online estimating solution gives you the same access to RSMeans' data with 24/7 access:

- Quickly locate costs in the searchable database.
- Build cost lists, estimates, and reports in minutes.
- Adjust costs to any location in the U.S. and Canada with the click of a button.

Start your free trial today at
www.RSMeansOnline.com

11 12 Parking Control Equipment

11 12 13 – Parking Key and Card Control Units

11 12 13.10 Parking Control Units	Crew	Daily Output	Labor-Hours	Unit	Material	2017 Bare Costs Labor	Equipment	Total	Total Incl O&P
0010 **PARKING CONTROL UNITS**									
5100 Card reader	1 Elec	2	4	Ea.	1,350	226		1,576	1,825
5120 Proximity with customer display	2 Elec	1	16		5,925	905		6,830	7,875
6000 Parking control software, basic functionality	1 Elec	.50	16		23,700	905		24,605	27,500
6020 Multi-function	"	.20	40		97,000	2,275		99,275	110,000

11 12 16 – Parking Ticket Dispensers

11 12 16.10 Ticket Dispensers

	Crew	Daily Output	Labor-Hours	Unit	Material	Labor	Equipment	Total	Total Incl O&P
0010 **TICKET DISPENSERS**									
5900 Ticket spitter with time/date stamp, standard	2 Elec	2	8	Ea.	6,550	455		7,005	7,875
5920 Mag stripe encoding	"	2	8	"	18,800	455		19,255	21,400

11 12 26 – Parking Fee Collection Equipment

11 12 26.13 Parking Fee Coin Collection Equipment

	Crew	Daily Output	Labor-Hours	Unit	Material	Labor	Equipment	Total	Total Incl O&P
0010 **PARKING FEE COIN COLLECTION EQUIPMENT**									
5200 Cashier booth, average	B-22	1	30	Ea.	10,500	1,400	207	12,107	14,000
5300 Collector station, pay on foot	2 Elec	.20	80		111,000	4,525		115,525	129,000
5320 Credit card only	"	.50	32		20,500	1,800		22,300	25,200

11 12 26.23 Fee Equipment

	Crew	Daily Output	Labor-Hours	Unit	Material	Labor	Equipment	Total	Total Incl O&P
0010 **FEE EQUIPMENT**									
5600 Fee computer	1 Elec	1.50	5.333	Ea.	12,000	300		12,300	13,700

11 12 33 – Parking Gates

11 12 33.13 Lift Arm Parking Gates

	Crew	Daily Output	Labor-Hours	Unit	Material	Labor	Equipment	Total	Total Incl O&P
0010 **LIFT ARM PARKING GATES**									
5000 Barrier gate with programmable controller	2 Elec	3	5.333	Ea.	3,275	300		3,575	4,050
5020 Industrial		3	5.333		5,150	300		5,450	6,100
5050 Non-programmable, with reader and 12' arm		3	5.333		1,950	300		2,250	2,575
5500 Exit verifier		1	16		19,200	905		20,105	22,500
5700 Full sign, 4" letters	1 Elec	2	4		1,225	226		1,451	1,700
5800 Inductive loop	2 Elec	4	4		207	226		433	570
5950 Vehicle detector, microprocessor based	1 Elec	3	2.667		435	151		586	705

11 21 Retail and Service Equipment

11 21 73 – Commercial Laundry and Dry Cleaning Equipment

11 21 73.13 Dry Cleaning Equipment

	Crew	Daily Output	Labor-Hours	Unit	Material	Labor	Equipment	Total	Total Incl O&P
0010 **DRY CLEANING EQUIPMENT**									
2000 Dry cleaners, electric, 20 lb. capacity, not incl. rough-in	L-1	.20	80	Ea.	34,100	4,725		38,825	44,600
2050 25 lb. capacity		.17	94.118		50,500	5,575		56,075	64,000
2100 30 lb. capacity		.15	106		53,000	6,325		59,325	68,000
2150 60 lb. capacity		.09	177		79,000	10,500		89,500	103,000

11 21 73.19 Finishing Equipment

	Crew	Daily Output	Labor-Hours	Unit	Material	Labor	Equipment	Total	Total Incl O&P
0010 **FINISHING EQUIPMENT**									
3500 Folders, blankets & sheets, minimum	1 Elec	.17	47.059	Ea.	34,400	2,675		37,075	41,900
3700 King size with automatic stacker		.10	80		62,500	4,525		67,025	75,500
3800 For conveyor delivery, add		.45	17.778		15,500	1,000		16,500	18,600

11 21 73.23 Commercial Ironing Equipment

	Crew	Daily Output	Labor-Hours	Unit	Material	Labor	Equipment	Total	Total Incl O&P
0010 **COMMERCIAL IRONING EQUIPMENT**									
4500 Ironers, institutional, 110", single roll	1 Elec	.20	40	Ea.	33,400	2,275		35,675	40,100

11 21 Retail and Service Equipment

11 21 73 – Commercial Laundry and Dry Cleaning Equipment

11 21 73.26 Commercial Washers and Extractors

		Daily Output	Labor-Hours	Unit	Material	2017 Bare Costs Labor	Equipment	Total	Total Incl O&P
0010	**COMMERCIAL WASHERS AND EXTRACTORS**, not including rough-in								
6000	Combination washer/extractor, 20 lb. capacity	L-6	1.50	8	Ea.	6,225	480		6,705	7,575
6100	30 lb. capacity		.80	15		9,650	900		10,550	12,000
6200	50 lb. capacity		.68	17.647		11,300	1,050		12,350	14,000
6300	75 lb. capacity		.30	40		21,300	2,400		23,700	27,000
6350	125 lb. capacity		.16	75		28,200	4,500		32,700	37,800

11 21 73.33 Coin-Operated Laundry Equipment

		Daily Output	Labor-Hours	Unit	Material	2017 Bare Costs Labor	Equipment	Total	Total Incl O&P
0010	**COIN-OPERATED LAUNDRY EQUIPMENT**								
5290	Clothes washer								
5300	Commercial, coin operated, average	1 Plum	3	2.667	Ea.	1,275	165		1,440	1,650

11 30 Residential Equipment

11 30 13 – Residential Appliances

11 30 13.15 Cooking Equipment

		Daily Output	Labor-Hours	Unit	Material	2017 Bare Costs Labor	Equipment	Total	Total Incl O&P
0010	**COOKING EQUIPMENT**								
0020	Cooking range, 30" free standing, 1 oven, minimum	2 Clab	10	1.600	Ea.	485	62.50		547.50	625
0050	Maximum		4	4		1,975	157		2,132	2,425
0700	Free standing, 1 oven, 21" wide range, minimum		10	1.600		515	62.50		577.50	665
0750	21" wide, maximum		4	4		610	157		767	910
0900	Countertop cooktops, 4 burner, standard, minimum	1 Elec	6	1.333		340	75.50		415.50	490
0950	Maximum		3	2.667		1,775	151		1,926	2,175
1050	As above, but with grill and griddle attachment, minimum		6	1.333		1,550	75.50		1,625.50	1,825
1100	Maximum		3	2.667		3,825	151		3,976	4,425
1200	Induction cooktop, 30" wide		3	2.667		1,325	151		1,476	1,700
1250	Microwave oven, minimum		4	2		119	113		232	300
1300	Maximum		2	4		475	226		701	865

11 30 13.17 Kitchen Cleaning Equipment

		Daily Output	Labor-Hours	Unit	Material	2017 Bare Costs Labor	Equipment	Total	Total Incl O&P
0010	**KITCHEN CLEANING EQUIPMENT**								
2750	Dishwasher, built-in, 2 cycles, minimum	L-1	4	4	Ea.	315	237		552	700
2800	Maximum		2	8		550	475		1,025	1,325
2950	4 or more cycles, minimum		4	4		415	237		652	815
2960	Average		4	4		555	237		792	965
3000	Maximum		2	8		1,250	475		1,725	2,075

11 30 13.18 Waste Disposal Equipment

		Daily Output	Labor-Hours	Unit	Material	2017 Bare Costs Labor	Equipment	Total	Total Incl O&P
0010	**WASTE DISPOSAL EQUIPMENT**								
3300	Garbage disposal, sink type, minimum	L-1	10	1.600	Ea.	97.50	94.50		192	249
3350	Maximum	"	10	1.600	"	246	94.50		340.50	415

11 30 13.19 Kitchen Ventilation Equipment

		Daily Output	Labor-Hours	Unit	Material	2017 Bare Costs Labor	Equipment	Total	Total Incl O&P
0010	**KITCHEN VENTILATION EQUIPMENT**								
4150	Hood for range, 2 speed, vented, 30" wide, minimum	L-3	5	3.200	Ea.	85.50	171		256.50	355
4200	Maximum		3	5.333		925	284		1,209	1,450
4300	42" wide, minimum		5	3.200		153	171		324	430
4330	Custom		5	3.200		1,600	171		1,771	2,025
4350	Maximum		3	5.333		1,950	284		2,234	2,575
4500	For ventless hood, 2 speed, add					22			22	24
4650	For vented 1 speed, deduct from maximum					66			66	72.50

11 30 13.24 Washers

		Daily Output	Labor-Hours	Unit	Material	2017 Bare Costs Labor	Equipment	Total	Total Incl O&P
0010	**WASHERS**								
5000	Residential, 4 cycle, average	1 Plum	3	2.667	Ea.	915	165		1,080	1,250

For customer support on your Electrical Costs with RSMeans Data, call 800.448.8182.

59

11 30 Residential Equipment

11 30 15 – Miscellaneous Residential Appliances

11 30 15.23 Water Heaters

		Crew	Daily Output	Labor-Hours	Unit	Material	2017 Bare Costs Labor	Equipment	Total	Total Incl O&P
0010	**WATER HEATERS**									
6900	Electric, glass lined, 30 gallon, minimum	L-1	5	3.200	Ea.	970	189		1,159	1,350
6950	Maximum		3	5.333		1,350	315		1,665	1,950
7100	80 gallon, minimum		2	8		1,800	475		2,275	2,675
7150	Maximum	▼	1	16	▼	2,500	945		3,445	4,175

11 30 15.43 Air Quality

		Crew	Daily Output	Labor-Hours	Unit	Material	2017 Bare Costs Labor	Equipment	Total	Total Incl O&P
0010	**AIR QUALITY**									
2450	Dehumidifier, portable, automatic, 15 pint	1 Elec	4	2	Ea.	191	113		304	380
2550	40 pint		3.75	2.133		218	121		339	420
3550	Heater, electric, built-in, 1250 watt, ceiling type, minimum		4	2		123	113		236	305
3600	Maximum		3	2.667		194	151		345	440
3700	Wall type, minimum		4	2		181	113		294	370
3750	Maximum		3	2.667		186	151		337	430
3900	1500 watt wall type, with blower		4	2		181	113		294	370
3950	3000 watt	▼	3	2.667		445	151		596	715
4850	Humidifier, portable, 8 gallons per day					157			157	173
5000	15 gallons per day				▼	224			224	246

11 32 Unit Kitchens

11 32 13 – Metal Unit Kitchens

11 32 13.10 Commercial Unit Kitchens

		Crew	Daily Output	Labor-Hours	Unit	Material	2017 Bare Costs Labor	Equipment	Total	Total Incl O&P
0010	**COMMERCIAL UNIT KITCHENS**									
1500	Combination range, refrigerator and sink, 30" wide, minimum	L-1	2	8	Ea.	1,100	475		1,575	1,925
1550	Maximum		1	16		1,350	945		2,295	2,900
1570	60" wide, average		1.40	11.429		1,475	675		2,150	2,650
1590	72" wide, average		1.20	13.333		1,850	790		2,640	3,200
1600	Office model, 48" wide		2	8		1,975	475		2,450	2,875
1620	Refrigerator and sink only	▼	2.40	6.667	▼	2,650	395		3,045	3,525
1640	Combination range, refrigerator, sink, microwave									
1660	Oven and ice maker	L-1	.80	20	Ea.	4,775	1,175		5,950	7,025

11 41 Foodservice Storage Equipment

11 41 13 – Refrigerated Food Storage Cases

11 41 13.20 Refrigerated Food Storage Equipment

		Crew	Daily Output	Labor-Hours	Unit	Material	2017 Bare Costs Labor	Equipment	Total	Total Incl O&P
0010	**REFRIGERATED FOOD STORAGE EQUIPMENT**									
2350	Cooler, reach-in, beverage, 6' long	Q-1	6	2.667	Ea.	3,225	148		3,373	3,775

11 42 Food Preparation Equipment

11 42 10 - Commercial Food Preparation Equipment

11 42 10.10 Choppers, Mixers and Misc. Equipment	Crew	Daily Output	Labor-Hours	Unit	Material	2017 Bare Costs Labor	Equipment	Total	Total Incl O&P
0010 **CHOPPERS, MIXERS AND MISC. EQUIPMENT**									
1850 Coffee urn, twin 6 gallon urns	1 Plum	2	4	Ea.	2,400	247		2,647	3,000
3800 Food mixers, bench type, 20 quarts	L-7	7	4		3,050	190		3,240	3,650
3900 60 quarts	"	5	5.600	↓	12,100	266		12,366	13,700

11 44 Food Cooking Equipment

11 44 13 - Commercial Ranges

11 44 13.10 Cooking Equipment

	Crew	Daily Output	Labor-Hours	Unit	Material	2017 Bare Costs Labor	Equipment	Total	Total Incl O&P
0010 **COOKING EQUIPMENT**									
0020 Bake oven, gas, one section	Q-1	8	2	Ea.	5,675	111		5,786	6,400
1300 Broiler, without oven, standard	"	8	2		3,900	111		4,011	4,475
1550 Infrared	L-7	4	7		7,500	330		7,830	8,750
6350 Kettle, w/steam jacket, tilting, w/positive lock, SS, 20 gallons		7	4		9,150	190		9,340	10,400
6600 60 gallons		6	4.667		12,300	221		12,521	13,800
8850 Steamer, electric 27 KW		7	4		11,500	190		11,690	13,000
9100 Electric, 10 KW or gas 100,000 BTU	↓	5	5.600		6,625	266		6,891	7,700
9150 Toaster, conveyor type, 16-22 slices per minute				↓	1,225			1,225	1,350
9200 For deluxe models of above equipment, add					75%				
9400 Rule of thumb: Equipment cost based									
9410 on kitchen work area									
9420 Office buildings, minimum	L-7	77	.364	S.F.	95	17.25		112.25	132
9450 Maximum		58	.483		161	23		184	212
9550 Public eating facilities, minimum		77	.364		125	17.25		142.25	164
9600 Maximum		46	.609		203	29		232	267
9750 Hospitals, minimum		58	.483		128	23		151	176
9800 Maximum	↓	39	.718	↓	236	34		270	310

11 46 Food Dispensing Equipment

11 46 16 - Service Line Equipment

11 46 16.10 Commercial Food Dispensing Equipment

	Crew	Daily Output	Labor-Hours	Unit	Material	2017 Bare Costs Labor	Equipment	Total	Total Incl O&P
0010 **COMMERCIAL FOOD DISPENSING EQUIPMENT**									
3300 Food warmer, counter, 1.2 KW				Ea.	720			720	790
3550 1.6 KW					2,175			2,175	2,400
5750 Ice dispenser 567 pound	Q-1	6	2.667	↓	5,450	148		5,598	6,225

11 48 Foodservice Cleaning and Disposal Equipment

11 48 13 - Commercial Dishwashers

11 48 13.10 Dishwashers

	Crew	Daily Output	Labor-Hours	Unit	Material	2017 Bare Costs Labor	Equipment	Total	Total Incl O&P
0010 **DISHWASHERS**									
2700 Dishwasher, commercial, rack type									
2720 10 to 12 racks per hour	Q-1	3.20	5	Ea.	3,425	278		3,703	4,200
2730 Energy star rated, 35 to 40 racks/hour [G]		1.30	12.308		5,000	685		5,685	6,525
2740 50 to 60 racks/hour [G]	↓	1.30	12.308	↓	11,100	685		11,785	13,200

For customer support on your Electrical Costs with RSMeans Data, call 800.448.8182.

61

11 52 Audio-Visual Equipment

11 52 16 – Projectors

11 52 16.10 Movie Equipment

		Crew	Daily Output	Labor-Hours	Unit	Material	2017 Bare Costs Labor	2017 Bare Costs Equipment	Total	Total Incl O&P
0010	**MOVIE EQUIPMENT**									
0020	Changeover, minimum				Ea.	505			505	555
0100	Maximum					960			960	1,050
0800	Lamphouses, incl. rectifiers, xenon, 1,000 watt	1 Elec	2	4		7,075	226		7,301	8,125
0900	1,600 watt		2	4		7,550	226		7,776	8,650
1000	2,000 watt		1.50	5.333		8,200	300		8,500	9,475
1100	4,000 watt		1.50	5.333		11,300	300		11,600	12,900
3700	Sound systems, incl. amplifier, mono, minimum		.90	8.889		3,650	505		4,155	4,775
3800	Dolby/Super Sound, maximum		.40	20		19,800	1,125		20,925	23,500
4100	Dual system, 2 channel, front surround, minimum		.70	11.429		5,075	645		5,720	6,550
4200	Dolby/Super Sound, 4 channel, maximum		.40	20		18,400	1,125		19,525	22,000
5300	Speakers, recessed behind screen, minimum		2	4		1,150	226		1,376	1,625
5400	Maximum		1	8		3,375	455		3,830	4,400
7000	For automation, varying sophistication, minimum		1	8	System	2,600	455		3,055	3,550
7100	Maximum	2 Elec	.30	53.333	"	6,100	3,025		9,125	11,200

11 52 16.20 Movie Equipment- Digital

		Crew	Daily Output	Labor-Hours	Unit	Material	2017 Bare Costs Labor	2017 Bare Costs Equipment	Total	Total Incl O&P
0010	**MOVIE EQUIPMENT- DIGITAL**									
1000	Digital 2K projection system, 98" DMD	1 Elec	2	4	Ea.	46,800	226		47,026	52,000
1100	OEM lens		2	4		5,875	226		6,101	6,825
2000	Pedestal with power distribution		2	4		2,250	226		2,476	2,825
3000	Software		2	4		1,900	226		2,126	2,425

11 53 Laboratory Equipment

11 53 19 – Laboratory Sterilizers

11 53 19.13 Sterilizers

		Crew	Daily Output	Labor-Hours	Unit	Material	2017 Bare Costs Labor	2017 Bare Costs Equipment	Total	Total Incl O&P
0010	**STERILIZERS**									
0700	Glassware washer, undercounter, minimum	L-1	1.80	8.889	Ea.	6,525	525		7,050	7,975
0710	Maximum	"	1	16	"	14,200	945		15,145	17,100

11 53 33 – Emergency Safety Appliances

11 53 33.13 Emergency Equipment

		Crew	Daily Output	Labor-Hours	Unit	Material	2017 Bare Costs Labor	2017 Bare Costs Equipment	Total	Total Incl O&P
0010	**EMERGENCY EQUIPMENT**									
1400	Safety equipment, eye wash, hand held				Ea.	405			405	445
1450	Deluge shower				"	810			810	895

11 53 43 – Service Fittings and Accessories

11 53 43.13 Fittings

		Crew	Daily Output	Labor-Hours	Unit	Material	2017 Bare Costs Labor	2017 Bare Costs Equipment	Total	Total Incl O&P
0010	**FITTINGS**									
8000	Alternate pricing method: as percent of lab furniture									
8050	Installation, not incl. plumbing & duct work				% Furn.				22%	22%
8100	Plumbing, final connections, simple system								10%	10%
8110	Moderately complex system								15%	15%
8120	Complex system								20%	20%
8150	Electrical, simple system								10%	10%
8160	Moderately complex system								20%	20%
8170	Complex system								35%	35%

11 61 Broadcast, Theater, and Stage Equipment

11 61 33 – Rigging Systems and Controls

11 61 33.10 Controls

		Crew	Daily Output	Labor-Hours	Unit	Material	2017 Bare Costs Labor	Equipment	Total	Total Incl O&P
0010	**CONTROLS**									
0050	Control boards with dimmers and breakers, minimum	1 Elec	1	8	Ea.	13,300	455		13,755	16,300
0100	Average		.50	16		42,500	905		43,405	48,100
0150	Maximum		.20	40		135,500	2,275		137,775	152,500

11 66 Athletic Equipment

11 66 43 – Interior Scoreboards

11 66 43.10 Scoreboards

		Crew	Daily Output	Labor-Hours	Unit	Material	2017 Bare Costs Labor	Equipment	Total	Total Incl O&P
0010	**SCOREBOARDS**									
7000	Baseball, minimum	R-3	1.30	15.385	Ea.	3,600	870	106	4,576	5,375
7200	Maximum		.05	400		20,300	22,600	2,750	45,650	59,500
7300	Football, minimum		.86	23.256		5,175	1,325	160	6,660	7,850
7400	Maximum		.20	100		18,300	5,650	690	24,640	29,400
7500	Basketball (one side), minimum		2.07	9.662		2,500	545	66.50	3,111.50	3,650
7600	Maximum		.30	66.667		7,475	3,775	460	11,710	14,400
7700	Hockey-basketball (four sides), minimum		.25	80		8,925	4,525	550	14,000	17,200
7800	Maximum		.15	133		15,800	7,550	920	24,270	29,600

11 71 Medical Sterilizing Equipment

11 71 10 – Medical Sterilizers & Distillers

11 71 10.10 Sterilizers and Distillers

		Crew	Daily Output	Labor-Hours	Unit	Material	2017 Bare Costs Labor	Equipment	Total	Total Incl O&P
0010	**STERILIZERS AND DISTILLERS**									
6200	Steam generators, electric 10 kW to 180 kW, freestanding									
6250	Minimum	1 Elec	3	2.667	Ea.	10,500	151		10,651	11,700
6300	Maximum	"	.70	11.429	"	23,100	645		23,745	26,400

11 72 Examination and Treatment Equipment

11 72 53 – Treatment Equipment

11 72 53.13 Medical Treatment Equipment

		Crew	Daily Output	Labor-Hours	Unit	Material	2017 Bare Costs Labor	Equipment	Total	Total Incl O&P
0010	**MEDICAL TREATMENT EQUIPMENT**									
6700	Surgical lights, doctor's office, single arm	2 Elec	2	8	Ea.	2,700	455		3,155	3,625
6750	Dual arm	"	1	16	"	5,000	905		5,905	6,825

11 76 Operating Room Equipment

11 76 10 – Operating Room Equipment

11 76 10.10 Surgical Equipment

		Crew	Daily Output	Labor-Hours	Unit	Material	2017 Bare Costs Labor	Equipment	Total	Total Incl O&P
0010	**SURGICAL EQUIPMENT**									
6800	Surgical lights, major operating room, dual head, minimum	2 Elec	1	16	Ea.	4,200	905		5,105	5,975
6850	Maximum	"	1	16	"	31,100	905		32,005	35,600

For customer support on your Electrical Costs with RSMeans Data, call 800.448.8182.

63

11 78 Mortuary Equipment

11 78 13 – Mortuary Refrigerators

11 78 13.10 Mortuary and Autopsy Equipment	Crew	Daily Output	Labor-Hours	Unit	Material	2017 Bare Costs Labor	Equipment	Total	Total Incl O&P
0010 **MORTUARY AND AUTOPSY EQUIPMENT**									
0015 Autopsy table, standard	1 Plum	1	8	Ea.	10,200	495		10,695	12,000

11 78 16 – Crematorium Equipment

11 78 16.10 Crematory

0010 **CREMATORY**									
1500 Crematory, not including building, 1 place	Q-3	.20	160	Ea.	77,500	9,425		86,925	99,500
1750 2 place	"	.10	320	"	111,000	18,800		129,800	150,500

11 82 Facility Solid Waste Handling Equipment

11 82 26 – Facility Waste Compactors

11 82 26.10 Compactors

0010 **COMPACTORS**									
0020 Compactors, 115 volt, 250#/hr., chute fed	L-4	1	24	Ea.	12,600	1,125		13,725	15,500
1000 Heavy duty industrial compactor, 0.5 C.Y. capacity		1	24		10,800	1,125		11,925	13,600
1050 1.0 C.Y. capacity		1	24		16,500	1,125		17,625	19,900
1100 3.0 C.Y. capacity		.50	48		27,700	2,250		29,950	33,900
1150 5.0 C.Y. capacity		.50	48		34,900	2,250		37,150	41,900
1200 Combination shredder/compactor (5,000 lb./hr.)	↓	.50	48		67,500	2,250		69,750	78,000
1400 For handling hazardous waste materials, 55 gallon drum packer, std.					21,100			21,100	23,200
1410 55 gallon drum packer w/HEPA filter					26,300			26,300	29,000
1420 55 gallon drum packer w/charcoal & HEPA filter					35,100			35,100	38,600
1430 All of the above made explosion proof, add					1,550			1,550	1,700
5800 Shredder, industrial, minimum					25,400			25,400	28,000
5850 Maximum					135,500			135,500	149,000
5900 Baler, industrial, minimum					10,100			10,100	11,200
5950 Maximum			↓	↓	591,500			591,500	651,000

Estimating Tips
General

- The items in this division are usually priced per square foot or each. Most of these items are purchased by the owner and installed by the contractor. Do not assume the items in Division 12 will be purchased and installed by the contractor. Check the specifications for responsibilities and include receiving, storage, installation, and mechanical and electrical hookups in the appropriate divisions.

- Some items in this division require some type of support system that is not usually furnished with the item. Examples of these systems include blocking for the attachment of casework and heavy drapery rods. The required blocking must be added to the estimate in the appropriate division.

Reference Numbers

Reference numbers are shown at the beginning of some major classifications. These numbers refer to related items in the Reference Section. The reference information may be an estimating procedure, an alternate pricing method, or technical information.

Note: Not all subdivisions listed here necessarily appear. ■

12 46 Furnishing Accessories

12 46 19 – Clocks

12 46 19.50 Wall Clocks	Crew	Daily Output	Labor-Hours	Unit	Material	2017 Bare Costs Labor	Equipment	Total	Total Incl O&P
0010	**WALL CLOCKS**								
0080	12" diameter, single face	1 Elec	8	1	Ea.	125	56.50		181.50	222
0100	Double face	"	6.20	1.290	"	310	73		383	450

Estimating Tips
General

- The items and systems in this division are usually estimated, purchased, supplied, and installed as a unit by one or more subcontractors. The estimator must ensure that all parties are operating from the same set of specifications and assumptions, and that all necessary items are estimated and will be provided. Many times the complex items and systems are covered, but the more common ones, such as excavation or a crane, are overlooked for the very reason that everyone assumes nobody could miss them. The estimator should be the central focus and be able to ensure that all systems are complete.

- Another area where problems can develop in this division is at the interface between systems. The estimator must ensure, for instance, that anchor bolts, nuts, and washers are estimated and included for the air-supported structures and pre-engineered buildings to be bolted to their foundations. Utility supply is a common area where essential items or pieces of equipment can be missed or overlooked, because each subcontractor may feel it is another's responsibility. The estimator should also be aware of certain items which may be supplied as part of a package but installed by others, and ensure that the installing contractor's estimate includes the cost of installation. Conversely, the estimator must also ensure that items are not costed by two different subcontractors, resulting in an inflated overall estimate.

13 30 00 Special Structures

- The foundations and floor slab, as well as rough mechanical and electrical, should be estimated, as this work is required for the assembly and erection of the structure. Generally, as noted in the data set, the pre-engineered building comes as a shell. Pricing is based on the size and structural design parameters stated in the reference section. Additional features, such as windows and doors with their related structural framing, must also be included by the estimator. Here again, the estimator must have a clear understanding of the scope of each portion of the work and all the necessary interfaces.

Reference Numbers

Reference numbers are shown at the beginning of some major classifications. These numbers refer to related items in the Reference Section. The reference information may be an estimating procedure, an alternate pricing method, or technical information.

Note: Not all subdivisions listed here necessarily appear. ■

Did you know?

Our online estimating solution gives you the same access to RSMeans' data with 24/7 access:

- Quickly locate costs in the searchable database.

- Build cost lists, estimates, and reports in minutes.

- Adjust costs to any location in the U.S. and Canada with the click of a button.

Start your free trial today at
www.RSMeansOnline.com

13 11 Swimming Pools

13 11 13 – Below-Grade Swimming Pools

13 11 13.50 Swimming Pools

		Crew	Daily Output	Labor-Hours	Unit	Material	2017 Bare Costs Labor	2017 Bare Costs Equipment	Total	Total Incl O&P
0010	**SWIMMING POOLS** Residential in-ground, vinyl lined									
0020	Concrete sides, w/equip, sand bottom	B-52	300	.187	SF Surf	26	8.50	2.14	36.64	44.50
0100	Metal or polystyrene sides	B-14	410	.117		22	4.85	.89	27.74	32.50
0200	Add for vermiculite bottom					1.67			1.67	1.84
0500	Gunite bottom and sides, white plaster finish									
0600	12' x 30' pool	B-52	145	.386	SF Surf	49	17.60	4.42	71.02	85.50
0720	16' x 32' pool		155	.361		44	16.45	4.13	64.58	78
0750	20' x 40' pool		250	.224		39.50	10.20	2.56	52.26	61.50
0810	Concrete bottom and sides, tile finish									
0820	12' x 30' pool	B-52	80	.700	SF Surf	49.50	32	8	89.50	111
0830	16' x 32' pool		95	.589		40.50	27	6.75	74.25	93.50
0840	20' x 40' pool		130	.431		32.50	19.60	4.93	57.03	71
1100	Motel, gunite with plaster finish, incl. medium									
1150	capacity filtration & chlorination	B-52	115	.487	SF Surf	60	22	5.55	87.55	106
1200	Municipal, gunite with plaster finish, incl. high									
1250	capacity filtration & chlorination	B-52	100	.560	SF Surf	77.50	25.50	6.40	109.40	132
1350	Add for formed gutters				L.F.	114			114	126
1360	Add for stainless steel gutters				"	340			340	370
1700	Filtration and deck equipment only, as % of total				Total				20%	20%
1800	Deck equipment, rule of thumb, 20' x 40' pool				SF Pool				1.18	1.30
1900	5000 S.F. pool				"				1.73	1.90

13 11 23 – On-Grade Swimming Pools

13 11 23.50 Swimming Pools

		Crew	Daily Output	Labor-Hours	Unit	Material	2017 Bare Costs Labor	2017 Bare Costs Equipment	Total	Total Incl O&P
0010	**SWIMMING POOLS** Residential above ground, steel construction									
0100	Round, 15' dia.	B-80A	3	8	Ea.	840	315	90	1,245	1,500
0120	18' dia.		2.50	9.600		910	375	108	1,393	1,700
0140	21' dia.		2	12		1,050	470	135	1,655	2,025
0160	24' dia.		1.80	13.333		1,150	520	150	1,820	2,225
0180	27' dia.		1.50	16		1,350	625	180	2,155	2,625
0200	30' dia.		1	24		1,500	940	270	2,710	3,400
0220	Oval, 12' x 24'		2.30	10.435		1,575	410	118	2,103	2,475
0240	15' x 30'		1.80	13.333		1,750	520	150	2,420	2,900
0260	18' x 33'		1	24		1,975	940	270	3,185	3,900

13 11 46 – Swimming Pool Accessories

13 11 46.50 Swimming Pool Equipment

		Crew	Daily Output	Labor-Hours	Unit	Material	2017 Bare Costs Labor	2017 Bare Costs Equipment	Total	Total Incl O&P
0010	**SWIMMING POOL EQUIPMENT**									
0020	Diving stand, stainless steel, 3 meter	2 Carp	.40	40	Ea.	16,100	1,975		18,075	20,700
2100	Lights, underwater, 12 volt, with transformer, 300 watt	1 Elec	1	8		350	455		805	1,075
2200	110 volt, 500 watt, standard		1	8		293	455		748	1,000
2400	Low water cutoff type		1	8		293	455		748	1,000
2800	Heaters, see Section 23 52 28.10									

13 12 Fountains

13 12 13 – Exterior Fountains

13 12 13.10 Outdoor Fountains

		Crew	Daily Output	Labor-Hours	Unit	Material	2017 Bare Costs Labor	Equipment	Total	Total Incl O&P
0010	**OUTDOOR FOUNTAINS**									
0100	Outdoor fountain, 48" high with bowl and figures	2 Clab	2	8	Ea.	570	315		885	1,100
0200	Commercial, concrete or cast stone, 40-60" H, simple		2	8		775	315		1,090	1,325
0220	Average		2	8		1,350	315		1,665	1,950
0240	Ornate		2	8		2,625	315		2,940	3,350
0260	Metal, 72" high		2	8		1,225	315		1,540	1,825
0280	90" high		2	8		1,875	315		2,190	2,525
0300	120" high		2	8		4,950	315		5,265	5,925
0320	Resin or fiberglass, 40-60" H, wall type		2	8		480	315		795	1,000
0340	Waterfall type		2	8		1,200	315		1,515	1,800

13 12 23 – Interior Fountains

13 12 23.10 Indoor Fountains

		Crew	Daily Output	Labor-Hours	Unit	Material	2017 Bare Costs Labor	Equipment	Total	Total Incl O&P
0010	**INDOOR FOUNTAINS**									
0100	Commercial, floor type, resin or fiberglass, lighted, cascade type	2 Clab	2	8	Ea.	296	315		611	805
0120	Tiered type		2	8		284	315		599	790
0140	Waterfall type		2	8		300	315		615	810

13 21 Controlled Environment Rooms

13 21 13 – Clean Rooms

13 21 13.50 Clean Room Components

		Crew	Daily Output	Labor-Hours	Unit	Material	2017 Bare Costs Labor	Equipment	Total	Total Incl O&P
0010	**CLEAN ROOM COMPONENTS**									
1100	Clean room, soft wall, 12' x 12', Class 100	1 Carp	.18	44.444	Ea.	18,000	2,200		20,200	23,200
1110	Class 1,000		.18	44.444		16,000	2,200		18,200	21,100
1120	Class 10,000		.21	38.095		13,200	1,875		15,075	17,400
1130	Class 100,000		.21	38.095		12,100	1,875		13,975	16,200
2800	Ceiling grid support, slotted channel struts 4'-0" O.C., ea. way				S.F.				5.90	6.50
3000	Ceiling panel, vinyl coated foil on mineral substrate									
3020	Sealed, non-perforated				S.F.				1.27	1.40
4000	Ceiling panel seal, silicone sealant, 150 L.F./gal.	1 Carp	150	.053	L.F.	.35	2.63		2.98	4.41
4100	Two sided adhesive tape	"	240	.033	"	.12	1.64		1.76	2.64
4200	Clips, one per panel				Ea.	1.02			1.02	1.12
6000	HEPA filter, 2' x 4', 99.97% eff., 3" dp beveled frame (silicone seal)					405			405	445
6040	6" deep skirted frame (channel seal)					465			465	510
6100	99.99% efficient, 3" deep beveled frame (silicone seal)					415			415	455
6140	6" deep skirted frame (channel seal)					470			470	520
6200	99.999% efficient, 3" deep beveled frame (silicone seal)					470			470	515
6240	6" deep skirted frame (channel seal)					505			505	555
7000	Wall panel systems, including channel strut framing									
7020	Polyester coated aluminum, particle board				S.F.				18.20	18.20
7100	Porcelain coated aluminum, particle board								32	32
7400	Wall panel support, slotted channel struts, to 12' high								16.35	16.35

For customer support on your Electrical Costs with RSMeans Data, call 800.448.8182.

69

13 24 Special Activity Rooms

13 24 16 – Saunas

13 24 16.50 Saunas and Heaters

		Crew	Daily Output	Labor-Hours	Unit	Material	2017 Bare Costs Labor	2017 Bare Costs Equipment	Total	Total Incl O&P
0010	**SAUNAS AND HEATERS**									
0020	Prefabricated, incl. heater & controls, 7' high, 6' x 4', C/C	L-7	2.20	12.727	Ea.	5,350	605		5,955	6,825
0050	6' x 4', C/P		2	14		4,825	665		5,490	6,325
0400	6' x 5', C/C		2	14		6,025	665		6,690	7,650
0450	6' x 5', C/P		2	14		5,350	665		6,015	6,900
0600	6' x 6', C/C		1.80	15.556		6,325	735		7,060	8,075
0650	6' x 6', C/P		1.80	15.556		5,600	735		6,335	7,300
0800	6' x 9', C/C		1.60	17.500		8,200	830		9,030	10,300
0850	6' x 9', C/P		1.60	17.500		7,150	830		7,980	9,150
1000	8' x 12', C/C		1.10	25.455		10,900	1,200		12,100	13,900
1050	8' x 12', C/P		1.10	25.455		9,675	1,200		10,875	12,600
1200	8' x 8', C/C		1.40	20		8,600	950		9,550	10,900
1250	8' x 8', C/P		1.40	20		7,650	950		8,600	9,875
1400	8' x 10', C/C		1.20	23.333		9,400	1,100		10,500	12,000
1450	8' x 10', C/P		1.20	23.333		8,300	1,100		9,400	10,800
1600	10' x 12', C/C		1	28		12,600	1,325		13,925	15,900
1650	10' x 12', C/P	▼	1	28		11,400	1,325		12,725	14,500
2500	Heaters only (incl. above), wall mounted, to 200 C.F.					800			800	880
2750	To 300 C.F.					1,075			1,075	1,175
3000	Floor standing, to 720 C.F., 10,000 watts, w/controls	1 Elec	3	2.667		2,625	151		2,776	3,125
3250	To 1,000 C.F., 16,000 watts	"	3	2.667	▼	3,900	151		4,051	4,500

13 24 26 – Steam Baths

13 24 26.50 Steam Baths and Components

		Crew	Daily Output	Labor-Hours	Unit	Material	2017 Bare Costs Labor	2017 Bare Costs Equipment	Total	Total Incl O&P
0010	**STEAM BATHS AND COMPONENTS**									
0020	Heater, timer & head, single, to 140 C.F.	1 Plum	1.20	6.667	Ea.	2,325	410		2,735	3,175
0500	To 300 C.F.		1.10	7.273		2,600	450		3,050	3,525
1000	Commercial size, with blow-down assembly, to 800 C.F.		.90	8.889		5,725	550		6,275	7,125
1500	To 2500 C.F.	▼	.80	10		8,000	620		8,620	9,725
2000	Multiple, motels, apts., 2 baths, w/blow-down assm., 500 C.F.	Q-1	1.30	12.308		6,675	685		7,360	8,375
2500	4 baths	"	.70	22.857	▼	10,700	1,275		11,975	13,600

13 47 Facility Protection

13 47 13 – Cathodic Protection

13 47 13.16 Cathodic Prot. for Underground Storage Tanks

		Crew	Daily Output	Labor-Hours	Unit	Material	2017 Bare Costs Labor	2017 Bare Costs Equipment	Total	Total Incl O&P
0010	**CATHODIC PROTECTION FOR UNDERGROUND STORAGE TANKS**									
1000	Anodes, magnesium type, 9 #	R-15	18.50	2.595	Ea.	35	145	15.60	195.60	273
1010	17 #		13	3.692		74.50	206	22	302.50	415
1020	32 #		10	4.800		117	268	29	414	560
1030	48 #	▼	7.20	6.667		161	370	40	571	780
1100	Graphite type w/epoxy cap, 3" x 60" (32 #)	R-22	8.40	4.438		120	230		350	475
1110	4" x 80" (68 #)		6	6.213		232	320		552	735
1120	6" x 72" (80 #)		5.20	7.169		1,500	370		1,870	2,200
1130	6" x 36" (45 #)	▼	9.60	3.883		760	201		961	1,125
2000	Rectifiers, silicon type, air cooled, 28 V/10 A	R-19	3.50	5.714		2,050	325		2,375	2,725
2010	20 V/20 A		3.50	5.714		2,100	325		2,425	2,800
2100	Oil immersed, 28 V/10 A		3	6.667		2,825	380		3,205	3,675
2110	20 V/20 A	▼	3	6.667	▼	3,000	380		3,380	3,875
3000	Anode backfill, coke breeze	R-22	3850	.010	Lb.	.28	.50		.78	1.06
4000	Cable, HMWPE, No. 8		2.40	15.533	M.L.F.	570	805		1,375	1,825
4010	No. 6	▼	2.40	15.533	▼	845	805		1,650	2,125

13 47 Facility Protection

13 47 13 – Cathodic Protection

13 47 13.16 Cathodic Prot. for Underground Storage Tanks	Crew	Daily Output	Labor-Hours	Unit	Material	2017 Bare Costs Labor	Equipment	Total	Total Incl O&P
4020	No. 4	R-22	2.40	15.533	M.L.F.	1,275	805		2,080	2,600
4030	No. 2		2.40	15.533		1,975	805		2,780	3,375
4040	No. 1		2.20	16.945		2,700	880		3,580	4,300
4050	No. 1/0		2.20	16.945		3,500	880		4,380	5,175
4060	No. 2/0		2.20	16.945		4,975	880		5,855	6,800
4070	No. 4/0		2	18.640		6,275	965		7,240	8,375
5000	Test station, 7 terminal box, flush curb type w/lockable cover	R-19	12	1.667	Ea.	76.50	94.50		171	227
5010	Reference cell, 2" dia PVC conduit, cplg., plug, set flush	"	4.80	4.167	"	151	236		387	520

13 49 Radiation Protection

13 49 13 – Integrated X-Ray Shielding Assemblies

13 49 13.50 Lead Sheets

		Crew	Daily Output	Labor-Hours	Unit	Material	Labor	Equipment	Total	Total Incl O&P
0010	**LEAD SHEETS**									
0300	Lead sheets, 1/16" thick	2 Lath	135	.119	S.F.	10.40	5.70		16.10	19.85
0400	1/8" thick		120	.133		19.60	6.40		26	31
0500	Lead shielding, 1/4" thick		135	.119		38	5.70		43.70	50
0550	1/2" thick		120	.133		75.50	6.40		81.90	92.50
0950	Lead headed nails (average 1 lb. per sheet)				Lb.	8.05			8.05	8.85
1000	Butt joints in 1/8" lead or thicker, 2" batten strip x 7' long	2 Lath	240	.067	Ea.	28.50	3.19		31.69	35.50
1200	X-ray protection, average radiography or fluoroscopy									
1210	room, up to 300 S.F. floor, 1/16" lead, economy	2 Lath	.25	64	Total	10,100	3,075		13,175	15,700
1500	7'-0" walls, deluxe	"	.15	106	"	12,200	5,100		17,300	21,000
1600	Deep therapy X-ray room, 250 kV capacity,									
1800	up to 300 S.F. floor, 1/4" lead, economy	2 Lath	.08	200	Total	28,300	9,575		37,875	45,300
1900	7'-0" walls, deluxe	"	.06	266	"	34,900	12,800		47,700	57,500

13 49 19 – Lead-Lined Materials

13 49 19.50 Shielding Lead

		Crew	Daily Output	Labor-Hours	Unit	Material	Labor	Equipment	Total	Total Incl O&P
0010	**SHIELDING LEAD**									
0100	Laminated lead in wood doors, 1/16" thick, no hardware				S.F.	53.50			53.50	59
0200	Lead lined door frame, not incl. hardware,									
0210	1/16" thick lead, butt prepared for hardware	1 Lath	2.40	3.333	Ea.	825	160		985	1,150
0850	Window frame with 1/16" lead and voice passage, 36" x 60"	2 Glaz	2	8		4,275	380		4,655	5,275
0870	24" x 36" frame		4	4		2,225	191		2,416	2,750
0900	Lead gypsum board, 5/8" thick with 1/16" lead		160	.100	S.F.	11.55	4.78		16.33	20
0910	1/8" lead		140	.114		23.50	5.45		28.95	34.50
0930	1/32" lead	2 Lath	200	.080		8.10	3.83		11.93	14.55

13 49 21 – Lead Glazing

13 49 21.50 Lead Glazing

		Crew	Daily Output	Labor-Hours	Unit	Material	Labor	Equipment	Total	Total Incl O&P
0010	**LEAD GLAZING**									
0600	Lead glass, 1/4" thick, 2.0 mm LE, 12" x 16"	2 Glaz	13	1.231	Ea.	370	59		429	500
0700	24" x 36"		8	2		1,300	95.50		1,395.50	1,575
0800	36" x 60"		2	8		3,600	380		3,980	4,550
2000	X-ray viewing panels, clear lead plastic									
2010	7 mm thick, 0.3 mm LE, 2.3 lb./S.F.	H-3	139	.115	S.F.	248	4.89		252.89	281
2020	12 mm thick, 0.5 mm LE, 3.9 lb./S.F.		82	.195		365	8.30		373.30	415
2030	18 mm thick, 0.8 mm LE, 5.9 lb./S.F.		54	.296		420	12.60		432.60	480
2040	22 mm thick, 1.0 mm LE, 7.2 lb./S.F.		44	.364		545	15.45		560.45	625
2050	35 mm thick, 1.5 mm LE, 11.5 lb./S.F.		28	.571		835	24.50		859.50	955
2060	46 mm thick, 2.0 mm LE, 15.0 lb./S.F.		21	.762		1,100	32.50		1,132.50	1,250
2090	For panels 12 S.F. to 48 S.F., add crating charge				Ea.				50	50

For customer support on your Electrical Costs with RSMeans Data, call 800.448.8182.

71

13 49 Radiation Protection

13 49 23 – Integrated RFI/EMI Shielding Assemblies

13 49 23.50 Modular Shielding Partitions	Crew	Daily Output	Labor-Hours	Unit	Material	2017 Bare Costs Labor	Equipment	Total	Total Incl O&P
0010 **MODULAR SHIELDING PARTITIONS**									
4000 X-ray barriers, modular, panels mounted within framework for									
4002 attaching to floor, wall or ceiling, upper portion is clear lead									
4005 plastic window panels 48"H, lower portion is opaque leaded									
4008 steel panels 36"H, structural supports not incl.									
4010 1-section barrier, 36"W x 84"H overall									
4020 0.5 mm LE panels	H-3	6.40	2.500	Ea.	8,375	106		8,481	9,400
4030 0.8 mm LE panels		6.40	2.500		9,050	106		9,156	10,100
4040 1.0 mm LE panels		5.33	3.002		10,600	127		10,727	11,800
4050 1.5 mm LE panels		5.33	3.002		14,100	127		14,227	15,700
4060 2-section barrier, 72"W x 84"H overall									
4070 0.5 mm LE panels	H-3	4	4	Ea.	12,100	170		12,270	13,700
4080 0.8 mm LE panels		4	4		13,500	170		13,670	15,100
4090 1.0 mm LE panels		3.56	4.494		16,500	191		16,691	18,500
5000 1.5 mm LE panels		3.20	5		23,500	212		23,712	26,200
5010 3-section barrier, 108"W x 84"H overall									
5020 0.5 mm LE panels	H-3	3.20	5	Ea.	18,200	212		18,412	20,300
5030 0.8 mm LE panels		3.20	5		20,200	212		20,412	22,500
5040 1.0 mm LE panels		2.67	5.993		24,800	254		25,054	27,600
5050 1.5 mm LE panels		2.46	6.504		35,200	276		35,476	39,200
7000 X-ray barriers, mobile, mounted within framework w/casters on									
7005 bottom, clear lead plastic window panels on upper portion,									
7010 opaque on lower, 30"W x 75"H overall, incl. framework									
7020 24"H upper w/0.5 mm LE, 48"H lower w/0.8 mm LE	1 Carp	16	.500	Ea.	4,025	24.50		4,049.50	4,475
7030 48"W x 75"H overall, incl. framework									
7040 36"H upper w/0.5 mm LE, 36"H lower w/0.8 mm LE	1 Carp	16	.500	Ea.	6,350	24.50		6,374.50	7,050
7050 36"H upper w/1.0 mm LE, 36"H lower w/1.5 mm LE	"	16	.500	"	7,525	24.50		7,549.50	8,325
7060 72"W x 75"H overall, incl. framework									
7070 36"H upper w/0.5 mm LE, 36"H lower w/0.8 mm LE	1 Carp	16	.500	Ea.	7,525	24.50		7,549.50	8,325
7080 36"H upper w/1.0 mm LE, 36"H lower w/1.5 mm LE	"	16	.500	"	9,425	24.50		9,449.50	10,400

13 49 33 – Radio Frequency Shielding

13 49 33.50 Shielding, Radio Frequency

	Crew	Daily Output	Labor-Hours	Unit	Material	Labor	Equipment	Total	Total Incl O&P
0010 **SHIELDING, RADIO FREQUENCY**									
0020 Prefabricated, galvanized steel	2 Carp	375	.043	SF Surf	5.30	2.10		7.40	9
0040 5 oz., copper floor panel		480	.033		4.48	1.64		6.12	7.45
0050 5 oz., copper wall/ceiling panel		155	.103		4.48	5.10		9.58	12.75
0100 12 oz., copper floor panel		470	.034		9.05	1.68		10.73	12.50
0110 12 oz., copper wall/ceiling panel		140	.114		9.05	5.65		14.70	18.55
0150 Door, copper/wood laminate, 4' x 7'		1.50	10.667	Ea.	8,050	525		8,575	9,650

For customer support on your Electrical Costs with RSMeans Data, call 800.448.8182.

Estimating Tips

Pipe for fire protection and all uses is located in Subdivisions 21 11 13 and 22 11 13.

The labor adjustment factors listed in Subdivision 22 01 02.20 also apply to Division 21.

Many, but not all, areas in the U.S. require backflow protection in the fire system. Insurance underwriters may have specific requirements for the type of materials to be installed or design requirements based on the hazard to be protected. Local jurisdictions may have requirements not covered by code. It is advisable to be aware of any special conditions.

For your reference, the following is a list of the most applicable Fire Codes and Standards which may be purchased from the NFPA, 1 Batterymarch Park, Quincy, MA 02169-7471.

- NFPA 1: Uniform Fire Code
- NFPA 10: Portable Fire Extinguishers
- NFPA 11: Low-, Medium-, and High-Expansion Foam
- NFPA 12: Carbon Dioxide Extinguishing Systems (Also companion 12A)
- NFPA 13: Installation of Sprinkler Systems (Also companion 13D, 13E, and 13R)
- NFPA 14: Installation of Standpipe and Hose Systems
- NFPA 15: Water Spray Fixed Systems for Fire Protection
- NFPA 16: Installation of Foam-Water Sprinkler and Foam-Water Spray Systems
- NFPA 17: Dry Chemical Extinguishing Systems (Also companion 17A)
- NFPA 18: Wetting Agents
- NFPA 20: Installation of Stationary Pumps for Fire Protection
- NFPA 22: Water Tanks for Private Fire Protection
- NFPA 24: Installation of Private Fire Service Mains and their Appurtenances
- NFPA 25: Inspection, Testing and Maintenance of Water-Based Fire Protection

Reference Numbers

Reference numbers are shown at the beginning of some major classifications. These numbers refer to related items in the Reference Section. The reference information may be an estimating procedure, an alternate pricing method, or technical information.

Note: Not all subdivisions listed here necessarily appear. ■

21 21 Carbon-Dioxide Fire-Extinguishing Systems

21 21 16 – Carbon-Dioxide Fire-Extinguishing Equipment

21 21 16.50 CO2 Fire Extinguishing System	Crew	Daily Output	Labor-Hours	Unit	Material	2017 Bare Costs Labor	Equipment	Total	Total Incl O&P
0010 **CO₂ FIRE EXTINGUISHING SYSTEM**									
0100 Control panel, single zone with batteries (2 zones det., 1 suppr.)	1 Elec	1	8	Ea.	350	455		805	1,075
0150 Multizone (4) with batteries (8 zones det., 4 suppr.)	"	.50	16		760	905		1,665	2,175
1000 Dispersion nozzle, CO₂, 3" x 5"	1 Plum	18	.444		67	27.50		94.50	115
2000 Extinguisher, CO₂ system, high pressure, 75 lb. cylinder	Q-1	6	2.667		1,275	148		1,423	1,625
2100 100 lb. cylinder	"	5	3.200		1,300	178		1,478	1,725
3000 Electro/mechanical release	L-1	4	4		188	237		425	560
3400 Manual pull station	1 Plum	6	1.333		60	82.50		142.50	190
4000 Pneumatic damper release	"	8	1		258	62		320	380

21 22 Clean-Agent Fire-Extinguishing Systems

21 22 16 – Clean-Agent Fire-Extinguishing Equipment

21 22 16.50 Clean-Agent Extinguishing Systems

	Crew	Daily Output	Labor-Hours	Unit	Material	2017 Bare Costs Labor	Equipment	Total	Total Incl O&P
0010 **CLEAN-AGENT EXTINGUISHING SYSTEMS**									
0020 FM200 fire extinguishing system									
1100 Dispersion nozzle FM200, 1-1/2"	1 Plum	14	.571	Ea.	92	35.50		127.50	155
2400 Extinguisher, FM200 system, filled, with mounting bracket									
2460 26 lb. container	Q-1	8	2	Ea.	2,600	111		2,711	3,025
2480 44 lb. container		7	2.286		3,000	127		3,127	3,500
2500 63 lb. container		6	2.667		4,550	148		4,698	5,250
2520 101 lb. container		5	3.200		5,325	178		5,503	6,125
2540 196 lb. container		4	4		7,850	223		8,073	8,950
6000 FM200 system, simple nozzle layout, with broad dispersion				C.F.	1.76			1.76	1.94
6010 Extinguisher, FM200 system, filled, with mounting bracket									
6020 Complex nozzle layout and/or including underfloor dispersion				C.F.	3.50			3.50	3.85
6100 20,000 cf 2 exits, 8' clng					2.75			2.75	3.03
6200 100,000 cf 4 exits, 8' clng					2.30			2.30	2.53
6300 250,000 cf 6 exits, 8' clng					1.85			1.85	2.04
7010 HFC-227ea fire extinguishing system									
7100 Cylinders with clean-agent									
7110 Does not include pallete jack/fork lift rental fees									
7120 70 lb cyl, w/ 35 lb agent, no solenoid	Q-12	14	1.143	Ea.	2,400	60.50		2,460.50	2,750
7130 70 lb cyl w/ 70 lb agent, no solenoid		10	1.600		3,075	85		3,160	3,525
7140 70 lb cyl w/ 35 lb agent, w/ solenoid		14	1.143		2,875	60.50		2,935.50	3,250
7150 70 lb cyl w/ 70 lb agent, w/ solenoid		10	1.600		3,625	85		3,710	4,125
7220 250 lb cyl, w/ 125 lb agent, no solenoid		8	2		5,425	106		5,531	6,100
7230 250 lb cyl, w/ 250 lb agent, no solenoid		5	3.200		5,425	170		5,595	6,200
7240 250 lb cyl, w/ 125 lb agent, w/ solenoid		8	2		6,225	106		6,331	7,000
7250 250 lb cyl, w/ 250 lb agent, w/ solenoid		5	3.200		8,925	170		9,095	10,100
7320 560 lb cyl, w/ 300 lb agent, no solenoid		4	4		10,200	212		10,412	11,500
7330 560 lb cyl, w/ 560 lb agent, no solenoid		2.50	6.400		15,200	340		15,540	17,300
7340 560 lb cyl, w/ 300 lb agent, w/ solenoid		4	4		11,500	212		11,712	13,000
7350 560 lb cyl, w/ 560 lb agent, w/ solenoid		2.50	6.400		17,100	340		17,440	19,400
7420 1200 lb cyl, w/ 600 lb agent, no solenoid	Q-13	4	8		19,200	450		19,650	21,800
7430 1200 lb cyl, w/ 1200 lb agent, no solenoid		3	10.667		30,900	600		31,500	34,900
7440 1200 lb cyl, w/ 600 lb agent, w/ solenoid		4	8		40,100	450		40,550	44,800
7450 1200 lb cyl, w/ 1200 lb agent, w/ solenoid		3	10.667		63,000	600		63,600	70,000
7500 Accessories									
7510 Dispersion nozzle	1 Spri	16	.500	Ea.	95	29.50		124.50	150
7520 Agent release panel	1 Elec	4	2		60	113		173	236
7530 Maintenance switch	"	6	1.333		35	75.50		110.50	152

21 22 16.50 Clean-Agent Extinguishing Systems	Crew	Daily Output	Labor-Hours	Unit	Material	2017 Bare Costs Labor	Equipment	Total	Total Incl O&P
7540	Solenoid valve, 12v dc	1 Spri	8	1	Ea.	232	59		291	345
7550	12v ac		8	1		415	59		474	545
7560	12v dc, exp.proof		8	1		390	59		449	520

Division Notes

	CREW	DAILY OUTPUT	LABOR-HOURS	UNIT	BARE COSTS				TOTAL INCL O&P
					MAT.	LABOR	EQUIP.	TOTAL	

Estimating Tips
22 10 00 Plumbing Piping and Pumps

This subdivision is primarily basic pipe and related materials. The pipe may be used by any of the mechanical disciplines, i.e., plumbing, fire protection, heating, and air conditioning.

Note: CPVC plastic piping approved for fire protection is located in 21 11 13.

- The labor adjustment factors listed in Subdivision 22 01 02.20 apply throughout Divisions 21, 22, and 23. CAUTION: the correct percentage may vary for the same items. For example, the percentage add for the basic pipe installation should be based on the maximum height that the installer must install for that particular section. If the pipe is to be located 14' above the floor but it is suspended on threaded rod from beams, the bottom flange of which is 18' high (4' rods), then the height is actually 18' and the add is 20%. The pipe cover, however, does not have to go above the 14', and so the add should be 10%.

- Most pipe is priced first as straight pipe with a joint (coupling, weld, etc.) every 10' and a hanger usually every 10'. There are exceptions with hanger spacing such as for cast iron pipe (5') and plastic pipe (3 per 10'). Following each type of pipe there are several lines listing sizes and the amount to be subtracted to delete couplings and hangers. This is for pipe that is to be buried or supported together on trapeze hangers. The reason that the couplings are deleted is that these runs are usually long, and frequently longer lengths of pipe are used. By deleting the couplings, the estimator is expected to look up and add back the correct reduced number of couplings.

- When preparing an estimate, it may be necessary to approximate the fittings. Fittings usually run between 25% and 50% of the cost of the pipe. The lower percentage is for simpler runs, and the higher number is for complex areas, such as mechanical rooms.

- For historic restoration projects, the systems must be as invisible as possible, and pathways must be sought for pipes, conduit, and ductwork. While installations in accessible spaces (such as basements and attics) are relatively straightforward to estimate, labor costs may be more difficult to determine when delivery systems must be concealed.

22 40 00 Plumbing Fixtures

- Plumbing fixture costs usually require two lines: the fixture itself and its "rough-in, supply, and waste."

- In the Assemblies Section (Plumbing D2010) for the desired fixture, the System Components Group at the center of the page shows the fixture on the first line. The rest of the list (fittings, pipe, tubing, etc.) will total up to what we refer to in the Unit Price section as "Rough-in, supply, waste, and vent." Note that for most fixtures we allow a nominal 5' of tubing to reach from the fixture to a main or riser.

- Remember that gas- and oil-fired units need venting.

Reference Numbers

Reference numbers are shown at the beginning of some major classifications. These numbers refer to related items in the Reference Section. The reference information may be an estimating procedure, an alternate pricing method, or technical information.

Note: Not all subdivisions listed here necessarily appear. ■

Did you know?

Our online estimating solution gives you the same access to RSMeans' data with 24/7 access:

- Quickly locate costs in the searchable database.
- Build cost lists, estimates, and reports in minutes.
- Adjust costs to any location in the U.S. and Canada with the click of a button.

Start your free trial today at
www.RSMeansOnline.com

22 01 02 – Labor Adjustments

22 01 02.10 Boilers, General	Crew	Daily Output	Labor-Hours	Unit	Material	2017 Bare Costs Labor	Equipment	Total	Total Incl O&P
0010 **BOILERS, GENERAL**, Prices do not include flue piping, elec. wiring,									
0020 gas or oil piping, boiler base, pad, or tankless unless noted									
0100 Boiler H.P.: 10 KW = 34 lb./steam/hr. = 33,475 BTU/hr.									
0150 To convert SFR to BTU rating: Hot water, 150 x SFR;									
0160 Forced hot water, 180 x SFR; steam, 240 x SFR									

22 01 02.20 Labor Adjustment Factors	Crew	Daily Output	Labor-Hours	Unit	Material	2017 Bare Costs Labor	Equipment	Total	Total Incl O&P
0010 **LABOR ADJUSTMENT FACTORS** (For Div. 21, 22 and 23) R220102-20									
0100 Labor factors, The below are reasonable suggestions, however									
0110 each project must be evaluated for its own peculiarities, and									
0120 the adjustments be increased or decreased depending on the									
0130 severity of the special conditions.									
1000 Add to labor for elevated installation (Above floor level)									
1080 10' to 14.5' high						10%			
1100 15' to 19.5' high						20%			
1120 20' to 24.5' high						25%			
1140 25' to 29.5' high						35%			
1160 30' to 34.5' high						40%			
1180 35' to 39.5' high						50%			
1200 40' and higher						55%			
2000 Add to labor for crawl space									
2100 3' high						40%			
2140 4' high						30%			
3000 Add to labor for multi-story building									
3010 For new construction (No elevator available)									
3100 Add for floors 3 thru 10						5%			
3110 Add for floors 11 thru 15						10%			
3120 Add for floors 16 thru 20						15%			
3130 Add for floors 21 thru 30						20%			
3140 Add for floors 31 and up						30%			
3170 For existing structure (Elevator available)									
3180 Add for work on floor 3 and above						2%			
4000 Add to labor for working in existing occupied buildings									
4100 Hospital						35%			
4140 Office building						25%			
4180 School						20%			
4220 Factory or warehouse						15%			
4260 Multi dwelling						15%			
5000 Add to labor, miscellaneous									
5100 Cramped shaft						35%			
5140 Congested area						15%			
5180 Excessive heat or cold						30%			
9000 Labor factors, The above are reasonable suggestions, however									
9010 each project should be evaluated for its own peculiarities.									
9100 Other factors to be considered are:									
9140 Movement of material and equipment through finished areas									
9180 Equipment room									
9220 Attic space									
9260 No service road									
9300 Poor unloading/storage area									
9340 Congested site area/heavy traffic									

78

For customer support on your Electrical Costs with RSMeans Data, call 800.448.8182.

22 05 Common Work Results for Plumbing

22 05 23 – General-Duty Valves for Plumbing Piping

22 05 23.20 Valves, Bronze	Crew	Daily Output	Labor-Hours	Unit	Material	2017 Bare Costs Labor	Equipment	Total	Total Incl O&P
0010 **VALVES, BRONZE**									
8800 Water heater water & gas safety shut off									
8810 Protection against a leaking water heater									
8814 Shut off valve	1 Plum	16	.500	Ea.	186	31		217	252
8818 Water heater dam		32	.250		31.50	15.45		46.95	58
8822 Gas control wiring harness	↓	32	.250	↓	24	15.45		39.45	50
8830 Whole house flood safety shut off									
8834 Connections									
8838 3/4" NPT	1 Plum	12	.667	Ea.	935	41		976	1,075
8842 1" NPT		11	.727		960	45		1,005	1,125
8846 1-1/4" NPT	↓	10	.800	↓	995	49.50		1,044.50	1,175

22 05 29 – Hangers and Supports for Plumbing Piping and Equipment

22 05 29.10 Hangers & Supp. for Plumb'g/HVAC Pipe/Equip.

	Crew	Daily Output	Labor-Hours	Unit	Material	2017 Bare Costs Labor	Equipment	Total	Total Incl O&P
0010 **HANGERS AND SUPPORTS FOR PLUMB'G/HVAC PIPE/EQUIP.**									
0011 TYPE numbers per MSS-SP58									
0050 Brackets									
0060 Beam side or wall, malleable iron, TYPE 34									
0070 3/8" threaded rod size	1 Plum	48	.167	Ea.	3.74	10.30		14.04	19.65
0080 1/2" threaded rod size		48	.167		3.41	10.30		13.71	19.30
0090 5/8" threaded rod size		48	.167		10.35	10.30		20.65	27
0100 3/4" threaded rod size		48	.167		12.10	10.30		22.40	29
0110 7/8" threaded rod size	↓	48	.167	↓	12.50	10.30		22.80	29.50
0120 For concrete installation, add						30%			
0150 Wall, welded steel, medium, TYPE 32									
0160 0 size, 12" wide, 18" deep	1 Plum	34	.235	Ea.	171	14.55		185.55	210
0170 1 size, 18" wide, 24" deep		34	.235		228	14.55		242.55	273
0180 2 size, 24" wide, 30" deep	↓	34	.235	↓	299	14.55		313.55	350
0300 Clamps									
0310 C-clamp, for mounting on steel beam flange, w/locknut, TYPE 23									
0320 3/8" threaded rod size	1 Plum	160	.050	Ea.	2.41	3.09		5.50	7.30
0330 1/2" threaded rod size		160	.050		2.45	3.09		5.54	7.35
0340 5/8" threaded rod size		160	.050		3.72	3.09		6.81	8.75
0350 3/4" threaded rod size	↓	160	.050	↓	4.58	3.09		7.67	9.70
0750 Riser or extension pipe, carbon steel, TYPE 8									
0760 3/4" pipe size	1 Plum	48	.167	Ea.	2.18	10.30		12.48	17.95
0770 1" pipe size		47	.170		2.63	10.50		13.13	18.75
0780 1-1/4" pipe size		46	.174		3.42	10.75		14.17	19.95
0790 1-1/2" pipe size		45	.178		3.49	11		14.49	20.50
0800 2" pipe size		43	.186		3.62	11.50		15.12	21.50
0810 2-1/2" pipe size		41	.195		3.81	12.05		15.86	22.50
0820 3" pipe size		40	.200		4.09	12.35		16.44	23
0830 3-1/2" pipe size		39	.205		5.15	12.70		17.85	25
0840 4" pipe size		38	.211		5.60	13		18.60	26
0850 5" pipe size		37	.216		7.15	13.35		20.50	28
0860 6" pipe size	↓	36	.222	↓	16.15	13.75		29.90	38.50
1150 Insert, concrete									
1160 Wedge type, carbon steel body, malleable iron nut, galvanized									
1170 1/4" threaded rod size	1 Plum	96	.083	Ea.	9.55	5.15		14.70	18.25
1180 3/8" threaded rod size		96	.083		39	5.15		44.15	50.50
1190 1/2" threaded rod size		96	.083		10.65	5.15		15.80	19.50
1200 5/8" threaded rod size		96	.083		60	5.15		65.15	74
1210 3/4" threaded rod size	↓	96	.083	↓	11.95	5.15		17.10	21

22 05 29.10 Hangers & Supp. for Plumb'g/HVAC Pipe/Equip.	Crew	Daily Output	Labor-Hours	Unit	Material	2017 Bare Costs Labor	Equipment	Total	Total Incl O&P
1220	7/8" threaded rod size	1 Plum	96	.083	Ea.	12.35	5.15		17.50	21.50
2650	Rods, carbon steel									
2660	Continuous thread									
2670	1/4" thread size	1 Plum	144	.056	L.F.	2.18	3.43		5.61	7.60
2680	3/8" thread size		144	.056		2.33	3.43		5.76	7.75
2690	1/2" thread size		144	.056		3.67	3.43		7.10	9.25
2700	5/8" thread size		144	.056		5.20	3.43		8.63	10.90
2710	3/4" thread size		144	.056		9.15	3.43		12.58	15.30
2720	7/8" thread size		144	.056		11.50	3.43		14.93	17.85
2725	1/4" thread size, bright finish		144	.056		1.24	3.43		4.67	6.55
2726	1/2" thread size, bright finish	↓	144	.056	↓	4.23	3.43		7.66	9.85
2730	For galvanized, add					40%				
4400	U-bolt, carbon steel									
4410	Standard, with nuts, TYPE 42									
4420	1/2" pipe size	1 Plum	160	.050	Ea.	1.01	3.09		4.10	5.75
4430	3/4" pipe size		158	.051		1.01	3.13		4.14	5.85
4450	1" pipe size		152	.053		1.05	3.25		4.30	6.05
4460	1-1/4" pipe size		148	.054		1.33	3.34		4.67	6.50
4470	1-1/2" pipe size		143	.056		1.42	3.46		4.88	6.75
4480	2" pipe size		139	.058		1.53	3.56		5.09	7.05
4490	2-1/2" pipe size		134	.060		2.50	3.69		6.19	8.30
4500	3" pipe size		128	.063		2.81	3.86		6.67	8.95
4510	3-1/2" pipe size		122	.066		3.03	4.05		7.08	9.45
4520	4" pipe size		117	.068		3.09	4.23		7.32	9.80
4530	5" pipe size		114	.070		3.63	4.34		7.97	10.55
4540	6" pipe size	↓	111	.072	↓	6.90	4.45		11.35	14.30
4580	For plastic coating on 1/2" thru 6" size, add					150%				
8800	Wire cable support system									
8810	Cable with hook terminal and locking device									
8830	2 mm (.079") dia cable (100 lb. cap.)									
8840	1 m (3.3') length, with hook	1 Shee	96	.083	Ea.	3.17	4.84		8.01	10.90
8850	2 m (6.6') length, with hook		84	.095		3.68	5.55		9.23	12.50
8860	3 m (9.9') length, with hook	↓	72	.111		4.15	6.45		10.60	14.40
8870	5 m (16.4') length, with hook	Q-9	60	.267		5.85	13.95		19.80	28
8880	10 m (32.8') length, with hook	"	30	.533	↓	7.45	28		35.45	50.50
8900	3 mm (.118") dia cable (200 lb. cap.)									
8910	1 m (3.3') length, with hook	1 Shee	96	.083	Ea.	3.96	4.84		8.80	11.75
8920	2 m (6.6') length, with hook		84	.095		4.45	5.55		10	13.35
8930	3 m (9.9') length, with hook	↓	72	.111		4.91	6.45		11.36	15.25
8940	5 m (16.4') length, with hook	Q-9	60	.267		6.05	13.95		20	28
8950	10 m (32.8') length, with hook	"	30	.533	↓	10.60	28		38.60	54
9000	Cable system accessories									
9010	Anchor bolt, 3/8", with nut	1 Shee	140	.057	Ea.	1	3.32		4.32	6.20
9020	Air duct corner protector		160	.050		.55	2.90		3.45	5.05
9030	Air duct support attachment	↓	140	.057	↓	1.75	3.32		5.07	7.05
9040	Flange clip, hammer-on style									
9044	For flange thickness 3/32" - 9/64", 160 lb. cap.	1 Shee	180	.044	Ea.	.26	2.58		2.84	4.24
9048	For flange thickness 1/8" - 1/4", 200 lb. cap.		160	.050		.29	2.90		3.19	4.76
9052	For flange thickness 5/16" - 1/2", 200 lb. cap.		150	.053		.59	3.10		3.69	5.40
9056	For flange thickness 9/16" - 3/4", 200 lb. cap.		140	.057		.78	3.32		4.10	5.95
9060	Wire insulation protection tube	↓	180	.044	L.F.	.41	2.58		2.99	4.40
9070	Wire cutter				Ea.	40.50			40.50	45

22 33 Electric Domestic Water Heaters

22 33 13 – Instantaneous Electric Domestic Water Heaters

22 33 13.10 Hot Water Dispensers

	Crew	Daily Output	Labor-Hours	Unit	Material	2017 Bare Costs Labor	Equipment	Total	Total Incl O&P
0010 **HOT WATER DISPENSERS**									
0160 Commercial, 100 cup, 11.3 amp	1 Plum	14	.571	Ea.	440	35.50		475.50	540
3180 Household, 60 cup	"	14	.571	"	241	35.50		276.50	320

22 33 30 – Residential, Electric Domestic Water Heaters

22 33 30.13 Residential, Small-Capacity Elec. Water Heaters

	Crew	Daily Output	Labor-Hours	Unit	Material	2017 Bare Costs Labor	Equipment	Total	Total Incl O&P
0010 **RESIDENTIAL, SMALL-CAPACITY ELECTRIC DOMESTIC WATER HEATERS**									
1000 Residential, electric, glass lined tank, 5 yr., 10 gal., single element R224000-10	1 Plum	2.30	3.478	Ea.	465	215		680	835
1040 20 gallon, single element R224000-20		2.20	3.636		615	225		840	1,025
1060 30 gallon, double element		2.20	3.636		1,075	225		1,300	1,550
1080 40 gallon, double element		2	4		1,150	247		1,397	1,650
1100 52 gallon, double element		2	4		1,300	247		1,547	1,825
1120 66 gallon, double element		1.80	4.444		1,775	275		2,050	2,375
1140 80 gallon, double element		1.60	5		2,000	310		2,310	2,675
1180 120 gallon, double element		1.40	5.714		2,775	355		3,130	3,575

22 33 33 – Light-Commercial Electric Domestic Water Heaters

22 33 33.10 Commercial Electric Water Heaters

	Crew	Daily Output	Labor-Hours	Unit	Material	2017 Bare Costs Labor	Equipment	Total	Total Incl O&P
0010 **COMMERCIAL ELECTRIC WATER HEATERS**									
4000 Commercial, 100° rise. NOTE: for each size tank, a range of									
4010 heaters between the ones shown are available									
4020 Electric									
4100 5 gal., 3 kW, 12 GPH, 208 volt	1 Plum	2	4	Ea.	5,175	247		5,422	6,050
4120 10 gal., 6 kW, 25 GPH, 208 volt		2	4		5,700	247		5,947	6,650
4130 30 gal., 24 kW, 98 GPH, 208 volt		1.92	4.167		9,400	258		9,658	10,800
4136 40 gal., 36 kW, 148 GPH, 208 volt		1.88	4.255		11,300	263		11,563	12,800
4140 50 gal., 9 kW, 37 GPH, 208 volt		1.80	4.444		7,875	275		8,150	9,075
4160 50 gal., 36 kW, 148 GPH, 208 volt		1.80	4.444		12,100	275		12,375	13,700
4180 80 gal., 12 kW, 49 GPH, 208 volt		1.50	5.333		9,650	330		9,980	11,100
4200 80 gal., 36 kW, 148 GPH, 208 volt		1.50	5.333		13,400	330		13,730	15,300
4220 100 gal., 36 kW, 148 GPH, 208 volt		1.20	6.667		14,000	410		14,410	16,000
4240 120 gal., 36 kW, 148 GPH, 208 volt		1.20	6.667		14,600	410		15,010	16,600
4260 150 gal., 15 kW, 61 GPH, 480 volt		1	8		34,200	495		34,695	38,300
4280 150 gal., 120 kW, 490 GPH, 480 volt		1	8		48,100	495		48,595	53,500
4300 200 gal., 15 kW, 61 GPH, 480 volt	Q-1	1.70	9.412		37,000	525		37,525	41,500
4320 200 gal., 120 kW, 490 GPH, 480 volt		1.70	9.412		50,500	525		51,025	56,500
4340 250 gal., 15 kW, 61 GPH, 480 volt		1.50	10.667		38,200	595		38,795	42,900
4360 250 gal., 150 kW, 615 GPH, 480 volt		1.50	10.667		55,500	595		56,095	62,000
4380 300 gal., 30 kW, 123 GPH, 480 volt		1.30	12.308		42,000	685		42,685	47,200
4400 300 gal., 180 kW, 738 GPH, 480 volt		1.30	12.308		60,500	685		61,185	67,500
4420 350 gal., 30 kW, 123 GPH, 480 volt		1.10	14.545		44,400	810		45,210	50,000
4440 350 gal., 180 kW, 738 GPH, 480 volt		1.10	14.545		62,500	810		63,310	70,000
4460 400 gal., 30 kW, 123 GPH, 480 volt		1	16		50,500	890		51,390	57,000
4480 400 gal., 210 kW, 860 GPH, 480 volt		1	16		72,500	890		73,390	81,000
4500 500 gal., 30 kW, 123 GPH, 480 volt		.80	20		58,500	1,125		59,625	66,000
4520 500 gal., 240 kW, 984 GPH, 480 volt		.80	20		96,000	1,125		97,125	107,000
4540 600 gal., 30 kW, 123 GPH, 480 volt	Q-2	1.20	20		67,500	1,150		68,650	76,000
4560 600 gal., 300 kW, 1230 GPH, 480 volt		1.20	20		102,000	1,150		103,150	114,000
4580 700 gal., 30 kW, 123 GPH, 480 volt		1	24		70,500	1,375		71,875	79,500
4600 700 gal., 300 kW, 1230 GPH, 480 volt		1	24		106,500	1,375		107,875	119,000
4620 800 gal., 60 kW, 245 GPH, 480 volt		.90	26.667		76,500	1,550		78,050	86,500
4640 800 gal., 300 kW, 1230 GPH, 480 volt		.90	26.667		108,500	1,550		110,050	122,000
4660 1000 gal., 60 kW, 245 GPH, 480 volt		.70	34.286		83,500	1,975		85,475	95,000
4680 1000 gal., 480 kW, 1970 GPH, 480 volt		.70	34.286		139,000	1,975		140,975	156,000

For customer support on your Electrical Costs with RSMeans Data, call 800.448.8182.

81

22 33 Electric Domestic Water Heaters

22 33 33 – Light-Commercial Electric Domestic Water Heaters

22 33 33.10 Commercial Electric Water Heaters	Crew	Daily Output	Labor-Hours	Unit	Material	2017 Bare Costs Labor	Equipment	Total	Total Incl O&P
4700	1200 gal., 60 kW, 245 GPH, 480 volt	Q-2	.60	40	Ea.	94,500	2,300		96,800	107,500
4720	1200 gal., 480 kW, 1970 GPH, 480 volt		.60	40		144,000	2,300		146,300	161,500
4740	1500 gal., 60 kW, 245 GPH, 480 volt		.50	48		124,500	2,775		127,275	141,000
4760	1500 gal., 480 kW, 1970 GPH, 480 volt		.50	48		173,000	2,775		175,775	194,500
5400	Modulating step control for under 90 kW, 2-5 steps	1 Elec	5.30	1.509		820	85.50		905.50	1,025
5440	For above 90 kW, 1 through 5 steps beyond standard, add		3.20	2.500		223	142		365	460
5460	For above 90 kW, 6 through 10 steps beyond standard, add		2.70	2.963		460	168		628	755
5480	For above 90 kW, 11 through 18 steps beyond standard, add		1.60	5		685	283		968	1,175

22 34 Fuel-Fired Domestic Water Heaters

22 34 30 – Residential Gas Domestic Water Heaters

22 34 30.13 Residential, Atmos, Gas Domestic Wtr Heaters

		Crew	Daily Output	Labor-Hours	Unit	Material	2017 Bare Costs Labor	Equipment	Total	Total Incl O&P
0010	**RESIDENTIAL, ATMOSPHERIC, GAS DOMESTIC WATER HEATERS**									
2000	Gas fired, foam lined tank, 10 yr., vent not incl.									
2040	30 gallon	1 Plum	2	4	Ea.	1,925	247		2,172	2,500
2060	40 gallon		1.90	4.211		1,925	260		2,185	2,525
2080	50 gallon		1.80	4.444		2,075	275		2,350	2,725
2090	60 gallon		1.70	4.706		1,725	291		2,016	2,325
2100	75 gallon		1.50	5.333		2,925	330		3,255	3,725
2120	100 gallon		1.30	6.154		3,075	380		3,455	3,975
2900	Water heater, safety-drain pan, 26" round		20	.400		34.50	24.50		59	75.50
3000	Tank leak safety, water & gas shut off see 22 05 23.20 8800									

22 34 46 – Oil-Fired Domestic Water Heaters

22 34 46.10 Residential Oil-Fired Water Heaters

		Crew	Daily Output	Labor-Hours	Unit	Material	2017 Bare Costs Labor	Equipment	Total	Total Incl O&P
0010	**RESIDENTIAL OIL-FIRED WATER HEATERS**									
3000	Oil fired, glass lined tank, 5 yr., vent not included, 30 gallon	1 Plum	2	4	Ea.	1,400	247		1,647	1,900
3040	50 gallon		1.80	4.444		1,700	275		1,975	2,300
3060	70 gallon		1.50	5.333		2,400	330		2,730	3,125

Estimating Tips

The labor adjustment factors listed in Subdivision 22 01 02.20 also apply to Division 23.

23 10 00 Facility Fuel Systems

- The prices in this subdivision for above- and below-ground storage tanks do not include foundations or hold-down slabs, unless noted. The estimator should refer to Divisions 3 and 31 for foundation system pricing. In addition to the foundations, required tank accessories, such as tank gauges, leak detection devices, and additional manholes and piping, must be added to the tank prices.

23 50 00 Central Heating Equipment

- When estimating the cost of an HVAC system, check to see who is responsible for providing and installing the temperature control system. It is possible to overlook controls, assuming that they would be included in the electrical estimate.

- When looking up a boiler, be careful on specified capacity. Some manufacturers rate their products on output while others use input.

- Include HVAC insulation for pipe, boiler, and duct (wrap and liner).

- Be careful when looking up mechanical items to get the correct pressure rating and connection type (thread, weld, flange).

23 70 00 Central HVAC Equipment

- Combination heating and cooling units are sized by the air conditioning requirements. (See Reference No. R236000-20 for the preliminary sizing guide.)

- A ton of air conditioning is nominally 400 CFM.

- Rectangular duct is taken off by the linear foot for each size, but its cost is usually estimated by the pound. Remember that SMACNA standards now base duct on internal pressure.

- Prefabricated duct is estimated and purchased like pipe: straight sections and fittings.

- Note that cranes or other lifting equipment are not included on any lines in Division 23. For example, if a crane is required to lift a heavy piece of pipe into place high above a gym floor, or to put a rooftop unit on the roof of a four-story building, etc., it must be added. Due to the potential for extreme variation—from nothing additional required to a major crane or helicopter—we feel that including a nominal amount for "lifting contingency" would be useless and detract from the accuracy of the estimate. When using equipment rental cost data from RSMeans, do not forget to include the cost of the operator(s).

Reference Numbers

Reference numbers are shown at the beginning of some major classifications. These numbers refer to related items in the Reference Section. The reference information may be an estimating procedure, an alternate pricing method, or technical information.

Note: Not all subdivisions listed here necessarily appear. ∎

Did you know?

Our online estimating solution gives you the same access to RSMeans' data with 24/7 access:

- Quickly locate costs in the searchable database.

- Build cost lists, estimates, and reports in minutes.

- Adjust costs to any location in the U.S. and Canada with the click of a button.

Start your free trial today at
www.RSMeansOnline.com

23 05 02 – HVAC General

23 05 02.10 Air Conditioning, General	Crew	Daily Output	Labor-Hours	Unit	Material	2017 Bare Costs Labor	2017 Bare Costs Equipment	Total	Total Incl O&P
0010 **AIR CONDITIONING, GENERAL** Prices are for standard efficiencies (SEER 13)									
0020 for upgrade to SEER 14 add					10%				

23 09 Instrumentation and Control for HVAC

23 09 23 – Direct-Digital Control System for HVAC

23 09 23.10 Control Components/DDC Systems

		Crew	Daily Output	Labor-Hours	Unit	Material	Labor	Equipment	Total	Total Incl O&P
0010	**CONTROL COMPONENTS/DDC SYSTEMS** (Sub's quote incl. M & L)									
0100	Analog inputs									
0110	Sensors (avg. 50' run in 1/2" EMT)									
0120	Duct temperature				Ea.				415	415
0130	Space temperature								665	665
0140	Duct humidity, +/- 3%								695	695
0150	Space humidity, +/- 2%								1,075	1,075
0160	Duct static pressure								565	565
0170	CFM/Transducer								765	765
0180	KW/Transducer								1,350	1,350
0182	KWH totalization (not incl. elec. meter pulse xmtr.)								625	625
0190	Space static pressure								1,075	1,075
1000	Analog outputs (avg. 50' run in 1/2" EMT)									
1010	P/I Transducer				Ea.				635	635
1020	Analog output, matl. in MUX								305	305
1030	Pneumatic (not incl. control device)								645	645
1040	Electric (not incl. control device)								380	380
2000	Status (Alarms)									
2100	Digital inputs (avg. 50' run in 1/2" EMT)									
2110	Freeze				Ea.				435	435
2120	Fire								395	395
2130	Differential pressure (air)								595	595
2140	Differential pressure (water)								975	975
2150	Current sensor								435	435
2160	Duct high temperature thermostat								570	570
2170	Duct smoke detector								705	705
2200	Digital output (avg. 50' run in 1/2" EMT)									
2210	Start/stop				Ea.				340	340
2220	On/off (maintained contact)				"				585	585
3000	Controller MUX panel, incl. function boards									
3100	48 point				Ea.				5,275	5,275
3110	128 point				"				7,225	7,225
3200	DDC controller (avg. 50' run in conduit)									
3210	Mechanical room									
3214	16 point controller (incl. 120 volt/1 phase power supply)				Ea.				3,275	3,275
3229	32 point controller (incl. 120 volt/1 phase power supply)				"				5,425	5,425
3230	Includes software programming and checkout									
3260	Space									
3266	VAV terminal box (incl. space temp. sensor)				Ea.				840	840
3280	Host computer (avg. 50' run in conduit)									
3281	Package complete with PC, keyboard,									
3282	printer, monitor, basic software				Ea.				3,150	3,150
4000	Front end costs									
4100	Computer (P.C.) with software program				Ea.				6,350	6,350
4200	Color graphics software								3,925	3,925

23 09 23 – Direct-Digital Control System for HVAC

23 09 23.10 Control Components/DDC Systems		Crew	Daily Output	Labor-Hours	Unit	Material	2017 Bare Costs Labor	Equipment	Total	Total Incl O&P
4300	Color graphics slides				Ea.				490	490
4350	Additional printer				▼				980	980
4400	Communications trunk cable				L.F.				3.80	3.80
4500	Engineering labor (not incl. dftg.)				Point				94	94
4600	Calibration labor								120	120
4700	Start-up, checkout labor				▼				120	120
4800	Programming labor, as req'd									
5000	Communications bus (data transmission cable)									
5010	#18 twisted shielded pair in 1/2" EMT conduit				C.L.F.				380	380
8000	Applications software									
8050	Basic maintenance manager software (not incl. data base entry)				Ea.				1,950	1,950
8100	Time program				Point				6.85	6.85
8120	Duty cycle								13.65	13.65
8140	Optimum start/stop								41.50	41.50
8160	Demand limiting								20.50	20.50
8180	Enthalpy program				▼				41.50	41.50
8200	Boiler optimization				Ea.				1,225	1,225
8220	Chiller optimization				"				1,625	1,625
8240	Custom applications									
8260	Cost varies with complexity									

23 09 43 – Pneumatic Control System for HVAC

23 09 43.10 Pneumatic Control Systems

			Crew	Daily Output	Labor-Hours	Unit	Material	2017 Bare Costs Labor	Equipment	Total	Total Incl O&P
0010	**PNEUMATIC CONTROL SYSTEMS**										
0011	Including a nominal 50 ft. of tubing. Add control panelboard if req'd.										
0100	Heating and ventilating, split system										
0200	Mixed air control, economizer cycle, panel readout, tubing										
0220	Up to 10 tons	G	Q-19	.68	35.294	Ea.	4,300	1,975		6,275	7,725
0240	For 10 to 20 tons	G		.63	37.915		4,600	2,125		6,725	8,275
0260	For over 20 tons	G		.58	41.096		5,000	2,300		7,300	8,975
0270	Enthalpy cycle, up to 10 tons			.50	48.387		4,750	2,725		7,475	9,325
0280	For 10 to 20 tons			.46	52.174		5,125	2,925		8,050	10,100
0290	For over 20 tons		▼	.42	56.604	▼	5,575	3,175		8,750	10,900
0300	Heating coil, hot water, 3 way valve,										
0320	Freezestat, limit control on discharge, readout		Q-5	.69	23.088	Ea.	3,200	1,300		4,500	5,475
0500	Cooling coil, chilled water, room										
0520	Thermostat, 3 way valve		Q-5	2	8	Ea.	1,425	450		1,875	2,250
0600	Cooling tower, fan cycle, damper control,										
0620	Control system including water readout in/out at panel		Q-19	.67	35.821	Ea.	5,675	2,025		7,700	9,250
1000	Unit ventilator, day/night operation,										
1100	freezestat, ASHRAE, cycle 2		Q-19	.91	26.374	Ea.	3,125	1,475		4,600	5,675
2000	Compensated hot water from boiler, valve control,										
2100	readout and reset at panel, up to 60 GPM		Q-19	.55	43.956	Ea.	5,875	2,475		8,350	10,200
2120	For 120 GPM			.51	47.059		6,275	2,650		8,925	10,900
2140	For 240 GPM			.49	49.180		6,575	2,775		9,350	11,400
3000	Boiler room combustion air, damper to 5 S.F., controls			1.37	17.582		2,825	990		3,815	4,600
3500	Fan coil, heating and cooling valves, 4 pipe control system			3	8		1,275	450		1,725	2,075
3600	Heat exchanger system controls		▼	.86	27.907	▼	2,750	1,575		4,325	5,375
3900	Multizone control (one per zone), includes thermostat, damper										
3910	motor and reset of discharge temperature		Q-5	.51	31.373	Ea.	2,825	1,750		4,575	5,775
4000	Pneumatic thermostat, including controlling room radiator valve		"	2.43	6.593		850	370		1,220	1,500
4040	Program energy saving optimizer	G	Q-19	1.21	19.786		7,075	1,100		8,175	9,450
4060	Pump control system		"	3	8	▼	1,300	450		1,750	2,125

For customer support on your Electrical Costs with RSMeans Data, call 800.448.8182.

85

23 09 43 – Pneumatic Control System for HVAC

23 09 43.10 Pneumatic Control Systems	Crew	Daily Output	Labor-Hours	Unit	Material	2017 Bare Costs Labor	Equipment	Total	Total Incl O&P
4080	Reheat coil control system, not incl. coil	Q-5	2.43	6.593	Ea.	1,100	370		1,470	1,775
4500	Air supply for pneumatic control system									
4600	Tank mounted duplex compressor, starter, alternator,									
4620	piping, dryer, PRV station and filter									
4630	1/2 HP	Q-19	.68	35.139	Ea.	10,500	1,975		12,475	14,600
4640	3/4 HP		.64	37.383		11,000	2,100		13,100	15,300
4650	1 HP		.61	39.539		12,100	2,225		14,325	16,700
4660	1-1/2 HP		.58	41.739		12,800	2,350		15,150	17,600
4680	3 HP		.55	43.956		17,500	2,475		19,975	22,900
4690	5 HP		.42	57.143		30,500	3,225		33,725	38,400
4800	Main air supply, includes 3/8" copper main and labor	Q-5	1.82	8.791	C.L.F.	355	495		850	1,125
4810	If poly tubing used, deduct								30%	30%
7000	Static pressure control for air handling unit, includes pressure									
7010	sensor, receiver controller, readout and damper motors	Q-19	.64	37.383	Ea.	8,375	2,100		10,475	12,400
7020	If return air fan requires control, add								70%	70%
8600	VAV boxes, incl. thermostat, damper motor, reheat coil & tubing	Q-5	1.46	10.989		1,325	615		1,940	2,375
8610	If no reheat coil, deduct								204	204

23 09 53 – Pneumatic and Electric Control System for HVAC

23 09 53.10 Control Components

		Crew	Daily Output	Labor-Hours	Unit	Material	2017 Bare Costs Labor	Equipment	Total	Total Incl O&P
0010	**CONTROL COMPONENTS**									
0700	Controller, receiver									
0850	Electric, single snap switch	1 Elec	4	2	Ea.	490	113		603	705
0860	Dual snap switches	"	3	2.667	"	655	151		806	945
3590	Sensor, electric operated									
3620	Humidity	1 Elec	8	1	Ea.	201	56.50		257.50	305
3650	Pressure		8	1		271	56.50		327.50	385
3680	Temperature		10	.800		119	45.50		164.50	199
5000	Thermostats									
5200	24 hour, automatic, clock G	1 Shee	8	1	Ea.	212	58		270	325
5220	Electric, low voltage, 2 wire	1 Elec	13	.615		50.50	35		85.50	108
5230	3 wire	"	10	.800		38.50	45.50		84	111
7090	Valves, motor controlled, including actuator									
7100	Electric motor actuated									
7200	Brass, two way, screwed									
7210	1/2" pipe size	L-6	36	.333	Ea.	355	20		375	420
7220	3/4" pipe size		30	.400		600	24		624	695
7230	1" pipe size		28	.429		715	25.50		740.50	825
7240	1-1/2" pipe size		19	.632		820	38		858	955
7250	2" pipe size		16	.750		1,150	45		1,195	1,350
7350	Brass, three way, screwed									
7360	1/2" pipe size	L-6	33	.364	Ea.	390	22		412	465
7370	3/4" pipe size		27	.444		430	26.50		456.50	515
7380	1" pipe size		25.50	.471		490	28.50		518.50	585
7384	1-1/4" pipe size		21	.571		560	34.50		594.50	665
7390	1-1/2" pipe size		17	.706		615	42.50		657.50	740
7400	2" pipe size		14	.857		930	51.50		981.50	1,100
7550	Iron body, two way, flanged									
7560	2-1/2" pipe size	L-6	4	3	Ea.	1,375	180		1,555	1,800
7570	3" pipe size		3	4		1,425	240		1,665	1,900
7580	4" pipe size		2	6		2,700	360		3,060	3,525
7850	Iron body, three way, flanged									
7860	2-1/2" pipe size	L-6	3	4	Ea.	1,400	240		1,640	1,900

23 09 Instrumentation and Control for HVAC

23 09 53 – Pneumatic and Electric Control System for HVAC

23 09 53 10 Control Components	Crew	Daily Output	Labor-Hours	Unit	Material	2017 Bare Costs Labor	2017 Bare Costs Equipment	Total	Total Incl O&P
7870	3" pipe size	L6	2.50	4.800	Ea.	1,600	288		1,888	2,175
7880	4" pipe size	▼	2	6	▼	2,050	360		2,410	2,800

23 34 HVAC Fans

23 34 13 – Axial HVAC Fans

23 34 13.10 Axial Flow HVAC Fans

		Crew	Daily Output	Labor-Hours	Unit	Material	Labor	Equipment	Total	Total Incl O&P
0010	**AXIAL FLOW HVAC FANS**									
0020	Air conditioning and process air handling									
1500	Vaneaxial, low pressure, 2000 CFM, 1/2 HP	Q-20	3.60	5.556	Ea.	2,250	295		2,545	2,950
1520	4,000 CFM, 1 HP		3.20	6.250		2,650	330		2,980	3,400
1540	8,000 CFM, 2 HP		2.80	7.143		3,350	380		3,730	4,275
1560	16,000 CFM, 5 HP	▼	2.40	8.333	▼	4,700	445		5,145	5,850

23 34 14 – Blower HVAC Fans

23 34 14.10 Blower Type HVAC Fans

		Crew	Daily Output	Labor-Hours	Unit	Material	Labor	Equipment	Total	Total Incl O&P
0010	**BLOWER TYPE HVAC FANS**									
2000	Blowers, direct drive with motor, complete									
2020	1045 CFM @ .5" S.P., 1/5 HP	Q-20	18	1.111	Ea.	370	59		429	500
2040	1385 CFM @ .5" S.P., 1/4 HP		18	1.111		365	59		424	490
2060	1640 CFM @ .5" S.P., 1/3 HP		18	1.111		330	59		389	450
2080	1760 CFM @ .5" S.P., 1/2 HP	▼	18	1.111	▼	340	59		399	465
2090	4 speed									
2100	1164 to 1739 CFM @ .5" S.P., 1/3 HP	Q-20	16	1.250	Ea.	345	66.50		411.50	480
2120	1467 to 2218 CFM @ 1.0" S.P., 3/4 HP	"	14	1.429	"	400	76		476	555
2500	Ceiling fan, right angle, extra quiet, 0.10" S.P.									
2520	95 CFM	Q-20	20	1	Ea.	315	53		368	430
2540	210 CFM		19	1.053		375	56		431	495
2560	385 CFM		18	1.111		475	59		534	610
2580	885 CFM		16	1.250		935	66.50		1,001.50	1,125
2600	1,650 CFM		13	1.538		1,300	81.50		1,381.50	1,550
2620	2,960 CFM	▼	11	1.818		1,725	96.50		1,821.50	2,050
2680	For speed control switch, add	1 Elec	16	.500	▼	173	28.50		201.50	233
7500	Utility set, steel construction, pedestal, 1/4" S.P.									
7520	Direct drive, 150 CFM, 1/8 HP	Q-20	6.40	3.125	Ea.	900	166		1,066	1,250
7540	485 CFM, 1/6 HP		5.80	3.448		1,125	183		1,308	1,525
7560	1950 CFM, 1/2 HP		4.80	4.167		1,325	221		1,546	1,775
7580	2410 CFM, 3/4 HP		4.40	4.545		2,450	241		2,691	3,075
7600	3328 CFM, 1-1/2 HP	▼	3	6.667	▼	2,725	355		3,080	3,550
7680	V-belt drive, drive cover, 3 phase									
7700	800 CFM, 1/4 HP	Q-20	6	3.333	Ea.	1,025	177		1,202	1,400
7720	1,300 CFM, 1/3 HP		5	4		1,075	212		1,287	1,500
7740	2,000 CFM, 1 HP		4.60	4.348		1,275	231		1,506	1,750
7760	2,900 CFM, 3/4 HP		4.20	4.762		1,725	253		1,978	2,250
7780	3,600 CFM, 3/4 HP		4	5		2,100	266		2,366	2,725
7800	4,800 CFM, 1 HP		3.50	5.714		2,500	305		2,805	3,225
7820	6,700 CFM, 1-1/2 HP		3	6.667		3,075	355		3,430	3,925
7830	7,500 CFM, 2 HP		2.50	8		4,175	425		4,600	5,225
7840	11,000 CFM, 3 HP		2	10		5,575	530		6,105	6,925
7860	13,000 CFM, 3 HP		1.60	12.500		5,650	665		6,315	7,225
7880	15,000 CFM, 5 HP		1	20		5,850	1,050		6,900	8,075
7900	17,000 CFM, 7-1/2 HP	▼	.80	25		6,275	1,325		7,600	8,925

23 34 14 – Blower HVAC Fans

23 34 14.10 Blower Type HVAC Fans	Crew	Daily Output	Labor-Hours	Unit	Material	2017 Bare Costs Labor	Equipment	Total	Total Incl O&P
7920	20,000 CFM, 7-1/2 HP	Q-20	.80	25	Ea.	7,475	1,325		8,800	10,300

23 34 16 – Centrifugal HVAC Fans

23 34 16.10 Centrifugal Type HVAC Fans

		Crew	Daily Output	Labor-Hours	Unit	Material	2017 Bare Costs Labor	Equipment	Total	Total Incl O&P
0010	**CENTRIFUGAL TYPE HVAC FANS**									
0200	In-line centrifugal, supply/exhaust booster									
0220	aluminum wheel/hub, disconnect switch, 1/4" S.P.									
0240	500 CFM, 10" diameter connection	Q-20	3	6.667	Ea.	1,450	355		1,805	2,150
0260	1,380 CFM, 12" diameter connection		2	10		1,475	530		2,005	2,425
0280	1,520 CFM, 16" diameter connection		2	10		1,525	530		2,055	2,475
0300	2,560 CFM, 18" diameter connection		1	20		1,650	1,050		2,700	3,450
0320	3,480 CFM, 20" diameter connection		.80	25		1,925	1,325		3,250	4,125
0326	5,080 CFM, 20" diameter connection		.75	26.667		2,100	1,425		3,525	4,450
3500	Centrifugal, airfoil, motor and drive, complete									
3520	1000 CFM, 1/2 HP	Q-20	2.50	8	Ea.	1,925	425		2,350	2,775
3540	2,000 CFM, 1 HP		2	10		2,175	530		2,705	3,200
3560	4,000 CFM, 3 HP		1.80	11.111		2,775	590		3,365	3,950
3580	8,000 CFM, 7-1/2 HP		1.40	14.286		4,175	760		4,935	5,750
3600	12,000 CFM, 10 HP		1	20		5,575	1,050		6,625	7,750
5000	Utility set, centrifugal, V belt drive, motor									
5020	1/4" S.P., 1200 CFM, 1/4 HP	Q-20	6	3.333	Ea.	1,875	177		2,052	2,350
5040	1520 CFM, 1/3 HP		5	4		2,475	212		2,687	3,050
5060	1850 CFM, 1/2 HP		4	5		2,450	266		2,716	3,100
5080	2180 CFM, 3/4 HP		3	6.667		2,900	355		3,255	3,750
5100	1/2" S.P., 3600 CFM, 1 HP		2	10		3,000	530		3,530	4,100
5120	4250 CFM, 1-1/2 HP		1.60	12.500		3,650	665		4,315	5,025
5140	4800 CFM, 2 HP		1.40	14.286		4,425	760		5,185	6,025
5160	6920 CFM, 5 HP		1.30	15.385		5,400	815		6,215	7,175
5180	7700 CFM, 7-1/2 HP		1.20	16.667		6,475	885		7,360	8,475
5200	For explosion proof motor, add					15%				
5500	Fans, industrial exhauster, for air which may contain granular matl.									
5520	1000 CFM, 1-1/2 HP	Q-20	2.50	8	Ea.	2,950	425		3,375	3,875
5540	2000 CFM, 3 HP		2	10		3,575	530		4,105	4,725
5560	4000 CFM, 7-1/2 HP		1.80	11.111		4,975	590		5,565	6,375
5580	8000 CFM, 15 HP		1.40	14.286		6,400	760		7,160	8,200
5600	12,000 CFM, 30 HP		1	20		10,400	1,050		11,450	13,100
7000	Roof exhauster, centrifugal, aluminum housing, 12" galvanized									
7020	curb, bird screen, back draft damper, 1/4" S.P.									
7100	Direct drive, 320 CFM, 11" sq. damper	Q-20	7	2.857	Ea.	770	152		922	1,075
7120	600 CFM, 11" sq. damper		6	3.333		985	177		1,162	1,350
7140	815 CFM, 13" sq. damper		5	4		985	212		1,197	1,400
7160	1450 CFM, 13" sq. damper		4.20	4.762		1,325	253		1,578	1,850
7180	2050 CFM, 16" sq. damper		4	5		1,700	266		1,966	2,275
7200	V-belt drive, 1650 CFM, 12" sq. damper		6	3.333		1,425	177		1,602	1,850
7220	2750 CFM, 21" sq. damper		5	4		1,700	212		1,912	2,200
7230	3500 CFM, 21" sq. damper		4.50	4.444		1,925	236		2,161	2,475
7240	4910 CFM, 23" sq. damper		4	5		2,325	266		2,591	2,975
7260	8525 CFM, 28" sq. damper		3	6.667		3,075	355		3,430	3,950
7280	13,760 CFM, 35" sq. damper		2	10		4,325	530		4,855	5,550
7300	20,558 CFM, 43" sq. damper		1	20		8,525	1,050		9,575	11,000
7320	For 2 speed winding, add					15%				
7340	For explosion proof motor, add					605			605	665
7360	For belt driven, top discharge, add					15%				

23 34 HVAC Fans

23 34 16 – Centrifugal HVAC Fans

23 34 16.10 Centrifugal Type HVAC Fans		Crew	Daily Output	Labor-Hours	Unit	Material	2017 Bare Costs Labor	Equipment	Total	Total Incl O&P
8500	Wall exhausters, centrifugal, auto damper, 1/8" S.P.									
8520	Direct drive, 610 CFM, 1/20 HP	Q-20	14	1.429	Ea.	445	76		521	605
8540	796 CFM, 1/12 HP		13	1.538		970	81.50		1,051.50	1,200
8560	822 CFM, 1/6 HP		12	1.667		1,125	88.50		1,213.50	1,375
8580	1,320 CFM, 1/4 HP		12	1.667		1,375	88.50		1,463.50	1,650
8600	1756 CFM, 1/4 HP		11	1.818		1,325	96.50		1,421.50	1,600
8620	1983 CFM, 1/4 HP		10	2		1,350	106		1,456	1,650
8640	2900 CFM, 1/2 HP		9	2.222		1,450	118		1,568	1,750
8660	3307 CFM, 3/4 HP	↓	8	2.500	↓	1,550	133		1,683	1,925
9500	V-belt drive, 3 phase									
9520	2,800 CFM, 1/4 HP	Q-20	9	2.222	Ea.	2,025	118		2,143	2,400
9540	3,740 CFM, 1/2 HP		8	2.500		2,100	133		2,233	2,500
9560	4400 CFM, 3/4 HP		7	2.857		2,125	152		2,277	2,550
9580	5700 CFM, 1-1/2 HP	↓	6	3.333	↓	2,200	177		2,377	2,700

23 34 23 – HVAC Power Ventilators

23 34 23.10 HVAC Power Circulators and Ventilators

			Crew	Daily Output	Labor-Hours	Unit	Material	2017 Bare Costs Labor	Equipment	Total	Total Incl O&P
0010	**HVAC POWER CIRCULATORS AND VENTILATORS**										
3000	Paddle blade air circulator, 3 speed switch										
3020	42", 5,000 CFM high, 3000 CFM low	G	1 Elec	2.40	3.333	Ea.	135	189		324	430
3040	52", 6,500 CFM high, 4000 CFM low	G	"	2.20	3.636	"	180	206		386	510
3100	For antique white motor, same cost										
3200	For brass plated motor, same cost										
3300	For light adaptor kit, add	G				Ea.	41			41	45.50
6000	Propeller exhaust, wall shutter										
6020	Direct drive, one speed, .075" S.P.										
6100	653 CFM, 1/30 HP		Q-20	10	2	Ea.	202	106		308	385
6120	1033 CFM, 1/20 HP			9	2.222		300	118		418	510
6140	1323 CFM, 1/15 HP			8	2.500		335	133		468	570
6160	2444 CFM, 1/4 HP		↓	7	2.857	↓	420	152		572	695
6300	V-belt drive, 3 phase										
6320	6175 CFM, 3/4 HP		Q-20	5	4	Ea.	1,250	212		1,462	1,725
6340	7500 CFM, 3/4 HP			5	4		1,325	212		1,537	1,800
6360	10,100 CFM, 1 HP			4.50	4.444		1,550	236		1,786	2,050
6380	14,300 CFM, 1-1/2 HP			4	5		1,825	266		2,091	2,400
6400	19,800 CFM, 2 HP			3	6.667		2,150	355		2,505	2,900
6420	26,250 CFM, 3 HP			2.60	7.692		2,275	410		2,685	3,125
6440	38,500 CFM, 5 HP			2.20	9.091		2,675	485		3,160	3,675
6460	46,000 CFM, 7-1/2 HP			2	10		2,875	530		3,405	3,950
6480	51,500 CFM, 10 HP		↓	1.80	11.111	↓	2,975	590		3,565	4,175
6650	Residential, bath exhaust, grille, back draft damper										
6660	50 CFM		Q-20	24	.833	Ea.	56.50	44.50		101	130
6670	110 CFM			22	.909		95	48.50		143.50	179
6680	Light combination, squirrel cage, 100 watt, 70 CFM		↓	24	.833	↓	108	44.50		152.50	187
6700	Light/heater combination, ceiling mounted										
6710	70 CFM, 1450 watt		Q-20	24	.833	Ea.	157	44.50		201.50	240
6800	Heater combination, recessed, 70 CFM			24	.833		65.50	44.50		110	140
6820	With 2 infrared bulbs			23	.870		102	46		148	183
6900	Kitchen exhaust, grille, complete, 160 CFM			22	.909		116	48.50		164.50	201
6910	180 CFM			20	1		97	53		150	188
6920	270 CFM			18	1.111		184	59		243	292
6930	350 CFM			16	1.250	↓	138	66.50		204.50	253
6940	Residential roof jacks and wall caps										

23 34 HVAC Fans

23 34 23 – HVAC Power Ventilators

23 34 23.10 HVAC Power Circulators and Ventilators	Crew	Daily Output	Labor-Hours	Unit	Material	2017 Bare Costs Labor	2017 Bare Costs Equipment	Total	Total Incl O&P
6944	Wall cap with back draft damper									
6946	3" & 4" diam. round duct	1 Shee	11	.727	Ea.	27	42		69	94
6948	6" diam. round duct	"	11	.727	"	64	42		106	135
6958	Roof jack with bird screen and back draft damper									
6960	3" & 4" diam. round duct	1 Shee	11	.727	Ea.	23.50	42		65.50	90.50
6962	3-1/4" x 10" rectangular duct	"	10	.800	"	47	46.50		93.50	123
6980	Transition									
6982	3-1/4" x 10" to 6" diam. round	1 Shee	20	.400	Ea.	28.50	23		51.50	66.50
8020	Attic, roof type									
8030	Aluminum dome, damper & curb									
8080	12" diameter, 1000 CFM (gravity)	1 Elec	10	.800	Ea.	600	45.50		645.50	730
8090	16" diameter, 1500 CFM (gravity)		9	.889		725	50.50		775.50	875
8100	20" diameter, 2500 CFM (gravity)		8	1		890	56.50		946.50	1,075
8110	26" diameter, 4000 CFM (gravity)		7	1.143		1,075	64.50		1,139.50	1,275
8120	32" diameter, 6500 CFM (gravity)		6	1.333		1,475	75.50		1,550.50	1,750
8130	38" diameter, 8000 CFM (gravity)		5	1.600		2,200	90.50		2,290.50	2,550
8140	50" diameter, 13,000 CFM (gravity)	↓	4	2	↓	3,175	113		3,288	3,675
8160	Plastic, ABS dome									
8180	1050 CFM	1 Elec	14	.571	Ea.	177	32.50		209.50	244
8200	1600 CFM	"	12	.667	"	265	37.50		302.50	350
8240	Attic, wall type, with shutter, one speed									
8250	12" diameter, 1000 CFM	1 Elec	14	.571	Ea.	415	32.50		447.50	505
8260	14" diameter, 1500 CFM		12	.667		450	37.50		487.50	550
8270	16" diameter, 2000 CFM	↓	9	.889	↓	510	50.50		560.50	635
8290	Whole house, wall type, with shutter, one speed									
8300	30" diameter, 4800 CFM	1 Elec	7	1.143	Ea.	1,100	64.50		1,164.50	1,300
8310	36" diameter, 7000 CFM		6	1.333		1,175	75.50		1,250.50	1,425
8320	42" diameter, 10,000 CFM		5	1.600		1,325	90.50		1,415.50	1,575
8330	48" diameter, 16,000 CFM	↓	4	2		1,650	113		1,763	2,000
8340	For two speed, add			↓		99			99	109
8350	Whole house, lay-down type, with shutter, one speed									
8360	30" diameter, 4500 CFM	1 Elec	8	1	Ea.	1,150	56.50		1,206.50	1,350
8370	36" diameter, 6500 CFM		7	1.143		1,250	64.50		1,314.50	1,475
8380	42" diameter, 9000 CFM		6	1.333		1,375	75.50		1,450.50	1,625
8390	48" diameter, 12,000 CFM	↓	5	1.600		1,550	90.50		1,640.50	1,825
8440	For two speed, add					74.50			74.50	82
8450	For 12 hour timer switch, add	1 Elec	32	.250	↓	74.50	14.15		88.65	103

23 52 Heating Boilers

23 52 13 – Electric Boilers

23 52 13.10 Electric Boilers, ASME

		Crew	Daily Output	Labor-Hours	Unit	Material	2017 Bare Costs Labor	2017 Bare Costs Equipment	Total	Total Incl O&P
0010	**ELECTRIC BOILERS, ASME**, Standard controls and trim									
1000	Steam, 6 KW, 20.5 MBH	Q-19	1.20	20	Ea.	4,100	1,125		5,225	6,200
1040	9 KW, 30.7 MBH		1.20	20		4,200	1,125		5,325	6,300
1060	18 KW, 61.4 MBH		1.20	20		4,325	1,125		5,450	6,450
1080	24 KW, 81.8 MBH		1.10	21.818		5,000	1,225		6,225	7,350
1120	36 KW, 123 MBH		1.10	21.818		5,525	1,225		6,750	7,925
1160	60 KW, 205 MBH		1	24		6,925	1,350		8,275	9,625
1220	112 KW, 382 MBH		.75	32		9,475	1,800		11,275	13,100
1240	148 KW, 505 MBH		.65	36.923		9,975	2,075		12,050	14,100
1260	168 KW, 573 MBH	↓	.60	40	↓	20,400	2,250		22,650	25,900

23 52 Heating Boilers

23 52 13 – Electric Boilers

23 52 13.10 Electric Boilers, ASME	Crew	Daily Output	Labor-Hours	Unit	Material	2017 Bare Costs Labor	Equipment	Total	Total Incl O&P
1280	222 KW, 758 MBH	Q-19	.55	43.636	Ea.	23,800	2,450		26,250	29,900
1300	296 KW, 1010 MBH		.45	53.333		25,000	3,000		28,000	32,100
1320	300 KW, 1023 MBH		.40	60		26,400	3,375		29,775	34,100
1340	370 KW, 1263 MBH		.35	68.571		29,200	3,850		33,050	37,900
1360	444 KW, 1515 MBH		.30	80		31,400	4,500		35,900	41,300
1380	518 KW, 1768 MBH	Q-21	.36	88.889		32,600	5,125		37,725	43,600
1400	592 KW, 2020 MBH		.34	94.118		35,400	5,425		40,825	47,100
1420	666 KW, 2273 MBH		.32	100		36,800	5,775		42,575	49,200
1460	740 KW, 2526 MBH		.28	114		38,300	6,600		44,900	52,000
1480	814 KW, 2778 MBH		.25	128		40,600	7,400		48,000	56,000
1500	962 KW, 3283 MBH		.22	145		44,900	8,400		53,300	62,000
1520	1036 KW, 3536 MBH		.20	160		47,600	9,225		56,825	66,500
1540	1110 KW, 3788 MBH		.19	168		49,600	9,725		59,325	69,000
1560	2070 KW, 7063 MBH		.18	177		68,000	10,300		78,300	90,500
1580	2250 KW, 7677 MBH		.17	188		80,000	10,900		90,900	104,500
1600	2,340 KW, 7984 MBH		.16	200		86,500	11,500		98,000	112,500
2000	Hot water, 7.5 KW, 25.6 MBH	Q-19	1.30	18.462		4,950	1,050		6,000	7,000
2020	15 KW, 51.2 MBH		1.30	18.462		5,000	1,050		6,050	7,050
2040	30 KW, 102 MBH		1.20	20		5,325	1,125		6,450	7,550
2060	45 KW, 164 MBH		1.20	20		5,425	1,125		6,550	7,650
2070	60 KW, 205 MBH		1.20	20		5,525	1,125		6,650	7,775
2080	75 KW, 256 MBH		1.10	21.818		5,900	1,225		7,125	8,350
2100	90 KW, 307 MBH		1.10	21.818		6,000	1,225		7,225	8,450
2120	105 KW, 358 MBH		1	24		6,275	1,350		7,625	8,925
2140	120 KW, 410 MBH		.90	26.667		6,375	1,500		7,875	9,275
2160	135 KW, 461 MBH		.75	32		7,400	1,800		9,200	10,900
2180	150 KW, 512 MBH		.65	36.923		7,500	2,075		9,575	11,400
2200	165 KW, 563 MBH		.60	40		7,600	2,250		9,850	11,800
2220	296 KW, 1010 MBH		.55	43.636		16,100	2,450		18,550	21,400
2280	370 KW, 1263 MBH		.40	60		17,900	3,375		21,275	24,800
2300	444 KW, 1515 MBH		.35	68.571		20,800	3,850		24,650	28,700
2340	518 KW, 1768 MBH	Q-21	.44	72.727		23,100	4,200		27,300	31,700
2360	592 KW, 2020 MBH		.43	74.419		26,100	4,300		30,400	35,300
2400	666 KW, 2273 MBH		.40	80		27,300	4,625		31,925	37,000
2420	740 KW, 2526 MBH		.39	82.051		28,500	4,725		33,225	38,500
2440	814 KW, 2778 MBH		.38	84.211		30,500	4,850		35,350	40,800
2460	888 KW, 3031 MBH		.37	86.486		32,500	5,000		37,500	43,300
2480	962 KW, 3283 MBH		.36	88.889		34,000	5,125		39,125	45,100
2500	1036 KW, 3536 MBH		.34	94.118		36,300	5,425		41,725	48,100
2520	1110 KW, 3788 MBH		.33	96.970		38,800	5,600		44,400	51,000
2540	1440 KW, 4915 MBH		.32	100		43,800	5,775		49,575	57,000
2560	1560 KW, 5323 MBH		.31	103		46,800	5,950		52,750	60,500
2580	1680 KW, 5733 MBH		.30	106		50,000	6,150		56,150	64,500
2600	1800 KW, 6143 MBH		.29	110		54,500	6,375		60,875	69,500
2620	1980 KW, 6757 MBH		.28	114		58,000	6,600		64,600	74,000
2640	2100 KW, 7167 MBH		.27	118		63,500	6,850		70,350	80,500
2660	2220 KW, 7576 MBH		.26	123		65,000	7,100		72,100	82,000
2680	2400 KW, 8191 MBH		.25	128		68,000	7,400		75,400	85,500
2700	2610 KW, 8905 MBH		.24	133		72,500	7,700		80,200	91,000
2720	2790 KW, 9519 MBH		.23	139		75,500	8,025		83,525	95,000
2740	2970 KW, 10133 MBH		.21	152		77,000	8,800		85,800	98,500
2760	3150 KW, 10748 MBH		.19	168		82,500	9,725		92,225	105,500
2780	3240 KW, 11055 MBH		.18	177		84,500	10,300		94,800	108,500

For customer support on your Electrical Costs with RSMeans Data, call 800.448.8182.

91

23 52 Heating Boilers

23 52 13 – Electric Boilers

23 52 13.10 Electric Boilers, ASME	Crew	Daily Output	Labor-Hours	Unit	Material	2017 Bare Costs Labor	2017 Bare Costs Equipment	Total	Total Incl O&P
2800	3420 KW, 11669 MBH	Q-21	.17	188	Ea.	90,000	10,900		100,900	115,500
2820	3600 KW, 12,283 MBH		.16	200		94,000	11,500		105,500	121,000

23 52 28 – Swimming Pool Boilers

23 52 28.10 Swimming Pool Heaters

		Crew	Daily Output	Labor-Hours	Unit	Material	2017 Bare Costs Labor	2017 Bare Costs Equipment	Total	Total Incl O&P
0010	**SWIMMING POOL HEATERS**, Not including wiring, external									
0020	piping, base or pad									
2000	Electric, 12 KW, 4,800 gallon pool	Q-19	3	8	Ea.	2,100	450		2,550	3,000
2020	15 KW, 7,200 gallon pool		2.80	8.571		2,150	480		2,630	3,075
2040	24 KW, 9,600 gallon pool		2.40	10		2,475	560		3,035	3,575
2060	30 KW, 12,000 gallon pool		2	12		2,525	675		3,200	3,800
2080	36 KW, 14,400 gallon pool		1.60	15		2,900	845		3,745	4,475
2100	57 KW, 24,000 gallon pool		1.20	20		3,650	1,125		4,775	5,700
9000	To select pool heater: 12 BTUH x S.F. pool area									
9010	X temperature differential = required output									
9050	For electric, KW = gallons x 2.5 divided by 1000									
9100	For family home type pool, double the									
9110	Rated gallon capacity = 1/2°F rise per hour									

23 54 Furnaces

23 54 13 – Electric-Resistance Furnaces

23 54 13.10 Electric Furnaces

		Crew	Daily Output	Labor-Hours	Unit	Material	2017 Bare Costs Labor	2017 Bare Costs Equipment	Total	Total Incl O&P
0010	**ELECTRIC FURNACES**, Hot air, blowers, std. controls									
1000	Electric, UL listed									
1100	34.1 MBH	Q-20	4.40	4.545	Ea.	530	241		771	955
1120	51.6 MBH		4.20	4.762		580	253		833	1,025
1140	68.3 MBH		4	5		605	266		871	1,075
1160	85.3 MBH		3.80	5.263		625	280		905	1,100

23 82 Convection Heating and Cooling Units

23 82 16 – Air Coils

23 82 16.20 Duct Heaters

		Crew	Daily Output	Labor-Hours	Unit	Material	2017 Bare Costs Labor	2017 Bare Costs Equipment	Total	Total Incl O&P
0010	**DUCT HEATERS**, Electric, 480 V, 3 Ph.									
0020	Finned tubular insert, 500°F									
0100	8" wide x 6" high, 4.0 kW	Q-20	16	1.250	Ea.	775	66.50		841.50	950
0120	12" high, 8.0 kW		15	1.333		1,275	71		1,346	1,525
0140	18" high, 12.0 kW		14	1.429		1,800	76		1,876	2,100
0160	24" high, 16.0 kW		13	1.538		2,325	81.50		2,406.50	2,675
0180	30" high, 20.0 kW		12	1.667		2,825	88.50		2,913.50	3,250
0300	12" wide x 6" high, 6.7 kW		15	1.333		825	71		896	1,025
0320	12" high, 13.3 kW		14	1.429		1,325	76		1,401	1,575
0340	18" high, 20.0 kW		13	1.538		1,850	81.50		1,931.50	2,175
0360	24" high, 26.7 kW		12	1.667		2,400	88.50		2,488.50	2,750
0380	30" high, 33.3 kW		11	1.818		2,925	96.50		3,021.50	3,375
0500	18" wide x 6" high, 13.3 kW		14	1.429		885	76		961	1,100
0520	12" high, 26.7 kW		13	1.538		1,525	81.50		1,606.50	1,800
0540	18" high, 40.0 kW		12	1.667		2,025	88.50		2,113.50	2,350
0560	24" high, 53.3 kW		11	1.818		2,700	96.50		2,796.50	3,100
0580	30" high, 66.7 kW		10	2		3,375	106		3,481	3,850
0700	24" wide x 6" high, 17.8 kW		13	1.538		975	81.50		1,056.50	1,200

23 82 16 – Air Coils

23 82 16 90 Duct Heaters	Crew	Daily Output	Labor-Hours	Unit	Material	2017 Bare Costs Labor	2017 Bare Costs Equipment	Total	Total Incl O&P
0720	12" high, 35.6 kW	Q-20	12	1.667	Ea.	1,650	88.50		1,738.50	1,950
0740	18" high, 53.3 kW		11	1.818		2,325	96.50		2,421.50	2,700
0760	24" high, 71.1 kW		10	2		3,000	106		3,106	3,450
0780	30" high, 88.9 kW		9	2.222		3,675	118		3,793	4,200
0900	30" wide x 6" high, 22.2 kW		12	1.667		1,025	88.50		1,113.50	1,250
0920	12" high, 44.4 kW		11	1.818		1,750	96.50		1,846.50	2,075
0940	18" high, 66.7 kW		10	2		2,450	106		2,556	2,850
0960	24" high, 88.9 kW		9	2.222		3,175	118		3,293	3,650
0980	30" high, 111.0 kW		8	2.500		3,875	133		4,008	4,450
1400	Note decreased kW available for									
1410	each duct size at same cost									
1420	See line 5000 for modifications and accessories									
2000	Finned tubular flange with insulated									
2020	terminal box, 500°F									
2100	12" wide x 36" high, 54 kW	Q-20	10	2	Ea.	3,825	106		3,931	4,350
2120	40" high, 60 kW		9	2.222		4,400	118		4,518	5,000
2200	24" wide x 36" high, 118.8 kW		9	2.222		4,900	118		5,018	5,550
2220	40" high, 132 kW		8	2.500		4,875	133		5,008	5,550
2400	36" wide x 8" high, 40 kW		11	1.818		1,925	96.50		2,021.50	2,275
2420	16" high, 80 kW		10	2		2,600	106		2,706	3,000
2440	24" high, 120 kW		9	2.222		3,400	118		3,518	3,900
2460	32" high, 160 kW		8	2.500		4,350	133		4,483	4,975
2480	36" high, 180 kW		7	2.857		5,350	152		5,502	6,125
2500	40" high, 200 kW		6	3.333		5,925	177		6,102	6,800
2600	40" wide x 8" high, 45 kW		11	1.818		2,025	96.50		2,121.50	2,375
2620	16" high, 90 kW		10	2		2,800	106		2,906	3,225
2640	24" high, 135 kW		9	2.222		3,550	118		3,668	4,075
2660	32" high, 180 kW		8	2.500		4,725	133		4,858	5,400
2680	36" high, 202.5 kW		7	2.857		5,425	152		5,577	6,200
2700	40" high, 225 kW		6	3.333		6,200	177		6,377	7,075
2800	48" wide x 8" high, 54.8 kW		10	2		2,125	106		2,231	2,475
2820	16" high, 109.8 kW		9	2.222		2,950	118		3,068	3,425
2840	24" high, 164.4 kW		8	2.500		3,750	133		3,883	4,325
2860	32" high, 219.2 kW		7	2.857		5,000	152		5,152	5,725
2880	36" high, 246.6 kW		6	3.333		5,750	177		5,927	6,600
2900	40" high, 274 kW		5	4		6,500	212		6,712	7,475
3000	56" wide x 8" high, 64 kW		9	2.222		2,425	118		2,543	2,825
3020	16" high, 128 kW		8	2.500		3,350	133		3,483	3,900
3040	24" high, 192 kW		7	2.857		4,075	152		4,227	4,700
3060	32" high, 256 kW		6	3.333		5,675	177		5,852	6,525
3080	36" high, 288 kW		5	4		6,525	212		6,737	7,500
3100	40" high, 320 kW		4	5		7,200	266		7,466	8,325
3200	64" wide x 8" high, 74 kW		8	2.500		2,500	133		2,633	2,950
3220	16" high, 148 kW		7	2.857		3,450	152		3,602	4,025
3240	24" high, 222 kW		6	3.333		4,400	177		4,577	5,100
3260	32" high, 296 kW		5	4		5,875	212		6,087	6,800
3280	36" high, 333 kW		4	5		7,025	266		7,291	8,125
3300	40" high, 370 kW		3	6.667		7,750	355		8,105	9,075
3800	Note decreased kW available for									
3820	each duct size at same cost									
5000	Duct heater modifications and accessories									
5120	T.C.O. limit auto or manual reset	Q-20	42	.476	Ea.	127	25.50		152.50	179
5140	Thermostat		28	.714		540	38		578	655

23 82 Convection Heating and Cooling Units

23 82 16 – Air Coils

23 82 16.20 Duct Heaters		Crew	Daily Output	Labor-Hours	Unit	Material	2017 Bare Costs Labor	Equipment	Total	Total Incl O&P
5160	Overheat thermocouple (removable)	Q-20	7	2.857	Ea.	765	152		917	1,075
5180	Fan interlock relay		18	1.111		185	59		244	294
5200	Air flow switch		20	1		160	53		213	257
5220	Split terminal box cover		100	.200		53	10.60		63.60	74
8000	To obtain BTU multiply kW by 3413									

23 83 Radiant Heating Units

23 83 33 – Electric Radiant Heaters

23 83 33.10 Electric Heating

		Crew	Daily Output	Labor-Hours	Unit	Material	2017 Bare Costs Labor	Equipment	Total	Total Incl O&P
0010	**ELECTRIC HEATING**, not incl. conduit or feed wiring									
1100	Rule of thumb: Baseboard units, including control	1 Elec	4.40	1.818	kW	106	103		209	271
1300	Baseboard heaters, 2' long, 350 watt		8	1	Ea.	26	56.50		82.50	114
1400	3' long, 750 watt		8	1		30	56.50		86.50	118
1600	4' long, 1000 watt		6.70	1.194		35	67.50		102.50	140
1800	5' long, 935 watt		5.70	1.404		43	79.50		122.50	166
2000	6' long, 1500 watt		5	1.600		49	90.50		139.50	190
2200	7' long, 1310 watt		4.40	1.818		53.50	103		156.50	213
2400	8' long, 2000 watt		4	2		59.50	113		172.50	236
2600	9' long, 1680 watt		3.60	2.222		93	126		219	290
2800	10' long, 1875 watt		3.30	2.424		184	137		321	410
2950	Wall heaters with fan, 120 to 277 volt									
3160	Recessed, residential, 750 watt	1 Elec	6	1.333	Ea.	84.50	75.50		160	206
3170	1000 watt		6	1.333		84.50	75.50		160	206
3180	1250 watt		5	1.600		84.50	90.50		175	229
3190	1500 watt		4	2		84.50	113		197.50	263
3210	2000 watt		4	2		84.50	113		197.50	263
3230	2500 watt		3.50	2.286		211	129		340	425
3240	3000 watt		3	2.667		310	151		461	565
3250	4000 watt		2.70	2.963		315	168		483	595
3260	Commercial, 750 watt		6	1.333		198	75.50		273.50	330
3270	1000 watt		6	1.333		198	75.50		273.50	330
3280	1250 watt		5	1.600		198	90.50		288.50	355
3290	1500 watt		4	2		198	113		311	390
3300	2000 watt		4	2		198	113		311	390
3310	2500 watt		3.50	2.286		198	129		327	410
3320	3000 watt		3	2.667		515	151		666	795
3330	4000 watt		2.70	2.963		515	168		683	820
3600	Thermostats, integral		16	.500		27	28.50		55.50	72
3800	Line voltage, 1 pole		8	1		15.65	56.50		72.15	102
3810	2 pole		8	1		24	56.50		80.50	111
4000	Heat trace system, 400 degree R238313-10									
4020	115 V, 2.5 watts per L.F.	1 Elec	530	.015	L.F.	8	.85		8.85	10.10
4030	5 watts per L.F. R238313-20		530	.015		8	.85		8.85	10.10
4050	10 watts per L.F.		530	.015		8	.85		8.85	10.10
4060	208 V, 5 watts per L.F.		530	.015		8	.85		8.85	10.10
4080	480 V, 8 watts per L.F.		530	.015		8	.85		8.85	10.10
4200	Heater raceway									
4260	Heat transfer cement									
4280	1 gallon				Ea.	60			60	66
4300	5 gallon				"	234			234	257
4320	Cable tie									

23 83 Radiant Heating Units

23 83 33 – Electric Radiant Heaters

23 83 33.10 Electric Heating	Crew	Daily Output	Labor-Hours	Unit	Material	2017 Bare Costs Labor	2017 Bare Costs Equipment	Total	Total Incl O&P
4340	3/4" pipe size	1 Eler	470	.017	Ea.	.05	.96		1.01	1.50
4360	1" pipe size		444	.018		.05	1.02		1.07	1.59
4380	1-1/4" pipe size		400	.020		.05	1.13		1.18	1.76
4400	1-1/2" pipe size		355	.023		.05	1.28		1.33	1.97
4420	2" pipe size		320	.025		.05	1.42		1.47	2.18
4440	3" pipe size		160	.050		.05	2.83		2.88	4.30
4460	4" pipe size		100	.080		.02	4.53		4.55	6.80
4480	Thermostat NEMA 3R, 22 amp, 0-150 Deg, 10' cap.		8	1		213	56.50		269.50	320
4500	Thermostat NEMA 4X, 25 amp, 40 Deg, 5-1/2' cap.		7	1.143		241	64.50		305.50	360
4520	Thermostat NEMA 4X, 22 amp, 25-325 Deg, 10' cap.		7	1.143		610	64.50		674.50	765
4540	Thermostat NEMA 4X, 22 amp, 15-140 Deg		6	1.333		535	75.50		610.50	705
4580	Thermostat NEMA 4, 7, 9, 22 amp, 25-325 Deg, 10' cap.		3.60	2.222		800	126		926	1,075
4600	Thermostat NEMA 4, 7, 9, 22 amp, 15-140 Deg		3	2.667		780	151		931	1,075
4720	Fiberglass application tape, 36 yard roll		11	.727		77.50	41		118.50	147
5000	Radiant heating ceiling panels, 2' x 4', 500 watt		16	.500		420	28.50		448.50	510
5050	750 watt		16	.500		465	28.50		493.50	555
5200	For recessed plaster frame, add		32	.250		122	14.15		136.15	155
5300	Infrared quartz heaters, 120 volts, 1000 watt		6.70	1.194		300	67.50		367.50	430
5350	1500 watt		5	1.600		300	90.50		390.50	465
5400	240 volts, 1500 watt		5	1.600		300	90.50		390.50	465
5450	2000 watt		4	2		300	113		413	500
5500	3000 watt		3	2.667		385	151		536	645
5550	4000 watt		2.60	3.077		385	174		559	680
5570	Modulating control	▼	.80	10	▼	156	565		721	1,025
5600	Unit heaters, heavy duty, with fan & mounting bracket									
5650	Single phase, 208-240-277 volt, 3 kW	1 Elec	6	1.333	Ea.	770	75.50		845.50	960
5750	5 kW		5.50	1.455		850	82.50		932.50	1,050
5800	7 kW		5	1.600		1,050	90.50		1,140.50	1,275
5850	10 kW		4	2		1,325	113		1,438	1,625
5950	15 kW		3.80	2.105		2,175	119		2,294	2,575
6000	480 volt, 3 kW		6	1.333		685	75.50		760.50	870
6020	4 kW		5.80	1.379		725	78		803	910
6040	5 kW		5.50	1.455		745	82.50		827.50	945
6060	7 kW		5	1.600		1,075	90.50		1,165.50	1,325
6080	10 kW		4	2		1,200	113		1,313	1,500
6100	13 kW		3.80	2.105		2,175	119		2,294	2,575
6120	15 kW		3.70	2.162		2,425	122		2,547	2,850
6140	20 kW		3.50	2.286		2,575	129		2,704	3,050
6300	3 phase, 208-240 volt, 5 kW		5.50	1.455		710	82.50		792.50	910
6320	7 kW		5	1.600		1,175	90.50		1,265.50	1,425
6340	10 kW		4	2		1,300	113		1,413	1,600
6360	15 kW		3.70	2.162		1,950	122		2,072	2,325
6380	20 kW		3.50	2.286		2,550	129		2,679	3,025
6400	25 kW		3.30	2.424		2,975	137		3,112	3,475
6500	480 volt, 5 kW		5.50	1.455		1,000	82.50		1,082.50	1,225
6520	7 kW		5	1.600		1,375	90.50		1,465.50	1,650
6540	10 kW		4	2		1,500	113		1,613	1,825
6560	13 kW		3.80	2.105		2,175	119		2,294	2,575
6580	15 kW		3.70	2.162		2,175	122		2,297	2,575
6600	20 kW		3.50	2.286		2,575	129		2,704	3,050
6620	25 kW		3.30	2.424		3,025	137		3,162	3,525
6630	30 kW		3	2.667		3,700	151		3,851	4,275
6640	40 kW		2	4		4,400	226		4,626	5,200

For customer support on your Electrical Costs with RSMeans Data, call 800.448.8182.

95

23 83 33.10 Electric Heating		Crew	Daily Output	Labor-Hours	Unit	Material	2017 Bare Costs Labor	Equipment	Total	Total Incl O&P
6650	50 kW	1 Elec	1.60	5	Ea.	5,375	283		5,658	6,350
6800	Vertical discharge heaters, with fan									
6820	Single phase, 208-240-277 volt, 10 kW	1 Elec	4	2	Ea.	1,250	113		1,363	1,550
6840	15 kW		3.70	2.162		1,850	122		1,972	2,225
6900	3 phase, 208-240 volt, 10 kW		4	2		1,300	113		1,413	1,600
6920	15 kW		3.70	2.162		1,950	122		2,072	2,325
6940	20 kW		3.50	2.286		2,550	129		2,679	3,025
6960	25 kW		3.30	2.424		2,975	137		3,112	3,475
6980	30 kW		3	2.667		3,500	151		3,651	4,075
7000	40 kW		2	4		4,450	226		4,676	5,250
7020	50 kW		1.60	5		5,300	283		5,583	6,275
7100	480 volt, 10 kW		4	2		1,325	113		1,438	1,625
7120	15 kW		3.70	2.162		2,175	122		2,297	2,575
7140	20 kW		3.50	2.286		2,575	129		2,704	3,050
7160	25 kW		3.30	2.424		3,025	137		3,162	3,525
7180	30 kW		3	2.667		3,700	151		3,851	4,275
7200	40 kW		2	4		4,400	226		4,626	5,200
7220	50 kW		1.60	5		5,375	283		5,658	6,350
7410	Sill height convector heaters, 5" high x 2' long, 500 watt		6.70	1.194		330	67.50		397.50	465
7420	3' long, 750 watt		6.50	1.231		390	69.50		459.50	535
7430	4' long, 1000 watt		6.20	1.290		455	73		528	610
7440	5' long, 1250 watt		5.50	1.455		515	82.50		597.50	690
7450	6' long, 1500 watt		4.80	1.667		585	94.50		679.50	780
7460	8' long, 2000 watt		3.60	2.222		790	126		916	1,050
7470	10' long, 2500 watt		3	2.667		985	151		1,136	1,300
7900	Cabinet convector heaters, 240 volt, three phase,									
7920	3' long, 2000 watt	1 Elec	5.30	1.509	Ea.	2,225	85.50		2,310.50	2,550
7940	3000 watt		5.30	1.509		2,300	85.50		2,385.50	2,675
7960	4000 watt		5.30	1.509		2,375	85.50		2,460.50	2,725
7980	6000 watt		4.60	1.739		2,700	98.50		2,798.50	3,125
8000	8000 watt		4.60	1.739		2,750	98.50		2,848.50	3,175
8020	4' long, 4000 watt		4.60	1.739		2,400	98.50		2,498.50	2,800
8040	6000 watt		4	2		2,500	113		2,613	2,925
8060	8000 watt		4	2		2,575	113		2,688	3,000
8080	10,000 watt		4	2		2,600	113		2,713	3,050
8100	Available also in 208 or 277 volt									
8200	Cabinet unit heaters, 120 to 277 volt, 1 pole,									
8220	wall mounted, 2 kW	1 Elec	4.60	1.739	Ea.	2,150	98.50		2,248.50	2,525
8230	3 kW		4.60	1.739		2,250	98.50		2,348.50	2,625
8240	4 kW		4.40	1.818		2,325	103		2,428	2,700
8250	5 kW		4.40	1.818		2,400	103		2,503	2,800
8260	6 kW		4.20	1.905		2,450	108		2,558	2,850
8270	8 kW		4	2		2,500	113		2,613	2,925
8280	10 kW		3.80	2.105		2,550	119		2,669	3,000
8290	12 kW		3.50	2.286		2,600	129		2,729	3,050
8300	13.5 kW		2.90	2.759		3,125	156		3,281	3,675
8310	16 kW		2.70	2.963		3,150	168		3,318	3,725
8320	20 kW		2.30	3.478		4,000	197		4,197	4,700
8330	24 kW		1.90	4.211		4,075	238		4,313	4,825
8350	Recessed, 2 kW		4.40	1.818		2,150	103		2,253	2,525
8370	3 kW		4.40	1.818		2,250	103		2,353	2,625
8380	4 kW		4.20	1.905		2,325	108		2,433	2,700
8390	5 kW		4.20	1.905		2,400	108		2,508	2,775

23 83 Radiant Heating Units

23 83 33 – Electric Radiant Heaters

23 83 33.10 Electric Heating		Crew	Daily Output	Labor-Hours	Unit	Material	2017 Bare Costs Labor	Equipment	Total	Total Incl O&P
8400	6 kW	1 Elec	4	2	Ea.	2,450	113		2,563	2,875
8410	8 kW		3.80	2.105		2,550	119		2,669	2,975
8420	10 kW		3.50	2.286		3,100	129		3,229	3,600
8430	12 kW		2.90	2.759		3,100	156		3,256	3,650
8440	13.5 kW		2.70	2.963		3,125	168		3,293	3,700
8450	16 kW		2.30	3.478		3,325	197		3,522	3,950
8460	20 kW		1.90	4.211		3,800	238		4,038	4,525
8470	24 kW		1.60	5		3,850	283		4,133	4,650
8490	Ceiling mounted, 2 kW		3.20	2.500		2,150	142		2,292	2,575
8510	3 kW		3.20	2.500		2,250	142		2,392	2,675
8520	4 kW		3	2.667		2,325	151		2,476	2,775
8530	5 kW		3	2.667		2,400	151		2,551	2,850
8540	6 kW		2.80	2.857		2,400	162		2,562	2,900
8550	8 kW		2.40	3.333		2,500	189		2,689	3,025
8560	10 kW		2.20	3.636		2,550	206		2,756	3,100
8570	12 kW		2	4		2,600	226		2,826	3,200
8580	13.5 kW		1.50	5.333		2,650	300		2,950	3,350
8590	16 kW		1.30	6.154		2,725	350		3,075	3,500
8600	20 kW		.90	8.889		3,800	505		4,305	4,925
8610	24 kW		.60	13.333		3,850	755		4,605	5,350
8630	208 to 480 V, 3 pole									
8650	Wall mounted, 2 kW	1 Elec	4.60	1.739	Ea.	2,300	98.50		2,398.50	2,675
8670	3 kW		4.60	1.739		2,400	98.50		2,498.50	2,775
8680	4 kW		4.40	1.818		2,450	103		2,553	2,850
8690	5 kW		4.40	1.818		2,525	103		2,628	2,925
8700	6 kW		4.20	1.905		2,550	108		2,658	2,950
8710	8 kW		4	2		2,625	113		2,738	3,075
8720	10 kW		3.80	2.105		2,675	119		2,794	3,125
8730	12 kW		3.50	2.286		2,725	129		2,854	3,200
8740	13.5 kW		2.90	2.759		2,775	156		2,931	3,275
8750	16 kW		2.70	2.963		2,825	168		2,993	3,375
8760	20 kW		2.30	3.478		3,925	197		4,122	4,625
8770	24 kW		1.90	4.211		4,175	238		4,413	4,925
8790	Recessed, 2 kW		4.40	1.818		2,300	103		2,403	2,675
8810	3 kW		4.40	1.818		2,325	103		2,428	2,700
8820	4 kW		4.20	1.905		2,425	108		2,533	2,800
8830	5 kW		4.20	1.905		2,450	108		2,558	2,825
8840	6 kW		4	2		2,475	113		2,588	2,875
8850	8 kW		3.80	2.105		2,550	119		2,669	2,975
8860	10 kW		3.50	2.286		2,725	129		2,854	3,175
8870	12 kW		2.90	2.759		2,825	156		2,981	3,350
8880	13.5 kW		2.70	2.963		2,875	168		3,043	3,425
8890	16 kW		2.30	3.478		4,200	197		4,397	4,900
8900	20 kW		1.90	4.211		4,250	238		4,488	5,025
8920	24 kW		1.60	5		4,325	283		4,608	5,175
8940	Ceiling mount, 2 kW		3.20	2.500		2,400	142		2,542	2,825
8950	3 kW		3.20	2.500		2,550	142		2,692	3,000
8960	4 kW		3	2.667		2,550	151		2,701	3,025
8970	5 kW		3	2.667		2,625	151		2,776	3,125
8980	6 kW		2.80	2.857		2,650	162		2,812	3,150
8990	8 kW		2.40	3.333		2,750	189		2,939	3,300
9000	10 kW		2.20	3.636		2,800	206		3,006	3,375
9020	13.5 kW		1.50	5.333		2,875	300		3,175	3,625

For customer support on your Electrical Costs with RSMeans Data, call 800.448.8182.

97

23 83 Radiant Heating Units

23 83 33 – Electric Radiant Heaters

23 83 33.10 Electric Heating	Crew	Daily Output	Labor-Hours	Unit	Material	2017 Bare Costs Labor	2017 Bare Costs Equipment	Total	Total Incl O&P
9030	16 kW	1 Elec	1.30	6.154	Ea.	4,200	350		4,550	5,125
9040	20 kW		.90	8.889		4,250	505		4,755	5,425
9060	24 kW		.60	13.333		4,725	755		5,480	6,325
9230	13.5 kW, 40,956 BTU		2.20	3.636		1,200	206		1,406	1,625
9250	24 kW, 81,912 BTU		2	4		2,100	226		2,326	2,650

Estimating Tips
26 05 00 Common Work Results for Electrical

- Conduit should be taken off in three main categories—power distribution, branch power, and branch lighting—so the estimator can concentrate on systems and components, therefore making it easier to ensure all items have been accounted for.

- For cost modifications for elevated conduit installation, add the percentages to labor according to the height of installation and only to the quantities exceeding the different height levels, not to the total conduit quantities. Refer to 26 01 02.20 for labor adjustment factors.

- Remember that aluminum wiring of equal ampacity is larger in diameter than copper and may require larger conduit.

- If more than three wires at a time are being pulled, deduct percentages from the labor hours of that grouping of wires.

- When taking off grounding systems, identify separately the type and size of wire, and list each unique type of ground connection.

- The estimator should take the weights of materials into consideration when completing a takeoff. Topics to consider include: How will the materials be supported? What methods of support are available? How high will the support structure have to reach? Will the final support structure be able to withstand the total burden? Is the support material included or separate from the fixture, equipment, and material specified?

- Do not overlook the costs for equipment used in the installation. If scaffolding or highlifts are available in the field, contractors may use them in lieu of the proposed ladders and rolling staging.

26 20 00 Low-Voltage Electrical Transmission

- Supports and concrete pads may be shown on drawings for the larger equipment, or the support system may be only a piece of plywood for the back of a panelboard. In either case, they must be included in the costs.

26 40 00 Electrical and Cathodic Protection

- When taking off cathodic protection systems, identify the type and size of cable, and list each unique type of anode connection.

26 50 00 Lighting

- Fixtures should be taken off room by room using the fixture schedule, specifications, and the ceiling plan. For large concentrations of lighting fixtures in the same area, deduct the percentages from labor hours.

Reference Numbers

Reference numbers are shown at the beginning of some major classifications. These numbers refer to related items in the Reference Section. The reference information may be an estimating procedure, an alternate pricing method, or technical information.

Note: Not all subdivisions listed here necessarily appear. ■

26 01 02.20 Labor Adjustment Factors	Crew	Daily Output	Labor-Hours	Unit	Material	2017 Bare Costs Labor	Equipment	Total	Total Incl O&P
0010 **LABOR ADJUSTMENT FACTORS** (For Div. 26, 27 and 28) R260519-90									
0100 Subtract from labor for Economy of Scale for Wire									
0110 4-5 wires						25%			
0120 6-10 wires						30%			
0130 11-15 wires						35%			
0140 over 15 wires						40%			
0150 Labor adjustment factors (For Div. 26, 27, 28 and 48)									
0200 Labor factors, The below are reasonable suggestions, however									
0210 each project must be evaluated for its own peculiarities, and									
0220 the adjustments be increased or decreased depending on the									
0230 severity of the special conditions.									
1000 Add to labor for elevated installation (above floor level)									
1010 10' to 14.5' high						10%			
1020 15' to 19.5' high						20%			
1030 20' to 24.5' high						25%			
1040 25' to 29.5' high						35%			
1050 30' to 34.5' high						40%			
1060 35' to 39.5' high						50%			
1070 40' and higher						55%			
2000 Add to labor for crawl space									
2010 3' high						40%			
2020 4' high						30%			
3000 Add to labor for multi-story building									
3100 For new construction (No elevator available)									
3110 Add for floors 3 thru 10						5%			
3120 Add for floors 11 thru 15						10%			
3130 Add for floors 16 thru 20						15%			
3140 Add for floors 21 thru 30						20%			
3150 Add for floors 31 and up						30%			
3200 For existing structure (Elevator available)									
3210 Add for work on floor 3 and above						2%			
4000 Add to labor for working in existing occupied buildings									
4010 Hospital						35%			
4020 Office building						25%			
4030 School						20%			
4040 Factory or warehouse						15%			
4050 Multi-dwelling						15%			
5000 Add to labor, miscellaneous									
5010 Cramped shaft						35%			
5020 Congested area						15%			
5030 Excessive heat or cold						30%			
6000 Labor factors, the above are reasonable suggestions, however									
6100 Each project should be evaluated for its own peculiarities									
6200 Other factors to be considered are:									
6210 Movement of material and equipment through finished areas						10%			
6220 Equipment room min security direct access w/authorization						15%			
6230 Attic space						25%			
6240 No service road						25%			
6250 Poor unloading/storage area, no hydraulic lifts or jacks						20%			
6260 Congested site area/heavy traffic						20%			
7000 Correctional facilities (no compounding division 1 adjustment factors)									
7010 Minimum security w/facilities escort						30%			
7020 Medium security w/ facilities and correctional officer escort						40%			

26 01 Operation and Maintenance of Electrical Systems

26 01 02 – Labor Adjustment

26 01 02.20 Labor Adjustment Factors	Crew	Daily Output	Labor-Hours	Unit	Material	2017 Bare Costs Labor	Equipment	Total	Total Incl O&P
7030 Mux security w/facilities & correctional officer escort (no inmate contact)						50%			

26 01 40 – Operation and Maintenance of Electrical Protection Systems

26 01 40.51 Electrical Systems Repair and Replacement

		Crew	Daily Output	Labor-Hours	Unit	Material	Labor	Equipment	Total	Total Incl O&P
0010	**ELECTRICAL SYSTEMS REPAIR AND REPLACEMENT**									
3000	Remove and replace (reinstall), switch cover	1 Elec	60	.133	Ea.		7.55		7.55	11.30
3020	Outlet cover	"	60	.133	"		7.55		7.55	11.30

26 01 50 – Operation and Maintenance of Lighting

26 01 50.81 Luminaire Replacement

		Crew	Daily Output	Labor-Hours	Unit	Material	Labor	Equipment	Total	Total Incl O&P
0010	**LUMINAIRE REPLACEMENT**									
0100	Fluorescent fixtures, elevate from work area	1 Elec	96	.083	Ea.	87	4.72		91.72	103
0962	Remove and install new replacement lens, 2' x 2' troffer		16	.500		15.90	28.50		44.40	60
0964	2' x 4' troffer		16	.500		14.90	28.50		43.40	59
3200	Remove and replace (reinstall), lighting fixture	↓	4	2	↓		113		113	170

26 05 Common Work Results for Electrical

26 05 05 – Selective Demolition for Electrical

26 05 05.10 Electrical Demolition

		Crew	Daily Output	Labor-Hours	Unit	Material	Labor	Equipment	Total	Total Incl O&P
0010	**ELECTRICAL DEMOLITION** R260105-30									
0020	Electrical dml, conduit to 10' high, including fittings & hangers									
0100	Rigid galvanized steel, 1/2" to 1" diameter	1 Elec	242	.033	L.F.		1.87		1.87	2.80
0120	1-1/4" to 2"	"	200	.040			2.26		2.26	3.39
0140	2-1/2" to 3-1/2"	2 Elec	302	.053			3		3	4.49
0160	4" to 6"	"	160	.100			5.65		5.65	8.50
0170	PVC #40, 1/2" to 1"	1 Elec	410	.020			1.10		1.10	1.65
0172	1-1/4" to 2"		350	.023			1.29		1.29	1.94
0174	2-1/2"	↓	250	.032			1.81		1.81	2.71
0176	3" to 3-1/2"	2 Elec	340	.047			2.66		2.66	3.99
0178	4" to 6"	"	230	.070			3.94		3.94	5.90
0200	Electric metallic tubing (EMT), 1/2" to 1"	1 Elec	394	.020			1.15		1.15	1.72
0220	1-1/4" to 1-1/2"		326	.025			1.39		1.39	2.08
0240	2" to 3"	↓	236	.034			1.92		1.92	2.87
0260	3-1/2" to 4"	2 Elec	310	.052	↓		2.92		2.92	4.38
0270	Armored cable (BX) avg. 50' runs									
0280	#14, 2 wire	1 Elec	690	.012	L.F.		.66		.66	.98
0290	#14, 3 wire		571	.014			.79		.79	1.19
0300	#12, 2 wire		605	.013			.75		.75	1.12
0310	#12, 3 wire		514	.016			.88		.88	1.32
0320	#10, 2 wire		514	.016			.88		.88	1.32
0330	#10, 3 wire		425	.019			1.07		1.07	1.60
0340	#8, 3 wire	↓	342	.023	↓		1.32		1.32	1.98
0350	Non metallic sheathed cable (Romex)									
0360	#14, 2 wire	1 Elec	720	.011	L.F.		.63		.63	.94
0370	#14, 3 wire		657	.012			.69		.69	1.03
0380	#12, 2 wire		629	.013			.72		.72	1.08
0390	#10, 3 wire	↓	450	.018	↓		1.01		1.01	1.51
0400	Wiremold raceway, including fittings & hangers									
0420	No. 3000	1 Elec	250	.032	L.F.		1.81		1.81	2.71
0440	No. 4000		217	.037			2.09		2.09	3.13
0460	No. 6000		166	.048			2.73		2.73	4.09
0462	Plugmold with receptacle	↓	114	.070	↓		3.97		3.97	5.95

26 05 Common Work Results for Electrical

26 05 05 – Selective Demolition for Electrical

26 05 05.10 Electrical Demolition	Crew	Daily Output	Labor-Hours	Unit	Material	2017 Bare Costs Labor	Equipment	Total	Total Incl O&P
0465	Telephone/power pole	1 Elec	12	.667	Ea.		37.50		37.50	56.50
0470	Non-metallic, straight section	↓	480	.017	L.F.		.94		.94	1.41
0500	Channels, steel, including fittings & hangers									
0520	3/4" x 1-1/2"	1 Elec	308	.026	L.F.		1.47		1.47	2.20
0540	1-1/2" x 1-1/2"	↓	269	.030			1.68		1.68	2.52
0560	1-1/2" x 1-7/8"	↓	229	.035	↓		1.98		1.98	2.96
0600	Copper bus duct, indoor, 3 phase									
0610	Including hangers & supports									
0620	225 amp	2 Elec	135	.119	L.F.		6.70		6.70	10.05
0640	400 amp		106	.151			8.55		8.55	12.80
0660	600 amp		86	.186			10.55		10.55	15.80
0680	1000 amp		60	.267			15.10		15.10	22.50
0700	1600 amp		40	.400			22.50		22.50	34
0720	3000 amp	↓	10	1.600	↓		90.50		90.50	136
0800	Plug-in switches, 600V 3 ph., incl. disconnecting									
0820	wire, conduit terminations, 30 amp	1 Elec	15.50	.516	Ea.		29		29	44
0840	60 amp		13.90	.576			32.50		32.50	49
0850	100 amp		10.40	.769			43.50		43.50	65
0860	200 amp	↓	6.20	1.290			73		73	109
0880	400 amp	2 Elec	5.40	2.963			168		168	251
0900	600 amp		3.40	4.706			266		266	400
0920	800 amp		2.60	6.154			350		350	520
0940	1200 amp		2	8			455		455	680
0960	1600 amp	↓	1.70	9.412	↓		535		535	800
1010	Safety switches, 250 or 600V, incl. disconnection									
1050	of wire & conduit terminations									
1100	30 amp	1 Elec	12.30	.650	Ea.		37		37	55
1120	60 amp		8.80	.909			51.50		51.50	77
1140	100 amp		7.30	1.096			62		62	93
1160	200 amp	↓	5	1.600			90.50		90.50	136
1180	400 amp	2 Elec	6.80	2.353			133		133	200
1200	600 amp	"	4.60	3.478			197		197	295
1202	Explosion proof, 60 amp	1 Elec	8.80	.909			51.50		51.50	77
1204	100 amp		5	1.600			90.50		90.50	136
1206	200 amp	↓	3.33	2.402	↓		136		136	204
1210	Panel boards, incl. removal of all breakers,									
1220	conduit terminations & wire connections									
1230	3 wire, 120/240 V, 100A, to 20 circuits	1 Elec	2.60	3.077	Ea.		174		174	261
1240	200 amps, to 42 circuits	2 Elec	2.60	6.154			350		350	520
1241	225 amps, to 42 circuits		5.60	2.857			162		162	242
1250	400 amps, to 42 circuits	↓	2.20	7.273			410		410	615
1260	4 wire, 120/208 V, 125A, to 20 circuits	1 Elec	2.40	3.333			189		189	283
1270	200 amps, to 42 circuits	2 Elec	2.40	6.667			375		375	565
1280	400 amps, to 42 circuits		1.92	8.333			470		470	705
1285	600 amps, to 42 circuits	↓	1.60	10	↓		565		565	850
1300	Transformer, dry type, 1 phase, incl. removal of									
1320	supports, wire & conduit terminations									
1340	1 kVA	1 Elec	7.70	1.039	Ea.		59		59	88
1360	5 kVA		4.70	1.702			96.50		96.50	144
1380	10 kVA	↓	3.60	2.222			126		126	188
1400	37.5 kVA	2 Elec	3	5.333			300		300	450
1420	75 kVA	"	2.50	6.400	↓		360		360	545
1440	3 phase to 600V, primary									

26 05 05 – Selective Demolition for Electrical

26 05 05.10 Electrical Demolition		Crew	Daily Output	Labor-Hours	Unit	Material	2017 Bare Costs Labor	Equipment	Total	Total Incl O&P
1460	3 kVA	1 Elec	3.87	2.067	Ea.		117		117	175
1480	15 kVA	2 Elec	3.67	4.360			247		247	370
1490	25 kVA		3.51	4.558			258		258	385
1500	30 kVA		3.42	4.678			265		265	395
1510	45 kVA		3.18	5.031			285		285	425
1520	75 kVA		2.69	5.948			335		335	505
1530	112.5 kVA	R-3	2.90	6.897			390	47.50	437.50	640
1540	150 kVA		2.70	7.407			420	51	471	685
1550	300 kVA		1.80	11.111			630	76.50	706.50	1,025
1560	500 kVA		1.40	14.286			810	98.50	908.50	1,325
1570	750 kVA		1.10	18.182			1,025	125	1,150	1,700
1600	Pull boxes & cabinets, sheet metal, incl. removal									
1620	of supports and conduit terminations									
1640	6" x 6" x 4"	1 Elec	31.10	.257	Ea.		14.55		14.55	22
1660	12" x 12" x 4"		23.30	.343			19.45		19.45	29
1680	24" x 24" x 6"		12.30	.650			37		37	55
1700	36" x 36" x 8"		7.70	1.039			59		59	88
1720	Junction boxes, 4" sq. & oct.		80	.100			5.65		5.65	8.50
1740	Handy box		107	.075			4.23		4.23	6.35
1760	Switch box		107	.075			4.23		4.23	6.35
1780	Receptacle & switch plates		257	.031			1.76		1.76	2.64
1790	Receptacles & switches, 15 to 30 amp		135	.059			3.35		3.35	5.05
1800	Wire, THW-THWN-THHN, removed from									
1810	in place conduit, to 10' high									
1830	#14	1 Elec	65	.123	C.L.F.		6.95		6.95	10.45
1840	#12		55	.145			8.25		8.25	12.35
1850	#10		45.50	.176			9.95		9.95	14.90
1860	#8		40.40	.198			11.20		11.20	16.80
1870	#6		32.60	.245			13.90		13.90	21
1880	#4	2 Elec	53	.302			17.10		17.10	25.50
1890	#3		50	.320			18.10		18.10	27
1900	#2		44.60	.359			20.50		20.50	30.50
1910	1/0		33.20	.482			27.50		27.50	41
1920	2/0		29.20	.548			31		31	46.50
1930	3/0		25	.640			36		36	54.50
1940	4/0		22	.727			41		41	61.50
1950	250 kcmil		20	.800			45.50		45.50	68
1960	300 kcmil		19	.842			47.50		47.50	71.50
1970	350 kcmil		18	.889			50.50		50.50	75.50
1980	400 kcmil		17	.941			53.50		53.50	80
1990	500 kcmil		16.20	.988			56		56	84
2000	Interior fluorescent fixtures, incl. supports									
2010	& whips, to 10' high									
2100	Recessed drop-in 2' x 2', 2 lamp	2 Elec	35	.457	Ea.		26		26	39
2110	2' x 2', 4 lamp		30	.533			30		30	45
2120	2' x 4', 2 lamp		33	.485			27.50		27.50	41
2140	2' x 4', 4 lamp		30	.533			30		30	45
2160	4' x 4', 4 lamp		20	.800			45.50		45.50	68
2180	Surface mount, acrylic lens & hinged frame									
2200	1' x 4', 2 lamp	2 Elec	44	.364	Ea.		20.50		20.50	31
2210	6" x 4', 2 lamp		44	.364			20.50		20.50	31
2220	2' x 2', 2 lamp		44	.364			20.50		20.50	31
2260	2' x 4', 4 lamp		33	.485			27.50		27.50	41

26 05 05.10 Electrical Demolition	Crew	Daily Output	Labor-Hours	Unit	Material	2017 Bare Costs Labor	2017 Bare Costs Equipment	Total	Total Incl O&P
2280	4' x 4', 4 lamp	2 Elec	23	.696	Ea.		39.50		39.50	59
2281	4' x 4', 6 lamp	↓	23	.696	↓		39.50		39.50	59
2300	Strip fixtures, surface mount									
2320	4' long, 1 lamp	2 Elec	53	.302	Ea.		17.10		17.10	25.50
2340	4' long, 2 lamp		50	.320			18.10		18.10	27
2360	8' long, 1 lamp		42	.381			21.50		21.50	32.50
2380	8' long, 2 lamp	↓	40	.400	↓		22.50		22.50	34
2400	Pendant mount, industrial, incl. removal									
2410	of chain or rod hangers, to 10' high									
2420	4' long, 2 lamp	2 Elec	35	.457	Ea.		26		26	39
2421	4' long, 4 lamp	↓	35	.457			26		26	39
2440	8' long, 2 lamp	↓	27	.593	↓		33.50		33.50	50.50
2460	Interior incandescent, surface, ceiling									
2470	or wall mount, to 12' high									
2480	Metal cylinder type, 75 Watt	2 Elec	62	.258	Ea.		14.60		14.60	22
2500	150 Watt		62	.258			14.60		14.60	22
2502	300 Watt	↓	53	.302			17.10		17.10	25.50
2520	Metal halide, high bay									
2540	400 Watt	2 Elec	15	1.067	Ea.		60.50		60.50	90.50
2560	1000 Watt		12	1.333			75.50		75.50	113
2580	150 Watt, low bay		20	.800			45.50		45.50	68
2585	Globe type, ceiling mount		62	.258			14.60		14.60	22
2586	Can type, recessed mount	↓	62	.258	↓		14.60		14.60	22
2600	Exterior fixtures, incandescent, wall mount									
2620	100 Watt	2 Elec	50	.320	Ea.		18.10		18.10	27
2640	Quartz, 500 Watt		33	.485			27.50		27.50	41
2660	1500 Watt	↓	27	.593	↓		33.50		33.50	50.50
2680	Wall pack, mercury vapor									
2700	175 Watt	2 Elec	25	.640	Ea.		36		36	54.50
2720	250 Watt	"	25	.640			36		36	54.50
7000	Weatherhead/mast, 2"	1 Elec	16	.500			28.50		28.50	42.50
7002	3"		10	.800			45.50		45.50	68
7004	3-1/2"		8.50	.941			53.50		53.50	80
7006	4"		8	1	↓		56.50		56.50	85
7100	Service entry cable, #6, +#6 neutral		420	.019	L.F.		1.08		1.08	1.62
7102	#4, +#4 neutral		360	.022			1.26		1.26	1.88
7104	#2, +#4 neutral		345	.023			1.31		1.31	1.97
7106	#2, +#2 neutral	↓	330	.024	↓		1.37		1.37	2.06
9900	Add to labor for higher elevated installation									
9905	10' to 14.5' high, add						10%			
9910	15' to 20' high, add						20%			
9920	20' to 25' high, add						25%			
9930	25' to 30' high, add						35%			
9940	30' to 35' high, add						40%			
9950	35' to 40' high, add						50%			
9960	Over 40' high, add						55%			

26 05 05.15 Electrical Demolition, Grounding

		Crew	Daily Output	Labor-Hours	Unit	Material	Labor	Equipment	Total	Total Incl O&P
0010	**ELECTRICAL DEMOLITION, GROUNDING** Addition									
0100	Ground clamp, bronze	1 Elec	64	.125	Ea.		7.10		7.10	10.60
0140	Water pipe ground clamp, bronze, heavy duty		24	.333			18.85		18.85	28.50
0150	Ground rod, 8' to 10'	↓	13	.615	↓		35		35	52
0200	Ground wire, bare armored	2 Elec	900	.018	L.F.		1.01		1.01	1.51

104

For customer support on your Electrical Costs with RSMeans Data, call 800.448.8182.

26 05 Common Work Results for Electrical

26 05 05 – Selective Demolition for Electrical

26 05 05.15 Electrical Demolition, Grounding

		Crew	Daily Output	Labor-Hours	Unit	Material	2017 Bare Costs Labor	Equipment	Total	Total Incl O&P
0240	Bare copper or aluminum	2 Elec	2800	.006	L.F.		.32		.32	.48

26 05 05.20 Electrical Demolition, Wiring Methods

		Crew	Daily Output	Labor-Hours	Unit	Material	2017 Bare Costs Labor	Equipment	Total	Total Incl O&P
0010	**ELECTRICAL DEMOLITION, WIRING METHODS** Addition									
0100	Armored cable, w/PVC jacket, in cable tray									
0110	#6	1 Elec	9.30	.860	C.L.F.		48.50		48.50	73
0120	#4	2 Elec	16.20	.988			56		56	84
0130	#2		13.80	1.159			65.50		65.50	98.50
0140	#1		12	1.333			75.50		75.50	113
0150	1/0		10.80	1.481			84		84	126
0160	2/0		10.20	1.569			89		89	133
0170	3/0		9.60	1.667			94.50		94.50	141
0180	4/0		9	1.778			101		101	151
0190	250 kcmil	3 Elec	10.80	2.222			126		126	188
0210	350 kcmil		9.90	2.424			137		137	206
0230	500 kcmil		9	2.667			151		151	226
0240	750 kcmil		8.10	2.963			168		168	251
1100	Control cable, 600 V or less									
1110	3 wires	1 Elec	24	.333	C.L.F.		18.85		18.85	28.50
1120	5 wires		20	.400			22.50		22.50	34
1130	7 wires		16.50	.485			27.50		27.50	41
1140	9 wires		15	.533			30		30	45
1150	12 wires	2 Elec	26	.615			35		35	52
1160	15 wires		22	.727			41		41	61.50
1170	19 wires		19	.842			47.50		47.50	71.50
1180	25 wires		16	1			56.50		56.50	85
1500	Mineral insulated (MI) cable, 600 V									
1510	#10	1 Elec	4.80	1.667	C.L.F.		94.50		94.50	141
1520	#8		4.50	1.778			101		101	151
1530	#6		4.20	1.905			108		108	162
1540	#4	2 Elec	7.20	2.222			126		126	188
1550	#2		6.60	2.424			137		137	206
1560	#1		6.30	2.540			144		144	215
1570	1/0		6	2.667			151		151	226
1580	2/0		5.70	2.807			159		159	238
1590	3/0		5.40	2.963			168		168	251
1600	4/0		4.80	3.333			189		189	283
1610	250 kcmil	3 Elec	7.20	3.333			189		189	283
1620	500 kcmil	"	5.90	4.068			230		230	345
2000	Shielded cable, XLP shielding, to 35 kV									
2010	#4	2 Elec	13.20	1.212	C.L.F.		68.50		68.50	103
2020	#1		12	1.333			75.50		75.50	113
2030	1/0		11.40	1.404			79.50		79.50	119
2040	2/0		10.80	1.481			84		84	126
2050	4/0		9.60	1.667			94.50		94.50	141
2060	250 kcmil	3 Elec	13.50	1.778			101		101	151
2070	350 kcmil		11.70	2.051			116		116	174
2080	500 kcmil		11.20	2.143			121		121	182
2090	750 kcmil		10.80	2.222			126		126	188
3000	Modular flexible wiring									
3010	Cable set	1 Elec	120	.067	Ea.		3.77		3.77	5.65
3020	Conversion module		48	.167			9.45		9.45	14.15
3030	Switching assembly		96	.083			4.72		4.72	7.05

Note: Row 0110 references R024119-10.

For customer support on your Electrical Costs with RSMeans Data, call 800.448.8182.

105

26 05 05.20 Electrical Demolition, Wiring Methods	Crew	Daily Output	Labor-Hours	Unit	Material	2017 Bare Costs Labor	Equipment	Total	Total Incl O&P
3200	Undercarpet									
3210	Power or telephone, flat cable	1 Elec	1320	.006	L.F.		.34		.34	.51
3220	Transition block assemblies w/fitting		75	.107	Ea.		6.05		6.05	9.05
3230	Floor box with fitting		60	.133			7.55		7.55	11.30
3300	Data system, cable with connection	▼	50	.160	▼		9.05		9.05	13.55
4000	Cable tray, including fitting & support									
4010	Galvanized steel, 6" wide	2 Elec	310	.052	L.F.		2.92		2.92	4.38
4020	9" wide		295	.054			3.07		3.07	4.60
4030	12" wide		285	.056			3.18		3.18	4.76
4040	18" wide		270	.059			3.35		3.35	5.05
4050	24" wide		260	.062			3.48		3.48	5.20
4060	30" wide		240	.067			3.77		3.77	5.65
4070	36" wide		220	.073			4.12		4.12	6.15
4110	Aluminum, 6" wide		420	.038			2.16		2.16	3.23
4120	9" wide		415	.039			2.18		2.18	3.27
4130	12" wide		390	.041			2.32		2.32	3.48
4140	18" wide		370	.043			2.45		2.45	3.67
4150	24" wide		350	.046			2.59		2.59	3.88
4160	30" wide		325	.049			2.79		2.79	4.17
4170	36" wide	▼	300	.053			3.02		3.02	4.52
4310	Cable channel, aluminum, 4" wide straight	1 Elec	240	.033	▼		1.89		1.89	2.83
4320	Cable tray fittings, 6" to 9" wide	2 Elec	27	.593	Ea.		33.50		33.50	50.50
4330	12" to 18" wide	"	19	.842	"		47.50		47.50	71.50
5000	Conduit nipples, with locknuts and bushings									
5020	1/2"	1 Elec	108	.074	Ea.		4.19		4.19	6.30
5040	3/4"		96	.083			4.72		4.72	7.05
5060	1"		81	.099			5.60		5.60	8.40
5080	1-1/4"		69	.116			6.55		6.55	9.85
5100	1-1/2"		60	.133			7.55		7.55	11.30
5120	2"		54	.148			8.40		8.40	12.55
5140	2-1/2"		45	.178			10.05		10.05	15.10
5160	3"		36	.222			12.60		12.60	18.85
5180	3-1/2"		33	.242			13.70		13.70	20.50
5200	4"		27	.296			16.75		16.75	25
5220	5"		21	.381			21.50		21.50	32.50
5240	6"		18	.444	▼		25		25	37.50
5500	Electric nonmetallic tubing (ENT), flexible, 1/2" to 1" diameter		690	.012	L.F.		.66		.66	.98
5510	1-1/4" to 2" diameter		300	.027			1.51		1.51	2.26
5600	Flexible metallic tubing, steel, 3/8" to 3/4" diameter		600	.013			.75		.75	1.13
5610	1" to 1-1/4" diameter		260	.031			1.74		1.74	2.61
5620	1-1/2" to 2" diameter		140	.057			3.23		3.23	4.85
5630	2-1/2" diameter	▼	100	.080			4.53		4.53	6.80
5640	3" to 3-1/2" diameter	2 Elec	150	.107			6.05		6.05	9.05
5650	4" diameter	"	100	.160			9.05		9.05	13.55
5700	Sealtite flexible conduit, 3/8" to 3/4" diameter	1 Elec	420	.019			1.08		1.08	1.62
5710	1" to 1-1/4" diameter		180	.044			2.52		2.52	3.77
5720	1-1/2" to 2" diameter		120	.067			3.77		3.77	5.65
5730	2-1/2" diameter	▼	80	.100			5.65		5.65	8.50
5740	3" diameter	2 Elec	150	.107			6.05		6.05	9.05
5750	4" diameter	"	100	.160			9.05		9.05	13.55
5800	Wiring duct, plastic, 1-1/2" to 2-1/2" wide	1 Elec	360	.022			1.26		1.26	1.88
5810	3" wide		330	.024			1.37		1.37	2.06
5820	4" wide	▼	300	.027	▼		1.51		1.51	2.26

For customer support on your Electrical Costs with RSMeans Data, call 800.448.8182.

26 05 05.20 Electrical Demolition, Wiring Methods

26 05 05.20 Electrical Demolition, Wiring Methods	Crew	Daily Output	Labor-Hours	Unit	Material	2017 Bare Costs Labor	Equipment	Total	Total Incl O&P
6000	Floor box and carpet flange	1 Elec	9	.889	Ea.		50.50		50.50	75.50
6300	Wireway, with fittings and supports, to 10' high									
6310	2-1/2" x 2-1/2"	1 Elec	180	.044	L.F.		2.52		2.52	3.77
6320	4" x 4"	"	160	.050			2.83		2.83	4.24
6330	6" x 6"	2 Elec	240	.067			3.77		3.77	5.65
6340	8" x 8"		160	.100			5.65		5.65	8.50
6350	10" x 10"		120	.133			7.55		7.55	11.30
6360	12" x 12"		80	.200			11.30		11.30	16.95
6400	Cable reel with receptacle, 120 V/208 V		13	1.231	Ea.		69.50		69.50	104
6500	Equipment connection, to 10 HP	1 Elec	23	.348			19.70		19.70	29.50
6510	To 15 to 30 HP		18	.444			25		25	37.50
6520	To 40 to 60 HP		15	.533			30		30	45
6530	To 75 to 100 HP		10	.800			45.50		45.50	68
7008	Receptacle, explosionproof, 120 V, to 30 A		16	.500			28.50		28.50	42.50
7020	Dimmer switch, 2000 W or less		62	.129			7.30		7.30	10.95

26 05 05.25 Electrical Demolition, Electrical Power

26 05 05.25 Electrical Demolition, Electrical Power	Crew	Daily Output	Labor-Hours	Unit	Material	2017 Bare Costs Labor	Equipment	Total	Total Incl O&P
0010	**ELECTRICAL DEMOLITION, ELECTRICAL POWER** R024119-10									
0100	Meter centers and sockets									
0120	Meter socket, 4 terminal R260105-30	1 Elec	8.40	.952	Ea.		54		54	81
0140	Trans-socket, 13 terminal, 400 A	"	3.60	2.222			126		126	188
0160	800 A	2 Elec	4.40	3.636			206		206	310
0200	Meter center, 400 A		5.80	2.759			156		156	234
0210	600 A		4	4			226		226	340
0220	800 A		3.30	4.848			274		274	410
0230	1200 A		2.80	5.714			325		325	485
0240	1600 A		2.50	6.400			360		360	545
0300	Base meter devices, 3 meter		3.60	4.444			252		252	375
0310	4 meter		3.30	4.848			274		274	410
0320	5 meter		2.90	5.517			310		310	470
0330	6 meter		2.20	7.273			410		410	615
0340	7 meter		2	8			455		455	680
0350	8 meter		1.90	8.421			475		475	715
0400	Branch meter devices									
0410	Socket w/circuit breaker 200 A, 2 meter	2 Elec	3.30	4.848	Ea.		274		274	410
0420	3 meter		2.90	5.517			310		310	470
0430	4 meter		2.60	6.154			350		350	520
0450	Main circuit breaker, 400 A		5.80	2.759			156		156	234
0460	600 A		4	4			226		226	340
0470	800 A		3.30	4.848			274		274	410
0480	1200 A		2.80	5.714			325		325	485
0490	1600 A		2.50	6.400			360		360	545
0500	Main lug terminal box, 800 A		3.40	4.706			266		266	400
0510	1200 A		2.60	6.154			350		350	520
1000	Motors, 230/460 V, 60 Hz, 3/4 HP	1 Elec	10.70	.748			42.50		42.50	63.50
1010	5 HP		9	.889			50.50		50.50	75.50
1020	10 HP		8	1			56.50		56.50	85
1030	15 HP		6.40	1.250			71		71	106
1040	20 HP	2 Elec	10.40	1.538			87		87	130
1050	50 HP		9.60	1.667			94.50		94.50	141
1060	75 HP		5.60	2.857			162		162	242
1070	100 HP	3 Elec	5.40	4.444			252		252	375
1080	150 HP		3.60	6.667			375		375	565

26 05 05.25 Electrical Demolition, Electrical Power	Crew	Daily Output	Labor-Hours	Unit	Material	2017 Bare Costs Labor	2017 Bare Costs Equipment	Total	Total Incl O&P
1090	200 HP	3 Elec	3	8	Ea.		455		455	680
1200	Variable frequency drive, 460 V, for 5 HP motor size	1 Elec	3.20	2.500			142		142	212
1210	10 HP motor size	"	2.70	2.963			168		168	251
1220	20 HP motor size	2 Elec	3.60	4.444			252		252	375
1230	50 HP motor size	"	2.10	7.619			430		430	645
1240	75 HP motor size	R-3	2.20	9.091			515	62.50	577.50	845
1250	100 HP motor size		2	10			565	69	634	925
1260	150 HP motor size		2	10			565	69	634	925
1270	200 HP motor size	▼	1.70	11.765	▼		665	81	746	1,100
2000	Generator set w/accessories, 3 phase 4 wire, 277/480 V									
2010	7.5 kW	3 Elec	2	12	Ea.		680		680	1,025
2020	20 kW		1.70	14.118			800		800	1,200
2040	30 kW		1.33	18.045			1,025		1,025	1,525
2060	50 kW		1	24			1,350		1,350	2,025
2080	100 kW		.75	32			1,800		1,800	2,725
2100	150 kW		.63	38.095			2,150		2,150	3,225
2120	250 kW		.59	40.678			2,300		2,300	3,450
2140	400 kW		.50	48			2,725		2,725	4,075
2160	500 kW	▼	.44	54.545			3,075		3,075	4,625
2180	750 kW	4 Elec	.56	57.143			3,225		3,225	4,850
2200	1000 kW	"	.46	69.565	▼		3,925		3,925	5,900
3000	Uninterruptible power supply system (UPS)									
3010	Single phase, 120 V, 1 kVA	1 Elec	3.20	2.500	Ea.		142		142	212
3020	2 kVA	2 Elec	3.60	4.444			252		252	375
3030	5 kVA	3 Elec	2.50	9.600			545		545	815
3040	10 kVA		2.30	10.435			590		590	885
3050	15 kVA	▼	1.80	13.333	▼		755		755	1,125
4000	Transformer, incl support, wire & conduit termination									
4010	Buck-boost, single phase, 120/240 V, 0.1 kVA	1 Elec	25	.320	Ea.		18.10		18.10	27
4020	0.5 kVA		12.50	.640			36		36	54.50
4030	1 kVA		6.30	1.270			72		72	108
4040	5 kVA	▼	3.80	2.105			119		119	179
4800	5 kV or 15 kV primary, 277/480 V second, 112.5 kVA	R-3	3.50	5.714			325	39.50	364.50	530
4810	150 kVA		2.70	7.407			420	51	471	685
4820	225 kVA		2.30	8.696			490	60	550	805
4830	500 kVA		1.45	13.793			780	95	875	1,275
4840	750 kVA		1.33	15.038			850	104	954	1,400
4850	1000 kVA		1.25	16			905	110	1,015	1,475
4860	2000 kVA		1.05	19.048			1,075	131	1,206	1,775
4870	3000 kVA	▼	.75	26.667			1,500	184	1,684	2,475
6010	Isolation panel, 3 kVA	1 Elec	2.30	3.478			197		197	295
6020	5 kVA		2.20	3.636			206		206	310
6030	7.5 kVA		2.10	3.810			216		216	325
6040	10 kVA		1.80	4.444			252		252	375
6050	15 kVA	▼	1.40	5.714	▼		325		325	485
7000	Power filters & conditioners									
7100	Automatic voltage regulator	2 Elec	6	2.667	Ea.		151		151	226
7200	Capacitor, 1 kVAR	1 Elec	8.60	.930			52.50		52.50	79
7210	5 kVAR		5.80	1.379			78		78	117
7220	10 kVAR		4.80	1.667			94.50		94.50	141
7230	15 kVAR		4.20	1.905			108		108	162
7240	20 kVAR		3.50	2.286			129		129	194
7250	30 kVAR	▼	3.40	2.353			133		133	200

26 05 05 – Selective Demolition for Electrical

26 05 05.25 Electrical Demolition, Electrical Power	Crew	Daily Output	Labor-Hours	Unit	Material	2017 Bare Costs Labor	Equipment	Total	Total Incl O&P
7260	50 kVAR	1 Elec	3.20	2.500	Ea.		142		142	212
7400	Computer isolator transformer									
7410	Single phase, 120/240 V, 0.5 kVAR	1 Elec	12.80	.625	Ea.		35.50		35.50	53
7420	1 kVAR		8.50	.941			53.50		53.50	80
7430	2.5 kVAR		6.40	1.250			71		71	106
7440	5 kVAR	▼	3.70	2.162	▼		122		122	183
7500	Computer regulator transformer									
7510	Single phase, 240 V, 0.5 kVAR	1 Elec	8.50	.941	Ea.		53.50		53.50	80
7520	1 kVAR		6.40	1.250			71		71	106
7530	2 kVAR		3.20	2.500			142		142	212
7540	Single phase, plug-in unit 120 V, 0.5 kVAR		26	.308			17.40		17.40	26
7550	1 kVAR	▼	17	.471	▼		26.50		26.50	40
7600	Power conditioner transformer									
7610	Single phase 115 V - 240 V, 3 kVA	2 Elec	5.10	3.137	Ea.		178		178	266
7620	5 kVA	"	3.70	4.324			245		245	365
7630	7.5 kVA	3 Elec	4.80	5			283		283	425
7640	10 kVA	"	4.30	5.581	▼		315		315	475
7700	Transient suppressor/voltage regulator									
7710	Single phase 115 or 220 V, 1 kVA	1 Elec	8.50	.941	Ea.		53.50		53.50	80
7720	2 kVA		7.30	1.096			62		62	93
7730	4 kVA	▼	6.80	1.176	▼		66.50		66.50	100
7800	Transient voltage suppressor transformer									
7810	Single phase, 115 or 220 V, 3.6 kVA	1 Elec	12.80	.625	Ea.		35.50		35.50	53
7820	7.2 kVA		11.50	.696			39.50		39.50	59
7830	14.4 kVA		10.20	.784			44.50		44.50	66.50
7840	Single phase, plug-in, 120 V, 1.8 kVA	▼	26	.308	▼		17.40		17.40	26
8000	Power measurement & control									
8010	Switchboard instruments, 3 phase 4 wire, indicating unit	1 Elec	25	.320	Ea.		18.10		18.10	27
8020	Recording unit		12	.667			37.50		37.50	56.50
8100	3 current transformers, 3 phase 4 wire, 5 to 800 A		6.40	1.250			71		71	106
8110	1000 to 1500 A		4.20	1.905			108		108	162
8120	2000 to 4000 A	▼	3.20	2.500	▼		142		142	212

26 05 05.30 Electrical Demolition, Transmission and Distribution

26 05 05.30		Crew	Daily Output	Labor-Hours	Unit	Material	Labor	Equipment	Total	Total Incl O&P
0010	**ELECTRICAL DEMOLITION, TRANSMISSION & DISTRIBUTION**									
0100	Load interrupter switch, 600 A, NEMA 1, 4.8 kV	R-3	1.33	15.038	Ea.		850	104	954	1,400
0120	13.8 kV	R024119-10	"	1.27	15.748			890	109	999	1,475
0200	Lightning arrester, 4.8 kV	1 Elec	9	.889			50.50		50.50	75.50
0220	13.8 kV	R260105-30		6.67	1.199			68		68	102
0300	Alarm or option items	▼	3.33	2.402	▼		136		136	204

26 05 05.35 Electrical Demolition, L.V. Distribution

26 05 05.35		Crew	Daily Output	Labor-Hours	Unit	Material	Labor	Equipment	Total	Total Incl O&P
0010	**ELECTRICAL DEMOLITION, L.V. DISTRIBUTION** Addition	R024119-10								
0100	Circuit breakers in enclosure									
0120	Enclosed (NEMA 1), 600 V, 3 pole, 30 A	R260105-30	1 Elec	12.30	.650	Ea.		37		37	55
0140	60 A		8.80	.909			51.50		51.50	77
0160	100 A		7.30	1.096			62		62	93
0180	225 A	▼	5	1.600			90.50		90.50	136
0200	400 A	2 Elec	6.80	2.353			133		133	200
0220	600 A		4.60	3.478			197		197	295
0240	800 A		3.60	4.444			252		252	375
0260	1200 A		3.10	5.161			292		292	440
0280	1600 A		2.80	5.714			325		325	485
0300	2000 A	▼	2.50	6.400	▼		360		360	545

For customer support on your Electrical Costs with RSMeans Data, call 800.448.8182.

109

26 05 05 – Selective Demolition for Electrical

26 05 05.35 Electrical Demolition, L.V. Distribution	Crew	Daily Output	Labor-Hours	Unit	Material	2017 Bare Costs Labor	Equipment	Total	Total Incl O&P
0400	Enclosed (NEMA 7), 600 V, 3 pole, 50 A	1 Elec	8.80	.909	Ea.		51.50		51.50	77
0410	100 A		5.80	1.379			78		78	117
0420	150 A		3.80	2.105			119		119	179
0430	250 A	2 Elec	6.20	2.581			146		146	219
0440	400 A	"	4.60	3.478			197		197	295
0460	Manual motor starter, NEMA 1	1 Elec	24	.333			18.85		18.85	28.50
0480	NEMA 4 or NEMA 7		15	.533			30		30	45
0500	Time switches, single pole single throw		15.40	.519			29.50		29.50	44
0520	Photo cell		30	.267			15.10		15.10	22.50
0540	Load management device, 4 loads		7.70	1.039			59		59	88
0550	8 loads		3.80	2.105			119		119	179
0560	Master light control panel	2 Elec	2	8			455		455	680
0600	Transfer switches, enclosed, 30 A	1 Elec	12	.667			37.50		37.50	56.50
0610	60 A		9.50	.842			47.50		47.50	71.50
0620	100 A		6.50	1.231			69.50		69.50	104
0630	150 A	2 Elec	12	1.333			75.50		75.50	113
0640	260 A		10	1.600			90.50		90.50	136
0660	400 A		8	2			113		113	170
0670	600 A		5	3.200			181		181	271
0680	800 A		4	4			226		226	340
0690	1200 A		3.50	4.571			259		259	390
0700	1600 A		3	5.333			300		300	450
0710	2000 A		2.50	6.400			360		360	545
0800	Air terminal with base and connector	1 Elec	24	.333			18.85		18.85	28.50
1000	Enclosed controller, NEMA 1, 30 A		13.80	.580			33		33	49
1020	60 A		11.50	.696			39.50		39.50	59
1040	100 A		9.60	.833			47		47	70.50
1060	150 A		7.70	1.039			59		59	88
1080	200 A		5.40	1.481			84		84	126
1100	400 A	2 Elec	6.90	2.319			131		131	197
1120	600 A		4.60	3.478			197		197	295
1140	800 A		3.80	4.211			238		238	355
1160	1200 A		3.10	5.161			292		292	440
1200	Control station, NEMA 1	1 Elec	30	.267			15.10		15.10	22.50
1220	NEMA 7		23	.348			19.70		19.70	29.50
1230	Control switches, push button		69	.116			6.55		6.55	9.85
1240	Indicating light unit		120	.067			3.77		3.77	5.65
1250	Relay		15	.533			30		30	45
2000	Motor control center components									
2020	Starter, NEMA 1, size 1	1 Elec	9	.889	Ea.		50.50		50.50	75.50
2040	Size 2	2 Elec	13.30	1.203			68		68	102
2060	Size 3		6.70	2.388			135		135	203
2080	Size 4		5.30	3.019			171		171	256
2100	Size 5		3.30	4.848			274		274	410
2120	NEMA 7, size 1	1 Elec	8.70	.920			52		52	78
2140	Size 2	2 Elec	12.70	1.260			71.50		71.50	107
2160	Size 3		6.30	2.540			144		144	215
2180	Size 4		5	3.200			181		181	271
2200	Size 5		3.20	5			283		283	425
2300	Fuse, light contactor, NEMA 1, 30 A	1 Elec	9	.889			50.50		50.50	75.50
2310	60 A		6.70	1.194			67.50		67.50	101
2320	100 A		3.30	2.424			137		137	206
2330	200 A		2.70	2.963			168		168	251

26 05 05.35 Electrical Demolition, L.V. Distribution	Crew	Daily Output	Labor-Hours	Unit	Material	2017 Bare Costs Labor	2017 Bare Costs Equipment	Total	Total Incl O&P
2350	Motor control center, incoming section	2 Elec	4	4	Ea.		226		226	340
2352	Structure per section	"	4.20	3.810			216		216	325
2400	Starter & structure, 10 HP	1 Elec	9	.889			50.50		50.50	75.50
2410	25 HP	2 Elec	13.30	1.203			68		68	102
2420	50 HP		6.70	2.388			135		135	203
2430	75 HP		5.30	3.019			171		171	256
2440	100 HP		4.70	3.404			193		193	289
2450	200 HP		3.30	4.848			274		274	410
2460	400 HP		2.70	5.926			335		335	505
2500	Motor starter & control									
2510	Motor starter, NEMA 1, 5 HP	1 Elec	8.90	.899	Ea.		51		51	76
2520	10 HP	"	6.20	1.290			73		73	109
2530	25 HP	2 Elec	8.40	1.905			108		108	162
2540	50 HP		6.90	2.319			131		131	197
2550	100 HP		4.60	3.478			197		197	295
2560	200 HP		3.50	4.571			259		259	390
2570	400 HP		3.10	5.161			292		292	440
2610	Motor starter, NEMA 7, 5 HP	1 Elec	6.20	1.290			73		73	109
2620	10 HP	"	4.20	1.905			108		108	162
2630	25 HP	2 Elec	6.90	2.319			131		131	197
2640	50 HP		4.60	3.478			197		197	295
2650	100 HP		3.50	4.571			259		259	390
2660	200 HP		1.90	8.421			475		475	715
2710	Combination control unit, NEMA 1, 5 HP	1 Elec	6.90	1.159			65.50		65.50	98.50
2720	10 HP	"	5	1.600			90.50		90.50	136
2730	25 HP	2 Elec	7.70	2.078			118		118	176
2740	50 HP		5.10	3.137			178		178	266
2750	100 HP		3.10	5.161			292		292	440
2810	NEMA 7, 5 HP	1 Elec	5	1.600			90.50		90.50	136
2820	10 HP	"	3.90	2.051			116		116	174
2830	25 HP	2 Elec	5.10	3.137			178		178	266
2840	50 HP		3.10	5.161			292		292	440
2850	100 HP		2.30	6.957			395		395	590
2860	200 HP		1.50	10.667			605		605	905
3000	Panelboard or load center circuit breaker									
3010	Bolt-on or plug in, 15 A to 50 A	1 Elec	20	.400	Ea.		22.50		22.50	34
3020	60 A to 70 A		16	.500			28.50		28.50	42.50
3030	Bolt-on, 80 A to 100 A		14	.571			32.50		32.50	48.50
3040	Up to 250 A		7.30	1.096			62		62	93
3050	Motor operated, 30 A		13	.615			35		35	52
3060	60 A		10	.800			45.50		45.50	68
3070	100 A		8	1			56.50		56.50	85
3200	Switchboard circuit breaker									
3210	15 A - 60 A	1 Elec	19	.421	Ea.		24		24	35.50
3220	70 A - 100 A		14	.571			32.50		32.50	48.50
3230	125 A - 400 A		10	.800			45.50		45.50	68
3240	450 A - 600 A		5.30	1.509			85.50		85.50	128
3250	700 A - 800 A		4.30	1.860			105		105	158
3260	1000 A		3.30	2.424			137		137	206
3270	1200 A		2.70	2.963			168		168	251
3500	Switchboard, incoming section, 400 A	2 Elec	3.70	4.324			245		245	365
3510	600 A		3.30	4.848			274		274	410
3520	800 A		2.90	5.517			310		310	470

For customer support on your Electrical Costs with RSMeans Data, call 800.448.8182.

111

26 05 05.35 Electrical Demolition, L.V. Distribution

		Crew	Daily Output	Labor-Hours	Unit	Material	2017 Bare Costs Labor	Equipment	Total	Total Incl O&P
3530	1200 A	2 Elec	2.40	6.667	Ea.		375		375	565
3540	1600 A		2.20	7.273			410		410	615
3550	2000 A		2.10	7.619			430		430	645
3560	3000 A		1.90	8.421			475		475	715
3570	4000 A		1.70	9.412			535		535	800
3610	Distribution section, 600 A		4	4			226		226	340
3620	800 A		3.60	4.444			252		252	375
3630	1200 A		3.10	5.161			292		292	440
3640	1600 A		2.90	5.517			310		310	470
3650	2000 A		2.70	5.926			335		335	505
3710	Transition section, 600 A		3.80	4.211			238		238	355
3720	800 A		3.30	4.848			274		274	410
3730	1200 A		2.70	5.926			335		335	505
3740	1600 A		2.40	6.667			375		375	565
3750	2000 A		2.20	7.273			410		410	615
3760	2500 A		2.10	7.619			430		430	645
3770	3000 A		1.90	8.421			475		475	715
4000	Bus duct, aluminum or copper, 30 A	1 Elec	200	.040	L.F.		2.26		2.26	3.39
4020	60 A		160	.050			2.83		2.83	4.24
4040	100 A		140	.057			3.23		3.23	4.85
5000	Feedrail, trolley busway, up to 60 A		160	.050			2.83		2.83	4.24
5020	100 A		120	.067			3.77		3.77	5.65
5040	Busway, 50 A		200	.040			2.26		2.26	3.39
6000	Fuse, 30 A		133	.060	Ea.		3.40		3.40	5.10
6010	60 A		133	.060			3.40		3.40	5.10
6020	100 A		105	.076			4.31		4.31	6.45
6030	200 A		95	.084			4.77		4.77	7.15
6040	400 A		80	.100			5.65		5.65	8.50
6050	600 A		53	.151			8.55		8.55	12.80
6060	601 A - 1200 A		42	.190			10.80		10.80	16.15
6070	1500 A - 1600 A		34	.235			13.30		13.30	19.95
6080	1800 A - 2500 A		26	.308			17.40		17.40	26
6090	4000 A		21	.381			21.50		21.50	32.50
6100	4500 A - 5000 A		18	.444			25		25	37.50
6120	6000 A		15	.533			30		30	45
6200	Fuse plug or fustat		100	.080			4.53		4.53	6.80

26 05 05.50 Electrical Demolition, Lighting

		Crew	Daily Output	Labor-Hours	Unit	Material	2017 Bare Costs Labor	Equipment	Total	Total Incl O&P
0010	**ELECTRICAL DEMOLITION, LIGHTING** Addition R024119-10									
0100	Fixture hanger, flexible, 1/2" diameter	1 Elec	36	.222	Ea.		12.60		12.60	18.85
0120	3/4" diameter R260105-30	"	30	.267	"		15.10		15.10	22.50
3000	Light pole, anchor base, excl concrete bases									
3010	Metal light pole, 10'	2 Elec	24	.667	Ea.		37.50		37.50	56.50
3020	16'	"	18	.889			50.50		50.50	75.50
3030	20'	R-3	8.70	2.299			130	15.85	145.85	212
3035	25'		8.60	2.326			132	16.05	148.05	216
3038	30'		6	3.333			189	23	212	310
3039	35'		6	3.333			189	23	212	310
3040	40'		6	3.333			189	23	212	310
3100	Wood light pole, 10'	2 Elec	36	.444			25		25	37.50
3120	20'	"	24	.667			37.50		37.50	56.50
3140	Bollard light, 42"	1 Elec	9	.889			50.50		50.50	75.50
3160	Walkway luminaire	"	8.10	.988			56		56	84

112

For customer support on your Electrical Costs with RSMeans Data, call 800.448.8182.

26 05 Common Work Results for Electrical

26 05 05 – Selective Demolition for Electrical

26 05 05.50 Electrical Demolition, Lighting

		Crew	Daily Output	Labor-Hours	Unit	Material	2017 Bare Costs Labor	Equipment	Total	Total Incl O&P
4000	Explosionproof									
4010	Metal halide, 175 W	1 Elec	8.70	.920	Ea.		52		52	78
4020	250 W	"	8.10	.988			56		56	84
4030	400 W	2 Elec	14.40	1.111			63		63	94
4050	High pressure sodium, 70 W	1 Elec	9	.889			50.50		50.50	75.50
4060	100 W		9	.889			50.50		50.50	75.50
4070	150 W		8.10	.988			56		56	84
4100	Incandescent		8.70	.920			52		52	78
4200	Fluorescent		8.10	.988			56		56	84
5000	Ballast, fluorescent fixture		24	.333			18.85		18.85	28.50
5040	High intensity discharge fixture	▼	24	.333	▼		18.85		18.85	28.50
5300	Exit and emergency lighting									
5310	Exit light	1 Elec	24	.333	Ea.		18.85		18.85	28.50
5320	Emergency battery pack lighting unit		12	.667			37.50		37.50	56.50
5330	Remote lamp only		80	.100			5.65		5.65	8.50
5340	Self-contained fluorescent lamp pack	▼	30	.267			15.10		15.10	22.50
5500	Track lighting, 8' section	2 Elec	40	.400			22.50		22.50	34
5510	Track lighting fixture	1 Elec	64	.125	▼		7.10		7.10	10.60
5800	Energy saving devices									
5810	Occupancy sensor	1 Elec	21	.381	Ea.		21.50		21.50	32.50
5820	Automatic wall switch		72	.111			6.30		6.30	9.40
5830	Remote power pack		30	.267			15.10		15.10	22.50
5840	Photoelectric control		24	.333			18.85		18.85	28.50
5850	Fixture whip	▼	100	.080	▼		4.53		4.53	6.80
6000	Lamps									
6010	Fluorescent	1 Elec	200	.040	Ea.		2.26		2.26	3.39
6030	High intensity discharge lamp, up to 400 W		68	.118			6.65		6.65	10
6040	Up to 1000 W		45	.178			10.05		10.05	15.10
6050	Quartz		90	.089			5.05		5.05	7.55
6070	Incandescent		360	.022			1.26		1.26	1.88
6080	Exterior, PAR		290	.028			1.56		1.56	2.34
6090	Guards for fluorescent lamp	▼	24	.333	▼		18.85		18.85	28.50

26 05 13 – Medium-Voltage Cables

26 05 13.10 Cable Terminations

		Crew	Daily Output	Labor-Hours	Unit	Material	2017 Bare Costs Labor	Equipment	Total	Total Incl O&P
0010	**CABLE TERMINATIONS**, 5 kV to 35 kV									
0100	Indoor, insulation diameter range .64" to 1.08"									
0300	Padmount, 5 kV	1 Elec	8	1	Ea.	61.50	56.50		118	153
0400	10 kV		6.40	1.250		75.50	71		146.50	190
0500	15 kV		6	1.333		92	75.50		167.50	214
0600	25 kV	▼	5.60	1.429	▼	132	81		213	266
0700	Insulation diameter range 1.05" to 1.8"									
0800	Padmount, 5 kV	1 Elec	8	1	Ea.	91.50	56.50		148	186
0900	10 kV		6	1.333		105	75.50		180.50	228
1000	15 kV		5.60	1.429		127	81		208	260
1100	25 kV	▼	5.30	1.509	▼	151	85.50		236.50	294
1200	Insulation diameter range 1.53" to 2.32"									
1300	Padmount, 5 kV	1 Elec	7.40	1.081	Ea.	135	61		196	241
1400	10 kV		5.60	1.429		115	81		196	248
1500	15 kV		5.30	1.509		162	85.50		247.50	305
1600	25 kV	▼	5	1.600	▼	266	90.50		356.50	430
1700	Outdoor systems, #4 stranded to 1/0 stranded									
1800	5 kV	1 Elec	7.40	1.081	Ea.	76.50	61		137.50	176

For customer support on your Electrical Costs with RSMeans Data, call 800.448.8182.

113

26 05 13 – Medium-Voltage Cables

26 05 13.10 Cable Terminations	Crew	Daily Output	Labor-Hours	Unit	Material	2017 Bare Costs Labor	2017 Bare Costs Equipment	Total	Total Incl O&P
1900	15 kV	1 Elec	5.30	1.509	Ea.	134	85.50		219.50	276
2000	25 kV		5	1.600		180	90.50		270.50	335
2100	35 kV		4.80	1.667		222	94.50		316.50	385
2200	#1 solid to 4/0 stranded, 5 kV		6.90	1.159		111	65.50		176.50	221
2300	15 kV		5	1.600		172	90.50		262.50	325
2400	25 kV		4.80	1.667		232	94.50		326.50	395
2500	35 kV		4.60	1.739		236	98.50		334.50	405
2600	2/0 solid to 350 kcmil stranded, 5 kV		6.40	1.250		175	71		246	298
2700	15 kV		4.80	1.667		194	94.50		288.50	355
2800	25 kV		4.60	1.739		300	98.50		398.50	475
2900	35 kV		4.40	1.818		345	103		448	530
3000	400 kcmil compact to 750 kcmil stranded, 5 kV		6	1.333		196	75.50		271.50	330
3100	15 kV		4.60	1.739		234	98.50		332.50	405
3200	25 kV		4.40	1.818		340	103		443	530
3300	35 kV		4.20	1.905		350	108		458	545
3400	1000 kcmil, 5 kV		5.60	1.429		190	81		271	330
3500	15 kV		4.40	1.818		315	103		418	505
3600	25 kV		4.20	1.905		350	108		458	545
3700	35 kV	▼	4	2	▼	315	113		428	515

26 05 13.16 Medium-Voltage, Single Cable

		Crew	Daily Output	Labor-Hours	Unit	Material	2017 Bare Costs Labor	2017 Bare Costs Equipment	Total	Total Incl O&P
0010	**MEDIUM-VOLTAGE, SINGLE CABLE** Splicing & terminations not included									
0040	Copper, XLP shielding, 5 kV, #6	2 Elec	4.40	3.636	C.L.F.	153	206		359	480
0050	#4		4.40	3.636		199	206		405	530
0100	#2		4	4		262	226		488	630
0200	#1		4	4		325	226		551	695
0400	1/0		3.80	4.211		350	238		588	735
0600	2/0		3.60	4.444		420	252		672	840
0800	4/0		3.20	5		570	283		853	1,050
1000	250 kcmil	3 Elec	4.50	5.333		680	300		980	1,200
1200	350 kcmil		3.90	6.154		885	350		1,235	1,500
1400	500 kcmil		3.60	6.667		1,050	375		1,425	1,725
1600	15 kV, ungrounded neutral, #1	2 Elec	4	4		330	226		556	700
1800	1/0		3.80	4.211		390	238		628	785
2000	2/0		3.60	4.444		445	252		697	865
2200	4/0		3.20	5		595	283		878	1,075
2400	250 kcmil	3 Elec	4.50	5.333		655	300		955	1,175
2600	350 kcmil		3.90	6.154		830	350		1,180	1,425
2800	500 kcmil		3.60	6.667		1,025	375		1,400	1,700
3000	25 kV, grounded neutral, 1/0	2 Elec	3.60	4.444		520	252		772	945
3200	2/0		3.40	4.706		570	266		836	1,025
3400	4/0		3	5.333		715	300		1,015	1,250
3600	250 kcmil	3 Elec	4.20	5.714		890	325		1,215	1,475
3800	350 kcmil		3.60	6.667		1,050	375		1,425	1,725
3900	500 kcmil		3.30	7.273		1,225	410		1,635	1,975
4000	35 kV, grounded neutral, 1/0	2 Elec	3.40	4.706		575	266		841	1,025
4200	2/0		3.20	5		645	283		928	1,125
4400	4/0		2.80	5.714		815	325		1,140	1,375
4600	250 kcmil	3 Elec	3.90	6.154		955	350		1,305	1,575
4800	350 kcmil		3.30	7.273		1,150	410		1,560	1,875
5000	500 kcmil		3	8		1,350	455		1,805	2,150
5050	Aluminum, XLP shielding, 5 kV, #2	2 Elec	5	3.200		181	181		362	470
5070	#1		4.40	3.636		187	206		393	515

26 05 13 – Medium-Voltage Cables

26 05 13.16 Medium-Voltage, Single Cable

	Crew	Daily Output	Labor-Hours	Unit	Material	2017 Bare Costs Labor	Equipment	Total	Total Incl O&P
5090	1/0	2 Elec	4	4	C.L.F.	217	226		443	580
5100	2/0		3.80	4.211		243	238		481	620
5150	4/0		3.60	4.444		288	252		540	690
5200	250 kcmil	3 Elec	4.80	5		350	283		633	810
5220	350 kcmil		4.50	5.333		410	300		710	900
5240	500 kcmil		3.90	6.154		525	350		875	1,100
5260	750 kcmil		3.60	6.667		695	375		1,070	1,325
5300	15 kV aluminum, XLP, #1	2 Elec	4.40	3.636		232	206		438	565
5320	1/0		4	4		240	226		466	605
5340	2/0		3.80	4.211		286	238		524	670
5360	4/0		3.60	4.444		315	252		567	725
5380	250 kcmil	3 Elec	4.80	5		380	283		663	840
5400	350 kcmil		4.50	5.333		425	300		725	920
5420	500 kcmil		3.90	6.154		590	350		940	1,175
5440	750 kcmil		3.60	6.667		780	375		1,155	1,425

26 05 19 – Low-Voltage Electrical Power Conductors and Cables

26 05 19.13 Undercarpet Electrical Power Cables

		Crew	Daily Output	Labor-Hours	Unit	Material	2017 Bare Costs Labor	Equipment	Total	Total Incl O&P
0010	**UNDERCARPET ELECTRICAL POWER CABLES** R260519-80									
0020	Power System									
0100	Cable flat, 3 conductor, #12, w/attached bottom shield	1 Elec	982	.008	L.F.	5.15	.46		5.61	6.35
0200	Shield, top, steel		1768	.005	"	5.50	.26		5.76	6.45
0250	Splice, 3 conductor		48	.167	Ea.	16.75	9.45		26.20	32.50
0300	Top shield		96	.083		1.49	4.72		6.21	8.70
0350	Tap		40	.200		21.50	11.30		32.80	40.50
0400	Insulating patch, splice, tap & end		48	.167		53	9.45		62.45	72
0450	Fold		230	.035			1.97		1.97	2.95
0500	Top shield, tap & fold		96	.083		1.49	4.72		6.21	8.70
0700	Transition, block assembly		77	.104		77	5.90		82.90	94
0750	Receptacle frame & base		32	.250		42.50	14.15		56.65	67.50
0800	Cover receptacle		120	.067		3.61	3.77		7.38	9.60
0850	Cover blank		160	.050		4.24	2.83		7.07	8.90
0860	Receptacle, direct connected, single		25	.320		90.50	18.10		108.60	127
0870	Dual		16	.500		149	28.50		177.50	206
0880	Combination high & low, tension		21	.381		109	21.50		130.50	153
0900	Box, floor with cover		20	.400		92	22.50		114.50	135
0920	Floor service w/barrier		4	2		259	113		372	455
1000	Wall, surface, with cover		20	.400		60.50	22.50		83	101
1100	Wall, flush, with cover		20	.400		42.50	22.50		65	80.50
1450	Cable flat, 5 conductor #12, w/attached bottom shield		800	.010	L.F.	8.45	.57		9.02	10.10
1550	Shield, top, steel		1768	.005	"	8.35	.26		8.61	9.60
1600	Splice, 5 conductor		48	.167	Ea.	27	9.45		36.45	44
1650	Top shield		96	.083		1.49	4.72		6.21	8.70
1700	Tap		48	.167		35.50	9.45		44.95	53
1750	Insulating patch, splice tap & end		83	.096		53	5.45		58.45	66
1800	Transition, block assembly		77	.104		55.50	5.90		61.40	70
1850	Box, wall, flush with cover		20	.400		56.50	22.50		79	96
1900	Cable flat, 4 conductor #12		933	.009	L.F.	6.15	.49		6.64	7.50
1950	3 conductor #10		982	.008		5.95	.46		6.41	7.25
1960	4 conductor #10		933	.009		7.80	.49		8.29	9.30
1970	5 conductor #10		884	.009		9.50	.51		10.01	11.20
2500	Telephone System									
2510	Transition fitting wall box, surface	1 Elec	24	.333	Ea.	61.50	18.85		80.35	96

For customer support on your Electrical Costs with RSMeans Data, call 800.448.8182.

115

26 05 19.13 Undercarpet Electrical Power Cables	Crew	Daily Output	Labor-Hours	Unit	Material	2017 Bare Costs Labor	Equipment	Total	Total Incl O&P
2520	Flush	1 Elec	24	.333	Ea.	61.50	18.85		80.35	96
2530	Flush, for PC board		24	.333		61.50	18.85		80.35	96
2540	Floor service box	▼	4	2		238	113		351	430
2550	Cover, surface					15.90			15.90	17.50
2560	Flush					15.90			15.90	17.50
2570	Flush for PC board					15.90			15.90	17.50
2700	Floor fitting w/duplex jack & cover	1 Elec	21	.381		47	21.50		68.50	84
2720	Low profile		53	.151		17.20	8.55		25.75	31.50
2740	Miniature w/duplex jack		53	.151		26	8.55		34.55	42
2760	25 pair kit		21	.381		49.50	21.50		71	87
2780	Low profile		53	.151		17.55	8.55		26.10	32
2800	Call director kit for 5 cable		19	.421		79	24		103	123
2820	4 pair kit		19	.421		94	24		118	139
2840	3 pair kit		19	.421		99.50	24		123.50	145
2860	Comb. 25 pair & 3 conductor power		21	.381		79	21.50		100.50	120
2880	5 conductor power		21	.381		90	21.50		111.50	132
2900	PC board, 8 per 3 pair		161	.050		68.50	2.81		71.31	79
2920	6 per 4 pair		161	.050		68.50	2.81		71.31	79
2940	3 pair adapter		161	.050		62	2.81		64.81	72.50
2950	Plug		77	.104		3.04	5.90		8.94	12.15
2960	Couplers		321	.025	▼	8.55	1.41		9.96	11.50
3000	Bottom shield for 25 pair cable		4420	.002	L.F.	.86	.10		.96	1.10
3020	4 pair		4420	.002		.40	.10		.50	.59
3040	Top shield for 25 pair cable		4420	.002	▼	.86	.10		.96	1.10
3100	Cable assembly, double-end, 50', 25 pair		11.80	.678	Ea.	241	38.50		279.50	325
3110	3 pair		23.60	.339		74.50	19.20		93.70	111
3120	4 pair		23.60	.339	▼	79	19.20		98.20	116
3140	Bulk 3 pair		1473	.005	L.F.	1.28	.31		1.59	1.87
3160	4 pair	▼	1473	.005	"	1.58	.31		1.89	2.20
3500	Data System									
3520	Cable 25 conductor w/connection 40', 75 ohm	1 Elec	14.50	.552	Ea.	71	31		102	126
3530	Single lead		22	.364		194	20.50		214.50	245
3540	Dual lead	▼	22	.364	▼	241	20.50		261.50	296
3560	Shields same for 25 conductor as 25 pair telephone									
3570	Single & dual, none required									
3590	BNC coax connectors, Plug	1 Elec	40	.200	Ea.	11.10	11.30		22.40	29
3600	TNC coax connectors, Plug	"	40	.200	"	15.50	11.30		26.80	34
3700	Cable-bulk									
3710	Single lead	1 Elec	1473	.005	L.F.	2.70	.31		3.01	3.43
3720	Dual lead	"	1473	.005	"	3.91	.31		4.22	4.76
3730	Hand tool crimp				Ea.	445			445	485
3740	Hand tool notch				"	19.55			19.55	21.50
3750	Boxes & floor fitting same as telephone									
3790	Data cable notching, 90°	1 Elec	97	.082	Ea.		4.67		4.67	7
3800	180°		60	.133	▼		7.55		7.55	11.30
8100	Drill floor		160	.050	▼	3.88	2.83		6.71	8.50
8200	Marking floor		1600	.005	L.F.		.28		.28	.42
8300	Tape, hold down		6400	.001	"	.17	.07		.24	.30
8350	Tape primer, 500 ft. per can	▼	96	.083	Ea.	41	4.72		45.72	52
8400	Tool, splicing				"	171			171	188

26 05 19 – Low-Voltage Electrical Power Conductors and Cables

26 05 19.20 Armored Cable		Crew	Daily Output	Labor-Hours	Unit	Material	2017 Bare Costs Labor	Equipment	Total	Total Incl O&P
0010	**ARMORED CABLE** R260519-20									
0050	600 volt, copper (BX), #14, 2 conductor, solid	1 Elec	2.40	3.333	C.L.F.	45.50	189		234.50	335
0100	3 conductor, solid		2.20	3.636		73	206		279	390
0120	4 conductor, solid		2	4		101	226		327	450
0150	#12, 2 conductor, solid		2.30	3.478		46	197		243	345
0200	3 conductor, solid		2	4		74.50	226		300.50	420
0220	4 conductor, solid		1.80	4.444		106	252		358	490
0250	#10, 2 conductor, solid		2	4		87.50	226		313.50	435
0300	3 conductor, solid		1.60	5		121	283		404	560
0320	4 conductor, solid		1.40	5.714		188	325		513	690
0340	#8, 2 conductor, stranded		1.50	5.333		229	300		529	700
0350	3 conductor, stranded		1.30	6.154		229	350		579	770
0370	4 conductor, stranded		1.10	7.273		325	410		735	975
0380	#6, 2 conductor, stranded		1.30	6.154		240	350		590	785
0390	#4, 3 conductor, stranded		1.40	5.714		555	325		880	1,100
0400	3 conductor with PVC jacket, in cable tray, #6		3.10	2.581		540	146		686	810
0450	#4	2 Elec	5.40	2.963		655	168		823	970
0500	#2		4.60	3.478		795	197		992	1,175
0550	#1		4	4		1,025	226		1,251	1,475
0600	1/0		3.60	4.444		1,100	252		1,352	1,575
0650	2/0		3.40	4.706		1,325	266		1,591	1,850
0700	3/0		3.20	5		1,775	283		2,058	2,375
0750	4/0		3	5.333		2,125	300		2,425	2,775
0800	250 kcmil	3 Elec	3.60	6.667		2,450	375		2,825	3,275
0850	350 kcmil		3.30	7.273		3,300	410		3,710	4,275
0900	500 kcmil		3	8		4,575	455		5,030	5,700
0910	4 conductor with PVC jacket, in cable tray, #6	1 Elec	2.70	2.963		770	168		938	1,100
0920	#4	2 Elec	4.60	3.478		820	197		1,017	1,200
0930	#2		4	4		1,250	226		1,476	1,725
0940	#1		3.60	4.444		1,450	252		1,702	1,950
0950	1/0		3.40	4.706		1,425	266		1,691	1,950
0960	2/0		3.20	5		1,750	283		2,033	2,350
0970	3/0		3	5.333		2,300	300		2,600	3,000
0980	4/0		2.40	6.667		2,675	375		3,050	3,525
0990	250 kcmil	3 Elec	3.30	7.273		3,225	410		3,635	4,175
1000	350 kcmil		3	8		4,325	455		4,780	5,450
1010	500 kcmil		2.70	8.889		6,000	505		6,505	7,350
1050	5 kV, copper, 3 conductor with PVC jacket,									
1060	non-shielded, in cable tray, #4	2 Elec	380	.042	L.F.	6.85	2.38		9.23	11.10
1100	#2		360	.044		8.90	2.52		11.42	13.55
1200	#1		300	.053		11.35	3.02		14.37	17
1400	1/0		290	.055		13.10	3.12		16.22	19.10
1600	2/0		260	.062		15.15	3.48		18.63	22
2000	4/0		240	.067		20	3.77		23.77	27.50
2100	250 kcmil	3 Elec	330	.073		27.50	4.12		31.62	36.50
2150	350 kcmil		315	.076		34	4.31		38.31	44
2200	500 kcmil		270	.089		46.50	5.05		51.55	58.50
2400	15 kV, copper, 3 conductor with PVC jacket galv., steel armored									
2500	grounded neutral, in cable tray, #2	2 Elec	300	.053	L.F.	15	3.02		18.02	21
2600	#1		280	.057		15.35	3.23		18.58	22
2800	1/0		260	.062		18.25	3.48		21.73	25
2900	2/0		220	.073		23.50	4.12		27.62	31.50

For customer support on your Electrical Costs with RSMeans Data, call 800.448.8182.

117

26 05 19.20 Armored Cable		Crew	Daily Output	Labor-Hours	Unit	Material	2017 Bare Costs Labor	Equipment	Total	Total Incl O&P
3000	4/0	2 Elec	190	.084	L.F.	26.50	4.77		31.27	36
3100	250 kcmil	3 Elec	270	.089		29.50	5.05		34.55	40
3150	350 kcmil		240	.100		34.50	5.65		40.15	46.50
3200	500 kcmil		210	.114		46.50	6.45		52.95	61
3400	15 kV, copper, 3 conductor with PVC jacket,									
3450	ungrounded neutral, in cable tray, #2	2 Elec	260	.062	L.F.	15.55	3.48		19.03	22.50
3500	#1		230	.070		17.20	3.94		21.14	25
3600	1/0		200	.080		19.70	4.53		24.23	28.50
3700	2/0		190	.084		24	4.77		28.77	33.50
3800	4/0		160	.100		29	5.65		34.65	40.50
4000	250 kcmil	3 Elec	210	.114		34	6.45		40.45	47
4050	350 kcmil		195	.123		45	6.95		51.95	59.50
4100	500 kcmil		180	.133		54.50	7.55		62.05	71.50
4200	600 volt, aluminum, 3 conductor in cable tray with PVC jacket									
4300	#2	2 Elec	540	.030	L.F.	3.61	1.68		5.29	6.50
4400	#1		460	.035		4.45	1.97		6.42	7.85
4500	1/0		400	.040		5.55	2.26		7.81	9.50
4600	2/0		360	.044		5.60	2.52		8.12	9.95
4700	3/0		340	.047		6.55	2.66		9.21	11.25
4800	4/0		320	.050		7.95	2.83		10.78	13
4900	250 kcmil	3 Elec	450	.053		9.55	3.02		12.57	15
5000	350 kcmil		360	.067		11.40	3.77		15.17	18.20
5200	500 kcmil		330	.073		14.20	4.12		18.32	22
5300	750 kcmil		285	.084		18.25	4.77		23.02	27
5400	600 volt, aluminum, 4 conductor in cable tray with PVC jacket									
5410	#2	2 Elec	520	.031	L.F.	4.64	1.74		6.38	7.70
5430	#1		440	.036		5.75	2.06		7.81	9.45
5450	1/0		380	.042		6.75	2.38		9.13	10.95
5470	2/0		340	.047		6.90	2.66		9.56	11.60
5480	3/0		320	.050		8.10	2.83		10.93	13.15
5500	4/0		300	.053		9.50	3.02		12.52	14.95
5520	250 kcmil	3 Elec	420	.057		10.20	3.23		13.43	16.05
5540	350 kcmil		330	.073		13.20	4.12		17.32	20.50
5560	500 kcmil		300	.080		16.50	4.53		21.03	25
5580	750 kcmil		270	.089		22.50	5.05		27.55	32.50
5600	5 kV, aluminum, unshielded in cable tray, #2 with PVC jacket	2 Elec	380	.042		5.60	2.38		7.98	9.75
5700	#1 with PVC jacket		360	.044		6.30	2.52		8.82	10.65
5800	1/0 with PVC jacket		300	.053		6.45	3.02		9.47	11.60
6000	2/0 with PVC jacket		290	.055		6.55	3.12		9.67	11.95
6200	3/0 with PVC jacket		260	.062		7.90	3.48		11.38	13.90
6300	4/0 with PVC jacket		240	.067		9.25	3.77		13.02	15.85
6400	250 kcmil with PVC jacket	3 Elec	330	.073		10.15	4.12		14.27	17.35
6500	350 kcmil with PVC jacket		315	.076		11.90	4.31		16.21	19.55
6600	500 kcmil with PVC jacket		300	.080		14.10	4.53		18.63	22.50
6800	750 kcmil with PVC jacket		270	.089		17.40	5.05		22.45	26.50
6900	15 kV, aluminum, shielded-grounded, #2 with PVC jacket	2 Elec	320	.050		12.80	2.83		15.63	18.30
7000	#1 with PVC jacket		300	.053		13.15	3.02		16.17	18.95
7200	1/0 with PVC jacket		280	.057		14.20	3.23		17.43	20.50
7300	2/0 with PVC jacket		260	.062		14.40	3.48		17.88	21
7400	3/0 with PVC jacket		240	.067		16.15	3.77		19.92	23.50
7500	4/0 with PVC jacket		220	.073		16.60	4.12		20.72	24.50
7600	250 kcmil with PVC jacket	3 Elec	300	.080		18.20	4.53		22.73	27
7700	350 kcmil with PVC jacket		270	.089		21.50	5.05		26.55	31

26 05 19.20 Armored Cable	Crew	Daily Output	Labor-Hours	Unit	Material	2017 Bare Costs Labor	Equipment	Total	Total Incl O&P
7800	500 kcmil with PVC jacket	3 Elec	240	.100	L.F.	25.50	5.65		31.15	36.50
8000	750 kcmil with PVC jacket		204	.118		30.50	6.65		37.15	43.50
8200	15 kV, aluminum, shielded-ungrounded, #1 with PVC jacket	2 Elec	250	.064		16	3.62		19.62	23
8300	1/0 with PVC jacket		230	.070		16.60	3.94		20.54	24
8400	2/0 with PVC jacket		210	.076		18.20	4.31		22.51	26.50
8500	3/0 with PVC jacket		200	.080		18.50	4.53		23.03	27.50
8600	4/0 with PVC jacket		190	.084		20	4.77		24.77	29
8700	250 kcmil with PVC jacket	3 Elec	270	.089		21.50	5.05		26.55	31
8800	350 kcmil with PVC jacket		240	.100		24.50	5.65		30.15	35.50
8900	500 kcmil with PVC jacket		210	.114		29.50	6.45		35.95	42
8950	750 kcmil with PVC jacket		174	.138		37	7.80		44.80	52
9010	600 volt, copper (MC) steel clad, #14, 2 wire	R-1A	8.16	1.961	C.L.F.	52	100		152	207
9020	3 wire		7.21	2.219		74.50	113		187.50	251
9030	4 wire		6.69	2.392		103	122		225	297
9040	#12, 2 wire		7.21	2.219		46.50	113		159.50	220
9050	3 wire		6.69	2.392		79	122		201	270
9060	4 wire		6.04	2.649		121	135		256	335
9070	#10, 2 wire		6.04	2.649		108	135		243	320
9080	3 wire		5.65	2.832		142	144		286	370
9090	4 wire		5.23	3.059		222	156		378	480
9100	#8, 2 wire, stranded		3.94	4.061		194	207		401	525
9110	3 wire, stranded		3.40	4.706		272	240		512	660
9120	4 wire, stranded		2.80	5.714		370	291		661	840
9130	#6, 2 wire, stranded		3.45	4.638		287	236		523	670
9200	600 volt, copper (MC) aluminum clad, #14, 2 wire		8.16	1.961		45	100		145	200
9210	3 wire		7.21	2.219		73	113		186	250
9220	4 wire		6.69	2.392		112	122		234	305
9230	#12, 2 wire		7.21	2.219		45	113		158	219
9240	3 wire		6.69	2.392		81.50	122		203.50	273
9250	4 wire		6.04	2.649		108	135		243	320
9260	#10, 2 wire		6.04	2.649		116	135		251	330
9270	3 wire		5.65	2.832		141	144		285	370
9280	4 wire		5.23	3.059		254	156		410	515
9600	Alum (MC) aluminum clad, #6, 3 conductor w/#6 grnd		2.75	5.818		291	296		587	765
9610	4 conductor w/#6 grnd		2.29	6.987		247	355		602	805
9620	#4, 3 conductor w/#6 grnd	R-1B	3.13	7.668		236	375		611	825
9630	4 conductor w/#6 grnd		2.67	8.989		255	440		695	940
9640	#2, 3 conductor w/#4 grnd		2.59	9.266		415	455		870	1,125
9650	4 conductor w/#4 grnd		2.21	10.860		465	535		1,000	1,325
9660	#1, 3 conductor w/#4 grnd		2.15	11.163		350	550		900	1,200
9670	4 conductor w/#4 grnd		1.85	12.973		635	635		1,270	1,650
9680	1/0, 3 conductor w/#4 grnd		2.16	11.111		400	545		945	1,250
9690	4 conductor w/#4 grnd		1.73	13.873		485	680		1,165	1,550
9700	2/0, 3 conductor w/#4 grnd		1.91	12.565		645	615		1,260	1,625
9710	4 conductor w/#4 grnd		1.53	15.686		545	770		1,315	1,750
9720	3/0, 3 conductor w/#4 grnd		1.75	13.714		825	675		1,500	1,900
9730	4 conductor w/#4 grnd		1.40	17.143		675	840		1,515	2,000
9740	4/0, 3 conductor w/#2 grnd		1.54	15.584		925	765		1,690	2,175
9750	4 conductor w/#2 grnd		1.23	19.512		920	955		1,875	2,450
9760	250 kcmil, 3 conductor w/#1 grnd	R-1C	1.90	16.842		1,175	860	68.50	2,103.50	2,650
9770	4 conductor w/#1 grnd		1.52	21.053		1,600	1,075	85.50	2,760.50	3,475
9780	350 kcmil, 3 conductor w/1/0 grnd		1.76	18.182		1,350	925	74	2,349	2,950
9790	4 conductor w/1/0 grnd		1.41	22.695		1,275	1,150	92.50	2,517.50	3,250

26 05 19.20 Armored Cable	Crew	Daily Output	Labor-Hours	Unit	Material	2017 Bare Costs Labor	Equipment	Total	Total Incl O&P
9800	500 kcmil, 3 conductor w/#1 grnd	R-1C	1.64	19.512	C.L.F.	1,850	995	79.50	2,924.50	3,625
9810	4 conductor w/2/0 grnd		1.31	24.427		1,575	1,250	99.50	2,924.50	3,700
9840	750 kcmil, 3 conductor w/1/0 grnd		1.31	24.427		2,825	1,250	99.50	4,174.50	5,075
9850	4 conductor w/3/0 grnd		1.04	30.769		2,650	1,575	125	4,350	5,425

26 05 19.25 Cable Connectors

		Crew	Daily Output	Labor-Hours	Unit	Material	2017 Bare Costs Labor	Equipment	Total	Total Incl O&P
0010	**CABLE CONNECTORS**									
0100	600 volt, nonmetallic, #14-2 wire	1 Elec	160	.050	Ea.	1.44	2.83		4.27	5.80
0200	#14-3 wire to #12-2 wire		133	.060		1.44	3.40		4.84	6.70
0300	#12-3 wire to #10-2 wire		114	.070		1.44	3.97		5.41	7.55
0400	#10-3 wire to #14-4 and #12-4 wire		100	.080		1.44	4.53		5.97	8.40
0500	#8-3 wire to #10-4 wire		80	.100		2.71	5.65		8.36	11.50
0600	#6-3 wire		40	.200		3.65	11.30		14.95	21
0800	SER, 3 #8 insulated + 1 #8 ground		32	.250		1.45	14.15		15.60	22.50
0900	3 #6 + 1 #6 ground		24	.333		1.81	18.85		20.66	30.50
1000	3 #4 + 1 #6 ground		22	.364		2.26	20.50		22.76	33.50
1100	3 #2 + 1 #4 ground		20	.400		4.12	22.50		26.62	38.50
1200	3 1/0 + 1 #2 ground		18	.444		10.60	25		35.60	49
1400	3 2/0 + 1 #1 ground		16	.500		12.80	28.50		41.30	56.50
1600	3 4/0 + 1 #2/0 ground		14	.571		28	32.50		60.50	79.50
1800	600 volt, armored, #14-2 wire		80	.100		1.16	5.65		6.81	9.80
2200	#14-4, #12-3 and #10-2 wire		40	.200		.91	11.30		12.21	17.95
2400	#12-4, #10-3 and #8-2 wire		32	.250		2.73	14.15		16.88	24
2600	#8-3 and #10-4 wire		26	.308		3.58	17.40		20.98	30
2650	#8-4 wire		22	.364		5.30	20.50		25.80	37
2652	Non-PVC jacket connector, #6-3 wire, #6-4 wire		22	.364		45	20.50		65.50	80.50
2660	1/0-3 wire		11	.727		62	41		103	130
2670	300 kcmil-3 wire		6	1.333		94	75.50		169.50	216
2680	700-kcmil-3 wire		4	2		139	113		252	325
2700	PVC jacket connector, #6-3 wire, #6-4 wire		16	.500		6.80	28.50		35.30	50
2800	#4-3 wire, #4-4 wire		16	.500		6.80	28.50		35.30	50
2900	#2-3 wire		12	.667		6.80	37.50		44.30	64
3000	#1-3 wire, #2-4 wire		12	.667		14.35	37.50		51.85	72.50
3200	1/0-3 wire		11	.727		14.35	41		55.35	77.50
3400	2/0-3 wire, 1/0-4 wire		10	.800		14.35	45.50		59.85	84
3500	3/0-3 wire, 2/0-4 wire		9	.889		21	50.50		71.50	98.50
3600	4/0-3 wire, 3/0-4 wire		7	1.143		21	64.50		85.50	120
3800	250 kcmil-3 wire, 4/0-4 wire		6	1.333		35.50	75.50		111	153
4000	350 kcmil-3 wire, 250 kcmil-4 wire		5	1.600		35.50	90.50		126	176
4100	350 kcmil-4 wire		4	2		196	113		309	385
4200	500 kcmil-3 wire		4	2		196	113		309	385
4250	500 kcmil-4 wire, 750 kcmil-3 wire		3.50	2.286		267	129		396	485
4300	750 kcmil-4 wire		3	2.667		267	151		418	520
4400	5 kV, armored, #4		8	1		67	56.50		123.50	159
4600	#2		8	1		67	56.50		123.50	159
4800	#1		8	1		86.50	56.50		143	180
5000	1/0		6.40	1.250		107	71		178	224
5200	2/0		5.30	1.509		107	85.50		192.50	246
5500	4/0		4	2		143	113		256	325
5600	250 kcmil		3.60	2.222		143	126		269	345
5650	350 kcmil		3.20	2.500		172	142		314	400
5700	500 kcmil		2.50	3.200		216	181		397	510
5720	750 kcmil		2.20	3.636		263	206		469	600

26 05 19 – Low-Voltage Electrical Power Conductors and Cables

26 05 19.25 Cable Connectors	Crew	Daily Output	Labor-Hours	Unit	Material	2017 Bare Costs Labor	Equipment	Total	Total Incl O&P
5750	1000 krmil	1 Elec	2	4	Ea.	325	226		551	695
5800	15 kV, armored, #1		4	2		129	113		242	310
5900	1/0		4	2		161	113		274	345
6000	3/0		3.60	2.222		246	126		372	460
6100	4/0		3.40	2.353		279	133		412	505
6200	250 kcmil		3.20	2.500		305	142		447	545
6300	350 kcmil		2.70	2.963		287	168		455	565
6400	500 kcmil		2	4		370	226		596	750

26 05 19.30 Cable Splicing	Crew	Daily Output	Labor-Hours	Unit	Material	2017 Bare Costs Labor	Equipment	Total	Total Incl O&P
0010	**CABLE SPLICING** URD or similar, ideal conditions									
0100	#6 stranded to #1 stranded, 5 kV	1 Elec	4	2	Ea.	132	113		245	315
0120	15 kV		3.60	2.222		182	126		308	390
0140	25 kV		3.20	2.500		212	142		354	445
0200	#1 stranded to 4/0 stranded, 5 kV		3.60	2.222		143	126		269	345
0210	15 kV		3.20	2.500		193	142		335	425
0220	25 kV		2.80	2.857		212	162		374	475
0300	4/0 stranded to 500 kcmil stranded, 5 kV		3.30	2.424		143	137		280	365
0310	15 kV		2.90	2.759		300	156		456	565
0320	25 kV		2.50	3.200		345	181		526	650
0400	500 kcmil, 5 kV		3.20	2.500		170	142		312	400
0410	15 kV		2.80	2.857		355	162		517	630
0420	25 kV		2.30	3.478		345	197		542	675
0500	600 kcmil, 5 kV		2.90	2.759		170	156		326	420
0510	15 kV		2.40	3.333		365	189		554	685
0520	25 kV		2	4		400	226		626	780
0600	750 kcmil, 5 kV		2.60	3.077		170	174		344	450
0610	15 kV		2.20	3.636		365	206		571	710
0620	25 kV		1.90	4.211		400	238		638	795
0700	1000 kcmil, 5 kV		2.30	3.478		170	197		367	480
0710	15 kV		1.90	4.211		395	238		633	790
0720	25 kV		1.60	5		415	283		698	880

26 05 19.35 Cable Terminations	Crew	Daily Output	Labor-Hours	Unit	Material	2017 Bare Costs Labor	Equipment	Total	Total Incl O&P
0010	**CABLE TERMINATIONS**									
0015	Wire connectors, screw type, #22 to #14	1 Elec	260	.031	Ea.	.06	1.74		1.80	2.68
0020	#18 to #12		240	.033		.07	1.89		1.96	2.91
0035	#16 to #10		230	.035		.27	1.97		2.24	3.25
0040	#14 to #8		210	.038		.30	2.16		2.46	3.56
0045	#12 to #6		180	.044		.62	2.52		3.14	4.45
0050	Terminal lugs, solderless, #16 to #10		50	.160		.37	9.05		9.42	13.95
0100	#8 to #4		30	.267		.73	15.10		15.83	23.50
0150	#2 to #1		22	.364		1.03	20.50		21.53	32
0200	1/0 to 2/0		16	.500		1.64	28.50		30.14	44.50
0250	3/0		12	.667		3.55	37.50		41.05	60.50
0300	4/0		11	.727		4.35	41		45.35	66.50
0350	250 kcmil		9	.889		3.41	50.50		53.91	79.50
0400	350 kcmil		7	1.143		4.44	64.50		68.94	102
0450	500 kcmil		6	1.333		8.20	75.50		83.70	122
0500	600 kcmil		5.80	1.379		9.30	78		87.30	127
0550	750 kcmil		5.20	1.538		10.95	87		97.95	142
0600	Split bolt connectors, tapped, #6		16	.500		3.78	28.50		32.28	46.50
0650	#4		14	.571		3.87	32.50		36.37	53
0700	#2		12	.667		5.40	37.50		42.90	62.50

26 05 19.35 Cable Terminations	Crew	Daily Output	Labor-Hours	Unit	Material	2017 Bare Costs Labor	Equipment	Total	Total Incl O&P
0750	#1	1 Elec	11	.727	Ea.	7.45	41		48.45	69.50
0800	1/0		10	.800		7.45	45.50		52.95	76
0850	2/0		9	.889		11.25	50.50		61.75	88
0900	3/0		7.20	1.111		16.25	63		79.25	112
1000	4/0		6.40	1.250		19.75	71		90.75	128
1100	250 kcmil		5.70	1.404		19.75	79.50		99.25	141
1200	300 kcmil		5.30	1.509		30.50	85.50		116	162
1400	350 kcmil		4.60	1.739		30.50	98.50		129	181
1500	500 kcmil	▼	4	2	▼	62.50	113		175.50	239
1600	Crimp 1 hole lugs, copper or aluminum, 600 volt									
1620	#14	1 Elec	60	.133	Ea.	.56	7.55		8.11	11.90
1630	#12		50	.160		.90	9.05		9.95	14.55
1640	#10		45	.178		.90	10.05		10.95	16.10
1780	#8		36	.222		1.80	12.60		14.40	21
1800	#6		30	.267		2.02	15.10		17.12	24.50
2000	#4		27	.296		2.56	16.75		19.31	28
2200	#2		24	.333		3.13	18.85		21.98	32
2400	#1		20	.400		4.61	22.50		27.11	39
2500	1/0		17.50	.457		4.98	26		30.98	44.50
2600	2/0		15	.533		6.15	30		36.15	52
2800	3/0		12	.667		6	37.50		43.50	63
3000	4/0		11	.727		6.65	41		47.65	69
3200	250 kcmil		9	.889		6.85	50.50		57.35	83
3400	300 kcmil		8	1		8.05	56.50		64.55	94
3500	350 kcmil		7	1.143		8.75	64.50		73.25	107
3600	400 kcmil		6.50	1.231		10.85	69.50		80.35	116
3800	500 kcmil		6	1.333		12.55	75.50		88.05	127
4000	600 kcmil		5.80	1.379		14.20	78		92.20	133
4200	700 kcmil		5.50	1.455		17.60	82.50		100.10	142
4400	750 kcmil	▼	5.20	1.538	▼	17.60	87		104.60	149
4500	Crimp 2-way connectors, copper or alum., 600 volt									
4510	#14	1 Elec	60	.133	Ea.	2.15	7.55		9.70	13.65
4520	#12		50	.160		2.28	9.05		11.33	16.05
4530	#10		45	.178		2.40	10.05		12.45	17.75
4540	#8		27	.296		2.43	16.75		19.18	27.50
4600	#6		25	.320		3.31	18.10		21.41	30.50
4800	#4		23	.348		4.09	19.70		23.79	34
5000	#2		20	.400		4.78	22.50		27.28	39.50
5200	#1		16	.500		7.80	28.50		36.30	51
5400	1/0		13	.615		8	35		43	61
5420	2/0		12	.667		6.95	37.50		44.45	64
5440	3/0		11	.727		7.85	41		48.85	70
5460	4/0		10	.800		11.50	45.50		57	80.50
5480	250 kcmil		9	.889		10.80	50.50		61.30	87.50
5500	300 kcmil		8.50	.941		11.85	53.50		65.35	93
5520	350 kcmil		8	1		12.25	56.50		68.75	98.50
5540	400 kcmil		7.30	1.096		14.70	62		76.70	109
5560	500 kcmil		6.20	1.290		18.50	73		91.50	130
5580	600 kcmil		5.50	1.455		27.50	82.50		110	154
5600	700 kcmil		4.50	1.778		40.50	101		141.50	196
5620	750 kcmil		4	2		35.50	113		148.50	209
7000	Compression equipment adapter, aluminum wire, #6		30	.267		10.30	15.10		25.40	34
7020	#4		27	.296		9.95	16.75		26.70	36

26 05 19 – Low-Voltage Electrical Power Conductors and Cables

26 05 19.35 Cable Terminations

		Crew	Daily Output	Labor-Hours	Unit	Material	2017 Bare Costs Labor	Equipment	Total	Total Incl O&P
7040	#2	1 Elec	24	.333	Ea.	10.40	18.85		29.25	40
7060	#1		20	.400		12.30	22.50		34.80	47.50
7080	1/0		18	.444		13.30	25		38.30	52
7100	2/0		15	.533		19.15	30		49.15	66
7140	4/0		11	.727		23	41		64	87
7160	250 kcmil		9	.889		26.50	50.50		77	105
7180	300 kcmil		8	1		26.50	56.50		83	115
7200	350 kcmil		7	1.143		30.50	64.50		95	131
7220	400 kcmil		6.50	1.231		39.50	69.50		109	148
7240	500 kcmil		6	1.333		41	75.50		116.50	159
7260	600 kcmil		5.80	1.379		46	78		124	168
7280	750 kcmil	▼	5.20	1.538		50.50	87		137.50	186
8000	Compression tool, hand					1,200			1,200	1,325
8100	Hydraulic					1,725			1,725	1,900
8500	Hydraulic dies				▼	325			325	360

26 05 19.50 Mineral Insulated Cable

		Crew	Daily Output	Labor-Hours	Unit	Material	2017 Bare Costs Labor	Equipment	Total	Total Incl O&P
0010	**MINERAL INSULATED CABLE** 600 volt									
0100	1 conductor, #12	1 Elec	1.60	5	C.L.F.	350	283		633	810
0200	#10		1.60	5		450	283		733	920
0400	#8		1.50	5.333		500	300		800	1,000
0500	#6	▼	1.40	5.714		595	325		920	1,150
0600	#4	2 Elec	2.40	6.667		800	375		1,175	1,450
0800	#2		2.20	7.273		1,125	410		1,535	1,875
0900	#1		2.10	7.619		1,300	430		1,730	2,075
1000	1/0		2	8		1,525	455		1,980	2,350
1100	2/0		1.90	8.421		1,825	475		2,300	2,725
1200	3/0		1.80	8.889		2,175	505		2,680	3,150
1400	4/0		1.60	10		2,525	565		3,090	3,625
1410	250 kcmil	3 Elec	2.40	10		2,850	565		3,415	3,975
1420	350 kcmil		1.95	12.308		3,250	695		3,945	4,625
1430	500 kcmil	▼	1.95	12.308		4,175	695		4,870	5,650
1500	2 conductor, #12	1 Elec	1.40	5.714		725	325		1,050	1,275
1600	#10		1.20	6.667		895	375		1,270	1,550
1800	#8		1.10	7.273		1,075	410		1,485	1,825
2000	#6	▼	1.05	7.619		1,400	430		1,830	2,200
2100	#4	2 Elec	2	8		1,900	455		2,355	2,775
2200	3 conductor, #12	1 Elec	1.20	6.667		910	375		1,285	1,575
2400	#10		1.10	7.273		1,025	410		1,435	1,750
2600	#8		1.05	7.619		1,300	430		1,730	2,075
2800	#6	▼	1	8		1,700	455		2,155	2,550
3000	#4	2 Elec	1.80	8.889		2,125	505		2,630	3,075
3100	4 conductor, #12	1 Elec	1.20	6.667		955	375		1,330	1,625
3200	#10		1.10	7.273		1,150	410		1,560	1,900
3400	#8		1	8		1,500	455		1,955	2,325
3600	#6		.90	8.889		1,950	505		2,455	2,900
3620	7 conductor, #12		1.10	7.273		1,225	410		1,635	1,975
3640	#10		1	8	▼	1,600	455		2,055	2,450
3800	Terminations, 600 volt, 1 conductor, #12		8	1	Ea.	15.40	56.50		71.90	102
4000	#10		7.60	1.053		15.40	59.50		74.90	106
4100	#8		7.30	1.096		15.40	62		77.40	110
4200	#6		6.70	1.194		15.40	67.50		82.90	118
4400	#4		6.20	1.290		15.40	73		88.40	126

For customer support on your Electrical Costs with RSMeans Data, call 800.448.8182.

123

26 05 19.50 Mineral Insulated Cable		Crew	Daily Output	Labor-Hours	Unit	Material	2017 Bare Costs Labor	Equipment	Total	Total Incl O&P
4600	#2	1 Elec	5.70	1.404	Ea.	23	79.50		102.50	145
4800	#1		5.30	1.509		23	85.50		108.50	154
5000	1/0		5	1.600		23	90.50		113.50	162
5100	2/0		4.70	1.702		23	96.50		119.50	170
5200	3/0		4.30	1.860		23	105		128	184
5400	4/0		4	2		51.50	113		164.50	227
5410	250 kcmil		4	2		51.50	113		164.50	227
5420	350 kcmil		4	2		80.50	113		193.50	259
5430	500 kcmil		4	2		80.50	113		193.50	259
5500	2 conductor, #12		6.70	1.194		15.40	67.50		82.90	118
5600	#10		6.40	1.250		23	71		94	132
5800	#8		6.20	1.290		23	73		96	135
6000	#6		5.70	1.404		23	79.50		102.50	145
6200	#4		5.30	1.509		51.50	85.50		137	185
6400	3 conductor, #12		5.70	1.404		23	79.50		102.50	145
6500	#10		5.50	1.455		23	82.50		105.50	149
6600	#8		5.20	1.538		23	87		110	156
6800	#6		4.80	1.667		23	94.50		117.50	167
7200	#4		4.60	1.739		51.50	98.50		150	204
7400	4 conductor, #12		4.60	1.739		25.50	98.50		124	176
7500	#10		4.40	1.818		25.50	103		128.50	183
7600	#8		4.20	1.905		25.50	108		133.50	191
8400	#6		4	2		54	113		167	230
8500	7 conductor, #12		3.50	2.286		25.50	129		154.50	223
8600	#10	▼	3	2.667		55.50	151		206.50	288
8800	Crimping tool, plier type					67.50			67.50	74.50
9000	Stripping tool					256			256	281
9200	Hand vise				▼	76			76	84

26 05 19.55 Non-Metallic Sheathed Cable		Crew	Daily Output	Labor-Hours	Unit	Material	2017 Bare Costs Labor	Equipment	Total	Total Incl O&P
0010	**NON-METALLIC SHEATHED CABLE** 600 volt									
0100	Copper with ground wire (Romex)									
0150	#14, 2 conductor	1 Elec	2.70	2.963	C.L.F.	21.50	168		189.50	275
0200	3 conductor		2.40	3.333		30.50	189		219.50	315
0220	4 conductor		2.20	3.636		44	206		250	360
0250	#12, 2 conductor		2.50	3.200		33	181		214	310
0300	3 conductor		2.20	3.636		46.50	206		252.50	360
0320	4 conductor		2	4		68.50	226		294.50	415
0350	#10, 2 conductor		2.20	3.636		50.50	206		256.50	365
0400	3 conductor		1.80	4.444		73.50	252		325.50	455
0420	4 conductor		1.60	5		106	283		389	540
0430	#8, 2 conductor		1.60	5		79.50	283		362.50	510
0450	3 conductor		1.50	5.333		118	300		418	580
0500	#6, 3 conductor	▼	1.40	5.714		192	325		517	695
0520	#4, 3 conductor	2 Elec	2.40	6.667		490	375		865	1,100
0540	#2, 3 conductor	"	2.20	7.273	▼	710	410		1,120	1,400
0550	SE type SER aluminum cable, 3 RHW and									
0600	1 bare neutral, 3 #8 & 1 #8	1 Elec	1.60	5	C.L.F.	69	283		352	500
0650	3 #6 & 1 #6	"	1.40	5.714		78	325		403	570
0700	3 #4 & 1 #6	2 Elec	2.40	6.667		87.50	375		462.50	660
0750	3 #2 & 1 #4		2.20	7.273		129	410		539	755
0800	3 #1/0 & 1 #2		2	8		195	455		650	895
0850	3 #2/0 & 1 #1	▼	1.80	8.889	▼	229	505		734	1,000

26 05 19 – Low-Voltage Electrical Power Conductors and Cables

26 05 19.55 Non-Metallic Sheathed Cable		Crew	Daily Output	Labor-Hours	Unit	Material	2017 Bare Costs Labor	Equipment	Total	Total Incl O&P
0900	3 #4/0 & 1 #2/0	2 Elec	1.60	10	C.L.F.	325	565		890	1,200
1000	URD - triplex underground distribution cable, alum. 2 #4 + #4 neutral		2.80	5.714		101	325		426	595
1010	2 #2 + #4 neutral		2.65	6.038		126	340		466	650
1020	2 #2 + #2 neutral		2.55	6.275		126	355		481	670
1030	2 1/0 + #2 neutral		2.40	6.667		152	375		527	735
1040	2 1/0 + 1/0 neutral		2.30	6.957		166	395		561	775
1050	2 2/0 + #1 neutral		2.20	7.273		181	410		591	815
1060	2 2/0 + 2/0 neutral		2.10	7.619		197	430		627	860
1070	2 3/0 + 1/0 neutral		1.95	8.205		218	465		683	935
1080	2 3/0 + 3/0 neutral		1.95	8.205		250	465		715	970
1090	2 4/0 + 2/0 neutral		1.85	8.649		249	490		739	1,000
1100	2 4/0 + 4/0 neutral	▼	1.85	8.649		276	490		766	1,050
1450	UF underground feeder cable, copper with ground, #14, 2 conductor	1 Elec	4	2		24.50	113		137.50	197
1500	#12, 2 conductor		3.50	2.286		37	129		166	235
1550	#10, 2 conductor		3	2.667		58	151		209	290
1600	#14, 3 conductor		3.50	2.286		35.50	129		164.50	233
1650	#12, 3 conductor		3	2.667		53.50	151		204.50	285
1700	#10, 3 conductor		2.50	3.200		83.50	181		264.50	365
1710	#8, 3 conductor		2	4		137	226		363	490
1720	#6, 3 conductor		1.80	4.444		222	252		474	620
2400	SEU service entrance cable, copper 2 conductors, #8 + #8 neutral		1.50	5.333		107	300		407	570
2600	#6 + #8 neutral		1.30	6.154		158	350		508	695
2800	#6 + #6 neutral	▼	1.30	6.154		180	350		530	720
3000	#4 + #6 neutral	2 Elec	2.20	7.273		248	410		658	890
3200	#4 + #4 neutral		2.20	7.273		280	410		690	925
3400	#3 + #5 neutral		2.10	7.619		345	430		775	1,025
3600	#3 + #3 neutral		2.10	7.619		370	430		800	1,050
3800	#2 + #4 neutral		2	8		400	455		855	1,125
4000	#1 + #1 neutral		1.90	8.421		445	475		920	1,200
4200	1/0 + 1/0 neutral		1.80	8.889		695	505		1,200	1,525
4400	2/0 + 2/0 neutral		1.70	9.412		875	535		1,410	1,750
4600	3/0 + 3/0 neutral		1.60	10		1,100	565		1,665	2,050
4620	4/0 + 4/0 neutral	▼	1.45	11.034		1,225	625		1,850	2,275
4800	Aluminum 2 conductors, #8 + #8 neutral	1 Elec	1.60	5		64.50	283		347.50	495
5000	#6 + #6 neutral	"	1.40	5.714		65	325		390	555
5100	#4 + #6 neutral	2 Elec	2.50	6.400		77.50	360		437.50	630
5200	#4 + #4 neutral		2.40	6.667		84.50	375		459.50	660
5300	#2 + #4 neutral		2.30	6.957		103	395		498	705
5400	#2 + #2 neutral		2.20	7.273		113	410		523	740
5450	1/0 + #2 neutral		2.10	7.619		163	430		593	825
5500	1/0 + 1/0 neutral		2	8		172	455		627	870
5550	2/0 + #1 neutral		1.90	8.421		184	475		659	920
5600	2/0 + 2/0 neutral		1.80	8.889		197	505		702	970
5800	3/0 + 1/0 neutral		1.70	9.412		214	535		749	1,025
6000	3/0 + 3/0 neutral		1.70	9.412		235	535		770	1,050
6200	4/0 + 2/0 neutral		1.60	10		254	565		819	1,125
6400	4/0 + 4/0 neutral	▼	1.60	10	▼	276	565		841	1,150
6500	Service entrance cap for copper SEU									
6600	100 amp	1 Elec	12	.667	Ea.	8.10	37.50		45.60	65.50
6700	150 amp		10	.800		13.80	45.50		59.30	83
6800	200 amp	▼	8	1	▼	21	56.50		77.50	108

26 05 19.70 Portable Cord

		Crew	Daily Output	Labor-Hours	Unit	Material	2017 Bare Costs Labor	Equipment	Total	Total Incl O&P
0010	**PORTABLE CORD** 600 volt									
0100	Type SO, #18, 2 conductor	1 Elec	980	.008	L.F.	.59	.46		1.05	1.34
0110	3 conductor		980	.008		.79	.46		1.25	1.56
0120	#16, 2 conductor		840	.010		.77	.54		1.31	1.66
0130	3 conductor		840	.010		1.10	.54		1.64	2.02
0140	4 conductor		840	.010		1.29	.54		1.83	2.23
0240	#14, 2 conductor		840	.010		1.27	.54		1.81	2.21
0250	3 conductor		840	.010		1.57	.54		2.11	2.54
0260	4 conductor		840	.010		1.84	.54		2.38	2.83
0280	#12, 2 conductor		840	.010		1.50	.54		2.04	2.46
0290	3 conductor		840	.010		2.24	.54		2.78	3.27
0300	4 conductor		840	.010		1.79	.54		2.33	2.78
0320	#10, 2 conductor		765	.010		2.54	.59		3.13	3.68
0330	3 conductor		765	.010		3.05	.59		3.64	4.25
0340	4 conductor		765	.010		3.45	.59		4.04	4.69
0360	#8, 2 conductor		555	.014		5.10	.82		5.92	6.80
0370	3 conductor		540	.015		4.47	.84		5.31	6.20
0380	4 conductor		525	.015		5.25	.86		6.11	7.10
0400	#6, 2 conductor		525	.015		4.19	.86		5.05	5.90
0410	3 conductor		490	.016		6.85	.92		7.77	8.90
0420	4 conductor		415	.019		7.45	1.09		8.54	9.85
0440	#4, 2 conductor	2 Elec	830	.019		7.05	1.09		8.14	9.40
0450	3 conductor		700	.023		9.45	1.29		10.74	12.35
0460	4 conductor		660	.024		13.60	1.37		14.97	17.05
0480	#2, 2 conductor		450	.036		10.45	2.01		12.46	14.50
0490	3 conductor		350	.046		10.45	2.59		13.04	15.40
0500	4 conductor		280	.057		18.55	3.23		21.78	25.50
2000	See 26 27 26.20 for Wiring Devices Elements									

26 05 19.75 Modular Flexible Wiring System

		Crew	Daily Output	Labor-Hours	Unit	Material	2017 Bare Costs Labor	Equipment	Total	Total Incl O&P
0010	**MODULAR FLEXIBLE WIRING SYSTEM**									
0020	Commercial system grid ceiling									
0100	Conversion Module	1 Elec	32	.250	Ea.	8.20	14.15		22.35	30
0120	Fixture cable, for fixture to fixture, 3 conductor, 15' long		40	.200		34	11.30		45.30	54
0150	Extender cable, 3 conductor, 15' long		48	.167		32	9.45		41.45	49
0200	Switch drop, 1 level, 9' long		32	.250		36.50	14.15		50.65	61
0220	2 level, 9' long		32	.250		30	14.15		44.15	54.50
0250	Power tee, 9' long		32	.250		34	14.15		48.15	58
1020	Industrial system open ceiling									
1100	Converter, interface between hardwiring and modular wiring	1 Elec	32	.250	Ea.	17.05	14.15		31.20	40
1120	Fixture cable, for fixture to fixture, 3 conductor, 21' long		32	.250		109	14.15		123.15	141
1125	3 conductor, 25' long		24	.333		126	18.85		144.85	168
1130	3 conductor, 31' long		19	.421		112	24		136	159
1150	Fixture cord drop, 10' long		40	.200		30	11.30		41.30	50

26 05 19.90 Wire

		Crew	Daily Output	Labor-Hours	Unit	Material	2017 Bare Costs Labor	Equipment	Total	Total Incl O&P
0010	**WIRE** R260519-90									
0020	600 volt, copper type THW, solid, #14	1 Elec	13	.615	C.L.F.	7	35		42	59.50
0030	#12		11	.727		10.65	41		51.65	73.50
0040	#10		10	.800		16.70	45.50		62.20	86.50
0050	Stranded, #14		13	.615		8.20	35		43.20	61
0100	#12		11	.727		12.55	41		53.55	75.50
0120	#10 R260519-92		10	.800		19.80	45.50		65.30	90
0140	#8		8	1		32.50	56.50		89	121

26 05 Common Work Results for Electrical

26 05 19 – Low-Voltage Electrical Power Conductors and Cables

26 05 19.90 Wire		Crew	Daily Output	Labor-Hours	Unit	Material	2017 Bare Costs Labor	Equipment	Total	Total Incl O&P
0160	#6	P260519-93	1 Elec	6.50	1.231	C.L.F.	55.50	69.50		125	165
0180	#4		2 Elec	10.60	1.509		85	85.50		170.50	222
0200	#3	R260519-94		10	1.600		106	90.50		196.50	252
0220	#2			9	1.778		133	101		234	297
0240	#1	R260533-22		8	2		175	113		288	365
0260	1/0			6.60	2.424		218	137		355	445
0280	2/0			5.80	2.759		274	156		430	535
0300	3/0			5	3.200		345	181		526	650
0350	4/0			4.40	3.636		440	206		646	790
0400	250 kcmil		3 Elec	6	4		495	226		721	885
0420	300 kcmil			5.70	4.211		560	238		798	970
0450	350 kcmil			5.40	4.444		650	252		902	1,100
0480	400 kcmil			5.10	4.706		745	266		1,011	1,225
0490	500 kcmil			4.80	5		925	283		1,208	1,450
0500	600 kcmil			3.90	6.154		1,175	350		1,525	1,825
0510	750 kcmil			3.30	7.273		1,925	410		2,335	2,750
0520	1000 kcmil			2.70	8.889		2,525	505		3,030	3,550
0540	600 volt, aluminum type THHN, stranded, #6		1 Elec	8	1		36.50	56.50		93	125
0560	#4		2 Elec	13	1.231		45.50	69.50		115	154
0580	#2			10.60	1.509		61.50	85.50		147	196
0600	#1			9	1.778		90	101		191	250
0620	1/0			8	2		108	113		221	289
0640	2/0			7.20	2.222		128	126		254	330
0680	3/0			6.60	2.424		158	137		295	380
0700	4/0			6.20	2.581		176	146		322	415
0720	250 kcmil		3 Elec	8.70	2.759		215	156		371	470
0740	300 kcmil			8.10	2.963		297	168		465	575
0760	350 kcmil			7.50	3.200		300	181		481	600
0780	400 kcmil			6.90	3.478		355	197		552	685
0800	500 kcmil			6	4		390	226		616	770
0850	600 kcmil			5.70	4.211		495	238		733	895
0880	700 kcmil			5.10	4.706		570	266		836	1,025
0900	750 kcmil			4.80	5		590	283		873	1,075
0910	1000 kcmil			3.78	6.349		875	360		1,235	1,500
0920	600 volt, copper type THWN-THHN, solid, #14		1 Elec	13	.615		7	35		42	59.50
0940	#12			11	.727		10.65	41		51.65	73.50
0960	#10			10	.800		16.70	45.50		62.20	86.50
1000	Stranded, #14			13	.615		7.30	35		42.30	60
1200	#12			11	.727		10.45	41		51.45	73
1250	#10			10	.800		16	45.50		61.50	85.50
1300	#8			8	1		28	56.50		84.50	116
1350	#6			6.50	1.231		48	69.50		117.50	157
1400	#4		2 Elec	10.60	1.509		68.50	85.50		154	204
1450	#3			10	1.600		93	90.50		183.50	238
1500	#2			9	1.778		116	101		217	278
1550	#1			8	2		150	113		263	335
1600	1/0			6.60	2.424		194	137		331	420
1650	2/0			5.80	2.759		219	156		375	475
1700	3/0			5	3.200		281	181		462	580
2000	4/0			4.40	3.636		345	206		551	690
2200	250 kcmil		3 Elec	6	4		425	226		651	810
2400	300 kcmil			5.70	4.211		500	238		738	905
2600	350 kcmil			5.40	4.444		585	252		837	1,025

For customer support on your Electrical Costs with RSMeans Data, call 800.448.8182.

127

26 05 19.90 Wire		Crew	Daily Output	Labor-Hours	Unit	Material	2017 Bare Costs Labor	Equipment	Total	Total Incl O&P
2700	400 kcmil	3 Elec	5.10	4.706	C.L.F.	670	266		936	1,150
2800	500 kcmil		4.80	5		835	283		1,118	1,350
2802	600 kcmil		3.90	6.154		755	350		1,105	1,350
2804	750 kcmil		3.30	7.273		1,875	410		2,285	2,700
2805	1000 kcmil		1.94	12.371		2,500	700		3,200	3,800
2900	600 volt, copper type XHHW, solid, #14	1 Elec	13	.615		11.25	35		46.25	64.50
2920	#12		11	.727		17.80	41		58.80	81
2940	#10		10	.800		27.50	45.50		73	98
3000	Stranded, #14		13	.615		9.05	35		44.05	62
3020	#12		11	.727		13.70	41		54.70	76.50
3040	#10		10	.800		20.50	45.50		66	90.50
3060	#8		8	1		30.50	56.50		87	119
3080	#6		6.50	1.231		51	69.50		120.50	160
3100	#4	2 Elec	10.60	1.509		78.50	85.50		164	214
3110	#3		10	1.600		97.50	90.50		188	243
3120	#2		9	1.778		122	101		223	285
3140	#1		8	2		166	113		279	355
3160	1/0		6.60	2.424		207	137		344	435
3180	2/0		5.80	2.759		259	156		415	520
3200	3/0		5	3.200		325	181		506	625
3220	4/0		4.40	3.636		405	206		611	755
3240	250 kcmil	3 Elec	6	4		450	226		676	835
3260	300 kcmil		5.70	4.211		510	238		748	915
3280	350 kcmil		5.40	4.444		595	252		847	1,025
3300	400 kcmil		5.10	4.706		675	266		941	1,150
3320	500 kcmil		4.80	5		840	283		1,123	1,350
3340	600 kcmil		3.90	6.154		1,175	350		1,525	1,800
3360	750 kcmil		3.30	7.273		1,950	410		2,360	2,775
3380	1000 kcmil		2.40	10		2,525	565		3,090	3,625
5020	600 volt, aluminum type XHHW, stranded, #6	1 Elec	8	1		35	56.50		91.50	124
5040	#4	2 Elec	13	1.231		43	69.50		112.50	152
5060	#2		10.60	1.509		58.50	85.50		144	193
5080	#1		9	1.778		85.50	101		186.50	245
5100	1/0		8	2		103	113		216	283
5120	2/0		7.20	2.222		121	126		247	320
5140	3/0		6.60	2.424		150	137		287	370
5160	4/0		6.20	2.581		167	146		313	405
5180	250 kcmil	3 Elec	8.70	2.759		204	156		360	460
5200	300 kcmil		8.10	2.963		282	168		450	560
5220	350 kcmil		7.50	3.200		287	181		468	585
5240	400 kcmil		6.90	3.478		335	197		532	665
5260	500 kcmil		6	4		370	226		596	745
5280	600 kcmil		5.70	4.211		470	238		708	870
5300	700 kcmil		5.40	4.444		540	252		792	970
5320	750 kcmil		5.10	4.706		545	266		811	1,000
5340	1000 kcmil		3.60	6.667		815	375		1,190	1,450
5390	600 volt, copper type XLPE-USE (RHW), solid, #14	1 Elec	12	.667		12.85	37.50		50.35	70.50
5400	#12		11	.727		16.80	41		57.80	80
5420	#10		10	.800		24.50	45.50		70	94.50
5440	Stranded, #14		13	.615		15	35		50	68.50
5460	#12		11	.727		18.05	41		59.05	81.50
5480	#10		10	.800		29	45.50		74.50	100
5500	#8		8	1		34	56.50		90.50	122

26 05 Common Work Results for Electrical

26 05 19 – Low-Voltage Electrical Power Conductors and Cables

26 05 19.90 Wire		Crew	Daily Output	Labor-Hours	Unit	Material	2017 Bare Costs Labor	Equipment	Total	Total Incl O&P
5520	#6	1 Elec	6.50	1.231	C.L.F.	56.50	69.50		126	166
5540	#4	2 Elec	10.60	1.509		86	85.50		171.50	223
5560	#2		9	1.778		140	101		241	305
5580	#1		8	2		188	113		301	375
5600	1/0		6.60	2.424		235	137		372	465
5620	2/0		5.80	2.759		310	156		466	580
5640	3/0		5	3.200		390	181		571	695
5660	4/0		4.40	3.636		420	206		626	775
5680	250 kcmil	3 Elec	6	4		490	226		716	880
5700	300 kcmil		5.70	4.211		610	238		848	1,025
5720	350 kcmil		5.40	4.444		690	252		942	1,125
5740	400 kcmil		5.10	4.706		785	266		1,051	1,275
5760	500 kcmil		4.80	5		830	283		1,113	1,350
5780	600 kcmil		3.90	6.154		1,250	350		1,600	1,900
5800	750 kcmil		3.30	7.273		2,150	410		2,560	3,000
5820	1000 kcmil		2.70	8.889		2,850	505		3,355	3,900
5840	600 volt, aluminum type XLPE-USE (RHW), stranded, #6	1 Elec	8	1		42	56.50		98.50	132
5860	#4	2 Elec	13	1.231		49	69.50		118.50	158
5880	#2		10.60	1.509		67.50	85.50		153	202
5900	#1		9	1.778		93.50	101		194.50	254
5920	1/0		8	2		115	113		228	297
5940	2/0		7.20	2.222		136	126		262	335
5960	3/0		6.60	2.424		160	137		297	380
5980	4/0		6.20	2.581		175	146		321	410
6000	250 kcmil	3 Elec	8.70	2.759		241	156		397	500
6020	300 kcmil		8.10	2.963		315	168		483	595
6040	350 kcmil		7.50	3.200		320	181		501	620
6060	400 kcmil		6.90	3.478		390	197		587	725
6080	500 kcmil		6	4		430	226		656	810
6100	600 kcmil		5.70	4.211		550	238		788	960
6110	700 kcmil		5.40	4.444		635	252		887	1,075
6120	750 kcmil		5.10	4.706		640	266		906	1,100

26 05 23 – Control-Voltage Electrical Power Cables

26 05 23.10 Control Cable

			Daily Output	Labor-Hours	Unit	Material	Labor	Equipment	Total	Total Incl O&P
0010	**CONTROL CABLE**									
0020	600 volt, copper, #14 THWN wire with PVC jacket, 2 wires	1 Elec	9	.889	C.L.F.	35	50.50		85.50	114
0030	3 wires		8	1		50.50	56.50		107	141
0100	4 wires		7	1.143		60	64.50		124.50	163
0150	5 wires		6.50	1.231		75	69.50		144.50	186
0200	6 wires		6	1.333		102	75.50		177.50	225
0300	8 wires		5.30	1.509		132	85.50		217.50	273
0400	10 wires		4.80	1.667		152	94.50		246.50	310
0500	12 wires		4.30	1.860		197	105		302	375
0600	14 wires		3.80	2.105		212	119		331	415
0700	16 wires		3.50	2.286		240	129		369	460
0800	18 wires		3.30	2.424		270	137		407	505
0810	19 wires		3.10	2.581		285	146		431	535
0900	20 wires		3	2.667		299	151		450	555
1000	22 wires		2.80	2.857		330	162		492	600

26 05 23 – Control-Voltage Electrical Power Cables

26 05 23.20 Special Wires and Fittings	Crew	Daily Output	Labor-Hours	Unit	Material	2017 Bare Costs Labor	Equipment	Total	Total Incl O&P
0010 **SPECIAL WIRES & FITTINGS**									
0100 Fixture TFFN 600 volt 90°C stranded, #18	1 Elec	13	.615	C.L.F.	9.50	35		44.50	62.50
0150 #16		13	.615		11.25	35		46.25	64.50
0500 Thermostat, jacket non-plenum, twisted, #18-2 conductor		8	1		15.60	56.50		72.10	102
0550 #18-3 conductor		7	1.143		20.50	64.50		85	120
0600 #18-4 conductor		6.50	1.231		30.50	69.50		100	138
0650 #18-5 conductor		6	1.333		34	75.50		109.50	151
0700 #18-6 conductor		5.50	1.455		42	82.50		124.50	170
0750 #18-7 conductor		5	1.600		43.50	90.50		134	184
0800 #18-8 conductor		4.80	1.667		55.50	94.50		150	203
2460 Tray cable, type TC, copper, #16-2 conductor		9.40	.851		28	48		76	103
2464 #16-3 conductor		8.40	.952		35.50	54		89.50	120
2468 #16-4 conductor		7.30	1.096		44.50	62		106.50	142
2472 #16-5 conductor		6.70	1.194		42.50	67.50		110	148
2476 #16-7 conductor		5.50	1.455		58	82.50		140.50	187
2480 #16-9 conductor		5	1.600		72.50	90.50		163	216
2484 #16-12 conductor	2 Elec	8.80	1.818		118	103		221	284
2488 #16-15 conductor		7.20	2.222		126	126		252	325
2492 #16-19 conductor		6.60	2.424		156	137		293	380
2496 #16-25 conductor		6.40	2.500		220	142		362	455
2500 #14-2 conductor	1 Elec	9	.889		34	50.50		84.50	113
2520 #14-3 conductor		8	1		47	56.50		103.50	137
2540 #14-4 conductor		7	1.143		55	64.50		119.50	157
2560 #14-5 conductor		6.50	1.231		71.50	69.50		141	183
2564 #14-7 conductor		5.30	1.509		91.50	85.50		177	229
2568 #14-9 conductor	2 Elec	9.60	1.667		135	94.50		229.50	289
2572 #14-12 conductor		8.60	1.860		183	105		288	360
2576 #14-15 conductor		7.20	2.222		173	126		299	380
2578 #14-19 conductor		6.20	2.581		218	146		364	460
2582 #14-25 conductor		5.30	3.019		286	171		457	570
2590 #12-2 conductor	1 Elec	8.40	.952		48	54		102	134
2592 #12-3 conductor		7.60	1.053		49.50	59.50		109	144
2594 #12-4 conductor		6.60	1.212		89.50	68.50		158	201
2596 #12-5 conductor		6.20	1.290		109	73		182	229
2598 #12-7 conductor	2 Elec	10.40	1.538		160	87		247	305
2602 #12-9 conductor		8.80	1.818		208	103		311	385
2604 #12-12 conductor		7.80	2.051		271	116		387	470
2606 #12-15 conductor		6.80	2.353		261	133		394	485
2608 #12-19 conductor		6	2.667		320	151		471	575
2610 #12-25 conductor	3 Elec	7.70	3.117		430	176		606	740
2618 #10-2 conductor	1 Elec	8	1		72.50	56.50		129	165
2622 #10-3 conductor	"	7.30	1.096		84	62		146	185
2624 #10-4 conductor	2 Elec	12.80	1.250		138	71		209	258
2626 #10-5 conductor		11.80	1.356		135	77		212	264
2628 #10-7 conductor		9.40	1.702		195	96.50		291.50	360
2630 #10-9 conductor		8.40	1.905		227	108		335	410
2632 #10-12 conductor		7.20	2.222		242	126		368	455
2640 300 V, copper braided shield, PVC jacket									
2650 2 conductor #18 stranded	1 Elec	7	1.143	C.L.F.	40.50	64.50		105	142
2660 3 conductor #18 stranded	"	6	1.333	"	57	75.50		132.50	176
3000 Strain relief grip for cable									
3050 Cord, top, #12-3	1 Elec	40	.200	Ea.	9.50	11.30		20.80	27.50

26 05 Common Work Results for Electrical

26 05 23 – Control-Voltage Electrical Power Cables

26 05 23.20 Special Wires and Fittings

		Crew	Daily Output	Labor-Hours	Unit	Material	2017 Bare Costs Labor	Equipment	Total	Total Incl O&P
3060	#12-4	1 Elec	40	.200	Ea.	9.50	11.30		20.80	27.50
3070	#12-5		39	.205		10.95	11.60		22.55	29.50
3100	#10-3		39	.205		10.95	11.60		22.55	29.50
3110	#10-4		38	.211		10.95	11.90		22.85	30
3120	#10-5		38	.211		13.40	11.90		25.30	32.50
3200	Bottom, #12-3		40	.200		22.50	11.30		33.80	41.50
3210	#12-4		40	.200		22.50	11.30		33.80	41.50
3220	#12-5		39	.205		22.50	11.60		34.10	42.50
3230	#10-3		39	.205		22.50	11.60		34.10	42.50
3300	#10-4		38	.211		22.50	11.90		34.40	43
3310	#10-5		38	.211		28.50	11.90		40.40	49
3400	Cable ties, standard, 4" length		190	.042		.17	2.38		2.55	3.76
3410	7" length		160	.050		.19	2.83		3.02	4.45
3420	14.5" length		90	.089		.46	5.05		5.51	8.05
3430	Heavy, 14.5" length		80	.100		.64	5.65		6.29	9.20

26 05 26 – Grounding and Bonding for Electrical Systems

26 05 26.80 Grounding

		Crew	Daily Output	Labor-Hours	Unit	Material	2017 Bare Costs Labor	Equipment	Total	Total Incl O&P
0010	**GROUNDING** R260526-80									
0030	Rod, copper clad, 8' long, 1/2" diameter	1 Elec	5.50	1.455	Ea.	20	82.50		102.50	145
0040	5/8" diameter		5.50	1.455		19.40	82.50		101.90	145
0050	3/4" diameter		5.30	1.509		34	85.50		119.50	166
0080	10' long, 1/2" diameter		4.80	1.667		22.50	94.50		117	166
0090	5/8" diameter		4.60	1.739		24.50	98.50		123	174
0100	3/4" diameter		4.40	1.818		39	103		142	197
0130	15' long, 3/4" diameter		4	2		51	113		164	226
0150	Coupling, bronze, 1/2" diameter					4.07			4.07	4.48
0160	5/8" diameter					5.45			5.45	6
0170	3/4" diameter					13.35			13.35	14.70
0190	Drive studs, 1/2" diameter					10.70			10.70	11.75
0210	5/8" diameter					15.55			15.55	17.10
0220	3/4" diameter					18.15			18.15	20
0230	Clamp, bronze, 1/2" diameter	1 Elec	32	.250		4.65	14.15		18.80	26
0240	5/8" diameter		32	.250		4.48	14.15		18.63	26
0250	3/4" diameter		32	.250		5.90	14.15		20.05	27.50
0260	Wire ground bare armored, #8-1 conductor		2	4	C.L.F.	69.50	226		295.50	415
0270	#6-1 conductor		1.80	4.444		83.50	252		335.50	465
0280	#4-1 conductor		1.60	5		134	283		417	570
0320	Bare copper wire, #14 solid		14	.571		6.65	32.50		39.15	56
0330	#12		13	.615		12.25	35		47.25	65.50
0340	#10		12	.667		16.25	37.50		53.75	74.50
0350	#8		11	.727		26	41		67	90.50
0360	#6		10	.800		46	45.50		91.50	119
0370	#4		8	1		101	56.50		157.50	196
0380	#2		5	1.600		112	90.50		202.50	259
0390	Bare copper wire, stranded, #8		11	.727		25.50	41		66.50	89.50
0400	#6		10	.800		45	45.50		90.50	118
0450	#4	2 Elec	16	1		75.50	56.50		132	168
0600	#2		10	1.600		93.50	90.50		184	239
0650	#1		9	1.778		163	101		264	330
0700	1/0		8	2		170	113		283	355
0750	2/0		7.20	2.222		214	126		340	425
0800	3/0		6.60	2.424		268	137		405	500

For customer support on your Electrical Costs with RSMeans Data, call 800.448.8182.

131

26 05 26.80 Grounding		Crew	Daily Output	Labor-Hours	Unit	Material	2017 Bare Costs Labor	Equipment	Total	Total Incl O&P
1000	4/0	2 Elec	5.70	2.807	C.L.F.	340	159		499	615
1200	250 kcmil	3 Elec	7.20	3.333		400	189		589	725
1210	300 kcmil		6.60	3.636		455	206		661	810
1220	350 kcmil		6	4		585	226		811	985
1230	400 kcmil		5.70	4.211		655	238		893	1,075
1240	500 kcmil		5.10	4.706		840	266		1,106	1,325
1260	750 kcmil		3.60	6.667		1,400	375		1,775	2,125
1270	1000 kcmil		3	8		1,875	455		2,330	2,725
1360	Bare aluminum, stranded, #6	1 Elec	9	.889		14.60	50.50		65.10	91.50
1370	#4	2 Elec	16	1		29.50	56.50		86	118
1380	#2		13	1.231		40.50	69.50		110	149
1390	#1		10.60	1.509		41.50	85.50		127	174
1400	1/0		9	1.778		53.50	101		154.50	210
1410	2/0		8	2		67.50	113		180.50	245
1420	3/0		7.20	2.222		91	126		217	288
1430	4/0		6.60	2.424		96.50	137		233.50	310
1440	250 kcmil	3 Elec	9.30	2.581		119	146		265	350
1450	300 kcmil		8.70	2.759		140	156		296	390
1460	400 kcmil		7.50	3.200		180	181		361	470
1470	500 kcmil		6.90	3.478		214	197		411	530
1480	600 kcmil		6	4		243	226		469	610
1490	700 kcmil		5.70	4.211		267	238		505	650
1500	750 kcmil		5.10	4.706		277	266		543	705
1510	1000 kcmil		4.80	5		350	283		633	810
1800	Water pipe ground clamps, heavy duty									
2000	Bronze, 1/2" to 1" diameter	1 Elec	8	1	Ea.	24	56.50		80.50	111
2100	1-1/4" to 2" diameter		8	1		33	56.50		89.50	122
2200	2-1/2" to 3" diameter		6	1.333		44.50	75.50		120	162
2730	Exothermic weld, 4/0 wire to 1" ground rod		7	1.143		10.25	64.50		74.75	108
2740	4/0 wire to building steel		7	1.143		10.25	64.50		74.75	108
2750	4/0 wire to motor frame		7	1.143		10.25	64.50		74.75	108
2760	4/0 wire to 4/0 wire		7	1.143		10.25	64.50		74.75	108
2770	4/0 wire to #4 wire		7	1.143		10.25	64.50		74.75	108
2780	4/0 wire to #8 wire		7	1.143		10.25	64.50		74.75	108
2790	Mold, reusable, for above					141			141	155
2800	Brazed connections, #6 wire	1 Elec	12	.667		16.50	37.50		54	74.50
3000	#2 wire		10	.800		22	45.50		67.50	92.50
3100	3/0 wire		8	1		33	56.50		89.50	121
3200	4/0 wire		7	1.143		37.50	64.50		102	138
3400	250 kcmil wire		5	1.600		43.50	90.50		134	184
3600	500 kcmil wire		4	2		54	113		167	230
3700	Insulated ground wire, copper #14		13	.615	C.L.F.	7.30	35		42.30	60
3710	#12		11	.727		10.45	41		51.45	73
3720	#10		10	.800		16	45.50		61.50	85.50
3730	#8		8	1		28	56.50		84.50	116
3740	#6		6.50	1.231		48	69.50		117.50	157
3750	#4	2 Elec	10.60	1.509		68.50	85.50		154	204
3770	#2		9	1.778		116	101		217	278
3780	#1		8	2		150	113		263	335
3790	1/0		6.60	2.424		194	137		331	420
3800	2/0		5.80	2.759		219	156		375	475
3810	3/0		5	3.200		281	181		462	580
3820	4/0		4.40	3.636		345	206		551	690

For customer support on your Electrical Costs with RSMeans Data, call 800.448.8182.

26 05 26 – Grounding and Bonding for Electrical Systems

26 05 26.80 Grounding		Crew	Daily Output	Labor-Hours	Unit	Material	2017 Bare Costs Labor	Equipment	Total	Total Incl O&P
3830	250 kcmil	3 Elec	6	4	C.L.F.	425	226		651	810
3840	300 kcmil		5.70	4.211		500	238		738	905
3850	350 kcmil		5.40	4.444		585	252		837	1,025
3860	400 kcmil		5.10	4.706		670	266		936	1,150
3870	500 kcmil		4.80	5		835	283		1,118	1,350
3880	600 kcmil		3.90	6.154		1,175	350		1,525	1,825
3890	750 kcmil		3.30	7.273		1,925	410		2,335	2,750
3900	1000 kcmil		2.70	8.889		2,525	505		3,030	3,550
3960	Insulated ground wire, aluminum, #6	1 Elec	8	1		36.50	56.50		93	125
3970	#4	2 Elec	13	1.231		45.50	69.50		115	154
3980	#2		10.60	1.509		61.50	85.50		147	196
3990	#1		9	1.778		90	101		191	250
4000	1/0		8	2		108	113		221	289
4010	2/0		7.20	2.222		128	126		254	330
4020	3/0		6.60	2.424		158	137		295	380
4030	4/0		6.20	2.581		176	146		322	415
4040	250 kcmil	3 Elec	8.70	2.759		215	156		371	470
4050	300 kcmil		8.10	2.963		297	168		465	575
4060	350 kcmil		7.50	3.200		300	181		481	600
4070	400 kcmil		6.90	3.478		355	197		552	685
4080	500 kcmil		6	4		390	226		616	770
4090	600 kcmil		5.70	4.211		495	238		733	895
4100	700 kcmil		5.10	4.706		570	266		836	1,025
4110	750 kcmil		4.80	5		590	283		873	1,075
5000	Copper Electrolytic ground rod system									
5010	Includes augering hole, mixing bentonite clay,									
5020	Installing rod, and terminating ground wire									
5100	Straight Vertical type, 2" diam.									
5120	8.5' long, clamp connection	1 Elec	2.67	2.996	Ea.	725	170		895	1,050
5130	With exothermic weld connection		1.95	4.103		735	232		967	1,150
5140	10' long		2.35	3.404		850	193		1,043	1,225
5150	With exothermic weld connection		1.78	4.494		860	254		1,114	1,325
5160	12' long		2.16	3.704		1,075	210		1,285	1,500
5170	With exothermic weld connection		1.67	4.790		1,075	271		1,346	1,600
5180	20' long		1.74	4.598		1,400	260		1,660	1,925
5190	With exothermic weld connection		1.40	5.714		1,400	325		1,725	2,025
5195	40' long with exothermic weld connection	2 Elec	2	8		3,050	455		3,505	4,025
5200	L-Shaped, 2" diam.									
5220	4' vert. x 10' horiz., clamp connection	1 Elec	5.33	1.501	Ea.	1,325	85		1,410	1,575
5230	With exothermic weld connection	"	3.08	2.597	"	1,325	147		1,472	1,700
5300	Protective Box at grade level, with breather slots									
5320	Round 12" long, fiberlyte	1 Elec	32	.250	Ea.	70	14.15		84.15	98
5330	Concrete	"	16	.500		110	28.50		138.50	164
5400	Bentonite Clay, 50# bag, 1 per 10' of rod					48.50			48.50	53.50
5500	Equipotential earthing bar	1 Elec	2	4		141	226		367	495

26 05 29 – Hangers and Supports for Electrical Systems

26 05 29.20 Hangers

		Crew	Daily Output	Labor-Hours	Unit	Material	Labor	Equipment	Total	Total Incl O&P
0010	**HANGERS** R260533-21									
0015	See section 22 05 29.10 for additional items									
0030	Conduit supports									
0050	Strap w/2 holes, rigid steel conduit									
0100	1/2" diameter	1 Elec	470	.017	Ea.	.10	.96		1.06	1.55

For customer support on your Electrical Costs with RSMeans Data, call 800.448.8182.

133

26 05 29.20 Hangers		Crew	Daily Output	Labor-Hours	Unit	Material	2017 Bare Costs Labor	Equipment	Total	Total Incl O&P
0150	3/4" diameter	1 Elec	440	.018	Ea.	.10	1.03		1.13	1.65
0200	1" diameter		400	.020		.15	1.13		1.28	1.87
0300	1-1/4" diameter		355	.023		.24	1.28		1.52	2.17
0350	1-1/2" diameter		320	.025		.30	1.42		1.72	2.45
0400	2" diameter		266	.030		.40	1.70		2.10	2.99
0500	2-1/2" diameter		160	.050		.72	2.83		3.55	5.05
0550	3" diameter		133	.060		.93	3.40		4.33	6.10
0600	3-1/2" diameter		100	.080		1.89	4.53		6.42	8.90
0650	4" diameter		80	.100		1.13	5.65		6.78	9.75
0700	EMT, 1/2" diameter		470	.017		.17	.96		1.13	1.63
0800	3/4" diameter		440	.018		.18	1.03		1.21	1.74
0850	1" diameter		400	.020		.29	1.13		1.42	2.02
0900	1-1/4" diameter		355	.023		.39	1.28		1.67	2.34
0950	1-1/2" diameter		320	.025		.45	1.42		1.87	2.62
1000	2" diameter		266	.030		.62	1.70		2.32	3.23
1100	2-1/2" diameter		160	.050		1.59	2.83		4.42	6
1150	3" diameter		133	.060		1.11	3.40		4.51	6.30
1200	3-1/2" diameter		100	.080		1.69	4.53		6.22	8.65
1250	4" diameter		80	.100		2.21	5.65		7.86	10.95
1400	Hanger, with bolt, 1/2" diameter		200	.040		.60	2.26		2.86	4.05
1450	3/4" diameter		190	.042		.60	2.38		2.98	4.23
1500	1" diameter		176	.045		.78	2.57		3.35	4.71
1550	1-1/4" diameter		160	.050		.96	2.83		3.79	5.30
1600	1-1/2" diameter		140	.057		1.33	3.23		4.56	6.30
1650	2" diameter		130	.062		1.67	3.48		5.15	7.05
1700	2-1/2" diameter		100	.080		2.18	4.53		6.71	9.20
1750	3" diameter		64	.125		1.98	7.10		9.08	12.80
1800	3-1/2" diameter		50	.160		2.59	9.05		11.64	16.40
1850	4" diameter		40	.200		4.90	11.30		16.20	22.50
1900	Riser clamps, conduit, 1/2" diameter		40	.200		7.80	11.30		19.10	25.50
1950	3/4" diameter		36	.222		8.05	12.60		20.65	27.50
2000	1" diameter		30	.267		7.85	15.10		22.95	31
2100	1-1/4" diameter		27	.296		9.65	16.75		26.40	35.50
2150	1-1/2" diameter		27	.296		10	16.75		26.75	36
2200	2" diameter		20	.400		10.75	22.50		33.25	46
2250	2-1/2" diameter		20	.400		12.85	22.50		35.35	48
2300	3" diameter		18	.444		13.65	25		38.65	52.50
2350	3-1/2" diameter		18	.444		14.05	25		39.05	53
2400	4" diameter		14	.571		14.55	32.50		47.05	64.50
2500	Threaded rod, painted, 1/4" diameter		260	.031	L.F.	.60	1.74		2.34	3.27
2600	3/8" diameter		200	.040		1.94	2.26		4.20	5.50
2700	1/2" diameter		140	.057		2.34	3.23		5.57	7.40
2800	5/8" diameter		100	.080		3.57	4.53		8.10	10.75
2900	3/4" diameter		60	.133		6.30	7.55		13.85	18.25
2940	Couplings painted, 1/4" diameter				C	340			340	375
2960	3/8" diameter					530			530	580
2970	1/2" diameter					745			745	820
2980	5/8" diameter					1,400			1,400	1,525
2990	3/4" diameter					1,025			1,025	1,125
3000	Nuts, galvanized, 1/4" diameter					15.25			15.25	16.80
3050	3/8" diameter					21			21	23.50
3100	1/2" diameter					42.50			42.50	47
3150	5/8" diameter					154			154	170

26 05 29.20 Hangers		Crew	Daily Output	Labor-Hours	Unit	Material	2017 Bare Costs Labor	Equipment	Total	Total Incl O&P
3200	0/1" diameter				C	128			128	141
3250	Washers, galvanized, 1/4" diameter					21.50			21.50	23.50
3300	3/8" diameter					19.90			19.90	22
3350	1/2" diameter					27			27	29.50
3400	5/8" diameter					131			131	144
3450	3/4" diameter					235			235	259
3500	Lock washers, galvanized, 1/4" diameter					10.65			10.65	11.75
3550	3/8" diameter					13.15			13.15	14.45
3600	1/2" diameter					17.55			17.55	19.30
3650	5/8" diameter					42			42	46.50
3700	3/4" diameter				▼	74.50			74.50	81.50
3800	Channels, steel, 3/4" x 1-1/2", 14 Ga.	1 Elec	80	.100	L.F.	2.47	5.65		8.12	11.20
3900	1-1/2" x 1-1/2", 12 Ga.		70	.114		3.16	6.45		9.61	13.20
4000	1-7/8" x 1-1/2"		60	.133		23	7.55		30.55	37
4100	3" x 1-1/2"		50	.160		39.50	9.05		48.55	57
4110	1-5/8" x 13/16", 16 Ga.		80	.100	▼	5.10	5.65		10.75	14.10
4114	Trapeze channel support, 12" wide, steel, 12 Ga.		8.80	.909	Ea.	17.95	51.50		69.45	97
4116	18" wide, steel		8.30	.964	"	19.55	54.50		74.05	103
4120	1-5/8" x 1-5/8", 14 Ga.		70	.114	L.F.	8.70	6.45		15.15	19.25
4130	1-5/8" x 7/8", 12 Ga.		70	.114		5.30	6.45		11.75	15.55
4140	1-5/8" x 1-3/8", 12 Ga.		60	.133		7.45	7.55		15	19.50
4150	1-5/8" x 1-5/8", 12 Ga.	▼	50	.160	▼	6.70	9.05		15.75	21
4160	Flat plate fitting, 2 hole, 3-1/2", material only				Ea.	3.13			3.13	3.44
4170	3 hole, 1-7/16" x 4-1/8"					3.35			3.35	3.69
4200	Spring nuts, long, 1/4"	1 Elec	120	.067		.90	3.77		4.67	6.65
4250	3/8"		100	.080		.99	4.53		5.52	7.90
4300	1/2"		80	.100		1.03	5.65		6.68	9.65
4350	Spring nuts, short, 1/4"		120	.067		1.41	3.77		5.18	7.20
4400	3/8"		100	.080		1.49	4.53		6.02	8.45
4450	1/2"		80	.100	▼	1.69	5.65		7.34	10.35
4500	Closure strip		200	.040	L.F.	4.67	2.26		6.93	8.55
4550	End cap		60	.133	Ea.	1.99	7.55		9.54	13.50
4600	End connector 3/4" conduit		40	.200		6.10	11.30		17.40	23.50
4650	Junction box, 1 channel		16	.500		31	28.50		59.50	76.50
4700	2 channel		14	.571		55.50	32.50		88	110
4750	3 channel		12	.667		94	37.50		131.50	161
4800	4 channel		10	.800		63.50	45.50		109	138
4850	Splice plate		40	.200		9.45	11.30		20.75	27.50
4900	Continuous concrete insert, 1-1/2" deep, 1' long		16	.500		19.85	28.50		48.35	64.50
4950	2' long		14	.571		24.50	32.50		57	75.50
5000	3' long		12	.667		23.50	37.50		61	82
5050	4' long		10	.800		31.50	45.50		77	103
5100	6' long		8	1		47	56.50		103.50	137
5150	3/4" deep, 1' long		16	.500		17.90	28.50		46.40	62
5200	2' long		14	.571		22.50	32.50		55	73
5250	3' long		12	.667		23	37.50		60.50	82
5300	4' long		10	.800		30.50	45.50		76	102
5350	6' long		8	1		46	56.50		102.50	136
5400	90° angle fitting 2-1/8" x 2-1/8"		60	.133		3.52	7.55		11.07	15.15
5450	Supports, suspension rod type, small		60	.133		83	7.55		90.55	103
5500	Large		40	.200		88	11.30		99.30	114
5550	Beam clamp, small		60	.133		25.50	7.55		33.05	39.50
5600	Large	▼	40	.200	▼	23	11.30		34.30	42

26 05 29.20 Hangers	Crew	Daily Output	Labor-Hours	Unit	Material	2017 Bare Costs Labor	2017 Bare Costs Equipment	Total	Total Incl O&P
5650	U-support, small	1 Elec	60	.133	Ea.	4.39	7.55		11.94	16.15
5700	Large		40	.200		9.85	11.30		21.15	28
5750	Concrete insert, cast, for up to 1/2" threaded rod		16	.500		15	28.50		43.50	59
5800	Beam clamp, 1/4" clamp, for 1/4" threaded drop rod		32	.250		2.67	14.15		16.82	24
5900	3/8" clamp, for 3/8" threaded drop rod		32	.250		3.27	14.15		17.42	24.50
6000	Strap, rigid conduit, 1/2" diameter		540	.015		1.61	.84		2.45	3.03
6050	3/4" diameter		440	.018		1.34	1.03		2.37	3.01
6100	1" diameter		420	.019		1.94	1.08		3.02	3.75
6150	1-1/4" diameter		400	.020		1.78	1.13		2.91	3.66
6200	1-1/2" diameter		400	.020		1.95	1.13		3.08	3.85
6250	2" diameter		267	.030		2.05	1.70		3.75	4.80
6300	2-1/2" diameter		267	.030		2.27	1.70		3.97	5.05
6350	3" diameter		160	.050		2.43	2.83		5.26	6.90
6400	3-1/2" diameter		133	.060		2.86	3.40		6.26	8.25
6450	4" diameter		100	.080		3.15	4.53		7.68	10.25
6500	5" diameter		80	.100		11.10	5.65		16.75	20.50
6550	6" diameter		60	.133		19.65	7.55		27.20	33
6600	EMT, 1/2" diameter		540	.015		.75	.84		1.59	2.09
6650	3/4" diameter		440	.018		.78	1.03		1.81	2.40
6700	1" diameter		420	.019		.88	1.08		1.96	2.59
6750	1-1/4" diameter		400	.020		1	1.13		2.13	2.80
6800	1-1/2" diameter		400	.020		1.27	1.13		2.40	3.10
6850	2" diameter		267	.030		1.32	1.70		3.02	3.99
6900	2-1/2" diameter		267	.030		1.92	1.70		3.62	4.65
6950	3" diameter		160	.050		2	2.83		4.83	6.45
6970	3-1/2" diameter		133	.060		2.25	3.40		5.65	7.60
6990	4" diameter		100	.080		2.21	4.53		6.74	9.25
7000	Clip, 1 hole for rigid conduit, 1/2" diameter		500	.016		.57	.91		1.48	1.99
7050	3/4" diameter		470	.017		.79	.96		1.75	2.31
7100	1" diameter		440	.018		1.95	1.03		2.98	3.69
7150	1-1/4" diameter		400	.020		2.03	1.13		3.16	3.93
7200	1-1/2" diameter		355	.023		2.22	1.28		3.50	4.35
7250	2" diameter		320	.025		1.96	1.42		3.38	4.28
7300	2-1/2" diameter		266	.030		5.70	1.70		7.40	8.80
7350	3" diameter		160	.050		5.55	2.83		8.38	10.35
7400	3-1/2" diameter		133	.060		8	3.40		11.40	13.90
7450	4" diameter		100	.080		15.45	4.53		19.98	24
7500	5" diameter		80	.100		140	5.65		145.65	163
7550	6" diameter		60	.133		109	7.55		116.55	131
7600	Hammer on purlin clip,1/4" hole, 1/16" flange		60	.133		.38	7.55		7.93	11.70
7610	1/4" hole threaded,1/4" flange, rod hanger		60	.133		1.16	7.55		8.71	12.60
7620	3/8" hole,threaded,1/4" flange, rod hanger		60	.133		.86	7.55		8.41	12.25
7630	Z purlin clip, 1/4" & 3/8" flange threaded rod hanger		60	.133		1.05	7.55		8.60	12.45
7640	1/2" rigid, 3/4" conduit, 1" flange		60	.133		1.18	7.55		8.73	12.60
7650	1" conduit, 1" flange		60	.133		1.21	7.55		8.76	12.65
7660	1-1/4" conduit, 1" flange		60	.133		1.53	7.55		9.08	13
7670	Push-in type conduit clip 3/4" EMT, with 9/32" hole		60	.133		.38	7.55		7.93	11.70
7680	3/4" EMT, 1/2" rigid		60	.133		.97	7.55		8.52	12.35
7690	Push-in type tandem conduit clip 3/4" - 1" EMT, 1/2" - 3/4" rigid		60	.133		.99	7.55		8.54	12.40
7820	Conduit hangers, with bolt & 12" rod, 1/2" diameter		150	.053		2.54	3.02		5.56	7.30
7830	3/4" diameter		145	.055		2.54	3.12		5.66	7.45
7840	1" diameter		135	.059		2.72	3.35		6.07	8.05
7850	1-1/4" diameter		120	.067		2.90	3.77		6.67	8.85

26 05 29 – Hangers and Supports for Electrical Systems

26 05 29.20 Hangers		Crew	Daily Output	Labor-Hours	Unit	Material	2017 Bare Costs Labor	Equipment	Total	Total Incl O&P
7860	1-1/2" diameter	1 Elec	110	.073	Ea.	3.27	4.12		7.39	9.75
7870	2" diameter		100	.080		4.01	4.53		8.54	11.20
7880	2-1/2" diameter		80	.100		4.52	5.65		10.17	13.45
7890	3" diameter		60	.133		4.32	7.55		11.87	16.05
7900	3-1/2" diameter		45	.178		4.93	10.05		14.98	20.50
7910	4" diameter		35	.229		7.25	12.95		20.20	27.50
7920	5" diameter		30	.267		8.45	15.10		23.55	32
7930	6" diameter		25	.320		17.10	18.10		35.20	46
7950	Jay clamp, 1/2" diameter		32	.250		4.33	14.15		18.48	26
7960	3/4" diameter		32	.250		6	14.15		20.15	27.50
7970	1" diameter		32	.250		7.05	14.15		21.20	29
7980	1-1/4" diameter		30	.267		5.85	15.10		20.95	29
7990	1-1/2" diameter		30	.267		9.55	15.10		24.65	33
8000	2" diameter		30	.267		14.10	15.10		29.20	38
8010	2-1/2" diameter		28	.286		24	16.15		40.15	50.50
8020	3" diameter		28	.286		24	16.15		40.15	50.50
8030	3-1/2" diameter		25	.320		24.50	18.10		42.60	54
8040	4" diameter		25	.320		24.50	18.10		42.60	54
8050	5" diameter		20	.400		96.50	22.50		119	140
8060	6" diameter		16	.500		184	28.50		212.50	245
8070	Channels, 3/4" x 1-1/2" w/12" rods for 1/2" to 1" conduit		30	.267		5.65	15.10		20.75	28.50
8080	1-1/2" x 1-1/2" w/12" rods for 1-1/4" to 2" conduit		28	.286		5.90	16.15		22.05	30.50
8090	1-1/2" x 1-1/2" w/12" rods for 2-1/2" to 4" conduit		26	.308		7.50	17.40		24.90	34.50
8100	1-1/2" x 1-7/8" w/12" rods for 5" to 6" conduit		24	.333		52.50	18.85		71.35	86.50
8110	Beam clamp, conduit, plastic coated steel, 1/2" diam.		30	.267		22.50	15.10		37.60	47
8120	3/4" diameter		30	.267		24	15.10		39.10	48.50
8130	1" diameter		30	.267		25	15.10		40.10	50
8140	1-1/4" diameter		28	.286		32	16.15		48.15	59
8150	1-1/2" diameter		28	.286		38.50	16.15		54.65	66
8160	2" diameter		28	.286		53	16.15		69.15	82
8170	2-1/2" diameter		26	.308		53	17.40		70.40	84.50
8180	3" diameter		26	.308		60	17.40		77.40	92
8190	3-1/2" diameter		23	.348		58	19.70		77.70	93.50
8200	4" diameter		23	.348		63	19.70		82.70	99
8210	5" diameter		18	.444		202	25		227	260
8220	Channels, plastic coated									
8250	3/4" x 1-1/2", w/12" rods for 1/2" to 1" conduit	1 Elec	28	.286	Ea.	35	16.15		51.15	62.50
8260	1-1/2" x 1-1/2", w/12" rods for 1-1/4" to 2" conduit		26	.308		39.50	17.40		56.90	69
8270	1-1/2" x 1-1/2", w/12" rods for 2-1/2" to 3-1/2" conduit		24	.333		42.50	18.85		61.35	75.50
8280	1-1/2" x 1-7/8", w/12" rods for 4" to 5" conduit		22	.364		71	20.50		91.50	109
8290	1-1/2" x 1-7/8", w/12" rods for 6" conduit		20	.400		78	22.50		100.50	120
8320	Conduit hangers, plastic coated steel, with bolt & 12" rod, 1/2" diam.		140	.057		20	3.23		23.23	27
8330	3/4" diameter		135	.059		20.50	3.35		23.85	28
8340	1" diameter		125	.064		21	3.62		24.62	28.50
8350	1-1/4" diameter		110	.073		22.50	4.12		26.62	30.50
8360	1-1/2" diameter		100	.080		25	4.53		29.53	34.50
8370	2" diameter		90	.089		27.50	5.05		32.55	38
8380	2-1/2" diameter		70	.114		33	6.45		39.45	45.50
8390	3" diameter		50	.160		40	9.05		49.05	57
8400	3-1/2" diameter		35	.229		40.50	12.95		53.45	64
8410	4" diameter		25	.320		59	18.10		77.10	92
8420	5" diameter		20	.400		64.50	22.50		87	105
9000	Parallel type, conduit beam clamp, 1/2"		32	.250		6.55	14.15		20.70	28.50

For customer support on your Electrical Costs with RSMeans Data, call 800.448.8182.

137

26 05 29.20 Hangers		Crew	Daily Output	Labor-Hours	Unit	Material	2017 Bare Costs Labor	Equipment	Total	Total Incl O&P
9010	3/4"	1 Elec	32	.250	Ea.	6.95	14.15		21.10	28.50
9020	1"		32	.250		7.80	14.15		21.95	29.50
9030	1-1/4"		30	.267		9.30	15.10		24.40	32.50
9040	1-1/2"		30	.267		10.55	15.10		25.65	34
9050	2"		30	.267		14	15.10		29.10	38
9060	2-1/2"		28	.286		14.70	16.15		30.85	40
9070	3"		28	.286		17.20	16.15		33.35	43
9090	4"		25	.320		18	18.10		36.10	47
9110	Right angle, conduit beam clamp, 1/2"		32	.250		2.43	14.15		16.58	23.50
9120	3/4"		32	.250		2.55	14.15		16.70	24
9130	1"		32	.250		2.19	14.15		16.34	23.50
9140	1-1/4"		30	.267		3.25	15.10		18.35	26
9150	1-1/2"		30	.267		3.65	15.10		18.75	26.50
9160	2"		30	.267		5.35	15.10		20.45	28.50
9170	2-1/2"		28	.286		6.60	16.15		22.75	31.50
9180	3"		28	.286		7.15	16.15		23.30	32
9190	3-1/2"		25	.320		7.40	18.10		25.50	35
9200	4"		25	.320		8.85	18.10		26.95	37
9230	Adjustable, conduit hanger, 1/2"		32	.250		7.70	14.15		21.85	29.50
9240	3/4"		32	.250		6.35	14.15		20.50	28
9250	1"		32	.250		7	14.15		21.15	28.50
9260	1-1/4"		30	.267		7.10	15.10		22.20	30.50
9270	1-1/2"		30	.267		7.75	15.10		22.85	31
9280	2"		30	.267		6.80	15.10		21.90	30
9290	2-1/2"		28	.286		16.70	16.15		32.85	42.50
9300	3"		28	.286		16.15	16.15		32.30	42
9310	3-1/2"		25	.320		21	18.10		39.10	50.50
9320	4"		25	.320		25	18.10		43.10	54.50
9330	5"		20	.400		28.50	22.50		51	65.50
9340	6"		16	.500		43	28.50		71.50	90
9350	Combination conduit hanger, 3/8"		32	.250		14.05	14.15		28.20	36.50
9360	Adjustable flange, 3/8"		32	.250		16.50	14.15		30.65	39

26 05 29.30 Fittings and Channel Support

		Crew	Daily Output	Labor-Hours	Unit	Material	2017 Bare Costs Labor	Equipment	Total	Total Incl O&P
0010	**FITTINGS & CHANNEL SUPPORT**									
0020	Rooftop Channel Support									
0200	2-7/8"l x 1-5/8"w, 12 Ga Pre Galv, Dbl base	1 Elec	46	.174	Ea.	4.07	9.85		13.92	19.25
0210	2-7/8"l x 1-5/8"w, 12 Ga hot dip Galv, Dbl base		46	.174		2.19	9.85		12.04	17.15
0220	2-7/16"l x 1-5/8"w, 12 Ga Pre Galv, Sngl base		48	.167		1.95	9.45		11.40	16.30
0230	2-7/16"l x 1-5/8"w, 12 Ga hot dip Galv, Sngl base		48	.167		6.95	9.45		16.40	22
0240	13/16"l x 1-5/8"w, 14 Ga Pre Galv, Sngl base		56	.143		1.66	8.10		9.76	13.95
0250	13/16"l x 1-5/8"w, 14 Ga hot dip Galv, Sngl base		56	.143		6.80	8.10		14.90	19.55
0260	1-5/8"l x 1-5/8"w, 12 Ga Pre Galv, Sngl base		54	.148		1.79	8.40		10.19	14.50
0270	1-5/8"l x 1-5/8"w, 12 Ga hot dip Galv, Sngl base		54	.148		1.76	8.40		10.16	14.50
0280	1-5/8"x 28", 12 Ga Pre Galv, Dbl H block base		42	.190		4.12	10.80		14.92	20.50
0290	1-5/8"x 36", 12 Ga Pre Galv, Dbl H block base		40	.200		4.36	11.30		15.66	22
0300	1-5/8"x 42", 12 Ga Pre Galv, Dbl H block base		34	.235		4.90	13.30		18.20	25.50
0310	1-5/8"x 50", 12 Ga Pre Galv, Dbl H block base		38	.211		5.20	11.90		17.10	23.50
0320	1-5/8"x 60", 12 Ga Pre Galv, Dbl H block base		36	.222		5.75	12.60		18.35	25
0330	13/16"x 8"H, threaded rod Pre Galv, H block base		35	.229		2.77	12.95		15.72	22.50
0340	13/16"x 12"H, threaded rod Pre Galv, H block base		34.60	.231		3.46	13.10		16.56	23.50
0350	1-5/8"x 16"H, threaded rod Dbl H block base		34	.235		5.15	13.30		18.45	25.50
0360	1-5/8"x 12"H, Pre Galv, Dbl H block base		34.60	.231		9.90	13.10		23	30.50

26 05 Common Work Results for Electrical

26 05 29 – Hangers and Supports for Electrical Systems

26 05 29.30 Fittings and Channel Support		Crew	Daily Output	Labor-Hours	Unit	Material	2017 Bare Costs Labor	Equipment	Total	Total Incl O&P
0370	1-5/8"x 24"H, Pre Galv, Dbl H block base	1 Elec	34	.235	Ea.	9.65	13.30		22.95	30.50
0380	3-1/4"x 24"H, Pre Galv, Dbl H block base		32	.250		23.50	14.15		37.65	47
0390	3-1/4"x 36"H, Pre Galv, Dbl H block base	↓	30	.267	↓	24	15.10		39.10	49

26 05 33 – Raceway and Boxes for Electrical Systems

26 05 33.13 Conduit

		Crew	Daily Output	Labor-Hours	Unit	Material	2017 Bare Costs Labor	Equipment	Total	Total Incl O&P
0010	**CONDUIT** To 10' high, includes 2 terminations, 2 elbows, R260533-20									
0020	11 beam clamps, and 11 couplings per 100 L.F.									
0300	Aluminum, 1/2" diameter	1 Elec	100	.080	L.F.	1.79	4.53		6.32	8.75
0500	3/4" diameter R260533-25		90	.089		2.54	5.05		7.59	10.35
0700	1" diameter		80	.100		3.48	5.65		9.13	12.35
1000	1-1/4" diameter		70	.114		4.28	6.45		10.73	14.40
1030	1-1/2" diameter		65	.123		5.45	6.95		12.40	16.45
1050	2" diameter		60	.133		7.70	7.55		15.25	19.80
1070	2-1/2" diameter	↓	50	.160		11.50	9.05		20.55	26
1100	3" diameter	2 Elec	90	.178		15.30	10.05		25.35	32
1130	3-1/2" diameter		80	.200		21	11.30		32.30	40
1140	4" diameter		70	.229		24.50	12.95		37.45	46.50
1150	5" diameter		50	.320		54.50	18.10		72.60	87
1160	6" diameter	↓	40	.400	↓	91	22.50		113.50	134
1161	Field bends, 45° to 90°, 1/2" diameter	1 Elec	53	.151	Ea.		8.55		8.55	12.80
1162	3/4" diameter		47	.170			9.65		9.65	14.45
1163	1" diameter		44	.182			10.30		10.30	15.40
1164	1-1/4" diameter		23	.348			19.70		19.70	29.50
1165	1-1/2" diameter		21	.381			21.50		21.50	32.50
1166	2" diameter		16	.500			28.50		28.50	42.50
1170	Elbows, 1/2" diameter		40	.200		8.60	11.30		19.90	26.50
1200	3/4" diameter		32	.250		10.95	14.15		25.10	33
1230	1" diameter		28	.286		15.75	16.15		31.90	41.50
1250	1-1/4" diameter		24	.333		26.50	18.85		45.35	57.50
1270	1-1/2" diameter		20	.400		34.50	22.50		57	72
1300	2" diameter		16	.500		50	28.50		78.50	97.50
1330	2-1/2" diameter		12	.667		94	37.50		131.50	160
1350	3" diameter		8	1		139	56.50		195.50	237
1370	3-1/2" diameter		6	1.333		243	75.50		318.50	380
1400	4" diameter		5	1.600		280	90.50		370.50	445
1410	5" diameter		4	2		745	113		858	990
1420	6" diameter		2.50	3.200		1,300	181		1,481	1,700
1430	Couplings, 1/2" diameter		320	.025		2.69	1.42		4.11	5.10
1450	3/4" diameter		192	.042		4.01	2.36		6.37	7.95
1470	1" diameter		160	.050		5.30	2.83		8.13	10.05
1500	1-1/4" diameter		120	.067		6.80	3.77		10.57	13.15
1530	1-1/2" diameter		96	.083		7.60	4.72		12.32	15.40
1550	2" diameter		80	.100		11.15	5.65		16.80	21
1570	2-1/2" diameter		69	.116		26.50	6.55		33.05	39
1600	3" diameter		64	.125		33.50	7.10		40.60	47
1630	3-1/2" diameter		56	.143		52.50	8.10		60.60	69.50
1650	4" diameter		53	.151		56	8.55		64.55	74.50
1670	5" diameter		48	.167		180	9.45		189.45	212
1690	6" diameter	↓	46	.174	↓	355	9.85		364.85	405
1691	See note on line 26 05 33.13 9995 R260533-30									
1750	Rigid galvanized steel, 1/2" diameter	1 Elec	90	.089	L.F.	2.50	5.05		7.55	10.30
1770	3/4" diameter	↓	80	.100	↓	4.66	5.65		10.31	13.65

For customer support on your Electrical Costs with RSMeans Data, call 800.448.8182.

139

26 05 33.13 Conduit		Crew	Daily Output	Labor-Hours	Unit	Material	2017 Bare Costs Labor	Equipment	Total	Total Incl O&P
1800	1" diameter	1 Elec	65	.123	L.F.	7.10	6.95		14.05	18.30
1830	1-1/4" diameter		60	.133		5.10	7.55		12.65	16.90
1850	1-1/2" diameter		55	.145		8	8.25		16.25	21
1870	2" diameter		45	.178		10.25	10.05		20.30	26.50
1900	2-1/2" diameter	▼	35	.229		12.95	12.95		25.90	33.50
1930	3" diameter	2 Elec	50	.320		14.95	18.10		33.05	43.50
1950	3-1/2" diameter		44	.364		18.95	20.50		39.45	52
1970	4" diameter		40	.400		22	22.50		44.50	58.50
1980	5" diameter		30	.533		43	30		73	92.50
1990	6" diameter	▼	20	.800	▼	61.50	45.50		107	136
1991	Field bends, 45° to 90°, 1/2" diameter	1 Elec	44	.182	Ea.		10.30		10.30	15.40
1992	3/4" diameter		40	.200			11.30		11.30	16.95
1993	1" diameter		36	.222			12.60		12.60	18.85
1994	1-1/4" diameter		19	.421			24		24	35.50
1995	1-1/2" diameter		18	.444			25		25	37.50
1996	2" diameter		13	.615			35		35	52
2000	Elbows, 1/2" diameter		32	.250		5.65	14.15		19.80	27.50
2030	3/4" diameter		28	.286		4.64	16.15		20.79	29
2050	1" diameter		24	.333		7.65	18.85		26.50	37
2070	1-1/4" diameter		18	.444		12.50	25		37.50	51.50
2100	1-1/2" diameter		16	.500		18.35	28.50		46.85	62.50
2130	2" diameter		12	.667		27.50	37.50		65	87
2150	2-1/2" diameter		8	1		41.50	56.50		98	131
2170	3" diameter		6	1.333		57.50	75.50		133	177
2200	3-1/2" diameter		4.20	1.905		91.50	108		199.50	263
2220	4" diameter		4	2		103	113		216	284
2230	5" diameter		3.50	2.286		286	129		415	510
2240	6" diameter		2	4		430	226		656	815
2250	Couplings, 1/2" diameter		267	.030		1.39	1.70		3.09	4.07
2270	3/4" diameter		160	.050		1.75	2.83		4.58	6.15
2300	1" diameter		133	.060		2.51	3.40		5.91	7.85
2330	1-1/4" diameter		100	.080		3.35	4.53		7.88	10.50
2350	1-1/2" diameter		80	.100		5.30	5.65		10.95	14.30
2370	2" diameter		67	.119		6.95	6.75		13.70	17.80
2400	2-1/2" diameter		57	.140		13.85	7.95		21.80	27
2430	3" diameter		53	.151		17.90	8.55		26.45	32.50
2450	3-1/2" diameter		47	.170		23	9.65		32.65	39.50
2470	4" diameter		44	.182		29	10.30		39.30	47.50
2480	5" diameter		40	.200		53	11.30		64.30	75
2490	6" diameter	▼	38	.211	▼	73.50	11.90		85.40	98.50
2491	See note on line 26 05 33.13 9995	R260533-30								
2500	Steel, intermediate conduit (IMC), 1/2" diameter	1 Elec	100	.080	L.F.	2.20	4.53		6.73	9.20
2530	3/4" diameter		90	.089		2.75	5.05		7.80	10.60
2550	1" diameter		70	.114		3.93	6.45		10.38	14
2570	1-1/4" diameter		65	.123		4.94	6.95		11.89	15.90
2600	1-1/2" diameter		60	.133		6.55	7.55		14.10	18.50
2630	2" diameter		50	.160		8.05	9.05		17.10	22.50
2650	2-1/2" diameter	▼	40	.200		14.05	11.30		25.35	32.50
2670	3" diameter	2 Elec	60	.267		18.50	15.10		33.60	43
2700	3-1/2" diameter		54	.296		23	16.75		39.75	50.50
2730	4" diameter	▼	50	.320	▼	13.65	18.10		31.75	42
2731	Field bends, 45° to 90°, 1/2" diameter	1 Elec	44	.182	Ea.		10.30		10.30	15.40
2732	3/4" diameter	▼	40	.200	▼		11.30		11.30	16.95

26 05 33.13 Conduit		Crew	Daily Output	Labor-Hours	Unit	Material	2017 Bare Costs Labor	Equipment	Total	Total Incl O&P
2733	1" diameter	1 Elec	36	.222	Ea.		12.60		12.60	18.85
2734	1-1/4" diameter		19	.421			24		24	35.50
2735	1-1/2" diameter		18	.444			25		25	37.50
2736	2" diameter		13	.615			35		35	52
2750	Elbows, 1/2" diameter		32	.250		6.95	14.15		21.10	28.50
2770	3/4" diameter		28	.286		7.45	16.15		23.60	32
2800	1" diameter		24	.333		10.90	18.85		29.75	40.50
2830	1-1/4" diameter		18	.444		16.55	25		41.55	56
2850	1-1/2" diameter		16	.500		20.50	28.50		49	65
2870	2" diameter		12	.667		22	37.50		59.50	80.50
2900	2-1/2" diameter		8	1		39.50	56.50		96	129
2930	3" diameter		6	1.333		57.50	75.50		133	176
2950	3-1/2" diameter		4.20	1.905		122	108		230	297
2970	4" diameter		4	2		117	113		230	299
3000	Couplings, 1/2" diameter		293	.027		1.39	1.55		2.94	3.85
3030	3/4" diameter		176	.045		1.75	2.57		4.32	5.80
3050	1" diameter		147	.054		2.51	3.08		5.59	7.35
3070	1-1/4" diameter		110	.073		3.35	4.12		7.47	9.85
3100	1-1/2" diameter		88	.091		5.30	5.15		10.45	13.50
3130	2" diameter		73	.110		6.95	6.20		13.15	16.95
3150	2-1/2" diameter		63	.127		13.85	7.20		21.05	26
3170	3" diameter		59	.136		17.90	7.65		25.55	31
3200	3-1/2" diameter		52	.154		23	8.70		31.70	38
3230	4" diameter		49	.163		29	9.25		38.25	46
3231	See note on line 26 05 33.13 9995	R260533-30								
4100	Rigid steel, plastic coated, 40 mil thick									
4130	1/2" diameter	1 Elec	80	.100	L.F.	7.10	5.65		12.75	16.30
4150	3/4" diameter		70	.114		8	6.45		14.45	18.50
4170	1" diameter		55	.145		9.80	8.25		18.05	23
4200	1-1/4" diameter		50	.160		13.40	9.05		22.45	28.50
4230	1-1/2" diameter		45	.178		15.05	10.05		25.10	31.50
4250	2" diameter		35	.229		19.85	12.95		32.80	41.50
4270	2-1/2" diameter		25	.320		31	18.10		49.10	61
4300	3" diameter	2 Elec	44	.364		35	20.50		55.50	69.50
4330	3-1/2" diameter		40	.400		46	22.50		68.50	85
4350	4" diameter		36	.444		49.50	25		74.50	92
4370	5" diameter		30	.533		120	30		150	177
4400	Elbows, 1/2" diameter	1 Elec	28	.286	Ea.	18.25	16.15		34.40	44
4430	3/4" diameter		24	.333		16.25	18.85		35.10	46.50
4450	1" diameter		18	.444		19	25		44	58.50
4470	1-1/4" diameter		16	.500		26.50	28.50		55	71.50
4500	1-1/2" diameter		12	.667		29	37.50		66.50	88.50
4530	2" diameter		8	1		37	56.50		93.50	126
4550	2-1/2" diameter		6	1.333		80	75.50		155.50	201
4570	3" diameter		4.20	1.905		121	108		229	295
4600	3-1/2" diameter		4	2		163	113		276	350
4630	4" diameter		3.80	2.105		168	119		287	365
4650	5" diameter		3.50	2.286		440	129		569	680
4680	Couplings, 1/2" diameter		213	.038		5.35	2.13		7.48	9.05
4700	3/4" diameter		128	.063		5.25	3.54		8.79	11.05
4730	1" diameter		107	.075		6.15	4.23		10.38	13.15
4750	1-1/4" diameter		80	.100		8.30	5.65		13.95	17.65
4770	1-1/2" diameter		64	.125		8.90	7.10		16	20.50

For customer support on your Electrical Costs with RSMeans Data, call 800.448.8182.

141

26 05 33.13 Conduit		Crew	Daily Output	Labor-Hours	Unit	Material	2017 Bare Costs Labor	Equipment	Total	Total Incl O&P
4800	2" diameter	1 Elec	53	.151	Ea.	13.10	8.55		21.65	27
4830	2-1/2" diameter		46	.174		33	9.85		42.85	51
4850	3" diameter		43	.186		37.50	10.55		48.05	57.50
4870	3-1/2" diameter		38	.211		50	11.90		61.90	73
4900	4" diameter		36	.222		54.50	12.60		67.10	79
4950	5" diameter		32	.250		188	14.15		202.15	227
4951	See note on line 26 05 33.13 9995 R260533-30									
5000	Electric metallic tubing (EMT), 1/2" diameter	1 Elec	170	.047	L.F.	.69	2.66		3.35	4.75
5020	3/4" diameter		130	.062		.98	3.48		4.46	6.30
5040	1" diameter		115	.070		1.65	3.94		5.59	7.70
5060	1-1/4" diameter		100	.080		2.66	4.53		7.19	9.70
5080	1-1/2" diameter		90	.089		3.38	5.05		8.43	11.25
5100	2" diameter		80	.100		4.24	5.65		9.89	13.15
5120	2-1/2" diameter		60	.133		8.70	7.55		16.25	21
5140	3" diameter	2 Elec	100	.160		10.20	9.05		19.25	25
5160	3-1/2" diameter		90	.178		12.85	10.05		22.90	29
5180	4" diameter		80	.200		13.85	11.30		25.15	32
5200	Field bends, 45° to 90°, 1/2" diameter	1 Elec	89	.090	Ea.		5.10		5.10	7.60
5220	3/4" diameter		80	.100			5.65		5.65	8.50
5240	1" diameter		73	.110			6.20		6.20	9.30
5260	1-1/4" diameter		38	.211			11.90		11.90	17.85
5280	1-1/2" diameter		36	.222			12.60		12.60	18.85
5300	2" diameter		26	.308			17.40		17.40	26
5320	Offsets, 1/2" diameter		65	.123			6.95		6.95	10.45
5340	3/4" diameter		62	.129			7.30		7.30	10.95
5360	1" diameter		53	.151			8.55		8.55	12.80
5380	1-1/4" diameter		30	.267			15.10		15.10	22.50
5400	1-1/2" diameter		28	.286			16.15		16.15	24
5420	2" diameter		20	.400			22.50		22.50	34
5700	Elbows, 1" diameter		40	.200		4.56	11.30		15.86	22
5720	1-1/4" diameter		32	.250		5.65	14.15		19.80	27
5740	1-1/2" diameter		24	.333		6.55	18.85		25.40	36
5760	2" diameter		20	.400		9.65	22.50		32.15	44.50
5780	2-1/2" diameter		12	.667		26.50	37.50		64	85.50
5800	3" diameter		9	.889		35	50.50		85.50	114
5820	3-1/2" diameter		7	1.143		47	64.50		111.50	149
5840	4" diameter		6	1.333		55.50	75.50		131	174
6200	Couplings, set screw, steel, 1/2" diameter		235	.034		1.07	1.93		3	4.07
6220	3/4" diameter		188	.043		1.68	2.41		4.09	5.45
6240	1" diameter		157	.051		2.82	2.88		5.70	7.40
6260	1-1/4" diameter		118	.068		5.80	3.84		9.64	12.15
6280	1-1/2" diameter		94	.085		8.15	4.82		12.97	16.15
6300	2" diameter		78	.103		10.95	5.80		16.75	21
6320	2-1/2" diameter		67	.119		31.50	6.75		38.25	44.50
6340	3" diameter		59	.136		34.50	7.65		42.15	49.50
6360	3-1/2" diameter		47	.170		38.50	9.65		48.15	57
6380	4" diameter		43	.186		42.50	10.55		53.05	63
6381	See note on line 26 05 33.13 9995 R260533-30									
6500	Box connectors, set screw, steel, 1/2" diameter	1 Elec	120	.067	Ea.	.85	3.77		4.62	6.60
6520	3/4" diameter		110	.073		1.38	4.12		5.50	7.65
6540	1" diameter		90	.089		2.60	5.05		7.65	10.40
6560	1-1/4" diameter		70	.114		5.05	6.45		11.50	15.25
6580	1-1/2" diameter		60	.133		7.30	7.55		14.85	19.35

26 05 33.13 Conduit		Crew	Daily Output	Labor-Hours	Unit	Material	2017 Bare Costs Labor	2017 Bare Costs Equipment	Total	Total Incl O&P
6600	2" diameter	1 Elec	50	.160	Ea.	10.05	9.05		19.10	24.50
6620	2-1/2" diameter		36	.222		35.50	12.60		48.10	58
6640	3" diameter		27	.296		42	16.75		58.75	71
6680	3-1/2" diameter		21	.381		58.50	21.50		80	97
6700	4" diameter		16	.500		65.50	28.50		94	115
6740	Insulated box connectors, set screw, steel, 1/2" diameter		120	.067		1.15	3.77		4.92	6.90
6760	3/4" diameter		110	.073		1.82	4.12		5.94	8.15
6780	1" diameter		90	.089		3.34	5.05		8.39	11.20
6800	1-1/4" diameter		70	.114		6.05	6.45		12.50	16.40
6820	1-1/2" diameter		60	.133		8.65	7.55		16.20	21
6840	2" diameter		50	.160		12.55	9.05		21.60	27.50
6860	2-1/2" diameter		36	.222		59.50	12.60		72.10	84
6880	3" diameter		27	.296		70	16.75		86.75	102
6900	3-1/2" diameter		21	.381		97.50	21.50		119	140
6920	4" diameter		16	.500		106	28.50		134.50	160
7000	EMT to conduit adapters, 1/2" diameter (compression)		70	.114		3.97	6.45		10.42	14.05
7020	3/4" diameter		60	.133		5.55	7.55		13.10	17.40
7040	1" diameter		50	.160		8.65	9.05		17.70	23
7060	1-1/4" diameter		40	.200		16.10	11.30		27.40	34.50
7080	1-1/2" diameter		30	.267		19.80	15.10		34.90	44.50
7100	2" diameter		25	.320		29	18.10		47.10	58.50
7200	EMT to Greenfield adapters, 1/2" to 3/8" diameter (compression)		90	.089		2.58	5.05		7.63	10.40
7220	1/2" diameter		90	.089		4.64	5.05		9.69	12.65
7240	3/4" diameter		80	.100		6.05	5.65		11.70	15.15
7260	1" diameter		70	.114		17	6.45		23.45	28.50
7270	1-1/4" diameter		60	.133		19.50	7.55		27.05	33
7280	1-1/2" diameter		50	.160		23	9.05		32.05	39
7290	2" diameter		40	.200		33.50	11.30		44.80	54
7400	EMT, LB, LR or LL fittings with covers, 1/2" dia, set screw		24	.333		6.40	18.85		25.25	35.50
7420	3/4" diameter		20	.400		9.25	22.50		31.75	44
7440	1" diameter		16	.500		11.45	28.50		39.95	55
7450	1-1/4" diameter		13	.615		15.10	35		50.10	68.50
7460	1-1/2" diameter		11	.727		21	41		62	84.50
7470	2" diameter		9	.889		30.50	50.50		81	109
7600	EMT, "T" fittings with covers, 1/2" diameter, set screw		16	.500		6.70	28.50		35.20	50
7620	3/4" diameter		15	.533		8.60	30		38.60	54.50
7640	1" diameter		12	.667		12.40	37.50		49.90	70
7650	1-1/4" diameter		11	.727		20	41		61	83.50
7660	1-1/2" diameter		10	.800		23	45.50		68.50	93
7670	2" diameter		8	1		29.50	56.50		86	118
8000	EMT, expansion fittings, no jumper, 1/2" diameter		24	.333		81	18.85		99.85	118
8020	3/4" diameter		20	.400		94.50	22.50		117	138
8040	1" diameter		16	.500		112	28.50		140.50	166
8060	1-1/4" diameter		13	.615		152	35		187	219
8080	1-1/2" diameter		11	.727		207	41		248	290
8100	2" diameter		9	.889		305	50.50		355.50	410
8110	2-1/2" diameter		7	1.143		490	64.50		554.50	630
8120	3" diameter		6	1.333		595	75.50		670.50	770
8140	4" diameter		5	1.600		955	90.50		1,045.50	1,175
8200	Split adapter, 1/2" diameter		110	.073		2.49	4.12		6.61	8.90
8210	3/4" diameter		90	.089		1.73	5.05		6.78	9.45
8220	1" diameter		70	.114		2.37	6.45		8.82	12.30
8230	1-1/4" diameter		60	.133		3.82	7.55		11.37	15.50

26 05 33.13 Conduit		Crew	Daily Output	Labor-Hours	Unit	Material	2017 Bare Costs Labor	2017 Bare Costs Equipment	Total	Total Incl O&P
8240	1-1/2" diameter	1 Elec	50	.160	Ea.	5.85	9.05		14.90	20
8250	2" diameter		36	.222		17.25	12.60		29.85	38
8300	1 hole clips, 1/2" diameter		500	.016		.34	.91		1.25	1.73
8320	3/4" diameter		470	.017		.42	.96		1.38	1.90
8340	1" diameter		444	.018		.78	1.02		1.80	2.39
8360	1-1/4" diameter		400	.020		1.07	1.13		2.20	2.88
8380	1-1/2" diameter		355	.023		1.62	1.28		2.90	3.69
8400	2" diameter		320	.025		2.55	1.42		3.97	4.93
8420	2-1/2" diameter		266	.030		4.74	1.70		6.44	7.75
8440	3" diameter		160	.050		5.95	2.83		8.78	10.80
8460	3-1/2" diameter		133	.060		9.40	3.40		12.80	15.45
8480	4" diameter		100	.080		12.20	4.53		16.73	20
8500	Clamp back spacers, 1/2" diameter		500	.016		1.01	.91		1.92	2.47
8510	3/4" diameter		470	.017		1.19	.96		2.15	2.75
8520	1" diameter		444	.018		2.06	1.02		3.08	3.80
8530	1-1/4" diameter		400	.020		3.70	1.13		4.83	5.75
8540	1-1/2" diameter		355	.023		4.14	1.28		5.42	6.45
8550	2" diameter		320	.025		6.95	1.42		8.37	9.75
8560	2-1/2" diameter		266	.030		13.50	1.70		15.20	17.40
8570	3" diameter		160	.050		19.20	2.83		22.03	25
8580	3-1/2" diameter		133	.060		26	3.40		29.40	33.50
8590	4" diameter		100	.080		56.50	4.53		61.03	69
8600	Offset connectors, 1/2" diameter		40	.200		3.63	11.30		14.93	21
8610	3/4" diameter		32	.250		5.25	14.15		19.40	27
8620	1" diameter		24	.333		5.85	18.85		24.70	35
8650	90° pulling elbows, female, 1/2" diameter, with gasket		24	.333		6.75	18.85		25.60	36
8660	3/4" diameter		20	.400		11.55	22.50		34.05	46.50
8700	Couplings, compression, 1/2" diameter, steel		78	.103		2.64	5.80		8.44	11.60
8710	3/4" diameter		67	.119		3.67	6.75		10.42	14.20
8720	1" diameter		59	.136		6.30	7.65		13.95	18.45
8730	1-1/4" diameter		47	.170		12	9.65		21.65	27.50
8740	1-1/2" diameter		38	.211		17.45	11.90		29.35	37
8750	2" diameter		31	.258		23.50	14.60		38.10	48
8760	2-1/2" diameter		24	.333		106	18.85		124.85	146
8770	3" diameter		21	.381		133	21.50		154.50	179
8780	3-1/2" diameter		19	.421		216	24		240	274
8790	4" diameter		16	.500		221	28.50		249.50	286
8791	See note on line 26 05 33.13 9995	R260533-30								
8800	Box connectors, compression, 1/2" diam., steel	1 Elec	120	.067	Ea.	2.22	3.77		5.99	8.10
8810	3/4" diameter		110	.073		3.06	4.12		7.18	9.50
8820	1" diameter		90	.089		4.56	5.05		9.61	12.55
8830	1-1/4" diameter		70	.114		11.55	6.45		18	22.50
8840	1-1/2" diameter		60	.133		13.55	7.55		21.10	26.50
8850	2" diameter		50	.160		19.60	9.05		28.65	35
8860	2-1/2" diameter		36	.222		48.50	12.60		61.10	72.50
8870	3" diameter		27	.296		67	16.75		83.75	98.50
8880	3-1/2" diameter		21	.381		101	21.50		122.50	144
8890	4" diameter		16	.500		103	28.50		131.50	157
8900	Box connectors, insulated compression, 1/2" diam., steel		120	.067		2.16	3.77		5.93	8.05
8910	3/4" diameter		110	.073		2.90	4.12		7.02	9.35
8920	1" diameter		90	.089		4.90	5.05		9.95	12.95
8930	1-1/4" diameter		70	.114		9.95	6.45		16.40	20.50
8940	1-1/2" diameter		60	.133		14.95	7.55		22.50	28

26 05 33.13 Conduit		Crew	Daily Output	Labor-Hours	Unit	Material	2017 Bare Costs Labor	Equipment	Total	Total Incl O&P
8950	2" diameter	1 Elec	50	.160	Ea.	21.50	9.05		30.55	37.50
8960	2-1/2" diameter		36	.222		56.50	12.60		69.10	81
8970	3" diameter		27	.296		74	16.75		90.75	106
8980	3-1/2" diameter		21	.381		108	21.50		129.50	152
8990	4" diameter		16	.500		110	28.50		138.50	164
9100	PVC, schedule 40, 1/2" diameter		190	.042	L.F.	.86	2.38		3.24	4.52
9110	3/4" diameter		145	.055		.95	3.12		4.07	5.70
9120	1" diameter		125	.064		2.06	3.62		5.68	7.70
9130	1-1/4" diameter		110	.073		2.53	4.12		6.65	8.95
9140	1-1/2" diameter		100	.080		2.86	4.53		7.39	9.95
9150	2" diameter		90	.089		3.73	5.05		8.78	11.65
9160	2-1/2" diameter		65	.123		4.60	6.95		11.55	15.50
9170	3" diameter	2 Elec	110	.145		5.25	8.25		13.50	18.10
9180	3-1/2" diameter		100	.160		6.85	9.05		15.90	21
9190	4" diameter		90	.178		8.05	10.05		18.10	24
9200	5" diameter		70	.229		10.50	12.95		23.45	31
9210	6" diameter		60	.267		12.40	15.10		27.50	36
9220	Elbows, 1/2" diameter	1 Elec	50	.160	Ea.	.76	9.05		9.81	14.40
9225	3/4" diameter		42	.190		.75	10.80		11.55	17
9230	1" diameter		35	.229		1.13	12.95		14.08	20.50
9235	1-1/4" diameter		28	.286		1.73	16.15		17.88	26
9240	1-1/2" diameter		20	.400		2.25	22.50		24.75	36.50
9245	2" diameter	R-1A	36.40	.440		3.05	22.50		25.55	37
9250	2-1/2" diameter		26.70	.599		5.50	30.50		36	51.50
9255	3" diameter		22.90	.699		9.20	35.50		44.70	63.50
9260	3-1/2" diameter		22.20	.721		11.90	36.50		48.40	68
9265	4" diameter		18.20	.879		14.65	45		59.65	83
9270	5" diameter		12.10	1.322		24	67.50		91.50	128
9275	6" diameter		11.10	1.441		55	73.50		128.50	171
9312	Couplings, 1/2" diameter	1 Elec	50	.160		.33	9.05		9.38	13.90
9314	3/4" diameter		42	.190		.27	10.80		11.07	16.45
9316	1" diameter		35	.229		.30	12.95		13.25	19.75
9318	1-1/4" diameter		28	.286		.43	16.15		16.58	24.50
9320	1-1/2" diameter		20	.400		.54	22.50		23.04	34.50
9322	2" diameter	R-1A	36.40	.440		.91	22.50		23.41	34.50
9324	2-1/2" diameter		26.70	.599		1.80	30.50		32.30	47.50
9326	3" diameter		22.90	.699		1.74	35.50		37.24	55.50
9328	3-1/2" diameter		22.20	.721		2.13	36.50		38.63	57.50
9330	4" diameter		18.20	.879		2.62	45		47.62	70
9332	5" diameter		12.10	1.322		7.55	67.50		75.05	109
9334	6" diameter		11.10	1.441		10.60	73.50		84.10	122
9335	See note on line 26 05 33.13 9995	R260533-30								
9340	Field bends, 45° & 90°, 1/2" diameter	1 Elec	45	.178	Ea.		10.05		10.05	15.10
9350	3/4" diameter		40	.200			11.30		11.30	16.95
9360	1" diameter		35	.229			12.95		12.95	19.40
9370	1-1/4" diameter		32	.250			14.15		14.15	21
9380	1-1/2" diameter		27	.296			16.75		16.75	25
9390	2" diameter		20	.400			22.50		22.50	34
9400	2-1/2" diameter		16	.500			28.50		28.50	42.50
9410	3" diameter		13	.615			35		35	52
9420	3-1/2" diameter		12	.667			37.50		37.50	56.50
9430	4" diameter		10	.800			45.50		45.50	68
9440	5" diameter		9	.889			50.50		50.50	75.50

26 05 33.13 Conduit		Crew	Daily Output	Labor-Hours	Unit	Material	2017 Bare Costs Labor	2017 Bare Costs Equipment	Total	Total Incl O&P
9450	6" diameter	1 Elec	8	1	Ea.		56.50		56.50	85
9460	PVC adapters, 1/2" diameter		50	.160		.21	9.05		9.26	13.80
9470	3/4" diameter		42	.190		.34	10.80		11.14	16.50
9480	1" diameter		38	.211		.48	11.90		12.38	18.40
9490	1-1/4" diameter		35	.229		.63	12.95		13.58	20
9500	1-1/2" diameter		32	.250		.84	14.15		14.99	22
9510	2" diameter		27	.296		1.03	16.75		17.78	26
9520	2-1/2" diameter		23	.348		1.82	19.70		21.52	31.50
9530	3" diameter		18	.444		2.52	25		27.52	40.50
9540	3-1/2" diameter		13	.615		3.89	35		38.89	56.50
9550	4" diameter		11	.727		4.49	41		45.49	66.50
9560	5" diameter		8	1		9.50	56.50		66	95.50
9570	6" diameter		6	1.333		15.90	75.50		91.40	130
9580	PVC-LB, LR or LL fittings & covers									
9590	1/2" diameter	1 Elec	20	.400	Ea.	2.74	22.50		25.24	37
9600	3/4" diameter		16	.500		3.91	28.50		32.41	47
9610	1" diameter		12	.667		4.28	37.50		41.78	61
9620	1-1/4" diameter		9	.889		6.65	50.50		57.15	83
9630	1-1/2" diameter		7	1.143		7.90	64.50		72.40	106
9640	2" diameter		6	1.333		12.50	75.50		88	127
9650	2-1/2" diameter		6	1.333		52	75.50		127.50	171
9660	3" diameter		5	1.600		50.50	90.50		141	192
9670	3-1/2" diameter		4	2		52.50	113		165.50	228
9680	4" diameter		3	2.667		60	151		211	292
9690	PVC-tee fitting & cover									
9700	1/2"	1 Elec	14	.571	Ea.	4.98	32.50		37.48	54
9710	3/4"		13	.615		4.97	35		39.97	57.50
9720	1"		10	.800		5.60	45.50		51.10	74
9730	1-1/4"		9	.889		9.75	50.50		60.25	86.50
9740	1-1/2"		8	1		11.50	56.50		68	97.50
9750	2"		7	1.143		17.40	64.50		81.90	116
9760	PVC-reducers, 3/4" x 1/2" diameter					1.37			1.37	1.51
9770	1" x 1/2" diameter					2.62			2.62	2.88
9780	1" x 3/4" diameter					2.84			2.84	3.12
9790	1-1/4" x 3/4" diameter					3.49			3.49	3.84
9800	1-1/4" x 1" diameter					3.69			3.69	4.06
9810	1-1/2" x 1-1/4" diameter					4.01			4.01	4.41
9820	2" x 1-1/4" diameter					4.61			4.61	5.05
9830	2-1/2" x 2" diameter					14.35			14.35	15.75
9840	3" x 2" diameter					14.80			14.80	16.30
9850	4" x 3" diameter					17.35			17.35	19.05
9860	Cement, quart					15.10			15.10	16.60
9870	Gallon					104			104	114
9880	Heat bender, to 6" diameter					1,225			1,225	1,350
9900	Add to labor for higher elevated installation									
9905	10' to 14.5' high, add						10%			
9910	15' to 20' high, add						20%			
9920	20' to 25' high, add						25%			
9930	25' to 30' high, add						35%			
9940	30' to 35' high, add						40%			
9950	35' to 40' high, add						50%			
9960	Over 40' high, add						55%			
9995	Do not include labor when adding couplings to a fitting installation	R260533-30								

26 05 33.14 Conduit

		Crew	Daily Output	Labor-Hours	Unit	Material	2017 Bare Costs Labor	Equipment	Total	Total Incl O&P
0010	**CONDUIT** To 10' high, includes 11 couplings per 100'									
0200	Electric metallic tubing, 1/2" diameter	1 Elec	435	.018	L.F.	.50	1.04		1.54	2.11
0220	3/4" diameter		253	.032		.78	1.79		2.57	3.54
0240	1" diameter		207	.039		1.32	2.19		3.51	4.73
0260	1-1/4" diameter		173	.046		2.25	2.62		4.87	6.40
0280	1-1/2" diameter		153	.052		2.90	2.96		5.86	7.60
0300	2" diameter		130	.062		3.63	3.48		7.11	9.20
0320	2-1/2" diameter		92	.087		7.05	4.92		11.97	15.10
0340	3" diameter	2 Elec	148	.108		8.30	6.10		14.40	18.25
0360	3-1/2" diameter		134	.119		10.30	6.75		17.05	21.50
0380	4" diameter		114	.140		10.85	7.95		18.80	24
0500	Steel rigid galvanized, 1/2" diameter	1 Elec	146	.055		1.90	3.10		5	6.75
0520	3/4" diameter		125	.064		3.89	3.62		7.51	9.75
0540	1" diameter		93	.086		6.15	4.87		11.02	14.05
0560	1-1/4" diameter		88	.091		4.16	5.15		9.31	12.25
0580	1-1/2" diameter		80	.100		6.50	5.65		12.15	15.65
0600	2" diameter		65	.123		8.05	6.95		15	19.30
0620	2-1/2" diameter		48	.167		11.05	9.45		20.50	26.50
0640	3" diameter	2 Elec	64	.250		12.65	14.15		26.80	35
0660	3-1/2" diameter		60	.267		16.15	15.10		31.25	40.50
0680	4" diameter		52	.308		18.40	17.40		35.80	46
0700	5" diameter		50	.320		35	18.10		53.10	65.50
0720	6" diameter		48	.333		46	18.85		64.85	79.50
1000	Steel intermediate conduit (IMC), 1/2" diameter R260533-25	1 Elec	155	.052		1.65	2.92		4.57	6.20
1010	3/4" diameter		130	.062		1.97	3.48		5.45	7.35
1020	1" diameter		100	.080		2.96	4.53		7.49	10.05
1030	1-1/4" diameter		93	.086		3.97	4.87		8.84	11.65
1040	1-1/2" diameter		85	.094		5.15	5.35		10.50	13.65
1050	2" diameter		70	.114		6.45	6.45		12.90	16.80
1060	2-1/2" diameter		53	.151		12.50	8.55		21.05	26.50
1070	3" diameter	2 Elec	80	.200		16.50	11.30		27.80	35
1080	3-1/2" diameter		70	.229		19.60	12.95		32.55	41
1090	4" diameter		60	.267		9.90	15.10		25	33.50

26 05 33.15 Conduit Nipples

		Crew	Daily Output	Labor-Hours	Unit	Material	2017 Bare Costs Labor	Equipment	Total	Total Incl O&P
0010	**CONDUIT NIPPLES** With locknuts and bushings									
0100	Aluminum, 1/2" diameter, close	1 Elec	36	.222	Ea.	7.90	12.60		20.50	27.50
0120	1-1/2" long		36	.222		7.95	12.60		20.55	27.50
0140	2" long		36	.222		8.25	12.60		20.85	28
0160	2-1/2" long		36	.222		9	12.60		21.60	29
0180	3" long		36	.222		9.15	12.60		21.75	29
0200	3-1/2" long		36	.222		9.70	12.60		22.30	29.50
0220	4" long		36	.222		9.95	12.60		22.55	30
0240	5" long		36	.222		11.05	12.60		23.65	31
0260	6" long		36	.222		11.30	12.60		23.90	31.50
0280	8" long		36	.222		12.45	12.60		25.05	32.50
0300	10" long		36	.222		15.30	12.60		27.90	35.50
0320	12" long		36	.222		15.70	12.60		28.30	36
0340	3/4" diameter, close		32	.250		10.10	14.15		24.25	32
0360	1-1/2" long		32	.250		10.25	14.15		24.40	32.50
0380	2" long		32	.250		10.40	14.15		24.55	32.50
0400	2-1/2" long		32	.250		11	14.15		25.15	33
0420	3" long		32	.250		11.30	14.15		25.45	33.50

26 05 33.15 Conduit Nipples		Crew	Daily Output	Labor-Hours	Unit	Material	2017 Bare Costs Labor	Equipment	Total	Total Incl O&P
0440	3-1/2" long	1 Elec	32	.250	Ea.	11.75	14.15		25.90	34
0460	4" long		32	.250		12.60	14.15		26.75	35
0480	5" long		32	.250		13.25	14.15		27.40	35.50
0500	6" long		32	.250		14.05	14.15		28.20	36.50
0520	8" long		32	.250		16.35	14.15		30.50	39
0540	10" long		32	.250		18.80	14.15		32.95	41.50
0560	12" long		32	.250		24	14.15		38.15	47.50
0580	1" diameter, close		27	.296		15.65	16.75		32.40	42
0600	2" long		27	.296		17.45	16.75		34.20	44
0620	2-1/2" long		27	.296		16.80	16.75		33.55	43.50
0640	3" long		27	.296		18.65	16.75		35.40	45.50
0660	3-1/2" long		27	.296		18.65	16.75		35.40	45.50
0680	4" long		27	.296		20.50	16.75		37.25	47.50
0700	5" long		27	.296		21	16.75		37.75	48
0720	6" long		27	.296		22.50	16.75		39.25	49.50
0740	8" long		27	.296		26	16.75		42.75	53.50
0760	10" long		27	.296		30	16.75		46.75	58
0780	12" long		27	.296		33.50	16.75		50.25	61.50
0800	1-1/4" diameter, close		23	.348		23	19.70		42.70	54.50
0820	2" long		23	.348		23	19.70		42.70	55
0840	2-1/2" long		23	.348		24	19.70		43.70	56
0860	3" long		23	.348		25	19.70		44.70	57
0880	3-1/2" long		23	.348		26.50	19.70		46.20	58.50
0900	4" long		23	.348		27.50	19.70		47.20	59.50
0920	5" long		23	.348		30	19.70		49.70	62.50
0940	6" long		23	.348		32	19.70		51.70	64.50
0960	8" long		23	.348		38.50	19.70		58.20	72
0980	10" long		23	.348		38.50	19.70		58.20	71.50
1000	12" long		23	.348		51	19.70		70.70	85.50
1020	1-1/2" diameter, close		20	.400		30.50	22.50		53	67.50
1040	2" long		20	.400		31	22.50		53.50	68
1060	2-1/2" long		20	.400		31.50	22.50		54	69
1080	3" long		20	.400		33	22.50		55.50	70.50
1100	3-1/2" long		20	.400		35.50	22.50		58	73
1120	4" long		20	.400		36	22.50		58.50	73.50
1140	5" long		20	.400		38.50	22.50		61	76.50
1160	6" long		20	.400		40.50	22.50		63	78.50
1180	8" long		20	.400		45	22.50		67.50	83
1200	10" long		20	.400		56.50	22.50		79	96
1220	12" long		20	.400		63	22.50		85.50	104
1240	2" diameter, close		18	.444		42	25		67	83.50
1260	2-1/2" long		18	.444		43.50	25		68.50	85.50
1280	3" long		18	.444		45	25		70	87
1300	3-1/2" long		18	.444		47	25		72	89.50
1320	4" long		18	.444		48	25		73	90.50
1340	5" long		18	.444		52	25		77	94.50
1360	6" long		18	.444		55	25		80	97.50
1380	8" long		18	.444		66.50	25		91.50	111
1400	10" long		18	.444		63	25		88	107
1420	12" long		18	.444		78	25		103	123
1440	2-1/2" diameter, close		15	.533		103	30		133	158
1460	3" long		15	.533		104	30		134	159
1480	3-1/2" long		15	.533		108	30		138	164

148

26 05 33.15 Conduit Nipples		Crew	Daily Output	Labor-Hours	Unit	Material	2017 Bare Costs Labor	Equipment	Total	Total Incl O&P
1500	4" long	1 Elec	15	.533	Ea.	113	30		143	170
1520	5" long		15	.533		113	30		143	169
1540	6" long		15	.533		114	30		144	170
1560	8" long		15	.533		121	30		151	178
1580	10" long		15	.533		130	30		160	188
1600	12" long		15	.533		138	30		168	197
1620	3" diameter, close		12	.667		112	37.50		149.50	180
1640	3" long		12	.667		120	37.50		157.50	189
1660	3-1/2" long		12	.667		117	37.50		154.50	185
1680	4" long		12	.667		125	37.50		162.50	195
1700	5" long		12	.667		123	37.50		160.50	193
1720	6" long		12	.667		133	37.50		170.50	203
1740	8" long		12	.667		155	37.50		192.50	228
1760	10" long		12	.667		160	37.50		197.50	233
1780	12" long		12	.667		178	37.50		215.50	253
1800	3-1/2" diameter, close		11	.727		250	41		291	335
1820	4" long		11	.727		261	41		302	350
1840	5" long		11	.727		263	41		304	350
1860	6" long		11	.727		270	41		311	360
1880	8" long		11	.727		280	41		321	370
1900	10" long		11	.727		294	41		335	385
1920	12" long		11	.727		345	41		386	435
1940	4" diameter, close		9	.889		258	50.50		308.50	360
1960	4" long		9	.889		275	50.50		325.50	380
1980	5" long		9	.889		288	50.50		338.50	390
2000	6" long		9	.889		281	50.50		331.50	385
2020	8" long		9	.889		315	50.50		365.50	425
2040	10" long		9	.889		330	50.50		380.50	440
2060	12" long		9	.889		325	50.50		375.50	435
2080	5" diameter, close		7	1.143		450	64.50		514.50	590
2100	5" long		7	1.143		505	64.50		569.50	650
2120	6" long		7	1.143		475	64.50		539.50	620
2140	8" long		7	1.143		525	64.50		589.50	670
2160	10" long		7	1.143		535	64.50		599.50	680
2180	12" long		7	1.143		555	64.50		619.50	705
2200	6" diameter, close		6	1.333		765	75.50		840.50	955
2220	5" long		6	1.333		800	75.50		875.50	995
2240	6" long		6	1.333		830	75.50		905.50	1,025
2260	8" long		6	1.333		855	75.50		930.50	1,050
2280	10" long		6	1.333		940	75.50		1,015.50	1,150
2300	12" long		6	1.333		885	75.50		960.50	1,100
2320	Rigid galvanized steel, 1/2" diameter, close		32	.250		2.83	14.15		16.98	24
2340	1-1/2" long		32	.250		3.08	14.15		17.23	24.50
2360	2" long		32	.250		3.22	14.15		17.37	24.50
2380	2-1/2" long		32	.250		3.34	14.15		17.49	24.50
2400	3" long		32	.250		3.50	14.15		17.65	25
2420	3-1/2" long		32	.250		3.64	14.15		17.79	25
2440	4" long		32	.250		3.79	14.15		17.94	25
2460	5" long		32	.250		4.04	14.15		18.19	25.50
2480	6" long		32	.250		4.50	14.15		18.65	26
2500	8" long		32	.250		6.50	14.15		20.65	28
2520	10" long		32	.250		7.25	14.15		21.40	29
2540	12" long		32	.250		8.05	14.15		22.20	30

For customer support on your Electrical Costs with RSMeans Data, call 800.448.8182.

149

26 05 33.15 Conduit Nipples		Crew	Daily Output	Labor-Hours	Unit	Material	2017 Bare Costs Labor	Equipment	Total	Total Incl O&P
2560	3/4" diameter, close	1 Elec	27	.296	Ea.	4.11	16.75		20.86	29.50
2580	2" long		27	.296		4.39	16.75		21.14	30
2600	2-1/2" long		27	.296		4.58	16.75		21.33	30
2620	3" long		27	.296		4.71	16.75		21.46	30
2640	3-1/2" long		27	.296		4.80	16.75		21.55	30.50
2660	4" long		27	.296		5.10	16.75		21.85	30.50
2680	5" long		27	.296		5.45	16.75		22.20	31
2700	6" long		27	.296		5.90	16.75		22.65	31.50
2720	8" long		27	.296		8	16.75		24.75	34
2740	10" long		27	.296		9.05	16.75		25.80	35
2760	12" long		27	.296		9.85	16.75		26.60	36
2780	1" diameter, close		23	.348		6.85	19.70		26.55	37
2800	2" long		23	.348		7.05	19.70		26.75	37.50
2820	2-1/2" long		23	.348		7.25	19.70		26.95	37.50
2840	3" long		23	.348		7.55	19.70		27.25	38
2860	3-1/2" long		23	.348		7.90	19.70		27.60	38
2880	4" long		23	.348		8.15	19.70		27.85	38.50
2900	5" long		23	.348		8.60	19.70		28.30	39
2920	6" long		23	.348		9	19.70		28.70	39.50
2940	8" long		23	.348		11.40	19.70		31.10	42
2960	10" long		23	.348		13.40	19.70		33.10	44.50
2980	12" long		23	.348		14.50	19.70		34.20	45.50
3000	1-1/4" diameter, close		20	.400		8.45	22.50		30.95	43.50
3020	2" long		20	.400		8.65	22.50		31.15	43.50
3040	3" long		20	.400		9.20	22.50		31.70	44
3060	3-1/2" long		20	.400		9.65	22.50		32.15	44.50
3080	4" long		20	.400		9.90	22.50		32.40	45
3100	5" long		20	.400		10.60	22.50		33.10	45.50
3120	6" long		20	.400		11.20	22.50		33.70	46.50
3140	8" long		20	.400		14.70	22.50		37.20	50
3160	10" long		20	.400		17	22.50		39.50	52.50
3180	12" long		20	.400		18.85	22.50		41.35	55
3200	1-1/2" diameter, close		18	.444		12.25	25		37.25	51
3220	2" long		18	.444		12.40	25		37.40	51
3240	2-1/2" long		18	.444		12.85	25		37.85	51.50
3260	3" long		18	.444		13.15	25		38.15	52
3280	3-1/2" long		18	.444		13.80	25		38.80	52.50
3300	4" long		18	.444		14.25	25		39.25	53
3320	5" long		18	.444		14.85	25		39.85	54
3340	6" long		18	.444		16.25	25		41.25	55.50
3360	8" long		18	.444		20	25		45	59.50
3380	10" long		18	.444		22.50	25		47.50	62
3400	12" long		18	.444		23.50	25		48.50	63.50
3420	2" diameter, close		16	.500		14.50	28.50		43	58.50
3440	2-1/2" long		16	.500		15.20	28.50		43.70	59.50
3460	3" long		16	.500		15.95	28.50		44.45	60
3480	3-1/2" long		16	.500		16.75	28.50		45.25	61
3500	4" long		16	.500		17.40	28.50		45.90	61.50
3520	5" long		16	.500		18.55	28.50		47.05	63
3540	6" long		16	.500		19.65	28.50		48.15	64
3560	8" long		16	.500		24	28.50		52.50	68.50
3580	10" long		16	.500		26.50	28.50		55	71.50
3600	12" long		16	.500		28.50	28.50		57	74

26 05 33.15 Conduit Nipples	Crew	Daily Output	Labor-Hours	Unit	Material	2017 Bare Costs Labor	Equipment	Total	Total Incl O&P
3620	2-1/2" diameter, close	1 Elec	13	.615	Ea.	53.50	35		88.50	111
3640	3" long		13	.615		53.50	35		88.50	111
3660	3-1/2" long		13	.615		56	35		91	114
3680	4" long		13	.615		56.50	35		91.50	114
3700	5" long		13	.615		59	35		94	117
3720	6" long		13	.615		61	35		96	120
3740	8" long		13	.615		67	35		102	126
3760	10" long		13	.615		71	35		106	131
3780	12" long		13	.615		76	35		111	136
3800	3" diameter, close		12	.667		53	37.50		90.50	115
3820	3" long		12	.667		54.50	37.50		92	117
3900	3-1/2" long		12	.667		55.50	37.50		93	118
3920	4" long		12	.667		57	37.50		94.50	119
3940	5" long		12	.667		59.50	37.50		97	122
3960	6" long		12	.667		62.50	37.50		100	125
3980	8" long		12	.667		69	37.50		106.50	133
4000	10" long		12	.667		74.50	37.50		112	139
4020	12" long		12	.667		82	37.50		119.50	147
4040	3-1/2" diameter, close		10	.800		105	45.50		150.50	184
4060	4" long		10	.800		109	45.50		154.50	188
4080	5" long		10	.800		112	45.50		157.50	191
4100	6" long		10	.800		116	45.50		161.50	195
4120	8" long		10	.800		122	45.50		167.50	203
4140	10" long		10	.800		129	45.50		174.50	210
4160	12" long		10	.800		137	45.50		182.50	218
4180	4" diameter, close		8	1		147	56.50		203.50	246
4200	4" long		8	1		150	56.50		206.50	251
4220	5" long		8	1		154	56.50		210.50	255
4240	6" long		8	1		157	56.50		213.50	258
4260	8" long		8	1		165	56.50		221.50	266
4280	10" long		8	1		173	56.50		229.50	275
4300	12" long		8	1		182	56.50		238.50	285
4320	5" diameter, close		6	1.333		247	75.50		322.50	385
4340	5" long		6	1.333		263	75.50		338.50	405
4360	6" long		6	1.333		268	75.50		343.50	410
4380	8" long		6	1.333		280	75.50		355.50	420
4400	10" long		6	1.333		291	75.50		366.50	435
4420	12" long		6	1.333		310	75.50		385.50	455
4440	6" diameter, close		5	1.600		460	90.50		550.50	640
4460	5" long		5	1.600		475	90.50		565.50	655
4480	6" long		5	1.600		480	90.50		570.50	665
4500	8" long		5	1.600		495	90.50		585.50	680
4520	10" long		5	1.600		515	90.50		605.50	700
4540	12" long		5	1.600		525	90.50		615.50	715
4560	Plastic coated, 40 mil thick, 1/2" diameter, 2" long		32	.250		17.65	14.15		31.80	40.50
4580	2-1/2" long		32	.250		20.50	14.15		34.65	43.50
4600	3" long		32	.250		20.50	14.15		34.65	43.50
4680	3-1/2" long		32	.250		23.50	14.15		37.65	47
4700	4" long		32	.250		23	14.15		37.15	46.50
4720	5" long		32	.250		23	14.15		37.15	46.50
4740	6" long		32	.250		24.50	14.15		38.65	48
4760	8" long		32	.250		23	14.15		37.15	46.50
4780	10" long		32	.250		24	14.15		38.15	47.50

26 05 33.15 Conduit Nipples		Crew	Daily Output	Labor-Hours	Unit	Material	2017 Bare Costs Labor	Equipment	Total	Total Incl O&P
4800	12" long	1 Elec	32	.250	Ea.	25	14.15		39.15	48.50
4820	3/4" diameter, 2" long		26	.308		19.20	17.40		36.60	47
4840	2-1/2" long		26	.308		22	17.40		39.40	50
4860	3" long		26	.308		21	17.40		38.40	49.50
4880	3-1/2" long		26	.308		24.50	17.40		41.90	53
4900	4" long		26	.308		24.50	17.40		41.90	53
4920	5" long		26	.308		25.50	17.40		42.90	54
4940	6" long		26	.308		24.50	17.40		41.90	53
4960	8" long		26	.308		24.50	17.40		41.90	53
4980	10" long		26	.308		25.50	17.40		42.90	54
5000	12" long		26	.308		29.50	17.40		46.90	58.50
5020	1" diameter, 2" long		22	.364		21.50	20.50		42	54.50
5040	2-1/2" long		22	.364		25.50	20.50		46	59
5060	3" long		22	.364		24.50	20.50		45	58
5080	3-1/2" long		22	.364		26	20.50		46.50	59.50
5100	4" long		22	.364		28.50	20.50		49	62.50
5120	5" long		22	.364		29	20.50		49.50	63
5140	6" long		22	.364		27.50	20.50		48	61
5160	8" long		22	.364		28.50	20.50		49	62
5180	10" long		22	.364		29.50	20.50		50	63.50
5200	12" long		22	.364		35.50	20.50		56	70
5220	1-1/4" diameter, 2" long		18	.444		26	25		51	66.50
5240	2-1/2" long		18	.444		28.50	25		53.50	69
5260	3" long		18	.444		30	25		55	70.50
5280	3-1/2" long		18	.444		30	25		55	70.50
5300	4" long		18	.444		31	25		56	72
5320	5" long		18	.444		32	25		57	72.50
5340	6" long		18	.444		36	25		61	77
5360	8" long		18	.444		33	25		58	74
5380	10" long		18	.444		37	25		62	78
5400	12" long		18	.444		47.50	25		72.50	90
5420	1-1/2" diameter, 2" long		16	.500		30	28.50		58.50	75.50
5440	2-1/2" long		16	.500		32.50	28.50		61	78
5460	3" long		16	.500		32	28.50		60.50	78
5480	3-1/2" long		16	.500		34	28.50		62.50	80
5500	4" long		16	.500		38	28.50		66.50	84.50
5520	5" long		16	.500		39.50	28.50		68	85.50
5540	6" long		16	.500		41	28.50		69.50	87.50
5560	8" long		16	.500		41.50	28.50		70	88
5580	10" long		16	.500		49.50	28.50		78	97
5600	12" long		16	.500		62	28.50		90.50	111
5620	2" diameter, 2-1/2" long		14	.571		39.50	32.50		72	92
5640	3" long		14	.571		39	32.50		71.50	91.50
5660	3-1/2" long		14	.571		40.50	32.50		73	93
5680	4" long		14	.571		43.50	32.50		76	96
5700	5" long		14	.571		47	32.50		79.50	101
5720	6" long		14	.571		49	32.50		81.50	102
5740	8" long		14	.571		52	32.50		84.50	106
5760	10" long		14	.571		63	32.50		95.50	118
5780	12" long		14	.571		75.50	32.50		108	132
5800	2-1/2" diameter, 3-1/2" long		12	.667		89.50	37.50		127	155
5820	4" long		12	.667		91.50	37.50		129	157
5840	5" long		12	.667		103	37.50		140.50	171

26 05 33 – Raceway and Boxes for Electrical Systems

26 05 33.15 Conduit Nipples

		Crew	Daily Output	Labor-Hours	Unit	Material	2017 Bare Costs Labor	Equipment	Total	Total Incl O&P
5860	6" long	1 Elec	12	.667	Ea.	112	37.50		149.50	180
5880	8" long		12	.667		117	37.50		154.50	186
5900	10" long		12	.667		127	37.50		164.50	196
5920	12" long		12	.667		141	37.50		178.50	212
5940	3" diameter, 3-1/2" long		11	.727		98	41		139	170
5960	4" long		11	.727		98	41		139	170
5980	5" long		11	.727		105	41		146	177
6000	6" long		11	.727		114	41		155	187
6020	8" long		11	.727		126	41		167	201
6040	10" long		11	.727		144	41		185	220
6060	12" long		11	.727		164	41		205	242
6080	3-1/2" diameter, 4" long		9	.889		162	50.50		212.50	254
6100	5" long		9	.889		163	50.50		213.50	255
6120	6" long		9	.889		180	50.50		230.50	274
6140	8" long		9	.889		191	50.50		241.50	286
6160	10" long		9	.889		208	50.50		258.50	305
6180	12" long		9	.889		225	50.50		275.50	325
6200	4" diameter, 4" long		7.50	1.067		206	60.50		266.50	320
6220	5" long		7.50	1.067		210	60.50		270.50	320
6240	6" long		7.50	1.067		224	60.50		284.50	335
6260	8" long		7.50	1.067		244	60.50		304.50	360
6280	10" long		7.50	1.067		280	60.50		340.50	400
6300	12" long		7.50	1.067		289	60.50		349.50	410
6320	5" diameter, 5" long		5.50	1.455		258	82.50		340.50	405
6340	6" long		5.50	1.455		297	82.50		379.50	450
6360	8" long		5.50	1.455		305	82.50		387.50	460
6380	10" long		5.50	1.455		320	82.50		402.50	480
6400	12" long		5.50	1.455		325	82.50		407.50	480
6420	6" diameter, 5" long		4.50	1.778		505	101		606	705
6440	6" long		4.50	1.778		515	101		616	715
6460	8" long		4.50	1.778		530	101		631	730
6480	10" long		4.50	1.778		540	101		641	745
6500	12" long		4.50	1.778		560	101		661	765

26 05 33.16 Boxes for Electrical Systems

		Crew	Daily Output	Labor-Hours	Unit	Material	2017 Bare Costs Labor	Equipment	Total	Total Incl O&P
0010	**BOXES FOR ELECTRICAL SYSTEMS** R260533-65									
0020	Pressed steel, octagon, 4"	1 Elec	20	.400	Ea.	2.22	22.50		24.72	36.50
0040	For Romex or BX		20	.400		3.33	22.50		25.83	37.50
0050	For Romex or BX, with bracket		20	.400		5.25	22.50		27.75	40
0060	Covers, blank		64	.125		.93	7.10		8.03	11.60
0100	Extension rings		40	.200		3.68	11.30		14.98	21
0150	Square, 4"		20	.400		2.88	22.50		25.38	37
0160	For Romex or BX		20	.400		5.95	22.50		28.45	40.50
0170	For Romex or BX, with bracket		20	.400		7.60	22.50		30.10	42.50
0200	Extension rings		40	.200		3.72	11.30		15.02	21
0220	2-1/8" deep, 1" KO		20	.400		3.84	22.50		26.34	38
0250	Covers, blank		64	.125		1	7.10		8.10	11.70
0260	Raised device		64	.125		1.89	7.10		8.99	12.70
0300	Plaster rings		64	.125		2.04	7.10		9.14	12.85
0350	Square, 4-11/16"		20	.400		5.20	22.50		27.70	39.50
0370	2-1/8" deep, 3/4" to 1-1/4" KO		20	.400		6.25	22.50		28.75	41
0400	Extension rings		40	.200		8.35	11.30		19.65	26
0450	Covers, blank		53	.151		1.88	8.55		10.43	14.85

For customer support on your Electrical Costs with RSMeans Data, call 800.448.8182.

153

26 05 33.16 Boxes for Electrical Systems	Crew	Daily Output	Labor-Hours	Unit	Material	2017 Bare Costs Labor	Equipment	Total	Total Incl O&P
0460	Raised device	1 Elec	53	.151	Ea.	5.60	8.55		14.15	18.95
0500	Plaster rings		53	.151		5.55	8.55		14.10	18.90
0550	Handy box		27	.296		2.45	16.75		19.20	27.50
0560	Covers, device		64	.125		.87	7.10		7.97	11.55
0600	Extension rings		54	.148		2.92	8.40		11.32	15.75
0650	Switchbox		27	.296		3.55	16.75		20.30	29
0660	Romex or BX		27	.296		5.10	16.75		21.85	30.50
0670	with bracket		27	.296		5.90	16.75		22.65	31.50
0680	Partition, metal		27	.296		2.22	16.75		18.97	27.50
0700	Masonry, 1 gang, 2-1/2" deep		27	.296		6.75	16.75		23.50	32.50
0710	3-1/2" deep		27	.296		6.80	16.75		23.55	32.50
0750	2 gang, 2-1/2" deep		20	.400		12.75	22.50		35.25	48
0760	3-1/2" deep		20	.400		10.25	22.50		32.75	45.50
0800	3 gang, 2-1/2" deep		13	.615		15.20	35		50.20	69
0850	4 gang, 2-1/2" deep		10	.800		17.60	45.50		63.10	87.50
0860	5 gang, 2-1/2" deep		9	.889		18.75	50.50		69.25	96
0870	6 gang, 2-1/2" deep		8	1		38	56.50		94.50	127
0880	Masonry thru-the-wall, 1 gang, 4" block		16	.500		26	28.50		54.50	71
0890	6" block		16	.500		42.50	28.50		71	89.50
0900	8" block		16	.500		45.50	28.50		74	92.50
0920	2 gang, 6" block		16	.500		64	28.50		92.50	113
0940	Bar hanger with 3/8" stud, for wood and masonry boxes		53	.151		4.74	8.55		13.29	18
0950	Concrete, set flush, 4" deep		20	.400		10.45	22.50		32.95	45.50
1000	Plate with 3/8" stud		80	.100		6.90	5.65		12.55	16.05
1100	Concrete, floor, 1 gang		5.30	1.509		89.50	85.50		175	227
1150	2 gang		4	2		137	113		250	320
1200	3 gang		2.70	2.963		203	168		371	475
1250	For duplex receptacle, pedestal mounted, add		24	.333		97.50	18.85		116.35	136
1270	Flush mounted, add		27	.296		30.50	16.75		47.25	58.50
1300	For telephone, pedestal mounted, add		30	.267		113	15.10		128.10	148
1350	Carpet flange, 1 gang		53	.151		50.50	8.55		59.05	68.50
1400	Cast, 1 gang, FS (2" deep), 1/2" hub		12	.667		18.25	37.50		55.75	76.50
1410	3/4" hub		12	.667		19.30	37.50		56.80	77.50
1420	FD (2-11/16" deep), 1/2" hub		12	.667		18.40	37.50		55.90	77
1430	3/4" hub		12	.667		20	37.50		57.50	78.50
1450	2 gang, FS, 1/2" hub		10	.800		33	45.50		78.50	104
1460	3/4" hub		10	.800		35.50	45.50		81	107
1470	FD, 1/2" hub		10	.800		39.50	45.50		85	112
1480	3/4" hub		10	.800		39.50	45.50		85	111
1500	3 gang, FS, 3/4" hub		9	.889		56	50.50		106.50	137
1510	Switch cover, 1 gang, FS		64	.125		4.83	7.10		11.93	15.90
1520	2 gang		53	.151		7.35	8.55		15.90	21
1530	Duplex receptacle cover, 1 gang, FS		64	.125		4.93	7.10		12.03	16
1540	2 gang, FS		53	.151		7.50	8.55		16.05	21
1542	Weatherproof blank cover, 1 gang		64	.125		1.22	7.10		8.32	11.95
1544	2 gang		53	.151		2.52	8.55		11.07	15.55
1550	Weatherproof switch cover, 1 gang		64	.125		6.40	7.10		13.50	17.65
1554	2 gang		53	.151		10.60	8.55		19.15	24.50
1600	Weatherproof receptacle cover, 1 gang		64	.125		4.10	7.10		11.20	15.10
1604	2 gang		53	.151		10.60	8.55		19.15	24.50
1620	Weatherproof receptacle cover, tamper resistant, 1 gang		58	.138		13.50	7.80		21.30	26.50
1624	2 gang		48	.167		27	9.45		36.45	43.50
1750	FSC, 1 gang, 1/2" hub		11	.727		20	41		61	83.50

For customer support on your Electrical Costs with RSMeans Data, call 800.448.8182.

26 05 33 – Raceway and Boxes for Electrical Systems

26 05 33.16 Boxes for Electrical Systems

		Crew	Daily Output	Labor-Hours	Unit	Material	2017 Bare Costs Labor	Equipment	Total	Total Incl O&P
1760	3/4" hub	1 Elec	11	.727	Ea.	22.50	41		63.50	86
1770	2 gang, 1/2" hub		9	.889		30.50	50.50		81	109
1780	3/4" hub		9	.889		39	50.50		89.50	119
1790	FDC, 1 gang, 1/2" hub		11	.727		23	41		64	86.50
1800	3/4" hub		11	.727		25.50	41		66.50	89.50
1810	2 gang, 1/2" hub		9	.889		47.50	50.50		98	128
1820	3/4" hub		9	.889		42	50.50		92.50	122
1850	Weatherproof in-use cover, 1 gang		64	.125		24	7.10		31.10	37
1870	2 gang		53	.151		27	8.55		35.55	42.50
2000	Poke-thru fitting, fire rated, for 3-3/4" floor		6.80	1.176		131	66.50		197.50	244
2040	For 7" floor		6.80	1.176		181	66.50		247.50	299
2100	Pedestal, 15 amp, duplex receptacle & blank plate		5.25	1.524		138	86.50		224.50	280
2120	Duplex receptacle and telephone plate		5.25	1.524		138	86.50		224.50	280
2140	Pedestal, 20 amp, duplex recept. & phone plate		5	1.600		139	90.50		229.50	288
2160	Telephone plate, both sides		5.25	1.524		131	86.50		217.50	273
2200	Abandonment plate		32	.250		38.50	14.15		52.65	63.50

26 05 33.17 Outlet Boxes, Plastic

		Crew	Daily Output	Labor-Hours	Unit	Material	2017 Bare Costs Labor	Equipment	Total	Total Incl O&P
0010	**OUTLET BOXES, PLASTIC**									
0050	4" diameter, round with 2 mounting nails	1 Elec	25	.320	Ea.	2.39	18.10		20.49	29.50
0100	Bar hanger mounted		25	.320		5.10	18.10		23.20	32.50
0200	4", square with 2 mounting nails		25	.320		4.63	18.10		22.73	32
0300	Plaster ring		64	.125		1.98	7.10		9.08	12.80
0400	Switch box with 2 mounting nails, 1 gang		30	.267		4.39	15.10		19.49	27.50
0500	2 gang		25	.320		3.33	18.10		21.43	30.50
0600	3 gang		20	.400		4.19	22.50		26.69	38.50
0700	Old work box		30	.267		4.85	15.10		19.95	28
1400	PVC, FSS, 1 gang, 1/2" hub		14	.571		13.90	32.50		46.40	64
1410	3/4" hub		14	.571		11.35	32.50		43.85	61
1420	FD, 1 gang for variable terminations		14	.571		9.35	32.50		41.85	59
1450	FS, 2 gang for variable terminations		12	.667		11.05	37.50		48.55	68.50
1480	Weatherproof blank cover, FS, 1 gang		64	.125		4.09	7.10		11.19	15.10
1500	2 gang		53	.151		4.74	8.55		13.29	18
1510	Weatherproof switch cover, FS, 1 gang		64	.125		9.85	7.10		16.95	21.50
1520	2 gang		53	.151		16.20	8.55		24.75	30.50
1530	Weatherproof duplex receptacle cover, FS, 1 gang		64	.125		13.55	7.10		20.65	25.50
1540	2 gang		53	.151		14.40	8.55		22.95	28.50
1750	FSC, 1 gang, 1/2" hub		13	.615		9.20	35		44.20	62
1760	3/4" hub		13	.615		9.90	35		44.90	63
1770	FSC, 2 gang, 1/2" hub		11	.727		14.10	41		55.10	77
1780	3/4" hub		11	.727		14.05	41		55.05	77
1790	FDC, 1 gang, 1/2" hub		13	.615		9.15	35		44.15	62
1800	3/4" hub		13	.615		10.35	35		45.35	63.50
1810	Weatherproof, T box w/3 holes		14	.571		9.90	32.50		42.40	59.50
1820	4" diameter round w/5 holes		14	.571		8.85	32.50		41.35	58
1850	In-use cover, 1 gang		64	.125		8.75	7.10		15.85	20.50
1870	2 gang		53	.151		11	8.55		19.55	25

26 05 33.18 Pull Boxes

		Crew	Daily Output	Labor-Hours	Unit	Material	2017 Bare Costs Labor	Equipment	Total	Total Incl O&P
0010	**PULL BOXES**	R260533-70								
0100	Steel, pull box, NEMA 1, type SC, 6" W x 6" H x 4" D	1 Elec	8	1	Ea.	9.65	56.50		66.15	95.50
0180	8" W x 6" H x 4" D		8	1		13.30	56.50		69.80	99.50
0200	8" W x 8" H x 4" D		8	1		13.20	56.50		69.70	99.50
0210	10" W x 10" H x 4" D		7	1.143		17.65	64.50		82.15	116

For customer support on your Electrical Costs with RSMeans Data, call 800.448.8182.

155

26 05 33.18 Pull Boxes		Crew	Daily Output	Labor-Hours	Unit	Material	2017 Bare Costs Labor	Equipment	Total	Total Incl O&P
0220	12" W x 12" H x 4" D	1 Elec	6.50	1.231	Ea.	22.50	69.50		92	129
0230	15" W x 15" H x 4" D		5.20	1.538		42	87		129	177
0240	18" W x 18" H x 4" D		4.40	1.818		42.50	103		145.50	201
0250	6" W x 6" H x 6" D		8	1		14.90	56.50		71.40	101
0260	8" W x 8" H x 6" D		7.50	1.067		16.15	60.50		76.65	108
0270	10" W x 10" H x 6" D		5.50	1.455		21	82.50		103.50	146
0300	10" W x 12" H x 6" D		5.30	1.509		22.50	85.50		108	153
0310	12" W x 12" H x 6" D		5.20	1.538		26.50	87		113.50	159
0320	15" W x 15" H x 6" D		4.60	1.739		43	98.50		141.50	194
0330	18" W x 18" H x 6" D		4.20	1.905		47.50	108		155.50	215
0340	24" W x 24" H x 6" D		3.20	2.500		95.50	142		237.50	315
0350	12" W x 12" H x 8" D		5	1.600		30.50	90.50		121	170
0360	15" W x 15" H x 8" D		4.50	1.778		45.50	101		146.50	201
0370	18" W x 18" H x 8" D		4	2		61	113		174	237
0380	24" W x 18" H x 6" D		3.70	2.162		87.50	122		209.50	280
0400	16" W x 20" H x 8" D		4	2		84.50	113		197.50	263
0500	20" W x 24" H x 8" D		3.20	2.500		98	142		240	320
0510	24" W x 24" H x 8" D		3	2.667		108	151		259	345
0600	24" W x 36" H x 8" D		2.70	2.963		153	168		321	420
0610	30" W x 30" H x 8" D		2.70	2.963		197	168		365	470
0620	36" W x 36" H x 8" D		2	4		223	226		449	585
0630	24" W x 24" H x 10" D		2.50	3.200		190	181		371	480
0650	Pull box, hinged, NEMA 1, 6" W x 6" H x 4" D		8	1		11.60	56.50		68.10	98
0660	8" W x 8" H x 4" D		8	1		16.45	56.50		72.95	103
0670	10" W x 10" H x 4" D		7	1.143		19.55	64.50		84.05	119
0680	12" W x 12" H x 4" D		6	1.333		27.50	75.50		103	143
0690	15" W x 15" H x 4" D		5.20	1.538		30	87		117	163
0700	18" W x 18" H x 4" D		4.40	1.818		35	103		138	193
0710	6" W x 6" H x 6" D		8	1		15.10	56.50		71.60	102
0720	8" W x 8" H x 6" D		7.50	1.067		20	60.50		80.50	113
0730	10" W x 10" H x 6" D		5.50	1.455		27	82.50		109.50	153
0740	12" W x 12" H x 6" D		5.20	1.538		32	87		119	166
0800	12" W x 16" H x 6" D		4.70	1.702		57	96.50		153.50	207
0810	15" W x 15" H x 6" D		4.60	1.739		33.50	98.50		132	184
0820	18" W x 18" H x 6" D		4.20	1.905		58.50	108		166.50	226
1000	20" W x 20" H x 6" D		3.60	2.222		99	126		225	297
1010	24" W x 24" H x 6" D		3.20	2.500		115	142		257	340
1020	12" W x 12" H x 8" D		5	1.600		74	90.50		164.50	217
1030	15" W x 15" H x 8" D		4.50	1.778		85.50	101		186.50	245
1040	18" W x 18" H x 8" D		4	2		120	113		233	300
1200	20" W x 20" H x 8" D		3.20	2.500		149	142		291	375
1210	24" W x 24" H x 8" D		3	2.667		169	151		320	410
1220	30" W x 30" H x 8" D		2.70	2.963		244	168		412	520
1400	24" W x 36" H x 8" D		2.70	2.963		237	168		405	510
1600	24" W x 42" H x 8" D		2	4		350	226		576	725
1610	36" W x 36" H x 8" D		2	4		375	226		601	750
2100	Pull box, NEMA 3R, type SC, raintight & weatherproof									
2150	6" L x 6" W x 6" D	1 Elec	10	.800	Ea.	16.95	45.50		62.45	86.50
2200	8" L x 6" W x 6" D		8	1		23.50	56.50		80	111
2250	10" L x 6" W x 6" D		7	1.143		32	64.50		96.50	132
2300	12" L x 12" W x 6" D		5	1.600		46.50	90.50		137	187
2350	16" L x 16" W x 6" D		4.50	1.778		89	101		190	249
2400	20" L x 20" W x 6" D		4	2		89	113		202	268

26 05 33.18 Pull Boxes		Crew	Daily Output	Labor-Hours	Unit	Material	2017 Bare Costs Labor	2017 Bare Costs Equipment	Total	Total Incl O&P
2450	24" L x 18" W x 8" D	1 Elec	3	2.667	Ea.	123	151		274	360
2500	24" L x 24" W x 10" D		2.50	3.200		247	181		428	545
2550	30" L x 24" W x 12" D		2	4		385	226		611	765
2600	36" L x 36" W x 12" D	↓	1.50	5.333	↓	430	300		730	925
2800	Cast iron, pull boxes for surface mounting									
3000	NEMA 4, watertight & dust tight									
3050	6" L x 6" W x 6" D	1 Elec	4	2	Ea.	267	113		380	465
3100	8" L x 6" W x 6" D		3.20	2.500		370	142		512	620
3150	10" L x 6" W x 6" D		2.50	3.200		415	181		596	730
3200	12" L x 12" W x 6" D		2.30	3.478		760	197		957	1,125
3250	16" L x 16" W x 6" D		1.30	6.154		1,100	350		1,450	1,750
3300	20" L x 20" W x 6" D		.80	10		1,525	565		2,090	2,525
3350	24" L x 18" W x 8" D		.70	11.429		2,600	645		3,245	3,825
3400	24" L x 24" W x 10" D		.50	16		4,900	905		5,805	6,750
3450	30" L x 24" W x 12" D		.40	20		6,275	1,125		7,400	8,600
3500	36" L x 36" W x 12" D		.20	40		5,075	2,275		7,350	9,000
3510	NEMA 4 clamp cover, 6" L x 6" W x 4" D		4	2		175	113		288	365
3520	8" L x 6" W x 4" D	↓	4	2	↓	217	113		330	410
4000	NEMA 7, explosionproof									
4050	6" L x 6" W x 6" D	1 Elec	2	4	Ea.	690	226		916	1,100
4100	8" L x 6" W x 6" D		1.80	4.444		995	252		1,247	1,475
4150	10" L x 6" W x 6" D		1.60	5		1,275	283		1,558	1,825
4200	12" L x 12" W x 6" D		1	8		2,300	455		2,755	3,225
4250	16" L x 14" W x 6" D		.60	13.333		3,400	755		4,155	4,875
4300	18" L x 18" W x 8" D		.50	16		6,025	905		6,930	7,975
4350	24" L x 18" W x 8" D		.40	20		7,675	1,125		8,800	10,100
4400	24" L x 24" W x 10" D		.30	26.667		10,500	1,500		12,000	13,800
4450	30" L x 24" W x 12" D		.20	40		14,300	2,275		16,575	19,100
5000	NEMA 9, dust tight 6" L x 6" W x 6" D		3.20	2.500		395	142		537	645
5050	8" L x 6" W x 6" D		2.70	2.963		470	168		638	770
5100	10" L x 6" W x 6" D		2	4		625	226		851	1,025
5150	12" L x 12" W x 6" D		1.60	5		1,200	283		1,483	1,750
5200	16" L x 16" W x 6" D		1	8		2,000	455		2,455	2,875
5250	18" L x 18" W x 8" D		.70	11.429		3,125	645		3,770	4,400
5300	24" L x 18" W x 8" D		.60	13.333		4,425	755		5,180	5,975
5350	24" L x 24" W x 10" D		.40	20		6,075	1,125		7,200	8,375
5400	30" L x 24" W x 12" D	↓	.30	26.667	↓	8,950	1,500		10,450	12,100
6000	J.I.C. wiring boxes, NEMA 12, dust tight & drip tight									
6050	6" L x 8" W x 4" D	1 Elec	10	.800	Ea.	62.50	45.50		108	137
6100	8" L x 10" W x 4" D		8	1		77.50	56.50		134	170
6150	12" L x 14" W x 6" D		5.30	1.509		131	85.50		216.50	272
6200	14" L x 16" W x 6" D		4.70	1.702		154	96.50		250.50	315
6250	16" L x 20" W x 6" D		4.40	1.818		229	103		332	405
6300	24" L x 30" W x 6" D		3.20	2.500		335	142		477	580
6350	24" L x 30" W x 8" D		2.90	2.759		345	156		501	615
6400	24" L x 36" W x 8" D		2.70	2.963		385	168		553	675
6450	24" L x 42" W x 8" D		2.30	3.478		435	197		632	770
6500	24" L x 48" W x 8" D	↓	2	4	↓	475	226		701	860

For customer support on your Electrical Costs with RSMeans Data, call 800.448.8182.

157

26 05 33.23 Wireway		Crew	Daily Output	Labor-Hours	Unit	Material	2017 Bare Costs Labor	Equipment	Total	Total Incl O&P
0010	**WIREWAY** to 10' high	R260533-60								
0020	For higher elevations, see Section 26 05 36.40									
0100	NEMA 1, Screw cover w/fittings and supports, 2-1/2" x 2-1/2"	1 Elec	45	.178	L.F.	10.80	10.05		20.85	27
0200	4" x 4"	"	40	.200		11.65	11.30		22.95	30
0400	6" x 6"	2 Elec	60	.267		19.60	15.10		34.70	44
0600	8" x 8"		40	.400		28.50	22.50		51	65.50
0620	10" x 10"		30	.533		48	30		78	97.50
0640	12" x 12"		20	.800		61	45.50		106.50	135
0800	Elbows, 90°, 2-1/2"	1 Elec	24	.333	Ea.	32.50	18.85		51.35	64
1000	4"		20	.400		36.50	22.50		59	74.50
1200	6"		18	.444		41.50	25		66.50	83
1400	8"		16	.500		66.50	28.50		95	116
1420	10"		12	.667		95	37.50		132.50	161
1440	12"		10	.800		121	45.50		166.50	201
1500	Elbows, 45°, 2-1/2"		24	.333		32.50	18.85		51.35	64
1510	4"		20	.400		39.50	22.50		62	77.50
1520	6"		18	.444		41.50	25		66.50	83
1530	8"		16	.500		66.50	28.50		95	116
1540	10"		12	.667		95	37.50		132.50	161
1550	12"		10	.800		169	45.50		214.50	253
1600	"T" box, 2-1/2"		18	.444		37	25		62	78.50
1800	4"		16	.500		45	28.50		73.50	92
2000	6"		14	.571		50.50	32.50		83	104
2200	8"		12	.667		93	37.50		130.50	159
2220	10"		10	.800		124	45.50		169.50	204
2240	12"		8	1		175	56.50		231.50	278
2300	Cross, 2-1/2"		16	.500		41.50	28.50		70	88
2310	4"		14	.571		50.50	32.50		83	104
2320	6"		12	.667		62.50	37.50		100	125
2400	Panel adapter, 2-1/2"		24	.333		11.25	18.85		30.10	41
2600	4"		20	.400		11.50	22.50		34	46.50
2800	6"		18	.444		12.30	25		37.30	51
3000	8"		16	.500		16.95	28.50		45.45	61
3020	10"		14	.571		31.50	32.50		64	83
3040	12"		12	.667		39.50	37.50		77	100
3200	Reducer, 4" to 2-1/2"		24	.333		12.80	18.85		31.65	42.50
3400	6" to 4"		20	.400		27	22.50		49.50	63.50
3600	8" to 6"		18	.444		33	25		58	74
3620	10" to 8"		16	.500		47	28.50		75.50	94
3640	12" to 10"		14	.571		52	32.50		84.50	106
3780	End cap, 2-1/2"		24	.333		4.62	18.85		23.47	33.50
3800	4"		20	.400		5.70	22.50		28.20	40.50
4000	6"		18	.444		6.85	25		31.85	45
4200	8"		16	.500		9.30	28.50		37.80	53
4220	10"		14	.571		15.10	32.50		47.60	65
4240	12"		12	.667		21	37.50		58.50	79.50
4300	U-connector, 2-1/2"		200	.040		3.85	2.26		6.11	7.65
4320	4"		200	.040		4.76	2.26		7.02	8.65
4340	6"		180	.044		6.05	2.52		8.57	10.40
4360	8"		170	.047		10.95	2.66		13.61	16
4380	10"		150	.053		15.40	3.02		18.42	21.50
4400	12"		130	.062		22.50	3.48		25.98	29.50

26 05 33 – Raceway and Boxes for Electrical Systems

26 05 33.23 Wireway		Crew	Daily Output	Labor-Hours	Unit	Material	2017 Bare Costs Labor	Equipment	Total	Total Incl O&P
4420	Hanger, 2-1/2"	1 Elec	100	.080	Ea.	12.60	4.53		17.13	20.50
4430	4"		100	.080		12.60	4.53		17.13	20.50
4440	6"		80	.100		13.85	5.65		19.50	24
4450	8"		65	.123		24.50	6.95		31.45	37.50
4460	10"		50	.160		44.50	9.05		53.55	62.50
4470	12"		40	.200		65	11.30		76.30	88.50
4475	NEMA 3R, Screw cover w/fittings and supports, 4" x 4"		36	.222	L.F.	14	12.60		26.60	34.50
4480	6" x 6"	2 Elec	55	.291		18.75	16.45		35.20	45
4485	8" x 8"		36	.444		29	25		54	69.50
4490	12" x 12"		18	.889		46.50	50.50		97	127
4500	Hinged cover, with fittings and supports, 2-1/2" x 2-1/2"	1 Elec	60	.133		17.85	7.55		25.40	31
4520	4" x 4"	"	45	.178		16.30	10.05		26.35	33
4540	6" x 6"	2 Elec	80	.200		26	11.30		37.30	45.50
4560	8" x 8"		60	.267		42.50	15.10		57.60	69.50
4580	10" x 10"		50	.320		54	18.10		72.10	86
4600	12" x 12"		24	.667		78	37.50		115.50	142
4700	Elbows 90°, 2-1/2" x 2-1/2"	1 Elec	32	.250	Ea.	46	14.15		60.15	71.50
4720	4"		27	.296		72	16.75		88.75	104
4730	6"		23	.348		82.50	19.70		102.20	120
4740	8"		18	.444		104	25		129	152
4750	10"		14	.571		110	32.50		142.50	170
4760	12"		12	.667		177	37.50		214.50	251
4800	Tee box, hinged cover, 2-1/2" x 2-1/2"		23	.348		59.50	19.70		79.20	95
4810	4"		20	.400		85	22.50		107.50	128
4820	6"		18	.444		94.50	25		119.50	142
4830	8"		16	.500		177	28.50		205.50	238
4840	10"		12	.667		162	37.50		199.50	235
4860	12"		10	.800		208	45.50		253.50	297
4880	Cross box, hinged cover, 2-1/2" x 2-1/2"		18	.444		60.50	25		85.50	105
4900	4"		16	.500		96.50	28.50		125	149
4920	6"		13	.615		122	35		157	186
4940	8"		11	.727		177	41		218	257
4960	10"		10	.800		238	45.50		283.50	330
4980	12"		9	.889		261	50.50		311.50	365
5000	NEMA 12, hinged cover, 2-1/2" x 2-1/2"		40	.200	L.F.	34	11.30		45.30	54
5020	4" x 4"		35	.229		38	12.95		50.95	61.50
5040	6" x 6"	2 Elec	60	.267		59	15.10		74.10	87.50
5060	8" x 8"	"	50	.320		78.50	18.10		96.60	113
5120	Elbows 90°, flanged, 2-1/2" x 2-1/2"	1 Elec	23	.348	Ea.	83.50	19.70		103.20	121
5140	4"		20	.400		105	22.50		127.50	149
5160	6"		18	.444		133	25		158	185
5180	8"		15	.533		194	30		224	258
5240	Tee box, flanged, 2-1/2" x 2-1/2"		18	.444		114	25		139	163
5260	4"		16	.500		133	28.50		161.50	190
5280	6"		15	.533		180	30		210	243
5300	8"		13	.615		262	35		297	340
5360	Cross box, flanged, 2-1/2" x 2-1/2"		15	.533		177	30		207	239
5380	4"		13	.615		195	35		230	267
5400	6"		12	.667		254	37.50		291.50	335
5420	8"		10	.800		320	45.50		365.50	425
5480	Flange gasket, 2-1/2"		160	.050		4.12	2.83		6.95	8.75
5500	4"		80	.100		5.70	5.65		11.35	14.80
5520	6"		53	.151		7.90	8.55		16.45	21.50

26 05 33.23 Wireway	Crew	Daily Output	Labor-Hours	Unit	Material	2017 Bare Costs Labor	Equipment	Total	Total Incl O&P
5530 8"	1 Elec	40	.200	Ea.	10.25	11.30		21.55	28

26 05 33.25 Conduit Fittings for Rigid Galvanized Steel

	Crew	Daily Output	Labor-Hours	Unit	Material	2017 Bare Costs Labor	Equipment	Total	Total Incl O&P
0010 **CONDUIT FITTINGS FOR RIGID GALVANIZED STEEL**									
0050 Standard, locknuts, 1/2" diameter				Ea.	.22			.22	.24
0100 3/4" diameter					.39			.39	.43
0300 1" diameter					.66			.66	.73
0500 1-1/4" diameter					.77			.77	.85
0700 1-1/2" diameter					1.37			1.37	1.51
1000 2" diameter					1.90			1.90	2.09
1030 2-1/2" diameter					4.82			4.82	5.30
1050 3" diameter					6.15			6.15	6.80
1070 3-1/2" diameter					8.90			8.90	9.80
1100 4" diameter					12.45			12.45	13.70
1110 5" diameter					26.50			26.50	29.50
1120 6" diameter					72			72	79
1130 Bushings, plastic, 1/2" diameter	1 Elec	40	.200		.09	11.30		11.39	17.05
1150 3/4" diameter		32	.250		.11	14.15		14.26	21
1170 1" diameter		28	.286		.20	16.15		16.35	24
1200 1-1/4" diameter		24	.333		.24	18.85		19.09	29
1230 1-1/2" diameter		18	.444		.42	25		25.42	38
1250 2" diameter		15	.533		.58	30		30.58	45.50
1270 2-1/2" diameter		13	.615		1.16	35		36.16	53.50
1300 3" diameter		12	.667		1.34	37.50		38.84	58
1330 3-1/2" diameter		11	.727		1.53	41		42.53	63
1350 4" diameter		9	.889		1.59	50.50		52.09	77.50
1360 5" diameter		7	1.143		12.05	64.50		76.55	110
1370 6" diameter		5	1.600		30	90.50		120.50	169
1390 Steel, 1/2" diameter		40	.200		.66	11.30		11.96	17.70
1400 3/4" diameter		32	.250		.97	14.15		15.12	22
1430 1" diameter		28	.286		1.70	16.15		17.85	26
1450 Steel insulated, 1-1/4" diameter		24	.333		4.90	18.85		23.75	34
1470 1-1/2" diameter		18	.444		5.70	25		30.70	44
1500 2" diameter		15	.533		8.30	30		38.30	54
1530 2-1/2" diameter		13	.615		16.95	35		51.95	70.50
1550 3" diameter		12	.667		23.50	37.50		61	82
1570 3-1/2" diameter		11	.727		30.50	41		71.50	95.50
1600 4" diameter		9	.889		37	50.50		87.50	116
1610 5" diameter		7	1.143		69.50	64.50		134	173
1620 6" diameter		5	1.600		175	90.50		265.50	330
1630 Sealing locknuts, 1/2" diameter		40	.200		1.40	11.30		12.70	18.50
1650 3/4" diameter		32	.250		1.50	14.15		15.65	22.50
1670 1" diameter		28	.286		2.20	16.15		18.35	26.50
1700 1-1/4" diameter		24	.333		3.32	18.85		22.17	32
1730 1-1/2" diameter		18	.444		4.22	25		29.22	42
1750 2" diameter		15	.533		5.40	30		35.40	51
1760 Grounding bushing, insulated, 1/2" diameter		32	.250		4.71	14.15		18.86	26
1770 3/4" diameter		28	.286		5.35	16.15		21.50	30
1780 1" diameter		20	.400		6.45	22.50		28.95	41
1800 1-1/4" diameter		18	.444		8	25		33	46.50
1830 1-1/2" diameter		16	.500		9.30	28.50		37.80	53
1850 2" diameter		13	.615		12.25	35		47.25	65.50
1870 2-1/2" diameter		12	.667		20	37.50		57.50	78.50

26 05 33.25 Conduit Fittings for Rigid Galvanized Steel	Crew	Daily Output	Labor-Hours	Unit	Material	2017 Bare Costs Labor	2017 Bare Costs Equipment	Total	Total Incl O&P
1900	3" diameter	1 Elec	11	.727	Ea.	22.50	41		63.50	86
1930	3-1/2" diameter		9	.889		26	50.50		76.50	105
1950	4" diameter		8	1		35	56.50		91.50	124
1960	5" diameter		6	1.333		70.50	75.50		146	191
1970	6" diameter		4	2		93	113		206	272
1990	Coupling, with set screw, 1/2" diameter		50	.160		3.69	9.05		12.74	17.60
2000	3/4" diameter		40	.200		4.77	11.30		16.07	22
2030	1" diameter		35	.229		7.35	12.95		20.30	27.50
2050	1-1/4" diameter		28	.286		11.15	16.15		27.30	36.50
2070	1-1/2" diameter		23	.348		16.55	19.70		36.25	47.50
2090	2" diameter		20	.400		35	22.50		57.50	72.50
2100	2-1/2" diameter		18	.444		82.50	25		107.50	128
2110	3" diameter		15	.533		94.50	30		124.50	149
2120	3-1/2" diameter		12	.667		138	37.50		175.50	209
2130	4" diameter		10	.800		183	45.50		228.50	269
2140	5" diameter		9	.889		325	50.50		375.50	430
2150	6" diameter		8	1		565	56.50		621.50	710
2160	Box connector with set screw, plain, 1/2" diameter		70	.114		2.53	6.45		8.98	12.50
2170	3/4" diameter		60	.133		3.49	7.55		11.04	15.15
2180	1" diameter		50	.160		5.25	9.05		14.30	19.35
2190	Insulated, 1-1/4" diameter		40	.200		13.85	11.30		25.15	32
2200	1-1/2" diameter		30	.267		20.50	15.10		35.60	45
2210	2" diameter		20	.400		41	22.50		63.50	79
2220	2-1/2" diameter		18	.444		109	25		134	158
2230	3" diameter		15	.533		157	30		187	218
2240	3-1/2" diameter		12	.667		221	37.50		258.50	300
2250	4" diameter		10	.800		264	45.50		309.50	360
2260	5" diameter		9	.889		230	50.50		280.50	330
2270	6" diameter		8	1		272	56.50		328.50	385
2280	LB, LR or LL fittings & covers, 1/2" diameter		16	.500		9	28.50		37.50	52.50
2290	3/4" diameter		13	.615		11.15	35		46.15	64.50
2300	1" diameter		11	.727		16.25	41		57.25	79.50
2330	1-1/4" diameter		8	1		25.50	56.50		82	113
2350	1-1/2" diameter		6	1.333		33.50	75.50		109	150
2370	2" diameter		5	1.600		55	90.50		145.50	197
2380	2-1/2" diameter		4	2		116	113		229	297
2390	3" diameter		3.50	2.286		148	129		277	355
2400	3-1/2" diameter		3	2.667		258	151		409	510
2410	4" diameter		2.50	3.200		282	181		463	580
2420	T fittings, with cover, 1/2" diameter		12	.667		11.50	37.50		49	69
2430	3/4" diameter		11	.727		13.25	41		54.25	76
2440	1" diameter		9	.889		22.50	50.50		73	101
2450	1-1/4" diameter		6	1.333		29	75.50		104.50	145
2470	1-1/2" diameter		5	1.600		40.50	90.50		131	181
2500	2" diameter		4	2		59	113		172	235
2510	2-1/2" diameter		3.50	2.286		130	129		259	335
2520	3" diameter		3	2.667		181	151		332	425
2530	3-1/2" diameter		2.50	3.200		315	181		496	615
2540	4" diameter		2	4		375	226		601	750
2550	Nipples chase, plain, 1/2" diameter		40	.200		.34	11.30		11.64	17.30
2560	3/4" diameter		32	.250		.73	14.15		14.88	22
2570	1" diameter		28	.286		2.06	16.15		18.21	26.50
2600	Insulated, 1-1/4" diameter		24	.333		6.70	18.85		25.55	36

26 05 33 - Raceway and Boxes for Electrical Systems

26 05 33.25 Conduit Fittings for Rigid Galvanized Steel	Crew	Daily Output	Labor-Hours	Unit	Material	2017 Bare Costs Labor	Equipment	Total	Total Incl O&P
2630	1-1/2" diameter	1 Elec	18	.444	Ea.	8.85	25		33.85	47
2650	2" diameter		15	.533		13.40	30		43.40	60
2660	2-1/2" diameter		12	.667		39.50	37.50		77	100
2670	3" diameter		10	.800		39	45.50		84.50	111
2680	3-1/2" diameter		9	.889		64	50.50		114.50	146
2690	4" diameter		8	1		78.50	56.50		135	172
2700	5" diameter		7	1.143		345	64.50		409.50	475
2710	6" diameter		6	1.333		550	75.50		625.50	720
2720	Nipples offset, plain, 1/2" diameter		40	.200		4.05	11.30		15.35	21.50
2730	3/4" diameter		32	.250		4.36	14.15		18.51	26
2740	1" diameter		24	.333		5.30	18.85		24.15	34.50
2750	Insulated, 1-1/4" diameter		20	.400		8.55	22.50		31.05	43.50
2760	1-1/2" diameter		18	.444		10.35	25		35.35	49
2770	2" diameter		16	.500		14.50	28.50		43	58.50
2780	3" diameter		14	.571		78.50	32.50		111	135
2850	Coupling, expansion, 1/2" diameter		12	.667		46	37.50		83.50	107
2880	3/4" diameter		10	.800		53.50	45.50		99	127
2900	1" diameter		8	1		62.50	56.50		119	154
2920	1-1/4" diameter		6.40	1.250		76	71		147	190
2940	1-1/2" diameter		5.30	1.509		118	85.50		203.50	258
2960	2" diameter		4.60	1.739		177	98.50		275.50	340
2980	2-1/2" diameter		3.60	2.222		248	126		374	460
3000	3" diameter		3	2.667		330	151		481	585
3020	3-1/2" diameter		2.80	2.857		405	162		567	685
3040	4" diameter		2.40	3.333		610	189		799	955
3060	5" diameter		2	4		930	226		1,156	1,375
3080	6" diameter		1.80	4.444		1,650	252		1,902	2,200
3100	Expansion deflection, 1/2" diameter		12	.667		257	37.50		294.50	340
3120	3/4" diameter		12	.667		289	37.50		326.50	370
3140	1" diameter		10	.800		298	45.50		343.50	400
3160	1-1/4" diameter		6.40	1.250		355	71		426	495
3180	1-1/2" diameter		5.30	1.509		415	85.50		500.50	585
3200	2" diameter		4.60	1.739		515	98.50		613.50	710
3220	2-1/2" diameter		3.60	2.222		700	126		826	960
3240	3" diameter		3	2.667		860	151		1,011	1,175
3260	3-1/2" diameter		2.80	2.857		1,100	162		1,262	1,475
3280	4" diameter		2.40	3.333		1,275	189		1,464	1,675
3300	5" diameter		2	4		1,925	226		2,151	2,475
3320	6" diameter		1.80	4.444		3,350	252		3,602	4,050
3340	Ericson, 1/2" diameter		16	.500		1.84	28.50		30.34	44.50
3360	3/4" diameter		14	.571		2.37	32.50		34.87	51
3380	1" diameter		11	.727		4.37	41		45.37	66.50
3400	1-1/4" diameter		8	1		9.30	56.50		65.80	95.50
3420	1-1/2" diameter		7	1.143		11.15	64.50		75.65	109
3440	2" diameter		5	1.600		22.50	90.50		113	161
3460	2-1/2" diameter		4	2		54.50	113		167.50	230
3480	3" diameter		3.50	2.286		82.50	129		211.50	285
3500	3-1/2" diameter		3	2.667		137	151		288	375
3520	4" diameter		2.70	2.963		162	168		330	430
3540	5" diameter		2.50	3.200		330	181		511	635
3560	6" diameter		2.30	3.478		440	197		637	780
3580	Split, 1/2" diameter		32	.250		3.81	14.15		17.96	25
3600	3/4" diameter		27	.296		4.78	16.75		21.53	30.50

26 05 33.25 Conduit Fittings for Rigid Galvanized Steel	Crew	Daily Output	Labor-Hours	Unit	Material	2017 Bare Costs Labor	Equipment	Total	Total Incl O&P
3620	1" diameter	1 Elec	20	.400	Ea.	8.60	22.50		31.10	43.50
3640	1-1/4" diameter		16	.500		13.20	28.50		41.70	57
3660	1-1/2" diameter		14	.571		15	32.50		47.50	65
3680	2" diameter		12	.667		30	37.50		67.50	89.50
3700	2-1/2" diameter		10	.800		64.50	45.50		110	139
3720	3" diameter		9	.889		99	50.50		149.50	185
3740	3-1/2" diameter		8	1		155	56.50		211.50	255
3760	4" diameter		7	1.143		188	64.50		252.50	305
3780	5" diameter		6	1.333		320	75.50		395.50	465
3800	6" diameter		5	1.600		415	90.50		505.50	595
4600	Reducing bushings, 3/4" to 1/2" diameter		54	.148		2.22	8.40		10.62	15
4620	1" to 3/4" diameter		46	.174		2.22	9.85		12.07	17.20
4640	1-1/4" to 1" diameter		40	.200		4.49	11.30		15.79	22
4660	1-1/2" to 1-1/4" diameter		36	.222		6.45	12.60		19.05	26
4680	2" to 1-1/2" diameter		32	.250		11.95	14.15		26.10	34
4740	2-1/2" to 2" diameter		30	.267		14.90	15.10		30	39
4760	3" to 2-1/2" diameter		28	.286		19.60	16.15		35.75	45.50
4800	Through-wall seal, 1/2" diameter		8	1		234	56.50		290.50	345
4820	3/4" diameter		7.50	1.067		254	60.50		314.50	370
4840	1" diameter		6.50	1.231		254	69.50		323.50	385
4860	1-1/4" diameter		5.50	1.455		292	82.50		374.50	445
4880	1-1/2" diameter		5	1.600		390	90.50		480.50	565
4900	2" diameter		4.20	1.905		273	108		381	460
4920	2-1/2" diameter		3.50	2.286		475	129		604	720
4940	3" diameter		3	2.667		505	151		656	785
4960	3-1/2" diameter		2.50	3.200		770	181		951	1,125
4980	4" diameter		2	4		780	226		1,006	1,200
5000	5" diameter		1.50	5.333		780	300		1,080	1,300
5020	6" diameter		1	8		780	455		1,235	1,525
5100	Cable supports, 2 or more wires									
5120	1-1/2" diameter	1 Elec	8	1	Ea.	147	56.50		203.50	247
5140	2" diameter		6	1.333		201	75.50		276.50	335
5160	2-1/2" diameter		4	2		217	113		330	410
5180	3" diameter		3.50	2.286		277	129		406	500
5200	3-1/2" diameter		2.60	3.077		360	174		534	655
5220	4" diameter		2	4		455	226		681	840
5240	5" diameter		1.50	5.333		600	300		900	1,100
5260	6" diameter		1	8		975	455		1,430	1,750
5280	Service entrance cap, 1/2" diameter		16	.500		4.99	28.50		33.49	48
5300	3/4" diameter		13	.615		5.95	35		40.95	58.50
5320	1" diameter		10	.800		7.10	45.50		52.60	76
5340	1-1/4" diameter		8	1		7.70	56.50		64.20	93.50
5360	1-1/2" diameter		6.50	1.231		14.15	69.50		83.65	120
5380	2" diameter		5.50	1.455		20	82.50		102.50	145
5400	2-1/2" diameter		4	2		64.50	113		177.50	241
5420	3" diameter		3.40	2.353		91.50	133		224.50	300
5440	3-1/2" diameter		3	2.667		122	151		273	360
5460	4" diameter		2.70	2.963		151	168		319	415
5750	90° pull elbows steel, female, 1/2" diameter		16	.500		7.15	28.50		35.65	50.50
5760	3/4" diameter		13	.615		7.90	35		42.90	60.50
5780	1" diameter		11	.727		14.80	41		55.80	78
5800	1-1/4" diameter		8	1		18.80	56.50		75.30	106
5820	1-1/2" diameter		6	1.333		27.50	75.50		103	144

26 05 33.25 Conduit Fittings for Rigid Galvanized Steel	Crew	Daily Output	Labor-Hours	Unit	Material	2017 Bare Costs Labor	Equipment	Total	Total Incl O&P
5840	2" diameter	1 Elec	5	1.600	Ea.	45	90.50		135.50	186
6000	Explosion proof, flexible coupling									
6010	1/2" diameter, 4" long	1 Elec	12	.667	Ea.	125	37.50		162.50	195
6020	6" long		12	.667		112	37.50		149.50	181
6050	12" long		12	.667		170	37.50		207.50	244
6070	18" long		12	.667		202	·37.50		239.50	279
6090	24" long		12	.667		251	37.50		288.50	335
6110	30" long		12	.667		330	37.50		367.50	420
6130	36" long		12	.667		320	37.50		357.50	410
6140	3/4" diameter, 4" long		10	.800		154	45.50		199.50	237
6150	6" long		10	.800		136	45.50		181.50	218
6180	12" long		10	.800		204	45.50		249.50	292
6200	18" long		10	.800		256	45.50		301.50	350
6220	24" long		10	.800		320	45.50		365.50	420
6240	30" long		10	.800		435	45.50		480.50	550
6260	36" long		10	.800		380	45.50		425.50	485
6270	1" diameter, 6" long		8	1		355	56.50		411.50	475
6300	12" long		8	1		345	56.50		401.50	465
6320	18" long		8	1		425	56.50		481.50	550
6340	24" long		8	1		550	56.50		606.50	690
6360	30" long		8	1		735	56.50		791.50	895
6380	36" long		8	1		805	56.50		861.50	970
6390	1-1/4" diameter, 12" long		6.40	1.250		620	71		691	790
6410	18" long		6.40	1.250		745	71		816	920
6430	24" long		6.40	1.250		855	71		926	1,050
6450	30" long		6.40	1.250		1,125	71		1,196	1,325
6470	36" long		6.40	1.250		1,375	71		1,446	1,625
6480	1-1/2" diameter, 12" long		5.30	1.509		640	85.50		725.50	835
6500	18" long		5.30	1.509		790	85.50		875.50	1,000
6520	24" long		5.30	1.509		1,125	85.50		1,210.50	1,375
6540	30" long		5.30	1.509		1,300	85.50		1,385.50	1,550
6560	36" long		5.30	1.509		1,375	85.50		1,460.50	1,650
6570	2" diameter, 12" long		4.60	1.739		1,100	98.50		1,198.50	1,350
6590	18" long		4.60	1.739		1,425	98.50		1,523.50	1,725
6610	24" long		4.60	1.739		1,550	98.50		1,648.50	1,850
6630	30" long		4.60	1.739		1,850	98.50		1,948.50	2,175
6650	36" long		4.60	1.739		1,950	98.50		2,048.50	2,300
7000	Close up plug, 1/2" diameter, explosion proof		40	.200		2.35	11.30		13.65	19.55
7010	3/4" diameter		32	.250		2.76	14.15		16.91	24
7020	1" diameter		28	.286		3.23	16.15		19.38	27.50
7030	1-1/4" diameter		24	.333		3.55	18.85		22.40	32.50
7040	1-1/2" diameter		18	.444		4.92	25		29.92	43
7050	2" diameter		15	.533		8.50	30		38.50	54.50
7060	2-1/2" diameter		13	.615		13.95	35		48.95	67.50
7070	3" diameter		12	.667		20.50	37.50		58	79.50
7080	3-1/2" diameter		11	.727		26	41		67	90
7090	4" diameter		9	.889		32.50	50.50		83	111
7091	Elbow female, 45°, 1/2"		16	.500		11.75	28.50		40.25	55.50
7092	3/4"		13	.615		14.60	35		49.60	68
7093	1"		11	.727		17.50	41		58.50	81
7094	1-1/4"		8	1		26.50	56.50		83	114
7095	1-1/2"		6	1.333		28.50	75.50		104	145
7096	2"		5	1.600		33	90.50		123.50	173

26 05 Common Work Results for Electrical

26 05 33 – Raceway and Boxes for Electrical Systems

26 05 33.25 Conduit Fittings for Rigid Galvanized Steel	Crew	Daily Output	Labor-Hours	Unit	Material	2017 Bare Costs Labor	Equipment	Total	Total Incl O&P
7097	2-1/2"	1 Elec	4.50	1.778	Ea.	97	101		198	258
7098	3"		4.20	1.905		98.50	108		206.50	270
7099	3-1/2"		4	2		151	113		264	335
7100	4"		3.80	2.105		167	119		286	360
7101	90°, 1/2"		16	.500		11.90	28.50		40.40	55.50
7102	3/4"		13	.615		12.85	35		47.85	66
7103	1"		11	.727		17.50	41		58.50	81
7104	1-1/4"		8	1		28	56.50		84.50	116
7105	1-1/2"		6	1.333		39	75.50		114.50	156
7106	2"		5	1.600		61	90.50		151.50	203
7107	2-1/2"		4.50	1.778		143	101		244	310
7110	Elbows 90°, long male & female, 1/2" diameter, explosion proof		16	.500		17.35	28.50		45.85	61.50
7120	3/4" diameter		13	.615		20	35		55	74
7130	1" diameter		11	.727		26	41		67	90
7140	1-1/4" diameter		8	1		30.50	56.50		87	119
7150	1-1/2" diameter		6	1.333		37.50	75.50		113	155
7160	2" diameter		5	1.600		55.50	90.50		146	197
7170	Capped elbow, 1/2" diameter, explosion proof		11	.727		18.95	41		59.95	82.50
7180	3/4" diameter		8	1		23	56.50		79.50	111
7190	1" diameter		6	1.333		25.50	75.50		101	141
7200	1-1/4" diameter		5	1.600		50.50	90.50		141	192
7210	Pulling elbow, 1/2" diameter, explosion proof		11	.727		75	41		116	144
7220	3/4" diameter		8	1		133	56.50		189.50	231
7230	1" diameter		6	1.333		190	75.50		265.50	325
7240	1-1/4" diameter		5	1.600		235	90.50		325.50	395
7250	1-1/2" diameter		5	1.600		280	90.50		370.50	445
7260	2" diameter		4	2		310	113		423	510
7270	2-1/2" diameter		3.50	2.286		765	129		894	1,050
7280	3" diameter		3	2.667		1,050	151		1,201	1,375
7290	3-1/2" diameter		2.50	3.200		1,325	181		1,506	1,725
7300	4" diameter		2.20	3.636		1,375	206		1,581	1,800
7310	LB conduit body, 1/2" diameter		11	.727		44	41		85	110
7320	3/4" diameter		8	1		53.50	56.50		110	144
7330	T conduit body, 1/2" diameter		9	.889		48	50.50		98.50	128
7340	3/4" diameter		6	1.333		56.50	75.50		132	175
7350	Explosion proof, round box w/cover, 3 threaded hubs, 1/2" diameter		8	1		65.50	56.50		122	157
7351	3/4" diameter		8	1		67.50	56.50		124	160
7352	1" diameter		7.50	1.067		72	60.50		132.50	170
7353	1-1/4" diameter		7	1.143		107	64.50		171.50	215
7354	1-1/2" diameter		7	1.143		266	64.50		330.50	390
7355	2" diameter		6	1.333		275	75.50		350.50	415
7356	Round box w/cover & mtng flange, 3 threaded hubs, 1/2" diameter		8	1		53.50	56.50		110	144
7357	3/4" diameter		8	1		60.50	56.50		117	152
7358	4 threaded hubs, 1" diameter		7	1.143		66	64.50		130.50	170
7400	Unions, 1/2" diameter		20	.400		11.80	22.50		34.30	47
7410	3/4" - 1/2" diameter		16	.500		17.10	28.50		45.60	61.50
7420	3/4" diameter		16	.500		16.25	28.50		44.75	60.50
7430	1" diameter		14	.571		29.50	32.50		62	81
7440	1-1/4" diameter		12	.667		43.50	37.50		81	104
7450	1-1/2" diameter		10	.800		55	45.50		100.50	129
7460	2" diameter		8.50	.941		71	53.50		124.50	158
7480	2-1/2" diameter		8	1		111	56.50		167.50	207
7490	3" diameter		7	1.143		145	64.50		209.50	256

For customer support on your Electrical Costs with RSMeans Data, call 800.448.8182.

165

26 05 33.25 Conduit Fittings for Rigid Galvanized Steel		Crew	Daily Output	Labor-Hours	Unit	Material	2017 Bare Costs Labor	Equipment	Total	Total Incl O&P
7500	3-1/2" diameter	1 Elec	6	1.333	Ea.	268	75.50		343.50	410
7510	4" diameter		5	1.600		270	90.50		360.50	435
7680	Reducer, 3/4" to 1/2"		54	.148		2.44	8.40		10.84	15.25
7690	1" to 1/2"		46	.174		4.40	9.85		14.25	19.60
7700	1" to 3/4"		46	.174		4.51	9.85		14.36	19.70
7710	1-1/4" to 3/4"		40	.200		5.55	11.30		16.85	23
7720	1-1/4" to 1"		40	.200		6.75	11.30		18.05	24.50
7730	1-1/2" to 1"		36	.222		10.35	12.60		22.95	30.50
7740	1-1/2" to 1-1/4"		36	.222		11.05	12.60		23.65	31
7750	2" to 3/4"		32	.250		18.15	14.15		32.30	41
7760	2" to 1-1/4"		32	.250		12.20	14.15		26.35	34.50
7770	2" to 1-1/2"		32	.250		13	14.15		27.15	35.50
7780	2-1/2" to 1-1/2"		30	.267		22	15.10		37.10	46.50
7790	3" to 2"		30	.267		22	15.10		37.10	46.50
7800	3-1/2" to 2-1/2"		28	.286		45	16.15		61.15	73.50
7810	4" to 3"		28	.286		54.50	16.15		70.65	84
7820	Sealing fitting, vertical/horizontal, 1/2" diameter		14.50	.552		15.85	31		46.85	64.50
7830	3/4" diameter		13.30	.602		18.50	34		52.50	71.50
7840	1" diameter		11.40	.702		23.50	39.50		63	85
7850	1-1/4" diameter		10	.800		29.50	45.50		75	101
7860	1-1/2" diameter		8.80	.909		44	51.50		95.50	126
7870	2" diameter		8	1		58	56.50		114.50	149
7880	2-1/2" diameter		6.70	1.194		80	67.50		147.50	189
7890	3" diameter		5.70	1.404		103	79.50		182.50	232
7900	3-1/2" diameter		4.70	1.702		273	96.50		369.50	445
7910	4" diameter		4	2		450	113		563	665
7920	Sealing hubs, 1" by 1-1/2"		12	.667		27.50	37.50		65	86.50
7930	1-1/4" by 2"		10	.800		53	45.50		98.50	126
7940	1-1/2" by 2"		9	.889		65.50	50.50		116	148
7950	2" by 2-1/2"		8	1		86	56.50		142.50	180
7960	3" by 4"		7	1.143		145	64.50		209.50	257
7970	4" by 5"		6	1.333		300	75.50		375.50	445
7980	Drain, 1/2"		32	.250		97.50	14.15		111.65	128
7990	Breather, 1/2"		32	.250		97.50	14.15		111.65	128
8000	Plastic coated 40 mil thick									
8010	LB, LR or LL conduit body w/cover, 1/2" diameter	1 Elec	13	.615	Ea.	49.50	35		84.50	107
8020	3/4" diameter		11	.727		51.50	41		92.50	118
8030	1" diameter		8	1		72	56.50		128.50	165
8040	1-1/4" diameter		6	1.333		107	75.50		182.50	231
8050	1-1/2" diameter		5	1.600		130	90.50		220.50	279
8060	2" diameter		4.50	1.778		190	101		291	360
8070	2-1/2" diameter		4	2		300	113		413	500
8080	3" diameter		3.50	2.286		440	129		569	680
8090	3-1/2" diameter		3	2.667		765	151		916	1,075
8100	4" diameter		2.50	3.200		860	181		1,041	1,225
8150	T conduit body with cover, 1/2" diameter		11	.727		61	41		102	129
8160	3/4" diameter		9	.889		57.50	50.50		108	139
8170	1" diameter		6	1.333		68.50	75.50		144	189
8180	1-1/4" diameter		5	1.600		122	90.50		212.50	271
8190	1-1/2" diameter		4.50	1.778		149	101		250	315
8200	2" diameter		4	2		203	113		316	395
8210	2-1/2" diameter		3.50	2.286		395	129		524	625
8220	3" diameter		3	2.667		510	151		661	790

For customer support on your Electrical Costs with RSMeans Data, call 800.448.8182.

26 05 33.25 Conduit Fittings for Rigid Galvanized Steel	Crew	Daily Output	Labor-Hours	Unit	Material	2017 Bare Costs Labor	Equipment	Total	Total Incl O&P
8230	3-1/2" diameter	1 Elec	2.50	3.200	Ea.	805	181		986	1,150
8240	4" diameter		2	4		875	226		1,101	1,300
8300	FS conduit body, 1 gang, 3/4" diameter		11	.727		59	41		100	127
8310	1" diameter		10	.800		61.50	45.50		107	136
8350	2 gang, 3/4" diameter		9	.889		107	50.50		157.50	194
8360	1" diameter		8	1		123	56.50		179.50	220
8400	Duplex receptacle cover		64	.125		43	7.10		50.10	58
8410	Switch cover		64	.125		62.50	7.10		69.60	79.50
8420	Switch, vaportight cover		53	.151		215	8.55		223.55	250
8430	Blank, cover		64	.125		41.50	7.10		48.60	56.50
8520	FSC conduit body, 1 gang, 3/4" diameter		10	.800		66.50	45.50		112	141
8530	1" diameter		9	.889		74	50.50		124.50	157
8550	2 gang, 3/4" diameter		8	1		121	56.50		177.50	218
8560	1" diameter		7	1.143		136	64.50		200.50	246
8590	Conduit hubs, 1/2" diameter		18	.444		37	25		62	78
8600	3/4" diameter		16	.500		47	28.50		75.50	94
8610	1" diameter		14	.571		58.50	32.50		91	113
8620	1-1/4" diameter		12	.667		63.50	37.50		101	126
8630	1-1/2" diameter		10	.800		80.50	45.50		126	157
8640	2" diameter		8.80	.909		111	51.50		162.50	199
8650	2-1/2" diameter		8.50	.941		149	53.50		202.50	244
8660	3" diameter		8	1		238	56.50		294.50	345
8670	3-1/2" diameter		7.50	1.067		288	60.50		348.50	405
8680	4" diameter		7	1.143		325	64.50		389.50	455
8690	5" diameter	▼	6	1.333	▼	425	75.50		500.50	585
8700	Plastic coated 40 mil thick									
8710	Pipe strap, stamped 1 hole, 1/2" diameter	1 Elec	470	.017	Ea.	11.50	.96		12.46	14.10
8720	3/4" diameter		440	.018		12.75	1.03		13.78	15.55
8730	1" diameter		400	.020		13.15	1.13		14.28	16.15
8740	1-1/4" diameter		355	.023		18.10	1.28		19.38	22
8750	1-1/2" diameter		320	.025		19.05	1.42		20.47	23
8760	2" diameter		266	.030		27	1.70		28.70	32
8770	2-1/2" diameter		200	.040		36.50	2.26		38.76	43.50
8780	3" diameter		133	.060		48	3.40		51.40	58
8790	3-1/2" diameter		110	.073		89.50	4.12		93.62	105
8800	4" diameter		90	.089		102	5.05		107.05	120
8810	5" diameter		70	.114		135	6.45		141.45	158
8840	Clamp back spacers, 3/4" diameter		440	.018		17.45	1.03		18.48	20.50
8850	1" diameter		400	.020		25	1.13		26.13	29
8860	1-1/4" diameter		355	.023		28.50	1.28		29.78	33.50
8870	1-1/2" diameter		320	.025		39	1.42		40.42	45
8880	2" diameter		266	.030		60	1.70		61.70	68
8900	3" diameter		133	.060		94	3.40		97.40	109
8920	4" diameter	▼	90	.089		77	5.05		82.05	92.50
8950	Touch-up plastic coating, spray, 12 oz.					52			52	57
8960	Sealing fittings, 1/2" diameter	1 Elec	11	.727		62	41		103	130
8970	3/4" diameter		9	.889		63.50	50.50		114	145
8980	1" diameter		7.50	1.067		74.50	60.50		135	173
8990	1-1/4" diameter		6.50	1.231		96.50	69.50		166	210
9000	1-1/2" diameter		5.50	1.455		126	82.50		208.50	262
9010	2" diameter		4.80	1.667		151	94.50		245.50	305
9020	2-1/2" diameter		4	2		210	113		323	400
9030	3" diameter	▼	3.50	2.286	▼	279	129		408	500

For customer support on your Electrical Costs with RSMeans Data, call 800.448.8182.

167

26 05 33.25 Conduit Fittings for Rigid Galvanized Steel

		Crew	Daily Output	Labor-Hours	Unit	Material	2017 Bare Costs Labor	Equipment	Total	Total Incl O&P
9040	3-1/2" diameter	1 Elec	3	2.667	Ea.	755	151		906	1,050
9050	4" diameter		2.50	3.200		1,025	181		1,206	1,400
9060	5" diameter		1.70	4.706		2,100	266		2,366	2,725
9070	Unions, 1/2" diameter		18	.444		55	25		80	98
9080	3/4" diameter		15	.533		60.50	30		90.50	112
9090	1" diameter		13	.615		81	35		116	141
9100	1-1/4" diameter		11	.727		124	41		165	199
9110	1-1/2" diameter		9.50	.842		150	47.50		197.50	237
9120	2" diameter		8	1		210	56.50		266.50	315
9130	2-1/2" diameter		7.50	1.067		296	60.50		356.50	415
9140	3" diameter		6.80	1.176		325	66.50		391.50	455
9150	3-1/2" diameter		5.80	1.379		510	78		588	675
9160	4" diameter		4.80	1.667		615	94.50		709.50	815
9170	5" diameter		4	2		945	113		1,058	1,225

26 05 33.30 Electrical Nonmetallic Tubing (ENT)

		Crew	Daily Output	Labor-Hours	Unit	Material	2017 Bare Costs Labor	Equipment	Total	Total Incl O&P
0010	**ELECTRICAL NONMETALLIC TUBING (ENT)**									
0050	Flexible, 1/2" diameter	1 Elec	270	.030	L.F.	.74	1.68		2.42	3.32
0100	3/4" diameter		230	.035		1.21	1.97		3.18	4.28
0200	1" diameter		145	.055		2.03	3.12		5.15	6.90
0210	1-1/4" diameter		125	.064		1.98	3.62		5.60	7.65
0220	1-1/2" diameter		100	.080		2.93	4.53		7.46	10
0230	2" diameter		75	.107		2.20	6.05		8.25	11.45
0300	Connectors, to outlet box, 1/2" diameter		230	.035	Ea.	1	1.97		2.97	4.05
0310	3/4" diameter		210	.038		1.82	2.16		3.98	5.25
0320	1" diameter		200	.040		2.55	2.26		4.81	6.20
0400	Couplings, to conduit, 1/2" diameter		145	.055		.99	3.12		4.11	5.75
0410	3/4" diameter		130	.062		1.29	3.48		4.77	6.60
0420	1" diameter		125	.064		2.14	3.62		5.76	7.80

26 05 33.35 Flexible Metallic Conduit

		Crew	Daily Output	Labor-Hours	Unit	Material	2017 Bare Costs Labor	Equipment	Total	Total Incl O&P
0010	**FLEXIBLE METALLIC CONDUIT**									
0050	Steel, 3/8" diameter	1 Elec	200	.040	L.F.	.23	2.26		2.49	3.64
0100	1/2" diameter		200	.040		.26	2.26		2.52	3.68
0200	3/4" diameter		160	.050		.36	2.83		3.19	4.64
0250	1" diameter		100	.080		.65	4.53		5.18	7.50
0300	1-1/4" diameter		70	.114		.84	6.45		7.29	10.60
0350	1-1/2" diameter		50	.160		1.37	9.05		10.42	15.05
0370	2" diameter		40	.200		1.67	11.30		12.97	18.80
0380	2-1/2" diameter		30	.267		3.66	15.10		18.76	26.50
0390	3" diameter	2 Elec	50	.320		6.35	18.10		24.45	34
0400	3-1/2" diameter		40	.400		7.20	22.50		29.70	42
0410	4" diameter		30	.533		8.15	30		38.15	54
0420	Connectors, plain, 3/8" diameter	1 Elec	100	.080	Ea.	1.36	4.53		5.89	8.30
0430	1/2" diameter		80	.100		1.69	5.65		7.34	10.35
0440	3/4" diameter		70	.114		1.96	6.45		8.41	11.85
0450	1" diameter		50	.160		4.03	9.05		13.08	18
0452	1-1/4" diameter		45	.178		4.80	10.05		14.85	20.50
0454	1-1/2" diameter		40	.200		7.30	11.30		18.60	25
0456	2" diameter		28	.286		10.95	16.15		27.10	36
0458	2-1/2" diameter		25	.320		19.25	18.10		37.35	48
0460	3" diameter		20	.400		27.50	22.50		50	64.50
0462	3-1/2" diameter		16	.500		90	28.50		118.50	142
0464	4" diameter		13	.615		113	35		148	177

26 05 33.35 Flexible Metallic Conduit	Crew	Daily Output	Labor-Hours	Unit	Material	2017 Bare Costs Labor	Equipment	Total	Total Incl O&P
0490 Insulated, 1" diameter	1 Elec	40	.200	Ea.	6.05	11.30		17.35	23.50
0500 1-1/4" diameter		40	.200		14.30	11.30		25.60	32.50
0550 1-1/2" diameter		32	.250		21.50	14.15		35.65	44.50
0600 2" diameter		23	.348		33	19.70		52.70	66
0610 2-1/2" diameter		20	.400		63.50	22.50		86	104
0620 3" diameter		17	.471		84	26.50		110.50	133
0630 3-1/2" diameter		13	.615		266	35		301	345
0640 4" diameter		10	.800		262	45.50		307.50	355
0650 Connectors 90°, plain, 3/8" diameter		80	.100		2.49	5.65		8.14	11.25
0660 1/2" diameter		60	.133		4.18	7.55		11.73	15.90
0700 3/4" diameter		50	.160		7.85	9.05		16.90	22
0750 1" diameter		40	.200		11.75	11.30		23.05	30
0790 Insulated, 1" diameter		40	.200		11.85	11.30		23.15	30
0800 1-1/4" diameter		30	.267		25.50	15.10		40.60	50.50
0850 1-1/2" diameter		23	.348		47.50	19.70		67.20	82
0900 2" diameter		18	.444		58	25		83	102
0910 2-1/2" diameter		16	.500		135	28.50		163.50	192
0920 3" diameter		14	.571		156	32.50		188.50	220
0930 3-1/2" diameter		11	.727		525	41		566	640
0940 4" diameter		8	1		730	56.50		786.50	890
0960 Couplings, to flexible conduit, 1/2" diameter		50	.160		.86	9.05		9.91	14.50
0970 3/4" diameter		40	.200		1.49	11.30		12.79	18.60
0980 1" diameter		35	.229		2.47	12.95		15.42	22
0990 1-1/4" diameter		28	.286		6.65	16.15		22.80	31.50
1000 1-1/2" diameter		23	.348		7.20	19.70		26.90	37.50
1010 2" diameter		20	.400		14.60	22.50		37.10	50
1020 2-1/2" diameter		18	.444		36.50	25		61.50	77.50
1030 3" diameter		15	.533		91.50	30		121.50	146
1032 Aluminum, 3/8" diameter		210	.038	L.F.	.44	2.16		2.60	3.71
1034 1/2" diameter		210	.038		.51	2.16		2.67	3.79
1036 3/4" diameter		165	.048		.71	2.74		3.45	4.89
1038 1" diameter		105	.076		1.33	4.31		5.64	7.90
1040 1-1/4" diameter		75	.107		1.85	6.05		7.90	11.10
1042 1-1/2" diameter		53	.151		2.65	8.55		11.20	15.70
1044 2" diameter		42	.190		3.38	10.80		14.18	19.85
1046 2-1/2" diameter		32	.250		4.35	14.15		18.50	26
1048 3" diameter	2 Elec	53	.302		8.20	17.10		25.30	34.50
1050 3-1/2" diameter		42	.381		8.20	21.50		29.70	41.50
1052 4" diameter		32	.500		9.15	28.50		37.65	52.50
1070 Sealtite, 3/8" diameter	1 Elec	140	.057		.70	3.23		3.93	5.60
1080 1/2" diameter		140	.057		1.05	3.23		4.28	6
1090 3/4" diameter		100	.080		1.47	4.53		6	8.40
1100 1" diameter		70	.114		2.42	6.45		8.87	12.35
1200 1-1/4" diameter		50	.160		3.24	9.05		12.29	17.10
1300 1-1/2" diameter		40	.200		3.46	11.30		14.76	21
1400 2" diameter		30	.267		4.42	15.10		19.52	27.50
1410 2-1/2" diameter		27	.296		7	16.75		23.75	32.50
1420 3" diameter	2 Elec	50	.320		8.30	18.10		26.40	36
1440 4" diameter	"	30	.533		9.35	30		39.35	55.50
1490 Connectors, plain, 3/8" diameter	1 Elec	70	.114	Ea.	2.58	6.45		9.03	12.55
1500 1/2" diameter		70	.114		3.23	6.45		9.68	13.25
1700 3/4" diameter		50	.160		4.73	9.05		13.78	18.75
1900 1" diameter		40	.200		8.10	11.30		19.40	26

26 05 33 – Raceway and Boxes for Electrical Systems

26 05 33.35 Flexible Metallic Conduit		Crew	Daily Output	Labor-Hours	Unit	Material	2017 Bare Costs Labor	Equipment	Total	Total Incl O&P
1910	Insulated, 1" diameter	1 Elec	40	.200	Ea.	5.45	11.30		16.75	23
2000	1-1/4" diameter		32	.250		8.50	14.15		22.65	30.50
2100	1-1/2" diameter		27	.296		11.10	16.75		27.85	37.50
2200	2" diameter		20	.400		19.90	22.50		42.40	56
2210	2-1/2" diameter		15	.533		117	30		147	174
2220	3" diameter		12	.667		131	37.50		168.50	201
2240	4" diameter		8	1		163	56.50		219.50	264
2290	Connectors, 90°, 3/8" diameter		70	.114		4.65	6.45		11.10	14.80
2300	1/2" diameter		70	.114		4.30	6.45		10.75	14.45
2400	3/4" diameter		50	.160		6.70	9.05		15.75	21
2600	1" diameter		40	.200		13.65	11.30		24.95	32
2790	Insulated, 1" diameter		40	.200		10.10	11.30		21.40	28
2800	1-1/4" diameter		32	.250		15.50	14.15		29.65	38
3000	1-1/2" diameter		27	.296		22	16.75		38.75	49
3100	2" diameter		20	.400		31.50	22.50		54	69
3110	2-1/2" diameter		14	.571		152	32.50		184.50	216
3120	3" diameter		11	.727		335	41		376	430
3140	4" diameter		7	1.143		237	64.50		301.50	355
4300	Coupling sealtite to rigid, 1/2" diameter		20	.400		3.42	22.50		25.92	38
4500	3/4" diameter		18	.444		5.50	25		30.50	43.50
4800	1" diameter		14	.571		5.80	32.50		38.30	55
4900	1-1/4" diameter		12	.667		8.40	37.50		45.90	66
5000	1-1/2" diameter		11	.727		36.50	41		77.50	102
5100	2" diameter		10	.800		21	45.50		66.50	91.50
5110	2-1/2" diameter		9.50	.842		178	47.50		225.50	268
5120	3" diameter		9	.889		172	50.50		222.50	265
5130	3-1/2" diameter		9	.889		193	50.50		243.50	288
5140	4" diameter		8.50	.941		213	53.50		266.50	315

26 05 33.95 Cutting and Drilling

		Crew	Daily Output	Labor-Hours	Unit	Material	2017 Bare Costs Labor	Equipment	Total	Total Incl O&P
0010	**CUTTING AND DRILLING**									
0100	Hole drilling to 10' high, concrete wall									
0110	8" thick, 1/2" pipe size	R-31	12	.667	Ea.	.24	37.50	4.61	42.35	62
0120	3/4" pipe size		12	.667		.24	37.50	4.61	42.35	62
0130	1" pipe size		9.50	.842		.38	47.50	5.80	53.68	78.50
0140	1-1/4" pipe size		9.50	.842		.38	47.50	5.80	53.68	78.50
0150	1-1/2" pipe size		9.50	.842		.38	47.50	5.80	53.68	78.50
0160	2" pipe size		4.40	1.818		.52	103	12.55	116.07	168
0170	2-1/2" pipe size		4.40	1.818		.52	103	12.55	116.07	168
0180	3" pipe size		4.40	1.818		.52	103	12.55	116.07	168
0190	3-1/2" pipe size		3.30	2.424		.67	137	16.75	154.42	225
0200	4" pipe size		3.30	2.424		.67	137	16.75	154.42	225
0500	12" thick, 1/2" pipe size		9.40	.851		.36	48	5.90	54.26	79
0520	3/4" pipe size		9.40	.851		.36	48	5.90	54.26	79
0540	1" pipe size		7.30	1.096		.58	62	7.55	70.13	102
0560	1-1/4" pipe size		7.30	1.096		.58	62	7.55	70.13	102
0570	1-1/2" pipe size		7.30	1.096		.58	62	7.55	70.13	102
0580	2" pipe size		3.60	2.222		.78	126	15.35	142.13	206
0590	2-1/2" pipe size		3.60	2.222		.78	126	15.35	142.13	206
0600	3" pipe size		3.60	2.222		.78	126	15.35	142.13	206
0610	3-1/2" pipe size		2.80	2.857		1	162	19.75	182.75	265
0630	4" pipe size		2.50	3.200		1	181	22	204	297
0650	16" thick, 1/2" pipe size		7.60	1.053		.49	59.50	7.25	67.24	98

For customer support on your Electrical Costs with RSMeans Data, call 800.448.8182.

26 05 33 – Raceway and Boxes for Electrical Systems

26 05 33.95 Cutting and Drilling	Crew	Daily Output	Labor-Hours	Unit	Material	2017 Bare Costs Labor	Equipment	Total	Total Incl O&P
0670	3/4" pipe size	R-31	7	1.143	Ea.	.49	64.50	7.90	72.89	106
0690	1" pipe size		6	1.333		.77	75.50	9.20	85.47	124
0710	1-1/4" pipe size		5.50	1.455		.77	82.50	10.05	93.32	135
0730	1-1/2" pipe size		5.50	1.455		.77	82.50	10.05	93.32	135
0750	2" pipe size		3	2.667		1.04	151	18.45	170.49	248
0770	2-1/2" pipe size		2.70	2.963		1.04	168	20.50	189.54	275
0790	3" pipe size		2.50	3.200		1.04	181	22	204.04	297
0810	3-1/2" pipe size		2.30	3.478		1.34	197	24	222.34	325
0830	4" pipe size		2	4		1.34	226	27.50	254.84	370
0850	20" thick, 1/2" pipe size		6.40	1.250		.61	71	8.65	80.26	116
0870	3/4" pipe size		6	1.333		.61	75.50	9.20	85.31	124
0890	1" pipe size		5	1.600		.96	90.50	11.05	102.51	149
0910	1-1/4" pipe size		4.80	1.667		.96	94.50	11.50	106.96	155
0930	1-1/2" pipe size		4.60	1.739		.96	98.50	12	111.46	161
0950	2" pipe size		2.70	2.963		1.30	168	20.50	189.80	275
0970	2-1/2" pipe size		2.40	3.333		1.30	189	23	213.30	310
0990	3" pipe size		2.20	3.636		1.30	206	25	232.30	340
1010	3-1/2" pipe size		2	4		1.67	226	27.50	255.17	370
1030	4" pipe size		1.70	4.706		1.67	266	32.50	300.17	440
1050	24" thick, 1/2" pipe size		5.50	1.455		.73	82.50	10.05	93.28	135
1070	3/4" pipe size		5.10	1.569		.73	89	10.85	100.58	146
1090	1" pipe size		4.30	1.860		1.15	105	12.85	119	173
1110	1-1/4" pipe size		4	2		1.15	113	13.80	127.95	186
1130	1-1/2" pipe size		4	2		1.15	113	13.80	127.95	186
1150	2" pipe size		2.40	3.333		1.56	189	23	213.56	310
1170	2-1/2" pipe size		2.20	3.636		1.56	206	25	232.56	340
1190	3" pipe size		2	4		1.56	226	27.50	255.06	370
1210	3-1/2" pipe size		1.80	4.444		2.01	252	30.50	284.51	410
1230	4" pipe size		1.50	5.333		2.01	300	37	339.01	495
1500	Brick wall, 8" thick, 1/2" pipe size		18	.444		.24	25	3.07	28.31	41
1520	3/4" pipe size		18	.444		.24	25	3.07	28.31	41
1540	1" pipe size		13.30	.602		.38	34	4.16	38.54	56
1560	1-1/4" pipe size		13.30	.602		.38	34	4.16	38.54	56
1580	1-1/2" pipe size		13.30	.602		.38	34	4.16	38.54	56
1600	2" pipe size		5.70	1.404		.52	79.50	9.70	89.72	130
1620	2-1/2" pipe size		5.70	1.404		.52	79.50	9.70	89.72	130
1640	3" pipe size		5.70	1.404		.52	79.50	9.70	89.72	130
1660	3-1/2" pipe size		4.40	1.818		.67	103	12.55	116.22	169
1680	4" pipe size		4	2		.67	113	13.80	127.47	186
1700	12" thick, 1/2" pipe size		14.50	.552		.36	31	3.81	35.17	51.50
1720	3/4" pipe size		14.50	.552		.36	31	3.81	35.17	51.50
1740	1" pipe size		11	.727		.58	41	5.05	46.63	67.50
1760	1-1/4" pipe size		11	.727		.58	41	5.05	46.63	67.50
1780	1-1/2" pipe size		11	.727		.58	41	5.05	46.63	67.50
1800	2" pipe size		5	1.600		.78	90.50	11.05	102.33	149
1820	2-1/2" pipe size		5	1.600		.78	90.50	11.05	102.33	149
1840	3" pipe size		5	1.600		.78	90.50	11.05	102.33	149
1860	3-1/2" pipe size		3.80	2.105		1	119	14.55	134.55	196
1880	4" pipe size		3.30	2.424		1	137	16.75	154.75	226
1900	16" thick, 1/2" pipe size		12.30	.650		.49	37	4.49	41.98	60.50
1920	3/4" pipe size		12.30	.650		.49	37	4.49	41.98	60.50
1940	1" pipe size		9.30	.860		.77	48.50	5.95	55.22	80.50
1960	1-1/4" pipe size		9.30	.860		.77	48.50	5.95	55.22	80.50

For customer support on your Electrical Costs with RSMeans Data, call 800.448.8182.

171

26 05 33 – Raceway and Boxes for Electrical Systems

26 05 33.95 Cutting and Drilling

		Crew	Daily Output	Labor-Hours	Unit	Material	2017 Bare Costs Labor	Equipment	Total	Total Incl O&P
1980	1-1/2" pipe size	R-31	9.30	.860	Ea.	.77	48.50	5.95	55.22	80.50
2000	2" pipe size		4.40	1.818		1.04	103	12.55	116.59	169
2010	2-1/2" pipe size		4.40	1.818		1.04	103	12.55	116.59	169
2030	3" pipe size		4.40	1.818		1.04	103	12.55	116.59	169
2050	3-1/2" pipe size		3.30	2.424		1.34	137	16.75	155.09	226
2070	4" pipe size		3	2.667		1.34	151	18.45	170.79	248
2090	20" thick, 1/2" pipe size		10.70	.748		.61	42.50	5.15	48.26	70
2110	3/4" pipe size		10.70	.748		.61	42.50	5.15	48.26	70
2130	1" pipe size		8	1		.96	56.50	6.90	64.36	93.50
2150	1-1/4" pipe size		8	1		.96	56.50	6.90	64.36	93.50
2170	1-1/2" pipe size		8	1		.96	56.50	6.90	64.36	93.50
2190	2" pipe size		4	2		1.30	113	13.80	128.10	187
2210	2-1/2" pipe size		4	2		1.30	113	13.80	128.10	187
2230	3" pipe size		4	2		1.30	113	13.80	128.10	187
2250	3-1/2" pipe size		3	2.667		1.67	151	18.45	171.12	248
2270	4" pipe size		2.70	2.963		1.67	168	20.50	190.17	275
2290	24" thick, 1/2" pipe size		9.40	.851		.73	48	5.90	54.63	79.50
2310	3/4" pipe size		9.40	.851		.73	48	5.90	54.63	79.50
2330	1" pipe size		7.10	1.127		1.15	64	7.80	72.95	105
2350	1-1/4" pipe size		7.10	1.127		1.15	64	7.80	72.95	105
2370	1-1/2" pipe size		7.10	1.127		1.15	64	7.80	72.95	105
2390	2" pipe size		3.60	2.222		1.56	126	15.35	142.91	207
2410	2-1/2" pipe size		3.60	2.222		1.56	126	15.35	142.91	207
2430	3" pipe size		3.60	2.222		1.56	126	15.35	142.91	207
2450	3-1/2" pipe size		2.80	2.857		2.01	162	19.75	183.76	266
2470	4" pipe size		2.50	3.200		2.01	181	22	205.01	298
3000	Knockouts to 8' high, metal boxes & enclosures									
3020	With hole saw, 1/2" pipe size	1 Elec	53	.151	Ea.		8.55		8.55	12.80
3040	3/4" pipe size		47	.170			9.65		9.65	14.45
3050	1" pipe size		40	.200			11.30		11.30	16.95
3060	1-1/4" pipe size		36	.222			12.60		12.60	18.85
3070	1-1/2" pipe size		32	.250			14.15		14.15	21
3080	2" pipe size		27	.296			16.75		16.75	25
3090	2-1/2" pipe size		20	.400			22.50		22.50	34
4010	3" pipe size		16	.500			28.50		28.50	42.50
4030	3-1/2" pipe size		13	.615			35		35	52
4050	4" pipe size		11	.727			41		41	61.50

26 05 36 – Cable Trays for Electrical Systems

26 05 36.10 Cable Tray Ladder Type

		Crew	Daily Output	Labor-Hours	Unit	Material	2017 Bare Costs Labor	Equipment	Total	Total Incl O&P
0010	**CABLE TRAY LADDER TYPE** w/ftngs. & supports, 4" dp., to 15' elev.									
0100	For higher elevations, see Section 26 05 36.40									
0160	Galvanized steel tray R260536-10									
0170	4" rung spacing, 6" wide	2 Elec	98	.163	L.F.	14.80	9.25		24.05	30
0180	9" wide R260536-11		92	.174		16.15	9.85		26	32.50
0200	12" wide		86	.186		17.80	10.55		28.35	35.50
0400	18" wide		82	.195		20.50	11.05		31.55	39
0600	24" wide		78	.205		24	11.60		35.60	43.50
0650	30" wide		68	.235		30	13.30		43.30	53
0700	36" wide		60	.267		34.50	15.10		49.60	60.50
0800	6" rung spacing, 6" wide		100	.160		13.45	9.05		22.50	28.50
0850	9" wide		94	.170		14.80	9.65		24.45	31
0860	12" wide		88	.182		15.55	10.30		25.85	32.50

26 05 36.10 Cable Tray Ladder Type	Crew	Daily Output	Labor-Hours	Unit	Material	2017 Bare Costs Labor	Equipment	Total	Total Incl O&P
0870	18" wide	2 Elec	84	.190	L.F.	17.70	10.80		28.50	35.50
0880	24" wide		80	.200		19.80	11.30		31.10	39
0890	30" wide		70	.229		23.50	12.95		36.45	45
0900	36" wide		64	.250		25.50	14.15		39.65	49
0910	9" rung spacing, 6" wide		102	.157		12.55	8.90		21.45	27
0920	9" wide		98	.163		12.85	9.25		22.10	28
0930	12" wide		94	.170		14.80	9.65		24.45	30.50
0940	18" wide		90	.178		16.65	10.05		26.70	33.50
0950	24" wide		86	.186		19	10.55		29.55	37
0960	30" wide		80	.200		21	11.30		32.30	40
0970	36" wide		74	.216		22	12.25		34.25	43
0980	12" rung spacing, 6" wide		106	.151		12.35	8.55		20.90	26.50
0990	9" wide		104	.154		12.65	8.70		21.35	27
1000	12" wide		100	.160		13.35	9.05		22.40	28.50
1010	18" wide		96	.167		14.35	9.45		23.80	30
1020	24" wide		94	.170		15.40	9.65		25.05	31.50
1030	30" wide		88	.182		17.50	10.30		27.80	34.50
1040	36" wide		84	.190		18.45	10.80		29.25	36.50
1041	18" rung spacing, 6" wide		108	.148		12.25	8.40		20.65	26
1042	9" wide		106	.151		12.45	8.55		21	26.50
1043	12" wide		102	.157		13.25	8.90		22.15	28
1044	18" wide		98	.163		13.95	9.25		23.20	29
1045	24" wide		96	.167		14.35	9.45		23.80	30
1046	30" wide		90	.178		15.15	10.05		25.20	32
1047	36" wide		86	.186		15.55	10.55		26.10	33
1050	Elbows horiz. 9" rung spacing, 90°, 12" radius, 6" wide		9.60	1.667	Ea.	57	94.50		151.50	204
1060	9" wide		8.40	1.905		60.50	108		168.50	229
1070	12" wide		7.60	2.105		65.50	119		184.50	252
1080	18" wide		6.20	2.581		86.50	146		232.50	315
1090	24" wide		5.40	2.963		97	168		265	360
1100	30" wide		4.80	3.333		128	189		317	425
1110	36" wide		4.20	3.810		149	216		365	490
1120	90°, 24" radius, 6" wide		9.20	1.739		118	98.50		216.50	276
1130	9" wide		8	2		121	113		234	305
1140	12" wide		7.20	2.222		125	126		251	325
1150	18" wide		5.80	2.759		135	156		291	380
1160	24" wide		5	3.200		145	181		326	430
1170	30" wide		4.40	3.636		157	206		363	485
1180	36" wide		3.80	4.211		187	238		425	560
1190	90°, 36" radius, 6" wide		8.80	1.818		130	103		233	297
1200	9" wide		7.60	2.105		137	119		256	330
1210	12" wide		6.80	2.353		144	133		277	360
1220	18" wide		5.40	2.963		164	168		332	430
1230	24" wide		4.60	3.478		180	197		377	495
1240	30" wide		4	4		216	226		442	580
1250	36" wide		3.40	4.706		235	266		501	660
1260	45°, 12" radius, 6" wide		13.20	1.212		44	68.50		112.50	152
1270	9" wide		11	1.455		46	82.50		128.50	174
1280	12" wide		9.60	1.667		47.50	94.50		142	194
1290	18" wide		7.60	2.105		50.50	119		169.50	235
1300	24" wide		6.20	2.581		65	146		211	291
1310	30" wide		5.40	2.963		83	168		251	340
1320	36" wide		4.60	3.478		86.50	197		283.50	390

For customer support on your Electrical Costs with RSMeans Data, call 800.448.8182.

173

26 05 36 – Cable Trays for Electrical Systems

26 05 36.10 Cable Tray Ladder Type	Crew	Daily Output	Labor-Hours	Unit	Material	2017 Bare Costs Labor	Equipment	Total	Total Incl O&P
1330	45°, 24" radius, 6" wide	2 Elec	12.80	1.250	Ea.	56	71		127	168
1340	9" wide		10.60	1.509		59.50	85.50		145	194
1350	12" wide		9.20	1.739		66.50	98.50		165	220
1360	18" wide		7.20	2.222		68.50	126		194.50	263
1370	24" wide		5.80	2.759		82.50	156		238.50	325
1380	30" wide		5	3.200		98.50	181		279.50	380
1390	36" wide		4.20	3.810		113	216		329	450
1400	45°, 36" radius, 6" wide		12.40	1.290		80	73		153	197
1410	9" wide		10.20	1.569		85	89		174	227
1420	12" wide		8.80	1.818		86.50	103		189.50	249
1430	18" wide		6.80	2.353		93.50	133		226.50	305
1440	24" wide		5.40	2.963		99	168		267	360
1450	30" wide		4.60	3.478		128	197		325	435
1460	36" wide		3.80	4.211		142	238		380	510
1470	Elbows horizontal, 4" rung spacing, use 9" rung x 1.50									
1480	6" rung spacing, use 9" rung x 1.20									
1490	12" rung spacing, use 9" rung x .93									
1500	Elbows vertical, 9" rung spacing, 90°, 12" radius, 6" wide	2 Elec	9.60	1.667	Ea.	78.50	94.50		173	227
1510	9" wide		8.40	1.905		80	108		188	250
1520	12" wide		7.60	2.105		82.50	119		201.50	270
1530	18" wide		6.20	2.581		86.50	146		232.50	315
1540	24" wide		5.40	2.963		90	168		258	350
1550	30" wide		4.80	3.333		97	189		286	390
1560	36" wide		4.20	3.810		100	216		316	435
1570	24" radius, 6" wide		9.20	1.739		111	98.50		209.50	269
1580	9" wide		8	2		114	113		227	296
1590	12" wide		7.20	2.222		118	126		244	315
1600	18" wide		5.80	2.759		125	156		281	370
1610	24" wide		5	3.200		131	181		312	415
1620	30" wide		4.40	3.636		137	206		343	460
1630	36" wide		3.80	4.211		154	238		392	525
1640	36" radius, 6" wide		8.80	1.818		149	103		252	320
1650	9" wide		7.60	2.105		154	119		273	350
1660	12" wide		6.80	2.353		156	133		289	370
1670	18" wide		5.40	2.963		170	168		338	435
1680	24" wide		4.60	3.478		171	197		368	485
1690	30" wide		4	4		194	226		420	555
1700	36" wide		3.40	4.706		208	266		474	630
1710	Elbows vertical, 4" rung spacing, use 9" rung x 1.25									
1720	6" rung spacing, use 9" rung x 1.15									
1730	12" rung spacing, use 9" rung x .90									
1740	Tee horizontal, 9" rung spacing, 12" radius, 6" wide	2 Elec	5	3.200	Ea.	121	181		302	405
1750	9" wide		4.60	3.478		130	197		327	440
1760	12" wide		4.40	3.636		137	206		343	460
1770	18" wide		4	4		156	226		382	510
1780	24" wide		3.60	4.444		183	252		435	575
1790	30" wide		3.40	4.706		220	266		486	640
1800	36" wide		3	5.333		249	300		549	725
1810	24" radius, 6" wide		4.60	3.478		189	197		386	500
1820	9" wide		4.20	3.810		197	216		413	540
1830	12" wide		4	4		204	226		430	565
1840	18" wide		3.60	4.444		221	252		473	620
1850	24" wide		3.20	5		240	283		523	690

26 05 36 – Cable Trays for Electrical Systems

26 05 36.10 Cable Tray Ladder Type		Crew	Daily Output	Labor-Hours	Unit	Material	2017 Bare Costs Labor	Equipment	Total	Total Incl O&P
1860	30" wide	2 Elec	3	5.333	Ea.	261	300		561	735
1870	36" wide		2.60	6.154		335	350		685	890
1880	36" radius, 6" wide		4.20	3.810		282	216		498	635
1890	9" wide		3.80	4.211		294	238		532	680
1900	12" wide		3.60	4.444		315	252		567	720
1910	18" wide		3.20	5		335	283		618	795
1920	24" wide		2.80	5.714		380	325		705	900
1930	30" wide		2.60	6.154		415	350		765	975
1940	36" wide		2.20	7.273		445	410		855	1,100
1980	Tee vertical, 9" rung spacing, 12" radius, 6" wide		5.40	2.963		206	168		374	475
1990	9" wide		5.20	3.077		208	174		382	490
2000	12" wide		5	3.200		209	181		390	500
2010	18" wide		4.60	3.478		211	197		408	525
2020	24" wide		4.40	3.636		216	206		422	550
2030	30" wide		4	4		230	226		456	595
2040	36" wide		3.60	4.444		239	252		491	640
2050	24" radius, 6" wide		5	3.200		370	181		551	675
2060	9" wide		4.80	3.333		375	189		564	700
2070	12" wide		4.60	3.478		380	197		577	715
2080	18" wide		4.20	3.810		395	216		611	755
2090	24" wide		4	4		405	226		631	785
2100	30" wide		3.60	4.444		415	252		667	830
2110	36" wide		3.20	5		430	283		713	900
2120	36" radius, 6" wide		4.60	3.478		690	197		887	1,050
2130	9" wide		4.40	3.636		700	206		906	1,075
2140	12" wide		4.20	3.810		710	216		926	1,100
2150	18" wide		3.80	4.211		720	238		958	1,150
2160	24" wide		3.60	4.444		730	252		982	1,175
2170	30" wide		3.20	5		755	283		1,038	1,250
2180	36" wide	▼	2.80	5.714	▼	765	325		1,090	1,325
2190	Tee, 4" rung spacing, use 9" rung x 1.30									
2200	6" rung spacing, use 9" rung x 1.20									
2210	12" rung spacing, use 9" rung x .90									
2220	Cross horizontal, 9" rung spacing, 12" radius, 6" wide	2 Elec	4	4	Ea.	149	226		375	505
2230	9" wide		3.80	4.211		157	238		395	525
2240	12" wide		3.60	4.444		171	252		423	565
2250	18" wide		3.40	4.706		187	266		453	605
2260	24" wide		3	5.333		208	300		508	680
2270	30" wide		2.80	5.714		251	325		576	760
2280	36" wide		2.60	6.154		278	350		628	825
2290	24" radius, 6" wide		3.60	4.444		291	252		543	695
2300	9" wide		3.40	4.706		299	266		565	730
2310	12" wide		3.20	5		310	283		593	765
2320	18" wide		3	5.333		330	300		630	810
2330	24" wide		2.60	6.154		350	350		700	905
2340	30" wide		2.40	6.667		370	375		745	975
2350	36" wide		2.20	7.273		430	410		840	1,100
2360	36" radius, 6" wide		3.20	5		405	283		688	870
2370	9" wide		3	5.333		420	300		720	915
2380	12" wide		2.80	5.714		440	325		765	970
2390	18" wide		2.60	6.154		485	350		835	1,050
2400	24" wide		2.20	7.273		540	410		950	1,200
2410	30" wide		2	8		585	455		1,040	1,325

For customer support on your Electrical Costs with RSMeans Data, call 800.448.8182.

175

26 05 36 – Cable Trays for Electrical Systems

26 05 36.10 Cable Tray Ladder Type	Crew	Daily Output	Labor-Hours	Unit	Material	2017 Bare Costs Labor	Equipment	Total	Total Incl O&P
2420	36" wide	2 Elec	1.80	8.889	Ea.	630	505		1,135	1,450
2430	Cross horizontal, 4" rung spacing, use 9" rung x 1.30									
2440	6" rung spacing, use 9" rung x 1.20									
2450	12" rung spacing, use 9" rung x .90									
2460	Reducer, 9" to 6" wide tray	2 Elec	13	1.231	Ea.	83	69.50		152.50	196
2470	12" to 9" wide tray		12	1.333		85	75.50		160.50	207
2480	18" to 12" wide tray		10.40	1.538		85	87		172	224
2490	24" to 18" wide tray		9	1.778		86.50	101		187.50	246
2500	30" to 24" wide tray		8	2		88	113		201	267
2510	36" to 30" wide tray		7	2.286		98.50	129		227.50	300
2511	Reducer, 18" to 6" wide tray		10.40	1.538		88	87		175	227
2512	24" to 12" wide tray		9	1.778		90	101		191	250
2513	30" to 18" wide tray		8	2		93.50	113		206.50	273
2514	30" to 12" wide tray		8	2		97	113		210	277
2515	36" to 24" wide tray		7	2.286		100	129		229	305
2516	36" to 18" wide tray		7	2.286		100	129		229	305
2517	36" to 12" wide tray		7	2.286		100	129		229	305
2520	Dropout or end plate, 6" wide		32	.500		9.25	28.50		37.75	52.50
2530	9" wide		28	.571		10.90	32.50		43.40	60.50
2540	12" wide		26	.615		11.95	35		46.95	65
2550	18" wide		22	.727		14	41		55	77
2560	24" wide		20	.800		16.95	45.50		62.45	86.50
2570	30" wide		18	.889		18.50	50.50		69	96
2580	36" wide		16	1		21.50	56.50		78	109
2590	Tray connector		48	.333		16.40	18.85		35.25	46.50
3200	Aluminum tray, 4" deep, 6" rung spacing, 6" wide		134	.119	L.F.	14.55	6.75		21.30	26
3210	9" wide		128	.125		15.40	7.10		22.50	27.50
3220	12" wide		124	.129		16.30	7.30		23.60	29
3230	18" wide		114	.140		18.15	7.95		26.10	32
3240	24" wide		106	.151		21	8.55		29.55	36
3250	30" wide		100	.160		23.50	9.05		32.55	39
3260	36" wide		94	.170		25	9.65		34.65	42
3270	9" rung spacing, 6" wide		140	.114		11.80	6.45		18.25	22.50
3280	9" wide		134	.119		12.40	6.75		19.15	24
3290	12" wide		130	.123		12.60	6.95		19.55	24.50
3300	18" wide		122	.131		14.75	7.40		22.15	27.50
3310	24" wide		116	.138		17.10	7.80		24.90	30.50
3320	30" wide		108	.148		18.95	8.40		27.35	33.50
3330	36" wide		100	.160		20	9.05		29.05	35.50
3340	12" rung spacing, 6" wide		146	.110		12.55	6.20		18.75	23
3350	9" wide		140	.114		12.70	6.45		19.15	23.50
3360	12" wide		134	.119		13.10	6.75		19.85	24.50
3370	18" wide		128	.125		13.85	7.10		20.95	26
3380	24" wide		124	.129		15.40	7.30		22.70	28
3390	30" wide		114	.140		16.50	7.95		24.45	30
3400	36" wide		106	.151		17.35	8.55		25.90	32
3401	18" rung spacing, 6" wide		150	.107		12.45	6.05		18.50	23
3402	9" wide tray		144	.111		12.60	6.30		18.90	23.50
3403	12" wide tray		140	.114		13.10	6.45		19.55	24
3404	18" wide tray		134	.119		13.80	6.75		20.55	25.50
3405	24" wide tray		130	.123		14.85	6.95		21.80	27
3406	30" wide tray		120	.133		15.40	7.55		22.95	28.50
3407	36" wide tray		110	.145		16.05	8.25		24.30	30

26 05 36 – Cable Trays for Electrical Systems

26 05 36.10 Cable Tray Ladder Type	Crew	Daily Output	Labor-Hours	Unit	Material	2017 Bare Costs Labor	2017 Bare Costs Equipment	Total	Total Incl O&P
3410	Elbows horiz., 9" rung spacing, 90°, 12" radius, 6" wide	2 Elec	9.60	1.667	Ea	56	94.50		150.50	203
3420	9" wide		8.40	1.905		57.50	108		165.50	225
3430	12" wide		7.60	2.105		68	119		187	254
3440	18" wide		6.20	2.581		77	146		223	305
3450	24" wide		5.40	2.963		95	168		263	355
3460	30" wide		4.80	3.333		101	189		290	395
3470	36" wide		4.20	3.810		122	216		338	460
3480	24" radius, 6" wide		9.20	1.739		99.50	98.50		198	257
3490	9" wide		8	2		104	113		217	284
3500	12" wide		7.20	2.222		108	126		234	305
3510	18" wide		5.80	2.759		118	156		274	365
3520	24" wide		5	3.200		130	181		311	415
3530	30" wide		4.40	3.636		143	206		349	470
3540	36" wide		3.80	4.211		160	238		398	530
3550	90°, 36" radius, 6" wide		8.80	1.818		109	103		212	274
3560	9" wide		7.60	2.105		112	119		231	300
3570	12" wide		6.80	2.353		126	133		259	340
3580	18" wide		5.40	2.963		141	168		309	405
3590	24" wide		4.60	3.478		158	197		355	470
3600	30" wide		4	4		175	226		401	530
3610	36" wide		3.40	4.706		201	266		467	620
3620	45°, 12" radius, 6" wide		13.20	1.212		37	68.50		105.50	144
3630	9" wide		11	1.455		38	82.50		120.50	165
3640	12" wide		9.60	1.667		39.50	94.50		134	185
3650	18" wide		7.60	2.105		47	119		166	231
3660	24" wide		6.20	2.581		58	146		204	283
3670	30" wide		5.40	2.963		67	168		235	325
3680	36" wide		4.60	3.478		69.50	197		266.50	370
3690	45°, 24" radius, 6" wide		12.80	1.250		49	71		120	160
3700	9" wide		10.60	1.509		56	85.50		141.50	190
3710	12" wide		9.20	1.739		57.50	98.50		156	210
3720	18" wide		7.20	2.222		61.50	126		187.50	256
3730	24" wide		5.80	2.759		71	156		227	310
3740	30" wide		5	3.200		84.50	181		265.50	365
3750	36" wide		4.20	3.810		90	216		306	425
3760	45°, 36" radius, 6" wide		12.40	1.290		67	73		140	183
3770	9" wide		10.20	1.569		68.50	89		157.50	208
3780	12" wide		8.80	1.818		69.50	103		172.50	231
3790	18" wide		6.80	2.353		76.50	133		209.50	284
3800	24" wide		5.40	2.963		94	168		262	355
3810	30" wide		4.60	3.478		99.50	197		296.50	405
3820	36" wide		3.80	4.211		109	238		347	475
3830	Elbows horizontal, 4" rung spacing, use 9" rung x 1.50									
3840	6" rung spacing, use 9" rung x 1.20									
3850	12" rung spacing, use 9" rung x .93									
3860	Elbows vertical, 9" rung spacing, 90°, 12" radius, 6" wide	2 Elec	9.60	1.667	Ea.	78	94.50		172.50	227
3870	9" wide		8.40	1.905		82	108		190	252
3880	12" wide		7.60	2.105		83.50	119		202.50	271
3890	18" wide		6.20	2.581		86	146		232	315
3900	24" wide		5.40	2.963		91.50	168		259.50	350
3910	30" wide		4.80	3.333		95.50	189		284.50	390
3920	36" wide		4.20	3.810		98.50	216		314.50	435
3930	24" radius, 6" wide		9.20	1.739		84.50	98.50		183	240

26 05 36.10 Cable Tray Ladder Type	Crew	Daily Output	Labor-Hours	Unit	Material	2017 Bare Costs Labor	Equipment	Total	Total Incl O&P
3940	9" wide	2 Elec	8	2	Ea.	87.50	113		200.50	266
3950	12" wide		7.20	2.222		90	126		216	287
3960	18" wide		5.80	2.759		95.50	156		251.50	340
3970	24" wide		5	3.200		101	181		282	380
3980	30" wide		4.40	3.636		107	206		313	425
3990	36" wide		3.80	4.211		113	238		351	480
4000	36" radius, 6" wide		8.80	1.818		131	103		234	298
4010	9" wide		7.60	2.105		134	119		253	325
4020	12" wide		6.80	2.353		142	133		275	355
4030	18" wide		5.40	2.963		147	168		315	415
4040	24" wide		4.60	3.478		153	197		350	465
4050	30" wide		4	4		165	226		391	520
4060	36" wide		3.40	4.706		172	266		438	590
4070	Elbows vertical, 4" rung spacing, use 9" rung x 1.25									
4080	6" rung spacing, use 9" rung x 1.15									
4090	12" rung spacing, use 9" rung x .90									
4100	Tee horizontal, 9" rung spacing, 12" radius, 6" wide	2 Elec	5	3.200	Ea.	86.50	181		267.50	365
4110	9" wide		4.60	3.478		93	197		290	395
4120	12" wide		4.40	3.636		103	206		309	425
4130	18" wide		4.20	3.810		112	216		328	450
4140	24" wide		4	4		123	226		349	475
4150	30" wide		3.60	4.444		143	252		395	535
4160	36" wide		3.40	4.706		172	266		438	590
4170	24" radius, 6" wide		4.60	3.478		147	197		344	455
4180	9" wide		4.20	3.810		156	216		372	495
4190	12" wide		4	4		160	226		386	515
4200	18" wide		3.80	4.211		175	238		413	545
4210	24" wide		3.60	4.444		191	252		443	585
4220	30" wide		3.20	5		208	283		491	655
4230	36" wide		3	5.333		320	300		620	800
4240	36" radius, 6" wide		4.20	3.810		209	216		425	555
4250	9" wide		3.80	4.211		214	238		452	590
4260	12" wide		3.60	4.444		235	252		487	635
4270	18" wide		3.40	4.706		247	266		513	670
4280	24" wide		3.20	5		273	283		556	725
4290	30" wide		2.80	5.714		345	325		670	865
4300	36" wide		2.60	6.154		380	350		730	940
4310	Tee vertical, 9" rung spacing, 12" radius, 6" wide		5.40	2.963		194	168		362	465
4320	9" wide		5.20	3.077		201	174		375	480
4330	12" wide		5	3.200		204	181		385	495
4340	18" wide		4.60	3.478		206	197		403	520
4350	24" wide		4.40	3.636		223	206		429	555
4360	30" wide		4.20	3.810		227	216		443	575
4370	36" wide		4	4		235	226		461	600
4380	24" radius, 6" wide		5	3.200		330	181		511	630
4390	9" wide		4.80	3.333		335	189		524	650
4400	12" wide		4.60	3.478		340	197		537	670
4410	18" wide		4.20	3.810		345	216		561	705
4420	24" wide		4	4		355	226		581	730
4430	30" wide		3.80	4.211		365	238		603	760
4440	36" wide		3.60	4.444		395	252		647	810
4450	36" radius, 6" wide		4.60	3.478		725	197		922	1,100
4460	9" wide		4.40	3.636		740	206		946	1,125

26 05 36 – Cable Trays for Electrical Systems

26 05 36.10 Cable Tray Ladder Type		Crew	Daily Output	Labor-Hours	Unit	Material	2017 Bare Costs Labor	Equipment	Total	Total Incl O&P
4470	12" wide	2 Elec	4.20	3.810	Ea.	765	216		981	1,175
4480	18" wide		3.80	4.211		775	238		1,013	1,200
4490	24" wide		3.60	4.444		795	252		1,047	1,250
4500	30" wide		3.40	4.706		805	266		1,071	1,275
4510	36" wide		3.20	5		815	283		1,098	1,325
4520	Tees, 4" rung spacing, use 9" rung x 1.30									
4530	6" rung spacing, use 9" rung x 1.20									
4540	12" rung spacing, use 9" rung x .90									
4550	Cross horizontal, 9" rung spacing, 12" radius, 6" wide	2 Elec	4.40	3.636	Ea.	120	206		326	440
4560	9" wide		4.20	3.810		134	216		350	470
4570	12" wide		4	4		149	226		375	505
4580	18" wide		3.60	4.444		164	252		416	555
4590	24" wide		3.40	4.706		169	266		435	585
4600	30" wide		3	5.333		199	300		499	670
4610	36" wide		2.80	5.714		249	325		574	760
4620	24" radius, 6" wide		4	4		231	226		457	595
4630	9" wide		3.80	4.211		239	238		477	620
4640	12" wide		3.60	4.444		246	252		498	645
4650	18" wide		3.20	5		258	283		541	710
4660	24" wide		3	5.333		281	300		581	760
4670	30" wide		2.60	6.154		300	350		650	850
4680	36" wide		2.40	6.667		340	375		715	940
4690	36" radius, 6" wide		3.60	4.444		273	252		525	675
4700	9" wide		3.40	4.706		284	266		550	710
4710	12" wide		3.20	5		300	283		583	755
4720	18" wide		2.80	5.714		320	325		645	840
4730	24" wide		2.60	6.154		395	350		745	955
4740	30" wide		2.20	7.273		440	410		850	1,100
4750	36" wide		2	8		490	455		945	1,225
4760	Cross horizontal, 4" rung spacing, use 9" rung x 1.30									
4770	6" rung spacing, use 9" rung x 1.20									
4780	12" rung spacing, use 9" rung x .90									
4790	Reducer, 9" to 6" wide tray	2 Elec	16	1	Ea.	64	56.50		120.50	156
4800	12" to 9" wide tray		14	1.143		67	64.50		131.50	171
4810	18" to 12" wide tray		12.40	1.290		67	73		140	183
4820	24" to 18" wide tray		10.60	1.509		68.50	85.50		154	203
4830	30" to 24" wide tray		9.20	1.739		69.50	98.50		168	224
4840	36" to 30" wide tray		8	2		73.50	113		186.50	251
4841	Reducer, 18" to 6" wide tray		12.40	1.290		67	73		140	183
4842	24" to 12" wide tray		10.60	1.509		68.50	85.50		154	203
4843	30" to 18" wide tray		9.20	1.739		69.50	98.50		168	224
4844	30" to 12" wide tray		9.20	1.739		69.50	98.50		168	224
4845	36" to 24" wide tray		8	2		73.50	113		186.50	251
4846	36" to 18" wide tray		8	2		73.50	113		186.50	251
4847	36" to 12" wide tray		8	2		73.50	113		186.50	251
4850	Dropout or end plate, 6" wide		32	.500		8.45	28.50		36.95	52
4860	9" wide tray		28	.571		9.05	32.50		41.55	58.50
4870	12" wide tray		26	.615		9.80	35		44.80	63
4880	18" wide tray		22	.727		13.10	41		54.10	76
4890	24" wide tray		20	.800		15.45	45.50		60.95	85
4900	30" wide tray		18	.889		18.30	50.50		68.80	95.50
4910	36" wide tray		16	1		20.50	56.50		77	108
4920	Tray connector		48	.333		12.30	18.85		31.15	42

26 05 36.10 Cable Tray Ladder Type		Crew	Daily Output	Labor-Hours	Unit	Material	2017 Bare Costs Labor	2017 Bare Costs Equipment	Total	Total Incl O&P
8000	Elbow 36" radius horiz., 60°, 6" wide tray	2 Elec	10.60	1.509	Ea.	93	85.50		178.50	230
8010	9" wide tray		9	1.778		101	101		202	262
8020	12" wide tray		7.80	2.051		104	116		220	288
8030	18" wide tray		6.20	2.581		111	146		257	340
8040	24" wide tray		5	3.200		130	181		311	415
8050	30" wide tray		4.40	3.636		132	206		338	455
8060	30°, 6" wide tray		14	1.143		71	64.50		135.50	175
8070	9" wide tray		11.40	1.404		75	79.50		154.50	202
8080	12" wide tray		9.80	1.633		76.50	92.50		169	222
8090	18" wide tray		7.40	2.162		80.50	122		202.50	272
8100	24" wide tray		5.80	2.759		98.50	156		254.50	340
8110	30" wide tray		4.80	3.333		101	189		290	395
8120	Adjustable, 6" wide tray		12.40	1.290		94	73		167	213
8130	9" wide tray		10.20	1.569		99.50	89		188.50	243
8140	12" wide tray		8.80	1.818		101	103		204	265
8150	18" wide tray		6.80	2.353		111	133		244	320
8160	24" wide tray		5.40	2.963		117	168		285	380
8170	30" wide tray		4.60	3.478		131	197		328	440
8180	Wye 36" radius horiz., 45°, 6" wide tray		4.60	3.478		102	197		299	410
8190	9" wide tray		4.40	3.636		108	206		314	430
8200	12" wide tray		4.20	3.810		112	216		328	450
8210	18" wide tray		3.80	4.211		127	238		365	495
8220	24" wide tray		3.60	4.444		142	252		394	530
8230	30" wide tray		3.40	4.706		158	266		424	575
8240	Elbow 36" radius vert. in/outside, 60°, 6" wide tray		10.60	1.509		102	85.50		187.50	241
8250	9" wide tray		9	1.778		107	101		208	268
8260	12" wide tray		7.80	2.051		108	116		224	293
8270	18" wide tray		6.20	2.581		112	146		258	340
8280	24" wide tray		5	3.200		119	181		300	400
8290	30" wide tray		4.40	3.636		127	206		333	450
8300	45°, 6" wide tray		12.40	1.290		92.50	73		165.50	211
8310	9" wide tray		10.20	1.569		98	89		187	241
8320	12" wide tray		8.80	1.818		99.50	103		202.50	263
8330	18" wide tray		6.80	2.353		102	133		235	315
8340	24" wide tray		5.40	2.963		108	168		276	370
8350	30" wide tray		4.60	3.478		111	197		308	415
8360	30°, 6" wide tray		14	1.143		81	64.50		145.50	186
8370	9" wide tray		11.40	1.404		82.50	79.50		162	210
8380	12" wide tray		9.80	1.633		88	92.50		180.50	235
8390	18" wide tray		7.40	2.162		89.50	122		211.50	282
8400	24" wide tray		5.80	2.759		91.50	156		247.50	335
8410	30" wide tray		4.80	3.333		96.50	189		285.50	390
8660	Adjustable, 6" wide tray		12.40	1.290		92.50	73		165.50	211
8670	9" wide tray		10.20	1.569		98	89		187	241
8680	12" wide tray		8.80	1.818		99.50	103		202.50	264
8690	18" wide tray		6.80	2.353		111	133		244	320
8700	24" wide tray		5.40	2.963		117	168		285	380
8710	30" wide tray		4.60	3.478		130	197		327	440
8720	Cross, vertical, 24" radius, 6" wide tray		3.60	4.444		630	252		882	1,075
8730	9" wide tray		3.40	4.706		645	266		911	1,100
8740	12" wide tray		3.20	5		660	283		943	1,150
8750	18" wide tray		2.80	5.714		690	325		1,015	1,250
8760	24" wide tray		2.60	6.154		715	350		1,065	1,300

26 05 Common Work Results for Electrical

26 05 36 – Cable Trays for Electrical Systems

26 05 36.10 Cable Tray Ladder Type

		Crew	Daily Output	Labor-Hours	Unit	Material	2017 Bare Costs Labor	Equipment	Total	Total Incl O&P
8770	30" wide tray	2 Elec	2.20	7.273	Ea.	755	410		1,165	1,450
9200	Splice plate	1 Elec	48	.167	Pr.	12.85	9.45		22.30	28.50
9210	Expansion joint		48	.167		15.45	9.45		24.90	31
9220	Horizontal hinged		48	.167		12.85	9.45		22.30	28.50
9230	Vertical hinged		48	.167		15.45	9.45		24.90	31
9240	Ladder hanger, vertical		28	.286	Ea.	3.82	16.15		19.97	28
9250	Ladder to channel connector		24	.333		45	18.85		63.85	78
9260	Ladder to box connector, 30" wide		19	.421		45	24		69	85
9270	24" wide		20	.400		45	22.50		67.50	83.50
9280	18" wide		21	.381		43.50	21.50		65	80
9290	12" wide		22	.364		40.50	20.50		61	75.50
9300	9" wide		23	.348		36	19.70		55.70	69.50
9310	6" wide		24	.333		32	18.85		50.85	64
9320	Ladder floor flange		24	.333		29	18.85		47.85	60.50
9330	Cable roller for tray, 30" wide		10	.800		239	45.50		284.50	330
9340	24" wide		11	.727		203	41		244	285
9350	18" wide		12	.667		193	37.50		230.50	270
9360	12" wide		13	.615		152	35		187	219
9370	9" wide		14	.571		135	32.50		167.50	197
9380	6" wide		15	.533		109	30		139	165
9390	Pulley, single wheel		12	.667		249	37.50		286.50	330
9400	Triple wheel		10	.800		495	45.50		540.50	615
9440	Nylon cable tie, 14" long		80	.100		.46	5.65		6.11	9
9450	Ladder, hold down clamp		60	.133		8.20	7.55		15.75	20.50
9460	Cable clamp		60	.133		8.35	7.55		15.90	20.50
9470	Wall bracket, 30" wide tray		19	.421		44	24		68	84
9480	24" wide tray		20	.400		34.50	22.50		57	71.50
9490	18" wide tray		21	.381		30.50	21.50		52	66
9500	12" wide tray		22	.364		28.50	20.50		49	62.50
9510	9" wide tray		23	.348		25	19.70		44.70	57
9520	6" wide tray		24	.333		24.50	18.85		43.35	55.50

26 05 36.20 Cable Tray Solid Bottom

			Crew	Daily Output	Labor-Hours	Unit	Material	2017 Bare Costs Labor	Equipment	Total	Total Incl O&P
0010	**CABLE TRAY SOLID BOTTOM** w/ftngs. & supports, 3" dp, to 15' high										
0200	For higher elevations, see Section 26 05 36.40										
0220	Galvanized steel, tray, 6" wide	R260536-10	2 Elec	120	.133	L.F.	11.70	7.55		19.25	24
0240	12" wide			100	.160		15	9.05		24.05	30
0260	18" wide			70	.229		18.30	12.95		31.25	39.50
0280	24" wide	R260536-11		60	.267		21.50	15.10		36.60	46
0300	30" wide			50	.320		25.50	18.10		43.60	55
0320	36" wide			44	.364		36.50	20.50		57	71
0340	Elbow horizontal, 90°, 12" radius, 6" wide			9.60	1.667	Ea.	89	94.50		183.50	239
0360	12" wide			6.80	2.353		99.50	133		232.50	310
0370	18" wide			5.40	2.963		114	168		282	375
0380	24" wide			4.40	3.636		139	206		345	465
0390	30" wide			3.80	4.211		166	238		404	540
0400	36" wide			3.40	4.706		188	266		454	605
0420	24" radius, 6" wide			9.20	1.739		127	98.50		225.50	286
0440	12" wide			6.40	2.500		147	142		289	375
0450	18" wide			5	3.200		171	181		352	460
0460	24" wide			4	4		199	226		425	560
0470	30" wide			3.40	4.706		233	266		499	655
0480	36" wide			3	5.333		262	300		562	740

For customer support on your Electrical Costs with RSMeans Data, call 800.448.8182.

181

26 05 36.20 Cable Tray Solid Bottom		Crew	Daily Output	Labor-Hours	Unit	Material	2017 Bare Costs Labor	2017 Bare Costs Equipment	Total	Total Incl O&P
0500	36" radius, 6" wide	2 Elec	8.80	1.818	Ea.	185	103		288	355
0520	12" wide		6	2.667		209	151		360	455
0530	18" wide		4.60	3.478		255	197		452	575
0540	24" wide		3.60	4.444		276	252		528	680
0550	30" wide		3	5.333		335	300		635	815
0560	36" wide		2.60	6.154		375	350		725	935
0580	Elbow vertical, 90°, 12" radius, 6" wide		9.60	1.667		108	94.50		202.50	260
0600	12" wide		6.80	2.353		117	133		250	330
0610	18" wide		5.40	2.963		126	168		294	390
0620	24" wide		4.40	3.636		135	206		341	460
0630	30" wide		3.80	4.211		144	238		382	515
0640	36" wide		3.40	4.706		149	266		415	565
0670	24" radius, 6" wide		9.20	1.739		152	98.50		250.50	315
0690	12" wide		6.40	2.500		168	142		310	395
0700	18" wide		5	3.200		182	181		363	470
0710	24" wide		4	4		197	226		423	555
0720	30" wide		3.40	4.706		209	266		475	630
0730	36" wide		3	5.333		228	300		528	700
0750	36" radius, 6" wide		8.80	1.818		209	103		312	385
0770	12" wide		6.60	2.424		233	137		370	460
0780	18" wide		4.60	3.478		255	197		452	575
0790	24" wide		3.60	4.444		279	252		531	680
0800	30" wide		3	5.333		305	300		605	785
0810	36" wide		2.60	6.154		330	350		680	885
0840	Tee horizontal, 12" radius, 6" wide		5	3.200		125	181		306	410
0860	12" wide		4	4		135	226		361	490
0870	18" wide		3.40	4.706		161	266		427	575
0880	24" wide		2.80	5.714		180	325		505	685
0890	30" wide		2.60	6.154		205	350		555	745
0900	36" wide		2.20	7.273		235	410		645	875
0940	24" radius, 6" wide		4.60	3.478		193	197		390	510
0960	12" wide		3.60	4.444		226	252		478	625
0970	18" wide		3	5.333		252	300		552	725
0980	24" wide		2.40	6.667		340	375		715	940
0990	30" wide		2.20	7.273		370	410		780	1,025
1000	36" wide		1.80	8.889		400	505		905	1,200
1020	36" radius, 6" wide		4.20	3.810		305	216		521	660
1040	12" wide		3.20	5		340	283		623	800
1050	18" wide		2.60	6.154		370	350		720	925
1060	24" wide		2.20	7.273		475	410		885	1,150
1070	30" wide		2	8		515	455		970	1,250
1080	36" wide		1.60	10		535	565		1,100	1,450
1100	Tee vertical, 12" radius, 6" wide		5	3.200		205	181		386	495
1120	12" wide		4	4		214	226		440	575
1130	18" wide		3.60	4.444		217	252		469	615
1140	24" wide		3.40	4.706		238	266		504	660
1150	30" wide		3	5.333		255	300		555	730
1160	36" wide		2.60	6.154		264	350		614	810
1180	24" radius, 6" wide		4.60	3.478		305	197		502	630
1200	12" wide		3.60	4.444		315	252		567	725
1210	18" wide		3.20	5		330	283		613	790
1220	24" wide		3	5.333		350	300		650	835
1230	30" wide		2.60	6.154		385	350		735	940

26 05 36 – Cable Trays for Electrical Systems

26 05 36.20 Cable Tray Solid Bottom	Crew	Daily Output	Labor-Hours	Unit	Material	2017 Bare Costs Labor	Equipment	Total	Total Incl O&P
1240	36" wide	2 Elec	2.20	7.273	Ea.	400	410		810	1,050
1260	36" radius, 6" wide		4.20	3.810		475	216		691	845
1280	12" wide		3.20	5		480	283		763	955
1290	18" wide		2.80	5.714		515	325		840	1,050
1300	24" wide		2.60	6.154		535	350		885	1,100
1310	30" wide		2.20	7.273		625	410		1,035	1,300
1320	36" wide		2	8		660	455		1,115	1,400
1340	Cross horizontal, 12" radius, 6" wide		4	4		149	226		375	505
1360	12" wide		3.40	4.706		163	266		429	580
1370	18" wide		2.80	5.714		190	325		515	695
1380	24" wide		2.40	6.667		214	375		589	800
1390	30" wide		2	8		238	455		693	940
1400	36" wide		1.80	8.889		262	505		767	1,050
1420	24" radius, 6" wide		3.60	4.444		272	252		524	675
1440	12" wide		3	5.333		305	300		605	785
1450	18" wide		2.40	6.667		340	375		715	940
1460	24" wide		2	8		435	455		890	1,150
1470	30" wide		1.80	8.889		475	505		980	1,275
1480	36" wide		1.60	10		500	565		1,065	1,400
1500	36" radius, 6" wide		3.20	5		445	283		728	915
1520	12" wide		2.60	6.154		490	350		840	1,050
1530	18" wide		2	8		535	455		990	1,275
1540	24" wide		1.80	8.889		630	505		1,135	1,450
1550	30" wide		1.60	10		685	565		1,250	1,600
1560	36" wide		1.40	11.429		730	645		1,375	1,775
1580	Drop out or end plate, 6" wide		32	.500		18.15	28.50		46.65	62.50
1600	12" wide		26	.615		22.50	35		57.50	77
1610	18" wide		22	.727		24	41		65	88
1620	24" wide		20	.800		28.50	45.50		74	99.50
1630	30" wide		18	.889		32	50.50		82.50	111
1640	36" wide		16	1		34.50	56.50		91	123
1660	Reducer, 12" to 6" wide		12	1.333		87.50	75.50		163	209
1680	18" to 12" wide		10.60	1.509		89	85.50		174.50	226
1700	18" to 6" wide		10.60	1.509		89	85.50		174.50	226
1720	24" to 18" wide		9.20	1.739		92.50	98.50		191	249
1740	24" to 12" wide		9.20	1.739		92.50	98.50		191	249
1760	30" to 24" wide		8	2		99.50	113		212.50	279
1780	30" to 18" wide		8	2		99.50	113		212.50	279
1800	30" to 12" wide		8	2		99.50	113		212.50	279
1820	36" to 30" wide		7.20	2.222		103	126		229	300
1840	36" to 24" wide		7.20	2.222		103	126		229	300
1860	36" to 18" wide		7.20	2.222		103	126		229	300
1880	36" to 12" wide		7.20	2.222		103	126		229	300
2000	Aluminum tray, 6" wide		150	.107	L.F.	11.25	6.05		17.30	21.50
2020	12" wide		130	.123		14.70	6.95		21.65	26.50
2030	18" wide		100	.160		18.45	9.05		27.50	34
2040	24" wide		90	.178		23.50	10.05		33.55	40.50
2050	30" wide		70	.229		27.50	12.95		40.45	49.50
2060	36" wide		64	.250		34.50	14.15		48.65	59
2080	Elbow horizontal, 90°, 12" radius, 6" wide		9.60	1.667	Ea.	90	94.50		184.50	240
2100	12" wide		7.60	2.105		101	119		220	290
2110	18" wide		6.80	2.353		124	133		257	335
2120	24" wide		5.80	2.759		142	156		298	390

26 05 36.20 Cable Tray Solid Bottom		Crew	Daily Output	Labor-Hours	Unit	Material	2017 Bare Costs Labor	Equipment	Total	Total Incl O&P
2130	30" wide	2 Elec	5	3.200	Ea.	173	181		354	460
2140	36" wide		4.40	3.636		195	206		401	525
2160	24" radius, 6" wide		9.20	1.739		128	98.50		226.50	288
2180	12" wide		7.20	2.222		151	126		277	355
2190	18" wide		6.40	2.500		173	142		315	400
2200	24" wide		5.40	2.963		214	168		382	485
2210	30" wide		4.60	3.478		245	197		442	565
2220	36" wide		4	4		281	226		507	650
2240	36" radius, 6" wide		8.80	1.818		189	103		292	360
2260	12" wide		6.80	2.353		227	133		360	450
2270	18" wide		6	2.667		270	151		421	525
2280	24" wide		5	3.200		289	181		470	590
2290	30" wide		4.20	3.810		325	216		541	685
2300	36" wide		3.60	4.444		385	252		637	795
2320	Elbow vertical, 90°, 12" radius, 6" wide		9.60	1.667		107	94.50		201.50	258
2340	12" wide		7.60	2.105		111	119		230	300
2350	18" wide		6.80	2.353		126	133		259	340
2360	24" wide		5.80	2.759		132	156		288	380
2370	30" wide		5	3.200		141	181		322	425
2380	36" wide		4.40	3.636		145	206		351	470
2400	24" radius, 6" wide		9.20	1.739		151	98.50		249.50	315
2420	12" wide		7.20	2.222		165	126		291	370
2430	18" wide		6.40	2.500		177	142		319	405
2440	24" wide		5.40	2.963		192	168		360	460
2450	30" wide		4.60	3.478		204	197		401	520
2460	36" wide		4	4		224	226		450	585
2480	36" radius, 6" wide		8.80	1.818		200	103		303	375
2500	12" wide		6.80	2.353		224	133		357	445
2510	18" wide		6	2.667		245	151		396	495
2520	24" wide		5	3.200		254	181		435	550
2530	30" wide		4.20	3.810		281	216		497	635
2540	36" wide		3.60	4.444		292	252		544	695
2560	Tee horizontal, 12" radius, 6" wide		5	3.200		139	181		320	425
2580	12" wide		4.40	3.636		169	206		375	495
2590	18" wide		4	4		189	226		415	550
2600	24" wide		3.60	4.444		212	252		464	610
2610	30" wide		3	5.333		245	300		545	720
2620	36" wide		2.40	6.667		281	375		656	875
2640	24" radius, 6" wide		4.60	3.478		230	197		427	550
2660	12" wide		4	4		258	226		484	625
2670	18" wide		3.60	4.444		292	252		544	695
2680	24" wide		3	5.333		360	300		660	845
2690	30" wide		2.40	6.667		410	375		785	1,025
2700	36" wide		2.20	7.273		455	410		865	1,125
2720	36" radius, 6" wide		4.20	3.810		375	216		591	735
2740	12" wide		3.60	4.444		410	252		662	825
2750	18" wide		3.20	5		470	283		753	945
2760	24" wide		2.60	6.154		550	350		900	1,125
2770	30" wide		2	8		605	455		1,060	1,350
2780	36" wide		1.80	8.889		675	505		1,180	1,500
2800	Tee vertical, 12" radius, 6" wide		5	3.200		199	181		380	490
2820	12" wide		4.40	3.636		203	206		409	535
2830	18" wide		4.20	3.810		211	216		427	555

26 05 36 – Cable Trays for Electrical Systems

26 05 36.20 Cable Tray Solid Bottom		Crew	Daily Output	Labor-Hours	Unit	Material	2017 Bare Costs Labor	Equipment	Total	Total Incl O&P
2840	24" wide	2 Elec	4	4	Ea.	224	226		450	585
2850	30" wide		3.60	4.444		245	252		497	645
2860	36" wide		3	5.333		258	300		558	735
2880	24" radius, 6" wide		4.60	3.478		292	197		489	615
2900	12" wide		4	4		310	226		536	680
2910	18" wide		3.80	4.211		330	238		568	720
2920	24" wide		3.60	4.444		360	252		612	770
2930	30" wide		3.20	5		395	283		678	860
2940	36" wide		2.60	6.154		415	350		765	975
2960	36" radius, 6" wide		4.20	3.810		455	216		671	830
2980	12" wide		3.40	4.706		480	266		746	925
2990	18" wide		3.40	4.706		505	266		771	955
3000	24" wide		3.20	5		520	283		803	1,000
3010	30" wide		2.80	5.714		560	325		885	1,100
3020	36" wide		2.20	7.273		620	410		1,030	1,300
3040	Cross horizontal, 12" radius, 6" wide		4.40	3.636		177	206		383	505
3060	12" wide		4	4		200	226		426	560
3070	18" wide		3.40	4.706		227	266		493	650
3080	24" wide		2.80	5.714		258	325		583	770
3090	30" wide		2.60	6.154		292	350		642	840
3100	36" wide		2.20	7.273		325	410		735	970
3120	24" radius, 6" wide		4	4		310	226		536	680
3140	12" wide		3.60	4.444		360	252		612	770
3150	18" wide		3	5.333		390	300		690	880
3160	24" wide		2.40	6.667		470	375		845	1,075
3170	30" wide		2.20	7.273		520	410		930	1,200
3180	36" wide		1.80	8.889		540	505		1,045	1,350
3200	36" radius, 6" wide		3.60	4.444		540	252		792	970
3220	12" wide		3.20	5		570	283		853	1,050
3230	18" wide		2.60	6.154		635	350		985	1,225
3240	24" wide		2	8		690	455		1,145	1,450
3250	30" wide		1.80	8.889		745	505		1,250	1,575
3260	36" wide		1.60	10		870	565		1,435	1,800
3280	Dropout, or end plate, 6" wide		32	.500		17.85	28.50		46.35	62
3300	12" wide		26	.615		20	35		55	74
3310	18" wide		22	.727		24	41		65	88
3320	24" wide		20	.800		26.50	45.50		72	97
3330	30" wide		18	.889		31	50.50		81.50	110
3340	36" wide		16	1		36	56.50		92.50	125
3380	Reducer, 12" to 6" wide		14	1.143		87	64.50		151.50	193
3400	18" to 12" wide		12	1.333		90	75.50		165.50	212
3420	18" to 6" wide		12	1.333		90	75.50		165.50	212
3440	24" to 18" wide		10.60	1.509		95.50	85.50		181	233
3460	24" to 12" wide		10.60	1.509		95.50	85.50		181	233
3480	30" to 24" wide		9.20	1.739		104	98.50		202.50	262
3500	30" to 18" wide		9.20	1.739		104	98.50		202.50	262
3520	30" to 12" wide		9.20	1.739		104	98.50		202.50	262
3540	36" to 30" wide		8	2		110	113		223	290
3560	36" to 24" wide		8	2		111	113		224	292
3580	36" to 18" wide		8	2		111	113		224	292
3600	36" to 12" wide		8	2		114	113		227	295

For customer support on your Electrical Costs with RSMeans Data, call 800.448.8182.

185

26 05 36.30 Cable Tray Trough	Crew	Daily Output	Labor-Hours	Unit	Material	2017 Bare Costs Labor	Equipment	Total	Total Incl O&P
0010 **CABLE TRAY TROUGH** vented, w/ftngs. & supports, 6" dp, to 10' high									
0020 For higher elevations, see Section 26 05 36.40									
0200 Galvanized steel, tray, 6" wide R260536-10	2 Elec	90	.178	L.F.	13.35	10.05		23.40	30
0240 12" wide		80	.200		12.65	11.30		23.95	31
0260 18" wide		70	.229		20.50	12.95		33.45	42
0280 24" wide R260536-11		60	.267		33	15.10		48.10	58.50
0300 30" wide		50	.320		48	18.10		66.10	79.50
0320 36" wide		40	.400		68.50	22.50		91	110
0340 Elbow horizontal, 90°, 12" radius, 6" wide		7.60	2.105	Ea.	116	119		235	305
0360 12" wide		5.60	2.857		138	162		300	395
0370 18" wide		4.40	3.636		159	206		365	485
0380 24" wide		3.60	4.444		196	252		448	590
0390 30" wide		3.20	5		221	283		504	670
0400 36" wide		2.80	5.714		257	325		582	770
0420 24" radius, 6" wide		7.20	2.222		171	126		297	375
0440 12" wide		5.20	3.077		198	174		372	480
0450 18" wide		4	4		238	226		464	600
0460 24" wide		3.20	5		270	283		553	720
0470 30" wide		2.80	5.714		310	325		635	825
0480 36" wide		2.40	6.667		330	375		705	930
0500 36" radius, 6" wide		6.80	2.353		236	133		369	460
0520 12" wide		4.80	3.333		269	189		458	580
0530 18" wide		3.60	4.444		320	252		572	730
0540 24" wide		2.80	5.714		330	325		655	850
0550 30" wide		2.40	6.667		375	375		750	975
0560 36" wide		2	8		415	455		870	1,150
0580 Elbow vertical, 90°, 12" radius, 6" wide		7.60	2.105		134	119		253	325
0600 12" wide		5.60	2.857		149	162		311	405
0610 18" wide		4.40	3.636		151	206		357	475
0620 24" wide		3.60	4.444		174	252		426	565
0630 30" wide		3.20	5		177	283		460	620
0640 36" wide		2.80	5.714		187	325		512	690
0660 24" radius, 6" wide		7.20	2.222		192	126		318	400
0680 12" wide		5.20	3.077		203	174		377	485
0690 18" wide		4	4		226	226		452	590
0700 24" wide		3.20	5		233	283		516	680
0710 30" wide		2.80	5.714		261	325		586	770
0720 36" wide		2.40	6.667		274	375		649	865
0740 36" radius, 6" wide		6.80	2.353		259	133		392	485
0760 12" wide		4.80	3.333		276	189		465	590
0770 18" wide		3.60	4.444		305	252		557	710
0780 24" wide		2.80	5.714		330	325		655	845
0790 30" wide		2.40	6.667		335	375		710	935
0800 36" wide		2	8		375	455		830	1,100
0820 Tee horizontal, 12" radius, 6" wide		4	4		157	226		383	510
0840 12" wide		3.20	5		175	283		458	620
0850 18" wide		2.80	5.714		198	325		523	705
0860 24" wide		2.40	6.667		230	375		605	820
0870 30" wide		2.20	7.273		261	410		671	900
0880 36" wide		2	8		287	455		742	995
0900 24" radius, 6" wide		3.60	4.444		259	252		511	660
0920 12" wide		2.80	5.714		284	325		609	795

26 05 36.30 Cable Tray Trough		Crew	Daily Output	Labor-Hours	Unit	Material	2017 Bare Costs Labor	2017 Bare Costs Equipment	Total	Total Incl O&P
0930	18" wide	2 Elec	2.40	6.667	Ea.	315	375		690	915
0940	24" wide		2	8		410	455		865	1,125
0950	30" wide		1.80	8.889		445	505		950	1,250
0960	36" wide		1.60	10		495	565		1,060	1,400
0980	36" radius, 6" wide		3.20	5		375	283		658	835
1000	12" wide		2.40	6.667		425	375		800	1,025
1010	18" wide		2	8		465	455		920	1,200
1020	24" wide		1.60	10		560	565		1,125	1,475
1030	30" wide		1.40	11.429		595	645		1,240	1,625
1040	36" wide		1.20	13.333		700	755		1,455	1,900
1060	Tee vertical, 12" radius, 6" wide		4	4		246	226		472	610
1080	12" wide		3.20	5		250	283		533	700
1090	18" wide		3	5.333		258	300		558	735
1100	24" wide		2.80	5.714		272	325		597	785
1110	30" wide		2.60	6.154		288	350		638	835
1120	36" wide		2.20	7.273		293	410		703	935
1140	24" radius, 6" wide		3.60	4.444		330	252		582	740
1160	12" wide		2.80	5.714		350	325		675	870
1170	18" wide		2.60	6.154		365	350		715	920
1180	24" wide		2.40	6.667		395	375		770	1,000
1190	30" wide		2.20	7.273		415	410		825	1,075
1200	36" wide		1.80	8.889		450	505		955	1,250
1220	36" radius, 6" wide		3.20	5		540	283		823	1,025
1240	12" wide		2.40	6.667		550	375		925	1,175
1250	18" wide		2.20	7.273		570	410		980	1,250
1260	24" wide		2	8		605	455		1,060	1,350
1270	30" wide		1.80	8.889		705	505		1,210	1,525
1280	36" wide		1.40	11.429		710	645		1,355	1,750
1300	Cross horizontal, 12" radius, 6" wide		3.20	5		194	283		477	640
1320	12" wide		2.80	5.714		196	325		521	700
1330	18" wide		2.40	6.667		219	375		594	805
1340	24" wide		2	8		230	455		685	935
1350	30" wide		1.80	8.889		259	505		764	1,050
1360	36" wide		1.60	10		290	565		855	1,175
1380	24" radius, 6" wide		2.80	5.714		305	325		630	820
1400	12" wide		2.40	6.667		320	375		695	915
1410	18" wide		2	8		350	455		805	1,075
1420	24" wide		1.60	10		450	565		1,015	1,350
1430	30" wide		1.40	11.429		495	645		1,140	1,525
1440	36" wide		1.20	13.333		525	755		1,280	1,700
1460	36" radius, 6" wide		2.40	6.667		525	375		900	1,150
1480	12" wide		2	8		540	455		995	1,275
1490	18" wide		1.60	10		550	565		1,115	1,450
1500	24" wide		1.20	13.333		665	755		1,420	1,850
1510	30" wide		1	16		730	905		1,635	2,150
1520	36" wide		.80	20		785	1,125		1,910	2,575
1540	Dropout or end plate, 6" wide		26	.615		23.50	35		58.50	77.50
1560	12" wide		22	.727		28.50	41		69.50	93
1580	18" wide		20	.800		31.50	45.50		77	103
1600	24" wide		18	.889		36	50.50		86.50	115
1620	30" wide		16	1		38.50	56.50		95	128
1640	36" wide		13.40	1.194		43.50	67.50		111	149
1660	Reducer, 12" to 6" wide		9.40	1.702		94.50	96.50		191	248

For customer support on your Electrical Costs with RSMeans Data, call 800.448.8182.

187

26 05 36.30 Cable Tray Trough		Crew	Daily Output	Labor-Hours	Unit	Material	2017 Bare Costs Labor	Equipment	Total	Total Incl O&P
1680	18" to 12" wide	2 Elec	8.40	1.905	Ea.	98	108		206	270
1700	18" to 6" wide		8.40	1.905		98	108		206	270
1720	24" to 18" wide		7.20	2.222		105	126		231	305
1740	24" to 12" wide		7.20	2.222		105	126		231	305
1760	30" to 24" wide		6.40	2.500		108	142		250	330
1780	30" to 18" wide		6.40	2.500		108	142		250	330
1800	30" to 12" wide		6.40	2.500		108	142		250	330
1820	36" to 30" wide		5.80	2.759		116	156		272	360
1840	36" to 24" wide		5.80	2.759		116	156		272	360
1860	36" to 18" wide		5.80	2.759		118	156		274	365
1880	36" to 12" wide		5.80	2.759		118	156		274	365
2000	Aluminum, tray, vented, 6" wide		120	.133	L.F.	16	7.55		23.55	29
2010	9" wide		110	.145		18.10	8.25		26.35	32.50
2020	12" wide		100	.160		21.50	9.05		30.55	37
2030	18" wide		90	.178		24	10.05		34.05	41.50
2040	24" wide		80	.200		28.50	11.30		39.80	48.50
2050	30" wide		70	.229		38	12.95		50.95	61.50
2060	36" wide		60	.267		41.50	15.10		56.60	68.50
2080	Elbow horiz., 90°, 12" radius, 6" wide		7.60	2.105	Ea.	100	119		219	289
2090	9" wide		7	2.286		109	129		238	315
2100	12" wide		6.20	2.581		116	146		262	345
2110	18" wide		5.60	2.857		135	162		297	390
2120	24" wide		4.60	3.478		156	197		353	465
2130	30" wide		4	4		192	226		418	550
2140	36" wide		3.60	4.444		210	252		462	605
2160	24" radius, 6" wide		7.20	2.222		145	126		271	345
2180	12" wide		5.80	2.759		170	156		326	420
2190	18" wide		5.20	3.077		195	174		369	475
2200	24" wide		4.20	3.810		223	216		439	570
2210	30" wide		3.60	4.444		255	252		507	655
2220	36" wide		3.20	5		276	283		559	730
2240	36" radius, 6" wide		6.80	2.353		209	133		342	430
2260	12" wide		5.40	2.963		237	168		405	510
2270	18" wide		4.80	3.333		270	189		459	580
2280	24" wide		3.80	4.211		295	238		533	680
2290	30" wide		3.40	4.706		345	266		611	780
2300	36" wide		2.80	5.714		375	325		700	900
2320	Elbow vertical, 90°, 12" radius, 6" wide		7.60	2.105		121	119		240	310
2330	9" wide		7	2.286		130	129		259	335
2340	12" wide		6.20	2.581		131	146		277	365
2350	18" wide		5.60	2.857		135	162		297	390
2360	24" wide		4.60	3.478		149	197		346	460
2370	30" wide		4	4		156	226		382	510
2380	36" wide		3.60	4.444		157	252		409	550
2400	24" radius, 6" wide		7.20	2.222		164	126		290	370
2420	12" wide		5.80	2.759		178	156		334	430
2430	18" wide		5.20	3.077		194	174		368	475
2440	24" wide		4.20	3.810		196	216		412	540
2450	30" wide		3.60	4.444		207	252		459	605
2460	36" wide		3.20	5		217	283		500	665
2480	36" radius, 6" wide		6.80	2.353		207	133		340	430
2500	12" wide		5.40	2.963		221	168		389	495
2510	18" wide		4.80	3.333		248	189		437	555

26 05 Common Work Results for Electrical

26 05 36 – Cable Trays for Electrical Systems

26 05 36.30 Cable Tray Trough

		Crew	Daily Output	Labor-Hours	Unit	Material	2017 Bare Costs Labor	Equipment	Total	Total Incl O&P
2520	24" wide	2 Elec	3.80	4.211	Ea.	268	238		506	650
2530	30" wide		3.40	4.706		295	266		561	725
2540	36" wide		2.80	5.714		305	325		630	820
2560	Tee horizontal, 12" radius, 6" wide		4	4		152	226		378	505
2570	9" wide		3.80	4.211		156	238		394	525
2580	12" wide		3.60	4.444		170	252		422	560
2590	18" wide		3.20	5		196	283		479	640
2600	24" wide		2.80	5.714		226	325		551	735
2610	30" wide		2.40	6.667		242	375		617	830
2620	36" wide		2.20	7.273		276	410		686	920
2640	24" radius, 6" wide		3.60	4.444		231	252		483	630
2660	12" wide		3.20	5		263	283		546	715
2670	18" wide		2.80	5.714		290	325		615	805
2680	24" wide		2.40	6.667		360	375		735	965
2690	30" wide		2	8		390	455		845	1,100
2700	36" wide		1.80	8.889		455	505		960	1,250
2720	36" radius, 6" wide		3.20	5		370	283		653	835
2740	12" wide		2.80	5.714		430	325		755	955
2750	18" wide		2.40	6.667		485	375		860	1,100
2760	24" wide		2	8		565	455		1,020	1,300
2770	30" wide		1.60	10		600	565		1,165	1,500
2780	36" wide		1.40	11.429		695	645		1,340	1,725
2800	Tee vertical, 12" radius, 6" wide		4	4		213	226		439	575
2810	9" wide		3.80	4.211		214	238		452	590
2820	12" wide		3.60	4.444		230	252		482	630
2830	18" wide		3.40	4.706		234	266		500	655
2840	24" wide		3.20	5		237	283		520	685
2850	30" wide		3	5.333		248	300		548	725
2860	36" wide		2.60	6.154		258	350		608	805
2880	24" radius, 6" wide		3.60	4.444		300	252		552	705
2900	12" wide		3.20	5		325	283		608	785
2910	18" wide		3	5.333		345	300		645	830
2920	24" wide		2.80	5.714		370	325		695	890
2930	30" wide		2.60	6.154		400	350		750	960
2940	36" wide		2.20	7.273		405	410		815	1,050
2960	36" radius, 6" wide		3.20	5		455	283		738	925
2980	12" wide		2.80	5.714		485	325		810	1,025
2990	18" wide		2.60	6.154		500	350		850	1,075
3000	24" wide		2.40	6.667		535	375		910	1,150
3010	30" wide		2.20	7.273		580	410		990	1,250
3020	36" wide		1.80	8.889		610	505		1,115	1,425
3040	Cross horizontal, 12" radius, 6" wide		3.60	4.444		189	252		441	585
3050	9" wide		3.40	4.706		203	266		469	625
3060	12" wide		3.20	5		209	283		492	655
3070	18" wide		2.80	5.714		219	325		544	725
3080	24" wide		2.40	6.667		244	375		619	835
3090	30" wide		2.20	7.273		310	410		720	960
3100	36" wide		1.80	8.889		355	505		860	1,150
3120	24" radius, 6" wide		3.20	5		340	283		623	800
3140	12" wide		2.80	5.714		370	325		695	895
3150	18" wide		2.40	6.667		400	375		775	1,000
3160	24" wide		2	8		465	455		920	1,200
3170	30" wide		1.80	8.889		500	505		1,005	1,300

For customer support on your Electrical Costs with RSMeans Data, call 800.448.8182.

189

26 05 36.30 Cable Tray Trough	Crew	Daily Output	Labor-Hours	Unit	Material	2017 Bare Costs Labor	2017 Bare Costs Equipment	Total	Total Incl O&P
3180	36" wide	2 Elec	1.40	11.429	Ea.	565	645		1,210	1,600
3200	36" radius, 6" wide		2.80	5.714		555	325		880	1,100
3220	12" wide		2.40	6.667		580	375		955	1,200
3230	18" wide		2	8		630	455		1,085	1,375
3240	24" wide		1.60	10		730	565		1,295	1,650
3250	30" wide		1.40	11.429		795	645		1,440	1,850
3260	36" wide		1.20	13.333		925	755		1,680	2,150
3280	Dropout, or end plate, 6" wide		26	.615		19.30	35		54.30	73
3300	12" wide		22	.727		23	41		64	86.50
3310	18" wide		20	.800		27.50	45.50		73	98.50
3320	24" wide		18	.889		33	50.50		83.50	112
3330	30" wide		16	1		35.50	56.50		92	124
3340	36" wide		14	1.143		40.50	64.50		105	142
3370	Reducer, 9" to 6" wide		12	1.333		94.50	75.50		170	217
3380	12" to 6" wide		11.40	1.404		99.50	79.50		179	228
3390	12" to 9" wide		11.40	1.404		99.50	79.50		179	228
3400	18" to 12" wide		9.60	1.667		106	94.50		200.50	258
3420	18" to 6" wide		9.60	1.667		106	94.50		200.50	258
3430	18" to 9" wide		9.60	1.667		106	94.50		200.50	258
3440	24" to 18" wide		8.40	1.905		114	108		222	287
3460	24" to 12" wide		8.40	1.905		114	108		222	287
3470	24" to 9" wide		8.40	1.905		115	108		223	289
3475	24" to 6" wide		8.40	1.905		115	108		223	289
3480	30" to 24" wide		7.20	2.222		116	126		242	315
3500	30" to 18" wide		7.20	2.222		116	126		242	315
3520	30" to 12" wide		7.20	2.222		119	126		245	320
3540	36" to 30" wide		6.40	2.500		121	142		263	345
3560	36" to 24" wide		6.40	2.500		121	142		263	345
3580	36" to 18" wide		6.40	2.500		121	142		263	345
3600	36" to 12" wide		6.40	2.500		121	142		263	345
3610	Elbow horizontal, 60°, 12" radius, 6" wide		7.80	2.051		82.50	116		198.50	265
3620	9" wide		7.20	2.222		90	126		216	287
3630	12" wide		6.40	2.500		99.50	142		241.50	320
3640	18" wide		5.80	2.759		103	156		259	345
3650	24" wide		4.80	3.333		131	189		320	425
3680	Elbow horizontal, 45°, 12" radius, 6" wide		8	2		75	113		188	253
3690	9" wide		7.40	2.162		75	122		197	266
3700	12" wide		6.60	2.424		79.50	137		216.50	294
3710	18" wide		6	2.667		89.50	151		240.50	325
3720	24" wide		5	3.200		104	181		285	385
3750	Elbow horizontal, 30°, 12" radius, 6" wide		8.20	1.951		62	110		172	233
3760	9" wide		7.60	2.105		65	119		184	251
3770	12" wide		6.80	2.353		71.50	133		204.50	279
3780	18" wide		6.20	2.581		75	146		221	300
3790	24" wide		5.20	3.077		82.50	174		256.50	350
3820	Elbow vertical, 60° in/outside, 12" radius, 6" wide		7.80	2.051		102	116		218	286
3830	9" wide		7.20	2.222		104	126		230	300
3840	12" wide		6.40	2.500		105	142		247	330
3850	18" wide		5.80	2.759		109	156		265	355
3860	24" wide		4.80	3.333		114	189		303	410
3890	Elbow vertical, 45° in/outside, 12" radius, 6" wide		8	2		88	113		201	267
3900	9" wide		7.40	2.162		84.50	122		206.50	276
3910	12" wide		6.60	2.424		90	137		227	305

26 05 Common Work Results for Electrical

26 05 36 – Cable Trays for Electrical Systems

26 05 36.30 Cable Tray Trough	Crew	Daily Output	Labor-Hours	Unit	Material	2017 Bare Costs Labor	Equipment	Total	Total Incl O&P
3920	18" wide	2 Elec	6	2.667	Ea.	93	151		244	330
3930	24" wide		5	3.200		102	181		283	385
3960	Elbow vertical, 30° in/outside, 12" radius, 6" wide		8.20	1.951		71	110		181	243
3970	9" wide		7.60	2.105		75	119		194	262
3980	12" wide		6.80	2.353		76.50	133		209.50	285
3990	18" wide		6.20	2.581		80	146		226	305
4000	24" wide		5.20	3.077		81	174		255	350
4250	Reducer, left or right hand, 24" to 18" wide		8.40	1.905		108	108		216	281
4260	24" to 12" wide		8.40	1.905		108	108		216	281
4270	24" to 9" wide		8.40	1.905		108	108		216	281
4280	24" to 6" wide		8.40	1.905		109	108		217	282
4290	18" to 12" wide		9.60	1.667		101	94.50		195.50	252
4300	18" to 9" wide		9.60	1.667		101	94.50		195.50	252
4310	18" to 6" wide		9.60	1.667		101	94.50		195.50	252
4320	12" to 9" wide		11.40	1.404		96.50	79.50		176	225
4330	12" to 6" wide		11.40	1.404		96.50	79.50		176	225
4340	9" to 6" wide		12	1.333		93.50	75.50		169	216
4350	Splice plate	1 Elec	48	.167		8.95	9.45		18.40	24
4360	Splice plate, expansion joint		48	.167		9.20	9.45		18.65	24.50
4370	Splice plate, hinged, horizontal		48	.167		7.40	9.45		16.85	22.50
4380	Vertical		48	.167		10.50	9.45		19.95	25.50
4390	Trough, hanger, vertical		28	.286		29.50	16.15		45.65	56.50
4400	Box connector, 24" wide		20	.400		37	22.50		59.50	75
4410	18" wide		21	.381		33	21.50		54.50	69
4420	12" wide		22	.364		32	20.50		52.50	66
4430	9" wide		23	.348		30	19.70		49.70	63
4440	6" wide		24	.333		29	18.85		47.85	60
4450	Floor flange		24	.333		30	18.85		48.85	62
4460	Hold down clamp		60	.133		3.47	7.55		11.02	15.10
4520	Wall bracket, 24" wide tray		20	.400		30.50	22.50		53	67.50
4530	18" wide tray		21	.381		30	21.50		51.50	65.50
4540	12" wide tray		22	.364		15.90	20.50		36.40	48.50
4550	9" wide tray		23	.348		14.20	19.70		33.90	45
4560	6" wide tray		24	.333		12.90	18.85		31.75	42.50
5000	Cable channel aluminum, vented, 1-1/4" deep, 4" wide, straight		80	.100	L.F.	7.60	5.65		13.25	16.85
5010	Elbow horizontal, 36" radius, 90°		5	1.600	Ea.	131	90.50		221.50	280
5020	60°		5.50	1.455		101	82.50		183.50	234
5030	45°		6	1.333		82	75.50		157.50	203
5040	30°		6.50	1.231		72	69.50		141.50	183
5050	Adjustable		6	1.333		68.50	75.50		144	189
5060	Elbow vertical, 36" radius, 90°		5	1.600		141	90.50		231.50	291
5070	60°		5.50	1.455		112	82.50		194.50	247
5080	45°		6	1.333		92	75.50		167.50	214
5090	30°		6.50	1.231		82	69.50		151.50	194
5100	Adjustable		6	1.333		68.50	75.50		144	189
5110	Splice plate, hinged, horizontal		48	.167		9.65	9.45		19.10	25
5120	Splice plate, hinged, vertical		48	.167		13.75	9.45		23.20	29.50
5130	Hanger, vertical		28	.286		15.15	16.15		31.30	40.50
5140	Single		28	.286		23	16.15		39.15	49.50
5150	Double		20	.400		23.50	22.50		46	60
5160	Channel to box connector		24	.333		31	18.85		49.85	63
5170	Hold down clip		80	.100		4.37	5.65		10.02	13.30
5180	Wall bracket, single		28	.286		10.05	16.15		26.20	35

For customer support on your Electrical Costs with RSMeans Data, call 800.448.8182.

191

26 05 36 – Cable Trays for Electrical Systems

26 05 36.30 Cable Tray Trough		Crew	Daily Output	Labor-Hours	Unit	Material	2017 Bare Costs Labor	Equipment	Total	Total Incl O&P
5190	Double	1 Elec	20	.400	Ea.	12.90	22.50		35.40	48
5200	Cable roller		16	.500		158	28.50		186.50	217
5210	Splice plate	↓	48	.167	↓	4.86	9.45		14.31	19.50

26 05 36.40 Cable Tray, Covers and Dividers

	26 05 36.40 Cable Tray, Covers and Dividers		Crew	Daily Output	Labor-Hours	Unit	Material	2017 Bare Costs Labor	Equipment	Total	Total Incl O&P
0010	**CABLE TRAY, COVERS AND DIVIDERS** To 10' high	R260536-10									
0011	For higher elevations, see lines 9900 – 9960										
0100	Covers, ventilated galv. steel, straight, 6" wide tray size		2 Elec	520	.031	L.F.	8.30	1.74		10.04	11.70
0200	9" wide tray size			460	.035		8.80	1.97		10.77	12.60
0300	12" wide tray size	R260536-11		400	.040		15.15	2.26		17.41	20
0400	18" wide tray size			300	.053		28.50	3.02		31.52	36
0500	24" wide tray size			220	.073		47	4.12		51.12	58
0600	30" wide tray size			180	.089		22.50	5.05		27.55	32.50
0700	36" wide tray size			160	.100	↓	24	5.65		29.65	35
1000	Elbow horizontal, 90°, 12" radius, 6" wide tray size			150	.107	Ea.	43	6.05		49.05	56.50
1020	9" wide tray size			128	.125		47.50	7.10		54.60	63
1040	12" wide tray size			108	.148		50.50	8.40		58.90	68
1060	18" wide tray size			84	.190		69.50	10.80		80.30	92.50
1080	24" wide tray size			66	.242		84.50	13.70		98.20	113
1100	30" wide tray size			60	.267		107	15.10		122.10	141
1120	36" wide tray size			50	.320		127	18.10		145.10	166
1160	24" radius, 6" wide tray size			136	.118		71.50	6.65		78.15	89
1180	9" wide tray size			116	.138		73.50	7.80		81.30	92
1200	12" wide tray size			96	.167		81.50	9.45		90.95	104
1220	18" wide tray size			76	.211		101	11.90		112.90	129
1240	24" wide tray size			60	.267		123	15.10		138.10	158
1260	30" wide tray size			52	.308		161	17.40		178.40	204
1280	36" wide tray size			44	.364		187	20.50		207.50	237
1320	36" radius, 6" wide tray size			120	.133		107	7.55		114.55	129
1340	9" wide tray size			104	.154		118	8.70		126.70	143
1360	12" wide tray size			84	.190		126	10.80		136.80	154
1380	18" wide tray size			72	.222		160	12.60		172.60	195
1400	24" wide tray size			52	.308		191	17.40		208.40	236
1420	30" wide tray size			46	.348		227	19.70		246.70	279
1440	36" wide tray size			40	.400		266	22.50		288.50	325
1480	Elbow horizontal, 45°, 12" radius, 6" wide tray size			150	.107		32.50	6.05		38.55	44.50
1500	9" wide tray size			128	.125		39	7.10		46.10	53
1520	12" wide tray size			108	.148		42	8.40		50.40	59
1540	18" wide tray size			88	.182		51.50	10.30		61.80	72
1560	24" wide tray size			76	.211		60	11.90		71.90	84
1580	30" wide tray size			66	.242		71	13.70		84.70	98.50
1600	36" wide tray size			60	.267		79.50	15.10		94.60	110
1640	24" radius, 6" wide tray size			136	.118		45	6.65		51.65	59.50
1660	9" wide tray size			116	.138		50.50	7.80		58.30	67
1680	12" wide tray size			96	.167		57	9.45		66.45	76.50
1700	18" wide tray size			80	.200		66	11.30		77.30	89.50
1720	24" wide tray size			70	.229		75	12.95		87.95	102
1740	30" wide tray size			60	.267		95.50	15.10		110.60	128
1760	36" wide tray size			52	.308		105	17.40		122.40	141
1800	36" radius, 6" wide tray size			120	.133		66.50	7.55		74.05	84.50
1820	9" wide tray size			104	.154		75	8.70		83.70	95.50
1840	12" wide tray size			84	.190		82.50	10.80		93.30	107
1860	18" wide tray size	↓		76	.211	↓	94.50	11.90		106.40	122

26 05 36 – Cable Trays for Electrical Systems

26 05 36.40 Cable Tray, Covers and Dividers	Crew	Daily Output	Labor-Hours	Unit	Material	2017 Bare Costs Labor	Equipment	Total	Total Incl O&P
1880	24" wide tray size	2 Elec	62	.258	Ea.	115	14.60		129.60	149
1900	30" wide tray size		52	.308		125	17.40		142.40	164
1920	36" wide tray size		48	.333		151	18.85		169.85	195
1960	Elbow vertical, 90°, 12" radius, 6" wide tray size		150	.107		38	6.05		44.05	51
1980	9" wide tray size		128	.125		39	7.10		46.10	53
2000	12" wide tray size		108	.148		42	8.40		50.40	58.50
2020	18" wide tray size		88	.182		47.50	10.30		57.80	68
2040	24" wide tray size		68	.235		48.50	13.30		61.80	73.50
2060	30" wide tray size		60	.267		53.50	15.10		68.60	81
2080	36" wide tray size		50	.320		69.50	18.10		87.60	104
2120	24" radius, 6" wide tray size		136	.118		46.50	6.65		53.15	61.50
2140	9" wide tray size		116	.138		51.50	7.80		59.30	68
2160	12" wide tray size		96	.167		53.50	9.45		62.95	72.50
2180	18" wide tray size		80	.200		71	11.30		82.30	95
2200	24" wide tray size		62	.258		79.50	14.60		94.10	110
2220	30" wide tray size		52	.308		87	17.40		104.40	122
2240	36" wide tray size		44	.364		99	20.50		119.50	140
2280	36" radius, 6" wide tray size		120	.133		52.50	7.55		60.05	69.50
2300	9" wide tray size		104	.154		67	8.70		75.70	87
2320	12" wide tray size		84	.190		75	10.80		85.80	98.50
2340	18" wide tray size		76	.211		94.50	11.90		106.40	122
2350	24" wide tray size		54	.296		105	16.75		121.75	140
2360	30" wide tray size		46	.348		125	19.70		144.70	168
2370	36" wide tray size		40	.400		148	22.50		170.50	197
2400	Tee horizontal, 12" radius, 6" wide tray size		92	.174		69	9.85		78.85	91
2410	9" wide tray size		80	.200		71	11.30		82.30	95
2420	12" wide tray size		68	.235		80.50	13.30		93.80	108
2430	18" wide tray size		60	.267		97	15.10		112.10	130
2440	24" wide tray size		52	.308		122	17.40		139.40	161
2460	30" wide tray size		36	.444		144	25		169	196
2470	36" wide tray size		30	.533		174	30		204	236
2500	24" radius, 6" wide tray size		88	.182		111	10.30		121.30	137
2510	9" wide tray size		76	.211		117	11.90		128.90	147
2520	12" wide tray size		64	.250		121	14.15		135.15	154
2530	18" wide tray size		56	.286		155	16.15		171.15	195
2540	24" wide tray size		48	.333		238	18.85		256.85	291
2560	30" wide tray size		32	.500		272	28.50		300.50	340
2570	36" wide tray size		26	.615		300	35		335	380
2600	36" radius, 6" wide tray size		84	.190		189	10.80		199.80	224
2610	9" wide tray size		72	.222		192	12.60		204.60	231
2620	12" wide tray size		60	.267		214	15.10		229.10	258
2630	18" wide tray size		52	.308		250	17.40		267.40	300
2640	24" wide tray size		44	.364		330	20.50		350.50	390
2660	30" wide tray size		28	.571		360	32.50		392.50	445
2670	36" wide tray size		22	.727		405	41		446	505
2700	Cross horizontal, 12" radius, 6" wide tray size		68	.235		103	13.30		116.30	133
2710	9" wide tray size		64	.250		109	14.15		123.15	140
2720	12" wide tray size		60	.267		121	15.10		136.10	156
2730	18" wide tray size		52	.308		144	17.40		161.40	184
2740	24" wide tray size		36	.444		169	25		194	224
2760	30" wide tray size		30	.533		192	30		222	257
2770	36" wide tray size		28	.571		225	32.50		257.50	296
2800	24" radius, 6" wide tray size		64	.250		185	14.15		199.15	225

26 05 36.40 Cable Tray, Covers and Dividers		Crew	Daily Output	Labor-Hours	Unit	Material	2017 Bare Costs Labor	Equipment	Total	Total Incl O&P
2810	9" wide tray size	2 Elec	60	.267	Ea.	201	15.10		216.10	244
2820	12" wide tray size		56	.286		217	16.15		233.15	263
2830	18" wide tray size		48	.333		260	18.85		278.85	315
2840	24" wide tray size		32	.500		315	28.50		343.50	390
2860	30" wide tray size		26	.615		350	35		385	435
2870	36" wide tray size		24	.667		395	37.50		432.50	485
2900	36" radius, 6" wide tray size		60	.267		315	15.10		330.10	375
2910	9" wide tray size		56	.286		315	16.15		331.15	370
2920	12" wide tray size		52	.308		345	17.40		362.40	400
2930	18" wide tray size		44	.364		390	20.50		410.50	455
2940	24" wide tray size		28	.571		485	32.50		517.50	585
2960	30" wide tray size		22	.727		520	41		561	635
2970	36" wide tray size		20	.800		555	45.50		600.50	685
3000	Reducer, 9" to 6" wide tray size		128	.125		44	7.10		51.10	59
3010	12" to 6" wide tray size		108	.148		46	8.40		54.40	63
3020	12" to 9" wide tray size		108	.148		46	8.40		54.40	63
3030	18" to 12" wide tray size		88	.182		49	10.30		59.30	69.50
3050	18" to 6" wide tray size		88	.182		49	10.30		59.30	69.50
3060	24" to 18" wide tray size		80	.200		68.50	11.30		79.80	92.50
3070	24" to 12" wide tray size		80	.200		62.50	11.30		73.80	86
3090	30" to 24" wide tray size		70	.229		72.50	12.95		85.45	99.50
3100	30" to 18" wide tray size		70	.229		72.50	12.95		85.45	99.50
3110	30" to 12" wide tray size		70	.229		62.50	12.95		75.45	88.50
3140	36" to 30" wide tray size		64	.250		79	14.15		93.15	108
3150	36" to 24" wide tray size		64	.250		79	14.15		93.15	108
3160	36" to 18" wide tray size		64	.250		79	14.15		93.15	108
3170	36" to 12" wide tray size		64	.250	↓	79	14.15		93.15	108
3250	Covers, aluminum, straight, 6" wide tray size		520	.031	L.F.	4.75	1.74		6.49	7.85
3270	9" wide tray size		460	.035		5.75	1.97		7.72	9.25
3290	12" wide tray size		400	.040		6.85	2.26		9.11	10.95
3310	18" wide tray size		320	.050		9.05	2.83		11.88	14.25
3330	24" wide tray size		260	.062		11.30	3.48		14.78	17.65
3350	30" wide tray size		200	.080		12.50	4.53		17.03	20.50
3370	36" wide tray size		180	.089	↓	13.25	5.05		18.30	22
3400	Elbow horizontal, 90°, 12" radius, 6" wide tray size		150	.107	Ea.	35.50	6.05		41.55	48
3410	9" wide tray size		128	.125		37	7.10		44.10	51.50
3420	12" wide tray size		108	.148		40	8.40		48.40	56.50
3430	18" wide tray size		88	.182		52	10.30		62.30	73
3440	24" wide tray size		70	.229		66	12.95		78.95	92
3460	30" wide tray size		64	.250		79	14.15		93.15	108
3470	36" wide tray size		54	.296		96.50	16.75		113.25	131
3500	24" radius, 6" wide tray size		136	.118		45.50	6.65		52.15	60
3510	9" wide tray size		116	.138		56.50	7.80		64.30	73.50
3520	12" wide tray size		96	.167		62.50	9.45		71.95	82.50
3530	18" wide tray size		80	.200		74	11.30		85.30	98
3540	24" wide tray size		64	.250		91	14.15		105.15	121
3560	30" wide tray size		56	.286		111	16.15		127.15	147
3570	36" wide tray size		48	.333		138	18.85		156.85	181
3600	36" radius, 6" wide tray size		120	.133		80	7.55		87.55	99.50
3610	9" wide tray size		104	.154		87	8.70		95.70	109
3620	12" wide tray size		84	.190		99	10.80		109.80	125
3630	18" wide tray size		76	.211		118	11.90		129.90	148
3640	24" wide tray size		56	.286	↓	143	16.15		159.15	182

26 05 36 – Cable Trays for Electrical Systems

26 05 36.40 Cable Tray, Covers and Dividers		Crew	Daily Output	Labor-Hours	Unit	Material	2017 Bare Costs Labor	Equipment	Total	Total Incl O&P
3660	30" wide tray size	2 Elec	50	.320	Ea.	165	18.10		183.10	208
3670	36" wide tray size		44	.364		193	20.50		213.50	243
3700	Elbow horizontal, 45°, 12" radius, 6" wide tray size		150	.107		26	6.05		32.05	37.50
3710	9" wide tray size		128	.125		27	7.10		34.10	40
3720	12" wide tray size		108	.148		30	8.40		38.40	45.50
3730	18" wide tray size		88	.182		34.50	10.30		44.80	53.50
3740	24" wide tray size		80	.200		38.50	11.30		49.80	59
3760	30" wide tray size		70	.229		48.50	12.95		61.45	72.50
3770	36" wide tray size		64	.250		58	14.15		72.15	85
3800	24" radius, 6" wide tray size		136	.118		28.50	6.65		35.15	41.50
3810	9" wide tray size		116	.138		36	7.80		43.80	51.50
3820	12" wide tray size		96	.167		37.50	9.45		46.95	55.50
3830	18" wide tray size		80	.200		45.50	11.30		56.80	67
3840	24" wide tray size		72	.222		56.50	12.60		69.10	81
3860	30" wide tray size		64	.250		65	14.15		79.15	92.50
3870	36" wide tray size		56	.286		75.50	16.15		91.65	107
3900	36" radius, 6" wide tray size		120	.133		50.50	7.55		58.05	67
3910	9" wide tray size		104	.154		54.50	8.70		63.20	73
3920	12" wide tray size		84	.190		57.50	10.80		68.30	79.50
3930	18" wide tray size		76	.211		69.50	11.90		81.40	94.50
3940	24" wide tray size		64	.250		84	14.15		98.15	114
3960	30" wide tray size		56	.286		96	16.15		112.15	130
3970	36" wide tray size		50	.320		109	18.10		127.10	147
4000	Elbow vertical, 90°, 12" radius, 6" wide tray size		150	.107		30	6.05		36.05	42
4010	9" wide tray size		128	.125		30	7.10		37.10	43.50
4020	12" wide tray size		108	.148		33	8.40		41.40	49
4030	18" wide tray size		88	.182		38.50	10.30		48.80	57.50
4040	24" wide tray size		70	.229		40	12.95		52.95	63.50
4060	30" wide tray size		64	.250		40.50	14.15		54.65	66
4070	36" wide tray size		54	.296		45.50	16.75		62.25	75
4100	24" radius, 6" wide tray size		136	.118		34.50	6.65		41.15	48
4110	9" wide tray size		116	.138		37.50	7.80		45.30	53
4120	12" wide tray size		96	.167		40.50	9.45		49.95	59
4130	18" wide tray size		80	.200		49	11.30		60.30	71
4140	24" wide tray size		64	.250		53.50	14.15		67.65	80
4160	30" wide tray size		56	.286		65	16.15		81.15	95.50
4170	36" wide tray size		48	.333		71	18.85		89.85	107
4200	36" radius, 6" wide tray size		120	.133		38.50	7.55		46.05	53.50
4210	9" wide tray size		104	.154		47.50	8.70		56.20	65
4220	12" wide tray size		84	.190		54.50	10.80		65.30	76
4230	18" wide tray size		76	.211		66.50	11.90		78.40	91
4240	24" wide tray size		56	.286		78	16.15		94.15	110
4260	30" wide tray size		50	.320		99	18.10		117.10	136
4270	36" wide tray size		44	.364		106	20.50		126.50	148
4300	Tee horizontal, 12" radius, 6" wide tray size		108	.148		49	8.40		57.40	66.50
4310	9" wide tray size		88	.182		52	10.30		62.30	73
4320	12" wide tray size		80	.200		58	11.30		69.30	81
4330	18" wide tray size		68	.235		69	13.30		82.30	96
4340	24" wide tray size		56	.286		87.50	16.15		103.65	120
4360	30" wide tray size		44	.364		103	20.50		123.50	144
4370	36" wide tray size		36	.444		124	25		149	175
4400	24" radius, 6" wide tray size		96	.167		79.50	9.45		88.95	102
4410	9" wide tray size		80	.200		84	11.30		95.30	109

For customer support on your Electrical Costs with RSMeans Data, call 800.448.8182.

195

26 05 36.40 Cable Tray, Covers and Dividers		Crew	Daily Output	Labor-Hours	Unit	Material	2017 Bare Costs Labor	Equipment	Total	Total Incl O&P
4420	12" wide tray size	2 Elec	72	.222	Ea.	94	12.60		106.60	123
4430	18" wide tray size		60	.267		110	15.10		125.10	144
4440	24" wide tray size		48	.333		175	18.85		193.85	222
4460	30" wide tray size		40	.400		194	22.50		216.50	247
4470	36" wide tray size		32	.500		216	28.50		244.50	280
4500	36" radius, 6" wide tray size		88	.182		141	10.30		151.30	170
4510	9" wide tray size		72	.222		143	12.60		155.60	177
4520	12" wide tray size		64	.250		158	14.15		172.15	194
4530	18" wide tray size		56	.286		179	16.15		195.15	221
4540	24" wide tray size		44	.364		227	20.50		247.50	281
4560	30" wide tray size		36	.444		256	25		281	320
4570	36" wide tray size		28	.571		288	32.50		320.50	365
4600	Cross horizontal, 12" radius, 6" wide tray size		80	.200		75	11.30		86.30	99.50
4610	9" wide tray size		72	.222		79.50	12.60		92.10	106
4620	12" wide tray size		64	.250		88.50	14.15		102.65	119
4630	18" wide tray size		56	.286		108	16.15		124.15	142
4640	24" wide tray size		48	.333		124	18.85		142.85	165
4660	30" wide tray size		40	.400		147	22.50		169.50	196
4670	36" wide tray size		32	.500		169	28.50		197.50	229
4700	24" radius, 6" wide tray size		72	.222		139	12.60		151.60	172
4710	9" wide tray size		64	.250		149	14.15		163.15	185
4720	12" wide tray size		56	.286		160	16.15		176.15	200
4730	18" wide tray size		48	.333		187	18.85		205.85	234
4740	24" wide tray size		40	.400		223	22.50		245.50	279
4760	30" wide tray size		32	.500		260	28.50		288.50	330
4770	36" wide tray size		24	.667		283	37.50		320.50	365
4800	36" radius, 6" wide tray size		64	.250		227	14.15		241.15	271
4810	9" wide tray size		56	.286		237	16.15		253.15	285
4820	12" wide tray size		50	.320		246	18.10		264.10	297
4830	18" wide tray size		44	.364		270	20.50		290.50	330
4840	24" wide tray size		36	.444		335	25		360	405
4860	30" wide tray size		28	.571		385	32.50		417.50	470
4870	36" wide tray size		22	.727		420	41		461	520
4900	Reducer, 9" to 6" wide tray size		128	.125		38	7.10		45.10	52
4910	12" to 6" wide tray size		108	.148		39.50	8.40		47.90	56
4920	12" to 9" wide tray size		108	.148		39.50	8.40		47.90	56
4930	18" to 12" wide tray size		88	.182		43.50	10.30		53.80	63
4950	18" to 6" wide tray size		88	.182		43.50	10.30		53.80	63
4960	24" to 18" wide tray size		80	.200		55.50	11.30		66.80	78
4970	24" to 12" wide tray size		80	.200		48	11.30		59.30	69.50
4990	30" to 24" wide tray size		70	.229		58	12.95		70.95	83.50
5000	30" to 18" wide tray size		70	.229		58	12.95		70.95	83.50
5010	30" to 12" wide tray size		70	.229		58	12.95		70.95	83.50
5040	36" to 30" wide tray size		64	.250		64.50	14.15		78.65	91.50
5050	36" to 24" wide tray size		64	.250		64.50	14.15		78.65	91.50
5060	36" to 18" wide tray size		64	.250		64.50	14.15		78.65	91.50
5070	36" to 12" wide tray size		64	.250		64.50	14.15		78.65	91.50
5710	Tray cover hold down clamp	1 Elec	60	.133		10.30	7.55		17.85	22.50
8000	Divider strip, straight, galvanized, 3" deep		200	.040	L.F.	5.50	2.26		7.76	9.45
8020	4" deep		180	.044		6.70	2.52		9.22	11.10
8040	6" deep		160	.050		8.75	2.83		11.58	13.90
8060	Aluminum, straight, 3" deep		210	.038		5.50	2.16		7.66	9.30
8080	4" deep		190	.042		6.80	2.38		9.18	11

26 05 36.40 Cable Tray, Covers and Dividers	Crew	Daily Output	Labor-Hours	Unit	Material	2017 Bare Costs Labor	Equipment	Total	Total Incl O&P
8100	6" deep	1 Elec	170	.047	L.F.	8.65	2.66		11.31	13.55
0110	Divider strip, vertical fitting, 3" deep									
8120	12" radius, galvanized, 30°	1 Elec	28	.286	Ea.	26.50	16.15		42.65	53
8140	45°		27	.296		33	16.75		49.75	61.50
8160	60°		26	.308		35	17.40		52.40	65
8180	90°		25	.320		44	18.10		62.10	75.50
8200	Aluminum, 30°		29	.276		17.70	15.60		33.30	43
8220	45°		28	.286		21	16.15		37.15	47
8240	60°		27	.296		24	16.75		40.75	51.50
8260	90°		26	.308		30.50	17.40		47.90	59.50
8280	24" radius, galvanized, 30°		25	.320		39.50	18.10		57.60	70.50
8300	45°		24	.333		42	18.85		60.85	75
8320	60°		23	.348		53.50	19.70		73.20	88
8340	90°		22	.364		72.50	20.50		93	111
8360	Aluminum, 30°		26	.308		27.50	17.40		44.90	56.50
8380	45°		25	.320		32	18.10		50.10	62
8400	60°		24	.333		40	18.85		58.85	72.50
8420	90°		23	.348		54.50	19.70		74.20	89
8440	36" radius, galvanized, 30°		22	.364		50.50	20.50		71	86.50
8460	45°		21	.381		59	21.50		80.50	97
8480	60°		20	.400		69	22.50		91.50	110
8500	90°		19	.421		95.50	24		119.50	141
8520	Aluminum, 30°		23	.348		42	19.70		61.70	76
8540	45°		22	.364		54.50	20.50		75	90.50
8560	60°		21	.381		70.50	21.50		92	110
8570	90°		20	.400		92	22.50		114.50	135
8590	Divider strip, vertical fitting, 4" deep									
8600	12" radius, galvanized, 30°	1 Elec	27	.296	Ea.	31.50	16.75		48.25	59.50
8610	45°		26	.308		36.50	17.40		53.90	66.50
8620	60°		25	.320		41.50	18.10		59.60	72.50
8630	90°		24	.333		50.50	18.85		69.35	84
8640	Aluminum, 30°		28	.286		23.50	16.15		39.65	50
8650	45°		27	.296		27	16.75		43.75	55
8660	60°		26	.308		31	17.40		48.40	60.50
8670	90°		25	.320		37	18.10		55.10	67.50
8680	24" radius, galvanized, 30°		24	.333		50.50	18.85		69.35	84
8690	45°		23	.348		63.50	19.70		83.20	99
8700	60°		22	.364		71.50	20.50		92	110
8710	90°		21	.381		95.50	21.50		117	138
8720	Aluminum, 30°		25	.320		37	18.10		55.10	67.50
8730	45°		24	.333		45	18.85		63.85	78
8740	60°		23	.348		53	19.70		72.70	87.50
8750	90°		22	.364		72.50	20.50		93	111
8760	36" radius, galvanized, 30°		23	.348		60	19.70		79.70	95.50
8770	45°		22	.364		68.50	20.50		89	106
8780	60°		21	.381		86	21.50		107.50	127
8790	90°		20	.400		115	22.50		137.50	160
8800	Aluminum, 30°		24	.333		57.50	18.85		76.35	92
8810	45°		23	.348		74	19.70		93.70	111
8820	60°		22	.364		90	20.50		110.50	130
8830	90°		21	.381		114	21.50		135.50	158
8840	Divider strip, vertical fitting, 6" deep									
8850	12" radius, galvanized, 30°	1 Elec	24	.333	Ea.	36.50	18.85		55.35	68.50

26 05 36 – Cable Trays for Electrical Systems

26 05 36.40 Cable Tray, Covers and Dividers	Crew	Daily Output	Labor-Hours	Unit	Material	2017 Bare Costs Labor	Equipment	Total	Total Incl O&P
8860	45°	1 Elec	23	.348	Ea.	40.50	19.70		60.20	74.50
8870	60°		22	.364		46.50	20.50		67	82.50
8880	90°		21	.381		58.50	21.50		80	96.50
8890	Aluminum, 30°		25	.320		27	18.10		45.10	57
8900	45°		24	.333		32	18.85		50.85	64
8910	60°		23	.348		33.50	19.70		53.20	66.50
8920	90°		22	.364		40	20.50		60.50	75
8930	24" radius, galvanized, 30°		23	.348		50.50	19.70		70.20	85
8940	45°		22	.364		63.50	20.50		84	101
8950	60°		21	.381		72.50	21.50		94	112
8960	90°		20	.400		95.50	22.50		118	139
8970	Aluminum, 30°		24	.333		37.50	18.85		56.35	70
8980	45°		23	.348		51.50	19.70		71.20	86
8990	60°		22	.364		56.50	20.50		77	93
9000	90°		21	.381		77	21.50		98.50	117
9010	36" radius, galvanized, 30°		22	.364		59	20.50		79.50	95.50
9020	45°		21	.381		72.50	21.50		94	112
9030	60°		20	.400		95.50	22.50		118	139
9040	90°		19	.421		125	24		149	174
9050	Aluminum, 30°		23	.348		58.50	19.70		78.20	93.50
9060	45°		22	.364		78	20.50		98.50	117
9070	60°		21	.381		92.50	21.50		114	135
9080	90°		20	.400		111	22.50		133.50	156
9120	Divider strip, horizontal fitting, galvanized, 3" deep		33	.242		36	13.70		49.70	60
9130	4" deep		30	.267		40.50	15.10		55.60	67
9140	6" deep		27	.296		51.50	16.75		68.25	81.50
9150	Aluminum, 3" deep		35	.229		27	12.95		39.95	49
9160	4" deep		32	.250		29.50	14.15		43.65	53.50
9170	6" deep		29	.276		39	15.60		54.60	66.50
9300	Divider strip protector		300	.027	L.F.	3.21	1.51		4.72	5.80
9310	Fastener, ladder tray				Ea.	.57			.57	.63
9320	Trough or solid bottom tray				"	.38			.38	.42
9900	Add to labor for higher elevated installation									
9905	10' to 14.5' high, add						10%			
9910	15' to 20' high, add						20%			
9920	20' to 25' high, add						25%			
9930	25' to 30' high, add						35%			
9940	30' to 35' high, add						40%			
9950	35' to 40' high, add						50%			
9960	Over 40' high, add						55%			

26 05 39 – Underfloor Raceways for Electrical Systems

26 05 39.30 Conduit In Concrete Slab

		Crew	Daily Output	Labor-Hours	Unit	Material	2017 Bare Costs Labor	Equipment	Total	Total Incl O&P
0010	**CONDUIT IN CONCRETE SLAB** Including terminations,	R260539-30								
0020	fittings and supports									
3230	PVC, schedule 40, 1/2" diameter	1 Elec	270	.030	L.F.	.49	1.68		2.17	3.05
3250	3/4" diameter		230	.035		.56	1.97		2.53	3.57
3270	1" diameter		200	.040		.76	2.26		3.02	4.23
3300	1-1/4" diameter		170	.047		1	2.66		3.66	5.10
3330	1-1/2" diameter		140	.057		1.21	3.23		4.44	6.20
3350	2" diameter		120	.067		1.53	3.77		5.30	7.35
3370	2-1/2" diameter		90	.089		2.64	5.05		7.69	10.45
3400	3" diameter	2 Elec	160	.100		3.33	5.65		8.98	12.15

26 05 39.30 Conduit In Concrete Slab		Crew	Daily Output	Labor-Hours	Unit	Material	2017 Bare Costs Labor	Equipment	Total	Total Incl O&P
3430	3-1/2" diameter	2 Elec	120	.133	L.F.	4.22	7.55		11.77	15.95
3440	4" diameter		100	.160		4.64	9.05		13.69	18.65
3450	5" diameter		80	.200		7.20	11.30		18.50	25
3460	6" diameter		60	.267		10.45	15.10		25.55	34
3530	Sweeps, 1" diameter, 30" radius	1 Elec	32	.250	Ea.	41	14.15		55.15	66
3550	1-1/4" diameter		24	.333		44.50	18.85		63.35	77.50
3570	1-1/2" diameter		21	.381		47	21.50		68.50	84
3600	2" diameter		18	.444		52	25		77	94.50
3630	2-1/2" diameter		14	.571		67.50	32.50		100	123
3650	3" diameter		10	.800		86	45.50		131.50	163
3670	3-1/2" diameter		8	1		105	56.50		161.50	201
3700	4" diameter		7	1.143		147	64.50		211.50	259
3710	5" diameter		6	1.333		168	75.50		243.50	298
3730	Couplings, 1/2" diameter					.13			.13	.14
3750	3/4" diameter					.15			.15	.17
3770	1" diameter					.24			.24	.26
3800	1-1/4" diameter					.33			.33	.36
3830	1-1/2" diameter					.45			.45	.50
3850	2" diameter					.61			.61	.67
3870	2-1/2" diameter					1.37			1.37	1.51
3900	3" diameter					1.91			1.91	2.10
3930	3-1/2" diameter					1.67			1.67	1.84
3950	4" diameter					2.83			2.83	3.11
3960	5" diameter					7.20			7.20	7.95
3970	6" diameter					9.90			9.90	10.85
4030	End bells, 1" diameter, PVC	1 Elec	60	.133		3.02	7.55		10.57	14.60
4050	1-1/4" diameter		53	.151		3.50	8.55		12.05	16.65
4100	1-1/2" diameter		48	.167		2.57	9.45		12.02	17
4150	2" diameter		34	.235		3.82	13.30		17.12	24
4170	2-1/2" diameter		27	.296		4.41	16.75		21.16	30
4200	3" diameter		20	.400		5.75	22.50		28.25	40.50
4250	3-1/2" diameter		16	.500		5.80	28.50		34.30	49
4300	4" diameter		14	.571		7.30	32.50		39.80	56.50
4310	5" diameter		12	.667		10.95	37.50		48.45	68.50
4320	6" diameter		9	.889		12	50.50		62.50	88.50
4350	Rigid galvanized steel, 1/2" diameter		200	.040	L.F.	2.37	2.26		4.63	6
4400	3/4" diameter		170	.047		4.34	2.66		7	8.75
4450	1" diameter		130	.062		6.70	3.48		10.18	12.55
4500	1-1/4" diameter		110	.073		4.78	4.12		8.90	11.40
4600	1-1/2" diameter		100	.080		7.30	4.53		11.83	14.80
4800	2" diameter		90	.089		9.05	5.05		14.10	17.50

26 05 39.40 Conduit In Trench

		Crew	Daily Output	Labor-Hours	Unit	Material	2017 Bare Costs Labor	Equipment	Total	Total Incl O&P
0010	**CONDUIT IN TRENCH** Includes terminations and fittings　R260539-40									
0020	Does not include excavation or backfill, see Section 31 23 16									
0200	Rigid galvanized steel, 2" diameter	1 Elec	150	.053	L.F.	8.70	3.02		11.72	14.05
0400	2-1/2" diameter	"	100	.080		12.10	4.53		16.63	20
0600	3" diameter	2 Elec	160	.100		14.10	5.65		19.75	24
0800	3-1/2" diameter		140	.114		18.35	6.45		24.80	29.50
1000	4" diameter		100	.160		21	9.05		30.05	36.50
1200	5" diameter		80	.200		42	11.30		53.30	63
1400	6" diameter		60	.267		58.50	15.10		73.60	86.50

26 05 43.10 Trench Duct	Crew	Daily Output	Labor-Hours	Unit	Material	2017 Bare Costs Labor	2017 Bare Costs Equipment	Total	Total Incl O&P
0010	**TRENCH DUCT** Steel with cover									
0020	Standard adjustable, depths to 4"									
0100	Straight, single compartment, 9" wide	2 Elec	40	.400	L.F.	224	22.50		246.50	280
0200	12" wide		32	.500		270	28.50		298.50	340
0400	18" wide		26	.615		325	35		360	410
0600	24" wide		22	.727		390	41		431	490
0700	27" wide		21	.762		213	43		256	299
0800	30" wide		20	.800		228	45.50		273.50	320
1000	36" wide		16	1		262	56.50		318.50	375
1020	Two compartment, 9" wide		38	.421		126	24		150	174
1030	12" wide		30	.533		147	30		177	207
1040	18" wide		24	.667		197	37.50		234.50	273
1050	24" wide		20	.800		253	45.50		298.50	345
1060	30" wide		18	.889		315	50.50		365.50	420
1070	36" wide		14	1.143		360	64.50		424.50	490
1090	Three compartment, 9" wide		36	.444		156	25		181	210
1100	12" wide		28	.571		175	32.50		207.50	241
1110	18" wide		22	.727		219	41		260	305
1120	24" wide		18	.889		274	50.50		324.50	375
1130	30" wide		16	1		330	56.50		386.50	450
1140	36" wide		12	1.333		390	75.50		465.50	545
1200	Horizontal elbow, 9" wide		5.40	2.963	Ea.	425	168		593	720
1400	12" wide		4.60	3.478		455	197		652	795
1600	18" wide		4	4		600	226		826	1,000
1800	24" wide		3.20	5		855	283		1,138	1,375
1900	27" wide		3	5.333		1,025	300		1,325	1,575
2000	30" wide		2.60	6.154		1,125	350		1,475	1,775
2200	36" wide		2.40	6.667		1,500	375		1,875	2,225
2220	Two compartment, 9" wide		3.80	4.211		685	238		923	1,100
2230	12" wide		3	5.333		760	300		1,060	1,275
2240	18" wide		2.40	6.667		915	375		1,290	1,575
2250	24" wide		2	8		1,125	455		1,580	1,900
2260	30" wide		1.80	8.889		1,500	505		2,005	2,400
2270	36" wide		1.60	10		1,800	565		2,365	2,850
2290	Three compartment, 9" wide		3.60	4.444		690	252		942	1,125
2300	12" wide		2.80	5.714		775	325		1,100	1,350
2310	18" wide		2.20	7.273		945	410		1,355	1,675
2320	24" wide		1.80	8.889		1,200	505		1,705	2,050
2330	30" wide		1.60	10		1,550	565		2,115	2,550
2350	36" wide		1.40	11.429		1,900	645		2,545	3,050
2400	Vertical elbow, 9" wide		5.40	2.963		171	168		339	440
2600	12" wide		4.60	3.478		161	197		358	470
2800	18" wide		4	4		185	226		411	545
3000	24" wide		3.20	5		230	283		513	680
3100	27" wide		3	5.333		239	300		539	715
3200	30" wide		2.60	6.154		253	350		603	800
3400	36" wide		2.40	6.667		279	375		654	870
3600	Cross, 9" wide		4	4		695	226		921	1,100
3800	12" wide		3.20	5		735	283		1,018	1,225
4000	18" wide		2.60	6.154		880	350		1,230	1,500
4200	24" wide		2.20	7.273		1,100	410		1,510	1,825
4300	27" wide		2.20	7.273		1,275	410		1,685	2,025

26 05 43.10 Trench Duct		Crew	Daily Output	Labor-Hours	Unit	Material	2017 Bare Costs Labor	2017 Bare Costs Equipment	Total	Total Incl O&P
4400	30" wide	2 Elec	2	8	Ea.	1,400	455		1,855	2,225
4600	36" wide		1.80	8.889		1,750	505		2,255	2,675
4620	Two compartment, 9" wide		3.80	4.211		700	238		938	1,125
4630	12" wide		3	5.333		735	300		1,035	1,250
4640	18" wide		2.40	6.667		890	375		1,265	1,550
4650	24" wide		2	8		1,125	455		1,580	1,925
4660	30" wide		1.80	8.889		1,500	505		2,005	2,400
4670	36" wide		1.60	10		1,800	565		2,365	2,825
4690	Three compartment, 9" wide		3.60	4.444		710	252		962	1,150
4700	12" wide		2.80	5.714		810	325		1,135	1,375
4710	18" wide		2.20	7.273		965	410		1,375	1,675
4720	24" wide		1.80	8.889		1,200	505		1,705	2,075
4730	30" wide		1.60	10		1,550	565		2,115	2,575
4740	36" wide		1.40	11.429		1,925	645		2,570	3,100
4800	End closure, 9" wide		14.40	1.111		42	63		105	140
5000	12" wide		12	1.333		48	75.50		123.50	166
5200	18" wide		10	1.600		73.50	90.50		164	217
5400	24" wide		8	2		97	113		210	277
5500	27" wide		7	2.286		112	129		241	315
5600	30" wide		6.60	2.424		148	137		285	370
5800	36" wide		5.80	2.759		144	156		300	395
6000	Tees, 9" wide		4	4		405	226		631	790
6200	12" wide		3.60	4.444		475	252		727	895
6400	18" wide		3.20	5		605	283		888	1,100
6600	24" wide		3	5.333		870	300		1,170	1,400
6700	27" wide		2.80	5.714		965	325		1,290	1,525
6800	30" wide		2.60	6.154		1,125	350		1,475	1,775
7000	36" wide		2	8		1,475	455		1,930	2,300
7020	Two compartment, 9" wide		3.80	4.211		475	238		713	875
7030	12" wide		3.40	4.706		510	266		776	960
7040	18" wide		3	5.333		680	300		980	1,200
7050	24" wide		2.80	5.714		920	325		1,245	1,475
7060	30" wide		2.40	6.667		1,250	375		1,625	1,950
7070	36" wide		1.90	8.421		1,550	475		2,025	2,450
7090	Three compartment, 9" wide		3.60	4.444		540	252		792	970
7100	12" wide		3.20	5		570	283		853	1,050
7110	18" wide		2.80	5.714		720	325		1,045	1,275
7120	24" wide		2.60	6.154		990	350		1,340	1,625
7130	30" wide		2.20	7.273		1,300	410		1,710	2,050
7140	36" wide		1.80	8.889		1,650	505		2,155	2,575
7200	Riser, and cabinet connector, 9" wide		5.40	2.963		178	168		346	445
7400	12" wide		4.60	3.478		208	197		405	525
7600	18" wide		4	4		209	226		435	570
7800	24" wide		3.20	5		310	283		593	765
7900	27" wide		3	5.333		310	300		610	795
8000	30" wide		2.60	6.154		355	350		705	910
8200	36" wide		2	8		415	455		870	1,125
8400	Insert assembly, cell to conduit adapter, 1-1/4"	1 Elec	16	.500		71	28.50		99.50	121
8500	Adjustable partition	"	320	.025	L.F.	25	1.42		26.42	29.50
8600	Depth of duct over 4", per 1", add					11.35			11.35	12.45
8700	Support post	1 Elec	240	.033		26	1.89		27.89	31.50
8800	Cover double tile trim, 2 sides					40			40	44
8900	4 sides					115			115	126

For customer support on your Electrical Costs with RSMeans Data, call 800.448.8182.

201

26 05 43.10 Trench Duct	Crew	Daily Output	Labor-Hours	Unit	Material	2017 Bare Costs Labor	Equipment	Total	Total Incl O&P
9160	Trench duct 3-1/2" x 4-1/2", add				L.F.	10.80			10.80	11.85
9170	Trench duct 4" x 5", add					10.80			10.80	11.85
9200	For carpet trim, add					36.50			36.50	40
9210	For double carpet trim, add					111			111	122

26 05 43.20 Underfloor Duct

		Crew	Daily Output	Labor-Hours	Unit	Material	Labor	Equipment	Total	Total Incl O&P
0010	**UNDERFLOOR DUCT** R260543-50									
0100	Duct, 1-3/8" x 3-1/8" blank, standard	2 Elec	160	.100	L.F.	12.70	5.65		18.35	22.50
0200	1-3/8" x 7-1/4" blank, super duct		120	.133		29.50	7.55		37.05	44
0400	7/8" or 1-3/8" insert type, 24" O.C., 1-3/8" x 3-1/8", std.		140	.114		19.90	6.45		26.35	31.50
0600	1-3/8" x 7-1/4", super duct		100	.160		34.50	9.05		43.55	51.50
0800	Junction box, single duct, 1 level, 3-1/8"	1 Elec	4	2	Ea.	445	113		558	660
0820	3-1/8" x 7-1/4"		4	2		560	113		673	785
0840	2 level, 3-1/8" upper & lower		3.20	2.500		515	142		657	775
0860	3-1/8" upper, 7-1/4" lower		2.70	2.963		520	168		688	820
0880	Carpet pan for above		80	.100		375	5.65		380.65	425
0900	Terrazzo pan for above		67	.119		850	6.75		856.75	940
1000	Junction box, single duct, 1 level, 7-1/4"		2.70	2.963		520	168		688	820
1020	2 level, 7-1/4" upper & lower		2.70	2.963		595	168		763	905
1040	2 duct, two 3-1/8" upper & lower		3.20	2.500		770	142		912	1,050
1200	1 level, 2 duct, 3-1/8"		3.20	2.500		585	142		727	850
1220	Carpet pan for above boxes		80	.100		370	5.65		375.65	415
1240	Terrazzo pan for above boxes		67	.119		860	6.75		866.75	955
1260	Junction box, 1 level, two 3-1/8" x one 3-1/8" + one 7-1/4"		2.30	3.478		1,000	197		1,197	1,400
1280	2 level, two 3-1/8" upper, one 3-1/8" + one 7-1/4" lower		2	4		1,100	226		1,326	1,575
1300	Carpet pan for above boxes		80	.100		370	5.65		375.65	415
1320	Terrazzo pan for above boxes		67	.119		860	6.75		866.75	955
1400	Junction box, 1 level, 2 duct, 7-1/4"		2.30	3.478		1,450	197		1,647	1,875
1420	Two 3-1/8" + one 7-1/4"		2	4		1,525	226		1,751	2,025
1440	Carpet pan for above		80	.100		370	5.65		375.65	415
1460	Terrazzo pan for above		67	.119		860	6.75		866.75	955
1580	Junction box, 1 level, one 3-1/8" + one 7-1/4" x same		2.30	3.478		995	197		1,192	1,400
1600	Triple duct, 3-1/8"		2.30	3.478		995	197		1,192	1,400
1700	Junction box, 1 level, one 3-1/8" + two 7-1/4"		2	4		1,700	226		1,926	2,225
1720	Carpet pan for above		80	.100		370	5.65		375.65	415
1740	Terrazzo pan for above		67	.119		860	6.75		866.75	955
1800	Insert to conduit adapter, 3/4" & 1"		32	.250		37	14.15		51.15	62
2000	Support, single cell		27	.296		55	16.75		71.75	85.50
2200	Super duct		16	.500		56	28.50		84.50	104
2400	Double cell		16	.500		55	28.50		83.50	103
2600	Triple cell		11	.727		53	41		94	120
2800	Vertical elbow, standard duct		10	.800		98.50	45.50		144	176
3000	Super duct		8	1		98.50	56.50		155	193
3200	Cabinet connector, standard duct		32	.250		77.50	14.15		91.65	107
3400	Super duct		27	.296		75.50	16.75		92.25	108
3600	Conduit adapter, 1" to 1-1/4"		32	.250		74.50	14.15		88.65	103
3800	2" to 1-1/4"		27	.296		89.50	16.75		106.25	124
4000	Outlet, low tension (tele, computer, etc.)		8	1		104	56.50		160.50	199
4200	High tension, receptacle (120 volt)		8	1		108	56.50		164.50	204
4300	End closure, standard duct		160	.050		4.34	2.83		7.17	9
4310	Super duct		160	.050		8.20	2.83		11.03	13.30
4350	Elbow, horiz., standard duct		26	.308		253	17.40		270.40	305
4360	Super duct		26	.308		244	17.40		261.40	294

26 05 43 – Underground Ducts and Raceways for Electrical Systems

26 05 43.20 Underfloor Duct		Crew	Daily Output	Labor-Hours	Unit	Material	2017 Bare Costs Labor	Equipment	Total	Total Incl O&P
4380	Elbow, offset, standard duct	1 Elec	26	.308	Ea.	98.50	17.40		115.90	134
4390	Super duct		26	.308		100	17.40		117.40	136
4400	Marker screw assembly for inserts		50	.160		18.45	9.05		27.50	34
4410	Y take off, standard duct		26	.308		151	17.40		168.40	192
4420	Super duct		26	.308		151	17.40		168.40	192
4430	Box opening plug, standard duct		160	.050		14.10	2.83		16.93	19.80
4440	Super duct		160	.050		14.10	2.83		16.93	19.80
4450	Sleeve coupling, standard duct		160	.050		37.50	2.83		40.33	45
4460	Super duct		160	.050		50	2.83		52.83	59
4470	Conduit adapter, standard duct, 3/4"		32	.250		77	14.15		91.15	106
4480	1" or 1-1/4"		32	.250		76	14.15		90.15	105
4500	1-1/2"		32	.250		75	14.15		89.15	104

26 05 80 – Wiring Connections

26 05 80.10 Motor Connections

		Crew	Daily Output	Labor-Hours	Unit	Material	2017 Bare Costs Labor	Equipment	Total	Total Incl O&P
0010	**MOTOR CONNECTIONS**									
0020	Flexible conduit and fittings, 115 volt, 1 phase, up to 1 HP motor	1 Elec	8	1	Ea.	4.92	56.50		61.42	90.50
0050	2 HP motor [R260580-75]		6.50	1.231		10.65	69.50		80.15	116
0100	3 HP motor		5.50	1.455		9.05	82.50		91.55	133
0110	230 volt, 3 phase, 3 HP motor		6.78	1.180		6.20	67		73.20	107
0112	5 HP motor		5.47	1.463		5.05	83		88.05	130
0114	7-1/2 HP motor		4.61	1.735		8.05	98		106.05	156
0120	10 HP motor		4.20	1.905		17.20	108		125.20	181
0150	15 HP motor		3.30	2.424		17.20	137		154.20	225
0200	25 HP motor		2.70	2.963		23	168		191	276
0400	50 HP motor		2.20	3.636		47.50	206		253.50	365
0600	100 HP motor		1.50	5.333		107	300		407	570
1500	460 volt, 5 HP motor, 3 phase		8	1		5.25	56.50		61.75	91
1520	10 HP motor		8	1		5.25	56.50		61.75	91
1530	25 HP motor		6	1.333		11.35	75.50		86.85	125
1540	30 HP motor		6	1.333		11.35	75.50		86.85	125
1550	40 HP motor		5	1.600		15.90	90.50		106.40	154
1560	50 HP motor		5	1.600		17.90	90.50		108.40	156
1570	60 HP motor		3.80	2.105		19.05	119		138.05	200
1580	75 HP motor		3.50	2.286		28	129		157	225
1590	100 HP motor		2.50	3.200		42.50	181		223.50	320
1600	125 HP motor		2	4		52.50	226		278.50	400
1610	150 HP motor		1.80	4.444		56	252		308	435
1620	200 HP motor		1.50	5.333		90.50	300		390.50	550
2005	460 Volt, 5 HP motor, 3 Phase, w/sealtite		8	1		9.50	56.50		66	95.50
2010	10 HP motor		8	1		9.50	56.50		66	95.50
2015	25 HP motor		6	1.333		18.55	75.50		94.05	134
2020	30 HP motor		6	1.333		18.55	75.50		94.05	134
2025	40 HP motor		5	1.600		23	90.50		113.50	162
2030	50 HP motor		5	1.600		23.50	90.50		114	162
2035	60 HP motor		3.80	2.105		34	119		153	216
2040	75 HP motor		3.50	2.286		39	129		168	237
2045	100 HP motor		2.50	3.200		53	181		234	330
2055	150 HP motor		1.80	4.444		58.50	252		310.50	440
2060	200 HP motor		1.50	5.333		294	300		594	775

26 05 90.10 Residential Wiring	Crew	Daily Output	Labor-Hours	Unit	Material	2017 Bare Costs Labor	Equipment	Total	Total Incl O&P
0010	**RESIDENTIAL WIRING**									
0020	20' avg. runs and #14/2 wiring incl. unless otherwise noted									
1000	Service & panel, includes 24' SE-AL cable, service eye, meter,									
1010	Socket, panel board, main bkr., ground rod, 15 or 20 amp									
1020	1-pole circuit breakers, and misc. hardware									
1100	100 amp, with 10 branch breakers	1 Elec	1.19	6.723	Ea.	490	380		870	1,100
1110	With PVC conduit and wire		.92	8.696		530	490		1,020	1,325
1120	With RGS conduit and wire		.73	10.959		745	620		1,365	1,750
1150	150 amp, with 14 branch breakers		1.03	7.767		845	440		1,285	1,600
1170	With PVC conduit and wire		.82	9.756		930	550		1,480	1,850
1180	With RGS conduit and wire		.67	11.940		1,250	675		1,925	2,400
1200	200 amp, with 18 branch breakers	2 Elec	1.80	8.889		1,050	505		1,555	1,925
1220	With PVC conduit and wire		1.46	10.959		1,150	620		1,770	2,175
1230	With RGS conduit and wire		1.24	12.903		1,550	730		2,280	2,800
1800	Lightning surge suppressor	1 Elec	32	.250		50.50	14.15		64.65	77
2000	Switch devices									
2100	Single pole, 15 amp, Ivory, with a 1-gang box, cover plate,									
2110	Type NM (Romex) cable	1 Elec	17.10	.468	Ea.	18.70	26.50		45.20	60
2120	Type MC (BX) cable		14.30	.559		27.50	31.50		59	77.50
2130	EMT & wire		5.71	1.401		36	79.50		115.50	159
2150	3-way, #14/3, type NM cable		14.55	.550		12.40	31		43.40	60
2170	Type MC cable		12.31	.650		24.50	37		61.50	82
2180	EMT & wire		5	1.600		29	90.50		119.50	168
2200	4-way, #14/3, type NM cable		14.55	.550		21	31		52	69.50
2220	Type MC cable		12.31	.650		33	37		70	91.50
2230	EMT & wire		5	1.600		37.50	90.50		128	177
2250	S.P., 20 amp, #12/2, type NM cable		13.33	.600		14.75	34		48.75	67
2270	Type MC cable		11.43	.700		21	39.50		60.50	82.50
2280	EMT & wire		4.85	1.649		33	93.50		126.50	177
2290	S.P. rotary dimmer, 600W, no wiring		17	.471		32.50	26.50		59	75.50
2300	S.P. rotary dimmer, 600W, type NM cable		14.55	.550		36.50	31		67.50	87
2320	Type MC cable		12.31	.650		45.50	37		82.50	105
2330	EMT & wire		5	1.600		55	90.50		145.50	197
2350	3-way rotary dimmer, type NM cable		13.33	.600		21	34		55	74
2370	Type MC cable		11.43	.700		29.50	39.50		69	92
2380	EMT & wire		4.85	1.649		39.50	93.50		133	184
2400	Interval timer wall switch, 20 amp, 1-30 min., #12/2									
2410	Type NM cable	1 Elec	14.55	.550	Ea.	57	31		88	110
2420	Type MC cable		12.31	.650		62	37		99	123
2430	EMT & wire		5	1.600		75.50	90.50		166	219
2500	Decorator style									
2510	S.P., 15 amp, type NM cable	1 Elec	17.10	.468	Ea.	23.50	26.50		50	65.50
2520	Type MC cable		14.30	.559		32.50	31.50		64	83
2530	EMT & wire		5.71	1.401		40.50	79.50		120	164
2550	3-way, #14/3, type NM cable		14.55	.550		17.30	31		48.30	65.50
2570	Type MC cable		12.31	.650		29.50	37		66.50	87.50
2580	EMT & wire		5	1.600		34	90.50		124.50	174
2600	4-way, #14/3, type NM cable		14.55	.550		25.50	31		56.50	75
2620	Type MC cable		12.31	.650		38	37		75	97
2630	EMT & wire		5	1.600		42.50	90.50		133	183
2650	S.P., 20 amp, #12/2, type NM cable		13.33	.600		19.65	34		53.65	72.50
2670	Type MC cable		11.43	.700		26	39.50		65.50	88

26 05 Common Work Results for Electrical

26 05 90 – Residential Applications

26 05 90.10 Residential Wiring	Crew	Daily Output	Labor-Hours	Unit	Material	2017 Bare Costs Labor	Equipment	Total	Total Incl O&P
2680	EMT & wire	1 Elec	4.85	1.649	Ea.	38	93.50		131.50	182
2700	S.P., slide dimmer, type NM cable		17.10	.468		24.50	26.50		51	66.50
2720	Type MC cable		14.30	.559		33	31.50		64.50	84
2730	EMT & wire		5.71	1.401		43	79.50		122.50	166
2750	S.P., touch dimmer, type NM cable		17.10	.468		41	26.50		67.50	84.50
2770	Type MC cable		14.30	.559		50	31.50		81.50	102
2780	EMT & wire		5.71	1.401		59.50	79.50		139	185
2800	3-way touch dimmer, type NM cable		13.33	.600		51.50	34		85.50	108
2820	Type MC cable		11.43	.700		60	39.50		99.50	126
2830	EMT & wire	▼	4.85	1.649	▼	70	93.50		163.50	217
3000	Combination devices									
3100	S.P. switch/15 amp recpt., Ivory, 1-gang box, plate									
3110	Type NM cable	1 Elec	11.43	.700	Ea.	24	39.50		63.50	86
3120	Type MC cable		10	.800		33	45.50		78.50	104
3130	EMT & wire		4.40	1.818		42.50	103		145.50	201
3150	S.P. switch/pilot light, type NM cable		11.43	.700		24.50	39.50		64	86.50
3170	Type MC cable		10	.800		33	45.50		78.50	105
3180	EMT & wire		4.43	1.806		43	102		145	200
3190	2-S.P. switches, 2-#14/2, no wiring		14	.571		13.70	32.50		46.20	63.50
3200	2-S.P. switches, 2-#14/2, type NM cables		10	.800		26.50	45.50		72	97.50
3220	Type MC cable		8.89	.900		40.50	51		91.50	121
3230	EMT & wire		4.10	1.951		45	110		155	215
3250	3-way switch/15 amp recpt., #14/3, type NM cable		10	.800		31.50	45.50		77	103
3270	Type MC cable		8.89	.900		44	51		95	125
3280	EMT & wire		4.10	1.951		48.50	110		158.50	218
3300	2-3 way switches, 2-#14/3, type NM cables		8.89	.900		40.50	51		91.50	121
3320	Type MC cable		8	1		61.50	56.50		118	153
3330	EMT & wire		4	2		55	113		168	231
3350	S.P. switch/20 amp recpt., #12/2, type NM cable		10	.800		31	45.50		76.50	103
3370	Type MC cable		8.89	.900		36	51		87	116
3380	EMT & wire	▼	4.10	1.951	▼	49.50	110		159.50	220
3400	Decorator style									
3410	S.P. switch/15 amp recpt., type NM cable	1 Elec	11.43	.700	Ea.	29	39.50		68.50	91.50
3420	Type MC cable		10	.800		37.50	45.50		83	110
3430	EMT & wire		4.40	1.818		47.50	103		150.50	207
3450	S.P. switch/pilot light, type NM cable		11.43	.700		29	39.50		68.50	91.50
3470	Type MC cable		10	.800		38	45.50		83.50	110
3480	EMT & wire		4.40	1.818		47.50	103		150.50	207
3500	2-S.P. switches, 2-#14/2, type NM cables		10	.800		31.50	45.50		77	103
3520	Type MC cable		8.89	.900		45	51		96	126
3530	EMT & wire		4.10	1.951		50	110		160	220
3550	3-way/15 amp recpt., #14/3, type NM cable		10	.800		36.50	45.50		82	108
3570	Type MC cable		8.89	.900		49	51		100	130
3580	EMT & wire		4.10	1.951		53	110		163	224
3650	2-3 way switches, 2-#14/3, type NM cables		8.89	.900		45.50	51		96.50	127
3670	Type MC cable		8	1		66	56.50		122.50	158
3680	EMT & wire		4	2		60	113		173	236
3700	S.P. switch/20 amp recpt., #12/2, type NM cable		10	.800		36	45.50		81.50	108
3720	Type MC cable		8.89	.900		41	51		92	122
3730	EMT & wire	▼	4.10	1.951	▼	54.50	110		164.50	225
4000	Receptacle devices									
4010	Duplex outlet, 15 amp recpt., Ivory, 1-gang box, plate									
4015	Type NM cable	1 Elec	14.55	.550	Ea.	10.30	31		41.30	58

26 05 90.10 Residential Wiring	Crew	Daily Output	Labor-Hours	Unit	Material	2017 Bare Costs Labor	2017 Bare Costs Equipment	Total	Total Incl O&P
4020	Type MC cable	1 Elec	12.31	.650	Ea.	19	37		56	76
4030	EMT & wire		5.33	1.501		27.50	85		112.50	157
4050	With #12/2, type NM cable		12.31	.650		12.65	37		49.65	69
4070	Type MC cable		10.67	.750		19	42.50		61.50	84.50
4080	EMT & wire		4.71	1.699		31	96		127	178
4100	20 amp recpt., #12/2, type NM cable		12.31	.650		19.30	37		56.30	76.50
4120	Type MC cable		10.67	.750		25.50	42.50		68	91.50
4130	EMT & wire	▼	4.71	1.699	▼	37.50	96		133.50	186
4140	For GFI see Section 26 05 90.10 line 4300 below									
4150	Decorator style, 15 amp recpt., type NM cable	1 Elec	14.55	.550	Ea.	15.20	31		46.20	63.50
4170	Type MC cable		12.31	.650		24	37		61	81.50
4180	EMT & wire		5.33	1.501		32.50	85		117.50	163
4200	With #12/2, type NM cable		12.31	.650		17.55	37		54.55	74.50
4220	Type MC cable		10.67	.750		24	42.50		66.50	90
4230	EMT & wire		4.71	1.699		36	96		132	184
4250	20 amp recpt., #12/2, type NM cable		12.31	.650		24	37		61	81.50
4270	Type MC cable		10.67	.750		30.50	42.50		73	97
4280	EMT & wire		4.71	1.699		42.50	96		138.50	191
4300	GFI, 15 amp recpt., type NM cable		12.31	.650		23	37		60	80
4320	Type MC cable		10.67	.750		31.50	42.50		74	98
4330	EMT & wire		4.71	1.699		40	96		136	188
4350	GFI with #12/2, type NM cable		10.67	.750		25	42.50		67.50	91
4370	Type MC cable		9.20	.870		31.50	49		80.50	108
4380	EMT & wire		4.21	1.900		43.50	108		151.50	209
4400	20 amp recpt., #12/2, type NM cable		10.67	.750		51.50	42.50		94	120
4420	Type MC cable		9.20	.870		58	49		107	137
4430	EMT & wire		4.21	1.900		70	108		178	238
4500	Weather-proof cover for above receptacles, add	▼	32	.250	▼	2.47	14.15		16.62	23.50
4550	Air conditioner outlet, 20 amp-240 volt recpt.									
4560	30' of #12/2, 2 pole circuit breaker									
4570	Type NM cable	1 Elec	10	.800	Ea.	62	45.50		107.50	137
4580	Type MC cable		9	.889		70	50.50		120.50	153
4590	EMT & wire		4	2		80.50	113		193.50	259
4600	Decorator style, type NM cable		10	.800		67	45.50		112.50	142
4620	Type MC cable		9	.889		74.50	50.50		125	158
4630	EMT & wire	▼	4	2	▼	85	113		198	264
4650	Dryer outlet, 30 amp-240 volt recpt., 20' of #10/3									
4660	2 pole circuit breaker									
4670	Type NM cable	1 Elec	6.41	1.248	Ea.	58	70.50		128.50	170
4680	Type MC cable		5.71	1.401		64	79.50		143.50	190
4690	EMT & wire	▼	3.48	2.299	▼	74	130		204	277
4700	Range outlet, 50 amp-240 volt recpt., 30' of #8/3									
4710	Type NM cable	1 Elec	4.21	1.900	Ea.	85	108		193	255
4720	Type MC cable		4	2		126	113		239	310
4730	EMT & wire		2.96	2.703		104	153		257	345
4750	Central vacuum outlet, Type NM cable		6.40	1.250		54	71		125	165
4770	Type MC cable		5.71	1.401		67	79.50		146.50	193
4780	EMT & wire	▼	3.48	2.299	▼	80.50	130		210.50	284
4800	30 amp-110 volt locking recpt., #10/2 circ. bkr.									
4810	Type NM cable	1 Elec	6.20	1.290	Ea.	62	73		135	177
4820	Type MC cable		5.40	1.481		78.50	84		162.50	213
4830	EMT & wire	▼	3.20	2.500	▼	91	142		233	310
4900	Low voltage outlets									

26 05 90 – Residential Applications

26 05 90.10 Residential Wiring	Crew	Daily Output	Labor-Hours	Unit	Material	2017 Bare Costs Labor	Equipment	Total	Total Incl O&P
4910	Telephone recpt., 20' of 4/C phone wire	1 Elec	26	.308	Ea.	8.20	17.40		25.60	35
4920	TV recpt., 20' of RG59U coax wire, F type connector	"	16	.500	"	15.75	28.50		44.25	60
4950	Door bell chime, transformer, 2 buttons, 60' of bellwire									
4970	Economy model	1 Elec	11.50	.696	Ea.	49.50	39.50		89	114
4980	Custom model		11.50	.696		99	39.50		138.50	168
4990	Luxury model, 3 buttons		9.50	.842		201	47.50		248.50	293
6000	Lighting outlets									
6050	Wire only (for fixture), type NM cable	1 Elec	32	.250	Ea.	6.35	14.15		20.50	28
6070	Type MC cable		24	.333		12.55	18.85		31.40	42.50
6080	EMT & wire		10	.800		20	45.50		65.50	90
6100	Box (4"), and wire (for fixture), type NM cable		25	.320		13.90	18.10		32	42.50
6120	Type MC cable		20	.400		20	22.50		42.50	56
6130	EMT & wire		11	.727		27.50	41		68.50	92
6200	Fixtures (use with line 6050 or 6100 above)									
6210	Canopy style, economy grade	1 Elec	40	.200	Ea.	27	11.30		38.30	46.50
6220	Custom grade		40	.200		53.50	11.30		64.80	76
6250	Dining room chandelier, economy grade		19	.421		67.50	24		91.50	110
6260	Custom grade		19	.421		315	24		339	380
6270	Luxury grade		15	.533		820	30		850	950
6310	Kitchen fixture (fluorescent), economy grade		30	.267		71.50	15.10		86.60	102
6320	Custom grade		25	.320		221	18.10		239.10	271
6350	Outdoor, wall mounted, economy grade		30	.267		25.50	15.10		40.60	50.50
6360	Custom grade		30	.267		120	15.10		135.10	155
6370	Luxury grade		25	.320		248	18.10		266.10	300
6410	Outdoor PAR floodlights, 1 lamp, 150 watt		20	.400		27.50	22.50		50	64
6420	2 lamp, 150 watt each		20	.400		45.50	22.50		68	84
6425	Motion sensing, 2 lamp, 150 watt each		20	.400		75.50	22.50		98	117
6430	For infrared security sensor, add		32	.250		132	14.15		146.15	166
6450	Outdoor, quartz-halogen, 300 watt flood		20	.400		33	22.50		55.50	70.50
6600	Recessed downlight, round, pre-wired, 50 or 75 watt trim		30	.267		68	15.10		83.10	97
6610	With shower light trim		30	.267		82.50	15.10		97.60	113
6620	With wall washer trim		28	.286		85	16.15		101.15	118
6630	With eye-ball trim		28	.286		84.50	16.15		100.65	117
6700	Porcelain lamp holder		40	.200		2.98	11.30		14.28	20
6710	With pull switch		40	.200		6.55	11.30		17.85	24
6750	Fluorescent strip, 2-20 watt tube, wrap around diffuser, 24"		24	.333		42	18.85		60.85	75
6760	1-34 watt tube, 48"		24	.333		100	18.85		118.85	139
6770	2-34 watt tubes, 48"		20	.400		118	22.50		140.50	164
6800	Bathroom heat lamp, 1-250 watt		28	.286		38.50	16.15		54.65	66
6810	2-250 watt lamps		28	.286		61	16.15		77.15	91.50
6820	For timer switch, see Section 26 05 90.10 line 2400									
6900	Outdoor post lamp, incl. post, fixture, 35' of #14/2									
6910	Type NM cable	1 Elec	3.50	2.286	Ea.	285	129		414	510
6920	Photo-eye, add		27	.296		27.50	16.75		44.25	55
6950	Clock dial time switch, 24 hr., w/enclosure, type NM cable		11.43	.700		73	39.50		112.50	140
6970	Type MC cable		11	.727		81.50	41		122.50	152
6980	EMT & wire		4.85	1.649		90	93.50		183.50	239
7000	Alarm systems									
7050	Smoke detectors, box, #14/3, type NM cable	1 Elec	14.55	.550	Ea.	34	31		65	84
7070	Type MC cable		12.31	.650		44.50	37		81.50	104
7080	EMT & wire		5	1.600		49	90.50		139.50	190
7090	For relay output to security system, add					10.20			10.20	11.20
8000	Residential equipment									

For customer support on your Electrical Costs with RSMeans Data, call 800.448.8182.

207

26 05 90.10 Residential Wiring	Crew	Daily Output	Labor-Hours	Unit	Material	2017 Bare Costs Labor	Equipment	Total	Total Incl O&P
8050	Disposal hook-up, incl. switch, outlet box, 3' of flex									
8060	20 amp-1 pole circ. bkr., and 25' of #12/2									
8070	Type NM cable	1 Elec	10	.800	Ea.	36	45.50		81.50	108
8080	Type MC cable		8	1		43	56.50		99.50	133
8090	EMT & wire	▼	5	1.600	▼	57.50	90.50		148	199
8100	Trash compactor or dishwasher hook-up, incl. outlet box,									
8110	3' of flex, 15 amp-1 pole circ. bkr., and 25' of #14/2									
8120	Type NM cable	1 Elec	10	.800	Ea.	21	45.50		66.50	91
8130	Type MC cable		8	1		30.50	56.50		87	119
8140	EMT & wire	▼	5	1.600	▼	42.50	90.50		133	183
8150	Hot water sink dispenser hook-up, use line 8100									
8200	Vent/exhaust fan hook-up, type NM cable	1 Elec	32	.250	Ea.	6.35	14.15		20.50	28
8220	Type MC cable		24	.333		12.55	18.85		31.40	42.50
8230	EMT & wire	▼	10	.800	▼	20	45.50		65.50	90
8250	Bathroom vent fan, 50 CFM (use with above hook-up)									
8260	Economy model	1 Elec	15	.533	Ea.	20	30		50	67.50
8270	Low noise model		15	.533		43.50	30		73.50	92.50
8280	Custom model	▼	12	.667	▼	131	37.50		168.50	201
8300	Bathroom or kitchen vent fan, 110 CFM									
8310	Economy model	1 Elec	15	.533	Ea.	67.50	30		97.50	120
8320	Low noise model	"	15	.533	"	130	30		160	188
8350	Paddle fan, variable speed (w/o lights)									
8360	Economy model (AC motor)	1 Elec	10	.800	Ea.	109	45.50		154.50	188
8362	With light kit		10	.800		150	45.50		195.50	233
8370	Custom model (AC motor)		10	.800		262	45.50		307.50	355
8372	With light kit		10	.800		305	45.50		350.50	405
8380	Luxury model (DC motor)		8	1		288	56.50		344.50	400
8382	With light kit		8	1		330	56.50		386.50	445
8390	Remote speed switch for above, add	▼	12	.667	▼	33.50	37.50		71	93.50
8500	Whole house exhaust fan, ceiling mount, 36", variable speed									
8510	Remote switch, incl. shutters, 20 amp-1 pole circ. bkr.									
8520	30' of #12/2, type NM cable	1 Elec	4	2	Ea.	1,350	113		1,463	1,650
8530	Type MC cable		3.50	2.286		1,350	129		1,479	1,675
8540	EMT & wire	▼	3	2.667	▼	1,375	151		1,526	1,725
8600	Whirlpool tub hook-up, incl. timer switch, outlet box									
8610	3' of flex, 20 amp-1 pole GFI circ. bkr.									
8620	30' of #12/2, type NM cable	1 Elec	5	1.600	Ea.	113	90.50		203.50	260
8630	Type MC cable		4.20	1.905		116	108		224	290
8640	EMT & wire	▼	3.40	2.353	▼	128	133		261	340
8650	Hot water heater hook-up, incl. 1-2 pole circ. bkr., box;									
8660	3' of flex, 20' of #10/2, type NM cable	1 Elec	5	1.600	Ea.	31	90.50		121.50	170
8670	Type MC cable		4.20	1.905		42	108		150	208
8680	EMT & wire	▼	3.40	2.353	▼	46	133		179	251
9000	Heating/air conditioning									
9050	Furnace/boiler hook-up, incl. firestat, local on-off switch									
9060	Emergency switch, and 40' of type NM cable	1 Elec	4	2	Ea.	52	113		165	227
9070	Type MC cable		3.50	2.286		65.50	129		194.50	266
9080	EMT & wire	▼	1.50	5.333	▼	83	300		383	540
9100	Air conditioner hook-up, incl. local 60 amp disc. switch									
9110	3' sealtite, 40 amp, 2 pole circuit breaker									
9130	40' of #8/2, type NM cable	1 Elec	3.50	2.286	Ea.	146	129		275	355
9140	Type MC cable		3	2.667		206	151		357	455
9150	EMT & wire	▼	1.30	6.154	▼	186	350		536	725

208

For customer support on your Electrical Costs with RSMeans Data, call 800.448.8182.

26 05 Common Work Results for Electrical

26 05 90 – Residential Applications

26 05 90.10 Residential Wiring

		Crew	Daily Output	Labor-Hours	Unit	Material	2017 Bare Costs Labor	Equipment	Total	Total Incl O&P
9200	Heat pump hook-up, 1-40 & 1-100 amp 2 pole circ. bkr.									
9210	Local disconnect switch, 0' conduit									
9220	40' of #8/2 & 30' of #3/2									
9230	Type NM cable	1 Elec	1.30	6.154	Ea.	460	350		810	1,025
9240	Type MC cable		1.08	7.407		515	420		935	1,200
9250	EMT & wire	↓	.94	8.511	↓	520	480		1,000	1,300
9500	Thermostat hook-up, using low voltage wire									
9520	Heating only, 25' of #18-3	1 Elec	24	.333	Ea.	8	18.85		26.85	37.50
9530	Heating/cooling, 25' of #18-4	"	20	.400	"	10.50	22.50		33	45.50

26 09 Instrumentation and Control for Electrical Systems

26 09 13 – Electrical Power Monitoring

26 09 13.10 Switchboard Instruments

		Crew	Daily Output	Labor-Hours	Unit	Material	2017 Bare Costs Labor	Equipment	Total	Total Incl O&P
0010	**SWITCHBOARD INSTRUMENTS** 3 phase, 4 wire R260913-80									
0100	AC indicating, ammeter & switch	1 Elec	8	1	Ea.	2,875	56.50		2,931.50	3,250
0200	Voltmeter & switch		8	1		2,900	56.50		2,956.50	3,250
0300	Wattmeter		8	1		4,150	56.50		4,206.50	4,650
0400	AC recording, ammeter		4	2		7,400	113		7,513	8,300
0500	Voltmeter		4	2		7,400	113		7,513	8,300
0600	Ground fault protection, zero sequence		2.70	2.963		6,525	168		6,693	7,425
0700	Ground return path		2.70	2.963		6,525	168		6,693	7,425
0800	3 current transformers, 5 to 800 amp		2	4		3,050	226		3,276	3,700
0900	1000 to 1500 amp		1.30	6.154		4,375	350		4,725	5,325
1200	2000 to 4000 amp		1	8		5,150	455		5,605	6,350
1300	Fused potential transformer, maximum 600 volt	↓	8	1	↓	1,150	56.50		1,206.50	1,325

26 09 13.20 Voltage Monitor Systems

		Crew	Daily Output	Labor-Hours	Unit	Material	2017 Bare Costs Labor	Equipment	Total	Total Incl O&P
0010	**VOLTAGE MONITOR SYSTEMS** (test equipment)									
0100	AC voltage monitor system, 120/240 V, one-channel				Ea.	2,700			2,700	2,975
0110	Modem adapter					335			335	370
0120	Add-on detector only					1,425			1,425	1,550
0150	AC voltage remote monitor sys., 3 channel, 120, 230, or 480 V					4,900			4,900	5,400
0160	With internal modem					5,175			5,175	5,675
0170	Combination temperature and humidity probe					760			760	835
0180	Add-on detector only					3,550			3,550	3,900
0190	With internal modem				↓	3,875			3,875	4,250

26 09 13.30 Smart Metering

		Crew	Daily Output	Labor-Hours	Unit	Material	2017 Bare Costs Labor	Equipment	Total	Total Incl O&P
0010	**SMART METERING**, In panel									
0100	Single phase, 120/208 volt, 100 amp G	1 Elec	8.78	.911	Ea.	380	51.50		431.50	500
0120	200 amp G		8.78	.911		380	51.50		431.50	500
0200	277 volt, 100 amp G		8.78	.911		405	51.50		456.50	530
0220	200 amp G		8.78	.911		405	51.50		456.50	530
1100	Three phase, 120/208 volt, 100 amp G		4.69	1.706		795	96.50		891.50	1,025
1120	200 amp G		4.69	1.706		795	96.50		891.50	1,025
1130	400 amp G		4.69	1.706		795	96.50		891.50	1,025
1140	800 amp G		4.69	1.706		795	96.50		891.50	1,025
1150	1600 amp G		4.69	1.706		795	96.50		891.50	1,025
1200	277/480 volt, 100 amp G		4.69	1.706		850	96.50		946.50	1,075
1220	200 amp G		4.69	1.706		850	96.50		946.50	1,075
1230	400 amp G		4.69	1.706		850	96.50		946.50	1,075
1240	800 amp G	↓	4.69	1.706	↓	850	96.50		946.50	1,075

For customer support on your Electrical Costs with RSMeans Data, call 800.448.8182.

209

26 09 13 – Electrical Power Monitoring

	26 09 13.30 Smart Metering		Crew	Daily Output	Labor-Hours	Unit	Material	2017 Bare Costs Labor	2017 Bare Costs Equipment	Total	Total Incl O&P
1250	1600 amp	G	1 Elec	4.69	1.706	Ea.	850	96.50		946.50	1,075
2000	Data recorder, 8 meters	G		10.97	.729		1,600	41.50		1,641.50	1,800
2100	16 meters	G		8.53	.938		4,000	53		4,053	4,475
3000	Software package, per meter, basic	G					246			246	271
3100	Premium	G					680			680	750

26 09 23 – Lighting Control Devices

26 09 23.10 Energy Saving Lighting Devices

	26 09 23.10 Energy Saving Lighting Devices		Crew	Daily Output	Labor-Hours	Unit	Material	Labor	Equipment	Total	Total Incl O&P
0010	**ENERGY SAVING LIGHTING DEVICES**										
0100	Occupancy sensors, passive infrared ceiling mounted	G	1 Elec	7	1.143	Ea.	79	64.50		143.50	184
0110	Ultrasonic ceiling mounted	G		7	1.143		89	64.50		153.50	195
0120	Dual technology ceiling mounted	G		6.50	1.231		165	69.50		234.50	285
0150	Automatic wall switches	G		24	.333		75	18.85		93.85	111
0160	Daylighting sensor, manual control, ceiling mounted	G		7	1.143		129	64.50		193.50	239
0170	Remote and dimming control with remote controller	G		6.50	1.231		159	69.50		228.50	279
0200	Passive infared ceiling mounted	G		6.50	1.231		32.50	69.50		102	140
0400	Remote power pack	G		10	.800		32.50	45.50		78	104
0450	Photoelectric control, S.P.S.T. 120 V	G		8	1		22.50	56.50		79	110
0500	S.P.S.T. 208 V/277 V	G		8	1		28.50	56.50		85	117
0550	D.P.S.T. 120 V	G		6	1.333		217	75.50		292.50	350
0600	D.P.S.T. 208 V/277 V	G		6	1.333		202	75.50		277.50	335
0650	S.P.D.T. 208 V/277 V	G		6	1.333		210	75.50		285.50	345
0660	Daylight level sensor, wall mounted, on/off or dimming	G		8	1		135	56.50		191.50	234

26 09 26 – Lighting Control Panelboards

26 09 26.10 Lighting Control Relay Panel

	26 09 26.10 Lighting Control Relay Panel		Crew	Daily Output	Labor-Hours	Unit	Material	Labor	Equipment	Total	Total Incl O&P
0010	**LIGHTING CONTROL RELAY PANEL** with timeclock										
0100	4 Relay	G	1 Elec	2.50	3.200	Ea.	1,175	181		1,356	1,575
0110	8 Relay	G		2.30	3.478		1,225	197		1,422	1,650
0120	16 Relay	G		1.80	4.444		1,800	252		2,052	2,350
0130	24 Relay	G		1.50	5.333		1,575	300		1,875	2,200
0140	48 Relay	G		1	8		1,425	455		1,880	2,225
0200	Room Controller, switching only										
0210	1 Relay	G	1 Elec	3	2.667	Ea.	1,350	151		1,501	1,700
0220	2 Relay	G		3	2.667		1,350	151		1,501	1,700
0230	3 Relay	G		3	2.667		1,425	151		1,576	1,775
0240	Dimming										
0250	1 Relay	G	1 Elec	3	2.667	Ea.	1,350	151		1,501	1,700
0260	2 Relay	G		3	2.667		1,350	151		1,501	1,700
0270	3 Relay	G		3	2.667		1,425	151		1,576	1,775

26 09 36 – Modular Dimming Controls

26 09 36.13 Manual Modular Dimming Controls

	26 09 36.13 Manual Modular Dimming Controls		Crew	Daily Output	Labor-Hours	Unit	Material	Labor	Equipment	Total	Total Incl O&P
0010	**MANUAL MODULAR DIMMING CONTROLS**										
2000	Lighting control module	G	1 Elec	2	4	Ea.	315	226		541	685

210

For customer support on your Electrical Costs with RSMeans Data, call 800.448.8182.

26 12 Medium-Voltage Transformers

26 12 19 – Pad-Mounted, Liquid-Filled, Medium-Voltage Transformers

26 12 19.10 Transformer, Oil-Filled

		Crew	Daily Output	Labor-Hours	Unit	Material	2017 Bare Costs Labor	Equipment	Total	Total Incl O&P
0010	**TRANSFORMER, OIL-FILLED** primary delta or Y, R262213-60									
0050	Pad mounted 5 kV or 15 kV, with lugs, 277/480 v secondary, 3 phase									
0100	150 kVA	R-3	.65	30.769	Ea.	9,550	1,750	212	11,512	13,400
0110	225 kVA		.55	36.364		10,900	2,050	251	13,201	15,400
0200	300 kVA		.45	44.444		13,600	2,525	305	16,430	19,100
0300	500 kVA		.40	50		19,400	2,825	345	22,570	25,900
0400	750 kVA		.38	52.632		24,500	2,975	365	27,840	31,900
0500	1000 kVA		.26	76.923		29,000	4,350	530	33,880	39,100
0600	1500 kVA		.23	86.957		34,500	4,925	600	40,025	46,100
0700	2000 kVA		.20	100		43,600	5,650	690	49,940	57,000
0710	2500 kVA		.19	105		52,500	5,950	725	59,175	68,000
0720	3000 kVA		.17	117		63,500	6,650	810	70,960	81,000
0800	3750 kVA	↓	.16	125	↓	81,500	7,075	865	89,440	101,500
1990	Pole mounted distribution type, single phase									
2000	13.8 kV primary, 120/240 V secondary, 10 kVA	R-15	7.45	6.443	Ea.	1,050	360	39	1,449	1,725
2010	50 kVA		3.70	12.973		2,075	725	78	2,878	3,425
2020	100 kVA		2.75	17.455		3,625	975	105	4,705	5,575
2030	167 kVA		2.15	22.326		5,975	1,250	134	7,359	8,600
2900	2400 V primary, 120/240 V secondary, 10 kVA		7.45	6.443		1,000	360	39	1,399	1,675
2910	15 kVA		6.70	7.164		1,250	400	43	1,693	2,025
2920	25 kVA		6	8		1,575	445	48	2,068	2,450
2930	37.5 kVA		4.30	11.163		1,925	620	67	2,612	3,100
2940	50 kVA		3.70	12.973		2,275	725	78	3,078	3,650
2950	75 kVA		3	16		3,300	890	96.50	4,286.50	5,075
2960	100 kVA	↓	2.75	17.455	↓	3,350	975	105	4,430	5,275

26 12 19.20 Transformer, Liquid-Filled

		Crew	Daily Output	Labor-Hours	Unit	Material	2017 Bare Costs Labor	Equipment	Total	Total Incl O&P
0010	**TRANSFORMER, LIQUID-FILLED** Pad mounted									
0020	5 kV or 15 kV primary, 277/480 volt secondary, 3 phase									
0050	225 kVA	R-3	.55	36.364	Ea.	14,000	2,050	251	16,301	18,800
0100	300 kVA		.45	44.444		16,600	2,525	305	19,430	22,400
0200	500 kVA		.40	50		21,000	2,825	345	24,170	27,700
0250	750 kVA		.38	52.632		27,100	2,975	365	30,440	34,700
0300	1000 kVA		.26	76.923		31,500	4,350	530	36,380	41,700
0350	1500 kVA		.23	86.957		36,700	4,925	600	42,225	48,500
0400	2000 kVA		.20	100		45,500	5,650	690	51,840	59,500
0450	2500 kVA	↓	.19	105	↓	54,000	5,950	725	60,675	69,500

26 13 Medium-Voltage Switchgear

26 13 16 – Medium-Voltage Fusible Interrupter Switchgear

26 13 16.10 Switchgear

		Crew	Daily Output	Labor-Hours	Unit	Material	2017 Bare Costs Labor	Equipment	Total	Total Incl O&P
0010	**SWITCHGEAR**, Incorporate switch with cable connections, transformer,									
0100	& Low Voltage section									
0200	Load interrupter switch, 600 amp, 2 position									
0300	NEMA 1, 4.8 kV, 300 kVA & below w/CLF fuses	R-3	.40	50	Ea.	22,300	2,825	345	25,470	29,100
0400	400 kVA & above w/CLF fuses		.38	52.632		24,900	2,975	365	28,240	32,300
0500	Non fusible		.41	48.780		18,100	2,750	335	21,185	24,400
0600	13.8 kV, 300 kVA & below w/CLF fuses		.38	52.632		28,000	2,975	365	31,340	35,700
0700	400 kVA & above w/CLF fuses		.36	55.556		28,000	3,150	385	31,535	35,900
0800	Non fusible	↓	.40	50		21,200	2,825	345	24,370	28,000
0900	Cable lugs for 2 feeders 4.8 kV or 13.8 kV	1 Elec	8	1		680	56.50		736.50	830
1000	Pothead, one 3 conductor or three 1 conductor	↓	4	2	↓	3,250	113		3,363	3,750

For customer support on your Electrical Costs with RSMeans Data, call 800.448.8182.

211

26 13 16 — Medium-Voltage Fusible Interrupter Switchgear

26 13 16.10 Switchgear		Crew	Daily Output	Labor-Hours	Unit	Material	2017 Bare Costs Labor	Equipment	Total	Total Incl O&P
1100	Two 3 conductor or six 1 conductor	1 Elec	2	4	Ea.	6,425	226		6,651	7,425
1200	Key interlocks	↓	8	1	↓	755	56.50		811.50	915
1300	Lightning arresters, Distribution class (no charge)									
1400	Intermediate class or line type 4.8 kV	1 Elec	2.70	2.963	Ea.	3,650	168		3,818	4,275
1500	13.8 kV		2	4		4,850	226		5,076	5,675
1600	Station class, 4.8 kV		2.70	2.963		6,275	168		6,443	7,150
1700	13.8 kV	↓	2	4		10,800	226		11,026	12,200
1800	Transformers, 4800 volts to 480/277 volts, 75 kVA	R-3	.68	29.412		19,100	1,675	203	20,978	23,700
1900	112.5 kVA		.65	30.769		23,300	1,750	212	25,262	28,500
2000	150 kVA		.57	35.088		26,500	1,975	242	28,717	32,300
2100	225 kVA		.48	41.667		30,400	2,350	288	33,038	37,400
2200	300 kVA		.41	48.780		34,000	2,750	335	37,085	41,900
2300	500 kVA		.36	55.556		44,800	3,150	385	48,335	54,500
2400	750 kVA		.29	68.966		51,000	3,900	475	55,375	62,500
2500	13,800 volts to 480/277 volts, 75 kVA		.61	32.787		26,900	1,850	226	28,976	32,500
2600	112.5 kVA		.55	36.364		35,600	2,050	251	37,901	42,600
2700	150 kVA		.49	40.816		36,000	2,300	282	38,582	43,400
2800	225 kVA		.41	48.780		41,500	2,750	335	44,585	50,000
2900	300 kVA		.37	54.054		42,400	3,050	375	45,825	51,500
3000	500 kVA		.31	64.516		46,900	3,650	445	50,995	57,500
3100	750 kVA	↓	.26	76.923		51,500	4,350	530	56,380	64,000
3200	Forced air cooling & temperature alarm	1 Elec	1	8	↓	4,150	455		4,605	5,250
3300	Low voltage components									
3400	Maximum panel height 49-1/2", single or twin row									
3500	Breaker heights, type FA or FH, 6"									
3600	type KA or KH, 8"									
3700	type LA, 11"									
3800	type MA, 14"									
3900	Breakers, 2 pole, 15 to 60 amp, type FA	1 Elec	5.60	1.429	Ea.	690	81		771	880
4000	70 to 100 amp, type FA		4.20	1.905		870	108		978	1,125
4100	15 to 60 amp, type FH		5.60	1.429		1,150	81		1,231	1,375
4200	70 to 100 amp, type FH		4.20	1.905		1,325	108		1,433	1,600
4300	125 to 225 amp, type KA		3.40	2.353		2,025	133		2,158	2,425
4400	125 to 225 amp, type KH		3.40	2.353		4,975	133		5,108	5,675
4500	125 to 400 amp, type LA		2.50	3.200		3,725	181		3,906	4,375
4600	125 to 600 amp, type MA		1.80	4.444		5,850	252		6,102	6,800
4700	700 & 800 amp, type MA		1.50	5.333		7,375	300		7,675	8,550
4800	3 pole, 15 to 60 amp, type FA		5.30	1.509		890	85.50		975.50	1,100
4900	70 to 100 amp, type FA		4	2		1,100	113		1,213	1,375
5000	15 to 60 amp, type FH		5.30	1.509		1,325	85.50		1,410.50	1,600
5100	70 to 100 amp, type FH		4	2		1,500	113		1,613	1,825
5200	125 to 225 amp, type KA		3.20	2.500		2,550	142		2,692	3,000
5300	125 to 225 amp, type KH		3.20	2.500		5,725	142		5,867	6,500
5400	125 to 400 amp, type LA		2.30	3.478		4,525	197		4,722	5,275
5500	125 to 600 amp, type MA		1.60	5		8,000	283		8,283	9,225
5600	700 & 800 amp, type MA	↓	1.30	6.154	↓	10,400	350		10,750	11,900

26 22 Low-Voltage Transformers

26 22 13 – Low-Voltage Distribution Transformers

26 22 13.10 Transformer, Dry-Type		Crew	Daily Output	Labor-Hours	Unit	Material	2017 Bare Costs		Total	Total Incl O&P
							Labor	Equipment		
0010	**TRANSFORMER, DRY-TYPE**	R262213-10								
0050	Single phase, 240/480 volt primary, 120/240 volt secondary									
0100	1 kVA	R262213-60	1 Elec	2	4	Ea.	375	226		601	750
0300	2 kVA			1.60	5		580	283		863	1,050
0500	3 kVA			1.40	5.714		720	325		1,045	1,275
0700	5 kVA		▼	1.20	6.667		980	375		1,355	1,650
0900	7.5 kVA		2 Elec	2.20	7.273		1,350	410		1,760	2,100
1100	10 kVA			1.60	10		1,550	565		2,115	2,550
1300	15 kVA			1.20	13.333		2,075	755		2,830	3,400
1500	25 kVA			1	16		2,325	905		3,230	3,900
1700	37.5 kVA			.80	20		2,825	1,125		3,950	4,800
1900	50 kVA			.70	22.857		3,425	1,300		4,725	5,725
2100	75 kVA		▼	.65	24.615		4,425	1,400		5,825	6,925
2110	100 kVA		R-3	.90	22.222		5,775	1,250	153	7,178	8,425
2120	167 kVA		"	.80	25		9,550	1,425	173	11,148	12,800
2190	480 V primary, 120/240 V secondary, nonvent., 15 kVA		2 Elec	1.20	13.333		1,625	755		2,380	2,925
2200	25 kVA			.90	17.778		2,425	1,000		3,425	4,150
2210	37 kVA			.75	21.333		2,875	1,200		4,075	4,950
2220	50 kVA			.65	24.615		3,375	1,400		4,775	5,800
2230	75 kVA			.60	26.667		4,500	1,500		6,000	7,200
2240	100 kVA			.50	32		5,850	1,800		7,650	9,150
2250	Low operating temperature (80°C), 25 kVA			1	16		4,375	905		5,280	6,150
2260	37 kVA			.80	20		4,700	1,125		5,825	6,875
2270	50 kVA			.70	22.857		6,150	1,300		7,450	8,725
2280	75 kVA			.65	24.615		9,750	1,400		11,150	12,800
2290	100 kVA		▼	.55	29.091	▼	10,200	1,650		11,850	13,700
2300	3 phase, 480 volt primary, 120/208 volt secondary									
2310	Ventilated, 3 kVA		1 Elec	1	8	Ea.	1,100	455		1,555	1,900
2700	6 kVA			.80	10		1,250	565		1,815	2,225
2900	9 kVA		▼	.70	11.429		1,250	645		1,895	2,350
3100	15 kVA		2 Elec	1.10	14.545		1,575	825		2,400	2,975
3300	30 kVA			.90	17.778		1,575	1,000		2,575	3,225
3500	45 kVA			.80	20		1,875	1,125		3,000	3,750
3700	75 kVA		▼	.70	22.857		2,500	1,300		3,800	4,700
3900	112.5 kVA		R-3	.90	22.222		4,150	1,250	153	5,553	6,625
4100	150 kVA			.85	23.529		5,025	1,325	162	6,512	7,700
4300	225 kVA			.65	30.769		7,325	1,750	212	9,287	10,900
4500	300 kVA			.55	36.364		9,175	2,050	251	11,476	13,500
4700	500 kVA			.45	44.444		15,300	2,525	305	18,130	20,900
4800	750 kVA			.35	57.143		22,200	3,225	395	25,820	29,700
4820	1000 kVA		▼	.32	62.500		26,100	3,550	430	30,080	34,500
4850	K-4 rated, 15 kVA		2 Elec	1.10	14.545		3,500	825		4,325	5,100
4855	30 kVA			.90	17.778		5,250	1,000		6,250	7,275
4860	45 kVA			.80	20		6,300	1,125		7,425	8,625
4865	75 kVA		▼	.70	22.857		9,650	1,300		10,950	12,600
4870	112.5 kVA		R-3	.90	22.222		12,600	1,250	153	14,003	16,000
4875	150 kVA			.85	23.529		16,600	1,325	162	18,087	20,400
4880	225 kVA			.65	30.769		23,000	1,750	212	24,962	28,200
4885	300 kVA			.55	36.364		30,100	2,050	251	32,401	36,500
4890	500 kVA		▼	.45	44.444		42,100	2,525	305	44,930	50,500
4900	K-13 rated, 15 kVA		2 Elec	1.10	14.545		3,975	825		4,800	5,600
4905	30 kVA			.90	17.778		5,975	1,000		6,975	8,075
4910	45 kVA		▼	.80	20	▼	7,200	1,125		8,325	9,625

26 22 13 – Low-Voltage Distribution Transformers

26 22 13.10 Transformer, Dry-Type	Crew	Daily Output	Labor-Hours	Unit	Material	2017 Bare Costs Labor	Equipment	Total	Total Incl O&P
4915	75 kVA	2 Elec	.70	22.857	Ea.	10,800	1,300		12,100	13,900
4920	112.5 kVA	R-3	.90	22.222		14,400	1,250	153	15,803	17,900
4925	150 kVA		.85	23.529		18,800	1,325	162	20,287	22,900
4930	225 kVA		.65	30.769		25,600	1,750	212	27,562	31,100
4935	300 kVA		.55	36.364		34,200	2,050	251	36,501	41,000
4940	500 kVA		.45	44.444		56,500	2,525	305	59,330	66,500
5020	480 volt primary, 120/208 volt secondary									
5030	Nonventilated, 15 kVA	2 Elec	1.10	14.545	Ea.	2,900	825		3,725	4,425
5040	30 kVA		.80	20		4,425	1,125		5,550	6,575
5050	45 kVA		.70	22.857		5,950	1,300		7,250	8,500
5060	75 kVA		.65	24.615		9,425	1,400		10,825	12,500
5070	112.5 kVA	R-3	.85	23.529		15,500	1,325	162	16,987	19,200
5081	150 kVA		.85	23.529		19,300	1,325	162	20,787	23,500
5090	225 kVA		.60	33.333		21,600	1,875	230	23,705	26,900
5100	300 kVA		.50	40		21,300	2,275	276	23,851	27,200
5200	Low operating temperature (80°C), 30 kVA	2 Elec	.90	17.778		4,775	1,000		5,775	6,750
5210	45 kVA		.80	20		5,750	1,125		6,875	8,000
5220	75 kVA		.70	22.857		8,650	1,300		9,950	11,500
5230	112.5 kVA	R-3	.90	22.222		11,500	1,250	153	12,903	14,800
5240	150 kVA		.85	23.529		14,800	1,325	162	16,287	18,500
5250	225 kVA		.65	30.769		20,100	1,750	212	22,062	25,000
5260	300 kVA		.55	36.364		27,000	2,050	251	29,301	33,100
5270	500 kVA		.45	44.444		36,200	2,525	305	39,030	44,000
5380	3 phase, 5 kV primary, 277/480 volt secondary									
5400	High voltage, 112.5 kVA	R-3	.85	23.529	Ea.	18,100	1,325	162	19,587	22,100
5410	150 kVA		.65	30.769		19,700	1,750	212	21,662	24,600
5420	225 kVA		.55	36.364		23,200	2,050	251	25,501	29,000
5430	300 kVA		.45	44.444		29,700	2,525	305	32,530	36,800
5440	500 kVA		.35	57.143		38,400	3,225	395	42,020	47,500
5450	750 kVA		.32	62.500		60,000	3,550	430	63,980	72,000
5460	1000 kVA		.30	66.667		70,000	3,775	460	74,235	83,000
5470	1500 kVA		.27	74.074		81,500	4,200	510	86,210	96,500
5480	2000 kVA		.25	80		95,500	4,525	550	100,575	113,000
5490	2500 kVA		.20	100		108,000	5,650	690	114,340	128,000
5500	3000 kVA		.18	111		141,000	6,300	765	148,065	166,000
5590	15 kV primary, 277/480 volt secondary									
5600	High voltage, 112.5 kVA	R-3	.85	23.529	Ea.	27,600	1,325	162	29,087	32,600
5610	150 kVA		.65	30.769		32,300	1,750	212	34,262	38,400
5620	225 kVA		.55	36.364		35,600	2,050	251	37,901	42,600
5630	300 kVA		.45	44.444		42,000	2,525	305	44,830	50,500
5640	500 kVA		.35	57.143		53,000	3,225	395	56,620	64,000
5650	750 kVA		.32	62.500		69,500	3,550	430	73,480	82,500
5660	1000 kVA		.30	66.667		79,000	3,775	460	83,235	93,000
5670	1500 kVA		.27	74.074		91,000	4,200	510	95,710	107,000
5680	2000 kVA		.25	80		101,000	4,525	550	106,075	118,500
5690	2500 kVA		.20	100		117,000	5,650	690	123,340	138,500
5700	3000 kVA		.18	111		139,500	6,300	765	146,565	164,000
6000	2400 volt primary, 480 volt secondary, 300 kVA		.45	44.444		29,700	2,525	305	32,530	36,800
6010	500 kVA		.35	57.143		38,400	3,225	395	42,020	47,500
6020	750 kVA		.32	62.500		55,000	3,550	430	58,980	66,500

26 22 Low-Voltage Transformers

26 22 13 – Low-Voltage Distribution Transformers

26 22 13.20 Isolating Panels		Crew	Daily Output	Labor-Hours	Unit	Material	2017 Bare Costs Labor	2017 Bare Costs Equipment	Total	Total Incl O&P
0010	**ISOLATING PANELS** used with isolating transformers									
0020	For hospital applications									
0100	Critical care area, 8 circuit, 3 kVA	1 Elec	.58	13.793	Ea.	6,825	780		7,605	8,675
0200	5 kVA		.54	14.815		3,225	840		4,065	4,800
0400	7.5 kVA		.52	15.385		5,975	870		6,845	7,875
0600	10 kVA		.44	18.182		8,100	1,025		9,125	10,500
0800	Operating room power & lighting, 8 circuit, 3 kVA		.58	13.793		4,750	780		5,530	6,400
1000	5 kVA		.54	14.815		5,300	840		6,140	7,075
1200	7.5 kVA		.52	15.385		4,900	870		5,770	6,675
1400	10 kVA		.44	18.182		5,450	1,025		6,475	7,550
1600	X-ray systems, 15 kVA, 90 amp		.44	18.182		10,400	1,025		11,425	13,000
1800	25 kVA, 125 amp		.36	22.222		12,600	1,250		13,850	15,700

26 22 13.30 Isolating Transformer

			Crew	Daily Output	Labor-Hours	Unit	Material	Labor	Equipment	Total	Total Incl O&P
0010	**ISOLATING TRANSFORMER**										
0100	Single phase, 120/240 volt primary, 120/240 volt secondary										
0200	0.50 kVA	R262213-60	1 Elec	4	2	Ea.	375	113		488	580
0400	1 kVA			2	4		935	226		1,161	1,375
0600	2 kVA			1.60	5		1,500	283		1,783	2,075
0800	3 kVA			1.40	5.714		800	325		1,125	1,375
1000	5 kVA			1.20	6.667		1,050	375		1,425	1,750
1200	7.5 kVA			1.10	7.273		1,325	410		1,735	2,100
1400	10 kVA			.80	10		1,700	565		2,265	2,725
1600	15 kVA			.60	13.333		2,175	755		2,930	3,525
1800	25 kVA			.50	16		3,150	905		4,055	4,800
1810	37.5 kVA		2 Elec	.80	20		5,200	1,125		6,325	7,400
1820	75 kVA		"	.65	24.615		7,800	1,400		9,200	10,700
1830	3 phase, 120/240 V primary, 120/240 V secondary, 112.5 kVA		R-3	.90	22.222		10,900	1,250	153	12,303	14,100
1840	150 kVA			.85	23.529		13,900	1,325	162	15,387	17,500
1850	225 kVA			.65	30.769		19,400	1,750	212	21,362	24,200
1860	300 kVA			.55	36.364		25,800	2,050	251	28,101	31,700
1870	500 kVA			.45	44.444		42,900	2,525	305	45,730	51,500
1880	750 kVA			.35	57.143		43,300	3,225	395	46,920	53,000

26 22 13.90 Transformer Handling

			Crew	Daily Output	Labor-Hours	Unit	Material	Labor	Equipment	Total	Total Incl O&P
0010	**TRANSFORMER HANDLING** Add to normal labor cost in restricted areas										
5000	Transformers										
5150	15 kVA, approximately 200 pounds		2 Elec	2.70	5.926	Ea.		335		335	505
5160	25 kVA, approximately 300 pounds			2.50	6.400			360		360	545
5170	37.5 kVA, approximately 400 pounds			2.30	6.957			395		395	590
5180	50 kVA, approximately 500 pounds			2	8			455		455	680
5190	75 kVA, approximately 600 pounds			1.80	8.889			505		505	755
5200	100 kVA, approximately 700 pounds			1.60	10			565		565	850
5210	112.5 kVA, approximately 800 pounds		3 Elec	2.20	10.909			615		615	925
5220	125 kVA, approximately 900 pounds			2	12			680		680	1,025
5230	150 kVA, approximately 1000 pounds			1.80	13.333			755		755	1,125
5240	167 kVA, approximately 1200 pounds			1.60	15			850		850	1,275
5250	200 kVA, approximately 1400 pounds			1.40	17.143			970		970	1,450
5260	225 kVA, approximately 1600 pounds			1.30	18.462			1,050		1,050	1,575
5270	250 kVA, approximately 1800 pounds			1.10	21.818			1,225		1,225	1,850
5280	300 kVA, approximately 2000 pounds			1	24			1,350		1,350	2,025
5290	500 kVA, approximately 3000 pounds			.75	32			1,800		1,800	2,725
5300	600 kVA, approximately 3500 pounds			.67	35.821			2,025		2,025	3,050
5310	750 kVA, approximately 4000 pounds			.60	40			2,275		2,275	3,400

For customer support on your Electrical Costs with RSMeans Data, call 800.448.8182.

215

26 22 Low-Voltage Transformers

26 22 13 – Low-Voltage Distribution Transformers

26 22 13.90 Transformer Handling	Crew	Daily Output	Labor-Hours	Unit	Material	2017 Bare Costs Labor	Equipment	Total	Total Incl O&P
5320	1000 kVA, approximately 5000 pounds	3 Elec	.50	48	Ea.		2,725		2,725	4,075

26 22 16 – Low-Voltage Buck-Boost Transformers

26 22 16.10 Buck-Boost Transformer

	26 22 16.10 Buck-Boost Transformer	Crew	Daily Output	Labor-Hours	Unit	Material	2017 Bare Costs Labor	Equipment	Total	Total Incl O&P
0010	**BUCK-BOOST TRANSFORMER** R262213-60									
0100	Single phase, 120/240 V primary, 12/24 V secondary									
0200	0.10 kVA	1 Elec	8	1	Ea.	132	56.50		188.50	230
0400	0.25 kVA		5.70	1.404		193	79.50		272.50	330
0600	0.50 kVA		4	2		263	113		376	460
0800	0.75 kVA		3.10	2.581		340	146		486	595
1000	1.0 kVA		2	4		425	226		651	805
1200	1.5 kVA		1.80	4.444		500	252		752	925
1400	2.0 kVA		1.60	5		630	283		913	1,125
1600	3.0 kVA		1.40	5.714		840	325		1,165	1,400
1800	5.0 kVA		1.20	6.667		1,025	375		1,400	1,700
2000	3 phase, 240 V primary, 208/120 V secondary, 15 kVA	2 Elec	2.40	6.667		2,200	375		2,575	3,000
2200	30 kVA		1.60	10		2,450	565		3,015	3,550
2400	45 kVA		1.40	11.429		2,950	645		3,595	4,225
2600	75 kVA		1.20	13.333		3,575	755		4,330	5,050
2800	112.5 kVA	R-3	1.40	14.286		4,450	810	98.50	5,358.50	6,225
3000	150 kVA		1.10	18.182		5,925	1,025	125	7,075	8,200
3200	225 kVA		1	20		7,700	1,125	138	8,963	10,300
3400	300 kVA		.90	22.222		10,500	1,250	153	11,903	13,600

26 24 Switchboards and Panelboards

26 24 13 – Switchboards

26 24 13.10 Incoming Switchboards

	26 24 13.10 Incoming Switchboards	Crew	Daily Output	Labor-Hours	Unit	Material	2017 Bare Costs Labor	Equipment	Total	Total Incl O&P
0010	**INCOMING SWITCHBOARDS** main service section R262419-84									
0100	Aluminum bus bars, not including CT's or PT's									
0200	No main disconnect, includes CT compartment									
0300	120/208 volt, 4 wire, 600 amp	2 Elec	1	16	Ea.	4,050	905		4,955	5,800
0400	800 amp		.88	18.182		4,050	1,025		5,075	6,000
0500	1000 amp		.80	20		4,875	1,125		6,000	7,050
0600	1200 amp		.72	22.222		4,875	1,250		6,125	7,225
0700	1600 amp		.66	24.242		4,875	1,375		6,250	7,400
0800	2000 amp		.62	25.806		5,250	1,450		6,700	7,975
1000	3000 amp		.56	28.571		6,925	1,625		8,550	10,000
1200	277/480 volt, 4 wire, 600 amp		1	16		4,050	905		4,955	5,800
1300	800 amp		.88	18.182		4,050	1,025		5,075	6,000
1400	1000 amp		.80	20		5,150	1,125		6,275	7,350
1500	1200 amp		.72	22.222		5,150	1,250		6,400	7,525
1600	1600 amp		.66	24.242		5,150	1,375		6,525	7,700
1700	2000 amp		.62	25.806		5,250	1,450		6,700	7,975
1800	3000 amp		.56	28.571		6,925	1,625		8,550	10,000
1900	4000 amp		.52	30.769		8,575	1,750		10,325	12,000
2000	Fused switch & CT compartment									
2100	120/208 volt, 4 wire, 400 amp	2 Elec	1.12	14.286	Ea.	2,700	810		3,510	4,175
2200	600 amp		.94	17.021		3,225	965		4,190	4,975
2300	800 amp		.84	19.048		11,000	1,075		12,075	13,600
2400	1200 amp		.68	23.529		14,300	1,325		15,625	17,700
2500	277/480 volt, 4 wire, 400 amp		1.14	14.035		4,975	795		5,770	6,675

26 24 Switchboards and Panelboards

26 24 13 – Switchboards

26 24 13.10 Incoming Switchboards		Crew	Daily Output	Labor-Hours	Unit	Material	2017 Bare Costs Labor	Equipment	Total	Total Incl O&P
2600	600 amp	2 Elec	.94	17.021	Ea.	3,200	965		4,165	4,975
2700	800 amp		.84	19.048		11,000	1,075		12,075	13,600
2800	1200 amp		.68	23.529		14,300	1,325		15,625	17,700
2900	Pressure switch & CT compartment									
3000	120/208 volt, 4 wire, 800 amp	2 Elec	.80	20	Ea.	9,850	1,125		10,975	12,500
3100	1200 amp		.66	24.242		19,000	1,375		20,375	23,100
3200	1600 amp		.62	25.806		20,300	1,450		21,750	24,500
3300	2000 amp		.56	28.571		21,500	1,625		23,125	26,100
3310	2500 amp		.50	32		26,500	1,800		28,300	31,800
3320	3000 amp		.44	36.364		35,700	2,050		37,750	42,400
3330	4000 amp		.40	40		45,800	2,275		48,075	54,000
3340	120/208 volt, 4 wire, 800 amp, with ground fault		.80	20		16,300	1,125		17,425	19,600
3350	1200 amp, with ground fault		.66	24.242		21,000	1,375		22,375	25,200
3360	1600 amp, with ground fault		.62	25.806		22,800	1,450		24,250	27,300
3370	2000 amp, with ground fault		.56	28.571		24,600	1,625		26,225	29,500
3400	277/480 volt, 4 wire, 800 amp, with ground fault		.80	20		16,300	1,125		17,425	19,600
3600	1200 amp, with ground fault		.66	24.242		21,000	1,375		22,375	25,200
4000	1600 amp, with ground fault		.62	25.806		22,800	1,450		24,250	27,300
4200	2000 amp, with ground fault		.56	28.571		24,600	1,625		26,225	29,500
4400	Circuit breaker, molded case & CT compartment									
4600	3 pole, 4 wire, 600 amp	2 Elec	.94	17.021	Ea.	8,475	965		9,440	10,800
4800	800 amp		.84	19.048		10,100	1,075		11,175	12,800
5000	1200 amp		.68	23.529		13,800	1,325		15,125	17,200
5100	Copper bus bars, not incl. CT's or PT's, add, minimum					15%				

26 24 13.20 In Plant Distribution Switchboards

		Crew	Daily Output	Labor-Hours	Unit	Material	2017 Bare Costs Labor	Equipment	Total	Total Incl O&P
0010	**IN PLANT DISTRIBUTION SWITCHBOARDS**									
0100	Main lugs only, to 600 volt, 3 pole, 3 wire, 200 amp	2 Elec	1.20	13.333	Ea.	1,275	755		2,030	2,525
0110	400 amp		1.20	13.333		1,275	755		2,030	2,525
0120	600 amp		1.20	13.333		1,300	755		2,055	2,550
0130	800 amp		1.08	14.815		1,425	840		2,265	2,800
0140	1200 amp		.92	17.391		1,725	985		2,710	3,375
0150	1600 amp		.86	18.605		2,250	1,050		3,300	4,050
0160	2000 amp		.82	19.512		2,500	1,100		3,600	4,400
0250	To 480 volt, 3 pole, 4 wire, 200 amp		1.20	13.333		1,100	755		1,855	2,325
0260	400 amp		1.20	13.333		1,275	755		2,030	2,525
0270	600 amp		1.20	13.333		1,375	755		2,130	2,650
0280	800 amp		1.08	14.815		1,500	840		2,340	2,900
0290	1200 amp		.92	17.391		1,875	985		2,860	3,525
0300	1600 amp		.86	18.605		2,125	1,050		3,175	3,925
0310	2000 amp		.82	19.512		2,475	1,100		3,575	4,375
0400	Main circuit breaker, to 600 volt, 3 pole, 3 wire, 200 amp		1.20	13.333		3,025	755		3,780	4,450
0410	400 amp		1.14	14.035		3,025	795		3,820	4,525
0420	600 amp		1.10	14.545		3,825	825		4,650	5,450
0430	800 amp		1.04	15.385		6,425	870		7,295	8,350
0440	1200 amp		.88	18.182		8,400	1,025		9,425	10,800
0450	1600 amp		.84	19.048		13,500	1,075		14,575	16,400
0460	2000 amp		.80	20		14,400	1,125		15,525	17,500
0550	277/480 volt, 3 pole, 4 wire, 200 amp		1.20	13.333		3,175	755		3,930	4,625
0560	400 amp		1.14	14.035		3,175	795		3,970	4,700
0570	600 amp		1.10	14.545		4,000	825		4,825	5,625
0580	800 amp		1.04	15.385		6,725	870		7,595	8,700
0590	1200 amp		.88	18.182		8,675	1,025		9,700	11,100

For customer support on your Electrical Costs with RSMeans Data, call 800.448.8182.

217

26 24 13.20 In Plant Distribution Switchboards	Crew	Daily Output	Labor-Hours	Unit	Material	2017 Bare Costs Labor	Equipment	Total	Total Incl O&P
0600	1600 amp	2 Elec	.84	19.048	Ea.	13,500	1,075		14,575	16,400
0610	2000 amp		.80	20		14,400	1,125		15,525	17,500
0700	Main fusible switch w/fuse, 208/240 volt, 3 pole, 3 wire, 200 amp		1.20	13.333		3,350	755		4,105	4,800
0710	400 amp		1.14	14.035		3,350	795		4,145	4,875
0720	600 amp		1.10	14.545		4,050	825		4,875	5,700
0730	800 amp		1.04	15.385		8,300	870		9,170	10,500
0740	1200 amp		.88	18.182		9,675	1,025		10,700	12,200
0800	120/208, 120/240 volt, 3 pole, 4 wire, 200 amp		1.20	13.333		2,975	755		3,730	4,375
0810	400 amp		1.14	14.035		2,975	795		3,770	4,450
0820	600 amp		1.10	14.545		3,875	825		4,700	5,475
0830	800 amp		1.04	15.385		6,150	870		7,020	8,075
0840	1200 amp		.88	18.182		7,150	1,025		8,175	9,425
0900	480 or 600 volt, 3 pole, 3 wire, 200 amp		1.20	13.333		3,200	755		3,955	4,650
0910	400 amp		1.14	14.035		3,200	795		3,995	4,725
0920	600 amp		1.10	14.545		3,850	825		4,675	5,450
0930	800 amp		1.04	15.385		5,925	870		6,795	7,825
0940	1200 amp		.88	18.182		6,875	1,025		7,900	9,125
1000	277 or 480 volt, 3 pole, 4 wire, 200 amp		1.20	13.333		3,325	755		4,080	4,800
1010	400 amp		1.14	14.035		3,325	795		4,120	4,875
1020	600 amp		1.10	14.545		4,025	825		4,850	5,650
1030	800 amp		1.04	15.385		6,175	870		7,045	8,075
1040	1200 amp		.88	18.182		7,150	1,025		8,175	9,425
1120	1600 amp		.76	21.053		13,100	1,200		14,300	16,200
1130	2000 amp		.68	23.529		17,200	1,325		18,525	20,900
1150	Pressure switch, bolted, 3 pole, 208/240 volt, 3 wire, 800 amp		.96	16.667		9,675	945		10,620	12,100
1160	1200 amp		.80	20		12,400	1,125		13,525	15,300
1170	1600 amp		.76	21.053		14,100	1,200		15,300	17,300
1180	2000 amp		.68	23.529		16,100	1,325		17,425	19,700
1200	120/208 or 120/240 volt, 3 pole, 4 wire, 800 amp		.96	16.667		7,650	945		8,595	9,825
1210	1200 amp		.80	20		8,950	1,125		10,075	11,500
1220	1600 amp		.76	21.053		14,100	1,200		15,300	17,300
1230	2000 amp		.68	23.529		16,100	1,325		17,425	19,700
1300	480 or 600 volt, 3 wire, 800 amp		.96	16.667		9,675	945		10,620	12,100
1310	1200 amp		.80	20		13,500	1,125		14,625	16,600
1320	1600 amp		.76	21.053		15,300	1,200		16,500	18,600
1330	2000 amp		.68	23.529		17,200	1,325		18,525	20,900
1400	277/480 volt, 4 wire, 800 amp		.96	16.667		9,675	945		10,620	12,100
1410	1200 amp		.80	20		13,500	1,125		14,625	16,600
1420	1600 amp		.76	21.053		15,300	1,200		16,500	18,600
1430	2000 amp		.68	23.529		17,200	1,325		18,525	20,900
1500	Main ground fault protector, 1200-2000 amp		5.40	2.963		3,225	168		3,393	3,800
1600	Busway connection, 200 amp		5.40	2.963		450	168		618	745
1610	400 amp		4.60	3.478		450	197		647	790
1620	600 amp		4	4		450	226		676	835
1630	800 amp		3.20	5		450	283		733	920
1640	1200 amp		2.60	6.154		450	350		800	1,025
1650	1600 amp		2.40	6.667		925	375		1,300	1,600
1660	2000 amp		2	8		925	455		1,380	1,700
1700	Shunt trip for remote operation, 200 amp		8	2		640	113		753	875
1710	400 amp		8	2		1,025	113		1,138	1,300
1720	600 amp		8	2		1,200	113		1,313	1,500
1730	800 amp		8	2		1,550	113		1,663	1,900
1740	1200-2000 amp		8	2		3,300	113		3,413	3,800

218

For customer support on your Electrical Costs with RSMeans Data, call 800.448.8182.

26 24 13 – Switchboards

26 24 13.20 In Plant Distribution Switchboards

		Crew	Daily Output	Labor-Hours	Unit	Material	2017 Bare Costs Labor	2017 Bare Costs Equipment	Total	Total Incl O&P
1800	Motor operated main breaker, 200 amp	2 Elec	8	2	Ea.	3,175	113		3,288	3,675
1810	400 amp		8	2		3,175	113		3,288	3,675
1820	600 amp		8	2		3,275	113		3,388	3,775
1830	800 amp		8	2		3,275	113		3,388	3,775
1840	1200-2000 amp		8	2		3,350	113		3,463	3,850
1900	Current/potential transformer metering compartment, 200-800 amp		5.40	2.963		2,500	168		2,668	3,000
1940	1200 amp		5.40	2.963		4,800	168		4,968	5,525
1950	1600-2000 amp		5.40	2.963		7,200	168		7,368	8,150
2000	With watt meter, 200-800 amp		4	4		8,175	226		8,401	9,350
2040	1200 amp		4	4		10,100	226		10,326	11,400
2050	1600-2000 amp		4	4		10,100	226		10,326	11,400
2100	Split bus, 60-200 amp	1 Elec	5.30	1.509		194	85.50		279.50	340
2130	400 amp	2 Elec	4.60	3.478		335	197		532	665
2140	600 amp		3.60	4.444		410	252		662	825
2150	800 amp		2.60	6.154		520	350		870	1,100
2170	1200 amp		2	8		595	455		1,050	1,325
2250	Contactor control, 60 amp	1 Elec	2	4		1,275	226		1,501	1,750
2260	100 amp		1.50	5.333		1,425	300		1,725	2,025
2270	200 amp		1	8		2,150	455		2,605	3,050
2280	400 amp	2 Elec	1	16		6,550	905		7,455	8,550
2290	600 amp		.84	19.048		7,325	1,075		8,400	9,675
2300	800 amp		.72	22.222		8,675	1,250		9,925	11,400
2500	Modifier, two distribution sections, add		.80	20		2,725	1,125		3,850	4,700
2520	Three distribution sections, add		.40	40		5,225	2,275		7,500	9,125
2560	Auxiliary pull section, 20", add		2	8		1,075	455		1,530	1,875
2580	24", add		1.80	8.889		1,075	505		1,580	1,950
2600	30", add		1.60	10		1,075	565		1,640	2,050
2620	36", add		1.40	11.429		1,300	645		1,945	2,400
2640	Dog house, 12", add		2.40	6.667		224	375		599	810
2660	18", add		2	8		445	455		900	1,175
3000	Transition section between switchboard and transformer									
3050	or motor control center, 4 wire alum. bus, 600 amp	2 Elec	1.14	14.035	Ea.	2,200	795		2,995	3,625
3100	800 amp		1	16		2,475	905		3,380	4,075
3150	1000 amp		.88	18.182		2,775	1,025		3,800	4,600
3200	1200 amp		.80	20		3,050	1,125		4,175	5,050
3250	1600 amp		.72	22.222		3,600	1,250		4,850	5,850
3300	2000 amp		.66	24.242		4,150	1,375		5,525	6,625
3350	2500 amp		.62	25.806		4,825	1,450		6,275	7,525
3400	3000 amp		.56	28.571		5,575	1,625		7,200	8,550
4000	Weatherproof construction, per vertical section		1.76	9.091		2,550	515		3,065	3,575

26 24 13.30 Distribution Switchboards Section

		Crew	Daily Output	Labor-Hours	Unit	Material	2017 Bare Costs Labor	2017 Bare Costs Equipment	Total	Total Incl O&P
0010	**DISTRIBUTION SWITCHBOARDS SECTION** R262419-80									
0100	Aluminum bus bars, not including breakers									
0160	Subfeed lug-rated at 60 amp	2 Elec	1.30	12.308	Ea.	1,075	695		1,770	2,225
0170	100 amp		1.26	12.698		1,450	720		2,170	2,650
0180	200 amp		1.20	13.333		1,225	755		1,980	2,475
0190	400 amp		1.10	14.545		1,300	825		2,125	2,650
0195	120/208 or 277/480 volt, 4 wire, 400 amp		1.10	14.545		1,550	825		2,375	2,925
0200	600 amp		1	16		1,450	905		2,355	2,925
0300	800 amp		.88	18.182		1,825	1,025		2,850	3,550
0400	1000 amp		.80	20		2,425	1,125		3,550	4,375
0500	1200 amp		.72	22.222		3,000	1,250		4,250	5,175

For customer support on your Electrical Costs with RSMeans Data, call 800.448.8182.

219

26 24 13 – Switchboards

26 24 13.30 Distribution Switchboards Section	Crew	Daily Output	Labor-Hours	Unit	Material	2017 Bare Costs Labor	Equipment	Total	Total Incl O&P
0600	1600 amp	2 Elec	.66	24.242	Ea.	4,000	1,375		5,375	6,425
0700	2000 amp		.62	25.806		4,975	1,450		6,425	7,675
0800	2500 amp		.60	26.667		5,975	1,500		7,475	8,825
0900	3000 amp		.56	28.571		6,975	1,625		8,600	10,100
0950	4000 amp		.52	30.769		7,975	1,750		9,725	11,400

26 24 13.40 Switchboards Feeder Section

		Crew	Daily Output	Labor-Hours	Unit	Material	2017 Bare Costs Labor	Equipment	Total	Total Incl O&P
0010	**SWITCHBOARDS FEEDER SECTION** group mounted devices R262419-82									
0030	Circuit breakers									
0160	FA frame, 15 to 60 amp, 240 volt, 1 pole	1 Elec	8	1	Ea.	116	56.50		172.50	212
0170	2 pole		7	1.143		243	64.50		307.50	365
0180	3 pole		5.30	1.509		365	85.50		450.50	530
0210	480 volt, 1 pole		8	1		161	56.50		217.50	262
0220	2 pole		7	1.143		445	64.50		509.50	585
0230	3 pole		5.30	1.509		575	85.50		660.50	760
0260	600 volt, 2 pole		7	1.143		515	64.50		579.50	660
0270	3 pole		5.30	1.509		660	85.50		745.50	860
0280	FA frame, 70 to 100 amp, 240 volt, 1 pole		7	1.143		213	64.50		277.50	330
0310	2 pole		5	1.600		395	90.50		485.50	570
0320	3 pole		4	2		515	113		628	735
0330	480 volt, 1 pole		7	1.143		292	64.50		356.50	415
0360	2 pole		5	1.600		580	90.50		670.50	770
0370	3 pole		4	2		675	113		788	910
0380	600 volt, 2 pole		5	1.600		650	90.50		740.50	850
0410	3 pole		4	2		815	113		928	1,075
0420	KA frame, 70 to 225 amp		3.20	2.500		1,525	142		1,667	1,900
0430	LA frame, 125 to 400 amp		2.30	3.478		4,150	197		4,347	4,875
0460	MA frame, 450 to 600 amp		1.60	5		6,175	283		6,458	7,200
0470	700 to 800 amp		1.30	6.154		8,000	350		8,350	9,325
0480	MAL frame, 1000 amp		1	8		8,300	455		8,755	9,825
0490	PA frame, 1200 amp		.80	10		16,900	565		17,465	19,500
0500	Branch circuit, fusible switch, 600 volt, double 30/30 amp		4	2		855	113		968	1,125
0550	60/60 amp		3.20	2.500		880	142		1,022	1,175
0600	100/100 amp		2.70	2.963		1,100	168		1,268	1,475
0650	Single, 30 amp		5.30	1.509		695	85.50		780.50	895
0700	60 amp		4.70	1.702		825	96.50		921.50	1,050
0750	100 amp		4	2		1,050	113		1,163	1,325
0800	200 amp		2.70	2.963		1,375	168		1,543	1,750
0850	400 amp		2.30	3.478		2,525	197		2,722	3,075
0900	600 amp		1.80	4.444		3,075	252		3,327	3,750
0950	800 amp		1.30	6.154		5,150	350		5,500	6,200
1000	1200 amp		.80	10		5,900	565		6,465	7,350
1080	Branch circuit, circuit breakers, high interrupting capacity									
1100	60 amp, 240, 480 or 600 volt, 1 pole	1 Elec	8	1	Ea.	315	56.50		371.50	430
1120	2 pole		7	1.143		800	64.50		864.50	980
1140	3 pole		5.30	1.509		660	85.50		745.50	855
1150	100 amp, 240, 480 or 600 volt, 1 pole		7	1.143		350	64.50		414.50	480
1160	2 pole		5	1.600		935	90.50		1,025.50	1,150
1180	3 pole		4	2		715	113		828	955
1200	225 amp, 240, 480 or 600 volt, 2 pole		3.50	2.286		2,200	129		2,329	2,625
1220	3 pole		3.20	2.500		2,225	142		2,367	2,650
1240	400 amp, 240, 480 or 600 volt, 2 pole		2.50	3.200		3,225	181		3,406	3,825
1260	3 pole		2.30	3.478		3,000	197		3,197	3,600

26 24 Switchboards and Panelboards

26 24 13 – Switchboards

26 24 13.40 Switchboards Feeder Section	Crew	Daily Output	Labor-Hours	Unit	Material	2017 Bare Costs Labor	2017 Bare Costs Equipment	Total	Total Incl O&P
1280	600 amp, 240, 480 or 600 volt, 2 pole	1 Elec	1.80	4.444	Ea.	4,025	252		4,277	4,800
1300	3 pole		1.60	5		3,675	283		3,958	4,475
1320	800 amp, 240, 480 or 600 volt, 2 pole		1.50	5.333		4,825	300		5,125	5,775
1340	3 pole		1.30	6.154		5,500	350		5,850	6,575
1360	1000 amp, 240, 480 or 600 volt, 2 pole		1.10	7.273		6,575	410		6,985	7,850
1380	3 pole		1	8		6,575	455		7,030	7,900
1400	1200 amp, 240, 480 or 600 volt, 2 pole		.90	8.889		6,550	505		7,055	7,975
1420	3 pole		.80	10		7,775	565		8,340	9,400
1700	Fusible switch, 240 V, 60 amp, 2 pole		3.20	2.500		430	142		572	680
1720	3 pole		3	2.667		590	151		741	875
1740	100 amp, 2 pole		2.70	2.963		435	168		603	730
1760	3 pole		2.50	3.200		660	181		841	995
1780	200 amp, 2 pole		2	4		910	226		1,136	1,350
1800	3 pole		1.90	4.211		1,075	238		1,313	1,525
1820	400 amp, 2 pole		1.50	5.333		1,700	300		2,000	2,325
1840	3 pole		1.30	6.154		2,125	350		2,475	2,875
1860	600 amp, 2 pole		1	8		2,425	455		2,880	3,350
1880	3 pole		.90	8.889		2,975	505		3,480	4,025
1900	240-600 V, 800 amp, 2 pole		.70	11.429		5,400	645		6,045	6,925
1920	3 pole		.60	13.333		6,625	755		7,380	8,400
2000	600 V, 60 amp, 2 pole		3.20	2.500		650	142		792	925
2040	100 amp, 2 pole		2.70	2.963		670	168		838	985
2080	200 amp, 2 pole		2	4		1,150	226		1,376	1,625
2120	400 amp, 2 pole		1.50	5.333		2,300	300		2,600	2,975
2160	600 amp, 2 pole		1	8		2,800	455		3,255	3,750
2500	Branch circuit, circuit breakers, 60 amp, 600 volt, 3 pole		5.30	1.509		620	85.50		705.50	815
2520	240, 480 or 600 volt, 1 pole		8	1		100	56.50		156.50	195
2540	240 volt, 2 pole		7	1.143		231	64.50		295.50	350
2560	480 or 600 volt, 2 pole		7	1.143		365	64.50		429.50	495
2580	240 volt, 3 pole		5.30	1.509		560	85.50		645.50	745
2600	480 volt, 3 pole		5.30	1.509		485	85.50		570.50	665
2620	100 amp, 600 volt, 2 pole		5	1.600		465	90.50		555.50	650
2640	3 pole		4	2		590	113		703	820
2660	480 volt, 2 pole		5	1.600		400	90.50		490.50	575
2680	240 volt, 2 pole		5	1.600		229	90.50		319.50	390
2700	3 pole		4	2		370	113		483	575
2720	480 volt, 3 pole		4	2		540	113		653	765
2740	225 amp, 240, 480 or 600 volt, 2 pole		3.50	2.286		610	129		739	870
2760	3 pole		3.20	2.500		705	142		847	985
2780	400 amp, 240, 480 or 600 volt, 2 pole		2.50	3.200		1,400	181		1,581	1,825
2800	3 pole		2.30	3.478		1,625	197		1,822	2,100
2820	600 amp, 240 or 480 volt, 2 pole		1.80	4.444		2,300	252		2,552	2,900
2840	3 pole		1.60	5		2,825	283		3,108	3,525
2860	800 amp, 240, 480 or 600 volt, 2 pole		1.50	5.333		3,450	300		3,750	4,250
2880	3 pole		1.30	6.154		4,025	350		4,375	4,950
2900	1000 amp, 240, 480 or 600 volt, 2 pole		1.10	7.273		4,225	410		4,635	5,275
2920	480 or 600 volt, 3 pole		1	8		4,850	455		5,305	6,025
2940	1200 amp, 240, 480 or 600 volt, 2 pole		.90	8.889		5,975	505		6,480	7,325
2960	3 pole		.80	10		6,525	565		7,090	8,025
2980	600 volt, 3 pole		.80	10		6,525	565		7,090	8,025

For customer support on your Electrical Costs with RSMeans Data, call 800.448.8182.

221

26 24 16 – Panelboards

26 24 16.10 Load Centers	Crew	Daily Output	Labor-Hours	Unit	Material	2017 Bare Costs Labor	2017 Bare Costs Equipment	Total	Total Incl O&P
0010 **LOAD CENTERS** (residential type) R262416-50									
0100 3 wire, 120/240 V, 1 phase, including 1 pole plug-in breakers									
0200 100 amp main lugs, indoor, 8 circuits	1 Elec	1.40	5.714	Ea.	126	325		451	625
0300 12 circuits		1.20	6.667		213	375		588	800
0400 Rainproof, 8 circuits		1.40	5.714		155	325		480	655
0500 12 circuits		1.20	6.667		166	375		541	750
0600 200 amp main lugs, indoor, 16 circuits	R-1A	1.80	8.889		214	455		669	915
0700 20 circuits		1.50	10.667		254	545		799	1,100
0800 24 circuits		1.30	12.308		305	625		930	1,275
0900 30 circuits		1.20	13.333		360	680		1,040	1,425
1000 40 circuits		.80	20		495	1,025		1,520	2,075
1200 Rainproof, 16 circuits		1.80	8.889		248	455		703	950
1300 20 circuits		1.50	10.667		287	545		832	1,125
1400 24 circuits		1.30	12.308		350	625		975	1,325
1500 30 circuits		1.20	13.333		410	680		1,090	1,475
1600 40 circuits		.80	20		530	1,025		1,555	2,100
1800 400 amp main lugs, indoor, 42 circuits		.72	22.222		1,325	1,125		2,450	3,150
1900 Rainproof, 42 circuits		.72	22.222		1,750	1,125		2,875	3,625
2200 Plug in breakers, 20 amp, 1 pole, 4 wire, 120/208 volts									
2210 125 amp main lugs, indoor, 12 circuits	1 Elec	1.20	6.667	Ea.	175	375		550	755
2300 18 circuits		.80	10		254	565		819	1,125
2400 Rainproof, 12 circuits		1.20	6.667		197	375		572	780
2500 18 circuits		.80	10		260	565		825	1,125
2600 200 amp main lugs, indoor, 24 circuits	R-1A	1.30	12.308		330	625		955	1,300
2700 30 circuits		1.20	13.333		400	680		1,080	1,475
2800 36 circuits		1	16		485	815		1,300	1,750
2900 42 circuits		.80	20		545	1,025		1,570	2,125
3000 Rainproof, 24 circuits		1.30	12.308		360	625		985	1,325
3100 30 circuits		1.20	13.333		420	680		1,100	1,475
3200 36 circuits		1	16		540	815		1,355	1,825
3300 42 circuits		.80	20		600	1,025		1,625	2,175
3500 400 amp main lugs, indoor, 42 circuits		.72	22.222		1,375	1,125		2,500	3,200
3600 Rainproof, 42 circuits		.72	22.222		1,750	1,125		2,875	3,625
3700 Plug-in breakers, 20 amp, 1 pole, 3 wire, 120/240 volts									
3800 100 amp main breaker, indoor, 12 circuits	1 Elec	1.20	6.667	Ea.	153	375		528	735
3900 18 circuits	"	.80	10		221	565		786	1,100
4000 200 amp main breaker, indoor, 20 circuits	R-1A	1.50	10.667		267	545		812	1,100
4200 24 circuits		1.30	12.308		335	625		960	1,300
4300 30 circuits		1.20	13.333		385	680		1,065	1,450
4400 40 circuits		.90	17.778		495	905		1,400	1,900
4500 Rainproof, 20 circuits		1.50	10.667		290	545		835	1,125
4600 24 circuits		1.30	12.308		355	625		980	1,325
4700 30 circuits		1.20	13.333		415	680		1,095	1,475
4800 40 circuits		.90	17.778		530	905		1,435	1,925
5000 400 amp main breaker, indoor, 42 circuits		.72	22.222		3,050	1,125		4,175	5,075
5100 Rainproof, 42 circuits		.72	22.222		3,575	1,125		4,700	5,625
5300 Plug in breakers, 20 amp, 1 pole, 4 wire, 120/208 volts									
5400 200 amp main breaker, indoor, 30 circuits	R-1A	1.20	13.333	Ea.	505	680		1,185	1,575
5500 42 circuits		.80	20		635	1,025		1,660	2,225
5600 Rainproof, 30 circuits		1.20	13.333		575	680		1,255	1,650
5700 42 circuits		.80	20		700	1,025		1,725	2,300

26 24 16 – Panelboards

26 24 16.20 Panelboard and Load Center Circuit Breakers	Crew	Daily Output	Labor-Hours	Unit	Material	2017 Bare Costs Labor	Equipment	Total	Total Incl O&P
0010 **PANELBOARD AND LOAD CENTER CIRCUIT BREAKERS** R262416-50									
0050 Bolt-on, 10,000 amp I.C., 120 volt, 1 pole									
0100 15 to 50 amp	1 Elec	10	.800	Ea.	19.60	45.50		65.10	89.50
0200 60 amp		8	1		19.20	56.50		75.70	106
0300 70 amp	↓	8	1	↓	28	56.50		84.50	116
0350 240 volt, 2 pole									
0400 15 to 50 amp	1 Elec	8	1	Ea.	84	56.50		140.50	178
0500 60 amp		7.50	1.067		57.50	60.50		118	154
0600 80 to 100 amp		5	1.600		110	90.50		200.50	257
0700 3 pole, 15 to 60 amp		6.20	1.290		136	73		209	258
0800 70 amp		5	1.600		171	90.50		261.50	325
0900 80 to 100 amp		3.60	2.222		195	126		321	405
1000 22,000 amp I.C., 240 volt, 2 pole, 70 – 225 amp		2.70	2.963		610	168		778	925
1100 3 pole, 70 – 225 amp		2.30	3.478		610	197		807	965
1200 14,000 amp I.C., 277 volts, 1 pole, 15 – 30 amp		8	1		52.50	56.50		109	143
1300 22,000 amp I.C., 480 volts, 2 pole, 70 – 225 amp		2.70	2.963		550	168		718	855
1400 3 pole, 70 – 225 amp		2.30	3.478		770	197		967	1,150
2000 Plug-in panel or load center, 120/240 volt, to 60 amp, 1 pole		12	.667		9.90	37.50		47.40	67.50
2004 Circuit breaker, 120/240 volt, 20 A, 1 pole with NM cable		6.50	1.231		16.55	69.50		86.05	122
2006 30 A, 1 pole with NM cable		6.50	1.231		16.55	69.50		86.05	122
2010 2 pole		9	.889		26	50.50		76.50	104
2014 50 A, 2 pole with NM cable		5.50	1.455		32.50	82.50		115	159
2020 3 pole		7.50	1.067		77.50	60.50		138	176
2030 100 amp, 2 pole		6	1.333		104	75.50		179.50	227
2040 3 pole		4.50	1.778		115	101		216	278
2050 150 to 200 amp, 2 pole		3	2.667		218	151		369	465
2060 Plug-in tandem, 120/240 V, 2-15 A, 1 pole		11	.727		37.50	41		78.50	103
2070 1-15 A & 1-20 A		11	.727		37.50	41		78.50	103
2080 2-20 A		11	.727		37.50	41		78.50	103
2082 Arc fault circuit interrupter, 120/240 V, 1-15 A & 1-20 A, 1 pole		11	.727		103	41		144	176
2100 High interrupting capacity, 120/240 volt, plug-in, 30 amp, 1 pole		12	.667		17.60	37.50		55.10	76
2110 60 amp, 2 pole		9	.889		29.50	50.50		80	108
2120 3 pole		7.50	1.067		207	60.50		267.50	320
2130 100 amp, 2 pole		6	1.333		176	75.50		251.50	305
2140 3 pole		4.50	1.778		296	101		397	475
2150 125 amp, 2 pole		3	2.667		970	151		1,121	1,300
2200 Bolt-on, 30 amp, 1 pole		10	.800		36	45.50		81.50	108
2210 60 amp, 2 pole		7.50	1.067		70.50	60.50		131	168
2220 3 pole		6.20	1.290		189	73		262	315
2230 100 amp, 2 pole		5	1.600		240	90.50		330.50	400
2240 3 pole		3.60	2.222		274	126		400	490
2300 Ground fault, 240 volt, 30 amp, 1 pole		7	1.143		74	64.50		138.50	179
2310 2 pole		6	1.333		132	75.50		207.50	259
2350 Key operated, 240 volt, 1 pole, 30 amp		7	1.143		113	64.50		177.50	222
2360 Switched neutral, 240 volt, 30 amp, 2 pole		6	1.333		48.50	75.50		124	167
2370 3 pole		5.50	1.455		73	82.50		155.50	204
2400 Shunt trip, for 240 volt breaker, 60 amp, 1 pole		4	2		71.50	113		184.50	249
2410 2 pole		3.50	2.286		71.50	129		200.50	273
2420 3 pole		3	2.667		71.50	151		222.50	305
2430 100 amp, 2 pole		3	2.667		71.50	151		222.50	305
2440 3 pole		2.50	3.200		71.50	181		252.50	350
2450 150 amp, 2 pole		2	4		170	226		396	525

For customer support on your Electrical Costs with RSMeans Data, call 800.448.8182.

223

26 24 16.20 Panelboard and Load Center Circuit Breakers	Crew	Daily Output	Labor-Hours	Unit	Material	2017 Bare Costs Labor	Equipment	Total	Total Incl O&P
2500 Auxiliary switch, for 240 volt breaker, 60 amp, 1 pole	1 Elec	4	2	Ea.	65	113		178	242
2510 2 pole		3.50	2.286		65	129		194	266
2520 3 pole		3	2.667		65	151		216	298
2530 100 amp, 2 pole		3	2.667		65	151		216	298
2540 3 pole		2.50	3.200		65	181		246	345
2550 150 amp, 2 pole		2	4		108	226		334	460
2600 Panel or load center, 277/480 volt, plug-in, 30 amp, 1 pole		12	.667		52.50	37.50		90	114
2610 60 amp, 2 pole		9	.889		157	50.50		207.50	249
2620 3 pole		7.50	1.067		230	60.50		290.50	345
2650 Bolt-on, 60 amp, 2 pole		7.50	1.067		157	60.50		217.50	264
2660 3 pole		6.20	1.290		230	73		303	360
2700 I-line, 277/480 volt, 30 amp, 1 pole		8	1		60	56.50		116.50	151
2710 60 amp, 2 pole		7.50	1.067		211	60.50		271.50	325
2720 3 pole		6.20	1.290		274	73		347	410
2730 100 amp, 1 pole		7.50	1.067		116	60.50		176.50	218
2740 2 pole		5	1.600		274	90.50		364.50	435
2750 3 pole		3.50	2.286		325	129		454	550
2800 High interrupting capacity, 277/480 volt, plug-in, 30 amp, 1 pole		12	.667		305	37.50		342.50	390
2810 60 amp, 2 pole		9	.889		465	50.50		515.50	590
2820 3 pole		7	1.143		545	64.50		609.50	695
2830 Bolt-on, 30 amp, 1 pole		8	1		305	56.50		361.50	420
2840 60 amp, 2 pole		7.50	1.067		615	60.50		675.50	765
2850 3 pole		6.20	1.290		690	73		763	870
2900 I-line, 30 amp, 1 pole		8	1		305	56.50		361.50	420
2910 60 amp, 2 pole		7.50	1.067		430	60.50		490.50	565
2920 3 pole		6.20	1.290		480	73		553	635
2930 100 amp, 1 pole		7.50	1.067		490	60.50		550.50	630
2940 2 pole		5	1.600		490	90.50		580.50	675
2950 3 pole		3.60	2.222		540	126		666	785
2960 Shunt trip, 277/480 volt breaker, remote oper., 30 amp, 1 pole		4	2		325	113		438	525
2970 60 amp, 2 pole		3.50	2.286		475	129		604	720
2980 3 pole		3	2.667		540	151		691	815
2990 100 amp, 1 pole		3.50	2.286		380	129		509	615
3000 2 pole		3	2.667		540	151		691	815
3010 3 pole		2.50	3.200		590	181		771	915
3050 Under voltage trip, 277/480 volt breaker, 30 amp, 1 pole		4	2		325	113		438	525
3060 60 amp, 2 pole		3.50	2.286		475	129		604	720
3070 3 pole		3	2.667		540	151		691	815
3080 100 amp, 1 pole		3.50	2.286		380	129		509	615
3090 2 pole		3	2.667		540	151		691	815
3100 3 pole		2.50	3.200		590	181		771	915
3150 Motor operated, 277/480 volt breaker, 30 amp, 1 pole		4	2		575	113		688	805
3160 60 amp, 2 pole		3.50	2.286		730	129		859	995
3170 3 pole		3	2.667		790	151		941	1,100
3180 100 amp, 1 pole		3.50	2.286		630	129		759	890
3190 2 pole		3	2.667		790	151		941	1,100
3200 3 pole		2.50	3.200		840	181		1,021	1,200
3250 Panelboard spacers, per pole		40	.200		3.82	11.30		15.12	21
5110 NEMA 1 enclosure only, 600V, 3 p, 14k AIC, 100A		2.20	3.636		164	206		370	490

26 24 16.30 Panelboards Commercial Applications

0010	PANELBOARDS COMMERCIAL APPLICATIONS	R262416-50							
0050	NQOD, w/20 amp 1 pole bolt-on circuit breakers								

26 24 Switchboards and Panelboards

26 24 16 – Panelboards

26 24 16.30 Panelboards Commercial Applications	Crew	Daily Output	Labor-Hours	Unit	Material	2017 Bare Costs Labor	Equipment	Total	Total Incl O&P
0100	3 wire, 120/240 volts, 100 amp main lugs									
0150	10 circuits	1 Elec	1	8	Ea.	735	455		1,190	1,500
0200	14 circuits		.88	9.091		815	515		1,330	1,675
0250	18 circuits		.75	10.667		885	605		1,490	1,875
0300	20 circuits		.65	12.308		995	695		1,690	2,150
0350	225 amp main lugs, 24 circuits	2 Elec	1.20	13.333		1,125	755		1,880	2,350
0400	30 circuits		.90	17.778		1,300	1,000		2,300	2,925
0450	36 circuits		.80	20		1,475	1,125		2,600	3,325
0500	38 circuits		.72	22.222		1,600	1,250		2,850	3,650
0550	42 circuits		.66	24.242		1,650	1,375		3,025	3,875
0600	4 wire, 120/208 volts, 100 amp main lugs, 12 circuits	1 Elec	1	8		785	455		1,240	1,550
0650	16 circuits		.75	10.667		905	605		1,510	1,900
0700	20 circuits		.65	12.308		1,050	695		1,745	2,200
0750	24 circuits		.60	13.333		1,025	755		1,780	2,250
0800	30 circuits		.53	15.094		1,300	855		2,155	2,700
0850	225 amp main lugs, 32 circuits	2 Elec	.90	17.778		1,450	1,000		2,450	3,100
0900	34 circuits		.84	19.048		1,475	1,075		2,550	3,250
0950	36 circuits		.80	20		1,525	1,125		2,650	3,375
1000	42 circuits		.68	23.529		1,700	1,325		3,025	3,875
1010	400 amp main lugs, 42 circs		.68	23.529		1,700	1,325		3,025	3,875
1040	225 amp main lugs, NEMA 7, 12 circuits		1	16		4,600	905		5,505	6,400
1100	24 circuits		.40	40		5,550	2,275		7,825	9,500
1200	NEHB, w/20 amp, 1 pole bolt-on circuit breakers									
1250	4 wire, 277/480 volts, 100 amp main lugs, 12 circuits	1 Elec	.88	9.091	Ea.	1,325	515		1,840	2,250
1300	20 circuits	"	.60	13.333		1,975	755		2,730	3,300
1350	225 amp main lugs, 24 circuits	2 Elec	.90	17.778		2,250	1,000		3,250	3,975
1400	30 circuits		.80	20		2,700	1,125		3,825	4,650
1448	32 circuits		4.90	3.265		3,125	185		3,310	3,725
1450	36 circuits		.72	22.222		3,125	1,250		4,375	5,325
1500	42 circuits		.60	26.667		3,575	1,500		5,075	6,175
1510	225 amp main lugs, NEMA 7, 12 circuits		.90	17.778		5,975	1,000		6,975	8,075
1590	24 circuits		.30	53.333		8,050	3,025		11,075	13,400
1600	NQOD panel, w/20 amp, 1 pole, circuit breakers									
1650	3 wire, 120/240 volt with main circuit breaker									
1700	100 amp main, 12 circuits	1 Elec	.80	10	Ea.	985	565		1,550	1,925
1750	20 circuits	"	.60	13.333		1,250	755		2,005	2,500
1800	225 amp main, 30 circuits	2 Elec	.68	23.529		2,350	1,325		3,675	4,600
1801	225 amp main, 32 circuits		5	3.200		2,350	181		2,531	2,875
1850	42 circuits		.52	30.769		2,725	1,750		4,475	5,600
1900	400 amp main, 30 circuits		.54	29.630		3,250	1,675		4,925	6,100
1950	42 circuits		.50	32		3,650	1,800		5,450	6,725
2000	4 wire, 120/208 volts with main circuit breaker									
2050	100 amp main, 24 circuits	1 Elec	.47	17.021	Ea.	1,525	965		2,490	3,125
2100	30 circuits	"	.40	20		1,650	1,125		2,775	3,525
2200	225 amp main, 32 circuits	2 Elec	.72	22.222		2,750	1,250		4,000	4,900
2250	42 circuits		.56	28.571		2,825	1,625		4,450	5,550
2300	400 amp main, 42 circuits		.48	33.333		4,025	1,875		5,900	7,250
2350	600 amp main, 42 circuits		.40	40		5,950	2,275		8,225	9,950
2400	NEHB, with 20 amp, 1 pole circuit breaker									
2450	4 wire, 277/480 volts with main circuit breaker									
2500	100 amp main, 24 circuits	1 Elec	.42	19.048	Ea.	2,600	1,075		3,675	4,475
2550	30 circuits	"	.38	21.053		3,025	1,200		4,225	5,100
2600	225 amp main, 30 circuits	2 Elec	.72	22.222		3,800	1,250		5,050	6,050

For customer support on your Electrical Costs with RSMeans Data, call 800.448.8182.

225

26 24 16.30 Panelboards Commercial Applications	Crew	Daily Output	Labor-Hours	Unit	Material	2017 Bare Costs Labor	Equipment	Total	Total Incl O&P
2650 42 circuits	2 Elec	.56	28.571	Ea.	4,675	1,625		6,300	7,575
2700 400 amp main, 42 circuits		.46	34.783		5,625	1,975		7,600	9,150
2750 600 amp main, 42 circuits	▼	.38	42.105	▼	7,700	2,375		10,075	12,100
2900 Note: the following line items don't include branch circuit breakers									
2910 For branch circuit breakers information, see Section 26 24 16.20									
3010 Main lug, no main breaker, 240 volt, 1 pole, 3 wire, 100 amp	1 Elec	2.30	3.478	Ea.	580	197		777	935
3020 225 amp	2 Elec	2.40	6.667		700	375		1,075	1,325
3030 400 amp	"	1.80	8.889		1,025	505		1,530	1,875
3060 3 pole, 3 wire, 100 amp	1 Elec	2.30	3.478		625	197		822	985
3070 225 amp	2 Elec	2.40	6.667		740	375		1,115	1,375
3080 400 amp		1.80	8.889		1,100	505		1,605	1,975
3090 600 amp	▼	1.60	10		1,275	565		1,840	2,275
3110 3 pole, 4 wire, 100 amp	1 Elec	2.30	3.478		695	197		892	1,050
3120 225 amp	2 Elec	2.40	6.667		865	375		1,240	1,525
3130 400 amp		1.80	8.889		1,100	505		1,605	1,975
3140 600 amp	▼	1.60	10		1,275	565		1,840	2,275
3160 480 volt, 3 pole, 3 wire, 100 amp	1 Elec	2.30	3.478		825	197		1,022	1,200
3170 225 amp	2 Elec	2.40	6.667		1,000	375		1,375	1,675
3180 400 amp		1.80	8.889		1,400	505		1,905	2,275
3190 600 amp	▼	1.60	10		1,550	565		2,115	2,550
3210 277/480 volt, 3 pole, 4 wire, 100 amp	1 Elec	2.30	3.478		805	197		1,002	1,175
3220 225 amp	2 Elec	2.40	6.667		975	375		1,350	1,650
3230 400 amp		1.80	8.889		1,350	505		1,855	2,250
3240 600 amp	▼	1.60	10		1,525	565		2,090	2,525
3260 Main circuit breaker, 240 volt, 1 pole, 3 wire, 100 amp	1 Elec	2	4		780	226		1,006	1,200
3270 225 amp	2 Elec	2	8		1,600	455		2,055	2,425
3280 400 amp	"	1.60	10		2,500	565		3,065	3,600
3310 3 pole, 3 wire, 100 amp	1 Elec	2	4		875	226		1,101	1,300
3320 225 amp	2 Elec	2	8		1,825	455		2,280	2,675
3330 400 amp		1.60	10		2,850	565		3,415	4,000
3360 120/208 volt, 3 pole, 4 wire, 100 amp		4	4		895	226		1,121	1,325
3370 225 amp		2	8		1,825	455		2,280	2,675
3380 400 amp	▼	1.60	10		2,850	565		3,415	4,000
3410 480 volt, 3 pole, 3 wire, 100 amp	1 Elec	2	4		1,250	226		1,476	1,725
3420 225 amp	2 Elec	2	8		2,150	455		2,605	3,025
3430 400 amp		1.60	10		3,225	565		3,790	4,375
3460 277/480 volt, 3 pole, 4 wire, 100 amp		4	4		1,225	226		1,451	1,700
3470 225 amp		2	8		2,100	455		2,555	2,975
3480 400 amp	▼	1.60	10		3,225	565		3,790	4,400
3510 Main circuit breaker, HIC, 240 volt, 1 pole, 3 wire, 100 amp	1 Elec	2	4		1,200	226		1,426	1,650
3520 225 amp	2 Elec	2	8		3,125	455		3,580	4,100
3530 400 amp	"	1.60	10		4,175	565		4,740	5,450
3560 3 pole, 3 wire, 100 amp	1 Elec	2	4		1,325	226		1,551	1,800
3570 225 amp	2 Elec	2	8		3,525	455		3,980	4,550
3580 400 amp	"	1.60	10		4,650	565		5,215	5,975
3610 120/208 volt, 3 pole, 4 wire, 100 amp	1 Elec	2	4		1,325	226		1,551	1,800
3620 225 amp	2 Elec	2	8		3,525	455		3,980	4,550
3630 400 amp	"	1.60	10		4,650	565		5,215	5,975
3660 480 volt, 3 pole, 3 wire, 100 amp	1 Elec	2	4		1,975	226		2,201	2,525
3670 225 amp	2 Elec	2	8		3,900	455		4,355	4,975
3680 400 amp	"	1.60	10		4,975	565		5,540	6,325
3710 277/480 volt, 3 pole, 4 wire, 100 amp	1 Elec	2	4		1,875	226		2,101	2,425
3720 225 amp	2 Elec	2	8		3,725	455		4,180	4,775

26 24 16 – Panelboards

26 24 16.30 Panelboards Commercial Applications

		Crew	Daily Output	Labor-Hours	Unit	Material	2017 Bare Costs Labor	Equipment	Total	Total Incl O&P
3730	400 amp	2 Elec	1.60	10	Ea.	4,925	565		5,490	6,275
3760	Main circuit breaker, shunt trip, 100 amp	1 Elec	1.20	6.667		1,000	375		1,375	1,675
3770	225 amp	2 Elec	1.60	10		2,300	565		2,865	3,375
3780	400 amp	"	1.40	11.429		3,350	645		3,995	4,650

26 24 19 – Motor-Control Centers

26 24 19.20 Motor Control Center Components

		Crew	Daily Output	Labor-Hours	Unit	Material	2017 Bare Costs Labor	Equipment	Total	Total Incl O&P
0010	**MOTOR CONTROL CENTER COMPONENTS** R262419-60									
0100	Starter, size 1, FVNR, NEMA 1, type A, fusible	1 Elec	2.70	2.963	Ea.	1,425	168		1,593	1,800
0120	Circuit breaker		2.70	2.963		1,550	168		1,718	1,950
0140	Type B, fusible		2.70	2.963		1,550	168		1,718	1,975
0160	Circuit breaker		2.70	2.963		1,700	168		1,868	2,125
0180	NEMA 12, type A, fusible		2.60	3.077		1,450	174		1,624	1,825
0200	Circuit breaker		2.60	3.077		1,575	174		1,749	1,975
0220	Type B, fusible		2.60	3.077		1,575	174		1,749	2,000
0240	Circuit breaker		2.60	3.077		1,725	174		1,899	2,150
0300	Starter, size 1, FVR, NEMA 1, type A, fusible		2	4		2,025	226		2,251	2,575
0320	Circuit breaker		2	4		2,025	226		2,251	2,575
0340	Type B, fusible		2	4		2,225	226		2,451	2,800
0360	Circuit breaker		2	4		2,225	226		2,451	2,800
0380	NEMA 12, type A, fusible		1.90	4.211		2,050	238		2,288	2,625
0400	Circuit breaker		1.90	4.211		2,050	238		2,288	2,625
0420	Type B, fusible		1.90	4.211		2,250	238		2,488	2,825
0440	Circuit breaker		1.90	4.211		2,250	238		2,488	2,825
0490	Starter size 1, 2 speed, separate winding									
0500	NEMA 1, type A, fusible	1 Elec	2.60	3.077	Ea.	2,675	174		2,849	3,200
0520	Circuit breaker		2.60	3.077		2,675	174		2,849	3,200
0540	Type B, fusible		2.60	3.077		2,950	174		3,124	3,500
0560	Circuit breaker		2.60	3.077		2,950	174		3,124	3,500
0580	NEMA 12, type A, fusible		2.50	3.200		2,725	181		2,906	3,275
0600	Circuit breaker		2.50	3.200		2,725	181		2,906	3,275
0620	Type B, fusible		2.50	3.200		3,000	181		3,181	3,575
0640	Circuit breaker		2.50	3.200		3,000	181		3,181	3,575
0650	Starter size 1, 2 speed, consequent pole									
0660	NEMA 1, type A, fusible	1 Elec	2.60	3.077	Ea.	2,675	174		2,849	3,200
0680	Circuit breaker		2.60	3.077		2,675	174		2,849	3,200
0700	Type B, fusible		2.60	3.077		2,950	174		3,124	3,500
0720	Circuit breaker		2.60	3.077		2,950	174		3,124	3,500
0740	NEMA 12, type A, fusible		2.50	3.200		2,725	181		2,906	3,275
0760	Circuit breaker		2.50	3.200		2,725	181		2,906	3,275
0780	Type B, fusible		2.50	3.200		2,975	181		3,156	3,550
0800	Circuit breaker		2.50	3.200		3,000	181		3,181	3,575
0810	Starter size 1, 2 speed, space only									
0820	NEMA 1, type A, fusible	1 Elec	16	.500	Ea.	600	28.50		628.50	705
0840	Circuit breaker		16	.500		600	28.50		628.50	705
0860	Type B, fusible		16	.500		600	28.50		628.50	705
0880	Circuit breaker		16	.500		600	28.50		628.50	705
0900	NEMA 12, type A, fusible		15	.533		625	30		655	735
0920	Circuit breaker		15	.533		625	30		655	735
0940	Type B, fusible		15	.533		625	30		655	735
0960	Circuit breaker		15	.533		625	30		655	735
1100	Starter size 2, FVNR, NEMA 1, type A, fusible	2 Elec	4	4		1,600	226		1,826	2,100
1120	Circuit breaker		4	4		1,750	226		1,976	2,275

For customer support on your Electrical Costs with RSMeans Data, call 800.448.8182.

227

26 24 19 – Motor-Control Centers

26 24 19.20 Motor Control Center Components	Crew	Daily Output	Labor-Hours	Unit	Material	2017 Bare Costs Labor	Equipment	Total	Total Incl O&P
1140	Type B, fusible	2 Elec	4	4	Ea.	1,750	226		1,976	2,300
1160	Circuit breaker		4	4		1,925	226		2,151	2,450
1180	NEMA 12, type A, fusible		3.80	4.211		1,625	238		1,863	2,150
1200	Circuit breaker		3.80	4.211		1,775	238		2,013	2,300
1220	Type B, fusible		3.80	4.211		1,775	238		2,013	2,300
1240	Circuit breaker		3.80	4.211		1,950	238		2,188	2,500
1300	FVR, NEMA 1, type A, fusible		3.20	5		2,700	283		2,983	3,400
1320	Circuit breaker		3.20	5		2,700	283		2,983	3,400
1340	Type B, fusible		3.20	5		2,975	283		3,258	3,700
1360	Circuit breaker		3.20	5		2,975	283		3,258	3,700
1380	NEMA type 12, type A, fusible		3	5.333		2,750	300		3,050	3,475
1400	Circuit breaker		3	5.333		2,750	300		3,050	3,475
1420	Type B, fusible		3	5.333		3,025	300		3,325	3,775
1440	Circuit breaker		3	5.333		3,025	300		3,325	3,775
1490	Starter size 2, 2 speed, separate winding									
1500	NEMA 1, type A, fusible	2 Elec	3.80	4.211	Ea.	3,025	238		3,263	3,675
1520	Circuit breaker		3.80	4.211		3,025	238		3,263	3,675
1540	Type B, fusible		3.80	4.211		3,325	238		3,563	4,000
1560	Circuit breaker		3.80	4.211		3,325	238		3,563	4,000
1570	NEMA 12, type A, fusible		3.60	4.444		3,075	252		3,327	3,750
1580	Circuit breaker		3.60	4.444		3,075	252		3,327	3,750
1600	Type B, fusible		3.60	4.444		3,375	252		3,627	4,100
1620	Circuit breaker		3.60	4.444		3,375	252		3,627	4,100
1630	Starter size 2, 2 speed, consequent pole									
1640	NEMA 1, type A, fusible	2 Elec	3.80	4.211	Ea.	3,425	238		3,663	4,125
1660	Circuit breaker		3.80	4.211		3,425	238		3,663	4,125
1680	Type B, fusible		3.80	4.211		3,625	238		3,863	4,350
1700	Circuit breaker		3.80	4.211		3,625	238		3,863	4,350
1720	NEMA 12, type A, fusible		3.80	4.211		3,450	238		3,688	4,150
1740	Circuit breaker		3.60	4.444		3,475	252		3,727	4,200
1760	Type B, fusible		3.60	4.444		3,675	252		3,927	4,425
1780	Circuit breaker		3.60	4.444		3,675	252		3,927	4,425
1830	Starter size 2, autotransformer									
1840	NEMA 1, type A, fusible	2 Elec	3.40	4.706	Ea.	5,350	266		5,616	6,300
1860	Circuit breaker		3.40	4.706		5,475	266		5,741	6,425
1880	Type B, fusible		3.40	4.706		5,850	266		6,116	6,850
1900	Circuit breaker		3.40	4.706		5,850	266		6,116	6,850
1920	NEMA 12, type A, fusible		3.20	5		5,450	283		5,733	6,425
1940	Circuit breaker		3.20	5		5,450	283		5,733	6,425
1960	Type B, fusible		3.20	5		5,950	283		6,233	6,975
1980	Circuit breaker		3.20	5		5,950	283		6,233	6,975
2030	Starter size 2, space only									
2040	NEMA 1, type A, fusible	1 Elec	16	.500	Ea.	600	28.50		628.50	705
2060	Circuit breaker		16	.500		600	28.50		628.50	705
2080	Type B, fusible		16	.500		600	28.50		628.50	705
2100	Circuit breaker		16	.500		600	28.50		628.50	705
2120	NEMA 12, type A, fusible		15	.533		625	30		655	735
2140	Circuit breaker		15	.533		625	30		655	735
2160	Type B, fusible		15	.533		625	30		655	735
2180	Circuit breaker		15	.533		625	30		655	735
2300	Starter size 3, FVNR, NEMA 1, type A, fusible	2 Elec	2	8		3,050	455		3,505	4,025
2320	Circuit breaker		2	8		2,700	455		3,155	3,650
2340	Type B, fusible		2	8		3,350	455		3,805	4,375

26 24 19 – Motor-Control Centers

26 24 19.20 Motor Control Center Components	Crew	Daily Output	Labor-Hours	Unit	Material	2017 Bare Costs Labor	Equipment	Total	Total Incl O&P
2360	Circuit breaker	2 Elec	2	8	Ea.	3,000	455		3,455	3,950
2380	NEMA 12, type A, fusible		1.90	8.421		3,100	475		3,575	4,150
2400	Circuit breaker		1.90	8.421		2,750	475		3,225	3,750
2420	Type B, fusible		1.90	8.421		3,475	475		3,950	4,550
2440	Circuit breaker		1.90	8.421		3,025	475		3,500	4,075
2500	Starter size 3, FVR, NEMA 1, type A, fusible		1.60	10		4,150	565		4,715	5,425
2520	Circuit breaker		1.60	10		3,975	565		4,540	5,225
2540	Type B, fusible		1.60	10		4,525	565		5,090	5,825
2560	Circuit breaker		1.60	10		4,350	565		4,915	5,625
2580	NEMA 12, type A, fusible		1.50	10.667		4,250	605		4,855	5,575
2600	Circuit breaker		1.50	10.667		4,050	605		4,655	5,350
2620	Type B, fusible		1.50	10.667		4,625	605		5,230	5,975
2640	Circuit breaker		1.50	10.667		4,775	605		5,380	6,175
2690	Starter size 3, 2 speed, separate winding									
2700	NEMA 1, type A, fusible	2 Elec	2	8	Ea.	4,775	455		5,230	5,925
2720	Circuit breaker		2	8		4,225	455		4,680	5,325
2740	Type B, fusible		2	8		5,225	455		5,680	6,425
2760	Circuit breaker		2	8		4,625	455		5,080	5,750
2780	NEMA 12, type A, fusible		1.90	8.421		4,875	475		5,350	6,100
2800	Circuit breaker		1.90	8.421		4,300	475		4,775	5,475
2820	Type B, fusible		1.90	8.421		5,325	475		5,800	6,600
2840	Circuit breaker		1.90	8.421		4,700	475		5,175	5,900
2850	Starter size 3, 2 speed, consequent pole									
2860	NEMA 1, type A, fusible	2 Elec	2	8	Ea.	5,350	455		5,805	6,550
2880	Circuit breaker		2	8		4,775	455		5,230	5,925
2900	Type B, fusible		2	8		5,800	455		6,255	7,050
2920	Circuit breaker		2	8		5,175	455		5,630	6,375
2940	NEMA 12, type A, fusible		1.90	8.421		5,425	475		5,900	6,700
2960	Circuit breaker		1.90	8.421		4,875	475		5,350	6,075
2980	Type B, fusible		1.90	8.421		5,900	475		6,375	7,200
3000	Circuit breaker		1.90	8.421		5,250	475		5,725	6,525
3100	Starter size 3, autotransformer, NEMA 1, type A, fusible		1.60	10		6,700	565		7,265	8,225
3120	Circuit breaker		1.60	10		6,650	565		7,215	8,150
3140	Type B, fusible		1.60	10		7,250	565		7,815	8,825
3160	Circuit breaker		1.60	10		7,250	565		7,815	8,825
3180	NEMA 12, type A, fusible		1.50	10.667		6,775	605		7,380	8,350
3200	Circuit breaker		1.50	10.667		6,775	605		7,380	8,350
3220	Type B, fusible		1.50	10.667		7,375	605		7,980	9,025
3240	Circuit breaker		1.50	10.667		7,375	605		7,980	9,025
3260	Starter size 3, space only, NEMA 1, type A, fusible	1 Elec	15	.533		1,025	30		1,055	1,175
3280	Circuit breaker		15	.533		800	30		830	925
3300	Type B, fusible		15	.533		1,025	30		1,055	1,175
3320	Circuit breaker		15	.533		800	30		830	925
3340	NEMA 12, type A, fusible		14	.571		1,100	32.50		1,132.50	1,250
3360	Circuit breaker		14	.571		850	32.50		882.50	985
3380	Type B, fusible		14	.571		1,100	32.50		1,132.50	1,250
3400	Circuit breaker		14	.571		850	32.50		882.50	985
3500	Starter size 4, FVNR, NEMA 1, type A, fusible	2 Elec	1.60	10		3,975	565		4,540	5,225
3520	Circuit breaker		1.60	10		3,600	565		4,165	4,825
3540	Type B, fusible		1.60	10		4,350	565		4,915	5,625
3560	Circuit breaker		1.60	10		3,975	565		4,540	5,225
3580	NEMA 12, type A, fusible		1.50	10.667		4,075	605		4,680	5,375
3600	Circuit breaker		1.50	10.667		3,675	605		4,280	4,925

For customer support on your Electrical Costs with RSMeans Data, call 800.448.8182.

229

26 24 19 – Motor-Control Centers

26 24 19.20 Motor Control Center Components	Crew	Daily Output	Labor-Hours	Unit	Material	2017 Bare Costs Labor	Equipment	Total	Total Incl O&P
3620	Type B, fusible	2 Elec	1.50	10.667	Ea.	4,450	605		5,055	5,775
3640	Circuit breaker		1.50	10.667		4,025	605		4,630	5,350
3700	Starter size 4, FVR, NEMA 1, type A, fusible		1.20	13.333		5,425	755		6,180	7,100
3720	Circuit breaker		1.20	13.333		4,900	755		5,655	6,525
3740	Type B, fusible		1.20	13.333		5,925	755		6,680	7,650
3760	Circuit breaker		1.20	13.333		5,400	755		6,155	7,050
3780	NEMA 12, type A, fusible		1.16	13.793		5,550	780		6,330	7,300
3800	Circuit breaker		1.16	13.793		4,975	780		5,755	6,650
3820	Type B, fusible		1.16	13.793		5,025	780		5,805	6,700
3840	Circuit breaker	▼	1.16	13.793	▼	5,475	780		6,255	7,175
3890	Starter size 4, 2 speed, separate windings									
3900	NEMA 1, type A, fusible	2 Elec	1.60	10	Ea.	6,850	565		7,415	8,400
3920	Circuit breaker		1.60	10		5,150	565		5,715	6,525
3940	Type B, fusible		1.60	10		7,525	565		8,090	9,150
3960	Circuit breaker		1.60	10		5,650	565		6,215	7,050
3980	NEMA 12, type A, fusible		1.50	10.667		6,975	605		7,580	8,575
4000	Circuit breaker		1.50	10.667		5,225	605		5,830	6,650
4020	Type B, fusible		1.50	10.667		7,650	605		8,255	9,325
4040	Circuit breaker	▼	1.50	10.667	▼	5,725	605		6,330	7,200
4050	Starter size 4, 2 speed, consequent pole									
4060	NEMA 1, type A, fusible	2 Elec	1.60	10	Ea.	8,000	565		8,565	9,650
4080	Circuit breaker		1.60	10		5,950	565		6,515	7,400
4100	Type B, fusible		1.60	10		8,800	565		9,365	10,600
4120	Circuit breaker		1.60	10		6,525	565		7,090	8,025
4140	NEMA 12, type A, fusible		1.50	10.667		8,125	605		8,730	9,850
4160	Circuit breaker		1.50	10.667		6,050	605		6,655	7,550
4180	Type B, fusible		1.50	10.667		8,925	605		9,530	10,700
4200	Circuit breaker		1.50	10.667		6,625	605		7,230	8,175
4300	Starter size 4, autotransformer, NEMA 1, type A, fusible		1.30	12.308		7,875	695		8,570	9,725
4320	Circuit breaker		1.30	12.308		7,950	695		8,645	9,800
4340	Type B, fusible		1.30	12.308		8,675	695		9,370	10,600
4360	Circuit breaker		1.30	12.308		8,675	695		9,370	10,600
4380	NEMA 12, type A, fusible		1.24	12.903		8,025	730		8,755	9,925
4400	Circuit breaker		1.24	12.903		8,050	730		8,780	9,975
4420	Type B, fusible		1.24	12.903		8,825	730		9,555	10,800
4440	Circuit breaker	▼	1.24	12.903		8,800	730		9,530	10,800
4500	Starter size 4, space only, NEMA 1, type A, fusible	1 Elec	14	.571		1,425	32.50		1,457.50	1,625
4520	Circuit breaker		14	.571		1,025	32.50		1,057.50	1,175
4540	Type B, fusible		14	.571		1,425	32.50		1,457.50	1,625
4560	Circuit breaker		14	.571		1,025	32.50		1,057.50	1,175
4580	NEMA 12, type A, fusible		13	.615		1,525	35		1,560	1,725
4600	Circuit breaker		13	.615		1,100	35		1,135	1,250
4620	Type B, fusible		13	.615		1,525	35		1,560	1,725
4640	Circuit breaker	▼	13	.615		1,100	35		1,135	1,250
4800	Starter size 5, FVNR, NEMA 1, type A, fusible	2 Elec	1	16		8,200	905		9,105	10,400
4820	Circuit breaker		1	16		5,825	905		6,730	7,750
4840	Type B, fusible		1	16		9,000	905		9,905	11,300
4860	Circuit breaker		1	16		6,400	905		7,305	8,400
4880	NEMA 12, type A, fusible		.96	16.667		8,325	945		9,270	10,600
4900	Circuit breaker		.96	16.667		5,925	945		6,870	7,950
4920	Type B, fusible		.96	16.667		9,125	945		10,070	11,400
4940	Circuit breaker		.96	16.667		6,525	945		7,470	8,600
5000	Starter size 5, FVR, NEMA 1, type A, fusible	▼	.80	20	▼	12,100	1,125		13,225	15,000

For customer support on your Electrical Costs with RSMeans Data, call 800.448.8182.

26 24 19 – Motor-Control Centers

26 24 19.20 Motor Control Center Components		Crew	Daily Output	Labor-Hours	Unit	Material	2017 Bare Costs Labor	Equipment	Total	Total Incl O&P
5020	Circuit breaker	2 Elec	.80	20	Ea.	9,500	1,125		10,625	12,100
5040	Type B, fusible		.80	20		13,200	1,125		14,325	16,300
5060	Circuit breaker		.80	20		10,400	1,125		11,525	13,200
5080	NEMA 12, type A, fusible		.76	21.053		12,300	1,200		13,500	15,400
5100	Circuit breaker		.76	21.053		9,625	1,200		10,825	12,400
5120	Type B, fusible		.76	21.053		13,500	1,200		14,700	16,600
5140	Circuit breaker		.76	21.053		10,600	1,200		11,800	13,400
5190	Starter size 5, 2 speed, separate windings									
5200	NEMA 1, type A, fusible	2 Elec	1	16	Ea.	16,700	905		17,605	19,700
5220	Circuit breaker		1	16		12,400	905		13,305	15,100
5240	Type B, fusible		1	16		18,300	905		19,205	21,500
5260	Circuit breaker		1	16		13,700	905		14,605	16,400
5280	NEMA 12, type A, fusible		.96	16.667		16,900	945		17,845	20,000
5300	Circuit breaker		.96	16.667		12,600	945		13,545	15,200
5320	Type B, fusible		.96	16.667		18,500	945		19,445	21,800
5340	Circuit breaker		.96	16.667		13,800	945		14,745	16,600
5400	Starter size 5, autotransformer, NEMA 1, type A, fusible		.70	22.857		13,600	1,300		14,900	17,000
5420	Circuit breaker		.70	22.857		11,300	1,300		12,600	14,500
5440	Type B, fusible		.70	22.857		15,000	1,300		16,300	18,500
5460	Circuit breaker		.70	22.857		12,400	1,300		13,700	15,700
5480	NEMA 12, type A, fusible		.68	23.529		13,800	1,325		15,125	17,200
5500	Circuit breaker		.68	23.529		11,400	1,325		12,725	14,600
5520	Type B, fusible		.68	23.529		15,100	1,325		16,425	18,600
5540	Circuit breakers		.68	23.529		12,600	1,325		13,925	15,800
5600	Starter size 5, space only, NEMA 1, type A, fusible	1 Elec	12	.667		1,825	37.50		1,862.50	2,075
5620	Circuit breaker		12	.667		1,825	37.50		1,862.50	2,075
5640	Type B, fusible		12	.667		1,825	37.50		1,862.50	2,075
5660	Circuit breaker		12	.667		1,200	37.50		1,237.50	1,375
5680	NEMA 12, type A, fusible		11	.727		1,950	41		1,991	2,200
5700	Circuit breaker		11	.727		1,275	41		1,316	1,450
5720	Type B, fusible		11	.727		1,950	41		1,991	2,200
5740	Circuit breaker		11	.727		1,275	41		1,316	1,450
5800	Fuse, light contactor NEMA 1, type A, 30 amp		2.70	2.963		1,650	168		1,818	2,075
5820	60 amp		2	4		1,875	226		2,101	2,400
5840	100 amp		1	8		3,550	455		4,005	4,575
5860	200 amp		.80	10		8,250	565		8,815	9,925
5880	Type B, 30 amp		2.70	2.963		1,800	168		1,968	2,225
5900	60 amp		2	4		2,000	226		2,226	2,550
5920	100 amp		1	8		3,900	455		4,355	4,975
5940	200 amp	2 Elec	1.60	10		9,025	565		9,590	10,800
5960	NEMA 12, type A, 30 amp	1 Elec	2.60	3.077		1,675	174		1,849	2,100
5980	60 amp		1.90	4.211		1,900	238		2,138	2,425
6000	100 amp		.95	8.421		3,625	475		4,100	4,700
6020	200 amp	2 Elec	1.50	10.667		8,375	605		8,980	10,100
6040	Type B, 30 amp	1 Elec	2.60	3.077		1,825	174		1,999	2,250
6060	60 amp		1.90	4.211		2,025	238		2,263	2,600
6080	100 amp		.95	8.421		3,975	475		4,450	5,100
6100	200 amp	2 Elec	1.50	10.667		9,175	605		9,780	11,000
6200	Circuit breaker, light contactor NEMA 1, type A, 30 amp	1 Elec	2.70	2.963		1,800	168		1,968	2,225
6220	60 amp		2	4		2,050	226		2,276	2,600
6240	100 amp		1	8		3,150	455		3,605	4,150
6260	200 amp	2 Elec	1.60	10		6,850	565		7,415	8,375
6280	Type B, 30 amp	1 Elec	2.70	2.963		1,975	168		2,143	2,425

For customer support on your Electrical Costs with RSMeans Data, call 800.448.8182.

231

26 24 19.20 Motor Control Center Components	Crew	Daily Output	Labor-Hours	Unit	Material	2017 Bare Costs Labor	Equipment	Total	Total Incl O&P
6300	60 amp	1 Elec	2	4	Ea.	2,250	226		2,476	2,825
6320	100 amp	▼	1	8		3,450	455		3,905	4,450
6340	200 amp	2 Elec	1.60	10		7,450	565		8,015	9,050
6360	NEMA 12, type A, 30 amp	1 Elec	2.60	3.077		1,825	174		1,999	2,250
6380	60 amp		1.90	4.211		2,075	238		2,313	2,625
6400	100 amp	▼	.95	8.421		3,225	475		3,700	4,250
6420	200 amp	2 Elec	1.50	10.667		6,875	605		7,480	8,450
6440	Type B, 30 amp	1 Elec	2.60	3.077		2,150	174		2,324	2,600
6460	60 amp		1.90	4.211		2,300	238		2,538	2,875
6480	100 amp	▼	.95	8.421		3,500	475		3,975	4,575
6500	200 amp	2 Elec	1.50	10.667		7,550	605		8,155	9,200
6600	Fusible switch, NEMA 1, type A, 30 amp	1 Elec	5.30	1.509		940	85.50		1,025.50	1,150
6620	60 amp		5	1.600		1,000	90.50		1,090.50	1,225
6640	100 amp		4	2		1,100	113		1,213	1,400
6660	200 amp	▼	3.20	2.500		1,900	142		2,042	2,300
6680	400 amp	2 Elec	4.60	3.478		4,500	197		4,697	5,250
6700	600 amp		3.20	5		4,875	283		5,158	5,775
6720	800 amp	▼	2.60	6.154		13,400	350		13,750	15,200
6740	NEMA 12, type A, 30 amp	1 Elec	5.20	1.538		965	87		1,052	1,175
6760	60 amp		4.90	1.633		1,025	92.50		1,117.50	1,275
6780	100 amp		3.90	2.051		1,125	116		1,241	1,425
6800	200 amp	▼	3.10	2.581		1,950	146		2,096	2,375
6820	400 amp	2 Elec	4.40	3.636		4,600	206		4,806	5,350
6840	600 amp		3	5.333		5,000	300		5,300	5,950
6860	800 amp	▼	2.40	6.667		13,500	375		13,875	15,400
6900	Circuit breaker, NEMA 1, type A, 30 amp	1 Elec	5.30	1.509		865	85.50		950.50	1,075
6920	60 amp		5	1.600		865	90.50		955.50	1,075
6940	100 amp		4	2		865	113		978	1,125
6960	225 amp	▼	3.20	2.500		1,550	142		1,692	1,900
6980	400 amp	2 Elec	4.60	3.478		2,925	197		3,122	3,525
7000	600 amp		3.20	5		3,425	283		3,708	4,175
7020	800 amp	▼	2.60	6.154		7,150	350		7,500	8,375
7040	NEMA 12, type A, 30 amp	1 Elec	5.20	1.538		885	87		972	1,100
7060	60 amp		4.90	1.633		885	92.50		977.50	1,125
7080	100 amp		3.90	2.051		885	116		1,001	1,150
7100	225 amp	▼	3.10	2.581		1,575	146		1,721	1,950
7120	400 amp	2 Elec	4.40	3.636		2,975	206		3,181	3,575
7140	600 amp		3	5.333		3,475	300		3,775	4,275
7160	800 amp		2.40	6.667		7,275	375		7,650	8,600
7300	Incoming line, main lug only, 600 amp, alum., NEMA 1		1.60	10		1,100	565		1,665	2,050
7320	NEMA 12		1.50	10.667		1,125	605		1,730	2,125
7340	Copper, NEMA 1		1.60	10		1,150	565		1,715	2,125
7360	800 amp, alum., NEMA 1		1.50	10.667		2,750	605		3,355	3,900
7380	NEMA 12		1.40	11.429		2,775	645		3,420	4,025
7400	Copper, NEMA 1		1.50	10.667		2,850	605		3,455	4,025
7420	1200 amp, copper, NEMA 1		1.40	11.429		2,950	645		3,595	4,200
7440	Incoming line, fusible switch, 400 amp, alum., NEMA 1		1.20	13.333		3,750	755		4,505	5,250
7460	NEMA 12		1.10	14.545		3,825	825		4,650	5,450
7480	Copper, NEMA 1		1.20	13.333		3,825	755		4,580	5,325
7500	600 amp, alum., NEMA 1		1.10	14.545		4,600	825		5,425	6,275
7520	NEMA 12		1	16		4,675	905		5,580	6,475
7540	Copper, NEMA 1		1.10	14.545		4,650	825		5,475	6,350
7560	Incoming line, circuit breaker, 225 amp, alum., NEMA 1	▼	1.20	13.333		1,950	755		2,705	3,275

For customer support on your Electrical Costs with RSMeans Data, call 800.448.8182.

26 24 19 – Motor-Control Centers

26 24 19.20 Motor Control Center Components

		Crew	Daily Output	Labor-Hours	Unit	Material	2017 Bare Costs Labor	Equipment	Total	Total Incl O&P
7580	NEMA 12	2 Elec	1.10	14.545	Ea.	2,000	825		2,825	3,425
7600	Copper, NEMA 1		1.20	13.333		2,025	755		2,780	3,350
7620	400 amp, alum., NEMA 1		1.20	13.333		2,925	755		3,680	4,350
7640	NEMA 12		1.10	14.545		2,975	825		3,800	4,500
7660	Copper, NEMA 1		1.20	13.333		2,975	755		3,730	4,400
7680	600 amp, alum., NEMA 1		1.10	14.545		3,425	825		4,250	4,975
7700	NEMA 12		1	16		3,475	905		4,380	5,175
7720	Copper, NEMA 1		1.10	14.545		3,475	825		4,300	5,050
7740	800 amp, copper, NEMA 1		.90	17.778		7,150	1,000		8,150	9,350
7760	Incoming line, for copper bus, add					108			108	119
7780	For 65000 amp bus bracing, add					160			160	176
7800	For NEMA 3R enclosure, add					5,025			5,025	5,525
7820	For NEMA 12 enclosure, add					139			139	152
7840	For 1/4" x 1" ground bus, add	1 Elec	16	.500		89.50	28.50		118	141
7860	For 1/4" x 2" ground bus, add	"	12	.667		89.50	37.50		127	155
7900	Main rating basic section, alum., NEMA 1, 800 amp	2 Elec	1.40	11.429		293	645		938	1,300
7920	1200 amp	"	1.20	13.333		575	755		1,330	1,750
7940	For copper bus, add					430			430	475
7960	For 65000 amp bus bracing, add					290			290	320
7980	For NEMA 3R enclosure, add					5,025			5,025	5,525
8000	For NEMA 12, enclosure, add					139			139	152
8020	For 1/4" x 1" ground bus, add	1 Elec	16	.500		89.50	28.50		118	141
8040	For 1/4" x 2" ground bus, add		12	.667		89.50	37.50		127	155
8060	Unit devices, pilot light, standard		16	.500		77	28.50		105.50	127
8080	Pilot light, push to test		16	.500		108	28.50		136.50	162
8100	Pilot light, standard, and push button		12	.667		185	37.50		222.50	260
8120	Pilot light, push to test, and push button		12	.667		216	37.50		253.50	294
8140	Pilot light, standard, and select switch		12	.667		185	37.50		222.50	260
8160	Pilot light, push to test, and select switch		12	.667		216	37.50		253.50	294

26 24 19.30 Motor Control Center

		Crew	Daily Output	Labor-Hours	Unit	Material	2017 Bare Costs Labor	Equipment	Total	Total Incl O&P
0010	**MOTOR CONTROL CENTER** Consists of starters & structures R262419-60									
0050	Starters, class 1, type B, comb. MCP, FVNR, with									
0100	control transformer, 10 HP, size 1, 12" high	1 Elec	2.70	2.963	Ea.	1,550	168		1,718	1,950
0200	25 HP, size 2, 18" high	2 Elec	4	4		1,750	226		1,976	2,275
0300	50 HP, size 3, 24" high		2	8		2,700	455		3,155	3,650
0350	75 HP, size 4, 24" high		1.60	10		3,600	565		4,165	4,825
0400	100 HP, size 4, 30" high		1.40	11.429		4,750	645		5,395	6,200
0500	200 HP, size 5, 48" high		1	16		7,100	905		8,005	9,150
0600	400 HP, size 6, 72" high		.80	20		14,600	1,125		15,725	17,700
0800	Structures, 600 amp, 22,000 rms, takes any									
0900	combination of starters up to 72" high	2 Elec	1.60	10	Ea.	1,800	565		2,365	2,825
1000	Back to back, 72" front & 66" back	"	1.20	13.333		2,350	755		3,105	3,725
1100	For copper bus, add per structure					240			240	264
1200	For NEMA 12, add per structure					139			139	152
1300	For 42,000 rms, add per structure					201			201	221
1400	For 100,000 rms, size 1 & 2, add					615			615	680
1500	Size 3, add					990			990	1,100
1600	Size 4, add					800			800	880
1700	For pilot lights, add per starter	1 Elec	16	.500		108	28.50		136.50	162
1800	For push button, add per starter		16	.500		108	28.50		136.50	162
1900	For auxiliary contacts, add per starter		16	.500		179	28.50		207.50	239

26 24 19.40 Motor Starters and Controls		Crew	Daily Output	Labor-Hours	Unit	Material	2017 Bare Costs Labor	Equipment	Total	Total Incl O&P
0010	**MOTOR STARTERS AND CONTROLS** R262419-65									
0050	Magnetic, FVNR, with enclosure and heaters, 480 volt									
0080	2 HP, size 00	1 Elec	3.50	2.286	Ea.	184	129		313	395
0100	5 HP, size 0		2.30	3.478		320	197		517	645
0200	10 HP, size 1	↓	1.60	5		250	283		533	700
0300	25 HP, size 2 R263413-33	2 Elec	2.20	7.273		470	410		880	1,125
0400	50 HP, size 3		1.80	8.889		765	505		1,270	1,600
0500	100 HP, size 4		1.20	13.333		1,700	755		2,455	3,000
0600	200 HP, size 5		.90	17.778		3,975	1,000		4,975	5,875
0610	400 HP, size 6	↓	.80	20		18,400	1,125		19,525	21,900
0620	NEMA 7, 5 HP, size 0	1 Elec	1.60	5		1,375	283		1,658	1,925
0630	10 HP, size 1	"	1.10	7.273		1,425	410		1,835	2,200
0640	25 HP, size 2	2 Elec	1.80	8.889		2,300	505		2,805	3,300
0650	50 HP, size 3		1.20	13.333		3,475	755		4,230	4,925
0660	100 HP, size 4		.90	17.778		5,600	1,000		6,600	7,650
0670	200 HP, size 5	↓	.50	32		13,400	1,800		15,200	17,400
0700	Combination, with motor circuit protectors, 5 HP, size 0	1 Elec	1.80	4.444		1,025	252		1,277	1,500
0800	10 HP, size 1	"	1.30	6.154		1,075	350		1,425	1,700
0900	25 HP, size 2	2 Elec	2	8		1,475	455		1,930	2,300
1000	50 HP, size 3		1.32	12.121		2,150	685		2,835	3,400
1200	100 HP, size 4	↓	.80	20		4,675	1,125		5,800	6,825
1220	NEMA 7, 5 HP, size 0	1 Elec	1.30	6.154		2,925	350		3,275	3,750
1230	10 HP, size 1	"	1	8		3,000	455		3,455	3,975
1240	25 HP, size 2	2 Elec	1.32	12.121		4,000	685		4,685	5,425
1250	50 HP, size 3		.80	20		6,625	1,125		7,750	8,975
1260	100 HP, size 4		.60	26.667		10,300	1,500		11,800	13,600
1270	200 HP, size 5	↓	.40	40		22,400	2,275		24,675	28,000
1400	Combination, with fused switch, 5 HP, size 0	1 Elec	1.80	4.444		550	252		802	980
1600	10 HP, size 1	"	1.30	6.154		590	350		940	1,175
1800	25 HP, size 2	2 Elec	2	8		960	455		1,415	1,725
2000	50 HP, size 3		1.32	12.121		1,625	685		2,310	2,800
2200	100 HP, size 4	↓	.80	20		2,825	1,125		3,950	4,800
2610	NEMA 4, with start-stop push button, size 1	1 Elec	1.30	6.154		1,475	350		1,825	2,150
2620	Size 2	2 Elec	2	8		1,975	455		2,430	2,850
2630	Size 3		1.32	12.121		3,150	685		3,835	4,475
2640	Size 4	↓	.80	20	↓	4,825	1,125		5,950	7,000
2650	NEMA 4, FVNR, including control transformer									
2660	Size 1	2 Elec	2.60	6.154	Ea.	1,575	350		1,925	2,250
2670	Size 2		2	8		2,225	455		2,680	3,125
2680	Size 3		1.32	12.121		3,550	685		4,235	4,950
2690	Size 4	↓	.80	20		5,500	1,125		6,625	7,750
2710	Magnetic, FVR, control circuit transformer, NEMA 1, size 1	1 Elec	1.30	6.154		925	350		1,275	1,550
2720	Size 2	2 Elec	2	8		1,475	455		1,930	2,300
2730	Size 3		1.32	12.121		2,250	685		2,935	3,500
2740	Size 4	↓	.80	20		4,875	1,125		6,000	7,075
2760	NEMA 4, size 1	1 Elec	1.10	7.273		1,325	410		1,735	2,075
2770	Size 2	2 Elec	1.60	10		2,125	565		2,690	3,200
2780	Size 3		1.20	13.333		3,200	755		3,955	4,650
2790	Size 4	↓	.70	22.857		6,600	1,300		7,900	9,200
2820	NEMA 12, size 1	1 Elec	1.10	7.273		1,075	410		1,485	1,825
2830	Size 2	2 Elec	1.60	10		1,725	565		2,290	2,750
2840	Size 3	↓	1.20	13.333		2,700	755		3,455	4,100

26 24 19 – Motor-Control Centers

26 24 19.40 Motor Starters and Controls		Crew	Daily Output	Labor-Hours	Unit	Material	2017 Bare Costs Labor	Equipment	Total	Total Incl O&P
2850	Size 4	2 Elec	.70	22.857	Ea.	5,575	1,300		6,875	8,075
2870	Combination FVR, fused, w/control XFMR & PB, NEMA 1, size 1	1 Elec	1	8		1,600	455		2,055	2,425
2880	Size 2	2 Elec	1.50	10.667		2,275	605		2,880	3,400
2890	Size 3		1.10	14.545		3,375	825		4,200	4,925
2900	Size 4	↓	.70	22.857		6,825	1,300		8,125	9,450
2910	NEMA 4, size 1	1 Elec	.90	8.889		2,350	505		2,855	3,350
2920	Size 2	2 Elec	1.40	11.429		3,450	645		4,095	4,750
2930	Size 3		1	16		5,425	905		6,330	7,325
2940	Size 4	↓	.60	26.667		9,000	1,500		10,500	12,200
2950	NEMA 12, size 1	1 Elec	1	8		1,800	455		2,255	2,650
2960	Size 2	2 Elec	1.40	11.429		2,550	645		3,195	3,775
2970	Size 3		1	16		3,725	905		4,630	5,450
2980	Size 4	↓	.60	26.667		7,425	1,500		8,925	10,400
3010	Manual, single phase, w/pilot, 1 pole, 120 V, NEMA 1	1 Elec	6.40	1.250		81	71		152	195
3020	NEMA 4		4	2		370	113		483	580
3030	2 pole, 120/240 V, NEMA 1		6.40	1.250		81.50	71		152.50	196
3040	NEMA 4		4	2		272	113		385	470
3041	3 phase, 3 pole, 600 V, NEMA 1		5.50	1.455		248	82.50		330.50	395
3042	NEMA 4		3.50	2.286		415	129		544	650
3043	NEMA 12	↓	3.50	2.286		276	129		405	500
3070	Auxiliary contact, normally open		↓		↓	90			90	99
3500	Magnetic FVNR with NEMA 12, enclosure & heaters, 480 volt									
3600	5 HP, size 0	1 Elec	2.20	3.636	Ea.	241	206		447	575
3700	10 HP, size 1	"	1.50	5.333		360	300		660	850
3800	25 HP, size 2	2 Elec	2	8		680	455		1,135	1,425
3900	50 HP, size 3		1.60	10		1,050	565		1,615	2,000
4000	100 HP, size 4		1	16		2,500	905		3,405	4,100
4100	200 HP, size 5	↓	.80	20		5,975	1,125		7,100	8,275
4200	Combination, with motor circuit protectors, 5 HP, size 0	1 Elec	1.70	4.706		795	266		1,061	1,275
4300	10 HP, size 1	"	1.20	6.667		830	375		1,205	1,475
4400	25 HP, size 2	2 Elec	1.80	8.889		1,250	505		1,755	2,100
4500	50 HP, size 3		1.20	13.333		2,025	755		2,780	3,350
4600	100 HP, size 4	↓	.74	21.622		4,550	1,225		5,775	6,850
4700	Combination, with fused switch, 5 HP, size 0	1 Elec	1.70	4.706		725	266		991	1,200
4800	10 HP, size 1	"	1.20	6.667		755	375		1,130	1,400
4900	25 HP, size 2	2 Elec	1.80	8.889		1,150	505		1,655	2,025
5000	50 HP, size 3		1.20	13.333		1,850	755		2,605	3,150
5100	100 HP, size 4	↓	.74	21.622	↓	3,750	1,225		4,975	5,950
5200	Factory installed controls, adders to size 0 thru 5									
5300	Start-stop push button	1 Elec	32	.250	Ea.	50.50	14.15		64.65	76.50
5400	Hand-off-auto-selector switch		32	.250		50.50	14.15		64.65	76.50
5500	Pilot light		32	.250		94.50	14.15		108.65	125
5600	Start-stop-pilot		32	.250		145	14.15		159.15	180
5700	Auxiliary contact, NO or NC		32	.250		69.50	14.15		83.65	97.50
5800	NO-NC		32	.250		139	14.15		153.15	174
5810	Magnetic FVR, NEMA 7, w/heaters, size 1	↓	.66	12.121		2,925	685		3,610	4,225
5830	Size 2	2 Elec	1.10	14.545		4,875	825		5,700	6,575
5840	Size 3		.70	22.857		7,825	1,300		9,125	10,600
5850	Size 4	↓	.60	26.667		8,900	1,500		10,400	12,100
5860	Combination w/circuit breakers, heaters, control XFMR PB, size 1	1 Elec	.60	13.333		1,550	755		2,305	2,825
5870	Size 2	2 Elec	.80	20		1,975	1,125		3,100	3,875
5880	Size 3		.50	32		2,625	1,800		4,425	5,625
5890	Size 4	↓	.40	40	↓	5,225	2,275		7,500	9,150

26 24 19.40 Motor Starters and Controls		Crew	Daily Output	Labor-Hours	Unit	Material	2017 Bare Costs Labor	Equipment	Total	Total Incl O&P
5900	Manual, 240 volt, .75 HP motor	1 Elec	4	2	Ea.	53.50	113		166.50	229
5910	2 HP motor		4	2		145	113		258	330
6000	Magnetic, 240 volt, 1 or 2 pole, .75 HP motor		4	2		180	113		293	370
6020	2 HP motor		4	2		199	113		312	390
6040	5 HP motor		3	2.667		284	151		435	540
6060	10 HP motor		2.30	3.478		705	197		902	1,075
6100	3 pole, .75 HP motor		3	2.667		184	151		335	430
6120	5 HP motor		2.30	3.478		250	197		447	570
6140	10 HP motor		1.60	5		470	283		753	940
6160	15 HP motor		1.60	5		470	283		753	940
6180	20 HP motor		1.10	7.273		765	410		1,175	1,450
6200	25 HP motor	2 Elec	2.20	7.273		800	410		1,210	1,500
6210	30 HP motor		1.80	8.889		800	505		1,305	1,625
6220	40 HP motor		1.80	8.889		1,775	505		2,280	2,700
6230	50 HP motor		1.80	8.889		1,775	505		2,280	2,700
6240	60 HP motor		1.20	13.333		4,150	755		4,905	5,700
6250	75 HP motor		1.20	13.333		4,150	755		4,905	5,700
6260	100 HP motor		1.20	13.333		4,150	755		4,905	5,700
6270	125 HP motor		.90	17.778		11,700	1,000		12,700	14,300
6280	150 HP motor		.90	17.778		11,700	1,000		12,700	14,300
6290	200 HP motor		.90	17.778		11,700	1,000		12,700	14,300
6400	Starter & nonfused disconnect, 240 volt, 1-2 pole, .75 HP motor	1 Elec	2	4		232	226		458	595
6410	2 HP motor		2	4		250	226		476	615
6420	5 HP motor		1.80	4.444		335	252		587	745
6430	10 HP motor		1.40	5.714		775	325		1,100	1,325
6440	3 pole, .75 HP motor		1.60	5		236	283		519	685
6450	5 HP motor		1.40	5.714		300	325		625	815
6460	10 HP motor		1.10	7.273		540	410		950	1,200
6470	15 HP motor		1	8		540	455		995	1,275
6480	20 HP motor	2 Elec	1.50	10.667		925	605		1,530	1,925
6490	25 HP motor		1.50	10.667		960	605		1,565	1,950
6500	30 HP motor		1.30	12.308		960	695		1,655	2,100
6510	40 HP motor		1.24	12.903		2,075	730		2,805	3,375
6520	50 HP motor		1.12	14.286		2,075	810		2,885	3,475
6530	60 HP motor		.90	17.778		4,450	1,000		5,450	6,400
6540	75 HP motor		.76	21.053		4,450	1,200		5,650	6,675
6550	100 HP motor		.70	22.857		4,450	1,300		5,750	6,850
6560	125 HP motor		.60	26.667		12,400	1,500		13,900	16,000
6570	150 HP motor		.52	30.769		12,400	1,750		14,150	16,300
6580	200 HP motor		.50	32		12,400	1,800		14,200	16,400
6600	Starter & fused disconnect, 240 volt, 1-2 pole, .75 HP motor	1 Elec	2	4		244	226		470	610
6610	2 HP motor		2	4		263	226		489	630
6620	5 HP motor		1.80	4.444		350	252		602	760
6630	10 HP motor		1.40	5.714		815	325		1,140	1,375
6640	3 pole, .75 HP motor		1.60	5		248	283		531	700
6650	5 HP motor		1.40	5.714		315	325		640	830
6660	10 HP motor		1.10	7.273		580	410		990	1,250
6690	15 HP motor		1	8		580	455		1,035	1,325
6700	20 HP motor	2 Elec	1.60	10		950	565		1,515	1,900
6710	25 HP motor		1.60	10		985	565		1,550	1,925
6720	30 HP motor		1.40	11.429		985	645		1,630	2,050
6730	40 HP motor		1.20	13.333		2,175	755		2,930	3,525
6740	50 HP motor		1.20	13.333		2,175	755		2,930	3,525

26 24 19.40 Motor Starters and Controls		Crew	Daily Output	Labor-Hours	Unit	Material	2017 Bare Costs Labor	Equipment	Total	Total Incl O&P
6750	60 HP motor	2 Elec	.90	17.778	Ea.	4,550	1,000		5,550	6,500
6760	75 HP motor		.90	17.778		4,550	1,000		5,550	6,500
6770	100 HP motor		.70	22.857		4,550	1,300		5,850	6,950
6780	125 HP motor		.54	29.630		12,600	1,675		14,275	16,400
6790	Combination starter & nonfusible disconnect									
6800	240 volt, 1-2 pole, .75 HP motor	1 Elec	2	4	Ea.	745	226		971	1,150
6810	2 HP motor		2	4		750	226		976	1,175
6820	5 HP motor		1.50	5.333		615	300		915	1,125
6830	10 HP motor		1.20	6.667		955	375		1,330	1,625
6840	3 pole, .75 HP motor		1.80	4.444		585	252		837	1,025
6850	5 HP motor		1.30	6.154		615	350		965	1,200
6860	10 HP motor		1	8		955	455		1,410	1,725
6870	15 HP motor		1	8		955	455		1,410	1,725
6880	20 HP motor	2 Elec	1.32	12.121		1,575	685		2,260	2,750
6890	25 HP motor		1.32	12.121		1,575	685		2,260	2,750
6900	30 HP motor		1.32	12.121		1,575	685		2,260	2,750
6910	40 HP motor		.80	20		3,000	1,125		4,125	5,025
6920	50 HP motor		.80	20		3,000	1,125		4,125	5,025
6930	60 HP motor		.70	22.857		6,725	1,300		8,025	9,350
6940	75 HP motor		.70	22.857		6,725	1,300		8,025	9,350
6950	100 HP motor		.70	22.857		6,725	1,300		8,025	9,350
6960	125 HP motor		.60	26.667		17,700	1,500		19,200	21,800
6970	150 HP motor		.60	26.667		17,700	1,500		19,200	21,800
6980	200 HP motor		.60	26.667		17,700	1,500		19,200	21,800
6990	Combination starter and fused disconnect									
7000	240 volt, 1-2 pole, .75 HP motor	1 Elec	2	4	Ea.	590	226		816	990
7010	2 HP motor		2	4		590	226		816	990
7020	5 HP motor		1.50	5.333		620	300		920	1,125
7030	10 HP motor		1.20	6.667		960	375		1,335	1,625
7040	3 pole, .75 HP motor		1.80	4.444		590	252		842	1,025
7050	5 HP motor		1.30	6.154		620	350		970	1,200
7060	10 HP motor		1	8		960	455		1,415	1,725
7070	15 HP motor		1	8		960	455		1,415	1,725
7080	20 HP motor	2 Elec	1.32	12.121		1,600	685		2,285	2,800
7090	25 HP motor		1.32	12.121		1,600	685		2,285	2,800
7100	30 HP motor		1.32	12.121		1,600	685		2,285	2,800
7110	40 HP motor		.80	20		3,050	1,125		4,175	5,050
7120	50 HP motor		.80	20		3,050	1,125		4,175	5,050
7130	60 HP motor		.80	20		6,800	1,125		7,925	9,175
7140	75 HP motor		.70	22.857		6,800	1,300		8,100	9,425
7150	100 HP motor		.70	22.857		6,800	1,300		8,100	9,425
7160	125 HP motor		.70	22.857		18,000	1,300		19,300	21,800
7170	150 HP motor		.60	26.667		18,000	1,500		19,500	22,100
7180	200 HP motor		.60	26.667		18,000	1,500		19,500	22,100
7190	Combination starter & circuit breaker disconnect									
7200	240 volt, 1-2 pole, .75 HP motor	1 Elec	2	4	Ea.	610	226		836	1,000
7210	2 HP motor		2	4		610	226		836	1,000
7220	5 HP motor		1.50	5.333		640	300		940	1,150
7230	10 HP motor		1.20	6.667		975	375		1,350	1,650
7240	3 pole, .75 HP motor		1.80	4.444		625	252		877	1,075
7250	5 HP motor		1.30	6.154		655	350		1,005	1,250
7260	10 HP motor		1	8		995	455		1,450	1,775
7270	15 HP motor		1	8		995	455		1,450	1,775

For customer support on your Electrical Costs with RSMeans Data, call 800.448.8182.

237

26 24 19.40 Motor Starters and Controls	Crew	Daily Output	Labor-Hours	Unit	Material	2017 Bare Costs Labor	Equipment	Total	Total Incl O&P
7280	20 HP motor	2 Elec	1.32	12.121	Ea.	1,700	685		2,385	2,875
7290	25 HP motor		1.32	12.121		1,700	685		2,385	2,875
7300	30 HP motor		1.32	12.121		1,700	685		2,385	2,875
7310	40 HP motor		.80	20		3,675	1,125		4,800	5,750
7320	50 HP motor		.80	20		3,675	1,125		4,800	5,750
7330	60 HP motor		.80	20		8,500	1,125		9,625	11,100
7340	75 HP motor		.70	22.857		8,500	1,300		9,800	11,300
7350	100 HP motor		.70	22.857		8,500	1,300		9,800	11,300
7360	125 HP motor		.70	22.857		18,400	1,300		19,700	22,300
7370	150 HP motor		.60	26.667		18,400	1,500		19,900	22,600
7380	200 HP motor	▼	.60	26.667	▼	18,400	1,500		19,900	22,600
7400	Magnetic FVNR with enclosure & heaters, 2 pole,									
7410	230 volt, 1 HP, size 00	1 Elec	4	2	Ea.	167	113		280	355
7420	2 HP, size 0		4	2		187	113		300	375
7430	3 HP, size 1		3	2.667		214	151		365	460
7440	5 HP, size 1P		3	2.667		275	151		426	525
7450	115 volt, 1/3 HP, size 00		4	2		167	113		280	355
7460	1 HP, size 0		4	2		187	113		300	375
7470	2 HP, size 1		3	2.667		214	151		365	460
7480	3 HP, size 1P	▼	3	2.667	▼	266	151		417	520
7500	3 pole, 480 volt, 600 HP, size 7	2 Elec	.70	22.857		15,700	1,300		17,000	19,200
7590	Magnetic FVNR with heater, NEMA 1									
7600	600 volt, 3 pole, 5 HP motor	1 Elec	2.30	3.478	Ea.	222	197		419	540
7610	10 HP motor	"	1.60	5		250	283		533	700
7620	25 HP motor	2 Elec	2.20	7.273		470	410		880	1,125
7630	30 HP motor		1.80	8.889		765	505		1,270	1,600
7640	40 HP motor		1.80	8.889		765	505		1,270	1,600
7650	50 HP motor		1.80	8.889		765	505		1,270	1,600
7660	60 HP motor		1.20	13.333		1,700	755		2,455	3,000
7670	75 HP motor		1.20	13.333		1,975	755		2,730	3,300
7680	100 HP motor		1.20	13.333		2,250	755		3,005	3,600
7690	125 HP motor		.90	17.778		3,900	1,000		4,900	5,775
7700	150 HP motor		.90	17.778		4,075	1,000		5,075	5,975
7710	200 HP motor	▼	.90	17.778		4,250	1,000		5,250	6,175
7750	Starter & nonfused disconnect, 600 volt, 3 pole, 5 HP motor	1 Elec	1.40	5.714		320	325		645	840
7760	10 HP motor	"	1.10	7.273		350	410		760	1,000
7770	25 HP motor	2 Elec	1.50	10.667		570	605		1,175	1,525
7780	30 HP motor		1.30	12.308		930	695		1,625	2,075
7790	40 HP motor		1.30	12.308		930	695		1,625	2,075
7800	50 HP motor		1.30	12.308		930	695		1,625	2,075
7810	60 HP motor		.92	17.391		1,950	985		2,935	3,625
7820	75 HP motor		.92	17.391		2,225	985		3,210	3,925
7830	100 HP motor		.84	19.048		2,500	1,075		3,575	4,375
7840	125 HP motor		.70	22.857		4,275	1,300		5,575	6,650
7850	150 HP motor		.70	22.857		4,475	1,300		5,775	6,875
7860	200 HP motor	▼	.60	26.667		4,650	1,500		6,150	7,375
7870	Starter & fused disconnect, 600 volt, 3 pole, 5 HP motor	1 Elec	1.40	5.714		400	325		725	925
7880	10 HP motor	"	1.10	7.273		425	410		835	1,075
7890	25 HP motor	2 Elec	1.50	10.667		645	605		1,250	1,625
7900	30 HP motor		1.30	12.308		980	695		1,675	2,125
7910	40 HP motor		1.30	12.308		980	695		1,675	2,125
7920	50 HP motor		1.30	12.308		980	695		1,675	2,125
7930	60 HP motor	▼	.92	17.391		2,100	985		3,085	3,775

26 24 Switchboards and Panelboards

26 24 19 - Motor-Control Centers

26 24 19.40 Motor Starters and Controls		Crew	Daily Output	Labor-Hours	Unit	Material	2017 Bare Costs Labor	Equipment	Total	Total Incl O&P
7940	75 HP motor	2 Elec	.92	17.391	Ea.	2,375	985		3,360	4,075
7950	100 HP motor		.84	19.048		2,625	1,075		3,700	4,525
7960	125 HP motor		.70	22.857		4,450	1,300		5,750	6,850
7970	150 HP motor		.70	22.857		4,650	1,300		5,950	7,050
7980	200 HP motor	↓	.60	26.667	↓	4,825	1,500		6,325	7,550
7990	Combination starter and nonfusible disconnect									
8000	600 volt, 3 pole, 5 HP motor	1 Elec	1.80	4.444	Ea.	665	252		917	1,100
8010	10 HP motor	"	1.30	6.154		740	350		1,090	1,325
8020	25 HP motor	2 Elec	2	8		1,075	455		1,530	1,850
8030	30 HP motor		1.32	12.121		1,625	685		2,310	2,825
8040	40 HP motor		1.32	12.121		1,625	685		2,310	2,825
8050	50 HP motor		1.32	12.121		1,925	685		2,610	3,150
8060	60 HP motor		.80	20		3,125	1,125		4,250	5,125
8070	75 HP motor		.80	20		3,125	1,125		4,250	5,125
8080	100 HP motor		.80	20		3,825	1,125		4,950	5,900
8090	125 HP motor		.70	22.857		6,750	1,300		8,050	9,375
8100	150 HP motor		.70	22.857		7,050	1,300		8,350	9,700
8110	200 HP motor	↓	.70	22.857	↓	7,250	1,300		8,550	9,925
8140	Combination starter and fused disconnect									
8150	600 volt, 3 pole, 5 HP motor	1 Elec	1.80	4.444	Ea.	590	252		842	1,025
8160	10 HP motor	"	1.30	6.154		645	350		995	1,225
8170	25 HP motor	2 Elec	2	8		1,050	455		1,505	1,825
8180	30 HP motor		1.32	12.121		1,625	685		2,310	2,825
8190	40 HP motor		1.32	12.121		1,750	685		2,435	2,950
8200	50 HP motor		1.32	12.121		1,750	685		2,435	2,950
8210	60 HP motor		.80	20		3,075	1,125		4,200	5,075
8220	75 HP motor		.80	20		3,075	1,125		4,200	5,075
8230	100 HP motor		.80	20		3,075	1,125		4,200	5,075
8240	125 HP motor		.70	22.857		6,800	1,300		8,100	9,425
8250	150 HP motor		.70	22.857		6,800	1,300		8,100	9,425
8260	200 HP motor	↓	.70	22.857	↓	6,800	1,300		8,100	9,425
8290	Combination starter & circuit breaker disconnect									
8300	600 volt, 3 pole, 5 HP motor	1 Elec	1.80	4.444	Ea.	910	252		1,162	1,375
8310	10 HP motor	"	1.30	6.154		845	350		1,195	1,450
8320	25 HP motor	2 Elec	2	8		1,325	455		1,780	2,125
8330	30 HP motor		1.32	12.121		1,700	685		2,385	2,875
8340	40 HP motor		1.32	12.121		1,700	685		2,385	2,875
8350	50 HP motor		1.32	12.121		1,675	685		2,360	2,875
8360	60 HP motor		.80	20		3,675	1,125		4,800	5,750
8370	75 HP motor		.80	20		3,675	1,125		4,800	5,750
8380	100 HP motor		.80	20		3,650	1,125		4,775	5,725
8390	125 HP motor		.70	22.857		8,500	1,300		9,800	11,300
8400	150 HP motor		.70	22.857		8,400	1,300		9,700	11,200
8410	200 HP motor	↓	.70	22.857	↓	8,450	1,300		9,750	11,300
8430	Starter & circuit breaker disconnect									
8440	600 volt, 3 pole, 5 HP motor	1 Elec	1.40	5.714	Ea.	715	325		1,040	1,275
8450	10 HP motor	"	1.10	7.273		740	410		1,150	1,425
8460	25 HP motor	2 Elec	1.50	10.667		960	605		1,565	1,950
8470	30 HP motor		1.30	12.308		1,375	695		2,070	2,550
8480	40 HP motor		1.30	12.308		1,375	695		2,070	2,550
8490	50 HP motor		1.30	12.308		1,375	695		2,070	2,550
8500	60 HP motor		.92	17.391		3,300	985		4,285	5,100
8510	75 HP motor	↓	.92	17.391	↓	3,575	985		4,560	5,400

26 24 Switchboards and Panelboards

26 24 19 – Motor-Control Centers

26 24 19.40 Motor Starters and Controls		Crew	Daily Output	Labor-Hours	Unit	Material	2017 Bare Costs Labor	Equipment	Total	Total Incl O&P
8520	100 HP motor	2 Elec	.84	19.048	Ea.	3,850	1,075		4,925	5,850
8530	125 HP motor		.70	22.857		5,475	1,300		6,775	7,975
8540	150 HP motor		.70	22.857		5,675	1,300		6,975	8,175
8550	200 HP motor		.60	26.667		6,975	1,500		8,475	9,925
8900	240 volt, 1-2 pole, .75 HP motor	1 Elec	2	4		670	226		896	1,075
8910	2 HP motor		2	4		690	226		916	1,100
8920	5 HP motor		1.80	4.444		775	252		1,027	1,225
8930	10 HP motor		1.40	5.714		1,300	325		1,625	1,925
8950	3 pole, .75 HP motor		1.60	5		675	283		958	1,175
8970	5 HP motor		1.40	5.714		740	325		1,065	1,300
8980	10 HP motor		1.10	7.273		1,075	410		1,485	1,800
8990	15 HP motor		1	8		1,075	455		1,530	1,850
9100	20 HP motor	2 Elec	1.50	10.667		1,450	605		2,055	2,500
9110	25 HP motor		1.50	10.667		1,500	605		2,105	2,550
9120	30 HP motor		1.30	12.308		1,500	695		2,195	2,700
9130	40 HP motor		1.24	12.903		3,375	730		4,105	4,800
9140	50 HP motor		1.12	14.286		3,375	810		4,185	4,900
9150	60 HP motor		.90	17.778		6,875	1,000		7,875	9,075
9160	75 HP motor		.76	21.053		6,875	1,200		8,075	9,350
9170	100 HP motor		.70	22.857		6,875	1,300		8,175	9,525
9180	125 HP motor		.60	26.667		15,600	1,500		17,100	19,500
9190	150 HP motor		.52	30.769		15,600	1,750		17,350	19,800
9200	200 HP motor		.50	32		15,600	1,800		17,400	19,900

26 25 Enclosed Bus Assemblies

26 25 13 – Bus Duct/Busway and Fittings

26 25 13.10 Aluminum Bus Duct

		Crew	Daily Output	Labor-Hours	Unit	Material	2017 Bare Costs Labor	Equipment	Total	Total Incl O&P
0010	**ALUMINUM BUS DUCT** 10 ft. long R262513-10									
0050	Indoor 3 pole 4 wire, plug-in, straight section, 225 amp	2 Elec	44	.364	L.F.	176	20.50		196.50	225
0100	400 amp		36	.444		222	25		247	282
0150	600 amp		32	.500		305	28.50		333.50	380
0200	800 amp		26	.615		355	35		390	440
0250	1000 amp		24	.667		445	37.50		482.50	545
0270	1200 amp		23	.696		565	39.50		604.50	685
0300	1350 amp		22	.727		251	41		292	340
0310	1600 amp		18	.889		267	50.50		317.50	370
0320	2000 amp		16	1		350	56.50		406.50	470
0330	2500 amp		14	1.143		400	64.50		464.50	535
0340	3000 amp		12	1.333		485	75.50		560.50	650
0350	Feeder, 600 amp		34	.471		106	26.50		132.50	157
0400	800 amp		28	.571		430	32.50		462.50	525
0450	1000 amp		26	.615		520	35		555	620
0455	1200 amp		25	.640		650	36		686	770
0500	1350 amp		24	.667		221	37.50		258.50	300
0550	1600 amp		20	.800		900	45.50		945.50	1,050
0600	2000 amp		18	.889		1,100	50.50		1,150.50	1,275
0620	2500 amp		14	1.143		1,350	64.50		1,414.50	1,575
0630	3000 amp		12	1.333		1,575	75.50		1,650.50	1,850
0640	4000 amp		10	1.600		635	90.50		725.50	835
0650	Elbow, 225 amp		4.40	3.636	Ea.	845	206		1,051	1,225
0700	400 amp		3.80	4.211		855	238		1,093	1,300

26 25 13.10 Aluminum Bus Duct		Crew	Daily Output	Labor-Hours	Unit	Material	2017 Bare Costs Labor	Equipment	Total	Total Incl O&P
0750	600 amp	2 Elec	3.40	4.706	Ea.	860	266		1,126	1,350
0800	800 amp		3	5.333		890	300		1,190	1,425
0850	1000 amp		2.80	5.714		1,150	325		1,475	1,725
0870	1200 amp		2.70	5.926		1,425	335		1,760	2,075
0900	1350 amp		2.60	6.154		1,125	350		1,475	1,750
0950	1600 amp		2.40	6.667		1,325	375		1,700	2,050
1000	2000 amp		2	8		1,475	455		1,930	2,275
1020	2500 amp		1.80	8.889		1,725	505		2,230	2,650
1030	3000 amp		1.60	10		2,000	565		2,565	3,050
1040	4000 amp		1.40	11.429		3,225	645		3,870	4,525
1100	Cable tap box end, 225 amp		3.60	4.444		1,700	252		1,952	2,250
1150	400 amp		3.20	5		1,725	283		2,008	2,325
1200	600 amp		2.60	6.154		1,500	350		1,850	2,175
1250	800 amp		2.20	7.273		1,800	410		2,210	2,600
1300	1000 amp		2	8		3,400	455		3,855	4,425
1320	1200 amp		2	8		1,600	455		2,055	2,450
1350	1350 amp		1.60	10		1,350	565		1,915	2,350
1400	1600 amp		1.40	11.429		1,525	645		2,170	2,650
1450	2000 amp		1.20	13.333		1,750	755		2,505	3,050
1460	2500 amp		1	16		1,950	905		2,855	3,500
1470	3000 amp		.80	20		1,950	1,125		3,075	3,850
1480	4000 amp		.60	26.667		2,600	1,500		4,100	5,125
1500	Switchboard stub, 225 amp		5.80	2.759		1,475	156		1,631	1,850
1550	400 amp		5.40	2.963		1,500	168		1,668	1,900
1600	600 amp		4.60	3.478		1,525	197		1,722	1,975
1650	800 amp		4	4		1,550	226		1,776	2,050
1700	1000 amp		3.20	5		1,550	283		1,833	2,150
1720	1200 amp		3.10	5.161		1,600	292		1,892	2,200
1750	1350 amp		3	5.333		1,500	300		1,800	2,100
1800	1600 amp		2.60	6.154		1,675	350		2,025	2,375
1850	2000 amp		2.40	6.667		1,675	375		2,050	2,400
1860	2500 amp		2.20	7.273		1,825	410		2,235	2,650
1870	3000 amp		2	8		1,875	455		2,330	2,725
1880	4000 amp		1.80	8.889		2,000	505		2,505	2,950
1890	Tee fittings, 225 amp		3.20	5		840	283		1,123	1,350
1900	400 amp		2.80	5.714		840	325		1,165	1,400
1950	600 amp		2.60	6.154		840	350		1,190	1,450
2000	800 amp		2.40	6.667		890	375		1,265	1,550
2050	1000 amp		2.20	7.273		945	410		1,355	1,675
2070	1200 amp		2.10	7.619		1,100	430		1,530	1,875
2100	1350 amp		2	8		1,525	455		1,980	2,350
2150	1600 amp		1.60	10		1,850	565		2,415	2,875
2200	2000 amp		1.20	13.333		2,050	755		2,805	3,375
2220	2500 amp		1	16		2,425	905		3,330	4,025
2230	3000 amp		.80	20		2,775	1,125		3,900	4,750
2240	4000 amp		.60	26.667		4,625	1,500		6,125	7,325
2300	Wall flange, 600 amp		20	.800		235	45.50		280.50	325
2310	800 amp		16	1		235	56.50		291.50	345
2320	1000 amp		13	1.231		235	69.50		304.50	365
2325	1200 amp		12	1.333		235	75.50		310.50	370
2330	1350 amp		10.80	1.481		235	84		319	385
2340	1600 amp		9	1.778		235	101		336	410
2350	2000 amp		8	2		235	113		348	430

26 25 13.10 Aluminum Bus Duct		Crew	Daily Output	Labor-Hours	Unit	Material	2017 Bare Costs Labor	Equipment	Total	Total Incl O&P
2360	2500 amp	2 Elec	6.60	2.424	Ea.	235	137		372	465
2370	3000 amp		5.40	2.963		235	168		403	510
2380	4000 amp		4	4		340	226		566	715
2390	5000 amp		3	5.333		340	300		640	825
2400	Vapor barrier		8	2		430	113		543	640
2420	Roof flange kit		4	4		680	226		906	1,075
2600	Expansion fitting, 225 amp		10	1.600		1,250	90.50		1,340.50	1,475
2610	400 amp		8	2		1,250	113		1,363	1,550
2620	600 amp		6	2.667		1,250	151		1,401	1,600
2630	800 amp		4.60	3.478		1,400	197		1,597	1,850
2640	1000 amp		4	4		1,600	226		1,826	2,100
2650	1350 amp		3.60	4.444		1,950	252		2,202	2,525
2660	1600 amp		3.20	5		2,325	283		2,608	3,000
2670	2000 amp		2.80	5.714		2,600	325		2,925	3,325
2680	2500 amp		2.40	6.667		3,150	375		3,525	4,025
2690	3000 amp		2	8		3,625	455		4,080	4,650
2700	4000 amp		1.60	10		4,750	565		5,315	6,075
2800	Reducer nonfused, 400 amp		8	2		820	113		933	1,075
2810	600 amp		6	2.667		820	151		971	1,125
2820	800 amp		4.60	3.478		985	197		1,182	1,375
2830	1000 amp		4	4		1,150	226		1,376	1,625
2840	1350 amp		3.60	4.444		1,500	252		1,752	2,025
2850	1600 amp		3.20	5		2,050	283		2,333	2,675
2860	2000 amp		2.80	5.714		2,350	325		2,675	3,050
2870	2500 amp		2.40	6.667		2,950	375		3,325	3,825
2880	3000 amp		2	8		3,400	455		3,855	4,425
2890	4000 amp		1.60	10		4,550	565		5,115	5,850
2950	Reducer fuse included, 225 amp		4.40	3.636		2,400	206		2,606	2,950
2960	400 amp		4.20	3.810		2,450	216		2,666	3,025
2970	600 amp		3.60	4.444		2,900	252		3,152	3,550
2980	800 amp		3.20	5		4,600	283		4,883	5,475
2990	1000 amp		3	5.333		5,250	300		5,550	6,225
3000	1200 amp		2.80	5.714		5,250	325		5,575	6,250
3010	1600 amp		2.20	7.273		12,000	410		12,410	13,800
3020	2000 amp		1.80	8.889		13,300	505		13,805	15,500
3100	Reducer circuit breaker, 225 amp		4.40	3.636		2,375	206		2,581	2,900
3110	400 amp		4.20	3.810		2,900	216		3,116	3,500
3120	600 amp		3.60	4.444		4,100	252		4,352	4,875
3130	800 amp		3.20	5		4,800	283		5,083	5,725
3140	1000 amp		3	5.333		5,450	300		5,750	6,450
3150	1200 amp		2.80	5.714		6,550	325		6,875	7,700
3160	1600 amp		2.20	7.273		9,700	410		10,110	11,300
3170	2000 amp		1.80	8.889		10,600	505		11,105	12,500
3250	Reducer circuit breaker, 75,000 AIC, 225 amp		4.40	3.636		3,700	206		3,906	4,375
3260	400 amp		4.20	3.810		3,700	216		3,916	4,400
3270	600 amp		3.60	4.444		4,950	252		5,202	5,825
3280	800 amp		3.20	5		5,450	283		5,733	6,425
3290	1000 amp		3	5.333		8,775	300		9,075	10,100
3300	1200 amp		2.80	5.714		8,775	325		9,100	10,100
3310	1600 amp		2.20	7.273		9,700	410		10,110	11,300
3320	2000 amp		1.80	8.889		10,600	505		11,105	12,500
3400	Reducer circuit breaker CLF 225 amp		4.40	3.636		3,800	206		4,006	4,500
3410	400 amp		4.20	3.810		4,525	216		4,741	5,300

For customer support on your Electrical Costs with RSMeans Data, call 800.448.8182.

26 25 13 – Bus Duct/Busway and Fittings

26 25 13.10 Aluminum Bus Duct		Crew	Daily Output	Labor-Hours	Unit	Material	2017 Bare Costs Labor	Equipment	Total	Total Incl O&P
3420	600 amp	2 Elec	3.60	4.444	Ea.	6,775	252		7,027	7,825
3430	800 amp		3.20	5		7,075	283		7,358	8,200
3440	1000 amp		3	5.333		7,375	300		7,675	8,575
3450	1200 amp		2.80	5.714		9,650	325		9,975	11,100
3460	1600 amp		2.20	7.273		9,700	410		10,110	11,300
3470	2000 amp		1.80	8.889	▼	10,600	505		11,105	12,500
3550	Ground bus added to bus duct, 225 amp		320	.050	L.F.	31.50	2.83		34.33	38.50
3560	400 amp		320	.050		31.50	2.83		34.33	38.50
3570	600 amp		280	.057		31.50	3.23		34.73	39.50
3580	800 amp		240	.067		31.50	3.77		35.27	40
3590	1000 amp		200	.080		31.50	4.53		36.03	41.50
3600	1350 amp		180	.089		31.50	5.05		36.55	42
3610	1600 amp		160	.100		31.50	5.65		37.15	43
3620	2000 amp		160	.100		31.50	5.65		37.15	43
3630	2500 amp		140	.114		31.50	6.45		37.95	44
3640	3000 amp		120	.133		31.50	7.55		39.05	46
3650	4000 amp		100	.160		31.50	9.05		40.55	48
3810	High short circuit, 400 amp		36	.444		212	25		237	271
3820	600 amp		32	.500		370	28.50		398.50	450
3830	800 amp		26	.615		425	35		460	520
3840	1000 amp		24	.667		535	37.50		572.50	645
3850	1350 amp		22	.727		177	41		218	256
3860	1600 amp		18	.889		203	50.50		253.50	300
3870	2000 amp		16	1		239	56.50		295.50	345
3880	2500 amp		14	1.143		400	64.50		464.50	530
3890	3000 amp		12	1.333	▼	450	75.50		525.50	610
3920	Cross, 225 amp		5.60	2.857	Ea.	1,250	162		1,412	1,625
3930	400 amp		4.60	3.478		1,250	197		1,447	1,675
3940	600 amp		4	4		1,250	226		1,476	1,725
3950	800 amp		3.40	4.706		1,325	266		1,591	1,850
3960	1000 amp		3	5.333		1,400	300		1,700	1,975
3970	1350 amp		2.80	5.714		2,250	325		2,575	2,950
3980	1600 amp		2.20	7.273		2,675	410		3,085	3,550
3990	2000 amp		1.80	8.889		2,925	505		3,430	3,975
4000	2500 amp		1.60	10		3,475	565		4,040	4,675
4010	3000 amp		1.20	13.333		4,000	755		4,755	5,525
4020	4000 amp		1	16		6,100	905		7,005	8,075
4040	Cable tap box center, 225 amp		3.60	4.444		3,100	252		3,352	3,775
4050	400 amp		3.20	5		3,550	283		3,833	4,325
4060	600 amp		2.60	6.154		4,725	350		5,075	5,725
4070	800 amp		2.20	7.273		5,225	410		5,635	6,375
4080	1000 amp		2	8		6,625	455		7,080	7,975
4090	1350 amp		1.60	10		1,350	565		1,915	2,350
4100	1600 amp		1.40	11.429		1,525	645		2,170	2,650
4110	2000 amp		1.20	13.333		1,750	755		2,505	3,050
4120	2500 amp		1	16		2,125	905		3,030	3,675
4130	3000 amp		.80	20		2,350	1,125		3,475	4,275
4140	4000 amp		.60	26.667	▼	3,125	1,500		4,625	5,700
4500	Weatherproof 3 pole 4 wire, feeder, 600 amp		30	.533	L.F.	127	30		157	185
4520	800 amp		24	.667		149	37.50		186.50	220
4540	1000 amp		22	.727		169	41		210	248
4550	1200 amp		21	.762		235	43		278	325
4560	1350 amp		20	.800		265	45.50		310.50	360

For customer support on your Electrical Costs with RSMeans Data, call 800.448.8182.

243

26 25 13.10 Aluminum Bus Duct	Crew	Daily Output	Labor-Hours	Unit	Material	2017 Bare Costs Labor	Equipment	Total	Total Incl O&P
4580	1600 amp	2 Elec	17	.941	L.F.	310	53.50		363.50	420
4600	2000 amp		16	1		360	56.50		416.50	480
4620	2500 amp		12	1.333		465	75.50		540.50	630
4640	3000 amp		10	1.600		530	90.50		620.50	720
4660	4000 amp		8	2		765	113		878	1,000
5000	Indoor 3 pole, 3 wire, feeder, 600 amp		40	.400		97	22.50		119.50	141
5010	800 amp		32	.500		355	28.50		383.50	435
5020	1000 amp		30	.533		395	30		425	480
5025	1200 amp		29	.552		535	31		566	630
5030	1350 amp		28	.571		168	32.50		200.50	234
5040	1600 amp		24	.667		755	37.50		792.50	885
5050	2000 amp		20	.800		905	45.50		950.50	1,075
5060	2500 amp		16	1		1,100	56.50		1,156.50	1,275
5070	3000 amp		14	1.143		1,250	64.50		1,314.50	1,475
5080	4000 amp		12	1.333		460	75.50		535.50	620
5200	Plug-in type, 225 amp		50	.320		143	18.10		161.10	184
5210	400 amp		42	.381		175	21.50		196.50	226
5220	600 amp		36	.444		217	25		242	277
5230	800 amp		30	.533		305	30		335	380
5240	1000 amp		28	.571		345	32.50		377.50	430
5245	1200 amp		27	.593		240	33.50		273.50	315
5250	1350 amp		26	.615		177	35		212	246
5260	1600 amp		20	.800		203	45.50		248.50	292
5270	2000 amp		18	.889		239	50.50		289.50	340
5280	2500 amp		16	1		325	56.50		381.50	445
5290	3000 amp		14	1.143		390	64.50		454.50	525
5300	4000 amp		12	1.333		470	75.50		545.50	630
5330	High short circuit, 400 amp		42	.381		210	21.50		231.50	264
5340	600 amp		36	.444		261	25		286	325
5350	800 amp		30	.533		365	30		395	450
5360	1000 amp		28	.571		415	32.50		447.50	505
5370	1350 amp		26	.615		177	35		212	246
5380	1600 amp		20	.800		203	45.50		248.50	292
5390	2000 amp		18	.889		239	50.50		289.50	340
5400	2500 amp		16	1		375	56.50		431.50	500
5410	3000 amp		14	1.143		390	64.50		454.50	525
5440	Elbow, 225 amp		5	3.200	Ea.	640	181		821	975
5450	400 amp		4.40	3.636		640	206		846	1,025
5460	600 amp		4	4		640	226		866	1,050
5470	800 amp		3.40	4.706		680	266		946	1,150
5480	1000 amp		3.20	5		700	283		983	1,200
5485	1200 amp		3.10	5.161		745	292		1,037	1,250
5490	1350 amp		3	5.333		685	300		985	1,200
5500	1600 amp		2.80	5.714		1,050	325		1,375	1,625
5510	2000 amp		2.40	6.667		1,150	375		1,525	1,850
5520	2500 amp		2	8		1,425	455		1,880	2,225
5530	3000 amp		1.80	8.889		1,675	505		2,180	2,600
5540	4000 amp		1.60	10		2,250	565		2,815	3,325
5560	Tee fittings, 225 amp		3.60	4.444		750	252		1,002	1,200
5570	400 amp		3.20	5		750	283		1,033	1,250
5580	600 amp		3	5.333		750	300		1,050	1,275
5590	800 amp		2.80	5.714		805	325		1,130	1,375
5600	1000 amp		2.60	6.154		830	350		1,180	1,425

26 25 Enclosed Bus Assemblies

26 25 13 — Bus Duct/Busway and Fittings

26 25 13.10 Aluminum Bus Duct		Crew	Daily Output	Labor- Hours	Unit	Material	2017 Bare Costs Labor	Equipment	Total	Total Incl O&P
5605	1200 amp	2 Elec	2.50	6.400	Ea.	885	360		1,245	1,525
5610	1350 amp		2.40	6.667		1,225	375		1,600	1,925
5620	1600 amp		1.80	8.889		1,450	505		1,955	2,350
5630	2000 amp		1.40	11.429		1,625	645		2,270	2,750
5640	2500 amp		1.20	13.333		2,000	755		2,755	3,325
5650	3000 amp		1	16		2,350	905		3,255	3,950
5660	4000 amp		.70	22.857		3,450	1,300		4,750	5,750
5680	Cross, 225 amp		6.40	2.500		1,225	142		1,367	1,525
5690	400 amp		5.40	2.963		1,225	168		1,393	1,575
5700	600 amp		4.60	3.478		1,225	197		1,422	1,625
5710	800 amp		4	4		1,275	226		1,501	1,775
5720	1000 amp		3.60	4.444		1,325	252		1,577	1,825
5730	1350 amp		3.20	5		1,975	283		2,258	2,600
5740	1600 amp		2.60	6.154		2,300	350		2,650	3,050
5750	2000 amp		2.20	7.273		2,500	410		2,910	3,375
5760	2500 amp		1.80	8.889		3,025	505		3,530	4,100
5770	3000 amp		1.40	11.429		3,625	645		4,270	4,950
5780	4000 amp		1.20	13.333		5,050	755		5,805	6,675
5800	Expansion fitting, 225 amp		11.60	1.379		910	78		988	1,125
5810	400 amp		9.20	1.739		910	98.50		1,008.50	1,150
5820	600 amp		7	2.286		910	129		1,039	1,200
5830	800 amp		5.20	3.077		1,075	174		1,249	1,425
5840	1000 amp		4.60	3.478		1,175	197		1,372	1,600
5850	1350 amp		4.20	3.810		1,375	216		1,591	1,850
5860	1600 amp		3.60	4.444		1,725	252		1,977	2,275
5870	2000 amp		3.20	5		2,025	283		2,308	2,650
5880	2500 amp		2.80	5.714		2,300	325		2,625	3,000
5890	3000 amp		2.40	6.667		2,675	375		3,050	3,525
5900	4000 amp		1.80	8.889		3,675	505		4,180	4,800
5940	Reducer, nonfused, 400 amp		9.20	1.739		705	98.50		803.50	920
5950	600 amp		7	2.286		705	129		834	970
5960	800 amp		5.20	3.077		740	174		914	1,075
5970	1000 amp		4.60	3.478		910	197		1,107	1,300
5980	1350 amp		4.20	3.810		1,350	216		1,566	1,800
5990	1600 amp		3.60	4.444		1,550	252		1,802	2,075
6000	2000 amp		3.20	5		1,800	283		2,083	2,400
6010	2500 amp		2.80	5.714		2,300	325		2,625	3,000
6020	3000 amp		2.20	7.273		2,675	410		3,085	3,575
6030	4000 amp		1.80	8.889		3,675	505		4,180	4,800
6050	Reducer, fuse included, 225 amp		5	3.200		1,850	181		2,031	2,300
6060	400 amp		4.80	3.333		2,450	189		2,639	2,975
6070	600 amp		4.20	3.810		3,150	216		3,366	3,775
6080	800 amp		3.60	4.444		4,875	252		5,127	5,725
6090	1000 amp		3.40	4.706		5,300	266		5,566	6,225
6100	1350 amp		3.20	5		9,700	283		9,983	11,100
6110	1600 amp		7.60	6.154		11,500	350		11,850	13,100
6120	2000 amp		2	8		13,300	455		13,755	15,400
6160	Reducer, circuit breaker, 225 amp		5	3.200		2,275	181		2,456	2,775
6170	400 amp		4.80	3.333		2,775	189		2,964	3,325
6180	600 amp		4.20	3.810		4,000	216		4,216	4,725
6190	800 amp		3.60	4.444		4,675	252		4,927	5,500
6200	1000 amp		3.40	4.706		5,300	266		5,566	6,225
6210	1350 amp		3.20	5		6,400	283		6,683	7,475

26 25 13.10 Aluminum Bus Duct

		Crew	Daily Output	Labor-Hours	Unit	Material	2017 Bare Costs Labor	2017 Bare Costs Equipment	Total	Total Incl O&P
6220	1600 amp	2 Elec	2.60	6.154	Ea.	9,550	350		9,900	11,000
6230	2000 amp		2	8		10,400	455		10,855	12,200
6270	Cable tap box center, 225 amp		4.20	3.810		1,025	216		1,241	1,450
6280	400 amp		3.60	4.444		1,025	252		1,277	1,500
6290	600 amp		3	5.333		1,025	300		1,325	1,575
6300	800 amp		2.60	6.154		1,125	350		1,475	1,750
6310	1000 amp		2.40	6.667		1,175	375		1,550	1,875
6320	1350 amp		1.80	8.889		1,175	505		1,680	2,050
6330	1600 amp		1.60	10		1,325	565		1,890	2,300
6340	2000 amp		1.40	11.429		1,525	645		2,170	2,650
6350	2500 amp		1.20	13.333		1,900	755		2,655	3,200
6360	3000 amp		1	16		2,150	905		3,055	3,700
6370	4000 amp		.70	22.857		2,550	1,300		3,850	4,750
6390	Cable tap box end, 225 amp		4.20	3.810		625	216		841	1,025
6400	400 amp		3.60	4.444		625	252		877	1,075
6410	600 amp		3	5.333		625	300		925	1,150
6420	800 amp		2.60	6.154		685	350		1,035	1,275
6430	1000 amp		2.40	6.667		740	375		1,115	1,375
6435	1200 amp		2.10	7.619		800	430		1,230	1,525
6440	1350 amp		1.80	8.889		735	505		1,240	1,575
6450	1600 amp		1.60	10		835	565		1,400	1,775
6460	2000 amp		1.40	11.429		945	645		1,590	2,000
6470	2500 amp		1.20	13.333		1,100	755		1,855	2,325
6480	3000 amp		1	16		1,300	905		2,205	2,775
6490	4000 amp		.70	22.857		1,550	1,300		2,850	3,650
7000	Weatherproof 3 pole 3 wire, feeder, 600 amp		34	.471	L.F.	125	26.50		151.50	178
7020	800 amp		28	.571		138	32.50		170.50	201
7040	1000 amp		26	.615		149	35		184	215
7050	1200 amp		25	.640		173	36		209	246
7060	1350 amp		24	.667		202	37.50		239.50	279
7080	1600 amp		20	.800		233	45.50		278.50	325
7100	2000 amp		18	.889		275	50.50		325.50	380
7120	2500 amp		14	1.143		380	64.50		444.50	515
7140	3000 amp		12	1.333		455	75.50		530.50	615
7160	4000 amp		10	1.600		550	90.50		640.50	740

26 25 13.20 Bus Duct

		Crew	Daily Output	Labor-Hours	Unit	Material	2017 Bare Costs Labor	2017 Bare Costs Equipment	Total	Total Incl O&P
0010	**BUS DUCT** 100 amp and less, aluminum or copper, plug-in									
0080	Bus duct, 3 pole 3 wire, 100 amp	1 Elec	42	.190	L.F.	73	10.80		83.80	96
0110	Elbow		4	2	Ea.	131	113		244	315
0120	Tee		2	4		186	226		412	545
0130	Wall flange		8	1		24.50	56.50		81	112
0140	Ground kit		.16	.500		61	28.50		89.50	110
0180	3 pole 4 wire, 100 amp		40	.200	L.F.	76	11.30		87.30	100
0200	Cable tap box		3.10	2.581	Ea.	228	146		374	470
0300	End closure		16	.500		30.50	28.50		59	76
0400	Elbow		4	2		186	113		299	375
0500	Tee		2	4		271	226		497	640
0600	Hangers		10	.800		18.20	45.50		63.70	88
0700	Circuit breakers, 15 to 50 amp, 1 pole		8	1		575	56.50		631.50	720
0800	15 to 60 amp, 2 pole		6.70	1.194		320	67.50		387.50	455
0900	3 pole		5.30	1.509		395	85.50		480.50	565
1000	60 to 100 amp, 1 pole		6.70	1.194		595	67.50		662.50	755

26 25 13.20 Bus Duct		Crew	Daily Output	Labor-Hours	Unit	Material	2017 Bare Costs Labor	Equipment	Total	Total Incl O&P
1100	70 to 100 amp, 2 pole	1 Elec	5.30	1.509	Ea.	1,250	85.50		1,335.50	1,500
1200	3 pole		4.50	1.778		1,550	101		1,651	1,850
1220	Switch, nonfused, 3 pole, 4 wire		8	1		192	56.50		248.50	297
1240	Fused, 3 fuses, 4 wire, 30 amp		8	1		360	56.50		416.50	480
1260	60 amp		5.30	1.509		425	85.50		510.50	595
1280	100 amp		4.50	1.778		580	101		681	790
1300	Plug, fusible, 3 pole 250 volt, 30 amp		5.30	1.509		515	85.50		600.50	695
1310	60 amp		5.30	1.509		595	85.50		680.50	785
1320	100 amp		4.50	1.778		800	101		901	1,025
1330	3 pole 480 volt, 30 amp		5.30	1.509		530	85.50		615.50	715
1340	60 amp		5.30	1.509		570	85.50		655.50	760
1350	100 amp		4.50	1.778		825	101		926	1,050
1360	Circuit breaker, 3 pole 250 volt, 60 amp		5.30	1.509		940	85.50		1,025.50	1,150
1370	3 pole 480 volt, 100 amp		4.50	1.778	▼	940	101		1,041	1,175
2000	Bus duct, 2 wire, 250 volt, 30 amp		60	.133	L.F.	7.25	7.55		14.80	19.30
2100	60 amp		50	.160		7.25	9.05		16.30	21.50
2200	300 volt, 30 amp		60	.133		7.25	7.55		14.80	19.30
2300	60 amp		50	.160		7.25	9.05		16.30	21.50
2400	3 wire, 250 volt, 30 amp		60	.133		9.80	7.55		17.35	22
2500	60 amp		50	.160		9.60	9.05		18.65	24
2600	480/277 volt, 30 amp		60	.133		9.80	7.55		17.35	22
2700	60 amp		50	.160	▼	9.80	9.05		18.85	24.50
2750	End feed, 300 volt 2 wire max. 30 amp		6	1.333	Ea.	73	75.50		148.50	194
2800	60 amp		5.50	1.455		73	82.50		155.50	204
2850	30 amp miniature		6	1.333		73	75.50		148.50	194
2900	3 wire, 30 amp		6	1.333		92	75.50		167.50	214
2950	60 amp		5.50	1.455		92	82.50		174.50	224
3000	30 amp miniature		6	1.333		92	75.50		167.50	214
3050	Center feed, 300 volt 2 wire, 30 amp		6	1.333		101	75.50		176.50	224
3100	60 amp		5.50	1.455		101	82.50		183.50	234
3150	3 wire, 30 amp		6	1.333		115	75.50		190.50	240
3200	60 amp		5.50	1.455		115	82.50		197.50	250
3220	Elbow, 30 amp		6	1.333		39.50	75.50		115	157
3240	60 amp		5.50	1.455		39.50	82.50		122	167
3260	End cap		40	.200		8.90	11.30		20.20	27
3280	Strength beam, 10 ft.		15	.533		23.50	30		53.50	71
3300	Hanger		24	.333		5.05	18.85		23.90	34
3320	Tap box, nonfusible		6.30	1.270		75.50	72		147.50	191
3340	Fusible switch 30 amp, 1 fuse		6	1.333		460	75.50		535.50	620
3360	2 fuse		6	1.333		485	75.50		560.50	645
3380	3 fuse		6	1.333		520	75.50		595.50	685
3400	Circuit breaker handle on cover, 1 pole		6	1.333		62.50	75.50		138	182
3420	2 pole		6	1.333		530	75.50		605.50	700
3440	3 pole		6	1.333		650	75.50		725.50	830
3460	Circuit breaker external operhandle, 1 pole		6	1.333		73.50	75.50		149	194
3480	2 pole		6	1.333		685	75.50		760.50	870
3500	3 pole		6	1.333		820	75.50		895.50	1,025
3520	Terminal plug only		16	.500		83.50	28.50		112	135
3540	Terminal with receptacle		16	.500		108	28.50		136.50	162
3560	Fixture plug		16	.500	▼	74.50	28.50		103	125
4000	Copper bus duct, lighting, 2 wire 300 volt, 20 amp		70	.114	L.F.	6.90	6.45		13.35	17.30
4020	35 amp		60	.133		6.90	7.55		14.45	18.90
4040	50 amp	▼	55	.145	▼	6.90	8.25		15.15	19.95

26 25 13 – Bus Duct/Busway and Fittings

26 25 13.20 Bus Duct		Crew	Daily Output	Labor-Hours	Unit	Material	2017 Bare Costs Labor	Equipment	Total	Total Incl O&P
4060	60 amp	1 Elec	50	.160	L.F.	6.90	9.05		15.95	21
4080	3 wire 300 volt, 20 amp		70	.114		6.90	6.45		13.35	17.30
4100	35 amp		60	.133		6.75	7.55		14.30	18.75
4120	50 amp		55	.145		6.90	8.25		15.15	19.95
4140	60 amp		50	.160		6.90	9.05		15.95	21
4160	Feeder in box, end, 1 circuit		6	1.333	Ea.	94	75.50		169.50	217
4180	2 circuit		5.50	1.455		98	82.50		180.50	231
4200	Center, 1 circuit		6	1.333		130	75.50		205.50	256
4220	2 circuit		5.50	1.455		135	82.50		217.50	271
4240	End cap		40	.200		15.85	11.30		27.15	34.50
4260	Hanger, surface mount		24	.333		9.50	18.85		28.35	39
4280	Coupling		40	.200		12.05	11.30		23.35	30

26 25 13.30 Copper Bus Duct

		Crew	Daily Output	Labor-Hours	Unit	Material	2017 Bare Costs Labor	Equipment	Total	Total Incl O&P
0010	**COPPER BUS DUCT**									
0100	Weatherproof 3 pole 4 wire, feeder duct, 600 amp	2 Elec	24	.667	L.F.	282	37.50		319.50	365
0110	800 amp		18	.889		385	50.50		435.50	500
0120	1000 amp		17	.941		430	53.50		483.50	555
0125	1200 amp		16.50	.970		505	55		560	635
0130	1350 amp		16	1		525	56.50		581.50	665
0140	1600 amp		12	1.333		565	75.50		640.50	735
0150	2000 amp		10	1.600		630	90.50		720.50	825
0160	2500 amp		7	2.286		685	129		814	950
0170	3000 amp		5	3.200		950	181		1,131	1,325
0180	4000 amp		3.60	4.444		1,475	252		1,727	2,000
0200	Indoor 3 pole 4 wire, plug-in, bus duct high short circuit, 400 amp		32	.500		465	28.50		493.50	555
0210	600 amp		26	.615		525	35		560	630
0220	800 amp		20	.800		765	45.50		810.50	915
0230	1000 amp		18	.889		895	50.50		945.50	1,050
0240	1350 amp		16	1		420	56.50		476.50	550
0250	1600 amp		12	1.333		475	75.50		550.50	640
0260	2000 amp		10	1.600		605	90.50		695.50	800
0270	2500 amp		8	2		745	113		858	985
0280	3000 amp		6	2.667		850	151		1,001	1,150
0310	Cross, 225 amp		3	5.333	Ea.	2,800	300		3,100	3,525
0320	400 amp		2.80	5.714		2,800	325		3,125	3,550
0330	600 amp		2.60	6.154		2,800	350		3,150	3,600
0340	800 amp		2.20	7.273		3,025	410		3,435	3,975
0350	1000 amp		2	8		3,400	455		3,855	4,400
0360	1350 amp		1.80	8.889		3,650	505		4,155	4,750
0370	1600 amp		1.70	9.412		4,050	535		4,585	5,250
0380	2000 amp		1.60	10		6,650	565		7,215	8,150
0390	2500 amp		1.40	11.429		8,050	645		8,695	9,825
0400	3000 amp		1.20	13.333		8,800	755		9,555	10,800
0410	4000 amp		1	16		11,500	905		12,405	14,000
0430	Expansion fitting, 225 amp		5.40	2.963		1,525	168		1,693	1,925
0440	400 amp		4.60	3.478		1,725	197		1,922	2,200
0450	600 amp		4	4		2,150	226		2,376	2,700
0460	800 amp		3.40	4.706		2,525	266		2,791	3,175
0470	1000 amp		3	5.333		2,900	300		3,200	3,625
0480	1350 amp		2.80	5.714		3,325	325		3,650	4,125
0490	1600 amp		2.60	6.154		4,625	350		4,975	5,600
0500	2000 amp		2.20	7.273		5,325	410		5,735	6,475

26 25 13.30 Copper Bus Duct		Crew	Daily Output	Labor-Hours	Unit	Material	2017 Bare Costs Labor	Equipment	Total	Total Incl O&P
0510	2500 amp	2 Elec	1.80	8.889	Ea.	6,475	505		6,980	7,875
0520	3000 amp		1.60	10		7,250	565		7,815	8,825
0530	4000 amp		1.20	13.333		9,350	755		10,105	11,400
0550	Reducer nonfused, 225 amp		5.40	2.963		1,675	168		1,843	2,100
0560	400 amp		4.60	3.478		1,675	197		1,872	2,150
0570	600 amp		4	4		1,675	226		1,901	2,200
0580	800 amp		3.40	4.706		2,025	266		2,291	2,650
0590	1000 amp		3	5.333		2,450	300		2,750	3,150
0600	1350 amp		2.80	5.714		3,525	325		3,850	4,350
0610	1600 amp		2.60	6.154		4,050	350		4,400	4,975
0620	2000 amp		2.20	7.273		4,875	410		5,285	5,975
0630	2500 amp		1.80	8.889		6,125	505		6,630	7,500
0640	3000 amp		1.60	10		6,925	565		7,490	8,450
0650	4000 amp		1.20	13.333		9,000	755		9,755	11,000
0670	Reducer fuse included, 225 amp		4.40	3.636		3,600	206		3,806	4,250
0680	400 amp		4.20	3.810		4,500	216		4,716	5,275
0690	600 amp		3.60	4.444		5,550	252		5,802	6,475
0700	800 amp		3.20	5		7,825	283		8,108	9,025
0710	1000 amp		3	5.333		9,800	300		10,100	11,300
0720	1350 amp		2.80	5.714		15,200	325		15,525	17,300
0730	1600 amp		2.20	7.273		20,700	410		21,110	23,300
0740	2000 amp		1.80	8.889		23,300	505		23,805	26,400
0790	Reducer, circuit breaker, 225 amp		4.40	3.636		4,550	206		4,756	5,300
0800	400 amp		4.20	3.810		5,300	216		5,516	6,175
0810	600 amp		3.60	4.444		7,525	252		7,777	8,650
0820	800 amp		3.20	5		8,825	283		9,108	10,200
0830	1000 amp		3	5.333		10,000	300		10,300	11,500
0840	1350 amp		2.80	5.714		11,400	325		11,725	13,100
0850	1600 amp		2.20	7.273		16,900	410		17,310	19,200
0860	2000 amp		1.80	8.889		18,500	505		19,005	21,200
0910	Cable tap box, center, 225 amp		3.20	5		2,075	283		2,358	2,700
0920	400 amp		2.60	6.154		2,075	350		2,425	2,800
0930	600 amp		2.20	7.273		2,075	410		2,485	2,900
0940	800 amp		2	8		2,300	455		2,755	3,200
0950	1000 amp		1.60	10		2,475	565		3,040	3,575
0960	1350 amp		1.40	11.429		2,425	645		3,070	3,650
0970	1600 amp		1.20	13.333		2,725	755		3,480	4,100
0980	2000 amp		1	16		3,275	905		4,180	4,950
1040	2500 amp		.80	20		3,875	1,125		5,000	5,950
1060	3000 amp		.60	26.667		4,225	1,500		5,725	6,900
1080	4000 amp		.40	40		5,350	2,275		7,625	9,275
1800	Weatherproof 3 pole 3 wire, feeder duct, 600 amp		28	.571	L.F.	248	32.50		280.50	320
1820	800 amp		22	.727		300	41		341	390
1840	1000 amp		20	.800		335	45.50		380.50	440
1850	1200 amp		19	.842		350	47.50		397.50	455
1860	1350 amp		18	.889		470	50.50		520.50	595
1880	1600 amp		14	1.143		540	64.50		604.50	685
1900	2000 amp		12	1.333		690	75.50		765.50	875
1920	2500 amp		8	2		860	113		973	1,125
1940	3000 amp		6	2.667		990	151		1,141	1,300
1960	4000 amp		4	4		1,300	226		1,526	1,800
2000	Indoor 3 pole 3 wire, feeder duct, 600 amp		32	.500		207	28.50		235.50	270
2010	800 amp		26	.615		580	35		615	690

For customer support on your Electrical Costs with RSMeans Data, call 800.448.8182.

249

26 25 13.30 Copper Bus Duct		Crew	Daily Output	Labor-Hours	Unit	Material	2017 Bare Costs Labor	Equipment	Total	Total Incl O&P
2020	1000 amp	2 Elec	24	.667	L.F.	280	37.50		317.50	365
2025	1200 amp		22	.727		370	41		411	465
2030	1350 amp		20	.800		395	45.50		440.50	500
2040	1600 amp		16	1		1,075	56.50		1,131.50	1,250
2050	2000 amp		14	1.143		1,375	64.50		1,439.50	1,600
2060	2500 amp		10	1.600		715	90.50		805.50	920
2070	3000 amp		8	2		825	113		938	1,075
2080	4000 amp		6	2.667		1,100	151		1,251	1,425
2090	5000 amp		5	3.200		1,325	181		1,506	1,725
2200	Indoor 3 pole 3 wire, bus duct plug-in, 225 amp		46	.348		176	19.70		195.70	224
2210	400 amp		36	.444		267	25		292	330
2220	600 amp		30	.533		340	30		370	420
2230	800 amp		24	.667		500	37.50		537.50	605
2240	1000 amp		20	.800		540	45.50		585.50	665
2250	1350 amp		18	.889		815	50.50		865.50	975
2260	1600 amp		14	1.143		870	64.50		934.50	1,050
2270	2000 amp		12	1.333		605	75.50		680.50	780
2280	2500 amp		10	1.600		745	90.50		835.50	950
2290	3000 amp		8	2		850	113		963	1,100
2330	High short circuit, 400 amp		36	.444		320	25		345	390
2340	600 amp		30	.533		400	30		430	480
2350	800 amp		24	.667		600	37.50		637.50	715
2360	1000 amp		20	.800		650	45.50		695.50	785
2370	1350 amp		18	.889		980	50.50		1,030.50	1,150
2380	1600 amp		14	1.143		1,050	64.50		1,114.50	1,250
2390	2000 amp		12	1.333		605	75.50		680.50	780
2400	2500 amp		10	1.600		745	90.50		835.50	950
2410	3000 amp		8	2		850	113		963	1,100
2440	Elbows, 225 amp		4.60	3.478	Ea.	1,425	197		1,622	1,850
2450	400 amp		4.20	3.810		1,425	216		1,641	1,875
2460	600 amp		3.60	4.444		1,425	252		1,677	1,925
2470	800 amp		3.20	5		1,525	283		1,808	2,100
2480	1000 amp		3	5.333		1,600	300		1,900	2,200
2485	1200 amp		2.90	5.517		1,425	310		1,735	2,050
2490	1350 amp		2.80	5.714		1,825	325		2,150	2,475
2500	1600 amp		2.60	6.154		1,950	350		2,300	2,675
2510	2000 amp		2	8		1,975	455		2,430	2,850
2520	2500 amp		1.80	8.889		3,000	505		3,505	4,050
2530	3000 amp		1.60	10		3,275	565		3,840	4,450
2540	4000 amp		1.40	11.429		4,200	645		4,845	5,600
2560	Tee fittings, 225 amp		2.80	5.714		1,400	325		1,725	2,000
2570	400 amp		2.40	6.667		1,400	375		1,775	2,100
2580	600 amp		2	8		1,400	455		1,855	2,200
2590	800 amp		1.80	8.889		1,525	505		2,030	2,425
2600	1000 amp		1.60	10		1,700	565		2,265	2,725
2605	1200 amp		1.50	10.667		1,800	605		2,405	2,900
2610	1350 amp		1.40	11.429		1,900	645		2,545	3,050
2620	1600 amp		1.20	13.333		2,200	755		2,955	3,550
2630	2000 amp		1	16		3,650	905		4,555	5,375
2640	2500 amp		.70	22.857		4,275	1,300		5,575	6,650
2650	3000 amp		.60	26.667		4,725	1,500		6,225	7,425
2660	4000 amp		.50	32		6,100	1,800		7,900	9,425
2680	Cross, 225 amp		3.60	4.444		2,125	252		2,377	2,725

26 25 13.30 Copper Bus Duct		Crew	Daily Output	Labor-Hours	Unit	Material	2017 Bare Costs Labor	2017 Bare Costs Equipment	Total	Total Incl O&P
2690	400 amp	2 Elec	3.20	5	Ea.	2,125	283		2,408	2,775
2700	600 amp		3	5.333		2,125	300		2,425	2,800
2710	800 amp		2.60	6.154		2,550	350		2,900	3,325
2720	1000 amp		2.40	6.667		2,650	375		3,025	3,500
2730	1350 amp		2.20	7.273		3,025	410		3,435	3,950
2740	1600 amp		2	8		3,250	455		3,705	4,250
2750	2000 amp		1.80	8.889		5,150	505		5,655	6,425
2760	2500 amp		1.60	10		6,000	565		6,565	7,450
2770	3000 amp		1.40	11.429		6,550	645		7,195	8,200
2780	4000 amp		1	16		8,400	905		9,305	10,600
2800	Expansion fitting, 225 amp		6.40	2.500		1,775	142		1,917	2,150
2810	400 amp		5.40	2.963		4,825	168		4,993	5,550
2820	600 amp		4.60	3.478		1,775	197		1,972	2,250
2830	800 amp		4	4		2,125	226		2,351	2,675
2840	1000 amp		3.60	4.444		2,325	252		2,577	2,925
2850	1350 amp		3.20	5		2,750	283		3,033	3,450
2860	1600 amp		3	5.333		3,025	300		3,325	3,775
2870	2000 amp		2.60	6.154		3,500	350		3,850	4,375
2880	2500 amp		2.20	7.273		4,875	410		5,285	6,000
2890	3000 amp		1.80	8.889		5,450	505		5,955	6,750
2900	4000 amp		1.40	11.429		6,950	645		7,595	8,625
2920	Reducer nonfused, 225 amp		6.40	2.500		1,375	142		1,517	1,725
2930	400 amp		5.40	2.963		1,375	168		1,543	1,775
2940	600 amp		4.60	3.478		1,375	197		1,572	1,825
2950	800 amp		4	4		1,600	226		1,826	2,125
2960	1000 amp		3.60	4.444		1,800	252		2,052	2,350
2970	1350 amp		3.20	5		2,275	283		2,558	2,925
2980	1600 amp		3	5.333		2,575	300		2,875	3,275
2990	2000 amp		2.60	6.154		3,100	350		3,450	3,925
3000	2500 amp		2.20	7.273		4,525	410		4,935	5,600
3010	3000 amp		1.80	8.889		5,075	505		5,580	6,325
3020	4000 amp		1.40	11.429		6,575	645		7,220	8,225
3040	Reducer fuse included, 225 amp		5	3.200		3,275	181		3,456	3,875
3050	400 amp		4.80	3.333		4,350	189		4,539	5,050
3060	600 amp		4.20	3.810		5,175	216		5,391	6,025
3070	800 amp		3.60	4.444		7,375	252		7,627	8,475
3080	1000 amp		3.40	4.706		8,725	266		8,991	10,000
3090	1350 amp		3.20	5		8,450	283		8,733	9,725
3100	1600 amp		2.60	6.154		19,700	350		20,050	22,100
3110	2000 amp		2	8		22,300	455		22,755	25,200
3160	Reducer circuit breaker, 225 amp		5	3.200		4,175	181		4,356	4,875
3170	400 amp		4.80	3.333		5,100	189		5,289	5,900
3180	600 amp		4.20	3.810		7,325	216		7,541	8,400
3190	800 amp		3.60	4.444		8,575	252		8,827	9,800
3200	1000 amp		3.40	4.706		9,750	266		10,016	11,100
3210	1350 amp		3.20	5		11,200	283		11,483	12,700
3220	1600 amp		2.60	6.154		16,700	350		17,050	18,800
3230	2000 amp		2	8		18,200	455		18,655	20,800
3280	3 pole, 3 wire, cable tap box center, 225 amp		3.60	4.444		2,350	252		2,602	2,975
3290	400 amp		3	5.333		2,350	300		2,650	3,050
3300	600 amp		2.60	6.154		2,350	350		2,700	3,125
3310	800 amp		2.40	6.667		2,625	375		3,000	3,475
3320	1000 amp		1.80	8.889		2,850	505		3,355	3,875

For customer support on your Electrical Costs with RSMeans Data, call 800.448.8182.

251

26 25 13 – Bus Duct/Busway and Fittings

26 25 13.30 Copper Bus Duct		Crew	Daily Output	Labor-Hours	Unit	Material	2017 Bare Costs Labor	Equipment	Total	Total Incl O&P
3330	1350 amp	2 Elec	1.60	10	Ea.	3,500	565		4,065	4,700
3340	1600 amp		1.40	11.429		3,900	645		4,545	5,275
3350	2000 amp		1.20	13.333		3,875	755		4,630	5,375
3360	2500 amp		1	16		4,625	905		5,530	6,425
3370	3000 amp		.70	22.857		5,075	1,300		6,375	7,550
3380	4000 amp		.50	32		6,450	1,800		8,250	9,825
3400	Cable tap box end, 225 amp		3.60	4.444		1,275	252		1,527	1,775
3410	400 amp		3	5.333		1,275	300		1,575	1,850
3420	600 amp		2.60	6.154		1,425	350		1,775	2,100
3430	800 amp		2.40	6.667		1,425	375		1,800	2,150
3440	1000 amp		1.80	8.889		1,575	505		2,080	2,475
3445	1200 amp		1.70	9.412		1,450	535		1,985	2,400
3450	1350 amp		1.60	10		1,875	565		2,440	2,900
3460	1600 amp		1.40	11.429		2,150	645		2,795	3,350
3470	2000 amp		1.20	13.333		2,000	755		2,755	3,325
3480	2500 amp		1	16		2,400	905		3,305	4,000
3490	3000 amp		.70	22.857		2,625	1,300		3,925	4,850
3500	4000 amp	▼	.50	32		3,325	1,800		5,125	6,400
4600	Plug-in, fusible switch w/3 fuses, 3 pole, 250 volt, 30 amp	1 Elec	4	2		410	113		523	620
4610	60 amp		3.60	2.222		535	126		661	775
4620	100 amp	▼	2.70	2.963		765	168		933	1,100
4630	200 amp	2 Elec	3.20	5		1,275	283		1,558	1,825
4640	400 amp		1.40	11.429		3,350	645		3,995	4,650
4650	600 amp	▼	.90	17.778		4,625	1,000		5,625	6,600
4700	4 pole, 120/208 volt, 30 amp	1 Elec	3.90	2.051		560	116		676	790
4710	60 amp		3.50	2.286		600	129		729	855
4720	100 amp	▼	2.60	3.077		840	174		1,014	1,175
4730	200 amp	2 Elec	3	5.333		1,400	300		1,700	2,000
4740	400 amp		1.30	12.308		3,300	695		3,995	4,675
4750	600 amp	▼	.80	20		4,625	1,125		5,750	6,800
4800	3 pole, 480 volt, 30 amp	1 Elec	4	2		420	113		533	630
4810	60 amp		3.60	2.222		445	126		571	675
4820	100 amp	▼	2.70	2.963		745	168		913	1,075
4830	200 amp	2 Elec	3.20	5		1,275	283		1,558	1,825
4840	400 amp		1.40	11.429		3,000	645		3,645	4,250
4850	600 amp		.90	17.778		4,250	1,000		5,250	6,175
4860	800 amp		.66	24.242		15,100	1,375		16,475	18,700
4870	1000 amp		.60	26.667		16,000	1,500		17,500	19,900
4880	1200 amp		.50	32		16,900	1,800		18,700	21,200
4890	1600 amp	▼	.44	36.364		18,500	2,050		20,550	23,500
4900	4 pole, 277/480 volt, 30 amp	1 Elec	3.90	2.051		605	116		721	840
4910	60 amp		3.50	2.286		645	129		774	905
4920	100 amp	▼	2.60	3.077		940	174		1,114	1,275
4930	200 amp	2 Elec	3	5.333		1,875	300		2,175	2,500
4940	400 amp		1.30	12.308		3,525	695		4,220	4,925
4950	600 amp		.80	20		4,825	1,125		5,950	7,000
5050	800 amp		.60	26.667		15,900	1,500		17,400	19,800
5060	1000 amp		.56	28.571		18,300	1,625		19,925	22,500
5070	1200 amp		.48	33.333		18,500	1,875		20,375	23,100
5080	1600 amp	▼	.42	38.095		20,400	2,150		22,550	25,600
5150	Fusible with starter, 3 pole 250 volt, 30 amp	1 Elec	3.50	2.286		2,800	129		2,929	3,275
5160	60 amp		3.20	2.500		2,950	142		3,092	3,450
5170	100 amp	▼	2.50	3.200		3,350	181		3,531	3,950

For customer support on your Electrical Costs with RSMeans Data, call 800.448.8182.

26 25 13.30 Copper Bus Duct		Crew	Daily Output	Labor-Hours	Unit	Material	2017 Bare Costs Labor	Equipment	Total	Total Incl O&P
5180	200 amp	2 Elec	2.80	5.714	Ea.	5,525	325		5,850	6,550
5200	3 pole 480 volt, 30 amp	1 Elec	3.50	2.286		2,800	129		2,929	3,275
5210	60 amp		3.20	2.500		2,950	142		3,092	3,450
5220	100 amp		2.50	3.200		3,350	181		3,531	3,950
5230	200 amp	2 Elec	2.80	5.714		5,525	325		5,850	6,550
5300	Fusible with contactor, 3 pole 250 volt, 30 amp	1 Elec	3.50	2.286		2,725	129		2,854	3,200
5310	60 amp		3.20	2.500		3,475	142		3,617	4,000
5320	100 amp		2.50	3.200		4,850	181		5,031	5,600
5330	200 amp	2 Elec	2.80	5.714		5,550	325		5,875	6,575
5400	3 pole 480 volt, 30 amp	1 Elec	3.50	2.286		2,925	129		3,054	3,425
5410	60 amp		3.20	2.500		4,125	142		4,267	4,750
5420	100 amp		2.50	3.200		5,675	181		5,856	6,525
5430	200 amp	2 Elec	2.80	5.714		5,800	325		6,125	6,875
5450	Fusible with capacitor, 3 pole 250 volt, 30 amp	1 Elec	3	2.667		7,075	151		7,226	8,000
5460	60 amp		2	4		8,225	226		8,451	9,400
5500	3 pole 480 volt, 30 amp		3	2.667		5,925	151		6,076	6,750
5510	60 amp		2	4		7,400	226		7,626	8,500
5600	Circuit breaker, 3 pole, 250 volt, 60 amp		4.50	1.778		575	101		676	780
5610	100 amp		3.20	2.500		705	142		847	985
5650	4 pole, 120/208 volt, 60 amp		4.40	1.818		650	103		753	870
5660	100 amp		3.10	2.581		770	146		916	1,075
5700	3 pole, 4 wire 277/480 volt, 60 amp		4.30	1.860		875	105		980	1,125
5710	100 amp		3	2.667		970	151		1,121	1,300
5720	225 amp	2 Elec	3.20	5		2,150	283		2,433	2,800
5730	400 amp		1.20	13.333		4,475	755		5,230	6,050
5740	600 amp		.96	16.667		6,000	945		6,945	8,025
5750	700 amp		.60	26.667		7,600	1,500		9,100	10,600
5760	800 amp		.60	26.667		7,600	1,500		9,100	10,600
5770	900 amp		.54	29.630		10,000	1,675		11,675	13,500
5780	1000 amp		.54	29.630		10,000	1,675		11,675	13,500
5790	1200 amp		.42	38.095		12,000	2,150		14,150	16,500
5810	Circuit breaker w/HIC fuses, 3 pole 480 volt, 60 amp	1 Elec	4.40	1.818		1,100	103		1,203	1,350
5820	100 amp	"	3.10	2.581		1,200	146		1,346	1,550
5830	225 amp	2 Elec	3.40	4.706		3,850	266		4,116	4,625
5840	400 amp		1.40	11.429		6,100	645		6,745	7,700
5850	600 amp		1	16		6,175	905		7,080	8,150
5860	700 amp		.64	25		8,200	1,425		9,625	11,200
5870	800 amp		.64	25		8,200	1,425		9,625	11,200
5880	900 amp		.56	28.571		17,700	1,625		19,325	21,900
5890	1000 amp		.56	28.571		17,700	1,625		19,325	21,900
5950	3 pole 4 wire 277/480 volt, 60 amp	1 Elec	4.30	1.860		1,100	105		1,205	1,350
5960	100 amp	"	3	2.667		1,200	151		1,351	1,550
5970	225 amp	2 Elec	3	5.333		3,850	300		4,150	4,675
5980	400 amp		1.10	14.545		6,100	825		6,925	7,950
5990	600 amp		.94	17.021		6,175	965		7,140	8,250
6000	700 amp		.58	27.586		8,200	1,550		9,750	11,400
6010	800 amp		.58	27.586		8,200	1,550		9,750	11,400
6020	900 amp		.52	30.769		17,700	1,750		19,450	22,100
6030	1000 amp		.52	30.769		17,700	1,750		19,450	22,100
6040	1200 amp		.40	40		17,700	2,275		19,975	22,900
6100	Circuit breaker with starter, 3 pole 250 volt, 60 amp	1 Elec	3.20	2.500		1,750	142		1,892	2,125
6110	100 amp	"	2.50	3.200		2,425	181		2,606	2,950
6120	225 amp	2 Elec	3	5.333		3,125	300		3,425	3,875

26 25 13.30 Copper Bus Duct

		Crew	Daily Output	Labor-Hours	Unit	Material	2017 Bare Costs Labor	Equipment	Total	Total Incl O&P
6130	3 pole 480 volt, 60 amp	1 Elec	3.20	2.500	Ea.	1,750	142		1,892	2,125
6140	100 amp	"	2.50	3.200		2,425	181		2,606	2,950
6150	225 amp	2 Elec	3	5.333		2,975	300		3,275	3,725
6200	Circuit breaker with contactor, 3 pole 250 volt, 60 amp	1 Elec	3.20	2.500		1,650	142		1,792	2,025
6210	100 amp	"	2.50	3.200		2,250	181		2,431	2,750
6220	225 amp	2 Elec	3	5.333		2,900	300		3,200	3,625
6250	3 pole 480 volt, 60 amp	1 Elec	3.20	2.500		1,650	142		1,792	2,025
6260	100 amp	"	2.50	3.200		2,250	181		2,431	2,750
6270	225 amp	2 Elec	3	5.333		2,775	300		3,075	3,500
6300	Circuit breaker with capacitor, 3 pole 250 volt, 60 amp	1 Elec	2	4		8,950	226		9,176	10,200
6310	3 pole 480 volt, 60 amp		2	4		9,000	226		9,226	10,200
6400	Add control transformer with pilot light to above starter		16	.500		495	28.50		523.50	590
6410	Switch, fusible, mechanically held contactor optional		16	.500		1,300	28.50		1,328.50	1,475
6430	Circuit breaker, mechanically held contactor optional		16	.500		1,300	28.50		1,328.50	1,475
6450	Ground neutralizer, 3 pole		16	.500		60.50	28.50		89	109

26 25 13.40 Copper Bus Duct

		Crew	Daily Output	Labor-Hours	Unit	Material	2017 Bare Costs Labor	Equipment	Total	Total Incl O&P
0010	**COPPER BUS DUCT** 10 ft. long									
0050	Indoor 3 pole 4 wire, plug-in, straight section, 225 amp	2 Elec	40	.400	L.F.	229	22.50		251.50	286
1000	400 amp		32	.500		385	28.50		413.50	470
1500	600 amp		26	.615		440	35		475	530
2400	800 amp		20	.800		640	45.50		685.50	770
2450	1000 amp		18	.889		300	50.50		350.50	405
2470	1200 amp		17	.941		395	53.50		448.50	510
2500	1350 amp		16	1		415	56.50		471.50	540
2510	1600 amp		12	1.333		470	75.50		545.50	630
2520	2000 amp		10	1.600		595	90.50		685.50	790
2530	2500 amp		8	2		730	113		843	975
2540	3000 amp		6	2.667		840	151		991	1,150
2550	Feeder, 600 amp		28	.571		204	32.50		236.50	273
2600	800 amp		22	.727		750	41		791	885
2700	1000 amp		20	.800		885	45.50		930.50	1,050
2750	1200 amp		19	.842		1,050	47.50		1,097.50	1,250
2800	1350 amp		18	.889		385	50.50		435.50	500
2900	1600 amp		14	1.143		1,425	64.50		1,489.50	1,675
3000	2000 amp		12	1.333		1,775	75.50		1,850.50	2,075
3010	2500 amp		8	2		705	113		818	945
3020	3000 amp		6	2.667		810	151		961	1,125
3030	4000 amp		4	4		1,075	226		1,301	1,525
3040	5000 amp		2	8		1,300	455		1,755	2,125
3100	Elbows, 225 amp		4	4	Ea.	1,575	226		1,801	2,075
3200	400 amp		3.60	4.444		1,575	252		1,827	2,100
3300	600 amp		3.20	5		1,575	283		1,858	2,150
3400	800 amp		2.80	5.714		1,700	325		2,025	2,350
3500	1000 amp		2.60	6.154		1,900	350		2,250	2,625
3550	1200 amp		2.50	6.400		1,850	360		2,210	2,600
3600	1350 amp		2.40	6.667		1,875	375		2,250	2,650
3700	1600 amp		2.20	7.273		2,050	410		2,460	2,875
3800	2000 amp		1.80	8.889		2,525	505		3,030	3,525
3810	2500 amp		1.60	10		4,000	565		4,565	5,250
3820	3000 amp		1.40	11.429		4,375	645		5,020	5,775
3830	4000 amp		1.20	13.333		5,650	755		6,405	7,350
3840	5000 amp		1	16		9,150	905		10,055	11,500

26 25 13.40 Copper Bus Duct		Crew	Daily Output	Labor-Hours	Unit	Material	2017 Bare Costs Labor	Equipment	Total	Total Incl O&P
4000	End box, 225 amp	2 Elec	34	.471	Ea.	174	26.50		200.50	231
4100	400 amp		32	.500		188	28.50		216.50	250
4200	600 amp		28	.571		188	32.50		220.50	256
4300	800 amp		26	.615		188	35		223	259
4400	1000 amp		24	.667		182	37.50		219.50	258
4410	1200 amp		23	.696		188	39.50		227.50	266
4500	1350 amp		22	.727		179	41		220	258
4600	1600 amp		20	.800		179	45.50		224.50	264
4700	2000 amp		18	.889		219	50.50		269.50	315
4710	2500 amp		16	1		219	56.50		275.50	325
4720	3000 amp		14	1.143		208	64.50		272.50	325
4730	4000 amp		12	1.333		251	75.50		326.50	390
4740	5000 amp		10	1.600		251	90.50		341.50	410
4800	Cable tap box end, 225 amp		3.20	5		1,200	283		1,483	1,750
5000	400 amp		2.60	6.154		1,200	350		1,550	1,850
5100	600 amp		2.20	7.273		1,650	410		2,060	2,450
5200	800 amp		2	8		1,750	455		2,205	2,575
5300	1000 amp		1.60	10		1,750	565		2,315	2,775
5350	1200 amp		1.50	10.667		2,000	605		2,605	3,100
5400	1350 amp		1.40	11.429		2,250	645		2,895	3,450
5500	1600 amp		1.20	13.333		2,500	755		3,255	3,875
5600	2000 amp		1	16		2,800	905		3,705	4,425
5610	2500 amp		.80	20		3,100	1,125		4,225	5,100
5620	3000 amp		.60	26.667		3,625	1,500		5,125	6,225
5630	4000 amp		.40	40		4,175	2,275		6,450	8,000
5640	5000 amp		.20	80		4,925	4,525		9,450	12,200
5700	Switchboard stub, 225 amp		5.40	2.963		1,250	168		1,418	1,650
5800	400 amp		4.60	3.478		1,325	197		1,522	1,750
5900	600 amp		4	4		1,375	226		1,601	1,875
6000	800 amp		3.20	5		1,675	283		1,958	2,250
6100	1000 amp		3	5.333		1,925	300		2,225	2,575
6150	1200 amp		2.80	5.714		2,275	325		2,600	2,975
6200	1350 amp		2.60	6.154		2,400	350		2,750	3,150
6300	1600 amp		2.40	6.667		2,700	375		3,075	3,550
6400	2000 amp		2	8		3,275	455		3,730	4,275
6410	2500 amp		1.80	8.889		3,975	505		4,480	5,125
6420	3000 amp		1.60	10		4,425	565		4,990	5,700
6430	4000 amp		1.40	11.429		5,750	645		6,395	7,300
6440	5000 amp		1.20	13.333		7,050	755		7,805	8,875
6490	Tee fittings, 225 amp		2.40	6.667		2,175	375		2,550	2,975
6500	400 amp		2	8		2,175	455		2,630	3,075
6600	600 amp		1.80	8.889		2,175	505		2,680	3,150
6700	800 amp		1.60	10		2,250	565		2,815	3,350
6750	1000 amp		1.40	11.429		2,575	645		3,220	3,800
6770	1200 amp		1.30	12.308		2,875	695		3,570	4,225
6800	1350 amp		1.20	13.333		3,025	755		3,700	4,475
7000	1600 amp		1	16		3,450	905		4,355	5,150
7100	2000 amp		.80	20		4,100	1,125		5,225	6,200
7110	2500 amp		.60	26.667		5,025	1,500		6,525	7,775
7120	3000 amp		.50	32		5,550	1,800		7,350	8,825
7130	4000 amp		.40	40		7,175	2,275		9,450	11,300
7140	5000 amp		.20	80		8,500	4,525		13,025	16,100
7200	Plug-in fusible switches w/3 fuses, 600 volt, 3 pole, 30 amp	1 Elec	4	2		860	113		973	1,125

For customer support on your Electrical Costs with RSMeans Data, call 800.448.8182.

255

26 25 13.40 Copper Bus Duct	Crew	Daily Output	Labor-Hours	Unit	Material	2017 Bare Costs Labor	Equipment	Total	Total Incl O&P
7300	60 amp	1 Elec	3.60	2.222	Ea.	970	126		1,096	1,275
7400	100 amp	↓	2.70	2.963		1,325	168		1,493	1,700
7500	200 amp	2 Elec	3.20	5		2,325	283		2,608	3,000
7600	400 amp		1.40	11.429		6,500	645		7,145	8,125
7700	600 amp		.90	17.778		7,850	1,000		8,850	10,100
7800	800 amp		.66	24.242		12,300	1,375		13,675	15,600
7900	1200 amp		.50	32		23,100	1,800		24,900	28,100
7910	1600 amp	↓	.44	36.364		21,900	2,050		23,950	27,200
8000	Plug-in circuit breakers, molded case, 15 to 50 amp	1 Elec	4.40	1.818		815	103		918	1,050
8100	70 to 100 amp	"	3.10	2.581		905	146		1,051	1,225
8200	150 to 225 amp	2 Elec	3.40	4.706		2,450	266		2,716	3,100
8300	250 to 400 amp		1.40	11.429		4,300	645		4,945	5,725
8400	500 to 600 amp		1	16		5,825	905		6,730	7,750
8500	700 to 800 amp		.64	25		7,175	1,425		8,600	10,000
8600	900 to 1000 amp		.56	28.571		10,300	1,625		11,925	13,700
8700	1200 amp		.44	36.364		12,400	2,050		14,450	16,700
8720	1400 amp		.40	40		17,300	2,275		19,575	22,500
8730	1600 amp	↓	.40	40		19,000	2,275		21,275	24,300
8750	Circuit breakers, with current limiting fuse, 15 to 50 amp	1 Elec	4.40	1.818		1,625	103		1,728	1,950
8760	70 to 100 amp	"	3.10	2.581		1,925	146		2,071	2,350
8770	150 to 225 amp	2 Elec	3.40	4.706		4,150	266		4,416	4,975
8780	250 to 400 amp		1.40	11.429		6,425	645		7,070	8,050
8790	500 to 600 amp		1	16		7,400	905		8,305	9,500
8800	700 to 800 amp		.64	25		12,200	1,425		13,625	15,500
8810	900 to 1000 amp	↓	.56	28.571		13,900	1,625		15,525	17,700
8850	Combination starter FVNR, fusible switch, NEMA size 0, 30 amp	1 Elec	2	4		2,200	226		2,426	2,775
8860	NEMA size 1, 60 amp		1.80	4.444		2,350	252		2,602	2,950
8870	NEMA size 2, 100 amp	↓	1.30	6.154		2,950	350		3,300	3,750
8880	NEMA size 3, 200 amp	2 Elec	2	8		4,675	455		5,130	5,825
8900	Circuit breaker, NEMA size 0, 30 amp	1 Elec	2	4		2,275	226		2,501	2,850
8910	NEMA size 1, 60 amp		1.80	4.444		2,350	252		2,602	2,975
8920	NEMA size 2, 100 amp	↓	1.30	6.154		3,375	350		3,725	4,250
8930	NEMA size 3, 200 amp	2 Elec	2	8		4,300	455		4,755	5,400
8950	Combination contactor, fusible switch, NEMA size 0, 30 amp	1 Elec	2	4		1,275	226		1,501	1,775
8960	NEMA size 1, 60 amp		1.80	4.444		1,325	252		1,577	1,825
8970	NEMA size 2, 100 amp	↓	1.30	6.154		1,975	350		2,325	2,700
8980	NEMA size 3, 200 amp	2 Elec	2	8		2,275	455		2,730	3,175
9000	Circuit breaker, NEMA size 0, 30 amp	1 Elec	2	4		1,475	226		1,701	1,975
9010	NEMA size 1, 60 amp		1.80	4.444		1,525	252		1,777	2,050
9020	NEMA size 2, 100 amp	↓	1.30	6.154		2,325	350		2,675	3,100
9030	NEMA size 3, 200 amp	2 Elec	2	8		2,825	455		3,280	3,800
9050	Control transformer for above, NEMA size 0, 30 amp	1 Elec	8	1		250	56.50		306.50	360
9060	NEMA size 1, 60 amp		8	1		250	56.50		306.50	360
9070	NEMA size 2, 100 amp	↓	7	1.143		350	64.50		414.50	480
9080	NEMA size 3, 200 amp	2 Elec	14	1.143		485	64.50		549.50	625
9100	Comb. fusible switch & lighting control, electrically held, 30 amp	1 Elec	2	4		1,025	226		1,251	1,475
9110	60 amp		1.80	4.444		1,475	252		1,727	2,000
9120	100 amp	↓	1.30	6.154		1,900	350		2,250	2,600
9130	200 amp	2 Elec	2	8		4,650	455		5,105	5,800
9150	Mechanically held, 30 amp	1 Elec	2	4		1,275	226		1,501	1,750
9160	60 amp		1.80	4.444		1,900	252		2,152	2,475
9170	100 amp	↓	1.30	6.154		2,450	350		2,800	3,225
9180	200 amp	2 Elec	2	8		5,000	455		5,455	6,175

26 25 Enclosed Bus Assemblies

26 25 13 – Bus Duct/Busway and Fittings

26 25 13.40 Copper Bus Duct

		Crew	Daily Output	Labor-Hours	Unit	Material	2017 Bare Costs Labor	Equipment	Total	Total Incl O&P
9200	Ground bus added to bus duct, 225 amp	2 Elec	370	.050	L.F.	44.50	2.83		47.33	52.50
9210	400 amp		240	.067		44.50	3.77		48.27	54
9220	600 amp		240	.067		44.50	3.77		48.27	54
9230	800 amp		160	.100		51.50	5.65		57.15	65.50
9240	1000 amp		160	.100		59	5.65		64.65	73.50
9250	1350 amp		140	.114		84	6.45		90.45	102
9260	1600 amp		120	.133		91	7.55		98.55	111
9270	2000 amp		110	.145		119	8.25		127.25	143
9280	2500 amp		100	.160		147	9.05		156.05	176
9290	3000 amp		90	.178		166	10.05		176.05	198
9300	4000 amp		80	.200		219	11.30		230.30	258
9310	5000 amp		70	.229		266	12.95		278.95	310
9320	High short circuit bracing, add					18.55			18.55	20.50

26 25 13.60 Copper or Aluminum Bus Duct Fittings

		Crew	Daily Output	Labor-Hours	Unit	Material	2017 Bare Costs Labor	Equipment	Total	Total Incl O&P
0010	**COPPER OR ALUMINUM BUS DUCT FITTINGS**									
0100	Flange, wall, with vapor barrier, 225 amp	2 Elec	6.20	2.581	Ea.	805	146		951	1,100
0110	400 amp		6	2.667		795	151		946	1,100
0120	600 amp		5.80	2.759		805	156		961	1,125
0130	800 amp		5.40	2.963		805	168		973	1,150
0140	1000 amp		5	3.200		805	181		986	1,150
0145	1200 amp		4.80	3.333		805	189		994	1,175
0150	1350 amp		4.60	3.478		805	197		1,002	1,175
0160	1600 amp		4.20	3.810		805	216		1,021	1,225
0170	2000 amp		4	4		805	226		1,031	1,225
0180	2500 amp		3.60	4.444		805	252		1,057	1,275
0190	3000 amp		3.20	5		805	283		1,088	1,325
0200	4000 amp		2.60	6.154		805	350		1,155	1,400
0300	Roof, 225 amp		6.20	2.581		930	146		1,076	1,250
0310	400 amp		6	2.667		930	151		1,081	1,250
0320	600 amp		5.80	2.759		930	156		1,086	1,250
0330	800 amp		5.40	2.963		930	168		1,098	1,275
0340	1000 amp		5	3.200		930	181		1,111	1,300
0345	1200 amp		4.80	3.333		930	189		1,119	1,300
0350	1350 amp		4.60	3.478		930	197		1,127	1,325
0360	1600 amp		4.20	3.810		930	216		1,146	1,350
0370	2000 amp		4	4		930	226		1,156	1,375
0380	2500 amp		3.60	4.444		930	252		1,182	1,400
0390	3000 amp		3.20	5		930	283		1,213	1,450
0400	4000 amp		2.60	6.154		930	350		1,280	1,550
0420	Support, floor mounted, 225 amp		20	.800		169	45.50		214.50	254
0430	400 amp		20	.800		169	45.50		214.50	254
0440	600 amp		18	.889		169	50.50		219.50	262
0450	800 amp		16	1		169	56.50		225.50	271
0460	1000 amp		13	1.231		169	69.50		238.50	290
0465	1200 amp		11.80	1.356		169	77		246	300
0470	1350 amp		10.60	1.509		169	85.50		254.50	315
0480	1600 amp		9.20	1.739		169	98.50		267.50	335
0490	2000 amp		8	2		169	113		282	355
0500	2500 amp		6.40	2.500		169	142		311	400
0510	3000 amp		5.40	2.963		169	168		337	435
0520	4000 amp		4	4		169	226		395	525
0540	Weather stop, 225 amp		12	1.333		520	75.50		595.50	690

For customer support on your Electrical Costs with RSMeans Data, call 800.448.8182.

257

26 25 13.60 Copper or Aluminum Bus Duct Fittings		Crew	Daily Output	Labor-Hours	Unit	Material	2017 Bare Costs Labor	Equipment	Total	Total Incl O&P
0550	400 amp	2 Elec	10	1.600	Ea.	520	90.50		610.50	710
0560	600 amp		9	1.778		520	101		621	725
0570	800 amp		8	2		520	113		633	745
0580	1000 amp		6.40	2.500		520	142		662	785
0585	1200 amp		5.90	2.712		520	153		673	805
0590	1350 amp		5.40	2.963		520	168		688	825
0600	1600 amp		4.60	3.478		520	197		717	870
0610	2000 amp		4	4		520	226		746	915
0620	2500 amp		3.20	5		520	283		803	1,000
0630	3000 amp		2.60	6.154		520	350		870	1,100
0640	4000 amp		2	8		520	455		975	1,250
0660	End closure, 225 amp		34	.471		194	26.50		220.50	253
0670	400 amp		32	.500		194	28.50		222.50	256
0680	600 amp		28	.571		194	32.50		226.50	262
0690	800 amp		26	.615		175	35		210	245
0700	1000 amp		24	.667		194	37.50		231.50	270
0705	1200 amp		23	.696		168	39.50		207.50	244
0710	1350 amp		22	.727		168	41		209	247
0720	1600 amp		20	.800		194	45.50		239.50	281
0730	2000 amp		18	.889		269	50.50		319.50	370
0740	2500 amp		16	1		249	56.50		305.50	360
0750	3000 amp		14	1.143		249	64.50		313.50	370
0760	4000 amp		12	1.333		249	75.50		324.50	385
0780	Switchboard stub, 3 pole 3 wire, 225 amp		6	2.667		1,000	151		1,151	1,325
0790	400 amp		5.20	3.077		1,000	174		1,174	1,350
0800	600 amp		4.60	3.478		1,000	197		1,197	1,400
0810	800 amp		3.60	4.444		1,225	252		1,477	1,725
0820	1000 amp		3.40	4.706		1,425	266		1,691	1,975
0825	1200 amp		3.20	5		1,425	283		1,708	2,000
0830	1350 amp		3	5.333		1,725	300		2,025	2,325
0840	1600 amp		2.80	5.714		2,025	325		2,350	2,700
0850	2000 amp		2.40	6.667		2,350	375		2,725	3,175
0860	2500 amp		2	8		2,850	455		3,305	3,825
0870	3000 amp		1.80	8.889		3,275	505		3,780	4,350
0880	4000 amp		1.60	10		4,225	565		4,790	5,500
0890	5000 amp		1.40	11.429		5,200	645		5,845	6,700
0900	3 pole 4 wire, 225 amp		5.40	2.963		1,250	168		1,418	1,625
0910	400 amp		4.60	3.478		1,250	197		1,447	1,675
0920	600 amp		4	4		1,250	226		1,476	1,725
0930	800 amp		3.20	5		1,525	283		1,808	2,100
0940	1000 amp		3	5.333		1,775	300		2,075	2,400
0950	1350 amp		2.60	6.154		2,275	350		2,625	3,025
0960	1600 amp		2.40	6.667		2,575	375		2,950	3,400
0970	2000 amp		2	8		3,100	455		3,555	4,100
0980	2500 amp		1.80	8.889		3,775	505		4,280	4,925
0990	3000 amp		1.60	10		4,425	565		4,990	5,725
1000	4000 amp		1.40	11.429		5,750	645		6,395	7,300
1050	Service head, weatherproof, 3 pole 3 wire, 225 amp		3	5.333		1,725	300		2,025	2,325
1060	400 amp		2.80	5.714		1,725	325		2,050	2,350
1070	600 amp		2.60	6.154		1,725	350		2,075	2,400
1080	800 amp		2.40	6.667		1,925	375		2,300	2,700
1090	1000 amp		2	8		2,075	455		2,530	2,975
1100	1350 amp		1.80	8.889		2,700	505		3,205	3,725

26 25 13.60 Copper or Aluminum Bus Duct Fittings		Crew	Daily Output	Labor-Hours	Unit	Material	2017 Bare Costs Labor	Equipment	Total	Total Incl O&P
1110	1600 amp	2 Elec	1.60	10	Ea.	3,025	565		3,590	4,175
1120	2000 amp		1.40	11.429		3,675	645		4,320	5,025
1130	2500 amp		1.20	13.333		4,400	755		5,155	5,950
1140	3000 amp		.90	17.778		5,125	1,000		6,125	7,125
1150	4000 amp		.70	22.857		6,500	1,300		7,800	9,100
1200	3 pole 4 wire, 225 amp		2.60	6.154		1,925	350		2,275	2,625
1210	400 amp		2.40	6.667		1,925	375		2,300	2,675
1220	600 amp		2.20	7.273		1,925	410		2,335	2,725
1230	800 amp		2	8		2,225	455		2,680	3,125
1240	1000 amp		1.70	9.412		2,575	535		3,110	3,625
1250	1350 amp		1.50	10.667		3,050	605		3,655	4,250
1260	1600 amp		1.40	11.429		3,325	645		3,970	4,625
1270	2000 amp		1.20	13.333		4,450	755		5,205	6,025
1280	2500 amp		1	16		5,475	905		6,380	7,375
1290	3000 amp		.80	20		6,400	1,125		7,525	8,750
1300	4000 amp		.60	26.667		8,325	1,500		9,825	11,400
1350	Flanged end, 3 pole 3 wire, 225 amp		6	2.667		935	151		1,086	1,250
1360	400 amp		5.20	3.077		935	174		1,109	1,275
1370	600 amp		4.60	3.478		935	197		1,132	1,325
1380	800 amp		3.60	4.444		1,025	252		1,277	1,525
1390	1000 amp		3.40	4.706		1,175	266		1,441	1,675
1395	1200 amp		3.20	5		1,300	283		1,583	1,850
1400	1350 amp		3	5.333		1,400	300		1,700	1,975
1410	1600 amp		2.80	5.714		1,575	325		1,900	2,225
1420	2000 amp		2.40	6.667		1,850	375		2,225	2,625
1430	2500 amp		2	8		2,175	455		2,630	3,075
1440	3000 amp		1.80	8.889		2,475	505		2,980	3,475
1450	4000 amp		1.60	10		3,075	565		3,640	4,250
1500	3 pole 4 wire, 225 amp		5.40	2.963		1,075	168		1,243	1,425
1510	400 amp		4.60	3.478		1,075	197		1,272	1,475
1520	600 amp		4	4		1,075	226		1,301	1,525
1530	800 amp		3.20	5		1,275	283		1,558	1,825
1540	1000 amp		3	5.333		1,400	300		1,700	2,000
1545	1200 amp		2.80	5.714		1,600	325		1,925	2,225
1550	1350 amp		2.60	6.154		1,725	350		2,075	2,425
1560	1600 amp		2.40	6.667		1,975	375		2,350	2,750
1570	2000 amp		2	8		2,325	455		2,780	3,225
1580	2500 amp		1.80	8.889		2,775	505		3,280	3,800
1590	3000 amp		1.60	10		3,150	565		3,715	4,325
1600	4000 amp		1.40	11.429		4,100	645		4,745	5,475
1650	Hanger, standard, 225 amp		64	.250		26	14.15		40.15	49.50
1660	400 amp		48	.333		26	18.85		44.85	57
1670	600 amp		40	.400		26	22.50		48.50	62.50
1680	800 amp		32	.500		26	28.50		54.50	71
1690	1000 amp		24	.667		26	37.50		63.50	85
1695	1200 amp		22	.727		26	41		67	90
1700	1350 amp		20	.800		26	45.50		71.50	96.50
1710	1600 amp		20	.800		26	45.50		71.50	96.50
1720	2000 amp		18	.889		26	50.50		76.50	104
1730	2500 amp		16	1		26	56.50		82.50	114
1740	3000 amp		16	1		26	56.50		82.50	114
1750	4000 amp		16	1		26	56.50		82.50	114
1800	Spring type, 225 amp		16	1		88	56.50		144.50	182

For customer support on your Electrical Costs with RSMeans Data, call 800.448.8182.

259

26 25 Enclosed Bus Assemblies

26 25 13 – Bus Duct/Busway and Fittings

26 25 13.60 Copper or Aluminum Bus Duct Fittings	Crew	Daily Output	Labor-Hours	Unit	Material	2017 Bare Costs Labor	Equipment	Total	Total Incl O&P
1810	400 amp	2 Elec	14	1.143	Ea.	88	64.50		152.50	194
1820	600 amp		14	1.143		88	64.50		152.50	194
1830	800 amp		14	1.143		88	64.50		152.50	194
1840	1000 amp		14	1.143		88	64.50		152.50	194
1845	1200 amp		14	1.143		88	64.50		152.50	194
1850	1350 amp		14	1.143		88	64.50		152.50	194
1860	1600 amp		12	1.333		88	75.50		163.50	210
1870	2000 amp		12	1.333		88	75.50		163.50	210
1880	2500 amp		12	1.333		88	75.50		163.50	210
1890	3000 amp		10	1.600		88	90.50		178.50	233
1900	4000 amp		10	1.600		88	90.50		178.50	233

26 25 13.70 Feedrail

		Crew	Daily Output	Labor-Hours	Unit	Material	2017 Bare Costs Labor	Equipment	Total	Total Incl O&P
0010	**FEEDRAIL**, 12 foot mounting									
0050	Trolley busway, 3 pole									
0100	300 volt 60 amp, plain, 10 ft. lengths	1 Elec	50	.160	L.F.	21	9.05		30.05	36.50
0300	Door track		50	.160		34	9.05		43.05	51
0500	Curved track		30	.267		14.95	15.10		30.05	39
0700	Coupling				Ea.	11.90			11.90	13.10
0900	Center feed	1 Elec	5.30	1.509		47	85.50		132.50	180
1100	End feed		5.30	1.509		48.50	85.50		134	181
1300	Hanger set		24	.333		2.80	18.85		21.65	31.50
3000	600 volt 100 amp, plain, 10 ft. lengths		35	.229	L.F.	60	12.95		72.95	85.50
3300	Door track		35	.229	"	89	12.95		101.95	117
3700	Coupling				Ea.	52			52	57
4000	End cap	1 Elec	40	.200		63.50	11.30		74.80	87
4200	End feed		4	2		233	113		346	425
4500	Trolley, 600 volt, 20 amp		5.30	1.509		247	85.50		332.50	400
4700	30 amp		5.30	1.509		247	85.50		332.50	400
4900	Duplex, 40 amp		4	2		880	113		993	1,150
5000	60 amp		4	2		880	113		993	1,150
5300	Fusible, 20 amp		4	2		495	113		608	715
5500	30 amp		4	2		495	113		608	715
5900	300 volt, 20 amp		5.30	1.509		232	85.50		317.50	385
6000	30 amp		5.30	1.509		282	85.50		367.50	440
6300	Fusible, 20 amp		4.70	1.702		345	96.50		441.50	525
6500	30 amp		4.70	1.702		480	96.50		576.50	675
7300	Busway, 250 volt 50 amp, 2 wire		70	.114	L.F.	20.50	6.45		26.95	32
7330	Coupling				Ea.	42.50			42.50	47
7340	Center feed	1 Elec	6	1.333		495	75.50		570.50	660
7350	End feed		6	1.333		109	75.50		184.50	233
7360	End cap		40	.200		29	11.30		40.30	49
7370	Hanger set		24	.333		2.80	18.85		21.65	31.50
7400	125/250 volt 50 amp, 3 wire		60	.133	L.F.	20.50	7.55		28.05	34
7430	Coupling		6	1.333	Ea.	61.50	75.50		137	181
7440	Center feed		6	1.333		495	75.50		570.50	660
7450	End feed		6	1.333		109	75.50		184.50	233
7460	End cap		40	.200		29	11.30		40.30	49
7470	Hanger set		24	.333		3.75	18.85		22.60	32.50
7480	Trolley, 250 volt, 2 pole, 20 amp		6	1.333		37	75.50		112.50	154
7490	30 amp		6	1.333		37	75.50		112.50	154
7500	125/250 volt, 3 pole, 20 amp		6	1.333		37	75.50		112.50	154
7510	30 amp		6	1.333		37	75.50		112.50	154

26 25 Enclosed Bus Assemblies

26 25 13 – Bus Duct/Busway and Fittings

26 25 13.70 Feedrail	Crew	Daily Output	Labor-Hours	Unit	Material	2017 Bare Costs Labor	Equipment	Total	Total Incl O&P
8000	Cleaning tools, 300 volt, dust remover				Ea.	107			107	118
8100	Bus bar cleaner					202			202	222
8300	600 volt, dust remover, 60 amp					297			297	325
8400	100 amp					650			650	715
8600	Bus bar cleaner, 60 amp					675			675	745
8700	100 amp					800			800	880

26 26 Power Distribution Units

26 26 13 – Power Distribution Unit Low-Voltage

26 26 13.10 Power Distribution Unit

	26 26 13.10 Power Distribution Unit	Crew	Daily Output	Labor-Hours	Unit	Material	2017 Bare Costs Labor	Equipment	Total	Total Incl O&P
0010	**POWER DISTRIBUTION UNIT**									
0050	3PH, 60KVA, PDU									
0100	208V-208V/120V	2 Elec	2	8	Ea.	13,500	455		13,955	15,600
0110	480V-208V/120V		2	8		13,500	455		13,955	15,600
0120	600V-208V/120V		2	8		13,500	455		13,955	15,600
0125	3PH, 80KVA, PDU									
0130	208V-208V/120V	2 Elec	2	8	Ea.	25,500	455		25,955	28,800
0140	480V-208V/120V		2	8		25,500	455		25,955	28,800
0150	600V-208V/120V		2	8		25,500	455		25,955	28,800
0200	3PH, 15KVA, 480-208/120V, 208-208/120V		3	5.333		11,700	300		12,000	13,400
0210	30KVA, 400-208/120V, 208-208/120V		3	5.333		18,300	300		18,600	20,700
0250	50KVA, 480-208/120V, 208-208/120V		2.50	6.400		7,825	360		8,185	9,175
0260	75KVA, 480-208/120V, 208-208/120V		2.50	6.400		8,500	360		8,860	9,900
0270	100KVA, 480-208/120V, 208-208/120V		2	8		9,275	455		9,730	10,900
0280	125KVA, 480-208/120V, 208-208/120V		2	8		10,200	455		10,655	11,900
0290	150KVA, 480-208/120V, 208-208/120V		2	8		12,400	455		12,855	14,300
0300	200KVA, 480-208/120V, 208-208/120V		1.50	10.667		13,600	605		14,205	15,900
0310	225KVA, 480-208/120V, 208-208/120V		1.50	10.667		14,400	605		15,005	16,700

26 27 Low-Voltage Distribution Equipment

26 27 13 – Electricity Metering

26 27 13.10 Meter Centers and Sockets

	26 27 13.10 Meter Centers and Sockets	Crew	Daily Output	Labor-Hours	Unit	Material	2017 Bare Costs Labor	Equipment	Total	Total Incl O&P
0010	**METER CENTERS AND SOCKETS**									
0100	Sockets, single position, 4 terminal, 100 amp	1 Elec	3.20	2.500	Ea.	43	142		185	260
0200	150 amp		2.30	3.478		48	197		245	350
0300	200 amp		1.90	4.211		92	238		330	455
0400	Transformer rated, 20 amp		3.20	2.500		152	142		294	380
0500	Double position, 4 terminal, 100 amp		2.80	2.857		204	162		366	465
0600	150 amp		2.10	3.810		203	216		419	550
0700	200 amp		1.70	4.706		450	266		716	895
0800	Trans-socket, 13 terminal, 3 CT mounts, 400 amp		1	8		1,250	455		1,705	2,050
0900	800 amp	2 Elec	1.20	13.333		1,400	755		2,155	2,675
1100	Meter centers and sockets, three phase, single pos, 7 terminal, 100 amp	1 Elec	2.80	2.857		107	162		269	360
1200	200 amp		2.10	3.810		217	216		433	565
1400	400 amp		1.70	4.706		810	266		1,076	1,300
2000	Meter center, main fusible switch, 1P 3W 120/240 volt									
2030	400 amp	2 Elec	1.60	10	Ea.	1,675	565		2,240	2,700
2040	600 amp		1.10	14.545		2,600	825		3,425	4,075
2050	800 amp		.90	17.778		4,325	1,000		5,325	6,275

For customer support on your Electrical Costs with RSMeans Data, call 800.448.8182.

261

26 27 13.10 Meter Centers and Sockets		Crew	Daily Output	Labor-Hours	Unit	Material	2017 Bare Costs Labor	Equipment	Total	Total Incl O&P
2060	Rainproof 1P 3W 120/240 volt, 400 amp	2 Elec	1.60	10	Ea.	1,550	565		2,115	2,550
2070	600 amp		1.10	14.545		2,675	825		3,500	4,175
2080	800 amp		.90	17.778		4,200	1,000		5,200	6,125
2100	3P 4W 120/208 V, 400 amp		1.60	10		2,425	565		2,990	3,525
2110	600 amp		1.10	14.545		3,350	825		4,175	4,925
2120	800 amp		.90	17.778		4,600	1,000		5,600	6,575
2130	Rainproof 3P 4W 120/208 V, 400 amp		1.60	10		1,750	565		2,315	2,800
2140	600 amp		1.10	14.545		3,300	825		4,125	4,850
2150	800 amp		.90	17.778		6,100	1,000		7,100	8,225
2170	Main circuit breaker, 1P 3W 120/240 V									
2180	400 amp	2 Elec	1.60	10	Ea.	1,300	565		1,865	2,275
2190	600 amp		1.10	14.545		1,675	825		2,500	3,050
2200	800 amp		.90	17.778		6,450	1,000		7,450	8,600
2210	1000 amp		.80	20		3,225	1,125		4,350	5,250
2220	1200 amp		.76	21.053		8,700	1,200		9,900	11,400
2230	1600 amp		.68	23.529		18,900	1,325		20,225	22,800
2240	Rainproof 1P 3W 120/240 V, 400 amp		1.60	10		2,750	565		3,315	3,875
2250	600 amp		1.10	14.545		3,700	825		4,525	5,300
2260	800 amp		.90	17.778		4,325	1,000		5,325	6,250
2270	1000 amp		.80	20		5,950	1,125		7,075	8,250
2280	1200 amp		.76	21.053		8,050	1,200		9,250	10,600
2300	3P 4W 120/208 V, 400 amp		1.60	10		3,300	565		3,865	4,475
2310	600 amp		1.10	14.545		4,425	825		5,250	6,075
2320	800 amp		.90	17.778		5,250	1,000		6,250	7,275
2330	1000 amp		.80	20		6,900	1,125		8,025	9,275
2340	1200 amp		.76	21.053		8,825	1,200		10,025	11,500
2350	1600 amp		.68	23.529		18,000	1,325		19,325	21,800
2360	Rainproof 3P 4W 120/208 V, 400 amp		1.60	10		3,125	565		3,690	4,300
2370	600 amp		1.10	14.545		4,425	825		5,250	6,075
2380	800 amp		.90	17.778		5,250	1,000		6,250	7,275
2390	1000 amp		.76	21.053		6,900	1,200		8,100	9,350
2400	1200 amp		.68	23.529		8,825	1,325		10,150	11,700
2420	Main lugs terminal box, 1P 3W 120/240 V									
2430	800 amp	2 Elec	.94	17.021	Ea.	360	965		1,325	1,850
2440	1200 amp		.72	22.222		440	1,250		1,690	2,350
2450	Rainproof 1P 3W 120/240 V, 225 amp		2.40	6.667		350	375		725	950
2460	800 amp		.94	17.021		515	965		1,480	2,025
2470	1200 amp		.72	22.222		1,025	1,250		2,275	3,025
2500	3P 4W 120/208 V, 800 amp		.94	17.021		575	965		1,540	2,075
2510	1200 amp		.72	22.222		1,150	1,250		2,400	3,150
2520	Rainproof 3P 4W 120/208 V, 225 amp		2.40	6.667		350	375		725	950
2530	800 amp		.94	17.021		575	965		1,540	2,075
2540	1200 amp		.72	22.222		1,150	1,250		2,400	3,150
2590	Basic meter device									
2600	1P 3W 120/240 V 4 jaw 125A sockets, 3 meter	2 Elec	1	16	Ea.	325	905		1,230	1,700
2610	4 meter		.90	17.778		385	1,000		1,385	1,925
2620	5 meter		.80	20		465	1,125		1,590	2,225
2630	6 meter		.60	26.667		610	1,500		2,110	2,925
2640	7 meter		.56	28.571		1,300	1,625		2,925	3,850
2650	8 meter		.52	30.769		1,425	1,750		3,175	4,150
2660	10 meter		.48	33.333		1,775	1,875		3,650	4,775
2680	Rainproof 1P 3W 120/240 V 4 jaw 125A sockets									
2690	3 meter	2 Elec	1	16	Ea.	590	905		1,495	2,000

26 27 13.10 Meter Centers and Sockets

		Crew	Daily Output	Labor-Hours	Unit	Material	2017 Bare Costs Labor	Equipment	Total	Total Incl O&P
2700	4 meter	2 Elec	.90	17.778	Ea.	710	1,000		1,710	2,275
2710	6 meter		.60	26.667		1,025	1,500		2,525	3,375
2720	7 meter		.56	28.571		1,300	1,625		2,925	3,850
2730	8 meter		.52	30.769		1,425	1,750		3,175	4,150
2750	1P 3W 120/240 V 4 jaw sockets									
2760	with 125A circuit breaker, 3 meter	2 Elec	1	16	Ea.	1,100	905		2,005	2,575
2770	4 meter		.90	17.778		1,400	1,000		2,400	3,025
2780	5 meter		.80	20		1,750	1,125		2,875	3,625
2790	6 meter		.60	26.667		2,050	1,500		3,550	4,500
2800	7 meter		.56	28.571		2,500	1,625		4,125	5,175
2810	8 meter		.52	30.769		2,800	1,750		4,550	5,675
2820	10 meter		.48	33.333		3,500	1,875		5,375	6,675
2830	Rainproof 1P 3W 120/240 V 4 jaw sockets									
2840	with 125A circuit breaker, 3 meter	2 Elec	1	16	Ea.	1,100	905		2,005	2,575
2850	4 meter		.90	17.778		1,400	1,000		2,400	3,025
2870	6 meter		.60	26.667		2,050	1,500		3,550	4,500
2880	7 meter		.56	28.571		2,500	1,625		4,125	5,175
2890	8 meter		.52	30.769		2,800	1,750		4,550	5,675
2920	1P 3W on 3P 4W 120/208 V system 5 jaw									
2930	125A sockets, 3 meter	2 Elec	1	16	Ea.	590	905		1,495	2,000
2940	4 meter		.90	17.778		710	1,000		1,710	2,275
2950	5 meter		.80	20		890	1,125		2,015	2,675
2960	6 meter		.60	26.667		1,025	1,500		2,525	3,375
2970	7 meter		.56	28.571		1,300	1,625		2,925	3,850
2980	8 meter		.52	30.769		1,425	1,750		3,175	4,150
2990	10 meter		.48	33.333		1,775	1,875		3,650	4,775
3000	Rainproof 1P 3W on 3P 4W 120/208 V system									
3020	5 jaw 125A sockets, 3 meter	2 Elec	1	16	Ea.	590	905		1,495	2,000
3030	4 meter		.90	17.778		710	1,000		1,710	2,275
3050	6 meter		.60	26.667		1,025	1,500		2,525	3,375
3060	7 meter		.56	28.571		1,300	1,625		2,925	3,850
3070	8 meter		.52	30.769		1,425	1,750		3,175	4,150
3090	1P 3W on 3P 4W 120/208 V system 5 jaw sockets									
3100	With 125A circuit breaker, 3 meter	2 Elec	1	16	Ea.	1,100	905		2,005	2,575
3110	4 meter		.90	17.778		1,400	1,000		2,400	3,025
3120	5 meter		.80	20		1,750	1,125		2,875	3,625
3130	6 meter		.60	26.667		2,050	1,500		3,550	4,500
3140	7 meter		.56	28.571		2,500	1,625		4,125	5,175
3150	8 meter		.52	30.769		2,800	1,750		4,550	5,675
3160	10 meter		.48	33.333		3,500	1,875		5,375	6,675
3170	Rainproof 1P 3W on 3P 4W 120/208 V system									
3180	5 jaw sockets w/125A circuit breaker, 3 meter	2 Elec	1	16	Ea.	1,100	905		2,005	2,575
3190	4 meter		.90	17.778		1,400	1,000		2,400	3,025
3210	6 meter		.60	26.667		2,050	1,500		3,550	4,500
3220	7 meter		.56	28.571		2,500	1,625		4,125	5,175
3230	8 meter		.52	30.769		2,800	1,750		4,550	5,675
3250	1P 3W 120/240 V 4 jaw sockets									
3260	with 200A circuit breaker, 3 meter	2 Elec	1	16	Ea.	1,650	905		2,555	3,175
3270	4 meter		.90	17.778		2,250	1,000		3,250	3,975
3290	6 meter		.60	26.667		3,325	1,500		4,825	5,900
3300	7 meter		.56	28.571		3,900	1,625		5,525	6,725
3310	8 meter		.56	28.571		4,500	1,625		6,125	7,375
3330	Rainproof 1P 3W 120/240 V 4 jaw sockets									

26 27 13.10 Meter Centers and Sockets	Crew	Daily Output	Labor-Hours	Unit	Material	2017 Bare Costs Labor	Equipment	Total	Total Incl O&P
3350	with 200A circuit breaker, 3 meter	2 Elec	1	16	Ea.	1,650	905		2,555	3,175
3360	4 meter		.90	17.778		2,250	1,000		3,250	3,975
3380	6 meter		.60	26.667		3,325	1,500		4,825	5,900
3390	7 meter		.56	28.571		3,900	1,625		5,525	6,725
3400	8 meter		.52	30.769		4,500	1,750		6,250	7,550
3420	1P 3W on 3P 4W 120/208 V 5 jaw sockets									
3430	with 200A circuit breaker, 3 meter	2 Elec	1	16	Ea.	1,650	905		2,555	3,175
3440	4 meter		.90	17.778		2,250	1,000		3,250	3,975
3460	6 meter		.60	26.667		3,325	1,500		4,825	5,900
3470	7 meter		.56	28.571		3,900	1,625		5,525	6,725
3480	8 meter		.52	30.769		4,500	1,750		6,250	7,550
3500	Rainproof 1P 3W on 3P 4W 120/208 V 5 jaw socket									
3510	with 200A circuit breaker, 3 meter	2 Elec	1	16	Ea.	1,650	905		2,555	3,175
3520	4 meter		.90	17.778		2,250	1,000		3,250	3,975
3540	6 meter		.60	26.667		3,325	1,500		4,825	5,900
3550	7 meter		.56	28.571		3,900	1,625		5,525	6,725
3560	8 meter		.52	30.769		4,500	1,750		6,250	7,550
3600	Automatic circuit closing, add					64			64	70.50
3610	Manual circuit closing, add					73.50			73.50	80.50
3650	Branch meter device									
3660	3P 4W 208/120 or 240/120 V 7 jaw sockets									
3670	with 200A circuit breaker, 2 meter	2 Elec	.90	17.778	Ea.	2,775	1,000		3,775	4,550
3680	3 meter		.80	20		4,175	1,125		5,300	6,275
3690	4 meter		.70	22.857		5,550	1,300		6,850	8,050
3700	Main circuit breaker 42,000 rms, 400 amp		1.60	10		1,825	565		2,390	2,850
3710	600 amp		1.10	14.545		2,450	825		3,275	3,925
3720	800 amp		.90	17.778		3,075	1,000		4,075	4,875
3730	Rainproof main circ. breaker 42,000 rms, 400 amp		1.60	10		2,425	565		2,990	3,525
3740	600 amp		1.10	14.545		3,900	825		4,725	5,525
3750	800 amp		.90	17.778		5,250	1,000		6,250	7,275
3760	Main circuit breaker 65,000 rms, 400 amp		1.60	10		3,300	565		3,865	4,475
3770	600 amp		1.10	14.545		4,625	825		5,450	6,325
3780	800 amp		.90	17.778		5,250	1,000		6,250	7,275
3790	1000 amp		.80	20		6,900	1,125		8,025	9,275
3800	1200 amp		.76	21.053		8,825	1,200		10,025	11,500
3810	1600 amp		.68	23.529		18,000	1,325		19,325	21,800
3820	Rainproof main circ. breaker 65,000 rms, 400 amp		1.60	10		3,300	565		3,865	4,475
3830	600 amp		1.10	14.545		4,625	825		5,450	6,325
3840	800 amp		.90	17.778		5,250	1,000		6,250	7,275
3850	1000 amp		.80	20		6,900	1,125		8,025	9,275
3860	1200 amp		.76	21.053		8,825	1,200		10,025	11,500
3880	Main circuit breaker 100,000 rms, 400 amp		1.60	10		3,300	565		3,865	4,475
3890	600 amp		1.10	14.545		4,625	825		5,450	6,325
3900	800 amp		.90	17.778		5,450	1,000		6,450	7,475
3910	Rainproof main circ. breaker 100,000 rms, 400 amp		1.60	10		3,300	565		3,865	4,475
3920	600 amp		1.10	14.545		4,625	825		5,450	6,325
3930	800 amp		.90	17.778		5,450	1,000		6,450	7,475
3940	Main lugs terminal box, 800 amp		.94	17.021		575	965		1,540	2,075
3950	1600 amp		.72	22.222		2,475	1,250		3,725	4,600
3960	Rainproof, 800 amp		.94	17.021		575	965		1,540	2,075
3970	1600 amp		.72	22.222		2,475	1,250		3,725	4,600

26 27 16.10 Cabinets		Crew	Daily Output	Labor-Hours	Unit	Material	2017 Bare Costs Labor	Equipment	Total	Total Incl O&P
0010	CABINETS R260533-70									
7000	Cabinets, current transformer									
7050	Single door, 24" H x 24" W x 10" D R262716-40	1 Elec	1.60	5	Ea.	176	283		459	620
7100	30" H x 24" W x 10" D		1.30	6.154		190	350		540	730
7150	36" H x 24" W x 10" D		1.10	7.273		252	410		662	895
7200	30" H x 30" W x 10" D		1	8		157	455		612	855
7250	36" H x 30" W x 10" D		.90	8.889		189	505		694	965
7300	36" H x 36" W x 10" D		.80	10		195	565		760	1,075
7500	Double door, 48" H x 36" W x 10" D		.60	13.333		370	755		1,125	1,525
7550	24" H x 24" W x 12" D		1	8		108	455		563	800
8000	NEMA 12, double door, floor mounted									
8020	54" H x 42" W x 8" D	2 Elec	6	2.667	Ea.	850	151		1,001	1,150
8040	60" H x 48" W x 8" D		5.40	2.963		1,125	168		1,293	1,500
8060	60" H x 48" W x 10" D		5.40	2.963		1,175	168		1,343	1,525
8080	60" H x 60" W x 10" D		5	3.200		1,300	181		1,481	1,725
8100	72" H x 60" W x 10" D		4	4		1,550	226		1,776	2,050
8120	72" H x 72" W x 10" D		3.40	4.706		1,700	266		1,966	2,275
8140	60" H x 48" W x 12" D		3.40	4.706		1,200	266		1,466	1,700
8160	60" H x 60" W x 12" D		3.20	5		1,350	283		1,633	1,900
8180	72" H x 60" W x 12" D		3	5.333		1,525	300		1,825	2,125
8200	72" H x 72" W x 12" D		3	5.333		1,700	300		2,000	2,325
8220	60" H x 48" W x 16" D		3.20	5		1,250	283		1,533	1,775
8240	72" H x 72" W x 16" D		2.60	6.154		1,800	350		2,150	2,500
8260	60" H x 48" W x 20" D		3	5.333		1,350	300		1,650	1,950
8280	72" H x 72" W x 20" D		2.20	7.273		1,925	410		2,335	2,750
8300	60" H x 48" W x 24" D		2.60	6.154		1,450	350		1,800	2,100
8320	72" H x 72" W x 24" D		2	8		2,050	455		2,505	2,925
8340	Pushbutton enclosure, oiltight									
8360	3-1/2" H x 3-1/4" W x 2-3/4" D, for 1 P.B.	1 Elec	12	.667	Ea.	37.50	37.50		75	97.50
8380	5-3/4" H x 3-1/4" W x 2-3/4" D, for 2 P.B.		11	.727		42.50	41		83.50	108
8400	8" H x 3-1/4" W x 2-3/4" D, for 3 P.B.		10.50	.762		47.50	43		90.50	117
8420	10-1/4" H x 3-1/4" W x 2-3/4" D, for 4 P.B.		10.50	.762		53	43		96	123
8460	12-1/2" H x 3-1/4" W x 3" D, for 5 P.B.		9	.889		92	50.50		142.50	177
8480	9-1/2" H x 6-1/4" W x 3" D, for 6 P.B.		8.50	.941		68.50	53.50		122	156
8500	9-1/2" H x 8-1/2" W x 3" D, for 9 P.B.		8	1		76	56.50		132.50	169
8510	11-3/4" H x 8-1/2" W x 3" D, for 12 P.B.		7	1.143		83	64.50		147.50	189
8520	11-3/4" H x 10-3/4" W x 3" D, for 16 P.B.		6.50	1.231		91	69.50		160.50	204
8540	14" H x 10-3/4" W x 3" D, for 20 P.B.		5	1.600		195	90.50		285.50	350
8560	14" H x 13" W x 3" D, for 25 P.B.		4.50	1.778		212	101		313	385
8580	Sloping front pushbutton enclosures									
8600	3-1/2" H x 7-3/4" W x 4-7/8" D, for 3 P.B.	1 Elec	10	.800	Ea.	63.50	45.50		109	138
8620	7-1/4" H x 8-1/2" W x 6-3/4" D, for 6 P.B.		8	1		93	56.50		149.50	187
8640	9-1/2" H x 8-1/2" W x 7-7/8" D, for 9 P.B.		7	1.143		111	64.50		175.50	219
8660	11-1/4" H x 8-1/2" W x 9" D, for 12 P.B.		5	1.600		125	90.50		215.50	274
8680	11-3/4" H x 10" W x 9" D, for 16 P.B.		5	1.600		138	90.50		228.50	288
8700	11-3/4" H x 13" W x 9" D, for 20 P.B.		5	1.600		159	90.50		249.50	310
8720	14" H x 13" W x 10-1/8" D, for 25 P.B.		4.50	1.778		179	101		280	350
8740	Pedestals, not including P.B. enclosure or base									
8760	Straight column 4" x 4"	1 Elec	4.50	1.778	Ea.	169	101		270	335
8780	6" x 6"		4	2		263	113		376	460
8800	Angled column 4" x 4"		4.50	1.778		194	101		295	365
8820	6" x 6"		4	2		291	113		404	490

For customer support on your Electrical Costs with RSMeans Data, call 800.448.8182.

265

26 27 16.10 Cabinets

		Crew	Daily Output	Labor-Hours	Unit	Material	2017 Bare Costs Labor	Equipment	Total	Total Incl O&P
8840	Pedestal, base 18" x 18"	1 Elec	10	.800	Ea.	99.50	45.50		145	178
8860	24" x 24"	↓	9	.889	↓	229	50.50		279.50	330
8900	Electronic rack enclosures									
8920	72" H x 19" W x 24" D	1 Elec	1.50	5.333	Ea.	2,000	300		2,300	2,625
8940	72" H x 23" W x 24" D		1.50	5.333		2,250	300		2,550	2,925
8960	72" H x 19" W x 30" D		1.30	6.154		2,375	350		2,725	3,150
8980	72" H x 19" W x 36" D		1.20	6.667		2,725	375		3,100	3,575
9000	72" H x 23" W x 36" D	↓	1.20	6.667	↓	3,025	375		3,400	3,900
9020	NEMA 12 & 4 enclosure panels									
9040	12" x 24"	1 Elec	20	.400	Ea.	23	22.50		45.50	59.50
9060	16" x 12"		20	.400		16.80	22.50		39.30	52.50
9080	20" x 16"		20	.400		24.50	22.50		47	61
9100	20" x 20"		19	.421		29.50	24		53.50	67.50
9120	24" x 20"		18	.444		38	25		63	79
9140	24" x 24"		17	.471		43.50	26.50		70	88
9160	30" x 20"		16	.500		54.50	28.50		83	103
9180	30" x 24"		16	.500		53	28.50		81.50	101
9200	36" x 24"		15	.533		62.50	30		92.50	114
9220	36" x 30"		15	.533		84	30		114	138
9240	42" x 24"		15	.533		71.50	30		101.50	124
9260	42" x 30"		14	.571		95	32.50		127.50	153
9280	42" x 36"		14	.571		111	32.50		143.50	171
9300	48" x 24"		14	.571		85.50	32.50		118	143
9320	48" x 30"		14	.571		111	32.50		143.50	171
9340	48" x 36"		13	.615		128	35		163	193
9360	60" x 36"	↓	12	.667	↓	156	37.50		193.50	229
9400	Wiring trough steel JIC, clamp cover									
9490	4" x 4", 12" long	1 Elec	12	.667	Ea.	59	37.50		96.50	122
9510	24" long		10	.800		74.50	45.50		120	150
9530	36" long		8	1		93	56.50		149.50	188
9540	48" long		7	1.143		108	64.50		172.50	216
9550	60" long		6	1.333		127	75.50		202.50	253
9560	6" x 6", 12" long		11	.727		78.50	41		119.50	148
9580	24" long		9	.889		104	50.50		154.50	190
9600	36" long		7	1.143		127	64.50		191.50	237
9610	48" long		6	1.333		155	75.50		230.50	283
9620	60" long	↓	5	1.600	↓	182	90.50		272.50	335

26 27 16.20 Cabinets and Enclosures

		Crew	Daily Output	Labor-Hours	Unit	Material	2017 Bare Costs Labor	Equipment	Total	Total Incl O&P
0010	**CABINETS AND ENCLOSURES** Nonmetallic									
0080	Enclosures fiberglass NEMA 4X									
0100	Wall mount, quick release latch door, 20"H x 16"W x 6"D	1 Elec	4.80	1.667	Ea.	390	94.50		484.50	570
0110	20"H x 20"W x 6"D		4.50	1.778		470	101		571	665
0120	24"H x 20"W x 6"D		4.20	1.905		500	108		608	710
0130	20"H x 16"W x 8"D		4.50	1.778		445	101		546	640
0140	20"H x 20"W x 8"D		4.20	1.905		500	108		608	710
0150	24"H x 24"W x 8"D		3.80	2.105		565	119		684	805
0160	30"H x 24"W x 8"D		3.20	2.500		610	142		752	885
0170	36"H x 30"W x 8"D		3	2.667		860	151		1,011	1,175
0180	20"H x 16"W x 10"D		3.50	2.286		520	129		649	765
0190	20"H x 20"W x 10"D		3.20	2.500		555	142		697	820
0200	24"H x 20"W x 10"D		3	2.667		590	151		741	875
0210	30"H x 24"W x 10"D	↓	2.80	2.857	↓	670	162		832	975

26 27 16 - Electrical Cabinets and Enclosures

26 27 16.20 Cabinets and Enclosures	Crew	Daily Output	Labor-Hours	Unit	Material	2017 Bare Costs Labor	Equipment	Total	Total Incl O&P
0220	20"H x 16"W x 12"D	1 Elec	3	2.667	Ea.	550	151		701	830
0230	20"H x 20"W x 12"D		2.80	2.857		590	162		752	890
0240	24"H x 24"W x 12"D		2.60	3.077		655	174		829	980
0250	30"H x 24"W x 12"D		2.40	3.333		730	189		919	1,100
0260	36"H x 30"W x 12"D		2.20	3.636		1,000	206		1,206	1,400
0270	36"H x 36"W x 12"D		2.10	3.810		1,125	216		1,341	1,550
0280	48"H x 36"W x 12"D		2	4		1,275	226		1,501	1,750
0290	60"H x 36"W x 12"D		1.80	4.444		1,450	252		1,702	1,975
0300	30"H x 24"W x 16"D		1.40	5.714		850	325		1,175	1,425
0310	48"H x 36"W x 16"D		1.20	6.667		1,425	375		1,800	2,125
0320	60"H x 36"W x 16"D		1	8		1,600	455		2,055	2,450
0480	Freestanding, one door, 72"H x 25"W x 25"D		.80	10		2,725	565		3,290	3,850
0490	Two doors with two panels, 72"H x 49"W x 24"D		.50	16		6,800	905		7,705	8,825
0500	Floor stand kits, for NEMA 4 & 12, 20"W or more, 6"H x 8"D		24	.333		102	18.85		120.85	142
0510	6"H x 10"D		24	.333		112	18.85		130.85	152
0520	6"H x 12"D		24	.333		125	18.85		143.85	167
0530	6"H x 18"D		24	.333		145	18.85		163.85	189
0540	12"H x 8"D		22	.364		129	20.50		149.50	173
0550	12"H x 10"D		22	.364		137	20.50		157.50	182
0560	12"H x 12"D		22	.364		146	20.50		166.50	192
0570	12"H x 16"D		22	.364		170	20.50		190.50	218
0580	12"H x 18"D		22	.364		174	20.50		194.50	223
0590	12"H x 20"D		22	.364		185	20.50		205.50	235
0600	18"H x 8"D		20	.400		154	22.50		176.50	203
0610	18"H x 10"D		20	.400		165	22.50		187.50	216
0620	18"H x 12"D		20	.400		177	22.50		199.50	229
0630	18"H x 16"D		20	.400		197	22.50		219.50	250
0640	24"H x 8"D		16	.500		190	28.50		218.50	252
0650	24"H x 10"D		16	.500		197	28.50		225.50	259
0660	24"H x 12"D		16	.500		212	28.50		240.50	277
0670	24"H x 16"D		16	.500		222	28.50		250.50	287
0680	Small, screw cover, 5-1/2"H x 4"W x 4-15/16"D		12	.667		60	37.50		97.50	123
0690	7-1/2"H x 4"W x 4-15/16"D		12	.667		64	37.50		101.50	127
0700	7-1/2"H x 6"W x 5-3/16"D		10	.800		74.50	45.50		120	150
0710	9-1/2"H x 6"W x 5-11/16"D		10	.800		76.50	45.50		122	152
0720	11-1/2"H x 8"W x 6-11/16"D		8	1		113	56.50		169.50	210
0730	13-1/2"H x 10"W x 7-3/16"D		7	1.143		136	64.50		200.50	247
0740	15-1/2"H x 12"W x 8-3/16"D		6	1.333		178	75.50		253.50	310
0750	17-1/2"H x 14"W x 8-11/16"D		5	1.600		212	90.50		302.50	370
0760	Screw cover with window, 6"H x 4"W x 5"D		12	.667		173	37.50		210.50	247
0770	8"H x 4"W x 5"D		11	.727		178	41		219	258
0780	8"H x 6"W x 5"D		11	.727		153	41		194	231
0790	10"H x 6"W x 6"D		10	.800		166	45.50		211.50	250
0800	12"H x 8"W x 7"D		8	1		222	56.50		278.50	330
0810	14"H x 10"W x 7"D		7	1.143		242	64.50		306.50	365
0820	16"H x 12"W x 8"D		6	1.333		305	75.50		380.50	450
0830	18"H x 14"W x 9"D		5	1.600		365	90.50		455.50	535
0840	Quick-release latch cover, 5-1/2"H x 4"W x 5"D		12	.667		82	37.50		119.50	147
0850	7-1/2"H x 4"W x 5"D		12	.667		87.50	37.50		125	153
0860	7-1/2"H x 6"W x 5-1/4"D		10	.800		94.50	45.50		140	172
0870	9-1/2"H x 6"W x 5-3/4"D		10	.800		104	45.50		149.50	182
0880	11-1/2"H x 8"W x 6-3/4"D		8	1		148	56.50		204.50	248
0890	13-1/2"H x 10"W x 7-1/4"D		7	1.143		186	64.50		250.50	300

For customer support on your Electrical Costs with RSMeans Data, call 800.448.8182.

267

26 27 16.20 Cabinets and Enclosures	Crew	Daily Output	Labor-Hours	Unit	Material	2017 Bare Costs Labor	Equipment	Total	Total Incl O&P
0900	15-1/2"H x 12"W x 8-1/4"D	1 Elec	6	1.333	Ea.	228	75.50		303.50	365
0910	17-1/2"H x 14"W x 8-3/4"D		5	1.600		275	90.50		365.50	440
0920	Pushbutton, 1 hole 5-1/2"H x 4"W x 4-15/16"D		12	.667		440	37.50		477.50	540
0930	2 hole 7-1/2"H x 4"W x 4-15/16"D		11	.727		615	41		656	735
0940	4 hole 7-1/2"H x 6"W x 5-3/16"D		10.50	.762		425	43		468	535
0950	6 hole 9-1/2"H x 6"W x 5-11/16"D		9	.889		515	50.50		565.50	645
0960	8 hole 11-1/2"H x 8"W x 6-11/16"D		8.50	.941		660	53.50		713.50	805
0970	12 hole 13-1/2"H x 10"W x 7-3/16"D		8	1		865	56.50		921.50	1,025
0980	20 hole 15-1/2"H x 12"W x 8-3/16"D		5	1.600		830	90.50		920.50	1,050
0990	30 hole 17-1/2"H x 14"W x 8-11/16"D	▼	4.50	1.778	▼	985	101		1,086	1,225
1450	Enclosures polyester NEMA 4X									
1460	Small, screw cover,									
1500	3-15/16"H x 3-15/16"W x 3-1/16"D	1 Elec	12	.667	Ea.	64	37.50		101.50	127
1510	5-3/16"H x 3-5/16"W x 3-1/16"D		12	.667		63	37.50		100.50	126
1520	5-7/8"H x 3-7/8"W x 4-3/16"D		12	.667		66.50	37.50		104	130
1530	5-7/8"H x 5-7/8"W x 4-3/16"D		12	.667		74.50	37.50		112	139
1540	7-5/8"H x 3-5/16"W x 3-1/16"D		12	.667		69	37.50		106.50	132
1550	10-3/16"H x 3-5/16"W x 3-1/16"D		10	.800		81.50	45.50		127	158
1560	Clear cover, 3-15/16"H x 3-15/16"W x 2-7/8"D		12	.667		72.50	37.50		110	136
1570	5-3/16"H x 3-5/16"W x 2-7/8"D		12	.667		77	37.50		114.50	141
1580	5-7/8"H x 3-7/8"W x 4"D		12	.667		95.50	37.50		133	162
1590	5-7/8"H x 5-7/8"W x 4"D		12	.667		118	37.50		155.50	187
1600	7-5/8"H x 3-5/16"W x 2-7/8"D		12	.667		86.50	37.50		124	152
1610	10-3/16"H x 3-5/16"W x 2-7/8"D		10	.800		109	45.50		154.50	187
1620	Pushbutton, 1 hole, 5-5/16"H x 3-5/16"W x 3-1/16"D		12	.667		56	37.50		93.50	118
1630	2 hole, 7-5/8"H x 3-5/16"W x 3-1/8"D		11	.727		63	41		104	131
1640	3 hole, 10-3/16"H x 3-5/16"W x 3-1/16"D		10.50	.762		74.50	43		117.50	147
8000	Wireway fiberglass, straight sect. screwcover, 12" L, 4" W x 4" D		40	.200		124	11.30		135.30	153
8010	6" W x 6" D		30	.267		165	15.10		180.10	204
8020	24" L, 4" W x 4" D		20	.400		150	22.50		172.50	199
8030	6" W x 6" D		15	.533		248	30		278	320
8040	36" L, 4" W x 4" D		13.30	.602		188	34		222	258
8050	6" W x 6" D		10	.800		294	45.50		339.50	395
8060	48" L, 4" W x 4" D		10	.800		225	45.50		270.50	315
8070	6" W x 6" D		7.50	1.067		370	60.50		430.50	495
8080	60" L, 4" W x 4" D		8	1		410	56.50		466.50	535
8090	6" W x 6" D		6	1.333		430	75.50		505.50	590
8100	Elbow, 90°, 4" W x 4" D		20	.400		127	22.50		149.50	174
8110	6" W x 6" D		18	.444		254	25		279	320
8120	Elbow, 45°, 4" W x 4" D		20	.400		121	22.50		143.50	167
8130	6" W x 6" D		18	.444		239	25		264	300
8140	Tee, 4" W x 4" D		16	.500		161	28.50		189.50	220
8150	6" W x 6" D		14	.571		292	32.50		324.50	370
8160	Cross, 4" W x 4" D		14	.571		345	32.50		377.50	430
8170	6" W x 6" D		12	.667		495	37.50		532.50	600
8180	Cut-off fitting, w/flange & adhesive, 4" W x 4" D		18	.444		90	25		115	137
8190	6" W x 6" D		16	.500		196	28.50		224.50	258
8200	Flexible ftng., hvy. neoprene coated nylon, 4" W x 4" D		20	.400		175	22.50		197.50	226
8210	6" W x 6" D		18	.444		258	25		283	320
8220	Closure plate, fiberglass, 4" W x 4" D		20	.400		35	22.50		57.50	72.50
8230	6" W x 6" D		18	.444		38	25		63	79.50
8240	Box connector, stainless steel type 304, 4" W x 4" D		20	.400		56.50	22.50		79	96
8250	6" W x 6" D	▼	18	.444		66.50	25		91.50	111

268

For customer support on your Electrical Costs with RSMeans Data, call 800.448.8182.

26 27 16 – Electrical Cabinets and Enclosures

26 27 16.20 Cabinets and Enclosures	Crew	Daily Output	Labor-Hours	Unit	Material	2017 Bare Costs Labor	Equipment	Total	Total Incl O&P
8260	Hanger, 4" W x 4" D	1 Elec	100	.080	Fn	14.70	4.53		19.23	23
8270	6" W x 6" D		80	.100		18.45	5.65		24.10	29
8280	Straight tube section fiberglass, 4"W x 4"D, 12" long		40	.200		107	11.30		118.30	135
8290	24" long		20	.400		195	22.50		217.50	248
8300	36" long		13.30	.602		243	34		277	320
8310	48" long		10	.800		156	45.50		201.50	240
8320	60" long		8	1		192	56.50		248.50	297
8330	120" long		4	2		294	113		407	495

26 27 19 – Multi-Outlet Assemblies

26 27 19.10 Wiring Duct

		Crew	Daily Output	Labor-Hours	Unit	Material	2017 Bare Costs Labor	Equipment	Total	Total Incl O&P
0010	**WIRING DUCT** Plastic									
1250	PVC, snap-in slots, adhesive backed									
1270	1-1/2"W x 2"H	2 Elec	120	.133	L.F.	5.50	7.55		13.05	17.35
1280	1-1/2"W x 3"H		120	.133		6.65	7.55		14.20	18.60
1290	1-1/2"W x 4"H		120	.133		7.85	7.55		15.40	19.95
1300	2"W x 1"H		120	.133		4.95	7.55		12.50	16.75
1310	2"W x 1-1/2"H		120	.133		5.35	7.55		12.90	17.20
1320	2"W x 2"H		120	.133		5.40	7.55		12.95	17.25
1340	2"W x 3"H		120	.133		7.05	7.55		14.60	19.05
1350	2"W x 4"H		120	.133		8.50	7.55		16.05	20.50
1360	2-1/2"W x 3"H		120	.133		7.60	7.55		15.15	19.65
1370	3"W x 1"H		110	.145		5.65	8.25		13.90	18.55
1390	3"W x 2"H		110	.145		6.70	8.25		14.95	19.75
1400	3"W x 3"H		110	.145		8.10	8.25		16.35	21.50
1410	3"W x 4"H		110	.145		10.15	8.25		18.40	23.50
1420	3"W x 5"H		110	.145		13.35	8.25		21.60	27
1430	4"W x 1-1/2"H		100	.160		6.70	9.05		15.75	21
1440	4"W x 2"H		100	.160		7.85	9.05		16.90	22
1450	4"W x 3"H		100	.160		8.85	9.05		17.90	23.50
1460	4"W x 4"H		100	.160		10.70	9.05		19.75	25.50
1470	4"W x 5"H		100	.160		15.10	9.05		24.15	30
1550	Cover, 1-1/2"W		200	.080		1.13	4.53		5.66	8.05
1560	2"W		200	.080		1.28	4.53		5.81	8.20
1570	2-1/2"W		200	.080		1.74	4.53		6.27	8.70
1580	3"W		200	.080		1.94	4.53		6.47	8.95
1590	4"W		200	.080		2.34	4.53		6.87	9.35

26 27 23 – Indoor Service Poles

26 27 23.40 Surface Raceway

		Crew	Daily Output	Labor-Hours	Unit	Material	2017 Bare Costs Labor	Equipment	Total	Total Incl O&P
0010	**SURFACE RACEWAY**									
0090	Metal, straight section									
0100	No. 500	1 Elec	100	.080	L.F.	1.07	4.53		5.60	8
0110	No. 700		100	.080		1.19	4.53		5.72	8.10
0200	No. 1000		90	.089		1.45	5.05		6.50	9.15
0400	No. 1500, small pancake		90	.089		2.20	5.05		7.25	9.95
0600	No. 2000, base & cover, blank		90	.089		2.24	5.05		7.29	10
0610	Receptacle, 6" O.C.		40	.200		20.50	11.30		31.80	39.50
0620	12" O.C.		44	.182		13.35	10.30		23.65	30
0630	18" O.C.		46	.174		11.05	9.85		20.90	27
0650	30" O.C.		50	.160		5.15	9.05		14.20	19.20
0660	60" O.C.		50	.160		4.75	9.05		13.80	18.80
0670	No. 2400, base & cover, blank		80	.100		2.05	5.65		7.70	10.75
0680	Receptacle, 6" O.C.		42	.190		39	10.80		49.80	58.50

For customer support on your Electrical Costs with RSMeans Data, call 800.448.8182.

269

26 27 23.40 Surface Raceway	Crew	Daily Output	Labor-Hours	Unit	Material	2017 Bare Costs Labor	Equipment	Total	Total Incl O&P
0690	12" O.C.	1 Elec	53	.151	L.F.	27.50	8.55		36.05	43
0700	18" O.C.		55	.145		19.90	8.25		28.15	34.50
0710	24" O.C.		57	.140		9.85	7.95		17.80	23
0720	30" O.C.		59	.136		6.75	7.65		14.40	18.95
0730	60" O.C.		61	.131		5.45	7.40		12.85	17.05
0800	No. 3000, base & cover, blank		75	.107		4.28	6.05		10.33	13.75
0810	Receptacle, 6" O.C.		45	.178		37.50	10.05		47.55	56.50
0820	12" O.C.		62	.129		21	7.30		28.30	34.50
0830	18" O.C.		64	.125		17.15	7.10		24.25	29.50
0840	24" O.C.		66	.121		12.85	6.85		19.70	24.50
0850	30" O.C.		68	.118		11.55	6.65		18.20	23
0860	60" O.C.		70	.114		8.45	6.45		14.90	19
1000	No. 4000, base & cover, blank		65	.123		8.15	6.95		15.10	19.45
1010	Receptacle, 6" O.C.		41	.195		50.50	11.05		61.55	72
1020	12" O.C.		52	.154		31.50	8.70		40.20	47.50
1030	18" O.C.		54	.148		25.50	8.40		33.90	40.50
1040	24" O.C.		56	.143		21	8.10		29.10	35
1050	30" O.C.		58	.138		19	7.80		26.80	32.50
1060	60" O.C.		60	.133		14.60	7.55		22.15	27.50
1200	No. 6000, base & cover, blank		50	.160		10.80	9.05		19.85	25.50
1210	Receptacle, 6" O.C.		30	.267		61.50	15.10		76.60	90.50
1220	12" O.C.		37	.216		41	12.25		53.25	63.50
1230	18" O.C.		39	.205		34.50	11.60		46.10	55.50
1240	24" O.C.		41	.195		28.50	11.05		39.55	47.50
1250	30" O.C.		43	.186		27	10.55		37.55	45.50
1260	60" O.C.		45	.178		21	10.05		31.05	38
2400	Fittings, elbows, No. 500		40	.200	Ea.	2.25	11.30		13.55	19.45
2800	Elbow cover, No. 2000		40	.200		3.25	11.30		14.55	20.50
2880	Tee, No. 500		42	.190		4.10	10.80		14.90	20.50
2900	No. 2000		27	.296		12.10	16.75		28.85	38.50
3000	Switch box, No. 500		16	.500		6.20	28.50		34.70	49.50
3400	Telephone outlet, No. 1500		16	.500		36	28.50		64.50	82
3600	Junction box, No. 1500		16	.500		15.75	28.50		44.25	60
3800	Plugmold wired sections, No. 2000									
4000	1 circuit, 6 outlets, 3 ft. long	1 Elec	8	1	Ea.	36.50	56.50		93	125
4100	2 circuits, 8 outlets, 6 ft. long		5.30	1.509		60	85.50		145.50	194
4110	Tele-power pole, alum, w/2 recept, 10'		4	2		209	113		322	400
4120	12'		3.85	2.078		200	118		318	395
4130	15'		3.70	2.162		315	122		437	530
4140	Steel, w/2 recept, 10'		4	2		132	113		245	315
4150	One phone fitting, 10'		4	2		142	113		255	325
4160	Alum, 4 outlets, 10'		3.70	2.162		262	122		384	470
4300	Overhead distribution systems, 125 volt									
4800	No. 2000, entrance end fitting	1 Elec	20	.400	Ea.	5.60	22.50		28.10	40
5000	Blank end fitting		40	.200		2.25	11.30		13.55	19.45
5200	Supporting clip		40	.200		1.33	11.30		12.63	18.40
5800	No. 3000, entrance end fitting		20	.400		9.20	22.50		31.70	44
6000	Blank end fitting		40	.200		2.62	11.30		13.92	19.85
6020	Internal elbow		20	.400		12.10	22.50		34.60	47.50
6030	External elbow		20	.400		17.10	22.50		39.60	53
6040	Device bracket		53	.151		4.10	8.55		12.65	17.30
6400	Hanger clamp		32	.250		6.25	14.15		20.40	28
7000	No. 4000 base		90	.089	L.F.	4.40	5.05		9.45	12.40

26 27 23.40 Surface Raceway	Crew	Daily Output	Labor-Hours	Unit	Material	2017 Bare Costs Labor	Equipment	Total	Total Incl O&P
7200	Divider	1 Elec	100	.080	L.F.	.85	4.53		5.38	7.75
7400	Entrance end fitting		16	.500	Ea.	22.50	28.50		51	67
7600	Blank end fitting		40	.200		6.20	11.30		17.50	24
7610	Recpt. & tele. cover		53	.151		10.55	8.55		19.10	24.50
7620	External elbow		16	.500		34.50	28.50		63	80.50
7630	Coupling		53	.151		5.25	8.55		13.80	18.60
7640	Divider clip & coupling		80	.100		1.04	5.65		6.69	9.65
7650	Panel connector		16	.500		22	28.50		50.50	66.50
7800	Take off connector		16	.500		72.50	28.50		101	123
8000	No. 6000, take off connector		16	.500		86.50	28.50		115	138
8100	Take off fitting		16	.500		64	28.50		92.50	113
8200	Hanger clamp		32	.250		15.55	14.15		29.70	38
8230	Coupling					8.50			8.50	9.35
8240	One gang device plate	1 Elec	53	.151		8.30	8.55		16.85	22
8250	Two gang device plate		40	.200		10.15	11.30		21.45	28
8260	Blank end fitting		40	.200		8.80	11.30		20.10	26.50
8270	Combination elbow		14	.571		36	32.50		68.50	88
8300	Panel connector		16	.500		15.75	28.50		44.25	60
8500	Chan-L-Wire system installed in 1-5/8" x 1-5/8" strut. Strut									
8600	not incl., 30 amp, 4 wire, 3 phase	1 Elec	200	.040	L.F.	5	2.26		7.26	8.90
8700	Junction box		8	1	Ea.	33.50	56.50		90	122
8800	Insulating end cap		40	.200		8.90	11.30		20.20	27
8900	Strut splice plate		40	.200		11.80	11.30		23.10	30
9000	Tap		40	.200		23.50	11.30		34.80	43
9100	Fixture hanger		60	.133		10.15	7.55		17.70	22.50
9200	Pulling tool					90			90	99
9300	Non-metallic, straight section									
9310	7/16" x 7/8", base & cover, blank	1 Elec	160	.050	L.F.	1.72	2.83		4.55	6.15
9320	Base & cover w/adhesive		160	.050		1.45	2.83		4.28	5.85
9340	7/16" x 1-5/16", base & cover, blank		145	.055		1.88	3.12		5	6.75
9350	Base & cover w/adhesive		145	.055		2.21	3.12		5.33	7.10
9370	11/16" x 2-1/4", base & cover, blank		130	.062		2.66	3.48		6.14	8.15
9380	Base & cover w/adhesive		130	.062		3.07	3.48		6.55	8.60
9385	1-11/16" x 5-1/4", two compartment base & cover w/screws		80	.100		9.95	5.65		15.60	19.45
9400	Fittings, elbows, 7/16" x 7/8"		50	.160	Ea.	1.92	9.05		10.97	15.65
9410	7/16" x 1-5/16"		45	.178		1.99	10.05		12.04	17.30
9420	11/16" x 2-1/4"		40	.200		2.15	11.30		13.45	19.30
9425	1-11/16" x 5-1/4"		28	.286		11.30	16.15		27.45	36.50
9430	Tees, 7/16" x 7/8"		35	.229		2.48	12.95		15.43	22
9440	7/16" x 1-5/16"		32	.250		2.54	14.15		16.69	24
9450	11/16" x 2-1/4"		30	.267		2.61	15.10		17.71	25.50
9455	1-11/16" x 5-1/4"		24	.333		18.10	18.85		36.95	48.50
9460	Cover clip, 7/16" x 7/8"		80	.100		.50	5.65		6.15	9.05
9470	7/16" x 1-5/16"		72	.111		.45	6.30		6.75	9.90
9480	11/16" x 2-1/4"		64	.125		.77	7.10		7.87	11.45
9484	1-11/16" x 5-1/4"		42	.190		2.67	10.80		13.47	19.10
9486	Wire clip, 1-11/16" x 5-1/4"		68	.118		.46	6.65		7.11	10.50
9490	Blank end, 7/16" x 7/8"		50	.160		.70	9.05		9.75	14.30
9500	7/16" x 1-5/16"		45	.178		.80	10.05		10.85	16
9510	11/16" x 2-1/4"		40	.200		1.20	11.30		12.50	18.25
9515	1-11/16" x 5-1/4"		38	.211		5.55	11.90		17.45	24
9520	Round fixture box, 5.5" dia x 1"		25	.320		11.30	18.10		29.40	39.50
9530	Device box, 1 gang		30	.267		5.10	15.10		20.20	28

For customer support on your Electrical Costs with RSMeans Data, call 800.448.8182.

271

26 27 23 – Indoor Service Poles

26 27 23.40 Surface Raceway	Crew	Daily Output	Labor-Hours	Unit	Material	2017 Bare Costs Labor	Equipment	Total	Total Incl O&P
9540	2 gang	1 Elec	25	.320	Ea.	7.40	18.10		25.50	35

26 27 26 – Wiring Devices

26 27 26.10 Low Voltage Switching

		Crew	Daily Output	Labor-Hours	Unit	Material	2017 Bare Costs Labor	Equipment	Total	Total Incl O&P
0010	**LOW VOLTAGE SWITCHING**									
3600	Relays, 120 V or 277 V standard	1 Elec	12	.667	Ea.	41	37.50		78.50	102
3800	Flush switch, standard		40	.200		11.50	11.30		22.80	29.50
4000	Interchangeable		40	.200		15.05	11.30		26.35	33.50
4100	Surface switch, standard		40	.200		8.20	11.30		19.50	26
4200	Transformer 115 V to 25 V		12	.667		128	37.50		165.50	198
4400	Master control, 12 circuit, manual		4	2		127	113		240	310
4500	25 circuit, motorized		4	2		141	113		254	325
4600	Rectifier, silicon		12	.667		46	37.50		83.50	107
4800	Switchplates, 1 gang, 1, 2 or 3 switch, plastic		80	.100		5	5.65		10.65	14
5000	Stainless steel		80	.100		11.35	5.65		17	21
5400	2 gang, 3 switch, stainless steel		53	.151		23	8.55		31.55	38
5500	4 switch, plastic		53	.151		10.45	8.55		19	24.50
5600	2 gang, 4 switch, stainless steel		53	.151		22	8.55		30.55	37
5700	6 switch, stainless steel		53	.151		43.50	8.55		52.05	61
5800	3 gang, 9 switch, stainless steel		32	.250		65.50	14.15		79.65	93
5900	Receptacle, triple, 1 return, 1 feed		26	.308		43	17.40		60.40	73.50
6000	2 feed		20	.400		43	22.50		65.50	81.50
6100	Relay gang boxes, flush or surface, 6 gang		5.30	1.509		90.50	85.50		176	228
6200	12 gang		4.70	1.702		102	96.50		198.50	256
6400	18 gang		4	2		113	113		226	294
6500	Frame, to hold up to 6 relays		12	.667		84	37.50		121.50	149
7200	Control wire, 2 conductor		6.30	1.270	C.L.F.	34	72		106	146
7400	3 conductor		5	1.600		47	90.50		137.50	188
7600	19 conductor		2.50	3.200		320	181		501	620
7800	26 conductor		2	4		430	226		656	815
8000	Weatherproof, 3 conductor		5	1.600		99	90.50		189.50	245

26 27 26.20 Wiring Devices Elements

		Crew	Daily Output	Labor-Hours	Unit	Material	2017 Bare Costs Labor	Equipment	Total	Total Incl O&P
0010	**WIRING DEVICES ELEMENTS** R262726-90									
0200	Toggle switch, quiet type, single pole, 15 amp	1 Elec	40	.200	Ea.	.54	11.30		11.84	17.55
0500	20 amp		27	.296		3.35	16.75		20.10	28.50
0510	30 amp		23	.348		20	19.70		39.70	51.50
0530	Lock handle, 20 amp		27	.296		23.50	16.75		40.25	50.50
0540	Security key, 20 amp		26	.308		119	17.40		136.40	157
0550	Rocker, 15 amp		40	.200		3.86	11.30		15.16	21
0560	20 amp		27	.296		7.80	16.75		24.55	33.50
0600	3 way, 15 amp		23	.348		1.90	19.70		21.60	31.50
0800	20 amp		18	.444		3.62	25		28.62	41.50
0810	30 amp		9	.889		24	50.50		74.50	102
0830	Lock handle, 20 amp		18	.444		26	25		51	66.50
0840	Security key, 20 amp		17	.471		114	26.50		140.50	165
0850	Rocker, 15 amp		23	.348		4.50	19.70		24.20	34.50
0860	20 amp		18	.444		10.70	25		35.70	49.50
0900	4 way, 15 amp		15	.533		7.75	30		37.75	53.50
1000	20 amp		11	.727		42.50	41		83.50	109
1020	Lock handle, 20 amp		11	.727		46.50	41		87.50	113
1030	Rocker, 15 amp		15	.533		17.50	30		47.50	64.50
1040	20 amp		11	.727		18.05	41		59.05	81.50
1100	Toggle switch, quiet type, double pole, 15 amp		15	.533		12.30	30		42.30	58.50

26 27 26.20 Wiring Devices Elements		Crew	Daily Output	Labor-Hours	Unit	Material	2017 Bare Costs Labor	Equipment	Total	Total Incl O&P
1200	20 amp	1 Elec	11	.727	Ea	17.10	41		58.10	80.50
1210	30 amp		9	.889		24.50	50.50		75	103
1230	Lock handle, 20 amp		11	.727		13.25	41		54.25	76
1250	Security key, 20 amp		10	.800		116	45.50		161.50	196
1420	Toggle switch quiet type, 1 pole, 2 throw center off, 15 amp		23	.348		58	19.70		77.70	93
1440	20 amp		18	.444		51	25		76	93.50
1460	2 pole, 2 throw center off, lock handle, 20 amp		11	.727		60	41		101	128
1480	1 pole, momentary contact, 15 amp		23	.348		17.65	19.70		37.35	49
1500	20 amp		18	.444		22.50	25		47.50	62
1520	Momentary contact, lock handle, 20 amp		18	.444		31	25		56	71.50
1650	Dimmer switch, 120 volt, incandescent, 600 watt, 1 pole	G	16	.500		22.50	28.50		51	67.50
1700	600 watt, 3 way	G	12	.667		6.90	37.50		44.40	64
1750	1000 watt, 1 pole	G	16	.500		35.50	28.50		64	81.50
1800	1000 watt, 3 way	G	12	.667		73	37.50		110.50	137
2000	1500 watt, 1 pole	G	11	.727		84	41		125	154
2100	2000 watt, 1 pole	G	8	1		129	56.50		185.50	227
2110	Fluorescent, 600 watt	G	15	.533		109	30		139	165
2120	1000 watt	G	15	.533		133	30		163	191
2130	1500 watt	G	10	.800		246	45.50		291.50	340
2160	Explosionproof, toggle switch, wall, single pole 20 amp		5.30	1.509		195	85.50		280.50	345
2180	Receptacle, single outlet, 20 amp		5.30	1.509		345	85.50		430.50	510
2190	30 amp		4	2		730	113		843	975
2290	60 amp		2.50	3.200		775	181		956	1,125
2360	Plug, 20 amp		16	.500		185	28.50		213.50	246
2370	30 amp		12	.667		315	37.50		352.50	400
2380	60 amp		8	1		410	56.50		466.50	535
2410	Furnace, thermal cutoff switch with plate		26	.308		15.90	17.40		33.30	43.50
2460	Receptacle, duplex, 120 volt, grounded, 15 amp		40	.200		1.26	11.30		12.56	18.35
2470	20 amp		27	.296		7.95	16.75		24.70	33.50
2480	Ground fault interrupting, 15 amp		27	.296		13.75	16.75		30.50	40
2482	20 amp		27	.296		40	16.75		56.75	69
2486	Clock receptacle, 15 amp		40	.200		27.50	11.30		38.80	47
2490	Dryer, 30 amp		15	.533		4.46	30		34.46	50
2500	Range, 50 amp		11	.727		12.15	41		53.15	75
2530	Surge suppressor receptacle, duplex, 20 amp		27	.296		41	16.75		57.75	70
2532	Quad, 20 amp		20	.400		81.50	22.50		104	124
2540	Isolated ground receptacle, duplex, 20 amp		27	.296		21	16.75		37.75	48
2542	Quad, 20 amp		20	.400		32	22.50		54.50	69
2550	Simplex, 20 amp		27	.296		23	16.75		39.75	50
2560	Simplex, 30 amp		15	.533		27.50	30		57.50	75.50
2570	Cable reel w/receptacle 50' w/3#12, 120 V, 20 A	2 Elec	2.67	5.999		1,050	340		1,390	1,650
2600	Wall plates, stainless steel, 1 gang	1 Elec	80	.100		2.56	5.65		8.21	11.30
2800	2 gang		53	.151		4.33	8.55		12.88	17.55
3000	3 gang		32	.250		8.45	14.15		22.60	30.50
3100	4 gang		27	.296		11	16.75		27.75	37
3110	Brown plastic, 1 gang		80	.100		.38	5.65		6.03	8.90
3120	2 gang		53	.151		.75	8.55		9.30	13.65
3130	3 gang		32	.250		1.11	14.15		15.26	22
3140	4 gang		27	.296		2.86	16.75		19.61	28
3150	Brushed brass, 1 gang		80	.100		5.30	5.65		10.95	14.30
3160	Anodized aluminum, 1 gang		80	.100		3.01	5.65		8.66	11.80
3170	Switch cover, weatherproof, 1 gang		60	.133		5.05	7.55		12.60	16.85
3180	Vandal proof lock, 1 gang		60	.133		14.20	7.55		21.75	27

For customer support on your Electrical Costs with RSMeans Data, call 800.448.8182.

273

26 27 26 – Wiring Devices

26 27 26.20 Wiring Devices Elements	Crew	Daily Output	Labor-Hours	Unit	Material	2017 Bare Costs Labor	Equipment	Total	Total Incl O&P
3200 Lampholder, keyless	1 Elec	26	.308	Ea.	16.85	17.40		34.25	44.50
3400 Pullchain with receptacle		22	.364		20.50	20.50		41	53.50
3500 Pilot light, neon with jewel		27	.296		9.55	16.75		26.30	35.50
3600 Receptacle, 20 amp, 250 volt, NEMA 6		27	.296		21.50	16.75		38.25	48.50
3620 277 volt NEMA 7		27	.296		15.95	16.75		32.70	42.50
3640 125/250 volt NEMA 10		27	.296		17.95	16.75		34.70	45
3680 125/250 volt NEMA 14		25	.320		23	18.10		41.10	52
3700 3 pole, 250 volt NEMA 15		25	.320		23	18.10		41.10	52.50
3720 120/208 volt NEMA 18		25	.320		24	18.10		42.10	53
3740 30 amp, 125 volt NEMA 5		15	.533		17.80	30		47.80	64.50
3760 250 volt NEMA 6		15	.533		20.50	30		50.50	67.50
3780 277 volt NEMA 7		15	.533		26.50	30		56.50	74.50
3820 125/250 volt NEMA 14		14	.571		46.50	32.50		79	100
3840 3 pole, 250 volt NEMA 15		14	.571		46	32.50		78.50	99
3880 50 amp, 125 volt NEMA 5		11	.727		22.50	41		63.50	86.50
3900 250 volt NEMA 6		11	.727		23	41		64	87
3920 277 volt NEMA 7		11	.727		26.50	41		67.50	90.50
3960 125/250 volt NEMA 14		10	.800		61	45.50		106.50	135
3980 3 pole 250 volt NEMA 15		10	.800		62	45.50		107.50	136
4020 60 amp, 125/250 volt, NEMA 14		8	1		70.50	56.50		127	163
4040 3 pole, 250 volt NEMA 15		8	1		74.50	56.50		131	167
4060 120/208 volt NEMA 18		8	1		105	56.50		161.50	201
4100 Receptacle locking, 20 amp, 125 volt NEMA L5		27	.296		16.60	16.75		33.35	43.50
4120 250 volt NEMA L6		27	.296		16.50	16.75		33.25	43
4140 277 volt NEMA L7		27	.296		17.15	16.75		33.90	44
4150 3 pole, 250 volt, NEMA L11		27	.296		24	16.75		40.75	51
4160 20 amp, 480 volt NEMA L8		27	.296		19.35	16.75		36.10	46.50
4180 600 volt NEMA L9		27	.296		29	16.75		45.75	57
4200 125/250 volt NEMA L10		27	.296		23.50	16.75		40.25	51
4230 125/250 volt NEMA L14		25	.320		27	18.10		45.10	56.50
4280 250 volt NEMA L15		25	.320		29	18.10		47.10	59
4300 480 volt NEMA L16		25	.320		23.50	18.10		41.60	52.50
4320 3 phase, 120/208 volt NEMA L18		25	.320		27	18.10		45.10	57
4340 277/480 volt NEMA L19		25	.320		28	18.10		46.10	58
4360 347/600 volt NEMA L20		25	.320		32	18.10		50.10	62.50
4380 120/208 volt NEMA L21		23	.348		29	19.70		48.70	61.50
4400 277/480 volt NEMA L22		23	.348		30	19.70		49.70	62.50
4420 347/600 volt NEMA L23		23	.348		32	19.70		51.70	64.50
4440 30 amp, 125 volt NEMA L5		15	.533		23	30		53	70.50
4460 250 volt NEMA L6		15	.533		25.50	30		55.50	73
4480 277 volt NEMA L7		15	.533		25.50	30		55.50	73.50
4500 480 volt NEMA L8		15	.533		26.50	30		56.50	74.50
4520 600 volt NEMA L9		15	.533		27.50	30		57.50	75
4540 125/250 volt NEMA L10		15	.533		30	30		60	78
4560 3 phase, 250 volt NEMA L11		15	.533		27	30		57	75
4620 125/250 volt NEMA L14		14	.571		36.50	32.50		69	88.50
4640 250 volt NEMA L15		14	.571		37	32.50		69.50	89.50
4660 480 volt NEMA L16		14	.571		38.50	32.50		71	90.50
4680 600 volt NEMA L17		14	.571		38	32.50		70.50	90
4700 120/208 volt NEMA L18		14	.571		41.50	32.50		74	94
4720 277/480 volt NEMA L19		14	.571		39.50	32.50		72	92
4740 347/600 volt NEMA L20		14	.571		43.50	32.50		76	96
4760 120/208 volt NEMA L21		13	.615		40	35		75	96

26 27 Low-Voltage Distribution Equipment

26 27 26 – Wiring Devices

26 27 26.20 Wiring Devices Elements	Crew	Daily Output	Labor-Hours	Unit	Material	2017 Bare Costs Labor	Equipment	Total	Total Incl O&P
4780	277/480 volt NEMA L22	1 Elec	13	.615	Ea.	40	35		75	96
4800	347/600 volt NEMA L23		13	.615		53	35		88	110
4840	Receptacle, corrosion resistant, 15 or 20 amp, 125 volt NEMA L5		27	.296		25.50	16.75		42.25	53
4860	250 volt NEMA L6		27	.296		22	16.75		38.75	49
4900	Receptacle, cover plate, phenolic plastic, NEMA 5 & 6		80	.100		.61	5.65		6.26	9.15
4910	NEMA 7-23		80	.100		.75	5.65		6.40	9.35
4920	Stainless steel, NEMA 5 & 6		80	.100		2.71	5.65		8.36	11.50
4930	NEMA 7-23		80	.100		3.21	5.65		8.86	12.05
4940	Brushed brass NEMA 5 & 6		80	.100		5.40	5.65		11.05	14.45
4950	NEMA 7-23		80	.100		5.85	5.65		11.50	14.95
4960	Anodized aluminum, NEMA 5 & 6		80	.100		3.51	5.65		9.16	12.35
4970	NEMA 7-23		80	.100		5.80	5.65		11.45	14.90
4980	Weatherproof NEMA 7-23		60	.133		33	7.55		40.55	47.50
5000	Duplex receptacle, combo 15A/125V, 3 wire W/ 2-5V 0.7A, port USB, AL		27	.296		16.80	16.75		33.55	43.50
5002	15A/125V, 3 wire W/ 2-5V 0.7A, port USB, BK		27	.296		16.80	16.75		33.55	43.50
5004	15A/125V, 3 wire W/ 2-5V 0.7A, port USB, LA		27	.296		16.80	16.75		33.55	43.50
5006	15A/125V, 3 wire W/ 2-5V 0.7A, port USB, IV		27	.296		16.80	16.75		33.55	43.50
5008	15A/125V, 3 wire W/ 2-5V 0.7A, port USB, WH		27	.296		16.80	16.75		33.55	43.50
5010	Duplex receptacle, combo 15A/125V, 3 wire W/ 2-5V 2.1A, port USB, AL		27	.296		45	16.75		61.75	74.50
5012	15A/125V, 3 wire W/ 2-5V 2.1A, port USB, BK		27	.296		45	16.75		61.75	74.50
5014	15A/125V, 3 wire W/ 2-5V 2.1A, port USB, LA		27	.296		45	16.75		61.75	74.50
5016	15A/125V, 3 wire W/ 2-5V 2.1A, port USB, IV		27	.296		45	16.75		61.75	74.50
5018	15A/125V, 3 wire W/ 2-5V 2.1A, port USB, WH		27	.296		45	16.75		61.75	74.50
5020	Duplex receptacle, combo 20A/125V, 3 wire W/ 2-5V 2.1A, port USB, AL		27	.296		49.50	16.75		66.25	79.50
5022	20A/125V, 3 wire W/ 2-5V 2.1A, port USB, BK		27	.296		49.50	16.75		66.25	79.50
5024	20A/125V, 3 wire W/ 2-5V 2.1A, port USB, LA		27	.296		49.50	16.75		66.25	79.50
5026	20A/125V, 3 wire W/ 2-5V 2.1A, port USB, IV		27	.296		49.50	16.75		66.25	79.50
5028	20A/125V, 3 wire W/ 2-5V 2.1A, port USB, WH		27	.296		49.50	16.75		66.25	79.50
5100	Plug, 20 amp, 250 volt NEMA 6		30	.267		15.65	15.10		30.75	39.50
5110	277 volt NEMA 7		30	.267		19.20	15.10		34.30	43.50
5120	3 pole, 120/250 volt NEMA 10		26	.308		18.15	17.40		35.55	46
5130	125/250 volt NEMA 14		26	.308		36.50	17.40		53.90	66.50
5140	250 volt NEMA 15		26	.308		41	17.40		58.40	71
5150	120/208 volt NEMA 8		26	.308		43.50	17.40		60.90	74
5160	30 amp, 125 volt NEMA 5		13	.615		56.50	35		91.50	114
5170	250 volt NEMA 6		13	.615		53.50	35		88.50	111
5180	277 volt NEMA 7		13	.615		62.50	35		97.50	121
5190	125/250 volt NEMA 14		13	.615		42.50	35		77.50	98.50
5200	3 pole, 250 volt NEMA 15		12	.667		44	37.50		81.50	105
5210	50 amp, 125 volt NEMA 5		9	.889		61.50	50.50		112	144
5220	250 volt NEMA 6		9	.889		64.50	50.50		115	147
5230	277 volt NEMA 7		9	.889		69	50.50		119.50	152
5240	125/250 volt NEMA 14		9	.889		54	50.50		104.50	135
5250	3 pole, 250 volt NEMA 15		8	1		55	56.50		111.50	146
5260	60 amp, 125/250 volt NEMA 14		7	1.143		61.50	64.50		126	165
5270	3 pole, 250 volt NEMA 15		7	1.143		65	64.50		129.50	169
5280	120/208 volt NEMA 18		7	1.143		82.50	64.50		147	188
5300	Plug angle, 20 amp, 250 volt NEMA 6		30	.267		24	15.10		39.10	49
5310	30 amp, 125 volt NEMA 5		13	.615		43	35		78	99.50
5320	250 volt NEMA 6		13	.615		44.50	35		79.50	101
5330	277 volt NEMA 7		13	.615		51	35		86	108
5340	125/250 volt NEMA 14		13	.615		47	35		82	104
5350	3 pole, 250 volt NEMA 15		12	.667		48.50	37.50		86	110

For customer support on your Electrical Costs with RSMeans Data, call 800.448.8182.

275

26 27 26.20 Wiring Devices Elements		Crew	Daily Output	Labor-Hours	Unit	Material	2017 Bare Costs Labor	Equipment	Total	Total Incl O&P
5360	50 amp, 125 volt NEMA 5	1 Elec	9	.889	Ea.	45	50.50		95.50	125
5370	250 volt NEMA 6		9	.889		46	50.50		96.50	127
5380	277 volt NEMA 7		9	.889		52	50.50		102.50	133
5390	125/250 volt NEMA 14		9	.889		58.50	50.50		109	140
5400	3 pole, 250 volt NEMA 15		8	1		60.50	56.50		117	152
5410	60 amp, 125/250 volt NEMA 14		7	1.143		68	64.50		132.50	172
5420	3 pole, 250 volt NEMA 15		7	1.143		71	64.50		135.50	175
5430	120/208 volt NEMA 18		7	1.143		71.50	64.50		136	176
5500	Plug, locking, 20 amp, 125 volt NEMA L5		30	.267		13.20	15.10		28.30	37
5510	250 volt NEMA L6		30	.267		13.15	15.10		28.25	37
5520	277 volt NEMA L7		30	.267		13.45	15.10		28.55	37.50
5530	480 volt NEMA L8		30	.267		14.95	15.10		30.05	39
5540	600 volt NEMA L9		30	.267		15	15.10		30.10	39
5550	3 pole, 125/250 volt NEMA L10		26	.308		22.50	17.40		39.90	50.50
5560	250 volt NEMA L11		26	.308		22.50	17.40		39.90	50.50
5570	480 volt NEMA L12		26	.308		26	17.40		43.40	54.50
5580	125/250 volt NEMA L14		26	.308		19.90	17.40		37.30	48
5590	250 volt NEMA L15		26	.308		21	17.40		38.40	49
5600	480 volt NEMA L16		26	.308		22.50	17.40		39.90	50.50
5610	4 pole, 120/208 volt NEMA L18		24	.333		25	18.85		43.85	56
5620	277/480 volt NEMA L19		24	.333		26	18.85		44.85	57
5630	347/600 volt NEMA L20		24	.333		29	18.85		47.85	60
5640	120/208 volt NEMA L21		24	.333		25.50	18.85		44.35	56.50
5650	277/480 volt NEMA L22		24	.333		27	18.85		45.85	58
5660	347/600 volt NEMA L23		24	.333		28	18.85		46.85	59
5670	30 amp, 125 volt NEMA L5		13	.615		20	35		55	74
5680	250 volt NEMA L6		13	.615		21	35		56	75
5690	277 volt NEMA L7		13	.615		20	35		55	74
5700	480 volt NEMA L8		13	.615		22	35		57	76
5710	600 volt NEMA L9		13	.615		21	35		56	75
5720	3 pole, 125/250 volt NEMA L10		11	.727		24.50	41		65.50	88
5730	250 volt NEMA L11		11	.727		24.50	41		65.50	88
5760	125/250 volt NEMA L14		11	.727		27	41		68	91.50
5770	250 volt NEMA L15		11	.727		27	41		68	91.50
5780	480 volt NEMA L16		11	.727		28.50	41		69.50	92.50
5790	600 volt NEMA L17		11	.727		29.50	41		70.50	94
5800	4 pole, 120/208 volt NEMA L18		10	.800		31	45.50		76.50	103
5810	120/208 volt NEMA L19		10	.800		31.50	45.50		77	103
5820	347/600 volt NEMA L20		10	.800		32.50	45.50		78	104
5830	120/208 volt NEMA L21		10	.800		30.50	45.50		76	102
5840	277/480 volt NEMA L22		10	.800		31	45.50		76.50	102
5850	347/600 volt NEMA L23		10	.800		35	45.50		80.50	107
6000	Connector, 20 amp, 250 volt NEMA 6		30	.267		24	15.10		39.10	49
6010	277 volt NEMA 7		30	.267		31.50	15.10		46.60	57
6020	3 pole, 120/250 volt NEMA 10		26	.308		35.50	17.40		52.90	65
6030	125/250 volt NEMA 14		26	.308		35.50	17.40		52.90	65
6040	250 volt NEMA 15		26	.308		35.50	17.40		52.90	65.50
6050	120/208 volt NEMA 18		26	.308		39	17.40		56.40	68.50
6060	30 amp, 125 volt NEMA 5		13	.615		61.50	35		96.50	120
6070	250 volt NEMA 6		13	.615		61.50	35		96.50	120
6080	277 volt NEMA 7		13	.615		61.50	35		96.50	120
6110	50 amp, 125 volt NEMA 5		9	.889		84.50	50.50		135	169
6120	250 volt NEMA 6		9	.889		84.50	50.50		135	169

For customer support on your Electrical Costs with RSMeans Data, call 800.448.8182.

26 27 26.20 Wiring Devices Elements	Crew	Daily Output	Labor-Hours	Unit	Material	2017 Bare Costs Labor	2017 Bare Costs Equipment	Total	Total Incl O&P
6130	277 volt NEMA 7	1 Elec	9	.889	Ea.	84.50	50.50		135	160
6200	Connector, locking, 20 amp, 125 volt NEMA L5		30	.267		20	15.10		35.10	44.50
6210	250 volt NEMA L6		30	.267		20.50	15.10		35.60	45
6220	277 volt NEMA L7		30	.267		20.50	15.10		35.60	45
6230	480 volt NEMA L8		30	.267		24	15.10		39.10	48.50
6240	600 volt NEMA L9		30	.267		24.50	15.10		39.60	49
6250	3 pole, 125/250 volt NEMA L10		26	.308		34	17.40		51.40	63.50
6260	250 volt NEMA L11		26	.308		34	17.40		51.40	63.50
6280	125/250 volt NEMA L14		26	.308		27.50	17.40		44.90	56.50
6290	250 volt NEMA L15		26	.308		28	17.40		45.40	56.50
6300	480 volt NEMA L16		26	.308		29.50	17.40		46.90	58.50
6310	4 pole, 120/208 volt NEMA L18		24	.333		35.50	18.85		54.35	67.50
6320	277/480 volt NEMA L19		24	.333		40.50	18.85		59.35	73
6330	347/600 volt NEMA L20		24	.333		40	18.85		58.85	72.50
6340	120/208 volt NEMA L21		24	.333		43	18.85		61.85	76
6350	277/480 volt NEMA L22		24	.333		45.50	18.85		64.35	78.50
6360	347/600 volt NEMA L23		24	.333		53	18.85		71.85	87
6370	30 amp, 125 volt NEMA L5		13	.615		41	35		76	97
6380	250 volt NEMA L6		13	.615		41.50	35		76.50	97.50
6390	277 volt NEMA L7		13	.615		41.50	35		76.50	98
6400	480 volt NEMA L8		13	.615		44	35		79	101
6410	600 volt NEMA L9		13	.615		43	35		78	99
6420	3 pole, 125/250 volt NEMA L10		11	.727		66	41		107	134
6430	250 volt NEMA L11		11	.727		66	41		107	134
6460	125/250 volt NEMA L14		11	.727		56	41		97	123
6470	250 volt NEMA L15		11	.727		56.50	41		97.50	124
6480	480 volt NEMA L16		11	.727		59.50	41		100.50	127
6490	600 volt NEMA L17		11	.727		61.50	41		102.50	129
6500	4 pole, 120/208 volt NEMA L18		10	.800		63	45.50		108.50	138
6510	120/208 volt NEMA L19		10	.800		69	45.50		114.50	144
6520	347/600 volt NEMA L20		10	.800		67.50	45.50		113	143
6530	120/208 volt NEMA L21		10	.800		57	45.50		102.50	131
6540	277/480 volt NEMA L22		10	.800		56	45.50		101.50	130
6550	347/600 volt NEMA L23		10	.800		66	45.50		111.50	141
7000	Receptacle computer, 250 volt, 15 amp, 3 pole 4 wire		8	1		82.50	56.50		139	176
7010	20 amp, 2 pole 3 wire		8	1		84	56.50		140.50	178
7020	30 amp, 2 pole 3 wire		6.50	1.231		137	69.50		206.50	254
7030	30 amp, 3 pole 4 wire		6.50	1.231		148	69.50		217.50	266
7040	60 amp, 3 pole 4 wire		4.50	1.778		249	101		350	425
7050	100 amp, 3 pole 4 wire		3	2.667		310	151		461	565
7100	Connector computer, 250 volt, 15 amp, 3 pole 4 wire		27	.296		130	16.75		146.75	168
7110	20 amp, 2 pole 3 wire		27	.296		118	16.75		134.75	154
7120	30 amp, 2 pole 3 wire		15	.533		181	30		211	244
7130	30 amp, 3 pole 4 wire		15	.533		185	30		215	249
7140	60 amp, 3 pole 4 wire		8	1		310	56.50		366.50	425
7150	100 amp, 3 pole 4 wire		4	2		425	113		538	640
7200	Plug, computer, 250 volt, 15 amp, 3 pole 4 wire		27	.296		116	16.75		132.75	153
7210	20 amp, 2 pole 3 wire		27	.296		109	16.75		125.75	145
7220	30 amp, 2 pole 3 wire		15	.533		190	30		220	254
7230	30 amp, 3 pole 4 wire		15	.533		184	30		214	247
7240	60 amp, 3 pole 4 wire		8	1		276	56.50		332.50	390
7250	100 amp, 3 pole 4 wire		4	2		345	113		458	550
7300	Connector adapter to flexible conduit, 1/2"		60	.133		2.90	7.55		10.45	14.50

26 27 Low-Voltage Distribution Equipment

26 27 26 – Wiring Devices

26 27 26.20 Wiring Devices Elements	Crew	Daily Output	Labor-Hours	Unit	Material	2017 Bare Costs Labor	Equipment	Total	Total Incl O&P
7310	3/4"	1 Elec	50	.160	Ea.	4.24	9.05		13.29	18.20
7320	1-1/4"		30	.267		11.45	15.10		26.55	35
7330	1-1/2"		23	.348		16.50	19.70		36.20	47.50

26 27 73 – Door Chimes

26 27 73.10 Doorbell System

		Crew	Daily Output	Labor-Hours	Unit	Material	Labor	Equipment	Total	Total Incl O&P
0010	**DOORBELL SYSTEM**, incl. transformer, button & signal									
0100	6" bell	1 Elec	4	2	Ea.	135	113		248	320
0200	Buzzer		4	2		109	113		222	290
1000	Door chimes, 2 notes		16	.500		24	28.50		52.50	69
1020	with ambient light		12	.667		116	37.50		153.50	185
1100	Tube type, 3 tube system		12	.667		199	37.50		236.50	276
1180	4 tube system		10	.800		440	45.50		485.50	555
1900	For transformer & button, add		5	1.600		15.60	90.50		106.10	153
3000	For push button only		24	.333		1.97	18.85		20.82	30.50
3200	Bell transformer		16	.500		19.35	28.50		47.85	64

26 28 Low-Voltage Circuit Protective Devices

26 28 13 – Fuses

26 28 13.10 Fuse Elements

		Crew	Daily Output	Labor-Hours	Unit	Material	Labor	Equipment	Total	Total Incl O&P
0010	**FUSE ELEMENTS**									
0020	Cartridge, nonrenewable									
0050	250 volt, 30 amp	1 Elec	50	.160	Ea.	2.40	9.05		11.45	16.20
0100	60 amp		50	.160		3.68	9.05		12.73	17.60
0150	100 amp		40	.200		16.10	11.30		27.40	34.50
0200	200 amp		36	.222		37	12.60		49.60	59.50
0250	400 amp		30	.267		74	15.10		89.10	104
0300	600 amp		24	.333		120	18.85		138.85	161
0400	600 volt, 30 amp		40	.200		8.65	11.30		19.95	26.50
0450	60 amp		40	.200		14.15	11.30		25.45	32.50
0500	100 amp		36	.222		28.50	12.60		41.10	50
0550	200 amp		30	.267		57.50	15.10		72.60	86
0600	400 amp		24	.333		140	18.85		158.85	183
0650	600 amp		20	.400		203	22.50		225.50	258
0800	Dual element, time delay, 250 volt, 30 amp		50	.160		9.95	9.05		19	24.50
0840	50 amp		50	.160		11.40	9.05		20.45	26
0850	60 amp		50	.160		11.60	9.05		20.65	26.50
0900	100 amp		40	.200		28	11.30		39.30	48
0950	200 amp		36	.222		61.50	12.60		74.10	86.50
1000	400 amp		30	.267		110	15.10		125.10	144
1050	600 amp		24	.333		181	18.85		199.85	228
1300	600 volt, 15 to 30 amp		40	.200		21.50	11.30		32.80	40.50
1350	35 to 60 amp		40	.200		31.50	11.30		42.80	51.50
1400	70 to 100 amp		36	.222		66.50	12.60		79.10	92
1450	110 to 200 amp		30	.267		129	15.10		144.10	165
1500	225 to 400 amp		24	.333		284	18.85		302.85	340
1550	600 amp		20	.400		355	22.50		377.50	430
1800	Class RK1, high capacity, 250 volt, 30 amp		50	.160		8	9.05		17.05	22.50
1850	60 amp		50	.160		14.75	9.05		23.80	30
1900	100 amp		40	.200		34.50	11.30		45.80	55
1950	200 amp		36	.222		78.50	12.60		91.10	105

26 28 Low-Voltage Circuit Protective Devices

26 28 13 – Fuses

26 28 13.10 Fuse Elements

		Crew	Daily Output	Labor-Hours	Unit	Material	2017 Bare Costs Labor	Equipment	Total	Total Incl O&P
2000	400 amp	1 Elec	30	.267	Ea.	130	15.10		145.10	166
2050	600 amp		24	.333		182	18.85		200.85	229
2200	600 volt, 30 amp		40	.200		14.90	11.30		26.20	33.50
2250	60 amp		40	.200		28	11.30		39.30	48
2300	100 amp		36	.222		71	12.60		83.60	97.50
2350	200 amp		30	.267		137	15.10		152.10	174
2400	400 amp		24	.333		230	18.85		248.85	282
2450	600 amp		20	.400		263	22.50		285.50	325
2700	Class J, current limiting, 250 or 600 volt, 30 amp		40	.200		24.50	11.30		35.80	44
2750	60 amp		40	.200		40.50	11.30		51.80	61.50
2800	100 amp		36	.222		56	12.60		68.60	80.50
2850	200 amp		30	.267		111	15.10		126.10	145
2900	400 amp		24	.333		274	18.85		292.85	330
2950	600 amp		20	.400		415	22.50		437.50	490
3100	Class L, current limiting, 250 or 600 volt, 601 to 1200 amp		16	.500		630	28.50		658.50	735
3150	1500 to 1600 amp		13	.615		1,025	35		1,060	1,175
3200	1800 to 2000 amp		10	.800		1,025	45.50		1,070.50	1,200
3250	2500 amp		10	.800		1,225	45.50		1,270.50	1,425
3300	3000 amp		8	1		1,650	56.50		1,706.50	1,875
3350	3500 to 4000 amp		8	1		1,725	56.50		1,781.50	1,975
3400	4500 to 5000 amp		6.70	1.194		2,250	67.50		2,317.50	2,575
3450	6000 amp		5.70	1.404		3,025	79.50		3,104.50	3,450
3600	Plug, 120 volt, 1 to 10 amp		50	.160		3.33	9.05		12.38	17.20
3650	15 to 30 amp		50	.160		4.11	9.05		13.16	18.05
3700	Dual element 0.3 to 14 amp		50	.160		5.30	9.05		14.35	19.35
3750	15 to 30 amp		50	.160		5.65	9.05		14.70	19.75
3800	Fustat, 120 volt, 15 to 30 amp		50	.160		5.75	9.05		14.80	19.90
3850	0.3 to 14 amp		50	.160		6.40	9.05		15.45	20.50
3900	Adapters 0.3 to 10 amp		50	.160		5.65	9.05		14.70	19.75
3950	15 to 30 amp		50	.160		8.65	9.05		17.70	23

26 28 16 – Enclosed Switches and Circuit Breakers

26 28 16.10 Circuit Breakers

		Crew	Daily Output	Labor-Hours	Unit	Material	2017 Bare Costs Labor	Equipment	Total	Total Incl O&P
0010	**CIRCUIT BREAKERS** (in enclosure)									
0100	Enclosed (NEMA 1), 600 volt, 3 pole, 30 amp	1 Elec	3.20	2.500	Ea.	490	142		632	750
0200	60 amp		2.80	2.857		605	162		767	905
0400	100 amp		2.30	3.478		690	197		887	1,050
0500	200 amp		1.50	5.333		1,450	300		1,750	2,050
0600	225 amp		1.50	5.333		1,600	300		1,900	2,200
0700	400 amp	2 Elec	1.60	10		2,725	565		3,290	3,850
0800	600 amp		1.20	13.333		3,950	755		4,705	5,475
1000	800 amp		.94	17.021		5,150	965		6,115	7,100
1200	1000 amp		.84	19.048		6,500	1,075		7,575	8,775
1220	1200 amp		.80	20		8,300	1,125		9,425	10,900
1240	1600 amp		.72	22.222		14,100	1,250		15,350	17,400
1260	2000 amp		.64	25		15,300	1,425		16,725	18,900
1400	1200 amp with ground fault		.80	20		12,200	1,125		13,325	15,100
1600	1600 amp with ground fault		.72	22.222		16,000	1,250		17,250	19,500
1800	2000 amp with ground fault		.64	25		17,100	1,425		18,525	21,000
2000	Disconnect, 240 volt 3 pole, 5 HP motor	1 Elec	3.20	2.500		425	142		567	675
2020	10 HP motor		3.20	2.500		425	142		567	675
2040	15 HP motor		2.80	2.857		425	162		587	705
2060	20 HP motor		2.30	3.478		515	197		712	860

For customer support on your Electrical Costs with RSMeans Data, call 800.448.8182.

279

26 28 16.10 Circuit Breakers

		Crew	Daily Output	Labor-Hours	Unit	Material	2017 Bare Costs Labor	Equipment	Total	Total Incl O&P
2080	25 HP motor	1 Elec	2.30	3.478	Ea.	515	197		712	860
2100	30 HP motor		2.30	3.478		515	197		712	860
2120	40 HP motor		2	4		880	226		1,106	1,300
2140	50 HP motor		1.50	5.333		880	300		1,180	1,425
2160	60 HP motor		1.50	5.333		2,025	300		2,325	2,675
2180	75 HP motor	2 Elec	2	8		2,025	455		2,480	2,900
2200	100 HP motor		1.60	10		2,025	565		2,590	3,075
2220	125 HP motor		1.60	10		2,025	565		2,590	3,075
2240	150 HP motor		1.20	13.333		3,950	755		4,705	5,475
2260	200 HP motor		1.20	13.333		5,150	755		5,905	6,775
2300	Enclosed (NEMA 7), explosion proof, 600 volt 3 pole, 50 amp	1 Elec	2.30	3.478		1,675	197		1,872	2,150
2350	100 amp		1.50	5.333		1,750	300		2,050	2,375
2400	150 amp		1	8		4,175	455		4,630	5,275
2450	250 amp	2 Elec	1.60	10		5,225	565		5,790	6,600
2500	400 amp	"	1.20	13.333		5,800	755		6,555	7,500

26 28 16.20 Safety Switches

		Crew	Daily Output	Labor-Hours	Unit	Material	2017 Bare Costs Labor	Equipment	Total	Total Incl O&P
0010	**SAFETY SWITCHES** R262816-80									
0100	General duty 240 volt, 3 pole NEMA 1, fusible, 30 amp	1 Elec	3.20	2.500	Ea.	64	142		206	283
0200	60 amp		2.30	3.478		109	197		306	415
0300	100 amp		1.90	4.211		186	238		424	560
0400	200 amp		1.30	6.154		400	350		750	960
0500	400 amp	2 Elec	1.80	8.889		980	505		1,485	1,825
0600	600 amp	"	1.20	13.333		1,900	755		2,655	3,200
0610	Nonfusible, 30 amp	1 Elec	3.20	2.500		52	142		194	269
0650	60 amp		2.30	3.478		68.50	197		265.50	370
0700	100 amp		1.90	4.211		160	238		398	530
0750	200 amp		1.30	6.154		294	350		644	845
0800	400 amp	2 Elec	1.80	8.889		750	505		1,255	1,575
0850	600 amp	"	1.20	13.333		1,625	755		2,380	2,900
1100	Heavy duty, 600 volt, 3 pole NEMA 1 nonfused									
1110	30 amp	1 Elec	3.20	2.500	Ea.	99	142		241	320
1500	60 amp		2.30	3.478		164	197		361	475
1700	100 amp		1.90	4.211		260	238		498	640
1900	200 amp		1.30	6.154		395	350		745	955
2100	400 amp	2 Elec	1.80	8.889		890	505		1,395	1,725
2300	600 amp		1.20	13.333		1,625	755		2,380	2,900
2500	800 amp		.94	17.021		3,300	965		4,265	5,075
2700	1200 amp		.80	20		4,875	1,125		6,000	7,050
2900	Heavy duty, 240 volt, 3 pole NEMA 1 fusible									
2910	30 amp	1 Elec	3.20	2.500	Ea.	103	142		245	325
3000	60 amp		2.30	3.478		174	197		371	485
3300	100 amp		1.90	4.211		275	238		513	655
3500	200 amp		1.30	6.154		485	350		835	1,050
3700	400 amp	2 Elec	1.80	8.889		1,225	505		1,730	2,100
3900	600 amp		1.20	13.333		2,875	755		3,630	4,275
4100	800 amp		.94	17.021		4,900	965		5,865	6,825
4300	1200 amp		.80	20		7,400	1,125		8,525	9,850
4340	2 pole fusible, 30 amp	1 Elec	3.50	2.286		80	129		209	282
4350	600 volt, 3 pole, fusible, 30 amp		3.20	2.500		176	142		318	405
4380	60 amp		2.30	3.478		213	197		410	530
4400	100 amp		1.90	4.211		390	238		628	785
4420	200 amp		1.30	6.154		565	350		915	1,150

26 28 16.20 Safety Switches	Crew	Daily Output	Labor-Hours	Unit	Material	2017 Bare Costs Labor	Equipment	Total	Total Incl O&P
4440	400 amp	2 Elec	1.80	8.889	Ea.	1,450	505		1,955	2,350
4450	600 amp		1.20	13.333		2,450	755		3,205	3,800
4460	800 amp		.94	17.021		4,900	965		5,865	6,825
4480	1200 amp		.80	20		7,400	1,125		8,525	9,850
4500	240 volt 3 pole NEMA 3R (no hubs), fusible									
4510	30 amp	1 Elec	3.10	2.581	Ea.	185	146		331	425
4700	60 amp		2.20	3.636		291	206		497	630
4900	100 amp		1.80	4.444		440	252		692	855
5100	200 amp		1.20	6.667		590	375		965	1,225
5300	400 amp	2 Elec	1.60	10		1,275	565		1,840	2,250
5500	600 amp	"	1	16		2,650	905		3,555	4,275
5510	Heavy duty, 600 volt, 3 pole 3ph. NEMA 3R fusible, 30 amp	1 Elec	3.10	2.581		310	146		456	560
5520	60 amp		2.20	3.636		370	206		576	720
5530	100 amp		1.80	4.444		545	252		797	975
5540	200 amp		1.20	6.667		740	375		1,115	1,375
5550	400 amp	2 Elec	1.60	10		1,750	565		2,315	2,775
5700	600 volt, 3 pole NEMA 3R nonfused									
5710	30 amp	1 Elec	3.10	2.581	Ea.	165	146		311	400
5900	60 amp		2.20	3.636		287	206		493	625
6100	100 amp		1.80	4.444		400	252		652	815
6300	200 amp		1.20	6.667		490	375		865	1,100
6500	400 amp	2 Elec	1.60	10		1,250	565		1,815	2,225
6700	600 amp	"	1	16		2,625	905		3,530	4,225
6900	600 volt, 6 pole NEMA 3R nonfused, 30 amp	1 Elec	2.70	2.963		1,175	168		1,343	1,550
7100	60 amp		2	4		1,425	226		1,651	1,925
7300	100 amp		1.50	5.333		1,500	300		1,800	2,075
7500	200 amp		1.20	6.667		6,750	375		7,125	8,000
7600	600 volt, 3 pole NEMA 7 explosion proof nonfused									
7610	30 amp	1 Elec	2.20	3.636	Ea.	1,350	206		1,556	1,775
7620	60 amp		1.80	4.444		1,625	252		1,877	2,150
7630	100 amp		1.20	6.667		1,950	375		2,325	2,725
7640	200 amp		.80	10		4,075	565		4,640	5,325
7710	600 volt 6 pole, NEMA 3R fusible, 30 amp		2.70	2.963		1,575	168		1,743	1,975
7900	60 amp		2	4		1,400	226		1,626	1,900
8100	100 amp		1.50	5.333		1,950	300		2,250	2,575
8110	240 volt 3 pole, NEMA 12 fusible, 30 amp		3.10	2.581		237	146		383	480
8120	60 amp		2.20	3.636		360	206		566	705
8130	100 amp		1.80	4.444		450	252		702	870
8140	200 amp		1.20	6.667		735	375		1,110	1,375
8150	400 amp	2 Elec	1.60	10		1,475	565		2,040	2,475
8160	600 amp	"	1	16		2,600	905		3,505	4,200
8180	600 volt 3 pole, NEMA 12 fusible, 30 amp	1 Elec	3.10	2.581		330	146		476	580
8190	60 amp		2.20	3.636		420	206		626	770
8200	100 amp		1.80	4.444		675	252		927	1,125
8210	200 amp		1.20	6.667		1,025	375		1,400	1,700
8220	400 amp	2 Elec	1.60	10		2,075	565		2,640	3,125
8230	600 amp	"	1	16		4,675	905		5,580	6,500
8240	600 volt 3 pole, NEMA 12 nonfused, 30 amp	1 Elec	3.10	2.581		225	146		371	465
8250	60 amp		2.20	3.636		320	206		526	660
8260	100 amp		1.80	4.444		455	252		707	875
8270	200 amp		1.20	6.667		560	375		935	1,175
8280	400 amp	2 Elec	1.60	10		1,275	565		1,840	2,250
8290	600 amp	"	1	16		3,625	905		4,530	5,325

26 28 Low-Voltage Circuit Protective Devices

26 28 16 – Enclosed Switches and Circuit Breakers

26 28 16.20 Safety Switches

		Crew	Daily Output	Labor-Hours	Unit	Material	2017 Bare Costs Labor	Equipment	Total	Total Incl O&P
8310	600 volt, 3 pole NEMA 4 fusible, 30 amp	1 Elec	3	2.667	Ea.	835	151		986	1,150
8320	60 amp		2.20	3.636		965	206		1,171	1,350
8330	100 amp		1.80	4.444		2,000	252		2,252	2,575
8340	200 amp		1.20	6.667		2,900	375		3,275	3,750
8350	400 amp	2 Elec	1.60	10		5,250	565		5,815	6,600
8360	600 volt 3 pole NEMA 4 nonfused, 30 amp	1 Elec	3	2.667		715	151		866	1,000
8370	60 amp		2.20	3.636		855	206		1,061	1,250
8380	100 amp		1.80	4.444		1,725	252		1,977	2,275
8390	200 amp		1.20	6.667		2,500	375		2,875	3,325
8400	400 amp	2 Elec	1.60	10		4,550	565		5,115	5,850
8490	Motor starters, manual, single phase, NEMA 1	1 Elec	6.40	1.250		65	71		136	178
8500	NEMA 4		4	2		182	113		295	370
8700	NEMA 7		4	2		200	113		313	390
8900	NEMA 1 with pilot		6.40	1.250		90	71		161	205
8920	3 pole, NEMA 1, 230/460 volt, 5 HP, size 0		3.50	2.286		207	129		336	420
8940	10 HP, size 1		2	4		245	226		471	610
9010	Disc. switch, 600 V 3 pole fusible, 30 amp, to 10 HP motor		3.20	2.500		355	142		497	600
9050	60 amp, to 30 HP motor		2.30	3.478		815	197		1,012	1,200
9070	100 amp, to 60 HP motor		1.90	4.211		815	238		1,053	1,250
9100	200 amp, to 125 HP motor		1.30	6.154		1,225	350		1,575	1,875
9110	400 amp, to 200 HP motor	2 Elec	1.80	8.889		3,075	505		3,580	4,150

26 28 16.40 Time Switches

		Crew	Daily Output	Labor-Hours	Unit	Material	2017 Bare Costs Labor	Equipment	Total	Total Incl O&P
0010	**TIME SWITCHES**									
0100	Single pole, single throw, 24 hour dial	1 Elec	4	2	Ea.	145	113		258	330
0200	24 hour dial with reserve power		3.60	2.222		615	126		741	865
0300	Astronomic dial		3.60	2.222		240	126		366	450
0400	Astronomic dial with reserve power		3.30	2.424		665	137		802	935
0500	7 day calendar dial		3.30	2.424		146	137		283	365
0600	7 day calendar dial with reserve power		3.20	2.500		285	142		427	525
0700	Photo cell 2000 watt		8	1		28.50	56.50		85	117
1080	Load management device, 4 loads		2	4		1,150	226		1,376	1,600
1100	8 loads		1	8		2,325	455		2,780	3,225

26 29 Low-Voltage Controllers

26 29 13 – Enclosed Controllers

26 29 13.10 Contactors, AC

		Crew	Daily Output	Labor-Hours	Unit	Material	2017 Bare Costs Labor	Equipment	Total	Total Incl O&P
0010	**CONTACTORS, AC** Enclosed (NEMA 1)									
0050	Lighting, 600 volt 3 pole, electrically held									
0100	20 amp	1 Elec	4	2	Ea.	380	113		493	585
0200	30 amp		3.60	2.222		370	126		496	595
0300	60 amp		3	2.667		695	151		846	990
0400	100 amp		2.50	3.200		1,050	181		1,231	1,425
0500	200 amp		1.40	5.714		2,600	325		2,925	3,325
0600	300 amp	2 Elec	1.60	10		6,975	565		7,540	8,525
0800	600 volt 3 pole, mechanically held, 30 amp	1 Elec	3.60	2.222		445	126		571	680
0900	60 amp		3	2.667		880	151		1,031	1,200
1000	75 amp		2.80	2.857		1,450	162		1,612	1,850
1100	100 amp		2.50	3.200		1,250	181		1,431	1,650
1200	150 amp		2	4		3,475	226		3,701	4,175
1300	200 amp		1.40	5.714		3,425	325		3,750	4,250
1500	Magnetic with auxiliary contact, size 00, 9 amp		4	2		177	113		290	365

26 29 Low-Voltage Controllers

26 29 13 – Enclosed Controllers

26 29 13.10 Contactors, AC		Crew	Daily Output	Labor-Hours	Unit	Material	2017 Bare Costs Labor	Equipment	Total	Total Incl O&P
1600	Size 0, 18 amp	1 Elec	4	2	Ea.	211	113		324	405
1700	Size 1, 27 amp		3.60	2.222		240	126		366	450
1800	Size 2, 45 amp		3	2.667		445	151		596	715
1900	Size 3, 90 amp		2.50	3.200		720	181		901	1,050
2000	Size 4, 135 amp		2.30	3.478		1,650	197		1,847	2,100
2100	Size 5, 270 amp	2 Elec	1.80	8.889		3,450	505		3,955	4,550
2200	Size 6, 540 amp		1.20	13.333		10,100	755		10,855	12,200
2300	Size 7, 810 amp		1	16		13,600	905		14,505	16,400
2310	Size 8, 1215 amp		.80	20		21,200	1,125		22,325	25,000
2500	Magnetic, 240 volt, 1-2 pole, .75 HP motor	1 Elec	4	2		143	113		256	325
2520	2 HP motor		3.60	2.222		196	126		322	405
2540	5 HP motor		2.50	3.200		390	181		571	695
2560	10 HP motor		1.40	5.714		640	325		965	1,200
2600	240 volt or less, 3 pole, .75 HP motor		4	2		143	113		256	325
2620	5 HP motor		3.60	2.222		177	126		303	385
2640	10 HP motor		3.60	2.222		206	126		332	415
2660	15 HP motor		2.50	3.200		410	181		591	720
2700	25 HP motor		2.50	3.200		410	181		591	720
2720	30 HP motor	2 Elec	2.80	5.714		685	325		1,010	1,250
2740	40 HP motor		2.80	5.714		685	325		1,010	1,250
2760	50 HP motor		1.60	10		685	565		1,250	1,600
2800	75 HP motor		1.60	10		1,600	565		2,165	2,625
2820	100 HP motor		1	16		1,600	905		2,505	3,125
2860	150 HP motor		1	16		3,425	905		4,330	5,125
2880	200 HP motor		1	16		3,425	905		4,330	5,125
3000	600 volt, 3 pole, 5 HP motor	1 Elec	4	2		177	113		290	365
3020	10 HP motor		3.60	2.222		206	126		332	415
3040	25 HP motor		3	2.667		410	151		561	675
3100	50 HP motor		2.50	3.200		685	181		866	1,025
3160	100 HP motor	2 Elec	2.80	5.714		1,600	325		1,925	2,250
3220	200 HP motor	"	1.60	10		3,425	565		3,990	4,625

26 29 13.20 Control Stations

		Crew	Daily Output	Labor-Hours	Unit	Material	2017 Bare Costs Labor	Equipment	Total	Total Incl O&P
0010	**CONTROL STATIONS**									
0050	NEMA 1, heavy duty, stop/start	1 Elec	8	1	Ea.	137	56.50		193.50	235
0100	Stop/start, pilot light		6.20	1.290		186	73		259	315
0200	Hand/off/automatic		6.20	1.290		101	73		174	220
0400	Stop/start/reverse		5.30	1.509		184	85.50		269.50	330
0500	NEMA 7, heavy duty, stop/start		6	1.333		485	75.50		560.50	645
0600	Stop/start, pilot light		4	2		590	113		703	820
0700	NEMA 7 or 9, 1 element		6	1.333		395	75.50		470.50	550
0800	2 element		6	1.333		510	75.50		585.50	675
0900	3 element		4	2		1,000	113		1,113	1,275
0910	Selector switch, 2 position		6	1.333		395	75.50		470.50	550
0920	3 position		4	2		395	113		508	605
0930	Oiltight, 1 element		8	1		107	56.50		163.50	203
0940	2 element		6.20	1.290		154	73		227	278
0950	3 element		5.30	1.509		207	85.50		292.50	355
0960	Selector switch, 2 position		6.20	1.290		114	73		187	234
0970	3 position		5.30	1.509		114	85.50		199.50	253

For customer support on your Electrical Costs with RSMeans Data, call 800.448.8182.

283

26 29 13 – Enclosed Controllers

26 29 13.30 Control Switches		Crew	Daily Output	Labor-Hours	Unit	Material	2017 Bare Costs Labor	Equipment	Total	Total Incl O&P
0010	**CONTROL SWITCHES** Field installed									
6000	Push button 600 V 10A, momentary contact									
6150	Standard operator with colored button	1 Elec	34	.235	Ea.	18.05	13.30		31.35	40
6160	With single block 1NO 1NC		18	.444		38	25		63	79.50
6170	With double block 2NO 2NC		15	.533		58	30		88	109
6180	Std operator w/mushroom button 1-9/16" diam.		34	.235		38	13.30		51.30	62
6190	Std operator w/mushroom button 2-1/4" diam.									
6200	With single block 1NO 1NC	1 Elec	18	.444	Ea.	51	25		76	94
6210	With double block 2NO 2NC		15	.533		69	30		99	121
6500	Maintained contact, selector operator		34	.235		51	13.30		64.30	76.50
6510	With single block 1NO 1NC		18	.444		69	25		94	113
6520	With double block 2NO 2NC		15	.533		86.50	30		116.50	140
6560	Spring-return selector operator		34	.235		51	13.30		64.30	76.50
6570	With single block 1NO 1NC		18	.444		69	25		94	113
6580	With double block 2NO 2NC		15	.533		86.50	30		116.50	140
6620	Transformer operator w/illuminated									
6630	button 6 V #12 lamp	1 Elec	32	.250	Ea.	86.50	14.15		100.65	116
6640	With single block 1NO 1NC w/guard		16	.500		104	28.50		132.50	157
6650	With double block 2NO 2NC w/guard		13	.615		122	35		157	186
6690	Combination operator		34	.235		51	13.30		64.30	76.50
6700	With single block 1NO 1NC		18	.444		69	25		94	113
6710	With double block 2NO 2NC		15	.533		86.50	30		116.50	140
9000	Indicating light unit, full voltage									
9010	110-125 V front mount	1 Elec	32	.250	Ea.	69	14.15		83.15	96.50
9020	130 V resistor type		32	.250		58	14.15		72.15	85
9030	6 V transformer type		32	.250		63	14.15		77.15	90

26 29 13.40 Relays

		Crew	Daily Output	Labor-Hours	Unit	Material	2017 Bare Costs Labor	Equipment	Total	Total Incl O&P
0010	**RELAYS** Enclosed (NEMA 1)									
0050	600 volt AC, 1 pole, 12 amp	1 Elec	5.30	1.509	Ea.	84	85.50		169.50	221
0100	2 pole, 12 amp		5	1.600		84	90.50		174.50	229
0200	4 pole, 10 amp		4.50	1.778		112	101		213	274
0500	250 volt DC, 1 pole, 15 amp		5.30	1.509		110	85.50		195.50	249
0600	2 pole, 10 amp		5	1.600		106	90.50		196.50	252
0700	4 pole, 4 amp		4.50	1.778		139	101		240	305

26 29 23 – Variable-Frequency Motor Controllers

26 29 23.10 Variable Frequency Drives/Adj. Frequency Drives

			Crew	Daily Output	Labor-Hours	Unit	Material	2017 Bare Costs Labor	Equipment	Total	Total Incl O&P
0010	**VARIABLE FREQUENCY DRIVES/ADJ. FREQUENCY DRIVES**										
0100	Enclosed (NEMA 1), 460 volt, for 3 HP motor size	G	1 Elec	.80	10	Ea.	1,900	565		2,465	2,950
0110	5 HP motor size	G		.80	10		2,175	565		2,740	3,250
0120	7.5 HP motor size	G		.67	11.940		2,275	675		2,950	3,550
0130	10 HP motor size	G		.67	11.940		2,500	675		3,175	3,775
0140	15 HP motor size	G	2 Elec	.89	17.978		3,225	1,025		4,250	5,075
0150	20 HP motor size	G		.89	17.978		4,375	1,025		5,400	6,350
0160	25 HP motor size	G		.67	23.881		5,400	1,350		6,750	7,950
0170	30 HP motor size	G		.67	23.881		5,850	1,350		7,200	8,475
0180	40 HP motor size	G		.67	23.881		6,775	1,350		8,125	9,475
0190	50 HP motor size	G		.53	30.189		9,975	1,700		11,675	13,600
0200	60 HP motor size	G	R-3	.56	35.714		12,100	2,025	246	14,371	16,600
0210	75 HP motor size	G		.56	35.714		13,900	2,025	246	16,171	18,600
0220	100 HP motor size	G		.50	40		15,600	2,275	276	18,151	20,900
0230	125 HP motor size	G		.50	40		17,000	2,275	276	19,551	22,300

26 29 Low-Voltage Controllers

26 29 23 – Variable-Frequency Motor Controllers

26 29 23.10 Variable Frequency Drives/Adj. Frequency Drives		Crew	Daily Output	Labor-Hours	Unit	Material	2017 Bare Costs Labor	Equipment	Total	Total Incl O&P
0240	150 HP motor size	G R-3	.50	40	Ea.	20,500	2,275	276	23,051	26,200
0250	200 HP motor size	G	.42	47.619		26,900	2,700	330	29,930	34,000
1100	Custom-engineered, 460 volt, for 3 HP motor size	G 1 Elec	.56	14.286		3,050	810		3,860	4,550
1110	5 HP motor size	G	.56	14.286		3,050	810		3,860	4,550
1120	7.5 HP motor size	G	.47	17.021		3,200	965		4,165	4,950
1130	10 HP motor size	G	.47	17.021		3,350	965		4,315	5,125
1140	15 HP motor size	G 2 Elec	.62	25.806		4,175	1,450		5,625	6,800
1150	20 HP motor size	G	.62	25.806		4,700	1,450		6,150	7,375
1160	25 HP motor size	G	.47	34.043		5,500	1,925		7,425	8,925
1170	30 HP motor size	G	.47	34.043		6,875	1,925		8,800	10,400
1180	40 HP motor size	G	.47	34.043		8,125	1,925		10,050	11,800
1190	50 HP motor size	G	.37	43.243		9,325	2,450		11,775	14,000
1200	60 HP motor size	G R-3	.39	51.282		14,100	2,900	355	17,355	20,200
1210	75 HP motor size	G	.39	51.282		15,000	2,900	355	18,255	21,200
1220	100 HP motor size	G	.35	57.143		16,400	3,225	395	20,020	23,300
1230	125 HP motor size	G	.35	57.143		17,500	3,225	395	21,120	24,600
1240	150 HP motor size	G	.35	57.143		20,100	3,225	395	23,720	27,400
1250	200 HP motor size	G	.29	68.966		26,200	3,900	475	30,575	35,200
2000	For complex & special design systems to meet specific									
2010	requirements, obtain quote from vendor.									

26 31 Photovoltaic Collectors

26 31 13 – Photovoltaics

26 31 13.50 Solar Energy - Photovoltaics

0010	**SOLAR ENERGY - PHOTOVOLTAICS**									
0220	Alt. energy source, photovoltaic module, 6 watt, 15 volts	G 1 Elec	8	1	Ea.	70.50	56.50		127	163
0230	10 watt, 16.3 volts	G	8	1		117	56.50		173.50	213
0240	20 watt, 14.5 volts	G	8	1		180	56.50		236.50	283
0250	36 watt, 17 volts	G	8	1		229	56.50		285.50	335
0260	55 watt, 17 volts	G	8	1		315	56.50		371.50	430
0270	75 watt, 17 volts	G	8	1		415	56.50		471.50	540
0280	130 watt, 33 volts	G	8	1		620	56.50		676.50	765
0290	140 watt, 33 volts	G	8	1		515	56.50		571.50	650
0300	150 watt, 33 volts	G	8	1		400	56.50		456.50	520
0310	DC to AC inverter for, 12 V, 2,000 watt	G	4	2		1,375	113		1,488	1,700
0320	12 V, 2,500 watt	G	4	2		1,075	113		1,188	1,375
0330	24 V, 2,500 watt	G	4	2		1,500	113		1,613	1,825
0340	12 V, 3,000 watt	G	3	2.667		1,500	151		1,651	1,875
0350	24 V, 3,000 watt	G	3	2.667		2,375	151		2,526	2,850
0360	24 V, 4,000 watt	G	2	4		2,525	226		2,751	3,125
0370	48 V, 4,000 watt	G	2	4		2,525	226		2,751	3,125
0380	48 V, 5,500 watt	G	2	4		2,975	226		3,201	3,625
0390	PV components, combiner box, 10 lug, NEMA 3R enclosure	G	4	2		270	113		383	465
0400	Fuse, 15 A for combiner box	G	40	.200		21.50	11.30		32.80	40.50
0410	Battery charger controller w/temperature sensor	G	4	2		495	113		608	710
0420	Digital readout panel, displays hours, volts, amps, etc.	G	4	2		202	113		315	390
0430	Deep cycle solar battery, 6 V, 180 Ah (C/20)	G	8	1		300	56.50		356.50	415
0440	Battery interconn, 15" AWG #2/0, sealed w/copper ring lugs	G	16	.500		18.10	28.50		46.60	62.50
0442	Battery interconn, 24" AWG #2/0, sealed w/copper ring lugs	G	16	.500		23.50	28.50		52	68.50
0444	Battery interconn, 60" AWG #2/0, sealed w/copper ring lugs	G	16	.500		59.50	28.50		88	108
0446	Batt temp computer probe, RJ11 jack, 15' cord	G	16	.500		22	28.50		50.50	67

For customer support on your Electrical Costs with RSMeans Data, call 800.448.8182.

285

26 31 Photovoltaic Collectors

26 31 13 – Photovoltaics

26 31 13.50 Solar Energy - Photovoltaics	Crew	Daily Output	Labor-Hours	Unit	Material	2017 Bare Costs Labor	Equipment	Total	Total Incl O&P
0450 System disconnect, DC 175 amp circuit breaker	1 Elec	8	1	Ea.	184	56.50		240.50	288
0460 Conduit box for inverter		8	1		62.50	56.50		119	154
0470 Low voltage disconnect		8	1		57	56.50		113.50	148
0480 Vented battery enclosure, wood	1 Carp	2	4		225	197		422	550
0490 PV rack system, roof, non-penetrating ballast, 1 panel	R-1A	30.50	.525		975	26.50		1,001.50	1,125
0500 Penetrating surface mount, on steel framing, 1 panel		5.13	3.122		57.50	159		216.50	300
0510 On wood framing, 1 panel		11	1.455		55.50	74		129.50	173
0520 With standoff, 1 panel		11	1.455		65.50	74		139.50	183
0530 Ground, ballast, fixed, 3 panel		20.50	.780		1,025	40		1,065	1,175
0540 4 panel		20.50	.780		1,400	40		1,440	1,600
0550 5 panel		20.50	.780		1,850	40		1,890	2,100
0560 6 panel		20.50	.780		2,150	40		2,190	2,400
0570 Adjustable, 3 panel		20.50	.780		1,100	40		1,140	1,250
0580 4 panel		20.50	.780		1,500	40		1,540	1,700
0590 5 panel		20.50	.780		1,975	40		2,015	2,225
0600 6 panel		20.50	.780		2,275	40		2,315	2,550
0605 Top of Pole, see 26 56 13.10 3800+, 5400+ & 33 71 16.33 7400+ for poles									
0610 Passive tracking, 1 panel	R-1A	20.50	.780	Ea.	630	40		670	755
0620 2 panel		20.50	.780		1,275	40		1,315	1,450
0630 3 panel		20.50	.780		1,800	40		1,840	2,025
0640 4 panel		20.50	.780		1,925	40		1,965	2,150
0650 6 panel		20.50	.780		2,175	40		2,215	2,425
0660 8 panel		20.50	.780		3,225	40		3,265	3,575

26 32 Packaged Generator Assemblies

26 32 13 – Engine Generators

26 32 13.13 Diesel-Engine-Driven Generator Sets

	Crew	Daily Output	Labor-Hours	Unit	Material	Labor	Equipment	Total	Total Incl O&P
0010 **DIESEL-ENGINE-DRIVEN GENERATOR SETS**									
2000 Diesel engine, including battery, charger,									
2010 muffler, & day tank, 30 kW	R-3	.55	36.364	Ea.	11,000	2,050	251	13,301	15,500
2100 50 kW		.42	47.619		20,000	2,700	330	23,030	26,400
2110 60 kW		.39	51.282		20,800	2,900	355	24,055	27,600
2200 75 kW		.35	57.143		23,100	3,225	395	26,720	30,700
2300 100 kW		.31	64.516		27,900	3,650	445	31,995	36,700
2400 125 kW		.29	68.966		29,300	3,900	475	33,675	38,700
2500 150 kW		.26	76.923		37,600	4,350	530	42,480	48,500
2501 Generator set, dsl eng in alum encl, incl btry, chgr, muf & day tank,150 kW		.26	76.923		41,400	4,350	530	46,280	52,500
2600 175 kW		.25	80		41,900	4,525	550	46,975	53,500
2700 200 kW		.24	83.333		45,200	4,725	575	50,500	57,500
2800 250 kW		.23	86.957		48,400	4,925	600	53,925	61,500
2850 275 kW		.22	90.909		49,600	5,150	625	55,375	63,000
2900 300 kW		.22	90.909		51,500	5,150	625	57,275	65,000
3000 350 kW		.20	100		59,000	5,650	690	65,340	74,000
3100 400 kW		.19	105		72,000	5,950	725	78,675	89,000
3200 500 kW		.18	111		91,500	6,300	765	98,565	111,000
3220 600 kW		.17	117		118,500	6,650	810	125,960	141,500
3230 650 kW	R-13	.38	110		146,000	6,075	570	152,645	170,500
3240 750 kW		.38	110		147,000	6,075	570	153,645	172,000
3250 800 kW		.36	116		154,500	6,425	600	161,525	180,500
3260 900 kW		.31	135		180,000	7,450	695	188,145	210,000
3270 1000 kW		.27	155		186,000	8,550	800	195,350	218,000

For customer support on your Electrical Costs with RSMeans Data, call 800.448.8182.

26 32 Packaged Generator Assemblies

26 32 13 – Engine Generators

26 32 13.16 Gas-Engine-Driven Generator Sets	Crew	Daily Output	Labor-Hours	Unit	Material	2017 Bare Costs Labor	Equipment	Total	Total Incl O&P
0010 **GAS-ENGINE-DRIVEN GENERATOR SETS**									
0020 Gas or gasoline operated, includes battery,									
0050 charger, & muffler									
0200 7.5 kW	R-3	.83	24.096	Ea.	8,550	1,375	166	10,091	11,700
0300 11.5 kW		.71	28.169		12,100	1,600	194	13,894	15,900
0400 20 kW		.63	31.746		14,300	1,800	219	16,319	18,600
0460 25 kW, steel enclosure		.63	31.746		23,100	1,800	219	25,119	28,300
0470 27 kW, aluminum enclosure		.63	31.746		28,900	1,800	219	30,919	34,600
0480 30 kW, steel enclosure		.63	31.746		26,100	1,800	219	28,119	31,600
0500 35 kW		.55	36.364		17,000	2,050	251	19,301	22,100
0510 45 kW, steel enclosure		.50	40		34,000	2,275	276	36,551	41,200
0515 48 kW, aluminum enclosure		.50	40		40,400	2,275	276	42,951	48,100
0520 60 kW	↓	.50	40		22,400	2,275	276	24,951	28,400
0550 70 kW, aluminum enclosure	R-13	.46	91.304		51,500	5,025	470	56,995	65,000
0600 80 kW		.40	105		27,900	5,775	540	34,215	40,000
0700 100 kW		.33	127		30,600	7,000	655	38,255	44,800
0800 125 kW		.28	150		62,500	8,250	770	71,520	82,500
0850 130 kW, aluminum enclosure		.28	150		79,000	8,250	770	88,020	100,000
0875 150 kW, aluminum enclosure		.25	168		85,500	9,250	865	95,615	109,000
0900 185 kW	↓	.25	168	↓	83,000	9,250	865	93,115	106,000

26 33 Battery Equipment

26 33 43 – Battery Chargers

26 33 43.55 Electric Vehicle Charging

26 33 43.55 Electric Vehicle Charging	Crew	Daily Output	Labor-Hours	Unit	Material	2017 Bare Costs Labor	Equipment	Total	Total Incl O&P
0010 **ELECTRIC VEHICLE CHARGING**									
0020 Level 2, wall mounted									
2200 Heavy duty [G]	R-1A	15.36	1.042	Ea.	2,525	53		2,578	2,850
2210 with RFID [G]		12.29	1.302		3,100	66.50		3,166.50	3,525
2300 Free standing, single connector [G]		10.24	1.563		2,900	79.50		2,979.50	3,300
2310 with RFID [G]		8.78	1.822		3,625	93		3,718	4,125
2320 Double connector [G]		7.68	2.083		4,850	106		4,956	5,475
2330 with RFID [G]	↓	6.83	2.343	↓	6,300	119		6,419	7,100

26 33 53 – Static Uninterruptible Power Supply

26 33 53.10 Uninterruptible Power Supply/Conditioner Trans.

26 33 53.10 Uninterruptible Power Supply/Conditioner Trans.	Crew	Daily Output	Labor-Hours	Unit	Material	2017 Bare Costs Labor	Equipment	Total	Total Incl O&P
0010 **UNINTERRUPTIBLE POWER SUPPLY/CONDITIONER TRANSFORMERS**									
0100 Volt. regulating, isolating transf., w/invert. & 10 min. battery pack									
0110 Single-phase, 120 V, 0.35 kVA R263353-80	1 Elec	2.29	3.493	Ea.	1,125	198		1,323	1,525
0120 0.5 kVA		2	4		1,175	226		1,401	1,650
0130 For additional 55 min. battery, add to 0.35 kVA		2.29	3.493		660	198		858	1,025
0140 Add to 0.5 kVA		1.14	7.018		695	395		1,090	1,350
0150 Single-phase, 120 V, 0.75 kVA		.80	10		1,500	565		2,065	2,500
0160 1.0 kVA		.80	10		2,125	565		2,690	3,200
0170 1.5 kVA	2 Elec	1.14	14.035		3,675	795		4,470	5,225
0180 2 kVA	"	.89	17.978		3,975	1,025		5,000	5,900
0190 3 kVA	R-3	.63	31.746		4,825	1,800	219	6,844	8,250
0200 5 kVA		.42	47.619		7,000	2,700	330	10,030	12,100
0210 7.5 kVA		.33	60.606		8,925	3,425	420	12,770	15,400
0220 10 kVA		.28	71.429		11,500	4,050	495	16,045	19,300
0230 15 kVA		.22	90.909		14,700	5,150	625	20,475	24,600
0240 3 phase, 120/208 V input 120/208 V output, 20 kVA, incl 17 min. battery	↓	.21	95.238	↓	27,000	5,400	655	33,055	38,500

For customer support on your Electrical Costs with RSMeans Data, call 800.448.8182.

287

26 33 Battery Equipment

26 33 53 – Static Uninterruptible Power Supply

26 33 53.10 Uninterruptible Power Supply/Conditioner Trans.	Crew	Daily Output	Labor-Hours	Unit	Material	2017 Bare Costs Labor	Equipment	Total	Total Incl O&P
0242	30 kVA, incl 11 min. battery	R-3	.20	100	Ea.	30,300	5,650	690	36,640	42,600
0250	40 kVA, incl 15 min. battery		.20	100		40,400	5,650	690	46,740	53,500
0260	480 V input 277/480 V output, 60 kVA, incl 6 min. battery		.19	105		45,400	5,950	725	52,075	60,000
0262	80 kVA, incl 4 min. battery		.19	105		54,000	5,950	725	60,675	69,500
0400	For additional 34 min./15 min. battery, add to 40 kVA	▼	.71	28.011	▼	14,100	1,575	193	15,868	18,100
0600	For complex & special design systems to meet specific									
0610	requirements, obtain quote from vendor									

26 35 Power Filters and Conditioners

26 35 13 – Capacitors

26 35 13.10 Capacitors Indoor

		Crew	Daily Output	Labor-Hours	Unit	Material	Labor	Equipment	Total	Total Incl O&P
0010	**CAPACITORS INDOOR**									
0020	240 volts, single & 3 phase, 0.5 kVAR	1 Elec	2.70	2.963	Ea.	470	168		638	765
0100	1.0 kVAR		2.70	2.963		565	168		733	875
0150	2.5 kVAR		2	4		640	226		866	1,050
0200	5.0 kVAR		1.80	4.444		790	252		1,042	1,250
0250	7.5 kVAR		1.60	5		885	283		1,168	1,400
0300	10 kVAR		1.50	5.333		1,025	300		1,325	1,575
0350	15 kVAR		1.30	6.154		1,325	350		1,675	1,975
0400	20 kVAR		1.10	7.273		1,600	410		2,010	2,375
0450	25 kVAR		1	8		1,825	455		2,280	2,700
1000	480 volts, single & 3 phase, 1 kVAR		2.70	2.963		425	168		593	720
1050	2 kVAR		2.70	2.963		490	168		658	790
1100	5 kVAR		2	4		620	226		846	1,025
1150	7.5 kVAR		2	4		670	226		896	1,075
1200	10 kVAR		2	4		710	226		936	1,125
1250	15 kVAR		2	4		840	226		1,066	1,250
1300	20 kVAR		1.60	5		915	283		1,198	1,425
1350	30 kVAR		1.50	5.333		1,100	300		1,400	1,675
1400	40 kVAR		1.20	6.667		1,375	375		1,750	2,075
1450	50 kVAR		1.10	7.273		1,600	410		2,010	2,400
2000	600 volts, single & 3 phase, 1 kVAR		2.70	2.963		440	168		608	735
2050	2 kVAR		2.70	2.963		505	168		673	805
2100	5 kVAR		2	4		620	226		846	1,025
2150	7.5 kVAR		2	4		670	226		896	1,075
2200	10 kVAR		2	4		710	226		936	1,125
2250	15 kVAR		1.60	5		840	283		1,123	1,350
2300	20 kVAR		1.60	5		915	283		1,198	1,425
2350	25 kVAR		1.50	5.333		1,000	300		1,300	1,550
2400	35 kVAR		1.40	5.714		1,250	325		1,575	1,850
2450	50 kVAR	▼	1.30	6.154	▼	1,600	350		1,950	2,300

26 35 26 – Harmonic Filters

26 35 26.10 Computer Isolation Transformer

		Crew	Daily Output	Labor-Hours	Unit	Material	Labor	Equipment	Total	Total Incl O&P
0010	**COMPUTER ISOLATION TRANSFORMER**									
0100	Computer grade									
0110	Single-phase, 120/240 V, 0.5 kVA	1 Elec	4	2	Ea.	405	113		518	620
0120	1.0 kVA		2.67	2.996		580	170		750	890
0130	2.5 kVA		2	4		880	226		1,106	1,300
0140	5 kVA	▼	1.14	7.018	▼	1,000	395		1,395	1,700

26 35 Power Filters and Conditioners

26 35 26 – Harmonic Filters

26 35 26.20 Computer Regulator Transformer

		Crew	Daily Output	Labor-Hours	Unit	Material	2017 Bare Costs Labor	Equipment	Total	Total Incl O&P
0010	**COMPUTER REGULATOR TRANSFORMER**									
0100	Ferro-resonant, constant voltage, variable transformer									
0110	Single-phase, 240 V, 0.5 kVA	1 Elec	2.67	2.996	Ea.	420	170		590	715
0120	1.0 kVA		2	4		575	226		801	970
0130	2.0 kVA		1	8		980	455		1,435	1,750
0210	Plug-in unit 120 V, 0.14 kVA		8	1		241	56.50		297.50	350
0220	0.25 kVA		8	1		282	56.50		338.50	395
0230	0.5 kVA		8	1		420	56.50		476.50	545
0240	1.0 kVA		5.33	1.501		575	85		660	755
0250	2.0 kVA		4	2		980	113		1,093	1,250

26 35 26.30 Power Conditioner Transformer

		Crew	Daily Output	Labor-Hours	Unit	Material	2017 Bare Costs Labor	Equipment	Total	Total Incl O&P
0010	**POWER CONDITIONER TRANSFORMER**									
0100	Electronic solid state, buck-boost, transformer, w/tap switch									
0110	Single-phase, 115 V, 3.0 kVA, + or - 3% accuracy	2 Elec	1.60	10	Ea.	2,250	565		2,815	3,325
0120	208, 220, 230, or 240 V, 5.0 kVA, + or - 1.5% accuracy	3 Elec	1.60	15		2,925	850		3,775	4,475
0130	5.0 kVA, + or - 6% accuracy	2 Elec	1.14	14.035		2,600	795		3,395	4,075
0140	7.5 kVA, + or - 1.5% accuracy	3 Elec	1.50	16		3,700	905		4,605	5,425
0150	7.5 kVA, + or - 6% accuracy		1.60	15		3,075	850		3,925	4,675
0160	10.0 kVA, + or - 1.5% accuracy		1.33	18.045		4,925	1,025		5,950	6,950
0170	10.0 kVA, + or - 6% accuracy		1.41	17.021		4,200	965		5,165	6,075

26 35 26.40 Transient Voltage Suppressor Transformer

		Crew	Daily Output	Labor-Hours	Unit	Material	2017 Bare Costs Labor	Equipment	Total	Total Incl O&P
0010	**TRANSIENT VOLTAGE SUPPRESSOR TRANSFORMER**									
0110	Single-phase, 120 V, 1.8 kVA	1 Elec	4	2	Ea.	1,225	113		1,338	1,500
0120	3.6 kVA		4	2		1,800	113		1,913	2,175
0130	7.2 kVA		3.20	2.500		2,125	142		2,267	2,550
0150	240 V, 3.6 kVA		4	2		2,675	113		2,788	3,125
0160	7.2 kVA		4	2		3,100	113		3,213	3,600
0170	14.4 kVA		3.20	2.500		3,525	142		3,667	4,100
0210	Plug-in unit, 120 V, 1.8 kVA		8	1		840	56.50		896.50	1,000

26 35 53 – Voltage Regulators

26 35 53.10 Automatic Voltage Regulators

		Crew	Daily Output	Labor-Hours	Unit	Material	2017 Bare Costs Labor	Equipment	Total	Total Incl O&P
0010	**AUTOMATIC VOLTAGE REGULATORS**									
0100	Computer grade, solid state, variable transf. volt. regulator									
0110	Single-phase, 120 V, 8.6 kVA	2 Elec	1.33	12.030	Ea.	5,225	680		5,905	6,775
0120	17.3 kVA		1.14	14.035		6,175	795		6,970	8,000
0130	208/240 V, 7.5/8.6 kVA		1.33	12.030		5,225	680		5,905	6,775
0140	13.5/15.6 kVA		1.33	12.030		6,175	680		6,855	7,825
0150	27.0/31.2 kVA		1.14	14.035		7,775	795		8,570	9,775
0210	Two-phase, single control, 208/240 V, 15.0/17.3 kVA		1.14	14.035		6,175	795		6,970	8,000
0220	Individual phase control, 15.0/17.3 kVA		1.14	14.035		6,175	795		6,970	8,000
0230	30.0/34.6 kVA	3 Elec	1.33	18.045		7,775	1,025		8,800	10,100
0310	Three-phase single control, 208/240 V, 26/30 kVA	2 Elec	1	16		6,175	905		7,080	8,150
0320	380/480 V, 24/30 kVA	"	1	16		6,175	905		7,080	8,150
0330	43/54 kVA	3 Elec	1.33	18.045		11,200	1,025		12,225	13,800
0340	Individual phase control, 208 V, 26 kVA	"	1.33	18.045		6,175	1,025		7,200	8,325
0350	52 kVA	R-3	.91	21.978		7,775	1,250	152	9,177	10,600
0360	340/480 V, 24/30 kVA	2 Elec	1	16		6,175	905		7,080	8,150
0370	43/54 kVA	"	1	16		7,775	905		8,680	9,925
0380	48/60 kVA	3 Elec	1.33	18.045		11,300	1,025		12,325	13,900
0390	86/108 kVA	R-3	.91	21.978		12,500	1,250	152	13,902	15,800
0500	Standard grade, solid state, variable transformer volt. regulator									

For customer support on your Electrical Costs with RSMeans Data, call 800.448.8182.

289

26 35 Power Filters and Conditioners

26 35 53 – Voltage Regulators

26 35 53.10 Automatic Voltage Regulators		Crew	Daily Output	Labor-Hours	Unit	Material	2017 Bare Costs Labor	Equipment	Total	Total Incl O&P
0510	Single-phase, 115 V, 2.3 kVA	1 Elec	2.29	3.493	Ea.	1,950	198		2,148	2,450
0520	4.2 kVA		2	4		3,125	226		3,351	3,800
0530	6.6 kVA		1.14	7.018		3,850	395		4,245	4,825
0540	13.0 kVA		1.14	7.018		6,625	395		7,020	7,900
0550	16.6 kVA	2 Elec	1.23	13.008		7,825	735		8,560	9,725
0610	230 V, 8.3 kVA		1.33	12.030		6,625	680		7,305	8,325
0620	21.4 kVA		1.23	13.008		7,825	735		8,560	9,725
0630	29.9 kVA		1.23	13.008		7,825	735		8,560	9,725
0710	460 V, 9.2 kVA		1.33	12.030		6,625	680		7,305	8,325
0720	20.7 kVA		1.23	13.008		7,825	735		8,560	9,725
0810	Three-phase, 230 V, 13.1 kVA	3 Elec	1.41	17.021		6,625	965		7,590	8,750
0820	19.1 kVA		1.41	17.021		7,825	965		8,790	10,100
0830	25.1 kVA		1.23	19.512		7,825	1,100		8,925	10,300
0840	57.8 kVA	R-3	.95	21.053		14,200	1,200	145	15,545	17,600
0850	74.9 kVA	"	.91	21.978		14,200	1,250	152	15,602	17,600
0910	460 V, 14.3 kVA	3 Elec	1.41	17.021		6,625	965		7,590	8,750
0920	19.1 kVA		1.41	17.021		7,825	965		8,790	10,100
0930	27.9 kVA		1.23	19.512		7,825	1,100		8,925	10,300
0940	59.8 kVA	R-3	1	20		14,200	1,125	138	15,463	17,500
0950	79.7 kVA		.95	21.053		15,900	1,200	145	17,245	19,500
0960	118 kVA		.95	21.053		16,700	1,200	145	18,045	20,400
1000	Laboratory grade, precision, electronic voltage regulator									
1110	Single-phase, 115 V, 0.5 kVA	1 Elec	2.29	3.493	Ea.	1,275	198		1,473	1,700
1120	1.0 kVA		2	4		1,375	226		1,601	1,850
1130	3.0 kVA		.80	10		1,900	565		2,465	2,950
1140	6.0 kVA	2 Elec	1.46	10.959		3,525	620		4,145	4,800
1150	10.0 kVA	3 Elec	1	24		4,600	1,350		5,950	7,075
1160	15.0 kVA	"	1.50	16		5,250	905		6,155	7,125
1210	230 V, 3.0 kVA	1 Elec	.80	10		2,150	565		2,715	3,225
1220	6.0 kVA	2 Elec	1.46	10.959		3,600	620		4,220	4,900
1230	10.0 kVA	3 Elec	1.71	14.035		4,800	795		5,595	6,475
1240	15.0 kVA	"	1.60	15		5,425	850		6,275	7,250

26 35 53.30 Transient Suppressor/Voltage Regulator

		Crew	Daily Output	Labor-Hours	Unit	Material	2017 Bare Costs Labor	Equipment	Total	Total Incl O&P
0010	**TRANSIENT SUPPRESSOR/VOLTAGE REGULATOR** (without isolation)									
0110	Single-phase, 115 V, 1.0 kVA	1 Elec	2.67	2.996	Ea.	1,100	170		1,270	1,450
0120	2.0 kVA		2.29	3.493		1,475	198		1,673	1,925
0130	4.0 kVA		2.13	3.756		1,825	213		2,038	2,350
0140	220 V, 1.0 kVA		2.67	2.996		1,100	170		1,270	1,450
0150	2.0 kVA		2.29	3.493		1,475	198		1,673	1,925
0160	4.0 kVA		2.13	3.756		1,925	213		2,138	2,450
0210	Plug-in unit, 120 V, 1.0 kVA		8	1		1,050	56.50		1,106.50	1,225
0220	2.0 kVA		8	1		1,475	56.50		1,531.50	1,700

26 36 13 – Manual Transfer Switches

26 36 13.10 Non-Automatic Transfer Switches	Crew	Daily Output	Labor-Hours	Unit	Material	2017 Bare Costs Labor	Equipment	Total	Total Incl O&P
0010 **NON-AUTOMATIC TRANSFER SWITCHES** enclosed									
0100 Manual operated, 480 volt 3 pole, 30 amp	1 Elec	2.30	3.478	Ea.	1,175	197		1,372	1,600
0150 60 amp		1.90	4.211		1,600	238		1,838	2,100
0200 100 amp		1.30	6.154		2,375	350		2,725	3,150
0250 200 amp	2 Elec	2	8		3,250	455		3,705	4,250
0300 400 amp		1.60	10		6,100	565		6,665	7,575
0350 600 amp		1	16		5,325	905		6,230	7,200
1000 250 volt 3 pole, 30 amp	1 Elec	2.30	3.478		850	197		1,047	1,225
1100 60 amp		1.90	4.211		1,225	238		1,463	1,700
1150 100 amp		1.30	6.154		2,000	350		2,350	2,700
1200 200 amp	2 Elec	2	8		3,025	455		3,480	4,000
1300 600 amp	"	1	16		7,075	905		7,980	9,125
1500 Electrically operated, 480 volt 3 pole, 60 amp	1 Elec	1.90	4.211		2,150	238		2,388	2,725
1600 100 amp	"	1.30	6.154		2,150	350		2,500	2,900
1650 200 amp	2 Elec	2	8		3,550	455		4,005	4,575
1700 400 amp		1.60	10		4,950	565		5,515	6,300
1750 600 amp		1	16		7,150	905		8,055	9,200
2000 250 volt 3 pole, 30 amp	1 Elec	2.30	3.478		2,000	197		2,197	2,500
2050 60 amp	"	1.90	4.211		2,000	238		2,238	2,550
2150 200 amp	2 Elec	2	8		3,300	455		3,755	4,300
2200 400 amp		1.60	10		4,625	565		5,190	5,925
2250 600 amp		1	16		6,650	905		7,555	8,675
2500 NEMA 3R, 480 volt 3 pole, 60 amp	1 Elec	1.80	4.444		2,350	252		2,602	2,975
2550 100 amp	"	1.20	6.667		3,050	375		3,425	3,925
2600 200 amp	2 Elec	1.80	8.889		3,650	505		4,155	4,775
2650 400 amp	"	1.40	11.429		5,425	645		6,070	6,950
2800 NEMA 3R, 250 volt 3 pole solid state, 100 amp	1 Elec	1.20	6.667		3,200	375		3,575	4,075
2850 150 amp	2 Elec	1.80	8.889		4,250	505		4,755	5,425
2900 250 volt 2 pole solid state, 100 amp	1 Elec	1.30	6.154		3,100	350		3,450	3,950
2950 150 amp	2 Elec	2	8		4,125	455		4,580	5,225

26 36 23 – Automatic Transfer Switches

26 36 23.10 Automatic Transfer Switch Devices

	Crew	Daily Output	Labor-Hours	Unit	Material	2017 Bare Costs Labor	Equipment	Total	Total Incl O&P
0010 **AUTOMATIC TRANSFER SWITCH DEVICES** R263623-60									
0015 Switches, enclosed 120/240 volt, 2 pole, 30 amp	1 Elec	2.40	3.333	Ea.	2,150	189		2,339	2,650
0020 70 amp		2	4		2,150	226		2,376	2,725
0030 100 amp		1.35	5.926		2,150	335		2,485	2,875
0040 225 amp	2 Elec	2.10	7.619		3,175	430		3,605	4,150
0050 400 amp		1.70	9.412		4,850	535		5,385	6,125
0060 600 amp		1.06	15.094		7,100	855		7,955	9,100
0070 800 amp		.84	19.048		8,350	1,075		9,425	10,800
0100 Switches, enclosed 480 volt, 3 pole, 30 amp	1 Elec	2.30	3.478		2,400	197		2,597	2,950
0200 60 amp		1.90	4.211		2,400	238		2,638	3,000
0300 100 amp		1.30	6.154		2,400	350		2,750	3,175
0400 150 amp	2 Elec	2.40	6.667		2,950	375		3,325	3,825
0500 225 amp		2	8		3,775	455		4,230	4,850
0600 260 amp		2	8		4,375	455		4,830	5,500
0700 400 amp		1.60	10		5,700	565		6,265	7,125
0800 600 amp		1	16		7,900	905		8,805	10,100
0900 800 amp		.80	20		9,275	1,125		10,400	11,900
1000 1000 amp		.76	21.053		15,400	1,200		16,600	18,800
1100 1200 amp		.70	22.857		21,200	1,300		22,500	25,300
1200 1600 amp		.60	26.667		24,100	1,500		25,600	28,800

For customer support on your Electrical Costs with RSMeans Data, call 800.448.8182.

291

26 36 Transfer Switches

26 36 23 – Automatic Transfer Switches

26 36 23.10 Automatic Transfer Switch Devices	Crew	Daily Output	Labor-Hours	Unit	Material	2017 Bare Costs Labor	Equipment	Total	Total Incl O&P
1300	2000 amp	2 Elec	.50	32	Ea.	27,000	1,800		28,800	32,400
1600	Accessories, time delay on engine starting					236			236	260
1700	Adjustable time delay on retransfer					236			236	260
1800	Shunt trips for customer connections					420			420	465
1900	Maintenance select switch					96			96	106
2000	Auxiliary contact when normal fails					104			104	115
2100	Pilot light-emergency					96			96	106
2200	Pilot light-normal					96			96	106
2300	Auxiliary contact-closed on normal					111			111	122
2400	Auxiliary contact-closed on emergency					111			111	122
2500	Emergency source sensing, frequency relay					490			490	540

26 41 Facility Lightning Protection

26 41 13 – Lightning Protection for Structures

26 41 13.13 Lightning Protection for Buildings

		Crew	Daily Output	Labor-Hours	Unit	Material	2017 Bare Costs Labor	Equipment	Total	Total Incl O&P
0010	**LIGHTNING PROTECTION FOR BUILDINGS**									
0200	Air terminals & base, copper									
0400	3/8" diameter x 10" (to 75' high)	1 Elec	8	1	Ea.	22.50	56.50		79	110
0500	1/2" diameter x 12" (over 75' high)		8	1		26	56.50		82.50	114
0520	1/2" diameter x 24"		7.30	1.096		35.50	62		97.50	132
0540	1/2" diameter x 60"		6.70	1.194		66.50	67.50		134	174
1000	Aluminum, 1/2" diameter x 12" (to 75' high)		8	1		17.65	56.50		74.15	104
1020	1/2" diameter x 24"		7.30	1.096		19.35	62		81.35	115
1040	1/2" diameter x 60"		6.70	1.194		26.50	67.50		94	130
1100	5/8" diameter x 12" (over 75' high)		8	1		18.95	56.50		75.45	106
2000	Cable, copper, 220 lb. per thousand ft. (to 75' high)		320	.025	L.F.	3.03	1.42		4.45	5.45
2100	375 lb. per thousand ft. (over 75' high)		230	.035		5.50	1.97		7.47	9
2500	Aluminum, 101 lb. per thousand ft. (to 75' high)		280	.029		.95	1.62		2.57	3.47
2600	199 lb. per thousand ft. (over 75' high)		240	.033		1.40	1.89		3.29	4.37
3000	Arrester, 175 volt AC to ground		8	1	Ea.	149	56.50		205.50	249
3100	650 volt AC to ground		6.70	1.194	"	149	67.50		216.50	265
4000	Air terminals, copper									
4010	3/8" x 10"	1 Elec	50	.160	Ea.	7.75	9.05		16.80	22
4020	1/2" x 12"		38	.211		11.30	11.90		23.20	30.50
4030	5/8" x 12"		33	.242		16	13.70		29.70	38
4040	1/2" x 24"		30	.267		21	15.10		36.10	45.50
4050	1/2" x 60"		19	.421		52	24		76	92.50
4060	Air terminals, aluminum									
4070	3/8" x 10"	1 Elec	50	.160	Ea.	2.79	9.05		11.84	16.60
4080	1/2" x 12"		38	.211		3.04	11.90		14.94	21
4090	5/8" x 12"		33	.242		4.32	13.70		18.02	25.50
4100	1/2" x 24"		30	.267		4.72	15.10		19.82	27.50
4110	1/2" x 60"		19	.421		11.90	24		35.90	48.50
4200	Air terminal bases, copper									
4210	Adhesive bases, 1/2"	1 Elec	15	.533	Ea.	16.45	30		46.45	63
4215	Adhesive base, lightning air terminal					16.45			16.45	18.05
4220	Bolted bases	1 Elec	9	.889		14.65	50.50		65.15	91.50
4230	Hinged bases		7	1.143		27.50	64.50		92	127
4240	Side mounted bases		9	.889		16.85	50.50		67.35	94
4250	Offset point support		9	.889		27	50.50		77.50	105
4260	Concealed base assembly		5	1.600		81.50	90.50		172	226

26 41 Facility Lightning Protection

26 41 13 – Lightning Protection for Structures

26 41 13.13 Lightning Protection for Buildings	Crew	Daily Output	Labor-Hours	Unit	Material	2017 Bare Costs Labor	2017 Bare Costs Equipment	Total	Total Incl O&P
4270	Tee connector base	1 Elec	13	.615	Ea.	46	35		81	103
4280	Tripod base, 36" for 60" air terminal		7	1.143		38.50	64.50		103	139
4290	Intermediate base, 1/2"	↓	15	.533	↓	28	30		58	76
4300	Air terminal bases, aluminum									
4310	Adhesive bases, 1/2"	1 Elec	15	.533	Ea.	8.75	30		38.75	54.50
4320	Bolted bases		9	.889		14.60	50.50		65.10	91.50
4330	Hinged bases		7	1.143		13.70	64.50		78.20	112
4340	Side mounted bases		9	.889		11.60	50.50		62.10	88.50
4350	Offset point support		9	.889		12.55	50.50		63.05	89.50
4360	Concealed base assembly		5	1.600		41.50	90.50		132	182
4370	Tee connector base		13	.615		14.10	35		49.10	67.50
4380	Tripod base, 36" for 60" air terminal		7	1.143		29	64.50		93.50	129
4390	Intermediate base, 1/2"	↓	15	.533	↓	13.25	30		43.25	59.50
4400	Connector cable, copper									
4410	Through wall connector	1 Elec	7	1.143	Ea.	80.50	64.50		145	186
4420	Through roof connector		5	1.600		97.50	90.50		188	243
4430	Beam connector		7	1.143		26	64.50		90.50	126
4440	Double bolt connector		38	.211		11.35	11.90		23.25	30.50
4450	Bar, copper	↓	40	.200	↓	12.70	11.30		24	31
4500	Connector cable, aluminum									
4510	Through wall connector	1 Elec	7	1.143	Ea.	32.50	64.50		97	133
4520	Through roof connector		5	1.600		35.50	90.50		126	175
4530	Beam connector		7	1.143		17.90	64.50		82.40	117
4540	Double bolt connector	↓	38	.211	↓	5.95	11.90		17.85	24.50
4600	Bonding plates, copper									
4610	I Beam, 8" square	1 Elec	7	1.143	Ea.	22.50	64.50		87	122
4620	Purlin, 8" square		7	1.143		26	64.50		90.50	126
4630	Large heavy duty, 16" square		5	1.600		31.50	90.50		122	171
4640	Aluminum, I Beam, 8" square		7	1.143		16.45	64.50		80.95	115
4650	Purlin, 8" square		7	1.143		16.25	64.50		80.75	115
4660	Large heavy duty, 16" square		5	1.600		17.75	90.50		108.25	156
4700	Cable support, copper, loop fastener		38	.211		1.09	11.90		12.99	19.05
4710	Adhesive cable holder		38	.211		1.41	11.90		13.31	19.40
4720	Aluminum, loop fastener		38	.211		.69	11.90		12.59	18.60
4730	Adhesive cable holder		38	.211		.76	11.90		12.66	18.70
4740	Bonding strap, copper, 3/4" x 9-1/2"		15	.533		11.15	30		41.15	57.50
4750	Aluminum, 3/4" x 9-1/2"		15	.533		4.78	30		34.78	50.50
4760	Swivel adapter, copper, 1/2"		73	.110		16.75	6.20		22.95	28
4770	Aluminum, 1/2"	↓	73	.110	↓	8.90	6.20		15.10	19.10

26 51 Interior Lighting

26 51 13 – Interior Lighting Fixtures, Lamps, and Ballasts

26 51 13.10 Fixture Hangers

		Crew	Daily Output	Labor-Hours	Unit	Material	Labor	Equipment	Total	Total Incl O&P
0010	**FIXTURE HANGERS**									
0220	Box hub cover	1 Elec	32	.250	Ea.	4.19	14.15		18.34	25.50
0240	Canopy		12	.667		9.95	37.50		47.45	67.50
0260	Connecting block		40	.200		2.78	11.30		14.08	20
0280	Cushion hanger		16	.500		22.50	28.50		51	67.50
0300	Box hanger, with mounting strap		8	1		10	56.50		66.50	96
0320	Connecting block		40	.200		2.39	11.30		13.69	19.60
0340	Flexible, 1/2" diameter, 4" long	↓	12	.667	↓	16.40	37.50		53.90	74.50

For customer support on your Electrical Costs with RSMeans Data, call 800.448.8182.

293

26 51 Interior Lighting

26 51 13 – Interior Lighting Fixtures, Lamps, and Ballasts

26 51 13.10 Fixture Hangers

		Crew	Daily Output	Labor-Hours	Unit	Material	2017 Bare Costs Labor	Equipment	Total	Total Incl O&P
0360	6" long	1 Elec	12	.667	Ea.	17.80	37.50		55.30	76
0380	8" long		12	.667		19.70	37.50		57.20	78
0400	10" long		12	.667		21	37.50		58.50	79.50
0420	12" long		12	.667		22	37.50		59.50	81
0440	15" long		12	.667		23.50	37.50		61	82
0460	18" long		12	.667		27.50	37.50		65	86.50
0480	3/4" diameter, 4" long		10	.800		21	45.50		66.50	91
0500	6" long		10	.800		23.50	45.50		69	93.50
0520	8" long		10	.800		23.50	45.50		69	93.50
0540	10" long		10	.800		26	45.50		71.50	96.50
0560	12" long		10	.800		27.50	45.50		73	98.50
0580	15" long		10	.800		31	45.50		76.50	103
0600	18" long	▼	10	.800	▼	35	45.50		80.50	107

26 51 13.40 Interior HID Fixtures

		Crew	Daily Output	Labor-Hours	Unit	Material	2017 Bare Costs Labor	Equipment	Total	Total Incl O&P
0010	**INTERIOR HID FIXTURES** Incl. lamps, and mounting hardware									
0700	High pressure sodium, recessed, round, 70 watt	1 Elec	3.50	2.286	Ea.	470	129		599	715
0720	100 watt		3.50	2.286		485	129		614	730
0740	150 watt		3.20	2.500		545	142		687	810
0760	Square, 70 watt		3.60	2.222		460	126		586	695
0780	100 watt		3.60	2.222		485	126		611	725
0820	250 watt	▼	3	2.667		745	151		896	1,050
0840	1000 watt	2 Elec	4.80	3.333		1,275	189		1,464	1,675
0860	Surface, round, 70 watt	1 Elec	3	2.667		650	151		801	940
0880	100 watt		3	2.667		670	151		821	960
0900	150 watt		2.70	2.963		700	168		868	1,025
0920	Square, 70 watt		3	2.667		615	151		766	905
0940	100 watt		3	2.667		650	151		801	940
0980	250 watt		2.50	3.200		665	181		846	1,000
1040	Pendent, round, 70 watt		3	2.667		675	151		826	970
1060	100 watt		3	2.667		650	151		801	940
1080	150 watt		2.70	2.963		660	168		828	975
1100	Square, 70 watt		3	2.667		705	151		856	1,000
1120	100 watt		3	2.667		715	151		866	1,000
1140	150 watt		2.70	2.963		735	168		903	1,050
1160	250 watt		2.50	3.200		990	181		1,171	1,375
1180	400 watt		2.40	3.333		1,050	189		1,239	1,425
1220	Wall, round, 70 watt		3	2.667		590	151		741	875
1240	100 watt		3	2.667		605	151		756	890
1260	150 watt		2.70	2.963		620	168		788	930
1300	Square, 70 watt		3	2.667		630	151		781	915
1320	100 watt		3	2.667		660	151		811	950
1340	150 watt		2.70	2.963		685	168		853	1,000
1360	250 watt	▼	2.50	3.200		760	181		941	1,100
1380	400 watt	2 Elec	4.80	3.333		940	189		1,129	1,300
1400	1000 watt	"	3.60	4.444		1,350	252		1,602	1,850
1500	Metal halide, recessed, round, 175 watt	1 Elec	3.40	2.353		405	133		538	645
1520	250 watt	"	3.20	2.500		510	142		652	770
1540	400 watt	2 Elec	5.80	2.759		720	156		876	1,025
1580	Square, 175 watt	1 Elec	3.40	2.353		410	133		543	650
1640	Surface, round, 175 watt		2.90	2.759		565	156		721	855
1660	250 watt	▼	2.70	2.963		915	168		1,083	1,250
1680	400 watt	2 Elec	4.80	3.333		995	189		1,184	1,375

For customer support on your Electrical Costs with RSMeans Data, call 800.448.8182.

26 51 Interior Lighting

26 51 13 – Interior Lighting Fixtures, Lamps, and Ballasts

26 51 13.40 Interior HID Fixtures

		Crew	Daily Output	Labor-Hours	Unit	Material	2017 Bare Costs Labor	Equipment	Total	Total Incl O&P
1720	Square, 175 watt	1 Elec	2.90	2.759	Ea.	615	156		771	910
1800	Pendent, round, 175 watt		2.90	2.759		745	156		901	1,050
1820	250 watt		2.70	2.963		990	168		1,158	1,350
1840	400 watt	2 Elec	4.80	3.333		1,075	189		1,264	1,475
1880	Square, 175 watt	1 Elec	2.90	2.759		445	156		601	720
1900	250 watt	"	2.70	2.963		640	168		808	955
1920	400 watt	2 Elec	4.80	3.333		1,025	189		1,214	1,400
1980	Wall, round, 175 watt	1 Elec	2.90	2.759		850	156		1,006	1,175
2000	250 watt	"	2.70	2.963		910	168		1,078	1,250
2020	400 watt	2 Elec	4.80	3.333		915	189		1,104	1,275
2060	Square, 175 watt	1 Elec	2.90	2.759		605	156		761	900
2080	250 watt	"	2.70	2.963		650	168		818	965
2100	400 watt	2 Elec	4.80	3.333		910	189		1,099	1,275
2800	High pressure sodium, vaporproof, recessed, 70 watt	1 Elec	3.50	2.286		660	129		789	920
2820	100 watt		3.50	2.286		675	129		804	935
2840	150 watt		3.20	2.500		690	142		832	970
2900	Surface, 70 watt		3	2.667		745	151		896	1,050
2920	100 watt		3	2.667		780	151		931	1,075
2940	150 watt		2.70	2.963		810	168		978	1,150
3000	Pendent, 70 watt		3	2.667		735	151		886	1,025
3020	100 watt		3	2.667		760	151		911	1,050
3040	150 watt		2.70	2.963		800	168		968	1,125
3100	Wall, 70 watt		3	2.667		790	151		941	1,100
3120	100 watt		3	2.667		825	151		976	1,125
3140	150 watt		2.70	2.963		860	168		1,028	1,200
3200	Metal halide, vaporproof, recessed, 175 watt		3.40	2.353		590	133		723	850
3220	250 watt		3.20	2.500		680	142		822	955
3240	400 watt	2 Elec	5.80	2.759		850	156		1,006	1,175
3260	1000 watt	"	4.80	3.333		1,550	189		1,739	1,975
3280	Surface, 175 watt	1 Elec	2.90	2.759		925	156		1,081	1,250
3300	250 watt	"	2.70	2.963		965	168		1,133	1,325
3320	400 watt	2 Elec	4.80	3.333		1,200	189		1,389	1,600
3340	1000 watt	"	3.60	4.444		1,750	252		2,002	2,300
3360	Pendent, 175 watt	1 Elec	2.90	2.759		910	156		1,066	1,225
3380	250 watt	"	2.70	2.963		995	168		1,163	1,350
3400	400 watt	2 Elec	4.80	3.333		1,200	189		1,389	1,575
3420	1000 watt	"	3.60	4.444		1,925	252		2,177	2,475
3440	Wall, 175 watt	1 Elec	2.90	2.759		960	156		1,116	1,275
3460	250 watt	"	2.70	2.963		1,050	168		1,218	1,400
3480	400 watt	2 Elec	4.80	3.333		1,250	189		1,439	1,650
3500	1000 watt	"	3.60	4.444		2,000	252		2,252	2,575

26 51 13.50 Interior Lighting Fixtures

		Crew	Daily Output	Labor-Hours	Unit	Material	2017 Bare Costs Labor	Equipment	Total	Total Incl O&P
0010	**INTERIOR LIGHTING FIXTURES** Including lamps, mounting R265113-40									
0030	hardware and connections									
0100	Fluorescent, C.W. lamps, troffer, recess mounted in grid, RS									
0130	Grid ceiling mount									
0200	Acrylic lens, 1'W x 4'L, two 40 watt	1 Elec	5.70	1.404	Ea.	51.50	79.50		131	176
0210	1'W x 4'L, three 40 watt		5.40	1.481		58.50	84		142.50	190
0300	2'W x 2'L, two U40 watt		5.70	1.404		55	79.50		134.50	180
0400	2'W x 4'L, two 40 watt		5.30	1.509		54	85.50		139.50	188
0500	2'W x 4'L, three 40 watt		5	1.600		59.50	90.50		150	202
0600	2'W x 4'L, four 40 watt		4.70	1.702		62	96.50		158.50	213

For customer support on your Electrical Costs with RSMeans Data, call 800.448.8182.

295

26 51 13.50 Interior Lighting Fixtures		Crew	Daily Output	Labor-Hours	Unit	Material	2017 Bare Costs Labor	Equipment	Total	Total Incl O&P
0700	4'W x 4'L, four 40 watt	2 Elec	6.40	2.500	Ea.	276	142		418	515
0800	4'W x 4'L, six 40 watt		6.20	2.581		296	146		442	545
0900	4'W x 4'L, eight 40 watt		5.80	2.759		340	156		496	605
0910	Acrylic lens, 1'W x 4'L, two 32 watt T8 [G]	1 Elec	5.70	1.404		61	79.50		140.50	187
0930	2'W x 2'L, two U32 watt T8 [G]		5.70	1.404		95.50	79.50		175	224
0940	2'W x 4'L, two 32 watt T8 [G]		5.30	1.509		79	85.50		164.50	215
0950	2'W x 4'L, three 32 watt T8 [G]		5	1.600		69.50	90.50		160	213
0960	2'W x 4'L, four 32 watt T8 [G]		4.70	1.702		74	96.50		170.50	226
1000	Surface mounted, RS									
1030	Acrylic lens with hinged & latched door frame									
1100	1'W x 4'L, two 40 watt	1 Elec	7	1.143	Ea.	65.50	64.50		130	169
1110	1'W x 4'L, three 40 watt		6.70	1.194		68	67.50		135.50	176
1200	2'W x 2'L, two U40 watt		7	1.143		70.50	64.50		135	175
1300	2'W x 4'L, two 40 watt		6.20	1.290		80	73		153	197
1400	2'W x 4'L, three 40 watt		5.70	1.404		83	79.50		162.50	210
1500	2'W x 4'L, four 40 watt		5.30	1.509		85	85.50		170.50	222
1501	2'W x 4'L, 6-40W T8		5.20	1.538		85	87		172	224
1600	4'W x 4'L, four 40 watt	2 Elec	7.20	2.222		420	126		546	650
1700	4'W x 4'L, six 40 watt		6.60	2.424		455	137		592	705
1800	4'W x 4'L, eight 40 watt		6.20	2.581		475	146		621	740
1900	2'W x 8'L, four 40 watt		6.40	2.500		167	142		309	395
2000	2'W x 8'L, eight 40 watt		6.20	2.581		179	146		325	415
2010	Acrylic wrap around lens									
2020	6"W x 4'L, one 40 watt	1 Elec	8	1	Ea.	68	56.50		124.50	160
2030	6"W x 8'L, two 40 watt	2 Elec	8	2		75	113		188	253
2040	11"W x 4'L, two 40 watt	1 Elec	7	1.143		45.50	64.50		110	147
2050	11"W x 8'L, four 40 watt	2 Elec	6.60	2.424		75.50	137		212.50	289
2060	16"W x 4'L, four 40 watt	1 Elec	5.30	1.509		75.50	85.50		161	211
2070	16"W x 8'L, eight 40 watt	2 Elec	6.40	2.500		164	142		306	390
2080	2'W x 2'L, two U40 watt	1 Elec	7	1.143		92	64.50		156.50	198
2100	Strip fixture									
2130	Surface mounted									
2200	4' long, one 40 watt, RS	1 Elec	8.50	.941	Ea.	31	53.50		84.50	114
2300	4' long, two 40 watt, RS		8	1		43	56.50		99.50	133
2310	4' long, two 32 watt T8, RS [G]		8	1		89	56.50		145.50	183
2400	4' long, one 40 watt, SL		8	1		53.50	56.50		110	144
2500	4' long, two 40 watt, SL		7	1.143		72.50	64.50		137	177
2580	8' long, one 60 watt T8, SL [G]	2 Elec	13.40	1.194		112	67.50		179.50	224
2590	8' long, two 60 watt T8, SL [G]		12.40	1.290		88	73		161	206
2600	8' long, one 75 watt, SL		13.40	1.194		55	67.50		122.50	162
2700	8' long, two 75 watt, SL		12.40	1.290		66.50	73		139.50	182
2800	4' long, two 60 watt, HO	1 Elec	6.70	1.194		107	67.50		174.50	219
2810	4' long, two 54 watt, T5HO [G]	"	6.70	1.194		174	67.50		241.50	292
2900	8' long, two 110 watt, HO	2 Elec	10.60	1.509		108	85.50		193.50	247
2910	4' long, two 115 watt, VHO	1 Elec	6.50	1.231		142	69.50		211.50	260
2920	8' long, two 215 watt, VHO	2 Elec	10.40	1.538		153	87		240	299
2950	High bay pendent mounted, 16" W x 4' L, four 54 watt, T5HO [G]		8.90	1.798		244	102		346	420
2952	2' W x 4' L, six 54 watt, T5HO [G]		8.50	1.882		310	107		417	500
2954	2' W x 4' L, six 32 watt, T8 [G]		8.50	1.882		179	107		286	355
3000	Strip, pendent mounted, industrial, white porcelain enamel									
3100	4' long, two 40 watt, RS	1 Elec	5.70	1.404	Ea.	53	79.50		132.50	177
3110	4' long, two 32 watt T8, RS [G]		5.70	1.404		68.50	79.50		148	195
3200	4' long, two 60 watt, HO		5	1.600		83	90.50		173.50	228

26 51 13.50 Interior Lighting Fixtures		Crew	Daily Output	Labor-Hours	Unit	Material	2017 Bare Costs Labor	Equipment	Total	Total Incl O&P
3290	8' long, two 60 watt T8, SL	G	2 Elec	8.80	1.818	Ea.	113	103		216	278
3300	8' long, two 75 watt, SL			8.80	1.818		98.50	103		201.50	262
3400	8' long, two 110 watt, HO			8	2		126	113		239	310
3410	Acrylic finish, 4' long, two 40 watt, RS		1 Elec	5.70	1.404		86.50	79.50		166	214
3420	4' long, two 60 watt, HO			5	1.600		161	90.50		251.50	315
3430	4' long, two 115 watt, VHO			4.80	1.667		208	94.50		302.50	370
3440	8' long, two 75 watt, SL		2 Elec	8.80	1.818		170	103		273	340
3450	8' long, two 110 watt, HO			8	2		193	113		306	380
3460	8' long, two 215 watt, VHO			7.60	2.105		273	119		392	480
3470	Troffer, air handling, 2'W x 4'L with four 32 watt T8	G	1 Elec	4	2		115	113		228	297
3480	2'W x 2'L with two U32 watt T8	G		5.50	1.455		111	82.50		193.50	245
3490	Air connector insulated, 5" diameter			20	.400		68	22.50		90.50	109
3500	6" diameter			20	.400		69	22.50		91.50	110
3502	Troffer, direct/indirect, 2'W x 4'L with two 32 W T8	G		5.30	1.509		281	85.50		366.50	440
3510	Troffer parabolic lay-in, 1'W x 4'L with one 32 W T8	G		5.70	1.404		117	79.50		196.50	248
3520	1'W x 4'L with two 32 W T8	G		5.30	1.509		140	85.50		225.50	282
3525	2'W x 2'L with two U32 W T8	G		5.70	1.404		118	79.50		197.50	249
3530	2'W x 4'L with three 32 W T8	G		5	1.600		131	90.50		221.50	280
3531	Intr fxtr, fluor, troffer prismatic lay-in, 2'w x 4'l W/three 32 W T8			5	1.600		152	90.50		242.50	305
3535	Downlight, recess mounted	G		8	1		148	56.50		204.50	247
3540	Wall wash reflector, recess mounted	G		8	1		105	56.50		161.50	201
3550	Direct/indirect, 4' long, stl., pendent mtd.	G		5	1.600		163	90.50		253.50	315
3560	4' long, alum., pendent mtd.	G		5	1.600		335	90.50		425.50	505
3565	Prefabricated cove, 4' long, stl. continuous row	G		5	1.600		204	90.50		294.50	360
3570	4' long, alum. continuous row	G		5	1.600		350	90.50		440.50	520
3580	Wet location, recess mounted, 2'W x 4'L with two 32 watt T8	G		5.30	1.509		243	85.50		328.50	395
3590	Pendent mounted, 2'W x 4'L with two 32 watt T8	G		5.70	1.404		375	79.50		454.50	535
4000	Induction lamp, integral ballast, ceiling mounted										
4110	High bay, aluminum reflector, 160 watt		1 Elec	3.20	2.500	Ea.	955	142		1,097	1,250
4120	320 watt		"	3	2.667		1,725	151		1,876	2,100
4130	480 watt		2 Elec	5.80	2.759		2,600	156		2,756	3,100
4150	Low bay, aluminum reflector, 250 watt		1 Elec	3.20	2.500		920	142		1,062	1,200
4170	Garage, aluminum reflector, 80 watt			3.60	2.222		920	126		1,046	1,225
4180	Vandalproof, aluminum reflector, 100 watt			3.20	2.500		660	142		802	940
4220	Metal halide, integral ballast, ceiling, recess mounted										
4230	prismatic glass lens, floating door										
4240	2'W x 2'L, 250 watt		1 Elec	3.20	2.500	Ea.	255	142		397	495
4250	2'W x 2'L, 400 watt		2 Elec	5.80	2.759		365	156		521	640
4260	Surface mounted, 2'W x 2'L, 250 watt		1 Elec	2.70	2.963		345	168		513	630
4270	400 watt		2 Elec	4.80	3.333		405	189		594	735
4280	High bay, aluminum reflector,										
4290	Single unit, 400 watt		2 Elec	4.60	3.478	Ea.	415	197		612	750
4300	Single unit, 1000 watt			4	4		595	226		821	995
4310	Twin unit, 400 watt			3.20	5		825	283		1,108	1,325
4320	Low bay, aluminum reflector, 250W DX lamp		1 Elec	3.20	2.500		365	142		507	610
4330	400 watt lamp		2 Elec	5	3.200		530	181		711	850
4340	High pressure sodium integral ballast ceiling, recess mounted										
4350	prismatic glass lens, floating door										
4360	2'W x 2'L, 150 watt lamp		1 Elec	3.20	2.500	Ea.	390	142		532	635
4370	2'W x 2'L, 400 watt lamp		2 Elec	5.80	2.759		465	156		621	745
4380	Surface mounted, 2'W x 2'L, 150 watt lamp		1 Elec	2.70	2.963		475	168		643	770
4390	400 watt lamp		2 Elec	4.80	3.333		530	189		719	870
4400	High bay, aluminum reflector,										

26 51 13.50 Interior Lighting Fixtures	Crew	Daily Output	Labor-Hours	Unit	Material	2017 Bare Costs Labor	Equipment	Total	Total Incl O&P
4410	Single unit, 400 watt lamp	2 Elec	4.60	3.478	Ea.	380	197		577	715
4430	Single unit, 1000 watt lamp	"	4	4		550	226		776	945
4440	Low bay, aluminum reflector, 150 watt lamp	1 Elec	3.20	2.500		330	142		472	570
4445	High bay H.I.D. quartz restrike	"	16	.500		164	28.50		192.50	223
4450	Incandescent, high hat can, round alzak reflector, prewired									
4470	100 watt	1 Elec	8	1	Ea.	64.50	56.50		121	156
4480	150 watt		8	1		105	56.50		161.50	200
4500	300 watt		6.70	1.194		242	67.50		309.50	365
4520	Round with reflector and baffles, 150 watt		8	1		51.50	56.50		108	142
4540	Round with concentric louver, 150 watt PAR		8	1		79	56.50		135.50	172
4600	Square glass lens with metal trim, prewired									
4630	100 watt	1 Elec	6.70	1.194	Ea.	55.50	67.50		123	162
4700	200 watt		6.70	1.194		97.50	67.50		165	208
4800	300 watt		5.70	1.404		146	79.50		225.50	279
4810	500 watt		5	1.600		286	90.50		376.50	450
4900	Ceiling/wall, surface mounted, metal cylinder, 75 watt		10	.800		50.50	45.50		96	124
4920	150 watt		10	.800		81	45.50		126.50	157
4930	300 watt		8	1		168	56.50		224.50	270
5000	500 watt		6.70	1.194		365	67.50		432.50	500
5010	Square, 100 watt		8	1		113	56.50		169.50	209
5020	150 watt		8	1		124	56.50		180.50	221
5030	300 watt		7	1.143		340	64.50		404.50	465
5040	500 watt		6	1.333		345	75.50		420.50	495
5200	Ceiling, surface mounted, opal glass drum									
5300	8", one 60 watt lamp	1 Elec	10	.800	Ea.	65.50	45.50		111	140
5400	10", two 60 watt lamps		8	1		72.50	56.50		129	165
5500	12", four 60 watt lamps		6.70	1.194		103	67.50		170.50	214
5510	Pendent, round, 100 watt		8	1		113	56.50		169.50	209
5520	150 watt		8	1		123	56.50		179.50	220
5530	300 watt		6.70	1.194		171	67.50		238.50	289
5540	500 watt		5.50	1.455		325	82.50		407.50	480
5550	Square, 100 watt		6.70	1.194		152	67.50		219.50	268
5560	150 watt		6.70	1.194		158	67.50		225.50	275
5570	300 watt		5.70	1.404		231	79.50		310.50	375
5580	500 watt		5	1.600		315	90.50		405.50	480
5600	Wall, round, 100 watt		8	1		65.50	56.50		122	157
5620	300 watt		8	1		143	56.50		199.50	242
5630	500 watt		6.70	1.194		380	67.50		447.50	515
5640	Square, 100 watt		8	1		104	56.50		160.50	199
5650	150 watt		8	1		106	56.50		162.50	201
5660	300 watt		7	1.143		166	64.50		230.50	280
5670	500 watt		6	1.333		292	75.50		367.50	435
6010	Vapor tight, incandescent, ceiling mounted, 200 watt		6.20	1.290		78.50	73		151.50	195
6020	Recessed, 200 watt		6.70	1.194		124	67.50		191.50	237
6030	Pendent, 200 watt		6.70	1.194		78.50	67.50		146	187
6040	Wall, 200 watt		8	1		80	56.50		136.50	173
6100	Fluorescent, surface mounted, 2 lamps, 4'L, RS, 40 watt		3.20	2.500		116	142		258	340
6110	Industrial, 2 lamps 4' long in tandem, 430 MA		2.20	3.636		213	206		419	545
6130	2 lamps 4' long, 800 MA		1.90	4.211		182	238		420	555
6160	Pendent, indust, 2 lamps 4'L in tandem, 430 MA		1.90	4.211		248	238		486	630
6170	2 lamps 4' long, 430 MA		2.30	3.478		166	197		363	480
6180	2 lamps 4' long, 800 MA		1.70	4.706		209	266		475	630
6850	Vandalproof, surface mounted, fluorescent, two 32 watt T8 [G]		3.20	2.500		252	142		394	490

26 51 13 – Interior Lighting Fixtures, Lamps, and Ballasts

26 51 13.50 Interior Lighting Fixtures	Crew	Daily Output	Labor-Hours	Unit	Material	2017 Bare Costs Labor	Equipment	Total	Total Incl O&P
6860	Incandescent, one 150 watt	1 Elec	8	1	Ea.	90	56.50		146.50	184
6900	Mirror light, fluorescent, RS, acrylic enclosure, two 10 watt		8	1		116	56.50		172.50	213
6910	One 40 watt		8	1		96	56.50		152.50	191
6920	One 20 watt		12	.667		82.50	37.50		120	147
7000	Low bay, aluminum reflector, 70 watt, high pressure sodium		4	2		275	113		388	475
7010	250 watt		3.20	2.500		365	142		507	615
7020	400 watt	2 Elec	5	3.200		385	181		566	690
7500	Ballast replacement, by weight of ballast, to 15' high									
7520	Indoor fluorescent, less than 2 lb.	1 Elec	10	.800	Ea.	23.50	45.50		69	94
7540	Two 40W, watt reducer, 2 to 5 lb.		9.40	.851		71	48		119	151
7560	Two F96 slimline, over 5 lb.		8	1		110	56.50		166.50	206
7580	Vaportite ballast, less than 2 lb.		9.40	.851		23.50	48		71.50	98
7600	2 lb. to 5 lb.		8.90	.899		71	51		122	155
7620	Over 5 lb.		7.60	1.053		110	59.50		169.50	211
7630	Electronic ballast for two tubes		8	1		33.50	56.50		90	122
7640	Dimmable ballast one-lamp ⒼG		8	1		94.50	56.50		151	189
7650	Dimmable ballast two-lamp ⒼG		7.60	1.053		100	59.50		159.50	200
7660	Dimmable ballast three-lamp		6.90	1.159		130	65.50		195.50	242
7690	Emergency ballast (factory installed in fixture)					166			166	183
7990	Decorator									
8000	Pendent RLM in colors, shallow dome, 12" diam., 100 W	1 Elec	8	1	Ea.	80.50	56.50		137	174
8010	Regular dome, 12" diam., 100 watt		8	1		83	56.50		139.50	177
8020	16" diam., 200 watt		7	1.143		84.50	64.50		149	190
8030	18" diam., 300 watt		6	1.333		93	75.50		168.50	215
8100	Picture framing light		16	.500		96	28.50		124.50	149
8150	Miniature low voltage, recessed, pinhole		8	1		129	56.50		185.50	227
8160	Star		8	1		134	56.50		190.50	232
8170	Adjustable cone		8	1		166	56.50		222.50	268
8180	Eyeball		8	1		107	56.50		163.50	202
8190	Cone		8	1		130	56.50		186.50	228
8200	Coilex baffle		8	1		118	56.50		174.50	215
8210	Surface mounted, adjustable cylinder		8	1		125	56.50		181.50	222
8250	Chandeliers, incandescent									
8260	24" diam. x 42" high, 6 light candle	1 Elec	6	1.333	Ea.	420	75.50		495.50	580
8270	24" diam. x 42" high, 6 light candle w/glass shade		6	1.333		430	75.50		505.50	590
8280	17" diam. x 12" high, 8 light w/glass panels		8	1		257	56.50		313.50	370
8300	27" diam. x 29" high, 10 light bohemian lead crystal		4	2		560	113		673	785
8310	21" diam. x 9" high, 6 light sculptured ice crystal		8	1		400	56.50		456.50	525
8500	Accent lights, on floor or edge, 0.5 W low volt incandescent									
8520	incl. transformer & fastenings, based on 100' lengths									
8550	Lights in clear tubing, 12" on center	1 Elec	230	.035	L.F.	8.35	1.97		10.32	12.15
8560	6" on center		160	.050		10.90	2.83		13.73	16.25
8570	4" on center		130	.062		16.70	3.48		20.18	23.50
8580	3" on center		125	.064		18.50	3.62		22.12	26
8590	2" on center		100	.080		27	4.53		31.53	36.50
8600	Carpet, lights both sides 6" OC, in alum. extrusion		270	.030		25.50	1.68		27.18	30.50
8610	In bronze extrusion		270	.030		28.50	1.68		30.18	34
8620	Carpet-bare floor, lights 18" OC, in alum. extrusion		270	.030		20	1.68		21.68	24.50
8630	In bronze extrusion		270	.030		23.50	1.68		25.18	28.50
8640	Carpet edge-wall, lights 6" OC in alum. extrusion		270	.030		25.50	1.68		27.18	30.50
8650	In bronze extrusion		270	.030		28.50	1.68		30.18	34
8660	Bare floor, lights 18" OC, in alum. extrusion		300	.027		20	1.51		21.51	24.50
8670	In bronze extrusion		300	.027		23.50	1.51		25.01	28.50

26 51 13 – Interior Lighting Fixtures, Lamps, and Ballasts

26 51 13.50 Interior Lighting Fixtures		Crew	Daily Output	Labor-Hours	Unit	Material	2017 Bare Costs Labor	Equipment	Total	Total Incl O&P
8680	Bare floor conduit, alum. extrusion	1 Elec	300	.027	L.F.	6.65	1.51		8.16	9.60
8690	In bronze extrusion		300	.027	↓	13.35	1.51		14.86	16.90
8700	Step edge to 36", lights 6" OC, in alum. extrusion		100	.080	Ea.	67	4.53		71.53	81
8710	In bronze extrusion		100	.080		70	4.53		74.53	84
8720	Step edge to 54", lights 6" OC, in alum. extrusion		100	.080		101	4.53		105.53	118
8730	In bronze extrusion		100	.080		106	4.53		110.53	124
8740	Step edge to 72", lights 6" OC, in alum. extrusion		100	.080		134	4.53		138.53	155
8750	In bronze extrusion		100	.080		146	4.53		150.53	168
8760	Connector, male		32	.250		2.48	14.15		16.63	23.50
8770	Female with pigtail		32	.250		5.20	14.15		19.35	27
8780	Clamps		400	.020		.49	1.13		1.62	2.24
8790	Transformers, 50 watt		8	1		66	56.50		122.50	158
8800	250 watt		4	2		217	113		330	410
8810	1000 watt		2.70	2.963	↓	325	168		493	610

26 51 13.55 Interior LED Fixtures

26 51 13.55 Interior LED Fixtures			Crew	Daily Output	Labor-Hours	Unit	Material	2017 Bare Costs Labor	Equipment	Total	Total Incl O&P
0010	**INTERIOR LED FIXTURES** Incl. lamps, and mounting hardware										
0100	Downlight, recess mounted, 7.5" diameter, 25 watt	G	1 Elec	8	1	Ea.	335	56.50		391.50	450
0120	10" diameter, 36 watt	G		8	1		360	56.50		416.50	480
0160	cylinder, 10 watts	G		8	1		102	56.50		158.50	197
0180	20 watts	G		8	1		166	56.50		222.50	268
1000	Troffer, recess mounted, 2' x 4', 3200 Lumens	G		5.30	1.509		138	85.50		223.50	279
1010	4800 Lumens	G		5	1.600		179	90.50		269.50	330
1020	6400 Lumens	G		4.70	1.702		198	96.50		294.50	360
1100	Troffer retrofit lamp, 38 watt	G		21	.381		238	21.50		259.50	294
1110	60 watt	G		20	.400		340	22.50		362.50	410
1120	100 watt	G		18	.444		510	25		535	600
1200	Troffer, volumetric recess mounted, 2' x 2'	G		5.70	1.404		279	79.50		358.50	425
2000	Strip, surface mounted, one light bar 4' long, 3500K	G		8.50	.941		260	53.50		313.50	365
2010	5000K	G		8	1		260	56.50		316.50	370
2020	Two light bar 4' long, 5000K	G		7	1.143		410	64.50		474.50	545
3000	Linear, suspended mounted, one light bar 4' long, 37 watt	G		6.70	1.194		153	67.50		220.50	269
3010	One light bar 8' long, 74 watt	G	2 Elec	12.20	1.311		283	74		357	420
3020	Two light bar 4' long, 74 watt	G	1 Elec	5.70	1.404		305	79.50		384.50	455
3030	Two light bar 8' long, 148 watt	G	2 Elec	8.80	1.818		350	103		453	540
4000	High bay, surface mounted, round, 150 watts	G		5.41	2.959		475	167		642	770
4010	2 bars, 164 watts	G		5.41	2.959		445	167		612	740
4020	3 bars, 246 watts	G		5.01	3.197		575	181		756	900
4030	4 bars, 328 watts	G		4.60	3.478		700	197		897	1,075
4040	5 bars, 410 watts	G	3 Elec	4.20	5.716		830	325		1,155	1,400
4050	6 bars, 492 watts	G		3.80	6.324		935	360		1,295	1,550
4060	7 bars, 574 watts	G		3.39	7.075		1,025	400		1,425	1,725
4070	8 bars, 656 watts	G		2.99	8.029		1,125	455		1,580	1,925
5000	Track, lighthead, 6 watt	G	1 Elec	32	.250		54.50	14.15		68.65	81
5010	9 watt	G	"	32	.250		61.50	14.15		75.65	88.50
6000	Garage, surface mounted, 103 watts	G	2 Elec	6.50	2.462		970	139		1,109	1,275
6100	pendent mounted, 80 watts	G		6.50	2.462		695	139		834	975
6200	95 watts	G		6.50	2.462		800	139		939	1,100
6300	125 watts	G		6.50	2.462	↓	840	139		979	1,125

26 51 13.70 Residential Fixtures

26 51 13.70 Residential Fixtures		Crew	Daily Output	Labor-Hours	Unit	Material	2017 Bare Costs Labor	Equipment	Total	Total Incl O&P
0010	**RESIDENTIAL FIXTURES**									
0400	Fluorescent, interior, surface, circline, 32 watt & 40 watt	1 Elec	20	.400	Ea.	141	22.50		163.50	189
0500	2' x 2', two U-tube 32 watt T8	↓	8	1	↓	165	56.50		221.50	266

For customer support on your Electrical Costs with RSMeans Data, call 800.448.8182.

26 51 Interior Lighting

26 51 13 – Interior Lighting Fixtures, Lamps, and Ballasts

26 51 13.70 Residential Fixtures

		Crew	Daily Output	Labor-Hours	Unit	Material	2017 Bare Costs Labor	Equipment	Total	Total Incl O&P
0700	Shallow under cabinet, two 20 watt	1 Elec	16	.500	Ea.	71.50	28.50		100	121
0900	Wall mounted, 1'L, two 32 watt TO, with baffle		10	.800		133	45.50		178.50	214
2000	Incandescent, exterior lantern, wall mounted, 60 watt		16	.500		60	28.50		88.50	109
2100	Post light, 150W, with 7' post		4	2		270	113		383	465
2500	Lamp holder, weatherproof with 150W PAR		16	.500		32	28.50		60.50	77.50
2550	With reflector and guard		12	.667		56	37.50		93.50	119
2600	Interior pendent, globe with shade, 150 watt		20	.400		201	22.50		223.50	255

26 51 13.90 Ballast, Replacement HID

		Crew	Daily Output	Labor-Hours	Unit	Material	2017 Bare Costs Labor	Equipment	Total	Total Incl O&P
0010	**BALLAST, REPLACEMENT HID**									
7510	Multi-tap 120/208/240/277 volt									
7550	High pressure sodium, 70 watt	1 Elec	10	.800	Ea.	116	45.50		161.50	195
7560	100 watt		9.40	.851		121	48		169	205
7570	150 watt		9	.889		130	50.50		180.50	219
7580	250 watt		8.50	.941		193	53.50		246.50	293
7590	400 watt		7	1.143		219	64.50		283.50	340
7600	1000 watt		6	1.333		300	75.50		375.50	445
7610	Metal halide, 175 watt		8	1		71	56.50		127.50	163
7620	250 watt		8	1		91.50	56.50		148	186
7630	400 watt		7	1.143		114	64.50		178.50	223
7640	1000 watt		6	1.333		196	75.50		271.50	330
7650	1500 watt		5	1.600		248	90.50		338.50	410

26 52 Emergency Lighting

26 52 13 – Emergency Lighting Equipments

26 52 13.10 Emergency Lighting and Battery Units

		Crew	Daily Output	Labor-Hours	Unit	Material	2017 Bare Costs Labor	Equipment	Total	Total Incl O&P
0010	**EMERGENCY LIGHTING AND BATTERY UNITS**									
0300	Emergency light units, battery operated									
0350	Twin sealed beam light, 25 watt, 6 volt each									
0500	Lead battery operated	1 Elec	4	2	Ea.	166	113		279	350
0700	Nickel cadmium battery operated		4	2		335	113		448	535
0780	Additional remote mount, sealed beam, 25 W 6 V		26.70	.300		28.50	16.95		45.45	57
0790	Twin sealed beam light, 25 W 6 V each		26.70	.300		56.50	16.95		73.45	87.50
0900	Self-contained fluorescent lamp pack		10	.800		166	45.50		211.50	251

26 53 Exit Signs

26 53 13 – Exit Lighting

26 53 13.10 Exit Lighting Fixtures

			Crew	Daily Output	Labor-Hours	Unit	Material	2017 Bare Costs Labor	Equipment	Total	Total Incl O&P
0010	**EXIT LIGHTING FIXTURES**										
0080	Exit light ceiling or wall mount, incandescent, single face		1 Elec	8	1	Ea.	70	56.50		126.50	162
0100	Double face			6.70	1.194		50	67.50		117.50	156
0120	Explosion proof			3.80	2.105		550	119		669	785
0150	Fluorescent, single face			8	1		85	56.50		141.50	179
0160	Double face			6.70	1.194		75	67.50		142.50	184
0200	LED standard, single face	G		8	1		47.50	56.50		104	137
0220	Double face	G		6.70	1.194		51	67.50		118.50	157
0230	LED vandal-resistant, single face	G		7.27	1.100		212	62.50		274.50	325
0240	LED w/battery unit, single face	G		4.40	1.818		184	103		287	355
0260	Double face	G		4	2		188	113		301	375
0262	LED w/battery unit, vandal-resistant, single face	G		4.40	1.818		245	103		348	425

26 53 Exit Signs

26 53 13 – Exit Lighting

26 53 13.10 Exit Lighting Fixtures		Crew	Daily Output	Labor-Hours	Unit	Material	2017 Bare Costs Labor	Equipment	Total	Total Incl O&P
0270	Combination emergency light units and exit sign	1 Elec	4	2	Ea.	179	113		292	365
0290	LED retrofit kits	G ↓	60	.133		50	7.55		57.55	66.50
1500	Exit sign, 12 V, 1 face, remote end mounted (Type 602A1)	R-19	18	1.111		63.50	63		126.50	165
1780	With emergency battery, explosion proof	"	7.70	2.597	↓	3,925	147		4,072	4,550

26 54 Classified Location Lighting

26 54 13 – Classified Lighting

26 54 13.20 Explosionproof

		Crew	Daily Output	Labor-Hours	Unit	Material	Labor	Equipment	Total	Total Incl O&P
0010	**EXPLOSIONPROOF**, incl lamps, mounting hardware and connections									
6310	Metal halide with ballast, ceiling, surface mounted, 175 watt	1 Elec	2.90	2.759	Ea.	1,075	156		1,231	1,400
6320	250 watt	"	2.70	2.963		1,275	168		1,443	1,675
6330	400 watt	2 Elec	4.80	3.333		1,375	189		1,564	1,800
6340	Ceiling, pendent mounted, 175 watt	1 Elec	2.60	3.077		1,025	174		1,199	1,375
6350	250 watt	"	2.40	3.333		1,225	189		1,414	1,625
6360	400 watt	2 Elec	4.20	3.810		1,325	216		1,541	1,775
6370	Wall, surface mounted, 175 watt	1 Elec	2.90	2.759		1,150	156		1,306	1,500
6380	250 watt	"	2.70	2.963		1,350	168		1,518	1,750
6390	400 watt	2 Elec	4.80	3.333		1,450	189		1,639	1,875
6400	High pressure sodium, ceiling surface mounted, 70 watt	1 Elec	3	2.667		1,500	151		1,651	1,875
6410	100 watt		3	2.667		1,550	151		1,701	1,925
6420	150 watt		2.70	2.963		1,600	168		1,768	2,025
6430	Pendent mounted, 70 watt		2.70	2.963		1,425	168		1,593	1,825
6440	100 watt		2.70	2.963		1,475	168		1,643	1,875
6450	150 watt		2.40	3.333		1,525	189		1,714	1,975
6460	Wall mounted, 70 watt		3	2.667		1,600	151		1,751	1,975
6470	100 watt		3	2.667		1,650	151		1,801	2,050
6480	150 watt		2.70	2.963		1,700	168		1,868	2,125
6510	Incandescent, ceiling mounted, 200 watt		4	2		1,250	113		1,363	1,575
6520	Pendent mounted, 200 watt		3.50	2.286		1,075	129		1,204	1,400
6530	Wall mounted, 200 watt		4	2		1,250	113		1,363	1,550
6600	Fluorescent, RS, 4' long, ceiling mounted, two 40 watt		2.70	2.963		3,325	168		3,493	3,925
6610	Three 40 watt		2.20	3.636		4,825	206		5,031	5,625
6620	Four 40 watt		1.90	4.211		6,200	238		6,438	7,175
6630	Pendent mounted, two 40 watt		2.30	3.478		3,875	197		4,072	4,575
6640	Three 40 watt		1.90	4.211		5,525	238		5,763	6,425
6650	Four 40 watt	↓	1.70	4.706	↓	7,250	266		7,516	8,400

26 55 Special Purpose Lighting

26 55 33 – Hazard Warning Lighting

26 55 33.10 Warning Beacons

		Crew	Daily Output	Labor-Hours	Unit	Material	Labor	Equipment	Total	Total Incl O&P
0010	**WARNING BEACONS**									
0015	Surface mount with colored or clear lens									
0100	Rotating beacon									
0110	120V, 40 watt halogen	1 Elec	3.50	2.286	Ea.	101	129		230	305
0120	24V, 20 watt halogen	"	3.50	2.286	"	211	129		340	425
0200	Steady beacon									
0210	120V, 40 watt halogen	1 Elec	3.50	2.286	Ea.	101	129		230	305
0220	24V, 20W		3.50	2.286		101	129		230	305
0230	12V DC, incandescent	↓	3.50	2.286	↓	101	129		230	305

26 55 Special Purpose Lighting

26 55 33 – Hazard Warning Lighting

26 55 33.10 Warning Beacons

		Crew	Daily Output	Labor-Hours	Unit	Material	2017 Bare Costs Labor	Equipment	Total	Total Incl O&P
0300	Flashing beacon									
0310	120V, 40 watt halogen	1 Elec	3.50	2.286	Ea.	101	129		230	305
0320	24V, 20 watt halogen		3.50	2.286		101	129		230	305
0410	12V DC with two 6V lantern batteries	↓	7	1.143	↓	101	64.50		165.50	208

26 55 59 – Display Lighting

26 55 59.10 Track Lighting

		Crew	Daily Output	Labor-Hours	Unit	Material	2017 Bare Costs Labor	Equipment	Total	Total Incl O&P
0010	**TRACK LIGHTING**									
0080	Track, 1 circuit, 4' section	1 Elec	6.70	1.194	Ea.	44.50	67.50		112	150
0100	8' section	2 Elec	10.60	1.509		69	85.50		154.50	204
0200	12' section	"	8.80	1.818		104	103		207	268
0300	3 circuits, 4' section	1 Elec	6.70	1.194		92.50	67.50		160	203
0400	8' section	2 Elec	10.60	1.509		109	85.50		194.50	248
0500	12' section	"	8.80	1.818		159	103		262	330
1000	Feed kit, surface mounting	1 Elec	16	.500		13	28.50		41.50	57
1100	End cover		24	.333		5.55	18.85		24.40	34.50
1200	Feed kit, stem mounting, 1 circuit		16	.500		42	28.50		70.50	88.50
1300	3 circuit		16	.500		42	28.50		70.50	88.50
2000	Electrical joiner, for continuous runs, 1 circuit		32	.250		24	14.15		38.15	47.50
2100	3 circuit		32	.250		59	14.15		73.15	86
2200	Fixtures, spotlight, 75W PAR halogen		16	.500		55.50	28.50		84	104
2210	50W MR16 halogen		16	.500		171	28.50		199.50	231
3000	Wall washer, 250 watt tungsten halogen		16	.500		132	28.50		160.50	188
3100	Low voltage, 25/50 watt, 1 circuit		16	.500		133	28.50		161.50	189
3120	3 circuit	↓	16	.500	↓	198	28.50		226.50	261

26 55 61 – Theatrical Lighting

26 55 61.10 Lights

		Crew	Daily Output	Labor-Hours	Unit	Material	2017 Bare Costs Labor	Equipment	Total	Total Incl O&P
0010	**LIGHTS**									
2000	Lights, border, quartz, reflector, vented,									
2100	colored or white	1 Elec	20	.400	L.F.	178	22.50		200.50	230
2500	Spotlight, follow spot, with transformer, 2,100 watt	"	4	2	Ea.	3,300	113		3,413	3,800
2600	For no transformer, deduct					940			940	1,025
3000	Stationary spot, fresnel quartz, 6" lens	1 Elec	4	2		184	113		297	370
3100	8" lens		4	2		238	113		351	430
3500	Ellipsoidal quartz, 1,000W, 6" lens		4	2		355	113		468	560
3600	12" lens		4	2		640	113		753	870
4000	Strobe light, 1 to 15 flashes per second, quartz		3	2.667		810	151		961	1,125
4500	Color wheel, portable, five hole, motorized	↓	4	2	↓	209	113		322	400

26 55 63 – Detention Lighting

26 55 63.10 Detention Lighting Fixtures

		Crew	Daily Output	Labor-Hours	Unit	Material	2017 Bare Costs Labor	Equipment	Total	Total Incl O&P
0010	**DETENTION LIGHTING FIXTURES**									
1000	Surface mounted, cold rolled steel, 14 ga., 1' x 4'	1 Elec	5.40	1.481	Ea.	695	84		779	890
1010	2' x 2'		5.40	1.481		745	84		829	945
1020	2' x 4'		5	1.600		875	90.50		965.50	1,100
1100	12 ga., 1' x 4'		5.40	1.481		910	84		994	1,125
1110	2' x 2'		5.40	1.481		745	84		829	945
1120	2' x 4'		5	1.600		985	90.50		1,075.50	1,200
3000	Fluorescent vandal resistant light fixture, high abuse troffer		5.40	1.481		220	84		304	370
3010	50"L x 8" W x 4" H		5.40	1.481		340	84		424	500
3020	32W		5.40	1.481		278	84		362	430
3030	T8/32W		5.40	1.481		270	84		354	425
3040	No lamp	↓	5.60	1.429	↓	335	81		416	485

For customer support on your Electrical Costs with RSMeans Data, call 800.448.8182.

303

26 55 Special Purpose Lighting

26 55 63 - Detention Lighting

26 55 63.10 Detention Lighting Fixtures	Crew	Daily Output	Labor-Hours	Unit	Material	2017 Bare Costs Labor	Equipment	Total	Total Incl O&P
3050	Lamp included	1 Elec	5.40	1.481	Ea.	385	84		469	550
3060	16 gauge cold rolled steel		5.40	1.481		232	84		316	380
3070	16 gauge cold rolled steel, ceiling/wall mount		5.40	1.481		271	84		355	425
3080	W/lamp		5.40	1.481		216	84		300	365
3090	WO/lamp		5.60	1.429		221	81		302	365
3100	W/lamp 6" L x 4-1/2" W x 8-1/2" H		5.40	1.481		44.50	84		128.50	175
3110	W/ lamp 5-7/8" W x 4-1/2" D x 8-1/2" H clear		5.40	1.481		51.50	84		135.50	183
3120	W/lamp white		5.40	1.481		226	84		310	375
3130	Tall wallpack, W/lamp, bronze		5.40	1.481		111	84		195	248
3140	Tall wallpack, W/lamp, white		5.40	1.481		110	84		194	247

26 56 Exterior Lighting

26 56 13 - Lighting Poles and Standards

26 56 13.10 Lighting Poles

		Crew	Daily Output	Labor-Hours	Unit	Material	2017 Bare Costs Labor	Equipment	Total	Total Incl O&P
0010	**LIGHTING POLES**									
2800	Light poles, anchor base									
2820	not including concrete bases									
2840	Aluminum pole, 8' high	1 Elec	4	2	Ea.	735	113		848	975
2850	10' high		4	2		775	113		888	1,025
2860	12' high		3.80	2.105		805	119		924	1,075
2870	14' high		3.40	2.353		840	133		973	1,125
2880	16' high		3	2.667		920	151		1,071	1,225
3000	20' high	R-3	2.90	6.897		975	390	47.50	1,412.50	1,725
3200	30' high		2.60	7.692		1,850	435	53	2,338	2,750
3400	35' high		2.30	8.696		2,000	490	60	2,550	3,000
3600	40' high		2	10		2,300	565	69	2,934	3,450
3800	Bracket arms, 1 arm	1 Elec	8	1		126	56.50		182.50	223
4000	2 arms		8	1		253	56.50		309.50	365
4200	3 arms		5.30	1.509		380	85.50		465.50	545
4400	4 arms		4.80	1.667		505	94.50		599.50	695
4500	Steel pole, galvanized, 8' high		3.80	2.105		635	119		754	880
4510	10' high		3.70	2.162		665	122		787	915
4520	12' high		3.40	2.353		720	133		853	990
4530	14' high		3.10	2.581		765	146		911	1,050
4540	16' high		2.90	2.759		810	156		966	1,125
4550	18' high		2.70	2.963		855	168		1,023	1,200
4600	20' high	R-3	2.60	7.692		1,025	435	53	1,513	1,850
4800	30' high		2.30	8.696		1,350	490	60	1,900	2,300
5000	35' high		2.20	9.091		1,500	515	62.50	2,077.50	2,500
5200	40' high		1.70	11.765		1,850	665	81	2,596	3,125
5400	Bracket arms, 1 arm	1 Elec	8	1		188	56.50		244.50	292
5600	2 arms		8	1		289	56.50		345.50	405
5800	3 arms		5.30	1.509		225	85.50		310.50	375
6000	4 arms		5.30	1.509		320	85.50		405.50	480
6100	Fiberglass pole, 1 or 2 fixtures, 20' high	R-3	4	5		735	283	34.50	1,052.50	1,275
6200	30' high		3.60	5.556		910	315	38.50	1,263.50	1,500
6300	35' high		3.20	6.250		1,425	355	43	1,823	2,150
6400	40' high		2.80	7.143		1,675	405	49.50	2,129.50	2,475
6420	Wood pole, 4-1/2" x 5-1/8", 8' high	1 Elec	6	1.333		350	75.50		425.50	500
6430	10' high		6	1.333		400	75.50		475.50	555
6440	12' high		5.70	1.404		505	79.50		584.50	680

26 56 Exterior Lighting

26 56 13 – Lighting Poles and Standards

26 56 13.10 Lighting Poles

26 56 13.10 Lighting Poles		Crew	Daily Output	Labor-Hours	Unit	Material	2017 Bare Costs Labor	Equipment	Total	Total Incl O&P
6450	15' high	1 Elec	5	1.600	Ea.	590	90.50		680.50	785
6460	20' high	↓	4	2		715	113		828	960
6461	Light poles, anchor base, w/o conc base, pwdr ct stl, 16' H	2 Elec	3.10	5.161		810	292		1,102	1,325
6462	20' high	R-3	2.90	6.897		1,025	390	47.50	1,462.50	1,775
6463	30' high		2.30	8.696		1,350	490	60	1,900	2,300
6464	35' high		2.40	8.333		1,500	470	57.50	2,027.50	2,425
6465	25' high	↓	2.70	7.407	↓	1,025	420	51	1,496	1,800
7300	Transformer bases, not including concrete bases									
7320	Maximum pole size, steel, 40' high	1 Elec	2	4	Ea.	1,475	226		1,701	1,975
7340	Cast aluminum, 30' high		3	2.667		785	151		936	1,075
7350	40' high	↓	2.50	3.200	↓	1,200	181		1,381	1,600
8000	Line cover protective devices									
8010	line cover									
8015	Refer to 26 01 02.20 for labor adjustment factors as they apply									
8100	MVLC 1" W x 1-1/2" H, 14/5'	1 Elec	60	.133	Ea.	4.50	7.55		12.05	16.25
8110	8'		58	.138		5	7.80		12.80	17.20
8120	MVLC 1" W x 1-1/2" H, 18/5'		60	.133		5.70	7.55		13.25	17.55
8130	8'		58	.138		6.35	7.80		14.15	18.65
8140	MVLC 1" W x 1-1/2" H, 38/5'		60	.133		10.25	7.55		17.80	22.50
8150	8'	↓	58	.138	↓	12.30	7.80		20.10	25.50

26 56 16 – Parking Lighting

26 56 16.55 Parking LED Lighting

			Crew	Daily Output	Labor-Hours	Unit	Material	Labor	Equipment	Total	Total Incl O&P
0010	**PARKING LED LIGHTING**										
0100	Round pole mounting, 88 lamp watts	G	1 Elec	2	4	Ea.	1,200	226		1,426	1,650

26 56 19 – Roadway Lighting

26 56 19.20 Roadway Luminaire

			Crew	Daily Output	Labor-Hours	Unit	Material	Labor	Equipment	Total	Total Incl O&P
0010	**ROADWAY LUMINAIRE**										
2650	Roadway area luminaire, low pressure sodium, 135 watt		1 Elec	2	4	Ea.	705	226		931	1,125
2700	180 watt		"	2	4		750	226		976	1,175
2750	Metal halide, 400 watt		2 Elec	4.40	3.636		605	206		811	975
2760	1000 watt			4	4		680	226		906	1,075
2780	High pressure sodium, 400 watt			4.40	3.636		630	206		836	1,000
2790	1000 watt	↓		4	4	↓	715	226		941	1,125

26 56 19.55 Roadway LED Luminaire

			Crew	Daily Output	Labor-Hours	Unit	Material	Labor	Equipment	Total	Total Incl O&P
0010	**ROADWAY LED LUMINAIRE**										
0100	LED fixture, 72 LEDs, 120 V AC or 12 V DC, equal to 60 watt	G	1 Elec	2.70	2.963	Ea.	585	168		753	895
0110	108 LEDs, 120 V AC or 12 V DC, equal to 90 watt	G		2.70	2.963		690	168		858	1,000
0120	144 LEDs, 120 V AC or 12 V DC, equal to 120 watt	G	↓	2.70	2.963		845	168		1,013	1,175
0130	252 LEDs, 120 V AC or 12 V DC, equal to 210 watt	G	2 Elec	4.40	3.636		1,175	206		1,381	1,600
0140	Replaces high pressure sodium fixture, 75 watt	G	1 Elec	2.70	2.963		395	168		563	685
0150	125 watt	G		2.70	2.963		450	168		618	745
0160	150 watt	G		2.70	2.963		530	168		698	830
0170	175 watt	G		2.70	2.963		780	168		948	1,100
0180	200 watt	G	↓	2.70	2.963		745	168		913	1,075
0190	250 watt	G	2 Elec	4.40	3.636		850	206		1,056	1,250
0200	320 watt	G	"	4.40	3.636	↓	930	206		1,136	1,325

26 56 23 – Area Lighting

26 56 23.10 Exterior Fixtures

		Crew	Daily Output	Labor-Hours	Unit	Material	Labor	Equipment	Total	Total Incl O&P
0010	**EXTERIOR FIXTURES** With lamps									
0200	Wall mounted, incandescent, 100 watt	1 Elec	8	1	Ea.	37.50	56.50		94	126
0400	Quartz, 500 watt	↓	5.30	1.509	↓	61.50	85.50		147	196

For customer support on your Electrical Costs with RSMeans Data, call 800.448.8182.

305

26 56 23.10 Exterior Fixtures		Crew	Daily Output	Labor-Hours	Unit	Material	2017 Bare Costs Labor	Equipment	Total	Total Incl O&P
0420	1500 watt	1 Elec	4.20	1.905	Ea.	107	108		215	280
1100	Wall pack, low pressure sodium, 35 watt		4	2		199	113		312	390
1150	55 watt		4	2		236	113		349	430
1160	High pressure sodium, 70 watt		4	2		195	113		308	385
1170	150 watt		4	2		213	113		326	405
1175	High pressure sodium, 250 watt		4	2		213	113		326	405
1180	Metal halide, 175 watt		4	2		210	113		323	400
1190	250 watt		4	2		246	113		359	440
1195	400 watt		4	2		415	113		528	625
1250	Induction lamp, 40 watt		4	2		450	113		563	665
1260	80 watt		4	2		685	113		798	925
1278	LED, poly lens, 26 watt		4	2		264	113		377	460
1280	110 watt		4	2		845	113		958	1,100
1500	LED, glass lens, 13 watt		4	2		264	113		377	460

26 56 23.55 Exterior LED Fixtures

			Crew	Daily Output	Labor-Hours	Unit	Material	Labor	Equipment	Total	Total Incl O&P
0010	**EXTERIOR LED FIXTURES**										
0100	Wall mounted, indoor/outdoor, 12 watt	G	1 Elec	10	.800	Ea.	191	45.50		236.50	278
0110	32 watt	G		10	.800		460	45.50		505.50	575
0120	66 watt	G		10	.800		705	45.50		750.50	845
0200	outdoor, 110 watt	G		10	.800		1,100	45.50		1,145.50	1,300
0210	220 watt	G		10	.800		1,750	45.50		1,795.50	2,000
0300	modular, type IV, 120 V, 50 lamp watts	G		9	.889		1,150	50.50		1,200.50	1,350
0310	101 lamp watts	G		9	.889		1,300	50.50		1,350.50	1,500
0320	126 lamp watts	G		9	.889		1,625	50.50		1,675.50	1,850
0330	202 lamp watts	G		9	.889		1,850	50.50		1,900.50	2,100
0340	240 V, 50 lamp watts	G		8	1		1,200	56.50		1,256.50	1,400
0350	101 lamp watts	G		8	1		1,350	56.50		1,406.50	1,550
0360	126 lamp watts	G		8	1		1,450	56.50		1,506.50	1,675
0370	202 lamp watts	G		8	1		1,900	56.50		1,956.50	2,150
0400	wall pack, glass, 13 lamp watts	G		4	2		445	113		558	660
0410	poly w/photocell, 26 lamp watts	G		4	2		297	113		410	495
0420	50 lamp watts	G		4	2		750	113		863	995
0430	replacement, 40 watts	G		4	2		365	113		478	570
0440	60 watts	G		4	2		460	113		573	675

26 56 26 – Landscape Lighting

26 56 26.20 Landscape Fixtures

		Crew	Daily Output	Labor-Hours	Unit	Material	Labor	Equipment	Total	Total Incl O&P
0010	**LANDSCAPE FIXTURES**									
7380	Landscape recessed uplight, incl. housing, ballast, transformer									
7390	& reflector, not incl. conduit, wire, trench									
7420	Incandescent, 250 watt	1 Elec	5	1.600	Ea.	640	90.50		730.50	840
7440	Quartz, 250 watt		5	1.600		605	90.50		695.50	805
7460	500 watt		4	2		625	113		738	855

26 56 26.50 Landscape LED Fixtures

		Crew	Daily Output	Labor-Hours	Unit	Material	Labor	Equipment	Total	Total Incl O&P
0010	**LANDSCAPE LED FIXTURES**									
0100	12 volt alum bullet hooded -BLK	1 Elec	5	1.600	Ea.	96	90.50		186.50	242
0200	12 volt alum bullet hooded -BRZ		5	1.600		96	90.50		186.50	242
0300	12 volt alum bullet hooded -GRN		5	1.600		96	90.50		186.50	242
1000	12 volt alum large bullet hooded -BLK		5	1.600		71	90.50		161.50	214
1100	12 volt alum large bullet hooded -BRZ		5	1.600		71	90.50		161.50	214
1200	12 volt alum large bullet hooded -GRN		5	1.600		71	90.50		161.50	214
2000	12 volt large bullet landscape light fixture		5	1.600		71	90.50		161.50	214
2100	12 volt alum light large bullet		5	1.600		71	90.50		161.50	214

26 56 Exterior Lighting

26 56 26 – Landscape Lighting

26 56 26.50 Landscape LED Fixtures		Crew	Daily Output	Labor-Hours	Unit	Material	2017 Bare Costs Labor	2017 Bare Costs Equipment	Total	Total Incl O&P
2200	12 volt alum bullet light	1 Elec	5	1.600	Ea.	71	90.50		161.50	214

26 56 33 – Walkway Lighting

26 56 33.10 Walkway Luminaire

		Crew	Daily Output	Labor-Hours	Unit	Material	Labor	Equipment	Total	Total Incl O&P
0010	**WALKWAY LUMINAIRE**									
6500	Bollard light, lamp & ballast, 42" high with polycarbonate lens									
6800	Metal halide, 175 watt	1 Elec	3	2.667	Ea.	850	151		1,001	1,150
6900	High pressure sodium, 70 watt		3	2.667		870	151		1,021	1,175
7000	100 watt		3	2.667		870	151		1,021	1,175
7100	150 watt		3	2.667		850	151		1,001	1,150
7200	Incandescent, 150 watt		3	2.667		620	151		771	910
7810	Walkway luminaire, square 16", metal halide 250 watt		2.70	2.963		665	168		833	985
7820	High pressure sodium, 70 watt		3	2.667		765	151		916	1,075
7830	100 watt		3	2.667		775	151		926	1,075
7840	150 watt		3	2.667		775	151		926	1,075
7850	200 watt		3	2.667		785	151		936	1,075
7910	Round 19", metal halide, 250 watt		2.70	2.963		970	168		1,138	1,325
7920	High pressure sodium, 70 watt		3	2.667		1,075	151		1,226	1,400
7930	100 watt		3	2.667		1,075	151		1,226	1,400
7940	150 watt		3	2.667		1,075	151		1,226	1,400
7950	250 watt		2.70	2.963		1,125	168		1,293	1,475
8000	Sphere 14" opal, incandescent, 200 watt		4	2		310	113		423	510
8020	Sphere 18" opal, incandescent, 300 watt		3.50	2.286		375	129		504	605
8040	Sphere 16" clear, high pressure sodium, 70 watt		3	2.667		645	151		796	935
8050	100 watt		3	2.667		690	151		841	980
8100	Cube 16" opal, incandescent, 300 watt		3.50	2.286		410	129		539	645
8120	High pressure sodium, 70 watt		3	2.667		600	151		751	885
8130	100 watt		3	2.667		615	151		766	900
8230	Lantern, high pressure sodium, 70 watt		3	2.667		535	151		686	815
8240	100 watt		3	2.667		575	151		726	860
8250	150 watt		3	2.667		540	151		691	820
8260	250 watt		2.70	2.963		755	168		923	1,075
8270	Incandescent, 300 watt		3.50	2.286		400	129		529	635
8330	Reflector 22" w/globe, high pressure sodium, 70 watt		3	2.667		515	151		666	790
8340	100 watt		3	2.667		520	151		671	800
8350	150 watt		3	2.667		530	151		681	805
8360	250 watt		2.70	2.963		675	168		843	995

26 56 33.55 Walkway LED Luminaire

			Crew	Daily Output	Labor-Hours	Unit	Material	Labor	Equipment	Total	Total Incl O&P
0010	**WALKWAY LED LUMINAIRE**										
0100	Pole mounted, 86 watts, 4350 lumens	G	1 Elec	3	2.667	Ea.	1,225	151		1,376	1,550
0110	4630 lumens	G		3	2.667		2,025	151		2,176	2,450
0120	80 watts, 4000 lumens	G		3	2.667		2,025	151		2,176	2,450

26 56 36 – Flood Lighting

26 56 36.20 Floodlights

		Crew	Daily Output	Labor-Hours	Unit	Material	Labor	Equipment	Total	Total Incl O&P
0010	**FLOODLIGHTS** with ballast and lamp,									
1290	floor mtd, mount with swivel bracket									
1300	Induction lamp, 40 watt	1 Elec	3	2.667	Ea.	550	151		701	830
1310	80 watt		3	2.667		835	151		986	1,150
1320	150 watt		3	2.667		1,500	151		1,651	1,875
1400	Pole mounted, pole not included									
1950	Metal halide, 175 watt	1 Elec	2.70	2.963	Ea.	231	168		399	505
2000	400 watt	2 Elec	4.40	3.636		390	206		596	740

For customer support on your Electrical Costs with RSMeans Data, call 800.448.8182.

307

26 56 Exterior Lighting

26 56 36 – Flood Lighting

26 56 36.20 Floodlights

		Crew	Daily Output	Labor-Hours	Unit	Material	2017 Bare Costs Labor	Equipment	Total	Total Incl O&P
2200	1000 watt	2 Elec	4	4	Ea.	755	226		981	1,175
2210	1500 watt		3.70	4.324		445	245		690	855
2250	Low pressure sodium, 55 watt	1 Elec	2.70	2.963		440	168		608	735
2270	90 watt		2	4		600	226		826	1,000
2290	180 watt		2	4		665	226		891	1,075
2340	High pressure sodium, 70 watt		2.70	2.963		250	168		418	525
2360	100 watt		2.70	2.963		256	168		424	535
2380	150 watt		2.70	2.963		310	168		478	590
2400	400 watt	2 Elec	4.40	3.636		315	206		521	660
2600	1000 watt	"	4	4		580	226		806	975
9005	Solar powered floodlight, w/motion det, incl batt pack for cloudy days G	1 Elec	8	1		59.50	56.50		116	151
9020	Replacement battery pack G	"	8	1		17.10	56.50		73.60	104

26 56 36.55 LED Floodlights

		Crew	Daily Output	Labor-Hours	Unit	Material	2017 Bare Costs Labor	Equipment	Total	Total Incl O&P
0010	**LED FLOODLIGHTS** with ballast and lamp,									
0020	Pole mounted, pole not included									
0100	11 watt G	1 Elec	4	2	Ea.	410	113		523	625
0110	46 watt G		4	2		1,225	113		1,338	1,525
0120	90 watt G		4	2		2,000	113		2,113	2,375
0130	288 watt G		4	2		1,800	113		1,913	2,150

26 61 Lighting Systems and Accessories

26 61 13 – Lighting Accessories

26 61 13.30 Fixture Whips

		Crew	Daily Output	Labor-Hours	Unit	Material	2017 Bare Costs Labor	Equipment	Total	Total Incl O&P
0010	**FIXTURE WHIPS**									
0080	3/8" Greenfield, 2 connectors, 6' long									
0100	TFFN wire, three #18	1 Elec	32	.250	Ea.	6.20	14.15		20.35	28
0150	Four #18		28	.286		6.55	16.15		22.70	31.50
0200	Three #16		32	.250		6.95	14.15		21.10	28.50
0250	Four #16		28	.286		7.25	16.15		23.40	32
0300	THHN wire, three #14		32	.250		7.35	14.15		21.50	29
0350	Four #14		28	.286		8.25	16.15		24.40	33
0360	Three #12		32	.250		9.40	14.15		23.55	31.50

26 61 23 – Lamps Applications

26 61 23.10 Lamps

		Crew	Daily Output	Labor-Hours	Unit	Material	2017 Bare Costs Labor	Equipment	Total	Total Incl O&P
0010	**LAMPS**									
0080	Fluorescent, rapid start, cool white, 2' long, 20 watt	1 Elec	1	8	C	360	455		815	1,075
0100	4' long, 40 watt		.90	8.889		275	505		780	1,050
0120	3' long, 30 watt		.90	8.889		475	505		980	1,275
0125	3' long, 25 watt energy saver R265723-10 G		.90	8.889		1,400	505		1,905	2,275
0150	U-40 watt		.80	10		1,175	565		1,740	2,150
0155	U-34 watt energy saver G		.80	10		1,200	565		1,765	2,175
0170	4' long, 34 watt energy saver G		.90	8.889		370	505		875	1,150
0176	2' long, T8, 17 watt energy saver G		1	8		410	455		865	1,125
0178	3' long, T8, 25 watt energy saver G		.90	8.889		440	505		945	1,225
0180	4' long, T8, 32 watt energy saver G		.90	8.889		305	505		810	1,100
0200	Slimline, 4' long, 40 watt		.90	8.889		1,450	505		1,955	2,350
0210	4' long, 30 watt energy saver G		.90	8.889		1,450	505		1,955	2,350
0300	8' long, 75 watt		.80	10		1,050	565		1,615	2,000
0350	8' long, 60 watt energy saver G		.80	10		450	565		1,015	1,350
0400	High output, 4' long, 60 watt		.90	8.889		755	505		1,260	1,600

26 61 23 – Lamps Applications

26 61 23.10 Lamps		Crew	Daily Output	Labor-Hours	Unit	Material	2017 Bare Costs Labor	Equipment	Total	Total Incl O&P
0410	8' long, 95 watt energy saver **G**	1 Elec	.80	10	C	545	565		1,110	1,450
0500	8' long, 110 watt		.80	10		545	565		1,110	1,450
0512	2' long, T5, 14 watt energy saver **G**		1	8		730	455		1,185	1,475
0514	3' long, T5, 21 watt energy saver **G**		.90	8.889		180	505		685	955
0516	4' long, T5, 28 watt energy saver **G**		.90	8.889		180	505		685	955
0517	4' long, T5, 54 watt energy saver **G**		.90	8.889		1,575	505		2,080	2,475
0520	Very high output, 4' long, 110 watt		.90	8.889		2,550	505		3,055	3,550
0525	8' long, 195 watt energy saver **G**		.70	11.429		2,075	645		2,720	3,250
0550	8' long, 215 watt		.70	11.429		1,575	645		2,220	2,725
0554	Full spectrum, 4' long, 60 watt		.90	8.889		1,450	505		1,955	2,350
0556	6' long, 85 watt		.90	8.889		1,100	505		1,605	1,950
0558	8' long, 110 watt		.80	10		1,825	565		2,390	2,850
0560	Twin tube compact lamp **G**		.90	8.889		355	505		860	1,150
0570	Double twin tube compact lamp **G**		.80	10		725	565		1,290	1,650
0600	Mercury vapor, mogul base, deluxe white, 100 watt		.30	26.667		11,400	1,500		12,900	14,900
0650	175 watt		.30	26.667		5,350	1,500		6,850	8,150
0700	250 watt		.30	26.667		9,300	1,500		10,800	12,500
0800	400 watt		.30	26.667		8,400	1,500		9,900	11,500
0900	1000 watt		.20	40		2,300	2,275		4,575	5,925
1000	Metal halide, mogul base, 175 watt		.30	26.667		2,450	1,500		3,950	4,950
1100	250 watt		.30	26.667		2,000	1,500		3,500	4,450
1200	400 watt		.30	26.667		2,075	1,500		3,575	4,525
1300	1000 watt		.20	40		41,900	2,275		44,175	49,500
1320	1000 watt, 125,000 initial lumens		.20	40		23,900	2,275		26,175	29,700
1330	1500 watt		.20	40		31,600	2,275		33,875	38,100
1350	High pressure sodium, 70 watt		.30	26.667		2,650	1,500		4,150	5,175
1360	100 watt		.30	26.667		2,750	1,500		4,250	5,275
1370	150 watt		.30	26.667		2,825	1,500		4,325	5,375
1380	250 watt		.30	26.667		2,225	1,500		3,725	4,700
1400	400 watt		.30	26.667		4,700	1,500		6,200	7,400
1450	1000 watt		.20	40		8,525	2,275		10,800	12,800
1500	Low pressure sodium, 35 watt		.30	26.667		37,600	1,500		39,100	43,600
1550	55 watt		.30	26.667		37,100	1,500		38,600	43,100
1600	90 watt		.30	26.667		18,300	1,500		19,800	22,400
1650	135 watt		.20	40		62,500	2,275		64,775	72,500
1700	180 watt		.20	40		72,000	2,275		74,275	82,500
1750	Quartz line, clear, 500 watt		1.10	7.273		1,550	410		1,960	2,325
1760	1500 watt		.20	40		2,000	2,275		4,275	5,600
1762	Spot, MR 16, 50 watt		1.30	6.154		1,075	350		1,425	1,700
1770	Tungsten halogen, T4, 400 watt		1.10	7.273		3,975	410		4,385	5,000
1775	T3, 1200 watt		.30	26.667		4,900	1,500		6,400	7,650
1778	PAR 30, 50 watt		1.30	6.154		1,150	350		1,500	1,775
1780	PAR 38, 90 watt		1.30	6.154		960	350		1,310	1,575
1800	Incandescent, interior, A21, 100 watt		1.60	5		239	283		522	690
1900	A21, 150 watt		1.60	5		166	283		449	610
2000	A23, 200 watt		1.60	5		390	283		673	855
2200	PS 35, 300 watt		1.60	5		1,025	283		1,308	1,550
2210	PS 35, 500 watt		1.60	5		1,425	283		1,708	1,975
2230	PS 52, 1000 watt		1.30	6.154		2,550	350		2,900	3,325
2240	PS 52, 1500 watt		1.30	6.154		6,825	350		7,175	8,050
2300	R30, 75 watt		1.30	6.154		620	350		970	1,200
2400	R40, 100 watt		1.30	6.154		620	350		970	1,200
2500	Exterior, PAR 38, 75 watt		1.30	6.154		2,100	350		2,450	2,825

For customer support on your Electrical Costs with RSMeans Data, call 800.448.8182.

309

26 61 23 – Lamps Applications

26 61 23.10 Lamps		Crew	Daily Output	Labor-Hours	Unit	Material	2017 Bare Costs Labor	2017 Bare Costs Equipment	Total	Total Incl O&P
2600	PAR 38, 150 watt	1 Elec	1.30	6.154	C	2,200	350		2,550	2,925
2700	PAR 46, 200 watt		1.10	7.273		4,050	410		4,460	5,075
2800	PAR 56, 300 watt		1.10	7.273		4,650	410		5,060	5,725
3000	Guards, fluorescent lamp, 4' long		1	8		1,325	455		1,780	2,125
3200	8' long		.90	8.889		2,650	505		3,155	3,650

26 61 23.55 LED Lamps

26 61 23.55			Crew	Daily Output	Labor-Hours	Unit	Material	Labor	Equipment	Total	Total Incl O&P
0010	**LED LAMPS**										
0100	LED lamp, interior, shape A60, equal to 60 watt	G	1 Elec	160	.050	Ea.	19	2.83		21.83	25
0110	7W LED decorative c, ca, f, g shape			160	.050		34.50	2.83		37.33	41.50
0120	12V mini lamp LED			160	.050		5	2.83		7.83	9.75
0200	Globe frosted A60, equal to 60 watt	G		160	.050		11.40	2.83		14.23	16.80
0205	LED lamp, interior, globe			160	.050		16.15	2.83		18.98	22
0210	2.2W LED LMP			160	.050		66	2.83		68.83	77
0220	2.2W LED replacement decorative lamp			160	.050		68	2.83		70.83	78.50
0230	3.5W LED replacement decorative lamp			160	.050		68	2.83		70.83	78.50
0240	4.5W 120V LED replacement decorative lamp			160	.050		68	2.83		70.83	78.50
0250	4.5W 120V LED, 2700k replacement decorative lamp			160	.050		68	2.83		70.83	78.50
0260	4.9W 120V LED, 2700k replacement decorative lamp candelabra base			160	.050		9.40	2.83		12.23	14.60
0270	4.9W 120V LED, 3000k replacement decorative lamp candelabra base			160	.050		9.40	2.83		12.23	14.60
0280	5 W LED PAR 20 Parabolic Reflector Lamp FL			140	.057		60	3.23		63.23	71
0300	Globe earth, equal to 100 watt	G		140	.057		27.50	3.23		30.73	35.50
0305	7 W LED Reflector Lamp 3000k DIM			140	.057		58	3.23		61.23	69
0310	10 watt omni LED warm white light bulb E26 medium base 120 volt card			140	.057		17.10	3.23		20.33	23.50
0315	7 W LED Reflector Lamp WFL 2700k DIM			140	.057		58	3.23		61.23	69
0320	9 watt omni LED warm white light bulb E26 medium base 120 volt card			140	.057		9.05	3.23		12.28	14.80
1100	MR16, 3 watt, replacement of halogen lamp 25 watt	G		130	.062		19	3.48		22.48	26
1200	6 watt replacement of halogen lamp 45 watt	G		130	.062		20	3.48		23.48	27
2100	10 watt, PAR20, equal to 60 watt	G		130	.062		26.50	3.48		29.98	34.50
2200	15 watt, PAR30, equal to 100 watt	G		130	.062		73.50	3.48		76.98	86
2210	LED lamp 50 watt w/6ft pri			130	.062		610	3.48		613.48	675
2220	11 Watt reflector dimmable warm white LED light bulb with medium base			130	.062		41.50	3.48		44.98	50.50
2221	12 W A-Line LED Lamp DIM			130	.062		78	3.48		81.48	91
2225	13 Watt reflector LED warm white e26 with medium base 120 volt box			130	.062		39	3.48		42.48	48
2226	13W br30 LED lamp			130	.062		54	3.48		57.48	64.50
2227	15W 120V br30 inc LED lamp, 2700k			130	.062		52.50	3.48		55.98	63
2228	15W 120V br30 inc LED lamp, 4000k			130	.062		50	3.48		53.48	60
2230	3 Watt dimmable warm white decorative LED lamp with medium base			160	.050		12.60	2.83		15.43	18.10
2240	.43 watt night light LED daylight bulb E12 candelabra base 120 volt 2 pack			160	.050		4.72	2.83		7.55	9.45
2250	15 watt omni-directional LED warm white e26 medium base 120 volt box			160	.050		40	2.83		42.83	48
2251	11watt omni-directional LED warm white e26 medium base 120 volt box			160	.050		28	2.83		30.83	34.50
2252	10watt omni-directional LED warm white e26 medium base 120 volt box			160	.050		28	2.83		30.83	34.50
2253	7 watt omni A19 LED warm white e26 medium base 120 volt box			160	.050		20.50	2.83		23.33	26.50
2255	8 PAR 20 parabolic reflector 2700 LED lamp			160	.050		33	2.83		35.83	40.50
2256	8 PAR 20 Parabolic Reflector 3000 LED Lamp			160	.050		33	2.83		35.83	40.50
2260	12W par38 120V LED 15 degree directional lamp			160	.050		203	2.83		205.83	227
2270	12W par38 120V LED 25 degree directional lamp			160	.050		203	2.83		205.83	227
2280	12W par38 120V LED 40 degree directional lamp			160	.050		203	2.83		205.83	227
2285	16W par38 120V 2700k LED parabolic reflector lamp			160	.050		21.50	2.83		24.33	28
2290	16W par38 120V 3000k LED parabolic reflector lamp			160	.050		21.50	2.83		24.33	28
3000	15W par30 LED daylight E26 medium base 120V box			160	.050		60	2.83		62.83	70
3100	17W LED3000k par38 100W replacement			160	.050		47	2.83		49.83	55.50
3110	17W LED par38 100W replacement			160	.050		47	2.83		49.83	55.50

26 61 23 – Lamps Applications

26 61 23.55 LED Lamps	Crew	Daily Output	Labor-Hours	Unit	Material	2017 Bare Costs Labor	Equipment	Total	Total Incl O&P
3120	17W LED par38 100W replacement parabolic reflector	1 Elec	160	.050	Ea.	47	2.83		49.83	55.50
3130	24 W LED T8 PW straight fluorescent lamp		8.89	.900		289	51		340	395
3135	Linear fluorescent LED lamp 120 V		8.89	.900		48	51		99	129
3200	30W LED 2700K recessed 8055E par 38 high power		160	.050		234	2.83		236.83	261
3210	30W LED 4200K 120 degree 8055E par 38 high power		160	.050		234	2.83		236.83	261
3220	30W LED 5700K 8055E par 38 high power		160	.050		234	2.83		236.83	261
3230	50W LED 2700K 8045M par38 277V high power		160	.050		340	2.83		342.83	380
3240	50W LED 4200K 8045M par38 277 V high power retro fit		160	.050		340	2.83		342.83	380
3250	50W LED 5700K 8045M par38 277V high power retro fit		160	.050		340	2.83		342.83	380
8000	10 watt LED par 30 / fl 10 pk		160	.050		96	2.83		98.83	110
8010	Gen 3 Par 30 15 watt short neck power LED 120 VAC E26 80 +cri 300k dimm		160	.050		12.95	2.83		15.78	18.50
8020	12 PAR 30 2700K parabolic reflector LED lamp		160	.050		39.50	2.83		42.33	47.50
8030	12 PAR 30 3000K parabolic reflector LED lamp		160	.050		39.50	2.83		42.33	47.50
8040	3500K LED advantage T8 9 W 800LM 2ft linear 2 BD frosted		69	.116		10.45	6.55		17	21.50
8050	3500K LED litespan T8 9 W 900LM 2ft linear frosted		69	.116		15.30	6.55		21.85	26.50
8060	4000K LED advantage T8 9 W 800LM 2ft linear 2BD frosted		69	.116		10.45	6.55		17	21.50
8070	4000K LED litespan T8 9 W 900LM 2ft linear frosted		69	.116		15.30	6.55		21.85	26.50
8080	5000K LED advantage T8 9 W 800LM 2ft linear 2BD frosted		69	.116		10.45	6.55		17	21.50
8090	5000K LED litespan T8 9 W 900LM 2ft linear frosted		69	.116		15.30	6.55		21.85	26.50
8100	3500K LED advantage T8 18 W 1600LM 4ft linear 2 BD frosted		69	.116		15.30	6.55		21.85	26.50
8105	18 W LED 4ft T8 4000K frost 1600L linear lamp		69	.116		18.50	6.55		25.05	30.50
8108	18 W LED 48 inch T8 4100K 1890LM linear lamp		69	.116		45.50	6.55		52.05	60
8110	3500K LED advantage T8 18 W 1800LM 4ft linear 2 BD frosted		69	.116		19.80	6.55		26.35	32
8120	4000K LED advantage T8 18 W 1600LM 4ft linear 2 BD frosted		69	.116		15.30	6.55		21.85	26.50
8130	4000K LED litespan T8 18 W 1800LM 4ft linear frosted		69	.116		19.80	6.55		26.35	32
8140	5000K LED advantage T8 18 W 1600LM 4ft linear 2BD frosted		69	.116		15.30	6.55		21.85	26.50
8150	5000K LED litespan T8 18 W 1800LM 4ft linear 2BD frosted		69	.116		19.80	6.55		26.35	32
8200	16.5 T8 3000 IF-6U U-shape fluorescent LED lamp		65	.123		38	6.95		44.95	52.50
8210	16.5 T8 3500 IF-6U U-shape fluorescent LED lamp		65	.123		38	6.95		44.95	52.50
8220	16.5 T8 4000 IF-6U U-shape fluorescent LED lamp		65	.123		38	6.95		44.95	52.50
8230	16.5 T8 5000 IF-6U U-shape fluorescent LED lamp		65	.123		38	6.95		44.95	52.50
8240	18 W 6 inch T8 4100 K U-shape frosted fluorescent LED lamp		60	.133		34	7.55		41.55	49
8250	18 W 6 inch T8 5000 K U-shape frosted fluorescent LED lamp		60	.133		34	7.55		41.55	49
8260	Circular 12 W linear fluorescent LED 2700K MOD lamp		62.40	.128		273	7.25		280.25	310
8270	Circular 12 W linear fluorescent LED 3000K MOD lamp		62.40	.128		273	7.25		280.25	310
8280	Circular 12 W linear fluorescent LED 3500K MOD lamp		62.40	.128		273	7.25		280.25	310
8290	Circular 18 W linear fluorescent LED 3000K MOD lamp		62.40	.128		375	7.25		382.25	420
8300	Circular 18 W linear fluorescent LED 3500K MOD lamp		62.40	.128		375	7.25		382.25	420
8310	Circular 18 W linear fluorescent LED 5000K MOD lamp		62.40	.128		375	7.25		382.25	420
8320	Circular 18 W linear fluorescent LED 4100K MOD lamp		62.40	.128		375	7.25		382.25	420

For customer support on your Electrical Costs with RSMeans Data, call 800.448.8182.

311

26 71 Electrical Machines

26 71 13 – Motors Applications

26 71 13.10 Handling

26 71 13.10 Handling	Crew	Daily Output	Labor-Hours	Unit	Material	2017 Bare Costs Labor	Equipment	Total	Total Incl O&P
0010 **HANDLING** Add to normal labor cost for restricted areas									
5000 Motors									
5100 1/2 HP, 23 pounds	1 Elec	4	2	Ea.		113		113	170
5110 3/4 HP, 28 pounds		4	2			113		113	170
5120 1 HP, 33 pounds		4	2			113		113	170
5130 1-1/2 HP, 44 pounds		3.20	2.500			142		142	212
5140 2 HP, 56 pounds		3	2.667			151		151	226
5150 3 HP, 71 pounds		2.30	3.478			197		197	295
5160 5 HP, 82 pounds		1.90	4.211			238		238	355
5170 7-1/2 HP, 124 pounds		1.50	5.333			300		300	450
5180 10 HP, 144 pounds		1.20	6.667			375		375	565
5190 15 HP, 185 pounds		1	8			455		455	680
5200 20 HP, 214 pounds	2 Elec	1.50	10.667			605		605	905
5210 25 HP, 266 pounds		1.40	11.429			645		645	970
5220 30 HP, 310 pounds		1.20	13.333			755		755	1,125
5230 40 HP, 400 pounds		1	16			905		905	1,350
5240 50 HP, 450 pounds		.90	17.778			1,000		1,000	1,500
5250 75 HP, 680 pounds		.80	20			1,125		1,125	1,700
5260 100 HP, 870 pounds	3 Elec	1	24			1,350		1,350	2,025
5270 125 HP, 940 pounds		.80	30			1,700		1,700	2,550
5280 150 HP, 1200 pounds		.70	34.286			1,950		1,950	2,900
5290 175 HP, 1300 pounds		.60	40			2,275		2,275	3,400
5300 200 HP, 1400 pounds		.50	48			2,725		2,725	4,075

26 71 13.20 Motors

26 71 13.20 Motors	Crew	Daily Output	Labor-Hours	Unit	Material	2017 Bare Costs Labor	Equipment	Total	Total Incl O&P
0010 **MOTORS** 230/460 volts, 60 HZ R263413-30									
0050 Dripproof, premium efficiency, 1.15 service factor									
0060 1800 RPM, 1/4 HP	1 Elec	5.33	1.501	Ea.	252	85		337	405
0070 1/3 HP		5.33	1.501		232	85		317	380
0080 1/2 HP		5.33	1.501		194	85		279	340
0090 3/4 HP		5.33	1.501		271	85		356	425
0100 1 HP		4.50	1.778		290	101		391	470
0150 2 HP		4.50	1.778		350	101		451	535
0200 3 HP		4.50	1.778		695	101		796	915
0250 5 HP		4.50	1.778		620	101		721	830
0300 7.5 HP		4.20	1.905		940	108		1,048	1,175
0350 10 HP		4	2		1,150	113		1,263	1,450
0400 15 HP		3.20	2.500		1,600	142		1,742	1,975
0450 20 HP	2 Elec	5.20	3.077		1,950	174		2,124	2,400
0500 25 HP		5	3.200		2,550	181		2,731	3,075
0550 30 HP		4.80	3.333		2,775	189		2,964	3,350
0600 40 HP		4	4		3,625	226		3,851	4,350
0650 50 HP		3.20	5		3,700	283		3,983	4,500
0700 60 HP		2.80	5.714		4,100	325		4,425	4,975
0750 75 HP		2.40	6.667		4,800	375		5,175	5,850
0800 100 HP	3 Elec	2.70	8.889		6,150	505		6,655	7,525
0850 125 HP		2.10	11.429		6,425	645		7,070	8,050
0900 150 HP		1.80	13.333		9,775	755		10,530	11,900
0950 200 HP		1.50	16		11,900	905		12,805	14,500
1000 1200 RPM, 1 HP	1 Elec	4.50	1.778		475	101		576	670
1050 2 HP		4.50	1.778		645	101		746	860
1100 3 HP		4.50	1.778		720	101		821	940
1150 5 HP		4.50	1.778		945	101		1,046	1,175

26 71 Electrical Machines

26 71 13 - Motors Applications

26 71 13.20 Motors

		Crew	Daily Output	Labor-Hours	Unit	Material	Labor	Equipment	Total	Total Incl O&P
1200	3600 RPM, 2 HP	1 Elec	4.50	1.778	Ea.	580	101		681	790
1250	3 HP		4.50	1.778		600	101		701	810
1300	5 HP		4.50	1.778		520	101		621	725
1350	Totally enclosed, premium efficiency 1.15 service factor									
1360	1800 RPM, 1/4 HP	1 Elec	5.33	1.501	Ea.	290	85		375	445
1370	1/3 HP		5.33	1.501		300	85		385	455
1380	1/2 HP		5.33	1.501		350	85		435	510
1390	3/4 HP		5.33	1.501		385	85		470	550
1400	1 HP		4.50	1.778		560	101		661	765
1450	2 HP		4.50	1.778		705	101		806	925
1500	3 HP		4.50	1.778		640	101		741	850
1550	5 HP		4.50	1.778		745	101		846	970
1600	7.5 HP		4.20	1.905		970	108		1,078	1,225
1650	10 HP		4	2		1,375	113		1,488	1,675
1700	15 HP		3.20	2.500		1,625	142		1,767	2,000
1750	20 HP	2 Elec	5.20	3.077		2,225	174		2,399	2,700
1800	25 HP		5	3.200		3,175	181		3,356	3,775
1850	30 HP		4.80	3.333		3,125	189		3,314	3,725
1900	40 HP		4	4		3,825	226		4,051	4,575
1950	50 HP		3.20	5		4,150	283		4,433	4,975
2000	60 HP		2.80	5.714		5,600	325		5,925	6,650
2050	75 HP		2.40	6.667		7,300	375		7,675	8,600
2100	100 HP	3 Elec	2.70	8.889		8,600	505		9,105	10,200
2150	125 HP		2.10	11.429		11,200	645		11,845	13,300
2200	150 HP		1.80	13.333		13,100	755		13,855	15,600
2250	200 HP		1.50	16		16,600	905		17,505	19,600
2300	1200 RPM, 1 HP	1 Elec	4.50	1.778		480	101		581	680
2350	2 HP		4.50	1.778		545	101		646	750
2400	3 HP		4.50	1.778		790	101		891	1,025
2450	5 HP		4.50	1.778		940	101		1,041	1,175
2500	3600 RPM, 2 HP		4.50	1.778		435	101		536	630
2550	3 HP		4.50	1.778		580	101		681	790
2600	5 HP		4.50	1.778		675	101		776	895

26 71 13.40 Motors Explosion Proof

		Crew	Daily Output	Labor-Hours	Unit	Material	Labor	Equipment	Total	Total Incl O&P
0010	**MOTORS EXPLOSION PROOF**, 208-230/460 volts, 60 HZ									
0020	1800 RPM, 1/4 HP	1 Elec	5	1.600	Ea.	565	90.50		655.50	760
0030	1/3 HP		5	1.600		272	90.50		362.50	435
0040	1/2 HP		5	1.600		485	90.50		575.50	665
0050	3/4 HP		5.33	1.501		430	85		515	600
0060	1 HP		4.20	1.905		555	108		663	770
0070	2 HP		4.20	1.905		645	108		753	870
0080	3 HP		4.20	1.905		725	108		833	955
0090	5 HP		4.20	1.905		890	108		998	1,125
0100	7.5 HP		4	2		1,100	113		1,213	1,375
0110	10 HP		3.70	2.162		1,300	122		1,422	1,600
0120	15 HP		3.20	2.500		1,700	142		1,842	2,075
0130	20 HP	2 Elec	5	3.200		2,125	181		2,306	2,600
0140	25 HP		4.80	3.333		2,550	189		2,739	3,075
0150	30 HP		4.40	3.636		2,950	206		3,156	3,550
0160	40 HP		3.80	4.211		3,775	238		4,013	4,500
0170	50 HP		3.20	5		4,125	283		4,408	4,950
0180	60 HP		2.60	6.154		6,000	350		6,350	7,125

For customer support on your Electrical Costs with RSMeans Data, call 800.448.8182.

313

26 71 13.40 Motors Explosion Proof		Crew	Daily Output	Labor-Hours	Unit	Material	2017 Bare Costs		Total	Total Incl O&P
							Labor	Equipment		
0190	75 HP	2 Elec	2	8	Ea.	7,400	455		7,855	8,800
0200	100 HP	3 Elec	2.50	9.600		9,425	545		9,970	11,200
0210	125 HP		2.20	10.909		12,300	615		12,915	14,400
0220	150 HP		1.60	15		14,500	850		15,350	17,200
0230	200 HP		1.20	20		17,800	1,125		18,925	21,300
1000	1200 RPM, 1 HP	1 Elec	4.20	1.905		470	108		578	675
1010	2 HP		4.20	1.905		540	108		648	755
1020	3 HP		4.20	1.905		735	108		843	970
1030	5 HP		4.20	1.905		1,000	108		1,108	1,250
2000	3600 RPM, 1/4 HP		5	1.600		405	90.50		495.50	580
2010	1/3 HP		5	1.600		425	90.50		515.50	600
2020	1/2 HP		5	1.600		390	90.50		480.50	565
2030	3/4 HP		5	1.600		530	90.50		620.50	715
2040	1 HP		4.20	1.905		610	108		718	830
2050	2 HP		4.20	1.905		670	108		778	895
2060	3 HP		4.20	1.905		730	108		838	965
2070	5 HP		4.20	1.905		975	108		1,083	1,225
2080	7.5 HP		4	2		1,100	113		1,213	1,375
2090	10 HP		3.70	2.162		1,275	122		1,397	1,575
2100	15 HP		3.20	2.500		1,725	142		1,867	2,100
2110	20 HP	2 Elec	5	3.200		2,150	181		2,331	2,625
2120	25 HP		4.80	3.333		2,650	189		2,839	3,200
2130	30 HP		4.40	3.636		3,100	206		3,306	3,700
2140	40 HP		3.80	4.211		3,825	238		4,063	4,550
2150	50 HP		3.20	5		4,125	283		4,408	4,950
2160	60 HP		2.60	6.154		6,050	350		6,400	7,175
2170	75 HP		2	8		7,400	455		7,855	8,800
2180	100 HP	3 Elec	2.50	9.600		9,425	545		9,970	11,200
2190	125 HP		2.20	10.909		12,700	615		13,315	14,900
2200	150 HP		1.60	15		14,500	850		15,350	17,200
2210	200 HP		1.20	20		18,300	1,125		19,425	21,800
2220	250 HP		1.20	20		18,300	1,125		19,425	21,800

Estimating Tips
27 20 00 Data Communications
27 30 00 Voice Communications
27 40 00 Audio-Video Communications

- When estimating material costs for special systems, it is always prudent to obtain manufacturers' quotations for equipment prices and special installation requirements that may affect the total cost.

- For cost modifications for elevated tray installation, add the percentages to labor according to the height of the installation and only to the quantities exceeding the different height levels, not to the total tray quantities. Refer to 26 01 02.20 for labor adjustment factors.

- Do not overlook the costs for equipment used in the installation. If scissor lifts and boom lifts are available in the field, contractors may use them in lieu of the proposed ladders and rolling staging.

Reference Numbers

Reference numbers are shown at the beginning of some major classifications. These numbers refer to related items in the Reference Section. The reference information may be an estimating procedure, an alternate pricing method, or technical information.

Note: Not all subdivisions listed here necessarily appear. ■

Did you know?

Our online estimating solution gives you the same access to RSMeans' data with 24/7 access:

- Quickly locate costs in the searchable database.
- Build cost lists, estimates, and reports in minutes.
- Adjust costs to any location in the U.S. and Canada with the click of a button.

Start your free trial today at
www.RSMeansOnline.com

27 01 Operation and Maintenance of Communications Systems

27 01 30 – Operation and Maintenance of Voice Communications

27 01 30.51 Operation and Maintenance of Voice Equipment	Crew	Daily Output	Labor-Hours	Unit	Material	2017 Bare Costs Labor	Equipment	Total	Total Incl O&P
0010 **OPERATION AND MAINTENANCE OF VOICE EQUIPMENT**									
3400 Remove and replace (reinstall), speaker	1 Elec	6	1.333	Ea.		75.50		75.50	113

27 05 Common Work Results for Communications

27 05 05 – Selective Demolition for Communications

27 05 05.20 Electrical Demolition, Communications

	Crew	Daily Output	Labor-Hours	Unit	Material	2017 Bare Costs Labor	Equipment	Total	Total Incl O&P
0010 **ELECTRICAL DEMOLITION, COMMUNICATIONS** R024119-10									
0100 Fiber optics									
0120 Cable R260105-30	1 Elec	2400	.003	L.F.		.19		.19	.28
0160 Multi-channel rack enclosure		6	1.333	Ea.		75.50		75.50	113
0180 Patch panel		18	.444	"		25		25	37.50
0200 Communication cables & fittings									
0220 Voice/data outlet	1 Elec	140	.057	Ea.		3.23		3.23	4.85
0240 Telephone cable		2800	.003	L.F.		.16		.16	.24
0260 Phone jack		135	.059	Ea.		3.35		3.35	5.05
0280 Data jack		135	.059	"		3.35		3.35	5.05
0300 High performance cable, 2 pair		3000	.003	L.F.		.15		.15	.23
0320 4 pair		2100	.004			.22		.22	.32
0340 25 pair		900	.009			.50		.50	.75
0400 Terminal cabinet		5	1.600	Ea.		90.50		90.50	136
1000 Nurse call system									
1020 Station	1 Elec	24	.333	Ea.		18.85		18.85	28.50
1040 Standard call button		24	.333			18.85		18.85	28.50
1060 Corridor dome light or zone indicator		24	.333			18.85		18.85	28.50
1080 Master control station	2 Elec	2	8			455		455	680

27 05 05.30 Electrical Demolition, Sound and Video

	Crew	Daily Output	Labor-Hours	Unit	Material	2017 Bare Costs Labor	Equipment	Total	Total Incl O&P
0010 **ELECTRICAL DEMOLITION, SOUND & VIDEO** R024119-10									
0100 Cables									
0120 TV antenna lead-in cable R260105-30	1 Elec	2100	.004	L.F.		.22		.22	.32
0140 Sound cable		2400	.003			.19		.19	.28
0160 Microphone cable		2400	.003			.19		.19	.28
0180 Coaxial cable		2400	.003			.19		.19	.28
0200 Doorbell system, not including wires, cables, and conduit		16	.500	Ea.		28.50		28.50	42.50
0220 Door chime or devices		36	.222	"		12.60		12.60	18.85
0300 Public address system, not including wires, cables, and conduit									
0320 Conventional office	1 Elec	16	.500	Speaker		28.50		28.50	42.50
0340 Conventional industrial	"	8	1	"		56.50		56.50	85
0352 PA cabinet/panel	2 Elec	5	3.200	Ea.		181		181	271
0400 Sound system, not including wires, cables, and conduit									
0410 Components	1 Elec	24	.333	Ea.		18.85		18.85	28.50
0412 Speaker		24	.333			18.85		18.85	28.50
0416 Volume control		24	.333			18.85		18.85	28.50
0420 Intercom, master station		6	1.333			75.50		75.50	113
0440 Remote station		24	.333			18.85		18.85	28.50
0460 Intercom outlets		24	.333			18.85		18.85	28.50
0480 Handset		12	.667			37.50		37.50	56.50
0500 Emergency call system, not including wires, cables, and conduit									
0520 Annunciator	1 Elec	4	2	Ea.		113		113	170
0540 Devices	"	16	.500			28.50		28.50	42.50
0600 Master door, buzzer type unit	2 Elec	1.60	10			565		565	850
0800 TV system, not including wires, cables, and conduit									

27 05 Common Work Results for Communications

27 05 05 – Selective Demolition for Communications

27 05 05.30 Electrical Demolition, Sound and Video	Crew	Daily Output	Labor-Hours	Unit	Material	2017 Bare Costs Labor	Equipment	Total	Total Incl O&P
0820	Master TV antenna system, per outlet	1 Elec	.02	.205	Outlet		11.60		11.60	17.40
0840	School application, per outlet		16	.500	"		28.50		28.50	42.50
0860	Amplifier		12	.667	Ea.		37.50		37.50	56.50
0880	Antenna		6	1.333	"		75.50		75.50	113
0900	One camera & one monitor	2 Elec	7.80	2.051	Total		116		116	174
0920	One camera	1 Elec	8	1	Ea.		56.50		56.50	85

27 05 29 – Hangers and Supports for Communications Systems

27 05 29.10 Cable Support

		Crew	Daily Output	Labor-Hours	Unit	Material	2017 Bare Costs Labor	Equipment	Total	Total Incl O&P
0010	CABLE SUPPORT									
0110	J-Hook, Single Tier, Single Sided, 1" dia	1 Elec	68.57	.117	Ea.	1.75	6.60		8.35	11.85
0120	1-1/2" dia		67.80	.118		2.53	6.70		9.23	12.80
0130	2" dia		67.30	.119		2.70	6.75		9.45	13.05
0140	4" dia		66.80	.120		5.15	6.80		11.95	15.80
0330	Double Tier, Single Sided, 2" dia		67	.119		9.80	6.75		16.55	21
0340	4" dia		66.20	.121		14.45	6.85		21.30	26
0430	Double Sided, 2" dia		65.80	.122		15.15	6.90		22.05	27
0440	4" dia		65.40	.122		20	6.90		26.90	32.50
0530	Triple Tier, Single Sided, 2" dia		66.40	.120		22	6.80		28.80	34
0540	4" dia		65.85	.121		19.65	6.90		26.55	32
0630	Double Sided, 2" dia		65.10	.123		20	6.95		26.95	32.50
0640	4" dia		64.70	.124		26	7		33	39

27 11 Communications Equipment Room Fittings

27 11 16 – Communications Cabinets, Racks, Frames and Enclosures

27 11 16.10 Public Phone

		Crew	Daily Output	Labor-Hours	Unit	Material	2017 Bare Costs Labor	Equipment	Total	Total Incl O&P
0010	PUBLIC PHONE									
7600	Telephone with wood backboard									
7620	Single door, 12" H x 12" W x 4" D	1 Elec	5.30	1.509	Ea.	96	85.50		181.50	234
7650	18" H x 12" W x 4" D		4.70	1.702		113	96.50		209.50	268
7700	24" H x 12" W x 4" D		4.20	1.905		123	108		231	298
7720	18" H x 18" W x 4" D		4.20	1.905		135	108		243	310
7750	24" H x 18" W x 4" D		4	2		191	113		304	380
7780	36" H x 36" W x 4" D		3.60	2.222		217	126		343	425
7800	24" H x 24" W x 6" D		3.60	2.222		238	126		364	450
7820	30" H x 24" W x 6" D		3.20	2.500		288	142		430	525
7850	30" H x 30" W x 6" D		2.70	2.963		330	168		498	615
7880	36" H x 30" W x 6" D		2.50	3.200		400	181		581	710
7900	48" H x 36" W x 6" D		2.20	3.636		470	206		676	825
7920	Double door, 48" H x 36" W x 6" D		2	4		535	226		761	930

27 11 16.20 Rack Mount Cabinet

		Crew	Daily Output	Labor-Hours	Unit	Material	2017 Bare Costs Labor	Equipment	Total	Total Incl O&P
0010	RACK MOUNT CABINET									
0100	80" H x 24" W x 40" D									
0110	No sides	1 Elec	9.60	.833	Ea.	1,200	47		1,247	1,400
0120	One side		8	1		1,275	56.50		1,331.50	1,475
0130	Two sides		7.86	1.018		1,350	57.50		1,407.50	1,550
0200	80" H x 24" W x 42" D									
0210	No sides	1 Elec	9.60	.833	Ea.	1,225	47		1,272	1,425
0220	One side		8	1		1,275	56.50		1,331.50	1,475
0230	Two sides		7.86	1.018		1,275	57.50		1,332.50	1,500
0300	80" H x 24" W x 48" D									

For customer support on your Electrical Costs with RSMeans Data, call 800.448.8182.

317

27 11 16.20 Rack Mount Cabinet		Crew	Daily Output	Labor-Hours	Unit	Material	2017 Bare Costs Labor	Equipment	Total	Total Incl O&P
0310	No sides	1 Elec	9.60	.833	Ea.	1,375	47		1,422	1,600
0320	One side		8	1		1,375	56.50		1,431.50	1,600
0330	Two sides	↓	7.86	1.018	↓	1,375	57.50		1,432.50	1,600
0400	80" H x 30" W x 40" D									
0410	No sides	1 Elec	9.60	.833	Ea.	1,375	47		1,422	1,600
0420	One side		8	1		1,375	56.50		1,431.50	1,600
0430	Two sides	↓	7.86	1.018	↓	1,375	57.50		1,432.50	1,600
0500	80" H x 30" W x 42" D									
0510	No sides	1 Elec	9.60	.833	Ea.	1,375	47		1,422	1,600
0520	One side		8	1		1,375	56.50		1,431.50	1,600
0530	Two sides	↓	7.86	1.018	↓	1,375	57.50		1,432.50	1,600
0600	80" H x 30" W x 48" D									
0610	No sides	1 Elec	9.60	.833	Ea.	1,375	47		1,422	1,600
0620	One side		8	1		1,375	56.50		1,431.50	1,600
0630	Two sides	↓	7.86	1.018	↓	1,375	57.50		1,432.50	1,600
0700	80" H x 32" W x 32" D									
0710	No sides	1 Elec	9.60	.833	Ea.	1,375	47		1,422	1,600
0720	One side		8	1		1,375	56.50		1,431.50	1,600
0730	Two sides	↓	7.86	1.018	↓	1,375	57.50		1,432.50	1,600
0800	80" H x 32" W x 40" D									
0810	No sides	1 Elec	9.60	.833	Ea.	1,375	47		1,422	1,600
0820	One side		8	1		1,375	56.50		1,431.50	1,600
0830	Two sides	↓	7.86	1.018	↓	1,375	57.50		1,432.50	1,600
0900	80" H x 32" W x 42" D									
0910	No sides	1 Elec	9.60	.833	Ea.	1,375	47		1,422	1,600
0920	One side		8	1		1,375	56.50		1,431.50	1,600
0930	Two sides	↓	7.86	1.018	↓	1,375	57.50		1,432.50	1,600
1000	80" H x 32" W x 48" D									
1010	No sides	1 Elec	9.60	.833	Ea.	1,375	47		1,422	1,600
1020	One side		8	1		1,375	56.50		1,431.50	1,600
1030	Two sides	↓	7.86	1.018	↓	1,375	57.50		1,432.50	1,600
1200	Freestanding cabinet with front and rear doors									
1300	84" H x 19" W x 24" D, gray									
1310	No sides	1 Elec	9.60	.833	Ea.	1,875	47		1,922	2,125
1320	One side		9.60	.833		2,225	47		2,272	2,500
1330	Two sides	↓	9.60	.833	↓	2,225	47		2,272	2,500
1400	84" H x 19" W x 24" D, white									
1410	No sides	1 Elec	9.60	.833	Ea.	1,875	47		1,922	2,125
1420	One side		9.60	.833		2,225	47		2,272	2,500
1430	Two sides	↓	9.60	.833	↓	2,225	47		2,272	2,500
1500	84" H x 19" W x 24" D, black									
1510	No sides	1 Elec	9.60	.833	Ea.	1,775	47		1,822	2,025
1520	One side		9.60	.833		2,100	47		2,147	2,400
1530	Two sides		9.60	.833		2,100	47		2,147	2,400
1600	84"H x 28"W x 34"D front glass, rear louvered door	↓	9.60	.833	↓	1,400	47		1,447	1,600

27 11 19.10 Termination Blocks and Patch Panels

		Crew	Daily Output	Labor-Hours	Unit	Material	Labor	Equipment	Total	Total Incl O&P
0010	**TERMINATION BLOCKS AND PATCH PANELS**									
2960	Patch panel, RJ-45/110 type, 24 ports	2 Elec	6	2.667	Ea.	177	151		328	420
3000	48 ports	3 Elec	6	4		279	226		505	645
3040	96 ports	"	4	6		505	340		845	1,075
3100	Punch down termination per port	1 Elec	107	.075	↓		4.23		4.23	6.35

27 13 Communications Backbone Cabling

27 13 23 – Communications Optical Fiber Backbone Cabling

27 13 23.13 Communications Optical Fiber	Crew	Daily Output	Labor-Hours	Unit	Material	2017 Bare Costs Labor	Equipment	Total	Total Incl O&P
0010 **COMMUNICATIONS OPTICAL FIBER**									
0040 Specialized tools & techniques cause installation costs to vary.									
0070 Fiber optic, cable, bulk simplex, single mode R271323-40	1 Elec	8	1	C.L.F.	24.50	56.50		81	112
0080 Multi mode		8	1		29.50	56.50		86	118
0090 4 strand, single mode		7.34	1.090		40.50	61.50		102	138
0095 Multi mode		7.34	1.090		50.50	61.50		112	148
0100 12 strand, single mode		6.67	1.199		78	68		146	188
0105 Multi mode		6.67	1.199		96.50	68		164.50	208
0150 Jumper				Ea.	33			33	36.50
0200 Pigtail					37			37	40.50
0300 Connector	1 Elec	24	.333		27	18.85		45.85	58
0350 Finger splice		32	.250		40	14.15		54.15	65.50
0400 Transceiver (low cost bi-directional)		8	1		480	56.50		536.50	610
0450 Rack housing, 4 rack spaces, 12 panels (144 fibers)		2	4		560	226		786	955
0500 Patch panel, 12 ports		6	1.333		300	75.50		375.50	445
1000 Cable, 62.5 microns, direct burial, 4 fiber	R-15	1200	.040	L.F.	.86	2.23	.24	3.33	4.56
1020 Indoor, 2 fiber	R-19	1000	.020		.43	1.13		1.56	2.17
1040 Outdoor, aerial/duct	"	1670	.012		.69	.68		1.37	1.78
1060 50 microns, direct burial, 8 fiber	R-22	4000	.009		1.34	.48		1.82	2.19
1080 12 fiber		4000	.009		2.18	.48		2.66	3.12
1100 Indoor, 12 fiber		759	.049		2.07	2.55		4.62	6.10
1120 Connectors, 62.5 micron cable, transmission	R-19	40	.500	Ea.	16.75	28.50		45.25	61
1140 Cable splice		40	.500		18.65	28.50		47.15	63
1160 125 micron cable, transmission		16	1.250		17.50	71		88.50	125
1180 Receiver, 1.2 mile range		20	1		247	56.50		303.50	355
1200 1.9 mile range		20	1		233	56.50		289.50	340
1220 6.2 mile range		5	4		290	227		517	660
1240 Transmitter, 1.2 mile range		20	1		271	56.50		327.50	385
1260 1.9 mile range		20	1		305	56.50		361.50	420
1280 6.2 mile range		5	4		390	227		617	765
1300 Modem, 1.2 mile range		5	4		168	227		395	525
1320 6.2 mile range		5	4		305	227		532	675
1340 1.9 mile range, 12 channel		5	4		1,925	227		2,152	2,450
1360 Repeater, 1.2 mile range		10	2		385	113		498	595
1380 1.9 mile range		10	2		480	113		593	700
1400 6.2 mile range		5	4		925	227		1,152	1,375
1420 1.2 mile range, digital		5	4		445	227		672	830
1440 Transceiver, 1.9 mile range		5	4		380	227		607	755
1460 1.2 mile range, digital		5	4		390	227		617	770
1480 Cable enclosure, interior NEMA 13		7	2.857		160	162		322	420
1500 Splice w/enclosure encapsulant		16	1.250		233	71		304	360
1510 1/4 inch, black, non-metalic, flexible, tube, liquid tight		8	2.500	C.L.F.	175	142		317	405
1520 3/8 inch		8	2.500		112	142		254	335
1530 1/2 inch		7.34	2.725		112	155		267	355
1540 3/4 inch		7.34	2.725		182	155		337	430
1550 1 inch		7.34	2.725		281	155		436	540
1560 1-1/4 inch		6.67	2.999		430	170		600	730
1570 1-1/2 inch		6.67	2.999		540	170		710	850
1580 2 inch		6.35	3.150		815	179		994	1,175

27 15 10 – Special Communications Cabling

27 15 10.23 Sound and Video Cables and Fittings	Crew	Daily Output	Labor-Hours	Unit	Material	2017 Bare Costs Labor	Equipment	Total	Total Incl O&P
0010 **SOUND AND VIDEO CABLES & FITTINGS**									
0900　TV antenna lead-in, 300 ohm, #20-2 conductor	1 Elec	7	1.143	C.L.F.	22.50	64.50		87	122
0950　　Coaxial, feeder outlet		7	1.143		19.95	64.50		84.45	119
1000　　Coaxial, main riser		6	1.333		21	75.50		96.50	136
1100　Sound, shielded with drain, #22-2 conductor		8	1		13.95	56.50		70.45	100
1150　　#22-3 conductor		7.50	1.067		17.55	60.50		78.05	110
1200　　#22-4 conductor		6.50	1.231		22	69.50		91.50	129
1250　　Nonshielded, #22-2 conductor		10	.800		14.25	45.50		59.75	83.50
1300　　#22-3 conductor		9	.889		21.50	50.50		72	99
1350　　#22-4 conductor		8	1		28.50	56.50		85	117
1400　Microphone cable		8	1		42	56.50		98.50	132

27 15 13 – Communications Copper Horizontal Cabling

27 15 13.13 Communication Cables and Fittings

	Crew	Daily Output	Labor-Hours	Unit	Material	2017 Bare Costs Labor	Equipment	Total	Total Incl O&P
0010 **COMMUNICATION CABLES AND FITTINGS**									
2200　Telephone twisted, PVC insulation, #22-2 conductor	1 Elec	10	.800	C.L.F.	10.40	45.50		55.90	79.50
2250　　#22-3 conductor		9	.889		13.65	50.50		64.15	90.50
2300　　#22-4 conductor		8	1		14.85	56.50		71.35	101
2350　　#18-2 conductor		9	.889		19.70	50.50		70.20	97
2370　Telephone jack, eight pins		32	.250	Ea.	3.50	14.15		17.65	25
5000　High performance unshielded twisted pair (UTP)									
5100　　Cable, category 3, #24, 2 pair solid, PVC jacket　R271513-75	1 Elec	10	.800	C.L.F.	9.85	45.50		55.35	79
5200　　4 pair solid, PVC jacket		7	1.143		13.90	64.50		78.40	112
5300　　25 pair solid, PVC jacket		3	2.667		105	151		256	340
5400　　2 pair solid, plenum		10	.800		13.75	45.50		59.25	83
5500　　4 pair solid, plenum		7	1.143		14.15	64.50		78.65	113
5600　　25 pair solid, plenum		3	2.667		98	151		249	335
5700　　4 pair stranded, PVC jacket		7	1.143		11.80	64.50		76.30	110
7000　　Category 5, #24, 4 pair solid, PVC jacket		7	1.143		10	64.50		74.50	108
7100　　4 pair solid, plenum		7	1.143		14.45	64.50		78.95	113
7200　　4 pair stranded, PVC jacket		7	1.143		20.50	64.50		85	120
7210　　Category 5e, #24, 4 pair solid, PVC jacket		7	1.143		14.90	64.50		79.40	113
7212　　4 pair solid, plenum		7	1.143		21	64.50		85.50	120
7214　　4 pair stranded, PVC jacket		7	1.143		23	64.50		87.50	122
7240　　Category 6, #24, 4 pair solid, PVC jacket		7	1.143		18	64.50		82.50	117
7242　　4 pair solid, plenum		7	1.143		13.50	64.50		78	112
7244　　4 pair stranded, PVC jacket		7	1.143		13.75	64.50		78.25	112
7300　　Connector, RJ45, category 5		80	.100	Ea.	.73	5.65		6.38	9.30
7302　　Shielded RJ45, category 5		72	.111		1.71	6.30		8.01	11.30
7310　　Jack, UTP RJ45, category 3		72	.111		.40	6.30		6.70	9.85
7312　　Category 5		65	.123		5.45	6.95		12.40	16.45
7314　　Category 5e		65	.123		4.94	6.95		11.89	15.90
7316　　Category 6		65	.123		3.17	6.95		10.12	13.95
7322　　Jack, shielded RJ45, category 5		60	.133		6.45	7.55		14	18.35
7324　　Category 5e		60	.133		6.45	7.55		14	18.40
7326　　Category 6		60	.133		6.90	7.55		14.45	18.90
7400　　Voice/data expansion module, category 5e		8	1		46.50	56.50		103	136
7401　　Modular jack, cat 6 keystone, RJ45, office white		16.50	.485		4.10	27.50		31.60	45.50
7402　　RJ45, green		16.50	.485		7.05	27.50		34.55	49
7404　　RJ45, grey		16.50	.485		7.05	27.50		34.55	49
7408　　RJ45, orange		16.50	.485		4.34	27.50		31.84	46
7420　　5M, RJ45, 568B, cord set		16.50	.485		32.50	27.50		60	76.50
7422　　3M, RJ45, 568B, cord set		16.50	.485		28	27.50		55.50	72

27 15 13.13 Communication Cables and Fittings		Crew	Daily Output	Labor-Hours	Unit	Material	2017 Bare Costs Labor	Equipment	Total	Total Incl O&P
7424	1M, RJ45, 568B, cord set	1 Elec	16.50	.485	Ea.	24	27.50		51.50	67.50
7450	M12 TO RJ45, 2M ultra-loch D-mode, cord set	▼	15.50	.516	▼	34.50	29		63.50	82
8000	Multipair unshielded non-plenum cable, 150 V PVC jacket									
8002	#22, 2 pair	1 Elec	8.40	.952	C.L.F.	16.75	54		70.75	99.50
8003	3 pair		8	1		22	56.50		78.50	110
8004	4 pair		7.30	1.096		47	62		109	145
8006	6 pair		6.20	1.290		42.50	73		115.50	156
8008	8 pair		5.70	1.404		55.50	79.50		135	180
8010	10 pair		5.30	1.509		64.50	85.50		150	199
8012	12 pair		4.20	1.905		165	108		273	345
8015	15 pair	▼	3.80	2.105		209	119		328	410
8020	20 pair	2 Elec	6.60	2.424		209	137		346	435
8025	25 pair		6	2.667		226	151		377	475
8030	30 pair		5.60	2.857		375	162		537	655
8040	40 pair		5.20	3.077		495	174		669	800
8050	50 pair	▼	4.90	3.265	▼	615	185		800	955
8100	Multipair unshielded non-plenum cable, 300 V PVC jacket									
8102	#20, 2 pair	1 Elec	7.30	1.096	C.L.F.	26	62		88	122
8103	3 pair		6.70	1.194		34	67.50		101.50	138
8104	4 pair		6	1.333		38	75.50		113.50	155
8106	6 pair		5.30	1.509		59	85.50		144.50	193
8108	8 pair	▼	4.40	1.818		97	103		200	260
8110	10 pair	2 Elec	7.30	2.192		107	124		231	305
8112	12 pair		6.20	2.581		135	146		281	365
8115	15 pair	▼	5.90	2.712		169	153		322	415
8201	#18, 1 pair	1 Elec	8	1		63	56.50		119.50	155
8202	2 pair		6.50	1.231		80	69.50		149.50	193
8203	3 pair		5.60	1.429		121	81		202	254
8204	4 pair		5	1.600		158	90.50		248.50	310
8206	6 pair		4.40	1.818		266	103		369	445
8208	8 pair	▼	4	2		252	113		365	450
8215	15 pair	2 Elec	5	3.200	▼	650	181		831	985
8300	Multipair shielded non-plenum cable, 300 V PVC jacket									
8303	#22, 3 pair	1 Elec	6.70	1.194	C.L.F.	62.50	67.50		130	170
8306	6 pair		5.70	1.404		125	79.50		204.50	256
8309	9 pair	▼	5	1.600		141	90.50		231.50	291
8312	12 pair	2 Elec	8	2		490	113		603	710
8315	15 pair		7.30	2.192		505	124		629	745
8317	17 pair		6.80	2.353		690	133		823	955
8319	19 pair		6.40	2.500		690	142		832	970
8327	27 pair	▼	5.90	2.712		1,250	153		1,403	1,600
8402	#20, 2 pair	1 Elec	6.70	1.194		77.50	67.50		145	187
8403	3 pair		6.20	1.290		97	73		170	215
8406	6 pair		4.40	1.818		244	103		347	420
8409	9 pair	▼	3.60	2.222		278	126		404	495
8412	12 pair	2 Elec	5.90	2.712		565	153		718	850
8415	15 pair	"	5.70	2.807		470	159		629	755
8502	#18, 2 pair	1 Elec	6.20	1.290		133	73		206	255
8503	3 pair		5.30	1.509		208	85.50		293.50	355
8504	4 pair		4.70	1.702		247	96.50		343.50	415
8506	6 pair		4	2		385	113		498	595
8509	9 pair	▼	3.40	2.353		590	133		723	850
8515	15 pair	2 Elec	4.80	3.333	▼	985	189		1,174	1,350

27 15 33 – Communications Coaxial Horizontal Cabling

27 15 33.10 Coaxial Cable and Fittings	Crew	Daily Output	Labor-Hours	Unit	Material	2017 Bare Costs Labor	Equipment	Total	Total Incl O&P
0010 **COAXIAL CABLE & FITTINGS**									
3500 Coaxial connectors, 50 ohm impedance quick disconnect									
3540 BNC plug, for RG A/U #58 cable	1 Elec	42	.190	Ea.	3.26	10.80		14.06	19.75
3550 RG A/U #59 cable		42	.190		3.26	10.80		14.06	19.75
3560 RG A/U #62 cable		42	.190		3.26	10.80		14.06	19.75
3600 BNC jack, for RG A/U #58 cable		42	.190		3.25	10.80		14.05	19.75
3610 RG A/U #59 cable		42	.190		2.75	10.80		13.55	19.20
3620 RG A/U #62 cable		42	.190		2.90	10.80		13.70	19.35
3660 BNC panel jack, for RG A/U #58 cable		40	.200		7.65	11.30		18.95	25.50
3670 RG A/U #59 cable		40	.200		6.20	11.30		17.50	24
3680 RG A/U #62 cable		40	.200		6.20	11.30		17.50	24
3720 BNC bulkhead jack, for RG A/U #58 cable		40	.200		6.20	11.30		17.50	24
3730 RG A/U #59 cable		40	.200		6.20	11.30		17.50	24
3740 RG A/U #62 cable		40	.200		6.20	11.30		17.50	24
3850 Coaxial cable, RG A/U #58, 50 ohm		8	1	C.L.F.	48.50	56.50		105	139
3860 RG A/U #59, 75 ohm		8	1		37.50	56.50		94	127
3870 RG A/U #62, 93 ohm		8	1		45.50	56.50		102	135
3875 RG 6/U, 75 ohm		8	1		30	56.50		86.50	118
3950 Fire rated, RG A/U #58, 50 ohm		8	1		94.50	56.50		151	189
3960 RG A/U #59, 75 ohm		8	1		125	56.50		181.50	222
3970 RG A/U #62, 93 ohm		8	1		110	56.50		166.50	206

27 15 43 – Communications Faceplates and Connectors

27 15 43.13 Communication Outlets

	Crew	Daily Output	Labor-Hours	Unit	Material	2017 Bare Costs Labor	Equipment	Total	Total Incl O&P
0010 **COMMUNICATION OUTLETS**									
0100 Voice/data devices not included									
0120 Voice/data outlets, single opening	1 Elec	48	.167	Ea.	7.85	9.45		17.30	23
0140 Two jack openings		48	.167		2.56	9.45		12.01	16.95
0160 One jack & one 3/4" round opening		48	.167		7.45	9.45		16.90	22.50
0180 One jack & one twinaxial opening		48	.167		4.83	9.45		14.28	19.45
0200 One jack & one connector cabling opening		48	.167		7.45	9.45		16.90	22.50
0220 Two 3/8" coaxial openings		48	.167		7.45	9.45		16.90	22.50
0300 Data outlets, single opening		48	.167		7.45	9.45		16.90	22.50
0320 One 25-pin subminiature opening		48	.167		7.45	9.45		16.90	22.50
1000 Voice/data wall plate plastic, 1 gang, 1-port		72	.111		2.08	6.30		8.38	11.70
1020 2-port		72	.111		2.76	6.30		9.06	12.45
1040 3-port		72	.111		2.08	6.30		8.38	11.70
1060 4-port		72	.111		2.08	6.30		8.38	11.70
1080 6-port		72	.111		2.08	6.30		8.38	11.70
1100 2 gang, 6-port		48	.167		6.25	9.45		15.70	21
1120 Voice/data wall plate, stainless steel, 1 gang, 1-port		72	.111		6.30	6.30		12.60	16.35
1140 2-port		72	.111		6.45	6.30		12.75	16.45
1160 3-port		72	.111		6.45	6.30		12.75	16.50
1180 4-port		72	.111		6.45	6.30		12.75	16.45
1200 2 gang, 6-port		48	.167		11.20	9.45		20.65	26.50

27 21 Data Communications Network Equipment

27 21 23 – Data Communications Switches and Hubs

27 21 23.10 Switching and Routing Equipment	Crew	Daily Output	Labor-Hours	Unit	Material	2017 Bare Costs Labor	Equipment	Total	Total Incl O&P
0010 **SWITCHING AND ROUTING EQUIPMENT**									
1100 Network hub, dual speed, 24 ports, includes cabinet	3 Elec	.66	36.364	Ea.	920	2,050		2,970	4,075
1300 Network switch, 50/60 HZ, 8 port, multi-platform, analog KVM	1 Elec	6.85	1.168		985	66		1,051	1,175
1310 16 port, multi-platform, analog KVM		6	1.333		1,225	75.50		1,300.50	1,475
1320 Network switch, 0x2x16,CAT5, analog KVM		6	1.333		1,025	75.50		1,100.50	1,250
1330 2x1x16, DIGITAL KVM, W/ VM		16	.500		3,225	28.50		3,253.50	3,600
1340 2x1x32, DIGITAL KVM, W/ VM		16	.500		3,850	28.50		3,878.50	4,275
1350 8x1x32, DIGITAL KVM, W/ VM		16	.500		4,300	28.50		4,328.50	4,800
1500 KVM,1 RMU 16 port, no keyboard		16	.500		1,250	28.50		1,278.50	1,425
1510 KVM,1 RMU, 17" LCD, 16 port, US keyboard		15.15	.528		2,400	30		2,430	2,700
1520 KVM,1 RMU, 17" LCD, 16 port, UK keyboard		15.15	.528		2,400	30		2,430	2,700
2000 10/100/1000 Mbps, 24 ports		14	.571		595	32.50		627.50	705
2040 10/100/1000 Mbps, 48 ports		12	.667		1,425	37.50		1,462.50	1,625
2050 10/100/Mbps, 5 Port, industrial ethernet type		32	.250		273	14.15		287.15	320
2060 10/100/Mbps, 6 Port, industrial ethernet type		32	.250		1,100	14.15		1,114.15	1,225
2070 10/100/1000 Mbps, 10 Port, X307-3		28	.286		2,600	16.15		2,616.15	2,875
2080 10/100/1000 Mbps, 10 Port, X308-2		28	.286		2,400	16.15		2,416.15	2,675
3000 10/100/1000 Mbps, 20 Port, front ports		20	.400		3,775	22.50		3,797.50	4,175
3010 10/100/1000 Mbps, 20 Port, rear ports		20	.400		3,775	22.50		3,797.50	4,175
3040 KVM, 10/100/1000/10000 Mbps, 28 Port, rear ports		16	.500		7,800	28.50		7,828.50	8,650
3050 KVM, 10/100/1000/10000 Mbps, 28 Port, front ports	▼	16	.500		9,175	28.50		9,203.50	10,100
3070 KVM, 10/100/1000/10000 Mbps, 52 port, front ports	2 Elec	12	1.333		9,625	75.50		9,700.50	10,700
3080 KVM, 10/100/1000/10000 Mbps, 52 port, rear ports	"	12	1.333	▼	9,625	75.50		9,700.50	10,700

27 32 Voice Communications Terminal Equipment

27 32 26 – Ring-Down Emergency Telephones

27 32 26.10 Emergency Phone Stations

	Crew	Daily Output	Labor-Hours	Unit	Material	2017 Bare Costs Labor	Equipment	Total	Total Incl O&P
0010 **EMERGENCY PHONE STATIONS**									
0100 Hands free emergency speaker phone w/LED strobe	1 Elec	7.22	1.108	Ea.	795	62.50		857.50	965
0110 Wall/pole mounted emergency phone station w/LED strobe	"	4.60	1.739	"	1,525	98.50		1,623.50	1,825

27 32 36 – TTY Equipment

27 32 36.10 TTY Telephone Equipment

	Crew	Daily Output	Labor-Hours	Unit	Material	2017 Bare Costs Labor	Equipment	Total	Total Incl O&P
0010 **TTY TELEPHONE EQUIPMENT**									
1620 Telephone, TTY, compact, pocket type				Ea.	299			299	330
1630 Advanced, desk type	2 Elec	20	.800		500	45.50		545.50	620
1640 Full-featured public, wall type	"	4	4	▼	700	226		926	1,100

27 41 Audio-Video Systems

27 41 33 – Master Antenna Television Systems

27 41 33.10 T.V. Systems

	Crew	Daily Output	Labor-Hours	Unit	Material	2017 Bare Costs Labor	Equipment	Total	Total Incl O&P
0010 **T.V. SYSTEMS**, not including rough-in wires, cables & conduits									
0100 Master TV antenna system									
0200 VHF reception & distribution, 12 outlets	1 Elec	6	1.333	Outlet	156	75.50		231.50	285
0400 30 outlets		10	.800		155	45.50		200.50	238
0600 100 outlets		13	.615		158	35		193	225
0800 VHF & UHF reception & distribution, 12 outlets		6	1.333		233	75.50		308.50	370
1000 30 outlets		10	.800		155	45.50		200.50	238
1200 100 outlets		13	.615		158	35		193	225
1400 School and deluxe systems, 12 outlets		2.40	3.333	▼	310	189		499	625

323

27 41 Audio-Video Systems

27 41 33 – Master Antenna Television Systems

27 41 33.10 T.V. Systems		Crew	Daily Output	Labor-Hours	Unit	Material	2017 Bare Costs Labor	Equipment	Total	Total Incl O&P
1600	30 outlets	1 Elec	4	2	Outlet	270	113		383	465
1800	80 outlets		5.30	1.509		259	85.50		344.50	415
1900	Amplifier		4	2	Ea.	775	113		888	1,025
5000	Antenna, small		6	1.333		51.50	75.50		127	170
5100	Large		4	2		217	113		330	410
5110	Rotor unit		8	1		63	56.50		119.50	155
5120	Single booster		8	1		31.50	56.50		88	120
5130	Antenna pole, 10'		3.20	2.500		20	142		162	234
6100	Satellite TV system	2 Elec	1	16		2,200	905		3,105	3,775
6110	Dish, mesh, 10' diam.	"	2.40	6.667		1,675	375		2,050	2,425
6111	Two way RF/IF tapeoff	1 Elec	36	.222		3.59	12.60		16.19	23
6112	Two way RF/IF splitter		24	.333		14	18.85		32.85	44
6113	Line amplifier		24	.333		15.15	18.85		34	45
6114	Line splitters		36	.222		5.05	12.60		17.65	24.50
6115	Line multi switches		8	1		670	56.50		726.50	820
6120	Motor unit		2.40	3.333		259	189		448	570
7000	Home theater, widescreen, 42", high definition, TV		10.24	.781		400	44		444	505
7050	Flat wall mount bracket		10.24	.781		80.50	44		124.50	155
7100	7 channel home theater receiver		10.24	.781		385	44		429	490
7200	Home theater speakers		10.24	.781	Set	216	44		260	305
7300	Home theater programmable remote		10.24	.781	Ea.	249	44		293	340
8000	Main video splitter		4	2		3,200	113		3,313	3,700
8010	Video distribution units		4	2		140	113		253	325

27 42 Electronic Digital Systems

27 42 13 – Point of Sale Systems

27 42 13.10 Bar Code Scanner

0010	BAR CODE SCANNER									
0100	CR3600, W/B4 battery, handle	1 Elec	6	1.333	Outlet	895	75.50		970.50	1,100
0110	Palm		12	.667		750	37.50		787.50	880
0120	Batch, B4 batt, handle, chgstn, 3ft USB		9	.889		850	50.50		900.50	1,000
0130	Palm, chgstn, 3ft USB		12	.667		715	37.50		752.50	840
0140	CR2500, W/H2 handle, no cable		10	.800		695	45.50		740.50	835
0150	Core unit, palm, no cable		16	.500		605	28.50		633.50	715

27 51 Distributed Audio-Video Communications Systems

27 51 16 – Public Address Systems

27 51 16.10 Public Address System

0010	PUBLIC ADDRESS SYSTEM									
0100	Conventional, office	1 Elec	5.33	1.501	Speaker	149	85		234	291
0200	Industrial	"	2.70	2.963	"	288	168		456	565

27 51 19 – Sound Masking Systems

27 51 19.10 Sound System

0010	SOUND SYSTEM, not including rough-in wires, cables & conduits									
0100	Components, projector outlet	1 Elec	8	1	Ea.	46.50	56.50		103	136
0200	Microphone		4	2		115	113		228	297
0400	Speakers, ceiling or wall		8	1		131	56.50		187.50	229
0600	Trumpets		4	2		243	113		356	435
0800	Privacy switch		8	1		97	56.50		153.50	192

27 51 Distributed Audio-Video Communications Systems

27 51 19 – Sound Masking Systems

27 51 19.10 Sound System

		Crew	Daily Output	Labor-Hours	Unit	Material	2017 Bare Costs Labor	2017 Bare Costs Equipment	Total	Total Incl O&P
1000	Monitor panel	1 Elec	4	2	Ea.	430	113		543	645
1200	Antenna, AM/FM		4	2		151	113		264	335
1400	Volume control		8	1		52	56.50		108.50	142
1600	Amplifier, 250 watts		1	8		1,425	455		1,880	2,250
1800	Cabinets	▼	1	8		940	455		1,395	1,700
2000	Intercom, 30 station capacity, master station	2 Elec	2	8		2,300	455		2,755	3,200
2020	10 station capacity	"	4	4		1,250	226		1,476	1,725
2200	Remote station	1 Elec	8	1		181	56.50		237.50	285
2400	Intercom outlets		8	1		107	56.50		163.50	202
2600	Handset		4	2		355	113		468	560
2800	Emergency call system, 12 zones, annunciator		1.30	6.154		1,075	350		1,425	1,700
3000	Bell		5.30	1.509		110	85.50		195.50	249
3200	Light or relay		8	1		55	56.50		111.50	146
3400	Transformer		4	2		241	113		354	435
3600	House telephone, talking station		1.60	5		520	283		803	995
3800	Press to talk, release to listen	▼	5.30	1.509		121	85.50		206.50	261
4000	System-on button					72.50			72.50	79.50
4200	Door release	1 Elec	4	2		129	113		242	310
4400	Combination speaker and microphone		8	1		220	56.50		276.50	325
4600	Termination box		3.20	2.500		69	142		211	288
4800	Amplifier or power supply		5.30	1.509	▼	795	85.50		880.50	1,000
5000	Vestibule door unit		16	.500	Name	146	28.50		174.50	204
5200	Strip cabinet		27	.296	Ea.	276	16.75		292.75	330
5400	Directory	▼	16	.500		130	28.50		158.50	186
6000	Master door, button buzzer type, 100 unit	2 Elec	.54	29.630		1,325	1,675		3,000	3,975
6020	200 unit		.30	53.333		2,500	3,025		5,525	7,275
6040	300 unit		.20	80		3,800	4,525		8,325	11,000
6060	Transformer	1 Elec	8	1		34	56.50		90.50	122
6080	Door opener		5.30	1.509		48.50	85.50		134	182
6100	Buzzer with door release and plate	▼	4	2		48.50	113		161.50	224
6200	Intercom type, 100 unit	2 Elec	.54	29.630		1,650	1,675		3,325	4,325
6220	200 unit		.30	53.333		3,200	3,025		6,225	8,050
6240	300 unit	▼	.20	80		4,850	4,525		9,375	12,100
6260	Amplifier	1 Elec	2	4		241	226		467	605
6280	Speaker with door release	"	4	2	▼	72.50	113		185.50	250

27 52 Healthcare Communications and Monitoring Systems

27 52 23 – Nurse Call/Code Blue Systems

27 52 23.10 Nurse Call Systems

		Crew	Daily Output	Labor-Hours	Unit	Material	2017 Bare Costs Labor	2017 Bare Costs Equipment	Total	Total Incl O&P
0010	**NURSE CALL SYSTEMS**									
0100	Single bedside call station	1 Elec	8	1	Ea.	239	56.50		295.50	350
0200	Ceiling speaker station		8	1		72.50	56.50		129	165
0400	Emergency call station		8	1		78	56.50		134.50	171
0600	Pillow speaker		8	1		191	56.50		247.50	295
0800	Double bedside call station		4	2		154	113		267	340
1000	Duty station		4	2		130	113		243	315
1200	Standard call button		8	1		93.50	56.50		150	188
1400	Lights, corridor, dome or zone indicator	▼	8	1	▼	53	56.50		109.50	144
1600	Master control station for 20 stations	2 Elec	.65	24.615	Total	3,450	1,400		4,850	5,875

27 53 Distributed Systems

27 53 13 – Clock Systems

27 53 13.50 Clock Equipments	Crew	Daily Output	Labor-Hours	Unit	Material	2017 Bare Costs Labor	Equipment	Total	Total Incl O&P
0010 **CLOCK EQUIPMENTS**, not including wires & conduits									
0100 Time system components, master controller	1 Elec	.33	24.242	Ea.	1,675	1,375		3,050	3,875
0200 Program bell		8	1		112	56.50		168.50	208
0400 Combination clock & speaker		3.20	2.500		200	142		342	430
0600 Frequency generator		2	4		2,425	226		2,651	3,025
0800 Job time automatic stamp recorder		4	2		565	113		678	790
1600 Master time clock system, clocks & bells, 20 room	4 Elec	.20	160		6,400	9,050		15,450	20,700
1800 50 room	"	.08	400		13,500	22,600		36,100	48,800
1900 Time clock	1 Elec	3.20	2.500		450	142		592	705
2000 100 cards in & out, 1 color					10			10	11
2200 2 colors					10			10	11
2800 Metal rack for 25 cards	1 Elec	7	1.143		50	64.50		114.50	152
4000 Wireless time systems component, master controller	"	2	4		630	226		856	1,025
4010 For transceiver and antenna, see Section 28 39 10.10									
4100 Wireless analog clock w/battery operated	1 Elec	8	1	Ea.	112	56.50		168.50	208
4200 Wireless digital clock w/battery operated	"	8	1	"	430	56.50		486.50	560

Estimating Tips

- When estimating material costs for electronic safety and security systems, it is always prudent to obtain manufacturers' quotations for equipment prices and special installation requirements that may affect the total cost.

- Fire alarm systems consist of control panels, annunciator panels, batteries with rack, charger, and fire alarm actuating and indicating devices. Some fire alarm systems include speakers, telephone lines, door closer controls, and other components. Be careful not to overlook the costs related to installation for these items. Also be aware of costs for integrated automation instrumentation and terminal devices, control equipment, control wiring, and programming. Insurance underwriters may have specific requirements for the type of materials to be installed or design requirements based on the hazard to be protected. Local jurisdictions may have requirements not covered by code. It is advisable to be aware of any special conditions.

- Security equipment includes items such as CCTV, access control, and other detection and identification systems to perform alert and alarm functions. Be sure to consider the costs related to installation for this security equipment, such as for integrated automation instrumentation and terminal devices, control equipment, control wiring, and programming.

Reference Numbers

Reference numbers are shown at the beginning of some major classifications. These numbers refer to related items in the Reference Section. The reference information may be an estimating procedure, an alternate pricing method, or technical information.

Note: Not all subdivisions listed here necessarily appear. ■

Did you know?

Our online estimating solution gives you the same access to RSMeans' data with 24/7 access:

- Quickly locate costs in the searchable database.

- Build cost lists, estimates, and reports in minutes.

- Adjust costs to any location in the U.S. and Canada with the click of a button.

Start your free trial today at
www.RSMeansOnline.com

28 01 Operation and Maint. of Electronic Safety and Security

28 01 30 – Operation and Maint. of Electronic Detection and Alarm

28 01 30.51 Maint. and Admin. of Elec. Detection and Alarm	Crew	Daily Output	Labor-Hours	Unit	Material	2017 Bare Costs Labor	Equipment	Total	Total Incl O&P
0010 **MAINT. AND ADMIN. OF ELEC. DETECTION AND ALARM**									
3300 Remove and replace (reinstall), fire alarm device	1 Elec	5.33	1.501	Ea.		85		85	127

28 05 Common Work Results for Electronic Safety and Security

28 05 05 – Selective Demolition for Electronic Safety and Security

28 05 05.10 Safety and Security Demolition

	Crew	Daily Output	Labor-Hours	Unit	Material	2017 Bare Costs Labor	Equipment	Total	Total Incl O&P
0010 **SAFETY AND SECURITY DEMOLITION**									
1050 Finger print/card reader	1 Elec	8	1	Ea.		56.50		56.50	85
1051 Electrical dml, CA 3000 card reader sys w/25 users		.31	25.600			1,450		1,450	2,175
1060 Video camera		8	1			56.50		56.50	85
1070 Motion detector, multi-channel		7	1.143			64.50		64.50	97
1090 Infrared detector		7	1.143			64.50		64.50	97
1130 Video monitor, 19"		8	1			56.50		56.50	85
1210 Fire alarm horn and strobe light		16	.500			28.50		28.50	42.50
1215 Remote fire alarm indicator light		23	.348			19.70		19.70	29.50
1220 Flame detector		23	.348			19.70		19.70	29.50
1230 Duct detector		10	.800			45.50		45.50	68
1240 Smoke detector		23	.348			19.70		19.70	29.50
1241 Fire alarm duct smoke remote test station		21.60	.370			21		21	31.50
1250 Fire alarm pull station		23	.348			19.70		19.70	29.50
1260 Fire alarm control panel, 4 to 8 zone	2 Elec	4	4			226		226	340
1270 12 to 16 zone	"	2.67	5.993			340		340	510
1280 Fire alarm annunciation panel, 4 to 8 zone	1 Elec	6	1.333			75.50		75.50	113
1290 12 to 16 zone	2 Elec	6	2.667			151		151	226
1300 Electrical dml, tamper switch	1 Elec	38	.211			11.90		11.90	17.85
1310 Electrical dml, flow switch	"	38	.211			11.90		11.90	17.85

28 05 13 – Conductors and Cables for Electronic Safety and Security

28 05 13.23 Fire Alarm Communications Conductors and Cables

	Crew	Daily Output	Labor-Hours	Unit	Material	2017 Bare Costs Labor	Equipment	Total	Total Incl O&P
0010 **FIRE ALARM COMMUNICATIONS CONDUCTORS AND CABLES**									
1500 Fire alarm FEP teflon 150 volt to 200°C									
1550 #22, 1 pair	1 Elec	10	.800	C.L.F.	98	45.50		143.50	176
1600 2 pair		8	1		96	56.50		152.50	191
1650 4 pair		7	1.143		350	64.50		414.50	480
1700 6 pair		6	1.333		425	75.50		500.50	585
1750 8 pair		5.50	1.455		625	82.50		707.50	815
1800 10 pair		5	1.600		755	90.50		845.50	965
1850 #18, 1 pair	2 Elec	16	1		67.50	56.50		124	160
1900 2 pair		13	1.231		143	69.50		212.50	261
1950 4 pair		9.60	1.667		212	94.50		306.50	375
2000 6 pair		8	2		281	113		394	480
2050 8 pair		7	2.286		365	129		494	595
2100 10 pair		6	2.667		420	151		571	685

28 13 Access Control

28 13 53 – Security Access Detection

28 13 53.13 Security Access Metal Detectors

28 13 53.13 Security Access Metal Detectors	Crew	Daily Output	Labor-Hours	Unit	Material	2017 Bare Costs Labor	2017 Bare Costs Equipment	Total	Total Incl O&P
0010 **SECURITY ACCESS METAL DETECTORS**									
0240 Metal detector, hand-held, wand type, unit only				Ea.	129			129	138
0250 Metal detector, walk through portal type, single zone	1 Elec	2	4		4,000	226		4,226	4,750
0260 Multi-zone	"	2	4		5,925	226		6,151	6,875

28 13 53.16 Security Access X-Ray Equipment

28 13 53.16 Security Access X-Ray Equipment	Crew	Daily Output	Labor-Hours	Unit	Material	2017 Bare Costs Labor	2017 Bare Costs Equipment	Total	Total Incl O&P
0010 **SECURITY ACCESS X-RAY EQUIPMENT**									
0290 X-ray machine, desk top, for mail/small packages/letters	1 Elec	4	2	Ea.	3,475	113		3,588	4,000
0300 Conveyor type, incl monitor		2	4		16,000	226		16,226	17,900
0310 Includes additional features		2	4		28,000	226		28,226	31,100
0320 X-ray machine, large unit, for airports, incl monitor	2 Elec	1	16		40,000	905		40,905	45,400
0330 Full console	"	.50	32		68,500	1,800		70,300	78,000

28 13 53.23 Security Access Explosive Detection Equipment

28 13 53.23 Security Access Explosive Detection Equipment	Crew	Daily Output	Labor-Hours	Unit	Material	2017 Bare Costs Labor	2017 Bare Costs Equipment	Total	Total Incl O&P
0010 **SECURITY ACCESS EXPLOSIVE DETECTION EQUIPMENT**									
0270 Explosives detector, walk through portal type	1 Elec	2	4	Ea.	44,200	226		44,426	48,900
0280 Hand-held, battery operated				"	25,500				28,100

28 16 Intrusion Detection

28 16 16 – Intrusion Detection Systems Infrastructure

28 16 16.50 Intrusion Detection

28 16 16.50 Intrusion Detection	Crew	Daily Output	Labor-Hours	Unit	Material	2017 Bare Costs Labor	2017 Bare Costs Equipment	Total	Total Incl O&P
0010 **INTRUSION DETECTION**, not including wires & conduits									
0100 Burglar alarm, battery operated, mechanical trigger	1 Elec	4	2	Ea.	280	113		393	480
0200 Electrical trigger		4	2		335	113		448	540
0400 For outside key control, add		8	1		87	56.50		143.50	181
0600 For remote signaling circuitry, add		8	1		138	56.50		194.50	237
0800 Card reader, flush type, standard		2.70	2.963		795	168		963	1,125
1000 Multi-code		2.70	2.963		1,200	168		1,368	1,575
1010 Card reader, proximity type		2.70	2.963		297	168		465	575
1200 Door switches, hinge switch		5.30	1.509		62.50	85.50		148	197
1400 Magnetic switch		5.30	1.509		77	85.50		162.50	213
1600 Exit control locks, horn alarm		4	2		213	113		326	405
1800 Flashing light alarm		4	2		244	113		357	440
2000 Indicating panels, 1 channel		2.70	2.963		271	168		439	550
2200 10 channel	2 Elec	3.20	5		1,075	283		1,358	1,600
2400 20 channel		2	8		2,500	455		2,955	3,400
2600 40 channel		1.14	14.035		4,500	795		5,295	6,150
2800 Ultrasonic motion detector, 12 volt	1 Elec	2.30	3.478		210	197		407	525
3000 Infrared photoelectric detector		4	2		146	113		259	330
3200 Passive infrared detector		4	2		236	113		349	430
3400 Glass break alarm switch		8	1		117	56.50		173.50	214
3420 Switchmats, 30" x 5'		5.30	1.509		105	85.50		190.50	244
3440 30" x 25'		4	2		205	113		318	395
3460 Police connect panel		4	2		272	113		385	470
3480 Telephone dialer		5.30	1.509		390	85.50		475.50	555
3500 Alarm bell		4	2		105	113		218	286
3520 Siren		4	2		147	113		260	330
3540 Microwave detector, 10' to 200'		2	4		585	226		811	985
3560 10' to 350'		2	4		1,775	226		2,001	2,300

For customer support on your Electrical Costs with RSMeans Data, call 800.448.8182.

329

28 23 Video Surveillance

28 23 13 - Video Surveillance Control and Management Systems

28 23 13.10 Closed Circuit Television System	Crew	Daily Output	Labor-Hours	Unit	Material	2017 Bare Costs Labor	Equipment	Total	Total Incl O&P
0010 **CLOSED CIRCUIT TELEVISION SYSTEM**									
2000 Surveillance, one station (camera & monitor)	2 Elec	2.60	6.154	Total	1,500	350		1,850	2,175
2200 For additional camera stations, add	1 Elec	2.70	2.963	Ea.	835	168		1,003	1,175
2400 Industrial quality, one station (camera & monitor)	2 Elec	2.60	6.154	Total	3,100	350		3,450	3,925
2600 For additional camera stations, add	1 Elec	2.70	2.963	Ea.	1,900	168		2,068	2,325
2610 For low light, add		2.70	2.963		1,525	168		1,693	1,925
2620 For very low light, add		2.70	2.963		11,200	168		11,368	12,600
2800 For weatherproof camera station, add		1.30	6.154		1,175	350		1,525	1,800
3000 For pan and tilt, add		1.30	6.154		3,025	350		3,375	3,850
3200 For zoom lens - remote control, add		2	4		2,775	226		3,001	3,400
3400 Extended zoom lens		2	4		10,200	226		10,426	11,500
3410 For automatic iris for low light, add		2	4		2,425	226		2,651	3,025
3600 Educational T.V. studio, basic 3 camera system, black & white,									
3800 electrical & electronic equip. only	4 Elec	.80	40	Total	14,400	2,275		16,675	19,300
4000 Full console		.28	114		61,500	6,475		67,975	77,000
4100 As above, but color system		.28	114		81,500	6,475		87,975	99,000
4120 Full console		.12	266		354,000	15,100		369,100	412,000
4200 For film chain, black & white, add	1 Elec	1	8	Ea.	16,500	455		16,955	18,900
4250 Color, add		.25	32		20,100	1,800		21,900	24,800
4400 For video recorders, add		1	8		3,475	455		3,930	4,500
4600 Premium	4 Elec	.40	80		28,900	4,525		33,425	38,600

28 23 19 - Digital Video Recorders and Analog Recording Devices

28 23 19.10 Digital Video Recorder (DVR)

	Crew	Daily Output	Labor-Hours	Unit	Material	2017 Bare Costs Labor	Equipment	Total	Total Incl O&P
0010 **DIGITAL VIDEO RECORDER (DVR)**									
0100 Pentaplex hybrid, internet protocol, and hard drive									
0200 4 channel	1 Elec	1.33	6.015	Ea.	1,350	340		1,690	1,975
0300 8 channel		1	8		3,050	455		3,505	4,025
0400 16 channel		1	8		3,375	455		3,830	4,375

28 23 23 - Video Surveillance Systems Infrastructure

28 23 23.50 Video Surveillance Equipments

	Crew	Daily Output	Labor-Hours	Unit	Material	2017 Bare Costs Labor	Equipment	Total	Total Incl O&P
0010 **VIDEO SURVEILLANCE EQUIPMENTS**									
0200 Video cameras, wireless, hidden in exit signs, clocks, etc., incl. receiver	1 Elec	3	2.667	Ea.	200	151		351	445
0210 Accessories for video recorder, single camera		3	2.667		183	151		334	425
0220 For multiple cameras		3	2.667		1,750	151		1,901	2,150
0230 Video cameras, wireless, for under vehicle searching, complete		2	4		16,000	226		16,226	17,900
0234 Master monitor station, 3 doors x 5 color monitor with tilt feature		2	4		810	226		1,036	1,225
0400 Internet protocol network camera, day/night, color & power supply		2.60	3.077		1,150	174		1,324	1,525
0500 Monitor, color flat screen, liquid crystal display (LCD), 15"		2.70	2.963		580	168		748	890
0520 17"		2.70	2.963		620	168		788	930
0540 19"		2.70	2.963		650	168		818	965

28 31 23 – Fire Detection and Alarm Annunciation Panels and Fire Stations

28 31 23.50 Alarm Panels and Devices	Crew	Daily Output	Labor-Hours	Unit	Material	2017 Bare Costs Labor	Equipment	Total	Total Incl O&P
0010 **ALARM PANELS AND DEVICES**, not including wires & conduits									
2200 Intercom remote station	1 Elec	8	1	Ea.	169	56.50		225.50	271
2400 Intercom outlet		8	1		99.50	56.50		156	194
2600 Sound system, intercom handset		8	1		330	56.50		386.50	445
3590 Signal device, beacon		8	1		202	56.50		258.50	310
3594 2 zone	▼	1.35	5.926		310	335		645	845
3600 4 zone	2 Elec	2	8		575	455		1,030	1,300
3610 3 zone		2	8		715	455		1,170	1,475
3800 8 zone		1	16		860	905		1,765	2,300
3810 5 zone		1.50	10.667		795	605		1,400	1,775
3900 10 zone		1.25	12.800		1,050	725		1,775	2,225
4000 12 zone	▼	.67	23.988		2,150	1,350		3,500	4,400
4020 Alarm device, tamper, flow	1 Elec	8	1		240	56.50		296.50	350
4025 Fire alarm, loop expander card		16	.500		740	28.50		768.50	855
4050 Actuating device	▼	8	1		340	56.50		396.50	460
4160 Alarm control panel, addressable w/o voice, up to 200 points	2 Elec	1.14	13.998		4,525	790		5,315	6,150
4170 addressable w/voice, up to 400 points	"	.73	22.008		9,525	1,250		10,775	12,400
4175 Addressable interface device	1 Elec	7.25	1.103		136	62.50		198.50	244
4200 Battery and rack		4	2		415	113		528	625
4400 Automatic charger		8	1		590	56.50		646.50	735
4600 Signal bell		8	1		130	56.50		186.50	228
4610 Fire alarm signal bell 10 Inch red 20-24 V P		8	1		136	56.50		192.50	234
4800 Trouble buzzer or manual station		8	1		84	56.50		140.50	178
5425 Duct smoke and heat detector 2 wire		8	1		131	56.50		187.50	229
5430 Fire alarm duct detector controller		3	2.667		197	151		348	445
5435 Fire alarm duct detector sensor kit		8	1		75	56.50		131.50	168
5440 Remote test station for smoke detector duct type		5.30	1.509		60.50	85.50		146	195
5460 Remote fire alarm indicator light		5.30	1.509		18.55	85.50		104.05	149
5600 Strobe and horn		5.30	1.509		154	85.50		239.50	297
5610 Strobe and horn (ADA type)		5.30	1.509		154	85.50		239.50	297
5620 Visual alarm (ADA type)		6.70	1.194		104	67.50		171.50	215
5800 Fire alarm horn		6.70	1.194		61.50	67.50		129	169
6000 Door holder, electro-magnetic		4	2		104	113		217	284
6200 Combination holder and closer		3.20	2.500		124	142		266	350
6600 Drill switch		8	1		375	56.50		431.50	495
6800 Master box		2.70	2.963		6,475	168		6,643	7,375
7000 Break glass station		8	1		61.50	56.50		118	153
7010 Break glass station, addressable		7.25	1.103		149	62.50		211.50	258
7800 Remote annunciator, 8 zone lamp	▼	1.80	4.444		213	252		465	610
8000 12 zone lamp	2 Elec	2.60	6.154		420	350		770	985
8200 16 zone lamp	"	2.20	7.273	▼	380	410		790	1,025

28 31 43 – Fire Detection Sensors

28 31 43.50 Fire and Heat Detectors

	Crew	Daily Output	Labor-Hours	Unit	Material	Labor	Equipment	Total	Total Incl O&P
0010 **FIRE & HEAT DETECTORS**									
5000 Detector,W/bell at rate of rise	1 Elec	8	1	Ea.	51.50	56.50		108	142
5010 Heat addressable type		7.25	1.103		259	62.50		321.50	380
5100 Fixed temp signal bell for fire alarm		7	1.143		51.50	64.50		116	154
5200 125 V SRF MT-135F		7.25	1.103		28	62.50		90.50	125
5300 MT-195F		7.25	1.103		28	62.50		90.50	125
5400 104/85 DB, indoor/outdoor, ceiling/wall, red		10.25	.780		64.50	44		108.50	137
5410 Ceiling/wall, white		10.25	.780		60.50	44		104.50	133
5420 102/98 DB, lumin 110cd, indoor/wall, red	▼	10.25	.780	▼	113	44		157	191

For customer support on your Electrical Costs with RSMeans Data, call 800.448.8182.

331

28 31 Fire Detection and Alarm

28 31 43 – Fire Detection Sensors

28 31 43.50 Fire and Heat Detectors	Crew	Daily Output	Labor-Hours	Unit	Material	2017 Bare Costs Labor	Equipment	Total	Total Incl O&P
5430 Lumin15/75cd, indoor/wall, red	1 Elec	10.25	.780	Ea.	110	44		154	187
5440 HI/LO DB, 24V, fire marking, red	↓	10.25	.780	↓	55	44		99	127

28 31 46 – Smoke Detection Sensors

28 31 46.50 Smoke Detectors

	Crew	Daily Output	Labor-Hours	Unit	Material	2017 Bare Costs Labor	Equipment	Total	Total Incl O&P
0010 **SMOKE DETECTORS**									
5200 Smoke detector, ceiling type	1 Elec	6.20	1.290	Ea.	130	73		203	252
5240 Smoke detector addressable type		6	1.333		224	75.50		299.50	360
5400 Duct type		3.20	2.500		330	142		472	575
5420 Duct addressable type		3.20	2.500		515	142		657	775
8300 Smoke alarm with w/integrated strobe light 120 V 16DB 60 FPM flash rate		16	.500		92	28.50		120.50	144
8310 Photoelectric smoke detector with strobe 120 V 90 DB ceiling mount		12	.667		160	37.50		197.50	233
8320 120 V, 90 DB wall mount		12	.667		159	37.50		196.50	232
8330 120 V, 9 VDC, 90 DB ceiling mount		12	.667		155	37.50		192.50	227
8340 120 V, 9 VDC backup 90 DB wall mount	↓	12	.667		155	37.50		192.50	227
8440 Fire alarm beam detector, motorised reflective, infrared optical beam	2 Elec	1.60	10	↓	800	565		1,365	1,725

28 31 49 – Carbon-Monoxide Detection Sensors

28 31 49.50 Carbon-Monoxide Detectors

	Crew	Daily Output	Labor-Hours	Unit	Material	2017 Bare Costs Labor	Equipment	Total	Total Incl O&P
0010 **CARBON-MONOXIDE DETECTORS**									
8400 Smoke and carbon monoxide alarm battery operated photoelectric low profile	1 Elec	24	.333	Ea.	46	18.85		64.85	79
8410 low profile photoelectric battery powered		24	.333		28.50	18.85		47.35	60
8420 photoelectric low profile sealed lithium		24	.333		48.50	18.85		67.35	81.50
8430 Photoelectric low profile sealed lithium smoke and CO with voice combo		24	.333		38	18.85		56.85	70.50
8500 Carbon monoxide sensor, wall mount 1Mod 1 relay output smoke & heat		24	.333		530	18.85		548.85	610
8510 1Mod, 1relay no display, smoke & heat		24	.333		500	18.85		518.85	580
8530 1Mod 1 relay no HW logo smoke & heat		24	.333		555	18.85		573.85	640
8700 Carbon monoxide detector, battery operated, wall mounted		16	.500		52.50	28.50		81	100
8710 Hardwired, wall and ceiling mounted		8	1		101	56.50		157.50	196
8720 Duct mounted	↓	8	1		345	56.50		401.50	460
8730 Continuous air monitoring system, PC based, incl remote sensors, min	2 Elec	.25	64		31,200	3,625		34,825	39,700
8740 Maximum	"	.10	160	↓	49,900	9,050		58,950	68,500

28 39 Mass Notification Systems

28 39 10 – Notification Systems

28 39 10.10 Mass Notification System

	Crew	Daily Output	Labor-Hours	Unit	Material	2017 Bare Costs Labor	Equipment	Total	Total Incl O&P
0010 **MASS NOTIFICATION SYSTEM**									
0100 Wireless command center, 10,000 devices	2 Elec	1.33	12.030	Ea.	2,275	680		2,955	3,525
0200 Option, email notification					1,700			1,700	1,850
0210 Remote device supervision & monitor					2,425			2,425	2,650
0300 Antenna VHF or UHF, for medium range	1 Elec	4	2		87	113		200	266
0310 For high-power transmitter		2	4		990	226		1,216	1,450
0400 Transmitter, 25 watt		4	2		1,650	113		1,763	1,975
0410 40 watt		2.66	3.008		1,900	170		2,070	2,350
0420 100 watt		1.33	6.015		6,175	340		6,515	7,300
0500 Wireless receiver/control module for speaker		8	1		279	56.50		335.50	390
0600 Desktop paging controller, stand alone		4	2		760	113		873	1,000
0700 Auxiliary level inputs	↓	8.36	.957	↓	76	54		130	165

28 41 Electronic Structural Monitoring Systems

28 41 13 – Building Systems

28 41 13.10 Load Cell Units	Crew	Daily Output	Labor- Hours	Unit	Material	2017 Bare Costs Labor	Equipment	Total	Total Incl O&P
0010 **LOAD CELL UNITS**									
0100 Load cell, stainless steel, 0.5/1 ton rated, mounting unit	2 Elec	1.33	12.030	Ea.	550	680		1,230	1,625
0110 2/3 to 5/5 ton rated, mounting unit		1.20	13.333		605	755		1,360	1,800
0120 0.5/1/2/3.5/5 ton, self aligning bottom base		1.66	9.639		175	545		720	1,000
0130 Combo mounting unit, 10/25 ton rated		.86	18.605		1,575	1,050		2,625	3,325
0140 40/60 ton rated		.66	24.242		2,400	1,375		3,775	4,700
0150 60kg/3m, rated		1.84	8.696		1,325	490		1,815	2,200
0160 130kg/3m, rated		1.55	10.323		1,275	585		1,860	2,275
0170 280 kg, rated		1.22	13.115		1,275	740		2,015	2,500

28 46 Electronic Detention Monitoring and Control Systems

28 46 13 – Hard-Wired Detention Monitoring and Control Systems

28 46 13.10 Detention Control Systems	Crew	Daily Output	Labor- Hours	Unit	Material	2017 Bare Costs Labor	Equipment	Total	Total Incl O&P
0010 **DETENTION CONTROL SYSTEMS**									
1000 Desk top control systems for 10 doors, 10 intercoms, and 10 lights	2 Elec	.30	53.333	Ea.	61,500	3,025		64,525	72,500
1020 Push button control panel systems for 10 doors, 10 intercoms, and 10 lights	"	.32	50	"	55,500	2,825		58,325	65,500

For customer support on your Electrical Costs with RSMeans Data, call 800.448.8182.

333

Division Notes

		CREW	DAILY OUTPUT	LABOR-HOURS	UNIT	BARE COSTS				TOTAL INCL O&P
						MAT.	LABOR	EQUIP.	TOTAL	

Estimating Tips
31 05 00 Common Work Results for Earthwork

- Estimating the actual cost of performing earthwork requires careful consideration of the variables involved. This includes items such as type of soil, whether water will be encountered, dewatering, whether banks need bracing, disposal of excavated earth, and length of haul to fill or spoil sites, etc. If the project has large quantities of cut or fill, consider raising or lowering the site to reduce costs, while paying close attention to the effect on site drainage and utilities.

- If the project has large quantities of fill, creating a borrow pit on the site can significantly lower the costs.

- It is very important to consider what time of year the project is scheduled for completion. Bad weather can create large cost overruns from dewatering, site repair, and lost productivity from cold weather.

Reference Numbers

Reference numbers are shown at the beginning of some major classifications. These numbers refer to related items in the Reference Section. The reference information may be an estimating procedure, an alternate pricing method, or technical information.

Note: Not all subdivisions listed here necessarily appear. ■

31 23 Excavation and Fill

31 23 16 – Excavation

31 23 16.13 Excavating, Trench

31 23 16.13 Excavating, Trench	Crew	Daily Output	Labor-Hours	Unit	Material	2017 Bare Costs Labor	Equipment	Total	Total Incl O&P
0010 **EXCAVATING, TRENCH**									
0011 Or continuous footing									
0020 Common earth with no sheeting or dewatering included									
0050 1' to 4' deep, 3/8 C.Y. excavator	B-11C	150	.107	B.C.Y.		4.94	2.44	7.38	10.20
0060 1/2 C.Y. excavator	B-11M	200	.080			3.71	1.97	5.68	7.80
0062 3/4 C.Y. excavator	B-12F	270	.059			2.81	2.50	5.31	7
1400 By hand with pick and shovel 2' to 6' deep, light soil	1 Clab	8	1			39		39	60
1500 Heavy soil	"	4	2	↓		78.50		78.50	120
3000 Backfill trench, F.E. loader, wheel mtd., 1 C.Y. bucket									
3020 Minimal haul	B-10R	400	.030	L.C.Y.		1.46	.78	2.24	3.08
5020 Loam & sandy clay with no sheeting or dewatering included									
5050 1' to 4' deep, 3/8 C.Y. tractor loader/backhoe	B-11C	162	.099	B.C.Y.		4.58	2.26	6.84	9.45
5060 1/2 C.Y. excavator	B-11M	216	.074			3.43	1.83	5.26	7.20
5070 3/4 C.Y. excavator	B-12F	292	.055	↓		2.60	2.31	4.91	6.50
6020 Sand & gravel with no sheeting or dewatering included									
6050 1' to 4' deep, 3/8 C.Y. excavator	B-11C	165	.097	B.C.Y.		4.49	2.22	6.71	9.30
6060 1/2 C.Y. excavator	B-11M	220	.073			3.37	1.79	5.16	7.10
6070 3/4 C.Y. excavator	B-12F	297	.054	↓		2.56	2.27	4.83	6.40
7020 Dense hard clay with no sheeting or dewatering included									
7050 1' to 4' deep, 3/8 C.Y. excavator	B-11C	132	.121	B.C.Y.		5.60	2.77	8.37	11.60
7060 1/2 C.Y. excavator	B-11M	176	.091			4.21	2.24	6.45	8.85
7070 3/4 C.Y. excavator	B-12F	238	.067	↓		3.19	2.83	6.02	7.95

31 23 16.14 Excavating, Utility Trench

31 23 16.14 Excavating, Utility Trench	Crew	Daily Output	Labor-Hours	Unit	Material	2017 Bare Costs Labor	Equipment	Total	Total Incl O&P
0010 **EXCAVATING, UTILITY TRENCH**									
0011 Common earth									
0050 Trenching with chain trencher, 12 H.P., operator walking									
0100 4" wide trench, 12" deep	B-53	800	.010	L.F.		.51	.08	.59	.86
0150 18" deep		750	.011			.54	.08	.62	.91
0200 24" deep		700	.011			.58	.09	.67	.98
0300 6" wide trench, 12" deep		650	.012			.63	.10	.73	1.06
0350 18" deep		600	.013			.68	.11	.79	1.15
0400 24" deep		550	.015			.74	.12	.86	1.25
0450 36" deep		450	.018			.91	.14	1.05	1.53
0600 8" wide trench, 12" deep		475	.017			.86	.13	.99	1.45
0650 18" deep		400	.020			1.02	.16	1.18	1.72
0700 24" deep		350	.023			1.17	.18	1.35	1.96
0750 36" deep	↓	300	.027	↓		1.36	.21	1.57	2.29
1000 Backfill by hand including compaction, add									
1050 4" wide trench, 12" deep	A-1G	800	.010	L.F.		.39	.07	.46	.68
1100 18" deep		530	.015			.59	.11	.70	1.03
1150 24" deep		400	.020			.78	.14	.92	1.36
1300 6" wide trench, 12" deep		540	.015			.58	.11	.69	1.01
1350 18" deep		405	.020			.77	.14	.91	1.34
1400 24" deep		270	.030			1.16	.21	1.37	2.01
1450 36" deep		180	.044			1.74	.32	2.06	3.02
1600 8" wide trench, 12" deep		400	.020			.78	.14	.92	1.36
1650 18" deep		265	.030			1.18	.21	1.39	2.05
1700 24" deep		200	.040			1.57	.28	1.85	2.71
1750 36" deep	↓	135	.059			2.32	.42	2.74	4.02
2000 Chain trencher, 40 H.P. operator riding									
2050 6" wide trench and backfill, 12" deep	B-54	1200	.007	L.F.		.34	.27	.61	.81
2100 18" deep	↓	1000	.008	↓		.41	.33	.74	.98

31 23 Excavation and Fill

31 23 16 – Excavation

31 23 16.14 Excavating, Utility Trench

		Crew	Daily Output	Labor-Hours	Unit	Material	2017 Bare Costs Labor	2017 Bare Costs Equipment	Total	Total Incl O&P
2150	24" deep	B-54	975	.008	L.F.		.47	.33	.75	1
2200	36" deep		900	.009			.45	.36	.81	1.09
2250	48" deep		750	.011			.54	.43	.97	1.30
2300	60" deep		650	.012			.63	.50	1.13	1.50
2400	8" wide trench and backfill, 12" deep		1000	.008			.41	.33	.74	.98
2450	18" deep		950	.008			.43	.34	.77	1.03
2500	24" deep		900	.009			.45	.36	.81	1.09
2550	36" deep		800	.010			.51	.41	.92	1.22
2600	48" deep		650	.012			.63	.50	1.13	1.50
2700	12" wide trench and backfill, 12" deep		975	.008			.42	.33	.75	1
2750	18" deep		860	.009			.47	.38	.85	1.14
2800	24" deep		800	.010			.51	.41	.92	1.22
2850	36" deep		725	.011			.56	.45	1.01	1.34
3000	16" wide trench and backfill, 12" deep		835	.010			.49	.39	.88	1.17
3050	18" deep		750	.011			.54	.43	.97	1.30
3100	24" deep	↓	700	.011	↓		.58	.46	1.04	1.39
3200	Compaction with vibratory plate, add								35%	35%
5100	Hand excavate and trim for pipe bells after trench excavation									
5200	8" pipe	1 Clab	155	.052	L.F.		2.02		2.02	3.10
5300	18" pipe	"	130	.062	"		2.41		2.41	3.69

31 23 16.15 Excavating, Utility Trench, Plow

		Crew	Daily Output	Labor-Hours	Unit	Material	2017 Bare Costs Labor	2017 Bare Costs Equipment	Total	Total Incl O&P
0010	**EXCAVATING, UTILITY TRENCH, PLOW**									
0100	Single cable, plowed into fine material	B-54C	3800	.004	L.F.		.20	.30	.50	.63
0200	Two cable		3200	.005			.23	.36	.59	.75
0300	Single cable, plowed into coarse material	↓	2000	.008	↓		.37	.58	.95	1.20

31 23 16.16 Structural Excavation for Minor Structures

		Crew	Daily Output	Labor-Hours	Unit	Material	2017 Bare Costs Labor	2017 Bare Costs Equipment	Total	Total Incl O&P
0010	**STRUCTURAL EXCAVATION FOR MINOR STRUCTURES**									
0015	Hand, pits to 6' deep, sandy soil	1 Clab	8	1	B.C.Y.		39		39	60
0100	Heavy soil or clay		4	2			78.50		78.50	120
0300	Pits 6' to 12' deep, sandy soil		5	1.600			62.50		62.50	96
0500	Heavy soil or clay		3	2.667			104		104	160
0700	Pits 12' to 18' deep, sandy soil		4	2			78.50		78.50	120
0900	Heavy soil or clay	↓	2	4			157		157	240
6030	Common earth, hydraulic backhoe, 1/2 C.Y. bucket	B-12E	55	.291			13.80	8.05	21.85	30
6035	3/4 C.Y. bucket	B-12F	90	.178			8.45	7.50	15.95	21
6040	1 C.Y. bucket	B-12A	108	.148			7.05	7.40	14.45	18.85
6050	1-1/2 C.Y. bucket	B-12B	144	.111			5.25	6.70	11.95	15.35
6060	2 C.Y. bucket	B-12C	200	.080			3.79	5.60	9.39	11.95
6070	Sand and gravel, 3/4 C.Y. bucket	B-12F	100	.160			7.60	6.75	14.35	18.95
6080	1 C.Y. bucket	B-12A	120	.133			6.30	6.65	12.95	16.90
6090	1-1/2 C.Y. bucket	B-12B	160	.100			4.74	6.05	10.79	13.85
6100	2 C.Y. bucket	B-12C	220	.073			3.45	5.10	8.55	10.85
6110	Clay, till, or blasted rock, 3/4 C.Y. bucket	B-12F	80	.200			9.50	8.45	17.95	23.50
6120	1 C.Y. bucket	B-12A	95	.168			8	8.40	16.40	21.50
6130	1-1/2 C.Y. bucket	B-12B	130	.123			5.85	7.40	13.25	17.05
6140	2 C.Y. bucket	B-12C	175	.091			4.34	6.40	10.74	13.65
6230	Sandy clay & loam, hydraulic backhoe, 1/2 C.Y. bucket	B-12E	60	.267			12.65	7.40	20.05	27.50
6235	3/4 C.Y. bucket	B-12F	98	.163			7.75	6.90	14.65	19.35
6240	1 C.Y. bucket	B-12A	116	.138			6.55	6.90	13.45	17.50
6250	1-1/2 C.Y. bucket	B-12B	156	.103			4.86	6.20	11.06	14.20

For customer support on your Electrical Costs with RSMeans Data, call 800.448.8182.

337

31 23 19 – Dewatering

31 23 19.20 Dewatering Systems	Crew	Daily Output	Labor-Hours	Unit	Material	2017 Bare Costs Labor	2017 Bare Costs Equipment	Total	Total Incl O&P
0010 DEWATERING SYSTEMS									
0020 Excavate drainage trench, 2' wide, 2' deep	B-11C	90	.178	C.Y.		8.25	4.07	12.32	17.05
0100 2' wide, 3' deep, with backhoe loader	"	135	.119			5.50	2.71	8.21	11.35
0200 Excavate sump pits by hand, light soil	1 Clab	7.10	1.127			44		44	67.50
0300 Heavy soil	"	3.50	2.286			89.50		89.50	137
0500 Pumping 8 hr., attended 2 hrs. per day, including 20 L.F.									
0550 of suction hose & 100 L.F. discharge hose									
0600 2" diaphragm pump used for 8 hours	B-10H	4	3	Day		146	18.70	164.70	243
0650 4" diaphragm pump used for 8 hours	B-10I	4	3			146	30.50	176.50	256
0800 8 hrs. attended, 2" diaphragm pump	B-10H	1	12			585	75	660	970
0900 3" centrifugal pump	B-10J	1	12			585	85	670	985
1000 4" diaphragm pump	B-10I	1	12			585	122	707	1,025
1100 6" centrifugal pump	B-10K	1	12			585	350	935	1,275

31 23 23 – Fill

31 23 23.13 Backfill

	Crew	Daily Output	Labor-Hours	Unit	Material	2017 Bare Costs Labor	2017 Bare Costs Equipment	Total	Total Incl O&P
0010 BACKFILL									
0015 By hand, no compaction, light soil	1 Clab	14	.571	L.C.Y.		22.50		22.50	34.50
0100 Heavy soil		11	.727	"		28.50		28.50	43.50
0300 Compaction in 6" layers, hand tamp, add to above		20.60	.388	E.C.Y.		15.20		15.20	23.50
0400 Roller compaction operator walking, add	B-10A	100	.120			5.85	1.83	7.68	10.90
0500 Air tamp, add	B-9D	190	.211			8.35	1.29	9.64	14.15
0600 Vibrating plate, add	A-1D	60	.133			5.20	.56	5.76	8.60
0800 Compaction in 12" layers, hand tamp, add to above	1 Clab	34	.235			9.20		9.20	14.10
0900 Roller compaction operator walking, add	B-10A	150	.080			3.90	1.22	5.12	7.25
1000 Air tamp, add	B-9	285	.140			5.55	.75	6.30	9.30
1100 Vibrating plate, add	A-1E	90	.089			3.48	.48	3.96	5.85
1300 Dozer backfilling, bulk, up to 300' haul, no compaction	B-10B	1200	.010	L.C.Y.		.49	1.15	1.64	2.01
1400 Air tamped, add	B-11B	80	.200	E.C.Y.		9	3.42	12.42	17.45
1600 Compacting backfill, 6" to 12" lifts, vibrating roller	B-10C	800	.015			.73	2.26	2.99	3.60
1700 Sheepsfoot roller	B-10D	750	.016			.78	2.45	3.23	3.87
1900 Dozer backfilling, trench, up to 300' haul, no compaction	B-10B	900	.013	L.C.Y.		.65	1.54	2.19	2.68
2000 Air tamped, add	B-11B	80	.200	E.C.Y.		9	3.42	12.42	17.45
2200 Compacting backfill, 6" to 12" lifts, vibrating roller	B-10C	700	.017			.84	2.59	3.43	4.12
2300 Sheepsfoot roller	B-10D	650	.018			.90	2.82	3.72	4.48

31 23 23.16 Fill By Borrow and Utility Bedding

	Crew	Daily Output	Labor-Hours	Unit	Material	2017 Bare Costs Labor	2017 Bare Costs Equipment	Total	Total Incl O&P
0010 FILL BY BORROW AND UTILITY BEDDING									
0049 Utility bedding, for pipe & conduit, not incl. compaction									
0050 Crushed or screened bank run gravel	B-6	150	.160	L.C.Y.	21.50	6.90	2.44	30.84	36.50
0100 Crushed stone 3/4" to 1/2"		150	.160		26	6.90	2.44	35.34	41.50
0200 Sand, dead or bank		150	.160		18.60	6.90	2.44	27.94	33.50
0500 Compacting bedding in trench	A-1D	90	.089	E.C.Y.		3.48	.37	3.85	5.75
0610 See Section 31 23 23.20 for hauling mileage add.									

31 23 23.20 Hauling

	Crew	Daily Output	Labor-Hours	Unit	Material	2017 Bare Costs Labor	2017 Bare Costs Equipment	Total	Total Incl O&P
0010 HAULING									
0011 Excavated or borrow, loose cubic yards									
0012 no loading equipment, including hauling, waiting, loading/dumping									
0013 time per cycle (wait, load, travel, unload or dump & return)									
0014 8 C.Y. truck, 15 MPH ave, cycle 0.5 miles, 10 min. wait/Ld./Uld.	B-34A	320	.025	L.C.Y.		1.14	1.22	2.36	3.06
0016 cycle 1 mile		272	.029			1.34	1.44	2.78	3.60
0018 cycle 2 miles		208	.038			1.75	1.88	3.63	4.71
0020 cycle 4 miles		144	.056			2.53	2.72	5.25	6.80

31 23 23.20 Hauling		Crew	Daily Output	Labor-Hours	Unit	Material	2017 Bare Costs Labor	Equipment	Total	Total Incl O&P
0022	cycle 8 miles	B-34A	112	.071	LCY		3.25	3.49	6.74	8.75
0024	cycle 8 miles		88	.091			4.14	4.44	8.58	11.15
0026	20 MPH ave, cycle 0.5 mile		336	.024			1.08	1.16	2.24	2.92
0028	cycle 1 mile		296	.027			1.23	1.32	2.55	3.31
0030	cycle 2 miles		240	.033			1.52	1.63	3.15	4.08
0032	cycle 4 miles		176	.045			2.07	2.22	4.29	5.55
0034	cycle 6 miles		136	.059			2.68	2.88	5.56	7.20
0036	cycle 8 miles		112	.071			3.25	3.49	6.74	8.75
0044	25 MPH ave, cycle 4 miles		192	.042			1.90	2.04	3.94	5.10
0046	cycle 6 miles		160	.050			2.28	2.44	4.72	6.15
0048	cycle 8 miles		128	.063			2.85	3.06	5.91	7.65
0050	30 MPH ave, cycle 4 miles		216	.037			1.69	1.81	3.50	4.53
0052	cycle 6 miles		176	.045			2.07	2.22	4.29	5.55
0054	cycle 8 miles		144	.056			2.53	2.72	5.25	6.80
0114	15 MPH ave, cycle 0.5 mile, 15 min. wait/Ld./Uld.		224	.036			1.63	1.75	3.38	4.37
0116	cycle 1 mile		200	.040			1.82	1.96	3.78	4.90
0118	cycle 2 miles		168	.048			2.17	2.33	4.50	5.85
0120	cycle 4 miles		120	.067			3.04	3.26	6.30	8.15
0122	cycle 6 miles		96	.083			3.80	4.07	7.87	10.20
0124	cycle 8 miles		80	.100			4.56	4.89	9.45	12.25
0126	20 MPH ave, cycle 0.5 mile		232	.034			1.57	1.69	3.26	4.22
0128	cycle 1 mile		208	.038			1.75	1.88	3.63	4.71
0130	cycle 2 miles		184	.043			1.98	2.13	4.11	5.35
0132	cycle 4 miles		144	.056			2.53	2.72	5.25	6.80
0134	cycle 6 miles		112	.071			3.25	3.49	6.74	8.75
0136	cycle 8 miles		96	.083			3.80	4.07	7.87	10.20
0144	25 MPH ave, cycle 4 miles		152	.053			2.40	2.57	4.97	6.45
0146	cycle 6 miles		128	.063			2.85	3.06	5.91	7.65
0148	cycle 8 miles		112	.071			3.25	3.49	6.74	8.75
0150	30 MPH ave, cycle 4 miles		168	.048			2.17	2.33	4.50	5.85
0152	cycle 6 miles		144	.056			2.53	2.72	5.25	6.80
0154	cycle 8 miles		120	.067			3.04	3.26	6.30	8.15
0214	15 MPH ave, cycle 0.5 mile, 20 min wait/Ld./Uld.		176	.045			2.07	2.22	4.29	5.55
0216	cycle 1 mile		160	.050			2.28	2.44	4.72	6.15
0218	cycle 2 miles		136	.059			2.68	2.88	5.56	7.20
0220	cycle 4 miles		104	.077			3.50	3.76	7.26	9.45
0222	cycle 6 miles		88	.091			4.14	4.44	8.58	11.15
0224	cycle 8 miles		72	.111			5.05	5.45	10.50	13.60
0226	20 MPH ave, cycle 0.5 mile		176	.045			2.07	2.22	4.29	5.55
0228	cycle 1 mile		168	.048			2.17	2.33	4.50	5.85
0230	cycle 2 miles		144	.056			2.53	2.72	5.25	6.80
0232	cycle 4 miles		120	.067			3.04	3.26	6.30	8.15
0234	cycle 6 miles		96	.083			3.80	4.07	7.87	10.20
0236	cycle 8 miles		88	.091			4.14	4.44	8.58	11.15
0244	25 MPH ave, cycle 4 miles		128	.063			2.85	3.06	5.91	7.65
0246	cycle 6 miles		112	.071			3.25	3.49	6.74	8.75
0248	cycle 8 miles		96	.083			3.80	4.07	7.87	10.20
0250	30 MPH ave, cycle 4 miles		136	.059			2.68	2.88	5.56	7.20
0252	cycle 6 miles		120	.067			3.04	3.26	6.30	8.15
0254	cycle 8 miles		104	.077			3.50	3.76	7.26	9.45
0314	15 MPH ave, cycle 0.5 mile, 25 min wait/Ld./Uld.		144	.056			2.53	2.72	5.25	6.80
0316	cycle 1 mile		128	.063			2.85	3.06	5.91	7.65
0318	cycle 2 miles		112	.071			3.25	3.49	6.74	8.75

31 23 Excavation and Fill

31 23 23 – Fill

31 23 23.20 Hauling		Crew	Daily Output	Labor-Hours	Unit	Material	2017 Bare Costs Labor	2017 Bare Costs Equipment	Total	Total Incl O&P
0320	cycle 4 miles	B-34A	96	.083	L.C.Y.		3.80	4.07	7.87	10.20
0322	cycle 6 miles		80	.100			4.56	4.89	9.45	12.25
0324	cycle 8 miles		64	.125			5.70	6.10	11.80	15.30
0326	20 MPH ave, cycle 0.5 mile		144	.056			2.53	2.72	5.25	6.80
0328	cycle 1 mile		136	.059			2.68	2.88	5.56	7.20
0330	cycle 2 miles		120	.067			3.04	3.26	6.30	8.15
0332	cycle 4 miles		104	.077			3.50	3.76	7.26	9.45
0334	cycle 6 miles		88	.091			4.14	4.44	8.58	11.15
0336	cycle 8 miles		80	.100			4.56	4.89	9.45	12.25
0344	25 MPH ave, cycle 4 miles		112	.071			3.25	3.49	6.74	8.75
0346	cycle 6 miles		96	.083			3.80	4.07	7.87	10.20
0348	cycle 8 miles		88	.091			4.14	4.44	8.58	11.15
0350	30 MPH ave, cycle 4 miles		112	.071			3.25	3.49	6.74	8.75
0352	cycle 6 miles		104	.077			3.50	3.76	7.26	9.45
0354	cycle 8 miles		96	.083			3.80	4.07	7.87	10.20
0414	15 MPH ave, cycle 0.5 mile, 30 min wait/Ld./Uld.		120	.067			3.04	3.26	6.30	8.15
0416	cycle 1 mile		112	.071			3.25	3.49	6.74	8.75
0418	cycle 2 miles		96	.083			3.80	4.07	7.87	10.20
0420	cycle 4 miles		80	.100			4.56	4.89	9.45	12.25
0422	cycle 6 miles		72	.111			5.05	5.45	10.50	13.60
0424	cycle 8 miles		64	.125			5.70	6.10	11.80	15.30
0426	20 MPH ave, cycle 0.5 mile		120	.067			3.04	3.26	6.30	8.15
0428	cycle 1 mile		112	.071			3.25	3.49	6.74	8.75
0430	cycle 2 miles		104	.077			3.50	3.76	7.26	9.45
0432	cycle 4 miles		88	.091			4.14	4.44	8.58	11.15
0434	cycle 6 miles		80	.100			4.56	4.89	9.45	12.25
0436	cycle 8 miles		72	.111			5.05	5.45	10.50	13.60
0444	25 MPH ave, cycle 4 miles		96	.083			3.80	4.07	7.87	10.20
0446	cycle 6 miles		88	.091			4.14	4.44	8.58	11.15
0448	cycle 8 miles		80	.100			4.56	4.89	9.45	12.25
0450	30 MPH ave, cycle 4 miles		96	.083			3.80	4.07	7.87	10.20
0452	cycle 6 miles		88	.091			4.14	4.44	8.58	11.15
0454	cycle 8 miles		80	.100			4.56	4.89	9.45	12.25
0514	15 MPH ave, cycle 0.5 mile, 35 min wait/Ld./Uld.		104	.077			3.50	3.76	7.26	9.45
0516	cycle 1 mile		96	.083			3.80	4.07	7.87	10.20
0518	cycle 2 miles		88	.091			4.14	4.44	8.58	11.15
0520	cycle 4 miles		72	.111			5.05	5.45	10.50	13.60
0522	cycle 6 miles		64	.125			5.70	6.10	11.80	15.30
0524	cycle 8 miles		56	.143			6.50	7	13.50	17.50
0526	20 MPH ave, cycle 0.5 mile		104	.077			3.50	3.76	7.26	9.45
0528	cycle 1 mile		96	.083			3.80	4.07	7.87	10.20
0530	cycle 2 miles		96	.083			3.80	4.07	7.87	10.20
0532	cycle 4 miles		80	.100			4.56	4.89	9.45	12.25
0534	cycle 6 miles		72	.111			5.05	5.45	10.50	13.60
0536	cycle 8 miles		64	.125			5.70	6.10	11.80	15.30
0544	25 MPH ave, cycle 4 miles		88	.091			4.14	4.44	8.58	11.15
0546	cycle 6 miles		80	.100			4.56	4.89	9.45	12.25
0548	cycle 8 miles		72	.111			5.05	5.45	10.50	13.60
0550	30 MPH ave, cycle 4 miles		88	.091			4.14	4.44	8.58	11.15
0552	cycle 6 miles		80	.100			4.56	4.89	9.45	12.25
0554	cycle 8 miles		72	.111			5.05	5.45	10.50	13.60
1014	12 C.Y. truck, cycle 0.5 mile, 15 MPH ave, 15 min. wait/Ld./Uld.	B-34B	336	.024			1.08	1.91	2.99	3.74
1016	cycle 1 mile		300	.027			1.21	2.14	3.35	4.19

340

31 23 23 – Fill

31 23 23.20 Hauling		Crew	Daily Output	Labor-Hours	Unit	Material	2017 Bare Costs Labor	Equipment	Total	Total Incl O&P
1018	cycle 2 miles	B-34B	252	.032	L.C.Y.		1.45	2.55	4	4.99
1020	cycle 4 miles		180	.044			2.02	3.57	5.59	7
1022	cycle 6 miles		144	.056			2.53	4.46	6.99	8.75
1024	cycle 8 miles		120	.067			3.04	5.35	8.39	10.50
1025	cycle 10 miles		96	.083			3.80	6.70	10.50	13.05
1026	20 MPH ave, cycle 0.5 mile		348	.023			1.05	1.85	2.90	3.61
1028	cycle 1 mile		312	.026			1.17	2.06	3.23	4.03
1030	cycle 2 miles		276	.029			1.32	2.33	3.65	4.55
1032	cycle 4 miles		216	.037			1.69	2.98	4.67	5.80
1034	cycle 6 miles		168	.048			2.17	3.83	6	7.50
1036	cycle 8 miles		144	.056			2.53	4.46	6.99	8.75
1038	cycle 10 miles		120	.067			3.04	5.35	8.39	10.50
1040	25 MPH ave, cycle 4 miles		228	.035			1.60	2.82	4.42	5.50
1042	cycle 6 miles		192	.042			1.90	3.35	5.25	6.55
1044	cycle 8 miles		168	.048			2.17	3.83	6	7.50
1046	cycle 10 miles		144	.056			2.53	4.46	6.99	8.75
1050	30 MPH ave, cycle 4 miles		252	.032			1.45	2.55	4	4.99
1052	cycle 6 miles		216	.037			1.69	2.98	4.67	5.80
1054	cycle 8 miles		180	.044			2.02	3.57	5.59	7
1056	cycle 10 miles		156	.051			2.34	4.12	6.46	8.05
1060	35 MPH ave, cycle 4 miles		264	.030			1.38	2.43	3.81	4.76
1062	cycle 6 miles		228	.035			1.60	2.82	4.42	5.50
1064	cycle 8 miles		204	.039			1.79	3.15	4.94	6.15
1066	cycle 10 miles		180	.044			2.02	3.57	5.59	7
1068	cycle 20 miles		120	.067			3.04	5.35	8.39	10.50
1069	cycle 30 miles		84	.095			4.34	7.65	11.99	14.95
1070	cycle 40 miles		72	.111			5.05	8.95	14	17.45
1072	40 MPH ave, cycle 6 miles		240	.033			1.52	2.68	4.20	5.25
1074	cycle 8 miles		216	.037			1.69	2.98	4.67	5.80
1076	cycle 10 miles		192	.042			1.90	3.35	5.25	6.55
1078	cycle 20 miles		120	.067			3.04	5.35	8.39	10.50
1080	cycle 30 miles		96	.083			3.80	6.70	10.50	13.05
1082	cycle 40 miles		72	.111			5.05	8.95	14	17.45
1084	cycle 50 miles		60	.133			6.05	10.70	16.75	21
1094	45 MPH ave, cycle 8 miles		216	.037			1.69	2.98	4.67	5.80
1096	cycle 10 miles		204	.039			1.79	3.15	4.94	6.15
1098	cycle 20 miles		132	.061			2.76	4.87	7.63	9.50
1100	cycle 30 miles		108	.074			3.37	5.95	9.32	11.65
1102	cycle 40 miles		84	.095			4.34	7.65	11.99	14.95
1104	cycle 50 miles		72	.111			5.05	8.95	14	17.45
1106	50 MPH ave, cycle 10 miles		216	.037			1.69	2.98	4.67	5.80
1108	cycle 20 miles		144	.056			2.53	4.46	6.99	8.75
1110	cycle 30 miles		108	.074			3.37	5.95	9.32	11.65
1112	cycle 40 miles		84	.095			4.34	7.65	11.99	14.95
1114	cycle 50 miles		72	.111			5.05	8.95	14	17.45
1214	15 MPH ave, cycle 0.5 mile, 20 min. wait/Ld./Uld.		264	.030			1.38	2.43	3.81	4.76
1216	cycle 1 mile		240	.033			1.52	2.68	4.20	5.25
1218	cycle 2 miles		204	.039			1.79	3.15	4.94	6.15
1220	cycle 4 miles		156	.051			2.34	4.12	6.46	8.05
1222	cycle 6 miles		132	.061			2.76	4.87	7.63	9.50
1224	cycle 8 miles		108	.074			3.37	5.95	9.32	11.65
1225	cycle 10 miles		96	.083			3.80	6.70	10.50	13.05
1226	20 MPH ave, cycle 0.5 mile		264	.030			1.38	2.43	3.81	4.76

For customer support on your Electrical Costs with RSMeans Data, call 800.448.8182.

341

31 23 23.20 Hauling		Crew	Daily Output	Labor-Hours	Unit	Material	2017 Bare Costs Labor	Equipment	Total	Total Incl O&P
1228	cycle 1 mile	B-34B	252	.032	L.C.Y.		1.45	2.55	4	4.99
1230	cycle 2 miles		216	.037			1.69	2.98	4.67	5.80
1232	cycle 4 miles		180	.044			2.02	3.57	5.59	7
1234	cycle 6 miles		144	.056			2.53	4.46	6.99	8.75
1236	cycle 8 miles		132	.061			2.76	4.87	7.63	9.50
1238	cycle 10 miles		108	.074			3.37	5.95	9.32	11.65
1240	25 MPH ave, cycle 4 miles		192	.042			1.90	3.35	5.25	6.55
1242	cycle 6 miles		168	.048			2.17	3.83	6	7.50
1244	cycle 8 miles		144	.056			2.53	4.46	6.99	8.75
1246	cycle 10 miles		132	.061			2.76	4.87	7.63	9.50
1250	30 MPH ave, cycle 4 miles		204	.039			1.79	3.15	4.94	6.15
1252	cycle 6 miles		180	.044			2.02	3.57	5.59	7
1254	cycle 8 miles		156	.051			2.34	4.12	6.46	8.05
1256	cycle 10 miles		144	.056			2.53	4.46	6.99	8.75
1260	35 MPH ave, cycle 4 miles		216	.037			1.69	2.98	4.67	5.80
1262	cycle 6 miles		192	.042			1.90	3.35	5.25	6.55
1264	cycle 8 miles		168	.048			2.17	3.83	6	7.50
1266	cycle 10 miles		156	.051			2.34	4.12	6.46	8.05
1268	cycle 20 miles		108	.074			3.37	5.95	9.32	11.65
1269	cycle 30 miles		72	.111			5.05	8.95	14	17.45
1270	cycle 40 miles		60	.133			6.05	10.70	16.75	21
1272	40 MPH ave, cycle 6 miles		192	.042			1.90	3.35	5.25	6.55
1274	cycle 8 miles		180	.044			2.02	3.57	5.59	7
1276	cycle 10 miles		156	.051			2.34	4.12	6.46	8.05
1278	cycle 20 miles		108	.074			3.37	5.95	9.32	11.65
1280	cycle 30 miles		84	.095			4.34	7.65	11.99	14.95
1282	cycle 40 miles		72	.111			5.05	8.95	14	17.45
1284	cycle 50 miles		60	.133			6.05	10.70	16.75	21
1294	45 MPH ave, cycle 8 miles		180	.044			2.02	3.57	5.59	7
1296	cycle 10 miles		168	.048			2.17	3.83	6	7.50
1298	cycle 20 miles		120	.067			3.04	5.35	8.39	10.50
1300	cycle 30 miles		96	.083			3.80	6.70	10.50	13.05
1302	cycle 40 miles		72	.111			5.05	8.95	14	17.45
1304	cycle 50 miles		60	.133			6.05	10.70	16.75	21
1306	50 MPH ave, cycle 10 miles		180	.044			2.02	3.57	5.59	7
1308	cycle 20 miles		132	.061			2.76	4.87	7.63	9.50
1310	cycle 30 miles		96	.083			3.80	6.70	10.50	13.05
1312	cycle 40 miles		84	.095			4.34	7.65	11.99	14.95
1314	cycle 50 miles		72	.111			5.05	8.95	14	17.45
1414	15 MPH ave, cycle 0.5 mile, 25 min. wait/Ld./Uld.		204	.039			1.79	3.15	4.94	6.15
1416	cycle 1 mile		192	.042			1.90	3.35	5.25	6.55
1418	cycle 2 miles		168	.048			2.17	3.83	6	7.50
1420	cycle 4 miles		132	.061			2.76	4.87	7.63	9.50
1422	cycle 6 miles		120	.067			3.04	5.35	8.39	10.50
1424	cycle 8 miles		96	.083			3.80	6.70	10.50	13.05
1425	cycle 10 miles		84	.095			4.34	7.65	11.99	14.95
1426	20 MPH ave, cycle 0.5 mile		216	.037			1.69	2.98	4.67	5.80
1428	cycle 1 mile		204	.039			1.79	3.15	4.94	6.15
1430	cycle 2 miles		180	.044			2.02	3.57	5.59	7
1432	cycle 4 miles		156	.051			2.34	4.12	6.46	8.05
1434	cycle 6 miles		132	.061			2.76	4.87	7.63	9.50
1436	cycle 8 miles		120	.067			3.04	5.35	8.39	10.50
1438	cycle 10 miles		96	.083			3.80	6.70	10.50	13.05

31 23 23 – Fill

31 23 23.20 Hauling	Crew	Daily Output	Labor-Hours	Unit	Material	2017 Bare Costs Labor	2017 Bare Costs Equipment	Total	Total Incl O&P
1440	25 MPH ave, cycle 4 miles	R-34B	168	.048	L.C.Y.		2.17	3.83	6	7.50
1442	cycle 6 miles		144	.056			2.53	4.46	6.99	8.75
1444	cycle 8 miles		132	.061			2.76	4.87	7.63	9.50
1446	cycle 10 miles		108	.074			3.37	5.95	9.32	11.65
1450	30 MPH ave, cycle 4 miles		168	.048			2.17	3.83	6	7.50
1452	cycle 6 miles		156	.051			2.34	4.12	6.46	8.05
1454	cycle 8 miles		132	.061			2.76	4.87	7.63	9.50
1456	cycle 10 miles		120	.067			3.04	5.35	8.39	10.50
1460	35 MPH ave, cycle 4 miles		180	.044			2.02	3.57	5.59	7
1462	cycle 6 miles		156	.051			2.34	4.12	6.46	8.05
1464	cycle 8 miles		144	.056			2.53	4.46	6.99	8.75
1466	cycle 10 miles		132	.061			2.76	4.87	7.63	9.50
1468	cycle 20 miles		96	.083			3.80	6.70	10.50	13.05
1469	cycle 30 miles		72	.111			5.05	8.95	14	17.45
1470	cycle 40 miles		60	.133			6.05	10.70	16.75	21
1472	40 MPH ave, cycle 6 miles		168	.048			2.17	3.83	6	7.50
1474	cycle 8 miles		156	.051			2.34	4.12	6.46	8.05
1476	cycle 10 miles		144	.056			2.53	4.46	6.99	8.75
1478	cycle 20 miles		96	.083			3.80	6.70	10.50	13.05
1480	cycle 30 miles		84	.095			4.34	7.65	11.99	14.95
1482	cycle 40 miles		60	.133			6.05	10.70	16.75	21
1484	cycle 50 miles		60	.133			6.05	10.70	16.75	21
1494	45 MPH ave, cycle 8 miles		156	.051			2.34	4.12	6.46	8.05
1496	cycle 10 miles		144	.056			2.53	4.46	6.99	8.75
1498	cycle 20 miles		108	.074			3.37	5.95	9.32	11.65
1500	cycle 30 miles		84	.095			4.34	7.65	11.99	14.95
1502	cycle 40 miles		72	.111			5.05	8.95	14	17.45
1504	cycle 50 miles		60	.133			6.05	10.70	16.75	21
1506	50 MPH ave, cycle 10 miles		156	.051			2.34	4.12	6.46	8.05
1508	cycle 20 miles		120	.067			3.04	5.35	8.39	10.50
1510	cycle 30 miles		96	.083			3.80	6.70	10.50	13.05
1512	cycle 40 miles		72	.111			5.05	8.95	14	17.45
1514	cycle 50 miles		60	.133			6.05	10.70	16.75	21
1614	15 MPH ave, cycle 0.5 mile, 30 min. wait/Ld./Uld.		180	.044			2.02	3.57	5.59	7
1616	cycle 1 mile		168	.048			2.17	3.83	6	7.50
1618	cycle 2 miles		144	.056			2.53	4.46	6.99	8.75
1620	cycle 4 miles		120	.067			3.04	5.35	8.39	10.50
1622	cycle 6 miles		108	.074			3.37	5.95	9.32	11.65
1624	cycle 8 miles		84	.095			4.34	7.65	11.99	14.95
1625	cycle 10 miles		84	.095			4.34	7.65	11.99	14.95
1626	20 MPH ave, cycle 0.5 mile		180	.044			2.02	3.57	5.59	7
1628	cycle 1 mile		168	.048			2.17	3.83	6	7.50
1630	cycle 2 miles		156	.051			2.34	4.12	6.46	8.05
1632	cycle 4 miles		132	.061			2.76	4.87	7.63	9.50
1634	cycle 6 miles		120	.067			3.04	5.35	8.39	10.50
1636	cycle 8 miles		108	.074			3.37	5.95	9.32	11.65
1638	cycle 10 miles		96	.083			3.80	6.70	10.50	13.05
1640	25 MPH ave, cycle 4 miles		144	.056			2.53	4.46	6.99	8.75
1642	cycle 6 miles		132	.061			2.76	4.87	7.63	9.50
1644	cycle 8 miles		108	.074			3.37	5.95	9.32	11.65
1646	cycle 10 miles		108	.074			3.37	5.95	9.32	11.65
1650	30 MPH ave, cycle 4 miles		144	.056			2.53	4.46	6.99	8.75
1652	cycle 6 miles		132	.061			2.76	4.87	7.63	9.50

For customer support on your Electrical Costs with RSMeans Data, call 800.448.8182.

343

31 23 23 – Fill

31 23 23.20 Hauling	Crew	Daily Output	Labor-Hours	Unit	Material	2017 Bare Costs Labor	2017 Bare Costs Equipment	Total	Total Incl O&P
1654	cycle 8 miles	B-34B	120	.067	L.C.Y.		3.04	5.35	8.39	10.50
1656	cycle 10 miles		108	.074			3.37	5.95	9.32	11.65
1660	35 MPH ave, cycle 4 miles		156	.051			2.34	4.12	6.46	8.05
1662	cycle 6 miles		144	.056			2.53	4.46	6.99	8.75
1664	cycle 8 miles		132	.061			2.76	4.87	7.63	9.50
1666	cycle 10 miles		120	.067			3.04	5.35	8.39	10.50
1668	cycle 20 miles		84	.095			4.34	7.65	11.99	14.95
1669	cycle 30 miles		72	.111			5.05	8.95	14	17.45
1670	cycle 40 miles		60	.133			6.05	10.70	16.75	21
1672	40 MPH ave, cycle 6 miles		144	.056			2.53	4.46	6.99	8.75
1674	cycle 8 miles		132	.061			2.76	4.87	7.63	9.50
1676	cycle 10 miles		120	.067			3.04	5.35	8.39	10.50
1678	cycle 20 miles		96	.083			3.80	6.70	10.50	13.05
1680	cycle 30 miles		72	.111			5.05	8.95	14	17.45
1682	cycle 40 miles		60	.133			6.05	10.70	16.75	21
1684	cycle 50 miles		48	.167			7.60	13.40	21	26
1694	45 MPH ave, cycle 8 miles		144	.056			2.53	4.46	6.99	8.75
1696	cycle 10 miles		132	.061			2.76	4.87	7.63	9.50
1698	cycle 20 miles		96	.083			3.80	6.70	10.50	13.05
1700	cycle 30 miles		84	.095			4.34	7.65	11.99	14.95
1702	cycle 40 miles		60	.133			6.05	10.70	16.75	21
1704	cycle 50 miles		60	.133			6.05	10.70	16.75	21
1706	50 MPH ave, cycle 10 miles		132	.061			2.76	4.87	7.63	9.50
1708	cycle 20 miles		108	.074			3.37	5.95	9.32	11.65
1710	cycle 30 miles		84	.095			4.34	7.65	11.99	14.95
1712	cycle 40 miles		72	.111			5.05	8.95	14	17.45
1714	cycle 50 miles		60	.133			6.05	10.70	16.75	21
2000	Hauling, 8 C.Y. truck, small project cost per hour	B-34A	8	1	Hr.		45.50	49	94.50	123
2100	12 C.Y. Truck	B-34B	8	1			45.50	80.50	126	157
2150	16.5 C.Y. Truck	B-34C	8	1			45.50	86	131.50	163
2175	18 C.Y. 8 wheel Truck	B-34I	8	1			45.50	102	147.50	181
2200	20 C.Y. Truck	B-34D	8	1			45.50	88	133.50	165
2300	Grading at dump, or embankment if required, by dozer	B-10B	1000	.012	L.C.Y.		.59	1.38	1.97	2.41
2310	Spotter at fill or cut, if required	1 Clab	8	1	Hr.		39		39	60
9014	18 C.Y. truck, 8 wheels,15 min. wait/Ld./Uld.,15 MPH, cycle 0.5 mi.	B-34I	504	.016	L.C.Y.		.72	1.62	2.34	2.87
9016	cycle 1 mile		450	.018			.81	1.81	2.62	3.21
9018	cycle 2 miles		378	.021			.96	2.16	3.12	3.82
9020	cycle 4 miles		270	.030			1.35	3.02	4.37	5.35
9022	cycle 6 miles		216	.037			1.69	3.78	5.47	6.70
9024	cycle 8 miles		180	.044			2.02	4.53	6.55	8.05
9025	cycle 10 miles		144	.056			2.53	5.65	8.18	10.05
9026	20 MPH ave, cycle 0.5 mile		522	.015			.70	1.56	2.26	2.77
9028	cycle 1 mile		468	.017			.78	1.74	2.52	3.09
9030	cycle 2 miles		414	.019			.88	1.97	2.85	3.50
9032	cycle 4 miles		324	.025			1.12	2.52	3.64	4.47
9034	cycle 6 miles		252	.032			1.45	3.24	4.69	5.75
9036	cycle 8 miles		216	.037			1.69	3.78	5.47	6.70
9038	cycle 10 miles		180	.044			2.02	4.53	6.55	8.05
9040	25 MPH ave, cycle 4 miles		342	.023			1.07	2.38	3.45	4.23
9042	cycle 6 miles		288	.028			1.27	2.83	4.10	5.05
9044	cycle 8 miles		252	.032			1.45	3.24	4.69	5.75
9046	cycle 10 miles		216	.037			1.69	3.78	5.47	6.70
9050	30 MPH ave, cycle 4 miles		378	.021			.96	2.16	3.12	3.82

31 23 23.20 Hauling		Crew	Daily Output	Labor-Hours	Unit	Material	2017 Bare Costs Labor	2017 Bare Costs Equipment	Total	Total Incl O&P
9052	cycle 6 miles	R-34I	324	.025	L.C.Y.		1.12	2.52	3.64	4.47
9054	cycle 8 miles		270	.030			1.35	3.02	4.37	5.35
9056	cycle 10 miles		234	.034			1.56	3.49	5.05	6.20
9060	35 MPH ave, cycle 4 miles		396	.020			.92	2.06	2.98	3.66
9062	cycle 6 miles		342	.023			1.07	2.38	3.45	4.23
9064	cycle 8 miles		288	.028			1.27	2.83	4.10	5.05
9066	cycle 10 miles		270	.030			1.35	3.02	4.37	5.35
9068	cycle 20 miles		162	.049			2.25	5.05	7.30	8.95
9070	cycle 30 miles		126	.063			2.89	6.45	9.34	11.45
9072	cycle 40 miles		90	.089			4.05	9.05	13.10	16.05
9074	40 MPH ave, cycle 6 miles		360	.022			1.01	2.27	3.28	4.02
9076	cycle 8 miles		324	.025			1.12	2.52	3.64	4.47
9078	cycle 10 miles		288	.028			1.27	2.83	4.10	5.05
9080	cycle 20 miles		180	.044			2.02	4.53	6.55	8.05
9082	cycle 30 miles		144	.056			2.53	5.65	8.18	10.05
9084	cycle 40 miles		108	.074			3.37	7.55	10.92	13.40
9086	cycle 50 miles		90	.089			4.05	9.05	13.10	16.05
9094	45 MPH ave, cycle 8 miles		324	.025			1.12	2.52	3.64	4.47
9096	cycle 10 miles		306	.026			1.19	2.67	3.86	4.73
9098	cycle 20 miles		198	.040			1.84	4.12	5.96	7.30
9100	cycle 30 miles		144	.056			2.53	5.65	8.18	10.05
9102	cycle 40 miles		126	.063			2.89	6.45	9.34	11.45
9104	cycle 50 miles		108	.074			3.37	7.55	10.92	13.40
9106	50 MPH ave, cycle 10 miles		324	.025			1.12	2.52	3.64	4.47
9108	cycle 20 miles		216	.037			1.69	3.78	5.47	6.70
9110	cycle 30 miles		162	.049			2.25	5.05	7.30	8.95
9112	cycle 40 miles		126	.063			2.89	6.45	9.34	11.45
9114	cycle 50 miles		108	.074			3.37	7.55	10.92	13.40
9214	20 min. wait/Ld./Uld.,15 MPH, cycle 0.5 mi.		396	.020			.92	2.06	2.98	3.66
9216	cycle 1 mile		360	.022			1.01	2.27	3.28	4.02
9218	cycle 2 miles		306	.026			1.19	2.67	3.86	4.73
9220	cycle 4 miles		234	.034			1.56	3.49	5.05	6.20
9222	cycle 6 miles		198	.040			1.84	4.12	5.96	7.30
9224	cycle 8 miles		162	.049			2.25	5.05	7.30	8.95
9225	cycle 10 miles		144	.056			2.53	5.65	8.18	10.05
9226	20 MPH ave, cycle 0.5 mile		396	.020			.92	2.06	2.98	3.66
9228	cycle 1 mile		378	.021			.96	2.16	3.12	3.82
9230	cycle 2 miles		324	.025			1.12	2.52	3.64	4.47
9232	cycle 4 miles		270	.030			1.35	3.02	4.37	5.35
9234	cycle 6 miles		216	.037			1.69	3.78	5.47	6.70
9236	cycle 8 miles		198	.040			1.84	4.12	5.96	7.30
9238	cycle 10 miles		162	.049			2.25	5.05	7.30	8.95
9240	25 MPH ave, cycle 4 miles		288	.028			1.27	2.83	4.10	5.05
9242	cycle 6 miles		252	.032			1.45	3.24	4.69	5.75
9244	cycle 8 miles		216	.037			1.69	3.78	5.47	6.70
9246	cycle 10 miles		198	.040			1.84	4.12	5.96	7.30
9250	30 MPH ave, cycle 4 miles		306	.026			1.19	2.67	3.86	4.73
9252	cycle 6 miles		270	.030			1.35	3.02	4.37	5.35
9254	cycle 8 miles		234	.034			1.56	3.49	5.05	6.20
9256	cycle 10 miles		216	.037			1.69	3.78	5.47	6.70
9260	35 MPH ave, cycle 4 miles		324	.025			1.12	2.52	3.64	4.47
9262	cycle 6 miles		288	.028			1.27	2.83	4.10	5.05
9264	cycle 8 miles		252	.032			1.45	3.24	4.69	5.75

31 23 23.20 Hauling		Crew	Daily Output	Labor-Hours	Unit	Material	2017 Bare Costs Labor	2017 Bare Costs Equipment	Total	Total Incl O&P
9266	cycle 10 miles	B-34I	234	.034	L.C.Y.		1.56	3.49	5.05	6.20
9268	cycle 20 miles		162	.049			2.25	5.05	7.30	8.95
9270	cycle 30 miles		108	.074			3.37	7.55	10.92	13.40
9272	cycle 40 miles		90	.089			4.05	9.05	13.10	16.05
9274	40 MPH ave, cycle 6 miles		288	.028			1.27	2.83	4.10	5.05
9276	cycle 8 miles		270	.030			1.35	3.02	4.37	5.35
9278	cycle 10 miles		234	.034			1.56	3.49	5.05	6.20
9280	cycle 20 miles		162	.049			2.25	5.05	7.30	8.95
9282	cycle 30 miles		126	.063			2.89	6.45	9.34	11.45
9284	cycle 40 miles		108	.074			3.37	7.55	10.92	13.40
9286	cycle 50 miles		90	.089			4.05	9.05	13.10	16.05
9294	45 MPH ave, cycle 8 miles		270	.030			1.35	3.02	4.37	5.35
9296	cycle 10 miles		252	.032			1.45	3.24	4.69	5.75
9298	cycle 20 miles		180	.044			2.02	4.53	6.55	8.05
9300	cycle 30 miles		144	.056			2.53	5.65	8.18	10.05
9302	cycle 40 miles		108	.074			3.37	7.55	10.92	13.40
9304	cycle 50 miles		90	.089			4.05	9.05	13.10	16.05
9306	50 MPH ave, cycle 10 miles		270	.030			1.35	3.02	4.37	5.35
9308	cycle 20 miles		198	.040			1.84	4.12	5.96	7.30
9310	cycle 30 miles		144	.056			2.53	5.65	8.18	10.05
9312	cycle 40 miles		126	.063			2.89	6.45	9.34	11.45
9314	cycle 50 miles		108	.074			3.37	7.55	10.92	13.40
9414	25 min. wait/Ld./Uld.,15 MPH, cycle 0.5 mi.		306	.026			1.19	2.67	3.86	4.73
9416	cycle 1 mile		288	.028			1.27	2.83	4.10	5.05
9418	cycle 2 miles		252	.032			1.45	3.24	4.69	5.75
9420	cycle 4 miles		198	.040			1.84	4.12	5.96	7.30
9422	cycle 6 miles		180	.044			2.02	4.53	6.55	8.05
9424	cycle 8 miles		144	.056			2.53	5.65	8.18	10.05
9425	cycle 10 miles		126	.063			2.89	6.45	9.34	11.45
9426	20 MPH ave, cycle 0.5 mile		324	.025			1.12	2.52	3.64	4.47
9428	cycle 1 mile		306	.026			1.19	2.67	3.86	4.73
9430	cycle 2 miles		270	.030			1.35	3.02	4.37	5.35
9432	cycle 4 miles		234	.034			1.56	3.49	5.05	6.20
9434	cycle 6 miles		198	.040			1.84	4.12	5.96	7.30
9436	cycle 8 miles		180	.044			2.02	4.53	6.55	8.05
9438	cycle 10 miles		144	.056			2.53	5.65	8.18	10.05
9440	25 MPH ave, cycle 4 miles		252	.032			1.45	3.24	4.69	5.75
9442	cycle 6 miles		216	.037			1.69	3.78	5.47	6.70
9444	cycle 8 miles		198	.040			1.84	4.12	5.96	7.30
9446	cycle 10 miles		180	.044			2.02	4.53	6.55	8.05
9450	30 MPH ave, cycle 4 miles		252	.032			1.45	3.24	4.69	5.75
9452	cycle 6 miles		234	.034			1.56	3.49	5.05	6.20
9454	cycle 8 miles		198	.040			1.84	4.12	5.96	7.30
9456	cycle 10 miles		180	.044			2.02	4.53	6.55	8.05
9460	35 MPH ave, cycle 4 miles		270	.030			1.35	3.02	4.37	5.35
9462	cycle 6 miles		234	.034			1.56	3.49	5.05	6.20
9464	cycle 8 miles		216	.037			1.69	3.78	5.47	6.70
9466	cycle 10 miles		198	.040			1.84	4.12	5.96	7.30
9468	cycle 20 miles		144	.056			2.53	5.65	8.18	10.05
9470	cycle 30 miles		108	.074			3.37	7.55	10.92	13.40
9472	cycle 40 miles		90	.089			4.05	9.05	13.10	16.05
9474	40 MPH ave, cycle 6 miles		252	.032			1.45	3.24	4.69	5.75
9476	cycle 8 miles		234	.034			1.56	3.49	5.05	6.20

31 23 23.20 Hauling		Crew	Daily Output	Labor-Hours	Unit	Material	Labor	Equipment	Total	Total Incl O&P
9478	cycle 10 miles	B-34I	216	.037	L.C.Y.		1.69	3.78	5.47	6.70
9480	cycle 20 miles		144	.056			2.53	5.65	8.18	10.05
9482	cycle 30 miles		126	.063			2.89	6.45	9.34	11.45
9484	cycle 40 miles		90	.089			4.05	9.05	13.10	16.05
9486	cycle 50 miles		90	.089			4.05	9.05	13.10	16.05
9494	45 MPH ave, cycle 8 miles		234	.034			1.56	3.49	5.05	6.20
9496	cycle 10 miles		216	.037			1.69	3.78	5.47	6.70
9498	cycle 20 miles		162	.049			2.25	5.05	7.30	8.95
9500	cycle 30 miles		126	.063			2.89	6.45	9.34	11.45
9502	cycle 40 miles		108	.074			3.37	7.55	10.92	13.40
9504	cycle 50 miles		90	.089			4.05	9.05	13.10	16.05
9506	50 MPH ave, cycle 10 miles		234	.034			1.56	3.49	5.05	6.20
9508	cycle 20 miles		180	.044			2.02	4.53	6.55	8.05
9510	cycle 30 miles		144	.056			2.53	5.65	8.18	10.05
9512	cycle 40 miles		108	.074			3.37	7.55	10.92	13.40
9514	cycle 50 miles		90	.089			4.05	9.05	13.10	16.05
9614	30 min. wait/Ld./Uld.,15 MPH, cycle 0.5 mi.		270	.030			1.35	3.02	4.37	5.35
9616	cycle 1 mile		252	.032			1.45	3.24	4.69	5.75
9618	cycle 2 miles		216	.037			1.69	3.78	5.47	6.70
9620	cycle 4 miles		180	.044			2.02	4.53	6.55	8.05
9622	cycle 6 miles		162	.049			2.25	5.05	7.30	8.95
9624	cycle 8 miles		126	.063			2.89	6.45	9.34	11.45
9625	cycle 10 miles		126	.063			2.89	6.45	9.34	11.45
9626	20 MPH ave, cycle 0.5 mile		270	.030			1.35	3.02	4.37	5.35
9628	cycle 1 mile		252	.032			1.45	3.24	4.69	5.75
9630	cycle 2 miles		234	.034			1.56	3.49	5.05	6.20
9632	cycle 4 miles		198	.040			1.84	4.12	5.96	7.30
9634	cycle 6 miles		180	.044			2.02	4.53	6.55	8.05
9636	cycle 8 miles		162	.049			2.25	5.05	7.30	8.95
9638	cycle 10 miles		144	.056			2.53	5.65	8.18	10.05
9640	25 MPH ave, cycle 4 miles		216	.037			1.69	3.78	5.47	6.70
9642	cycle 6 miles		198	.040			1.84	4.12	5.96	7.30
9644	cycle 8 miles		180	.044			2.02	4.53	6.55	8.05
9646	cycle 10 miles		162	.049			2.25	5.05	7.30	8.95
9650	30 MPH ave, cycle 4 miles		216	.037			1.69	3.78	5.47	6.70
9652	cycle 6 miles		198	.040			1.84	4.12	5.96	7.30
9654	cycle 8 miles		180	.044			2.02	4.53	6.55	8.05
9656	cycle 10 miles		162	.049			2.25	5.05	7.30	8.95
9660	35 MPH ave, cycle 4 miles		234	.034			1.56	3.49	5.05	6.20
9662	cycle 6 miles		216	.037			1.69	3.78	5.47	6.70
9664	cycle 8 miles		198	.040			1.84	4.12	5.96	7.30
9666	cycle 10 miles		180	.044			2.02	4.53	6.55	8.05
9668	cycle 20 miles		126	.063			2.89	6.45	9.34	11.45
9670	cycle 30 miles		108	.074			3.37	7.55	10.92	13.40
9672	cycle 40 miles		90	.089			4.05	9.05	13.10	16.05
9674	40 MPH ave, cycle 6 miles		216	.037			1.69	3.78	5.47	6.70
9676	cycle 8 miles		198	.040			1.84	4.12	5.96	7.30
9678	cycle 10 miles		180	.044			2.02	4.53	6.55	8.05
9680	cycle 20 miles		144	.056			2.53	5.65	8.18	10.05
9682	cycle 30 miles		108	.074			3.37	7.55	10.92	13.40
9684	cycle 40 miles		90	.089			4.05	9.05	13.10	16.05
9686	cycle 50 miles		72	.111			5.05	11.35	16.40	20
9694	45 MPH ave, cycle 8 miles		216	.037			1.69	3.78	5.47	6.70

31 23 Excavation and Fill

31 23 23 – Fill

31 23 23.20 Hauling		Crew	Daily Output	Labor-Hours	Unit	Material	2017 Bare Costs Labor	2017 Bare Costs Equipment	Total	Total Incl O&P
9696	cycle 10 miles	B-34I	198	.040	L.C.Y.		1.84	4.12	5.96	7.30
9698	cycle 20 miles		144	.056			2.53	5.65	8.18	10.05
9700	cycle 30 miles		126	.063			2.89	6.45	9.34	11.45
9702	cycle 40 miles		108	.074			3.37	7.55	10.92	13.40
9704	cycle 50 miles		90	.089			4.05	9.05	13.10	16.05
9706	50 MPH ave, cycle 10 miles		198	.040			1.84	4.12	5.96	7.30
9708	cycle 20 miles		162	.049			2.25	5.05	7.30	8.95
9710	cycle 30 miles		126	.063			2.89	6.45	9.34	11.45
9712	cycle 40 miles		108	.074			3.37	7.55	10.92	13.40
9714	cycle 50 miles	↓	90	.089	↓		4.05	9.05	13.10	16.05

31 23 23.23 Compaction

		Crew	Daily Output	Labor-Hours	Unit	Material	2017 Bare Costs Labor	2017 Bare Costs Equipment	Total	Total Incl O&P
0010	**COMPACTION**									
7000	Walk behind, vibrating plate 18" wide, 6" lifts, 2 passes	A-1D	200	.040	E.C.Y.		1.57	.17	1.74	2.58
7020	3 passes		185	.043			1.69	.18	1.87	2.79
7040	4 passes	↓	140	.057	↓		2.24	.24	2.48	3.69

Estimating Tips
32 01 00 Operations and Maintenance of Exterior Improvements

- Recycling of asphalt pavement is becoming very popular and is an alternative to removal and replacement. It can be a good value engineering proposal if removed pavement can be recycled, either at the project site or at another site that is reasonably close to the project site. Sections on repair of flexible and rigid pavement are included.

32 10 00 Bases, Ballasts, and Paving

- When estimating paving, keep in mind the project schedule. Also note that prices for asphalt and concrete are generally higher in the cold seasons. Lines for pavement markings, including tactile warning systems and fence lines, are included.

32 90 00 Planting

- The timing of planting and guarantee specifications often dictate the costs for establishing tree and shrub growth and a stand of grass or ground cover. Establish the work performance schedule to coincide with the local planting season. Maintenance and growth guarantees can add from 20%–100% to the total landscaping cost and can be contractually cumbersome. The cost to replace trees and shrubs can be as high as 5% of the total cost, depending on the planting zone, soil conditions, and time of year.

Reference Numbers

Reference numbers are shown at the beginning of some major classifications. These numbers refer to related items in the Reference Section. The reference information may be an estimating procedure, an alternate pricing method, or technical information.

Note: Not all subdivisions listed here necessarily appear. ■

Did you know?

Our online estimating solution gives you the same access to RSMeans' data with 24/7 access:

- Quickly locate costs in the searchable database.
- Build cost lists, estimates, and reports in minutes.
- Adjust costs to any location in the U.S. and Canada with the click of a button.

Start your free trial today at
www.RSMeansOnline.com

32 31 13 – Chain Link Fences and Gates

32 31 13.30 Fence, Chain Link, Gates and Posts	Crew	Daily Output	Labor-Hours	Unit	Material	2017 Bare Costs Labor	Equipment	Total	Total Incl O&P
0010 **FENCE, CHAIN LINK, GATES & POSTS**									
0011 (1/3 post length in ground)									
6710 Corner post, galv. steel, 4" OD, set in conc., 4'	B-80	65	.492	Ea.	100	21.50	10.35	131.85	154
6715 6'		63	.508		114	22.50	10.70	147.20	171
6720 7'		61	.525		133	23	11.05	167.05	193
6725 8'		65	.492		152	21.50	10.35	183.85	211
7900 Auger fence post hole, 3' deep, medium soil, by hand	1 Clab	30	.267			10.45		10.45	16
7925 By machine	B-80	175	.183			8	3.85	11.85	16.45
7950 Rock, with jackhammer	B-9	32	1.250			49.50	6.65	56.15	83.50
7975 With rock drill	B-47C	65	.246			11.10	23.50	34.60	43

Estimating Tips

33 10 00 Water Utilities
33 30 00 Sanitary Sewerage Utilities
33 40 00 Storm Drainage Utilities

- Never assume that the water, sewer, and drainage lines will go in at the early stages of the project. Consider the site access needs before dividing the site in half with open trenches, loose pipe, and machinery obstructions. Always inspect the site to establish that the site drawings are complete. Check off all existing utilities on your drawings as you locate them. Be especially careful with underground utilities because appurtenances are sometimes buried during regrading or repaving operations. If you find any discrepancies, mark up the site plan for further research. Differing site conditions can be very costly if discovered later in the project.

- See also Section 33 01 00 for restoration of pipe where removal/replacement may be undesirable. Use of new types of piping materials can reduce the overall project cost. Owners/design engineers should consider the installing contractor as a valuable source of current information on utility products and local conditions that could lead to significant cost savings.

Reference Numbers

Reference numbers are shown at the beginning of some major classifications. These numbers refer to related items in the Reference Section. The reference information may be an estimating procedure, an alternate pricing method, or technical information.

Note: Not all subdivisions listed here necessarily appear. ■

Division 33 Utilities

33 05 16 – Utility Structures

33 05 16.13 Precast Concrete Utility Structures	Crew	Daily Output	Labor-Hours	Unit	Material	2017 Bare Costs Labor	Equipment	Total	Total Incl O&P
0010 **PRECAST CONCRETE UTILITY STRUCTURES**, 6" thick									
0050 5' x 10' x 6' high, I.D.	B-13	2	28	Ea.	1,800	1,200	335	3,335	4,200
0100 6' x 10' x 6' high, I.D.		2	28		1,875	1,200	335	3,410	4,300
0150 5' x 12' x 6' high, I.D.		2	28		1,975	1,200	335	3,510	4,400
0200 6' x 12' x 6' high, I.D.		1.80	31.111		2,225	1,350	375	3,950	4,900
0250 6' x 13' x 6' high, I.D.		1.50	37.333		2,925	1,600	450	4,975	6,150
0300 8' x 14' x 7' high, I.D.		1	56		3,150	2,400	675	6,225	7,900

33 05 23 – Trenchless Utility Installation

33 05 23.19 Microtunneling

	Crew	Daily Output	Labor-Hours	Unit	Material	2017 Bare Costs Labor	Equipment	Total	Total Incl O&P
0010 **MICROTUNNELING**									
0011 Not including excavation, backfill, shoring,									
0020 or dewatering, average 50'/day, slurry method									
0100 24" to 48" outside diameter, minimum				L.F.				875	965
0110 Adverse conditions, add				%				50%	50%
1000 Rent microtunneling machine, average monthly lease				Month				97,500	107,000
1010 Operating technician				Day				630	705
1100 Mobilization and demobilization, minimum				Job				41,200	45,900
1110 Maximum				"				445,500	490,500

33 05 23.20 Horizontal Boring

	Crew	Daily Output	Labor-Hours	Unit	Material	2017 Bare Costs Labor	Equipment	Total	Total Incl O&P
0010 **HORIZONTAL BORING**									
0011 Casing only, 100' minimum,									
0020 not incl. jacking pits or dewatering									
0100 Roadwork, 1/2" thick wall, 24" diameter casing	B-42	20	3.200	L.F.	117	142	63.50	322.50	420
0200 36" diameter		16	4		215	178	79.50	472.50	600
0300 48" diameter		15	4.267		297	190	84.50	571.50	710
0500 Railroad work, 24" diameter		15	4.267		117	190	84.50	391.50	515
0600 36" diameter		14	4.571		215	203	90.50	508.50	650
0700 48" diameter		12	5.333		297	237	106	640	805
0900 For ledge, add								20%	20%
1000 Small diameter boring, 3", sandy soil	B-82	900	.018		21	.80	.09	21.89	24.50
1040 Rocky soil	"	500	.032		21	1.44	.16	22.60	25.50
1100 Prepare jacking pits, incl. mobilization & demobilization, minimum				Ea.				3,225	3,700
1101 Maximum				"				22,000	25,500

33 05 23.22 Directional Drilling

	Crew	Daily Output	Labor-Hours	Unit	Material	2017 Bare Costs Labor	Equipment	Total	Total Incl O&P
0010 **DIRECTIONAL DRILLING**									
0011 Excluding access and splice pits (if required) and conduit (required)									
0012 Drilled hole diameters shown should be 50% larger than conduit									
0013 Assume access to H2O & removal of spoil/drilling mud as non-hazard material									
0014 Actual production rates adj. to account for risk factors for each soil type									
0100 Sand, silt, clay, common earth									
0110 Mobilization or demobilization	B-82A	1	32	Ea.	1,450	2,350		3,800	4,775
0120 6" diameter		480	.067	L.F.		3.01	4.89	7.90	9.95
0130 12" diameter		270	.119			5.35	8.70	14.05	17.70
0140 18" diameter		180	.178			8	13.05	21.05	26.50
0150 24" diameter		135	.237			10.70	17.40	28.10	35.50
0200 Hard clay, cobble, random boulders									
0210 Mobilization or demobilization	B-82B	1	32	Ea.	1,450	2,625		4,075	5,075
0220 6" diameter		400	.080	L.F.		3.61	6.55	10.16	12.70
0230 12" diameter		220	.145			6.55	11.95	18.50	23
0240 18" diameter		145	.221			9.95	18.10	28.05	35
0250 24" diameter		105	.305			13.75	25	38.75	48.50
0260 30" diameter		80	.400			18.05	33	51.05	63.50

33 05 Common Work Results for Utilities

33 05 23 – Trenchless Utility Installation

33 05 23.22 Directional Drilling		Crew	Daily Output	Labor-Hours	Unit	Material	2017 Bare Costs Labor	Equipment	Total	Total Incl O&P
0270	36" diameter	B 82B	60	.533	L.F.		24	43.50	67.50	84.50
0300	Hard rock (solid bed, 24,000+ psi)									
0310	Mobilization or demobilization	B-82C	1	32	Ea.		1,450	2,925	4,375	5,425
0320	6" diameter		75	.427	L.F.		19.25	39	58.25	72.50
0330	12" diameter		40	.800			36	73	109	136
0340	18" diameter		25	1.280			57.50	117	174.50	217
0350	24" diameter		20	1.600			72	146	218	271
0360	30" diameter		15	2.133			96	195	291	360
0370	36" diameter		12	2.667			120	244	364	450

33 05 26 – Utility Identification

33 05 26.05 Utility Connection

		Crew	Daily Output	Labor-Hours	Unit	Material	2017 Bare Costs Labor	Equipment	Total	Total Incl O&P
0010	**UTILITY CONNECTION**									
0020	Water, sanitary, stormwater, gas, single connection	B-14	1	48	Ea.	2,975	2,000	365	5,340	6,725
0030	Telecommunication	"	3	16	"	385	665	122	1,172	1,575

33 05 26.10 Utility Accessories

		Crew	Daily Output	Labor-Hours	Unit	Material	2017 Bare Costs Labor	Equipment	Total	Total Incl O&P
0010	**UTILITY ACCESSORIES**									
0400	Underground tape, detectable, reinforced, alum. foil core, 2"	1 Clab	150	.053	C.L.F.	6	2.09		8.09	9.80
0500	6"	"	140	.057	"	35	2.24		37.24	42

33 44 Storm Utility Water Drains

33 44 13 – Utility Area Drains

33 44 13.13 Catch Basins

		Crew	Daily Output	Labor-Hours	Unit	Material	2017 Bare Costs Labor	Equipment	Total	Total Incl O&P
0010	**CATCH BASINS**									
0011	Not including footing & excavation									
1600	Frames & grates, C.I., 24" square, 500 lb.	B-6	7.80	3.077	Ea.	350	133	47	530	640
1700	26" D shape, 600 lb.		7	3.429		605	148	52.50	805.50	950
1800	Light traffic, 18" diameter, 100 lb.		10	2.400		200	103	36.50	339.50	420
1900	24" diameter, 300 lb.		8.70	2.759		195	119	42	356	440
2000	36" diameter, 900 lb.		5.80	4.138		630	178	63	871	1,025
2100	Heavy traffic, 24" diameter, 400 lb.		7.80	3.077		260	133	47	440	540
2200	36" diameter, 1150 lb.		3	8		860	345	122	1,327	1,600
2300	Mass. State standard, 26" diameter, 475 lb.		7	3.429		635	148	52.50	835.50	980
2400	30" diameter, 620 lb.		7	3.429		340	148	52.50	540.50	660
2500	Watertight, 24" diameter, 350 lb.		7.80	3.077		360	133	47	540	650
2600	26" diameter, 500 lb.		7	3.429		415	148	52.50	615.50	740
2700	32" diameter, 575 lb.		6	4		900	172	61	1,133	1,325
2800	3 piece cover & frame, 10" deep,									
2900	1200 lb., for heavy equipment	B-6	3	8	Ea.	1,050	345	122	1,517	1,800
3000	Raised for paving 1-1/4" to 2" high									
3100	4 piece expansion ring									
3200	20" to 26" diameter	1 Clab	3	2.667	Ea.	174	104		278	350
3300	30" to 36" diameter	"	3	2.667	"	241	104		345	425
3320	Frames and covers, existing, raised for paving, 2", including									
3340	row of brick, concrete collar, up to 12" wide frame	B-6	18	1.333	Ea.	50.50	57.50	20.50	128.50	166
3360	20" to 26" wide frame		11	2.182		75	94	33.50	202.50	262
3380	30" to 36" wide frame		9	2.667		93	115	40.50	248.50	320
3400	Inverts, single channel brick	D-1	3	5.333		104	231		335	470
3500	Concrete		5	3.200		121	139		260	345
3600	Triple channel, brick		2	8		163	345		508	710
3700	Concrete		3	5.333		157	231		388	525

For customer support on your Electrical Costs with RSMeans Data, call 800.448.8182.

353

33 49 Storm Drainage Structures

33 49 13 – Storm Drainage Manholes, Frames, and Covers

33 49 13.10 Storm Drainage Manholes, Frames and Covers

33 49 13.10 Storm Drainage Manholes, Frames and Covers	Crew	Daily Output	Labor-Hours	Unit	Material	2017 Bare Costs Labor	2017 Bare Costs Equipment	Total	Total Incl O&P
0010 **STORM DRAINAGE MANHOLES, FRAMES & COVERS**									
0020 Excludes footing, excavation, backfill (See line items for frame & cover)									
0050 Brick, 4' inside diameter, 4' deep	D-1	1	16	Ea.	545	690		1,235	1,675
0100 6' deep		.70	22.857		775	990		1,765	2,375
0150 8' deep		.50	32	▼	995	1,375		2,370	3,225
0200 For depths over 8', add		4	4	V.L.F.	88	173		261	365
0400 Concrete blocks (radial), 4' I.D., 4' deep		1.50	10.667	Ea.	415	460		875	1,175
0500 6' deep		1	16		555	690		1,245	1,675
0600 8' deep		.70	22.857	▼	690	990		1,680	2,275
0700 For depths over 8', add	▼	5.50	2.909	V.L.F.	71.50	126		197.50	273
0800 Concrete, cast in place, 4' x 4', 8" thick, 4' deep	C-14H	2	24	Ea.	560	1,150	14.15	1,724.15	2,400
0900 6' deep		1.50	32		810	1,550	18.90	2,378.90	3,250
1000 8' deep		1	48		1,175	2,325	28.50	3,528.50	4,850
1100 For depths over 8', add	▼	8	6	V.L.F.	129	290	3.54	422.54	590
1110 Precast, 4' I.D., 4' deep	B-22	4.10	7.317	Ea.	840	340	50.50	1,230.50	1,500
1120 6' deep		3	10		1,500	465	69	2,034	2,425
1130 8' deep		2	15		1,950	695	104	2,749	3,325
1140 For depths over 8', add		16	1.875	V.L.F.	175	87	12.95	274.95	340
1150 5' I.D., 4' deep	B-6	3	8	Ea.	1,775	345	122	2,242	2,600
1160 6' deep		2	12		2,150	515	183	2,848	3,375
1170 8' deep		1.50	16	▼	3,000	690	244	3,934	4,625
1180 For depths over 8', add		12	2	V.L.F.	380	86	30.50	496.50	580
1190 6' I.D., 4' deep		2	12	Ea.	2,475	515	183	3,173	3,725
1200 6' deep		1.50	16		3,200	690	244	4,134	4,850
1210 8' deep		1	24	▼	3,775	1,025	365	5,165	6,150
1220 For depths over 8', add	▼	8	3	V.L.F.	500	129	46	675	800
1250 Slab tops, precast, 8" thick									
1300 4' diameter manhole	B-6	8	3	Ea.	255	129	46	430	530
1400 5' diameter manhole		7.50	3.200		420	138	49	607	725
1500 6' diameter manhole	▼	7	3.429		645	148	52.50	845.50	995
3800 Steps, heavyweight cast iron, 7" x 9"	1 Bric	40	.200		18.05	9.55		27.60	34.50
3900 8" x 9"		40	.200		21.50	9.55		31.05	38.50
3928 12" x 10-1/2"		40	.200		26	9.55		35.55	43.50
4000 Standard sizes, galvanized steel		40	.200		24.50	9.55		34.05	41.50
4100 Aluminum		40	.200		28	9.55		37.55	45.50
4150 Polyethylene	▼	40	.200	▼	31.50	9.55		41.05	49

33 71 Electrical Utility Transmission and Distribution

33 71 13 – Electrical Utility Towers

33 71 13.23 Steel Electrical Utility Towers

33 71 13.23 Steel Electrical Utility Towers	Crew	Daily Output	Labor-Hours	Unit	Material	2017 Bare Costs Labor	2017 Bare Costs Equipment	Total	Total Incl O&P
0010 **STEEL ELECTRICAL UTILITY TOWERS**									
0100 Excavation and backfill, earth	R-5	135.38	.650	C.Y.		32	10.10	42.10	59.50
0105 Rock		21.46	4.101	"		203	63.50	266.50	375
0200 Steel footings (grillage) in earth		3.91	22.506	Ton	2,150	1,125	350	3,625	4,425
0205 In rock	▼	3.20	27.500	"	2,150	1,375	425	3,950	4,900
0290 See also Section 33 05 23.19									
0300 Rock anchors	R-5	5.87	14.991	Ea.	575	745	233	1,553	2,025
0400 Concrete foundations	"	12.85	6.848	C.Y.	149	340	106	595	795
0490 See also Section 03 30 53.40									
0500 Towers-material handling and spotting	R-7	22.56	2.128	Ton		86	8.25	94.25	141
0540 Steel tower erection	R-5	7.65	11.503	▼	2,100	570	178	2,848	3,350

33 71 Electrical Utility Transmission and Distribution

33 71 13 – Electrical Utility Towers

33 71 13.23 Steel Electrical Utility Towers	Crew	Daily Output	Labor-Hours	Unit	Material	2017 Bare Costs Labor	Equipment	Total	Total Incl O&P
0550	Lace and box	R-5	7.10	12.394	Ton	2,100	615	192	2,907	3,450
0560	Painting total structure	↓	1.47	59.864	Ea.	480	2,975	930	4,385	6,025
0570	Disposal of surplus material	R-7	20.87	2.300	Mile		93	8.90	101.90	153
0600	Special towers-material handling and spotting	"	12.31	3.899	Ton		158	15.10	173.10	260
0640	Special steel structure erection	R-6	6.52	13.497		2,625	670	520	3,815	4,450
0650	Special steel lace and box	"	6.29	13.990	↓	2,625	695	540	3,860	4,525
0670	Disposal of surplus material	R-7	7.87	6.099	Mile		247	23.50	270.50	405

33 71 13.80 Transmission Line Right of Way

		Crew	Daily Output	Labor-Hours	Unit	Material	2017 Bare Costs Labor	Equipment	Total	Total Incl O&P
0010	**TRANSMISSION LINE RIGHT OF WAY**									
0100	Clearing right of way	B-87	6.67	5.997	Acre		305	475	780	985
0200	Restoration & seeding	B-10D	4	3	"	425	146	460	1,031	1,200

33 71 16 – Electrical Utility Poles

33 71 16.23 Steel Electrical Utility Poles

		Crew	Daily Output	Labor-Hours	Unit	Material	2017 Bare Costs Labor	Equipment	Total	Total Incl O&P
0010	**STEEL ELECTRICAL UTILITY POLES**									
0100	Steel, square, tapered shaft, 20'	R-15A	6	8	Ea.	385	400	48	833	1,075
0120	25'		5.35	8.972		415	450	54	919	1,200
0140	30'		4.80	10		470	500	60	1,030	1,350
0160	35'		4.35	11.034		500	550	66.50	1,116.50	1,450
0180	40'		4	12		690	600	72	1,362	1,750
0300	Galvanized, round, tapered shaft, 40'		4	12		2,025	600	72	2,697	3,200
0320	45'		3.70	12.973		2,275	650	78	3,003	3,575
0340	50'		3.45	13.913		2,475	695	84	3,254	3,875
0360	55'		3	16		2,650	800	96.50	3,546.50	4,225
0380	60'		2.65	18.113		2,900	905	109	3,914	4,675
0400	65'	R-13	2.20	19.091		3,675	1,050	98	4,823	5,700
0420	70'		1.90	22.105		4,050	1,225	114	5,389	6,400
0440	75'		1.70	24.706		5,275	1,350	127	6,752	8,000
0460	80'		1.50	28		4,750	1,550	144	6,444	7,700
0480	85'		1.40	30		5,250	1,650	154	7,054	8,425
0500	90'		1.25	33.600		5,550	1,850	173	7,573	9,075
0520	95'		1.15	36.522		6,000	2,000	188	8,188	9,825
0540	100'		1	42		6,500	2,300	216	9,016	10,800
0700	12 sided, tapered shaft, 40'	R-15A	4	12		1,175	600	72	1,847	2,275
0720	45'		3.70	12.973		1,300	650	78	2,028	2,500
0740	50'		3.45	13.913		1,500	695	84	2,279	2,800
0760	55'		3	16		1,700	800	96.50	2,596.50	3,175
0780	60'	↓	2.65	18.113		1,800	905	109	2,814	3,475
0800	65'	R-13	2.20	19.091		2,075	1,050	98	3,223	3,975
0820	70'		1.90	22.105		2,275	1,225	114	3,614	4,450
0840	75'		1.70	24.706		2,450	1,350	127	3,927	4,900
0860	80'		1.50	28		4,225	1,550	144	5,919	7,125
0880	85'		1.40	30		6,775	1,650	154	8,579	10,100
0900	90'		1.25	33.600		8,875	1,850	173	10,898	12,700
0920	95'		1.15	36.522		11,100	2,000	188	13,288	15,400
0940	100'		1	42		13,600	2,300	216	16,116	18,600
0960	105'	↓	.90	46.667		14,900	2,575	240	17,715	20,500
0980	Ladder clips					237			237	261
1000	Galvanized steel, round, tapered, w/one 6' arm, 20'	R-15A	9.20	5.217		955	261	31.50	1,247.50	1,475
1020	25'		7.65	6.275		1,050	315	38	1,403	1,675
1040	30'		6.55	7.328		1,150	365	44	1,559	1,850
1060	35'		5.75	8.348		1,225	415	50.50	1,690.50	2,025
1080	40'	↓	5.15	9.320	↓	1,325	465	56	1,846	2,225

For customer support on your Electrical Costs with RSMeans Data, call 800.448.8182.

355

33 71 16 – Electrical Utility Poles

33 71 16.23 Steel Electrical Utility Poles

		Crew	Daily Output	Labor-Hours	Unit	Material	2017 Bare Costs Labor	Equipment	Total	Total Incl O&P
1200	Two 6' arms, 20'	R-15A	6.55	7.328	Ea.	1,225	365	44	1,634	1,950
1220	25'		5.75	8.348		1,300	415	50.50	1,765.50	2,100
1240	30'		5.15	9.320		1,375	465	56	1,896	2,300
1260	35'		4.60	10.435		1,500	520	63	2,083	2,500
1280	40'		4.20	11.429		1,725	570	69	2,364	2,825
1400	One 12' truss arm, 25'		7.65	6.275		1,200	315	38	1,553	1,825
1420	30'		6.55	7.328		1,225	365	44	1,634	1,950
1440	35'		5.75	8.348		1,350	415	50.50	1,815.50	2,150
1460	40'		5.15	9.320		1,500	465	56	2,021	2,425
1480	45'		4.60	10.435		1,725	520	63	2,308	2,750
1600	Two 12' truss arms, 25'		5.75	8.348		1,425	415	50.50	1,890.50	2,225
1620	30'		5.15	9.320		1,450	465	56	1,971	2,375
1640	35'		4.60	10.435		1,575	520	63	2,158	2,575
1660	40'		4.20	11.429		1,725	570	69	2,364	2,825
1680	45'		3.85	12.468		1,950	625	75	2,650	3,175
3400	Galvanized steel, tapered, 10'		15.50	3.097		320	155	18.65	493.65	605
3420	12'		11.50	4.174		465	208	25	698	855
3440	14'		9.20	5.217		345	261	31.50	637.50	805
3460	16'		8.45	5.680		355	284	34	673	865
3480	18'		7.65	6.275		365	315	38	718	920
3500	20'		7.10	6.761		345	340	40.50	725.50	935
5200	Galvanized steel, bracket type, 2", 6' long		18.50	2.595		148	130	15.60	293.60	375
5220	8' long		15.50	3.097		184	155	18.65	357.65	455
5240	10' long	↓	12.50	3.840		310	192	23	525	655
6000	Digging holes in earth, average	R-5	25.14	3.500			173	54.50	227.50	320
6010	In rock, average	"	4.51	19.512	↓		965	305	1,270	1,800
6020	Formed plate pole structure									
6030	Material handling and spotting	R-7	2.40	20	Ea.		810	77.50	887.50	1,325
6040	Erect steel plate pole	R-5	1.95	45.128		9,800	2,225	700	12,725	14,900
6050	Guys, anchors and hardware for pole, in earth		7.04	12.500		595	620	194	1,409	1,800
6060	In rock	↓	17.96	4.900	↓	710	243	76	1,029	1,225
6070	Foundations for line poles									
6080	Excavation, in earth	R-5	135.38	.650	C.Y.		32	10.10	42.10	59.50
6090	In rock		20	4.400			218	68	286	405
6110	Concrete foundations	↓	11	8	↓	149	395	124	668	900

33 71 16.33 Wood Electrical Utility Poles

		Crew	Daily Output	Labor-Hours	Unit	Material	2017 Bare Costs Labor	Equipment	Total	Total Incl O&P
0010	**WOOD ELECTRICAL UTILITY POLES**									
0011	Excludes excavation, backfill and cast-in-place concrete									
1020	12" Ponderosa Pine Poles treated 0.40 ACQ, 16'	R-3	3.20	6.250	Ea.	875	355	43	1,273	1,550
5000	Wood, class 3 yellow pine, penta-treated, 25'	R-15A	8.60	5.581		270	279	33.50	582.50	755
5020	30'		7.70	6.234		310	310	37.50	657.50	850
5040	35'		5.80	8.276		385	415	50	850	1,100
5060	40'		5.30	9.057		460	450	54.50	964.50	1,250
5080	45'		4.70	10.213		500	510	61.50	1,071.50	1,400
5100	50'		4.20	11.429		615	570	69	1,254	1,625
5120	55'		3.80	12.632		725	630	76	1,431	1,825
5140	60'		3.50	13.714		965	685	82.50	1,732.50	2,175
5160	65'		3.20	15		1,250	750	90.50	2,090.50	2,600
5180	70'		3	16		1,775	800	96.50	2,671.50	3,250
5200	75'		2.80	17.143		2,275	855	103	3,233	3,925
6000	Wood, class 1 type C, CCA/ACA-treated, 25'		8.60	5.581		270	279	33.50	582.50	755
6020	30'	↓	7.70	6.234	↓	330	310	37.50	677.50	875

33 71 Electrical Utility Transmission and Distribution

33 71 16 – Electrical Utility Poles

33 71 16.33 Wood Electrical Utility Poles

		Crew	Daily Output	Labor-Hours	Unit	Material	2017 Bare Costs Labor	Equipment	Total	Total Incl O&P
6040	35'	R-15A	5.80	8.276	Ea.	460	415	50	925	1,200
6060	40'		5.30	9.057		540	450	54.50	1,044.50	1,350
6080	45'		4.70	10.213		655	510	61.50	1,226.50	1,550
6100	50'		4.20	11.429		715	570	69	1,354	1,725
6120	55'		3.80	12.632		810	630	76	1,516	1,925
6200	Electric & tel sitework, 20' high, treated wd., see Section 26 56 13.10	R-3	3.10	6.452		213	365	44.50	622.50	835
6400	25' high		2.90	6.897		282	390	47.50	719.50	950
6600	30' high		2.60	7.692		375	435	53	863	1,125
6800	35' high		2.40	8.333		500	470	57.50	1,027.50	1,325
7000	40' high		2.30	8.696		670	490	60	1,220	1,550
7200	45' high		1.70	11.765		900	665	81	1,646	2,075
7400	Cross arms with hardware & insulators									
7600	4' long	1 Elec	2.50	3.200	Ea.	149	181		330	435
7800	5' long		2.40	3.333		165	189		354	465
8000	6' long		2.20	3.636		171	206		377	500
9000	Disposal of pole & hardware surplus material	R-7	20.87	2.300	Mile		93	8.90	101.90	153
9100	Disposal of crossarms & hardware surplus material	"	40	1.200	"		48.50	4.64	53.14	79.50

33 71 19 – Electrical Underground Ducts and Manholes

33 71 19.15 Underground Ducts and Manholes

		Crew	Daily Output	Labor-Hours	Unit	Material	2017 Bare Costs Labor	Equipment	Total	Total Incl O&P
0010	**UNDERGROUND DUCTS AND MANHOLES**									
0011	Not incl. excavation, backfill and concrete, in slab or duct bank									
1000	Direct burial									
1010	PVC, schedule 40, w/coupling, 1/2" diameter	1 Elec	340	.024	L.F.	.30	1.33		1.63	2.33
1020	3/4" diameter		290	.028		.40	1.56		1.96	2.78
1030	1" diameter		260	.031		.66	1.74		2.40	3.34
1040	1-1/2" diameter		210	.038		.97	2.16		3.13	4.30
1050	2" diameter		180	.044		1.26	2.52		3.78	5.15
1060	3" diameter	2 Elec	240	.067		2.39	3.77		6.16	8.30
1070	4" diameter		160	.100		3.35	5.65		9	12.20
1080	5" diameter		120	.133		4.87	7.55		12.42	16.65
1090	6" diameter		90	.178		6.45	10.05		16.50	22
1110	Elbows, 1/2" diameter	1 Elec	48	.167	Ea.	.76	9.45		10.21	15
1120	3/4" diameter		38	.211		.75	11.90		12.65	18.70
1130	1" diameter		32	.250		1.13	14.15		15.28	22
1140	1-1/2" diameter		21	.381		2.25	21.50		23.75	35
1150	2" diameter		16	.500		3.05	28.50		31.55	46
1160	3" diameter		12	.667		9.20	37.50		46.70	66.50
1170	4" diameter		9	.889		14.65	50.50		65.15	91.50
1180	5" diameter		8	1		24	56.50		80.50	112
1190	6" diameter		5	1.600		55	90.50		145.50	197
1210	Adapters, 1/2" diameter		52	.154		.21	8.70		8.91	13.30
1220	3/4" diameter		43	.186		.34	10.55		10.89	16.15
1230	1" diameter		39	.205		.48	11.60		12.08	17.95
1240	1-1/2" diameter		35	.229		.84	12.95		13.79	20.50
1250	2" diameter		26	.308		1.03	17.40		18.43	27
1260	3" diameter		20	.400		2.52	22.50		25.02	37
1270	4" diameter		14	.571		4.49	32.50		36.99	53.50
1280	5" diameter		12	.667		9.50	37.50		47	67
1290	6" diameter		9	.889		15.90	50.50		66.40	93
1340	Bell end & cap, 1-1/2" diameter		35	.229		4.01	12.95		16.96	24
1350	Bell end & plug, 2" diameter		26	.308		5.85	17.40		23.25	32.50
1360	3" diameter		20	.400		8.55	22.50		31.05	43.50

R337119-30

For customer support on your Electrical Costs with RSMeans Data, call 800.448.8182.

357

33 71 19.15 Underground Ducts and Manholes	Crew	Daily Output	Labor-Hours	Unit	Material	2017 Bare Costs Labor	Equipment	Total	Total Incl O&P
1370	4" diameter	1 Elec	14	.571	Ea.	10.40	32.50		42.90	60
1380	5" diameter		12	.667		15.65	37.50		53.15	73.50
1390	6" diameter		9	.889		17.45	50.50		67.95	94.50
1450	Base spacer, 2" diameter		56	.143		1.19	8.10		9.29	13.40
1460	3" diameter		46	.174		1.55	9.85		11.40	16.45
1470	4" diameter		41	.195		1.60	11.05		12.65	18.30
1480	5" diameter		37	.216		1.74	12.25		13.99	20.50
1490	6" diameter		34	.235		2.37	13.30		15.67	22.50
1550	Intermediate spacer, 2" diameter		60	.133		1.12	7.55		8.67	12.55
1560	3" diameter		46	.174		1.63	9.85		11.48	16.55
1570	4" diameter		41	.195		1.49	11.05		12.54	18.20
1580	5" diameter		37	.216		1.95	12.25		14.20	20.50
1590	6" diameter		34	.235		2.58	13.30		15.88	23
4010	PVC, schedule 80, w/coupling, 1/2" diameter		215	.037	L.F.	.83	2.11		2.94	4.07
4020	3/4" diameter		180	.044		1.14	2.52		3.66	5
4030	1" diameter		145	.055		1.55	3.12		4.67	6.40
4040	1-1/2" diameter		120	.067		2.50	3.77		6.27	8.40
4050	2" diameter		100	.080		3.82	4.53		8.35	11
4060	3" diameter	2 Elec	130	.123		7.20	6.95		14.15	18.35
4070	4" diameter		90	.178		10.50	10.05		20.55	26.50
4080	5" diameter		70	.229		16.30	12.95		29.25	37.50
4090	6" diameter		50	.320		18.25	18.10		36.35	47
4110	Elbows, 1/2" diameter	1 Elec	29	.276	Ea.	2.36	15.60		17.96	26
4120	3/4" diameter		23	.348		5.70	19.70		25.40	36
4130	1" diameter		20	.400		6.30	22.50		28.80	41
4140	1-1/2" diameter		16	.500		10.45	28.50		38.95	54
4150	2" diameter		12	.667		17.25	37.50		54.75	75.50
4160	3" diameter		9	.889		37	50.50		87.50	116
4170	4" diameter		7	1.143		76	64.50		140.50	181
4180	5" diameter		6	1.333		187	75.50		262.50	320
4190	6" diameter		4	2		385	113		498	595
4210	Adapter, 1/2" diameter		39	.205		.21	11.60		11.81	17.65
4220	3/4" diameter		33	.242		.34	13.70		14.04	21
4230	1" diameter		29	.276		.48	15.60		16.08	24
4240	1-1/2" diameter		26	.308		.84	17.40		18.24	27
4250	2" diameter		23	.348		1.03	19.70		20.73	30.50
4260	3" diameter		18	.444		2.52	25		27.52	40.50
4270	4" diameter		13	.615		4.49	35		39.49	57
4280	5" diameter		11	.727		9.50	41		50.50	72
4290	6" diameter		8	1		15.90	56.50		72.40	102
4310	Bell end & cap, 1-1/2" diameter		26	.308		4.01	17.40		21.41	30.50
4320	Bell end & plug, 2" diameter		23	.348		5.85	19.70		25.55	36
4330	3" diameter		18	.444		8.55	25		33.55	47
4340	4" diameter		13	.615		10.40	35		45.40	63.50
4350	5" diameter		11	.727		15.65	41		56.65	78.50
4360	6" diameter		8	1		17.45	56.50		73.95	104
4370	Base spacer, 2" diameter		42	.190		1.19	10.80		11.99	17.45
4380	3" diameter		33	.242		1.55	13.70		15.25	22
4390	4" diameter		29	.276		1.60	15.60		17.20	25.50
4400	5" diameter		26	.308		1.74	17.40		19.14	28
4410	6" diameter		25	.320		2.37	18.10		20.47	29.50
4420	Intermediate spacer, 2" diameter		45	.178		1.12	10.05		11.17	16.35
4430	3" diameter		34	.235		1.63	13.30		14.93	21.50

33 71 19 – Electrical Underground Ducts and Manholes

33 71 19.15 Underground Ducts and Manholes	Crew	Daily Output	Labor-Hours	Unit	Material	2017 Bare Costs Labor	Equipment	Total	Total Incl O&P
4440	4" diameter	1 Elec	31	.258	Ea.	1.49	14.60		16.09	23.50
4450	5" diameter		28	.286		1.95	16.15		18.10	26
4460	6" diameter		25	.320		2.58	18.10		20.68	30

33 71 19.17 Electric and Telephone Underground

		Crew	Daily Output	Labor-Hours	Unit	Material	Labor	Equipment	Total	Total Incl O&P
0010	**ELECTRIC AND TELEPHONE UNDERGROUND**									
0011	Not including excavation									
0200	backfill and cast in place concrete									
0250	For bedding, see Section 31 23 23.16 R337119-30									
0400	Hand holes, precast concrete, with concrete cover									
0600	2' x 2' x 3' deep	R-3	2.40	8.333	Ea.	430	470	57.50	957.50	1,250
0800	3' x 3' x 3' deep		1.90	10.526		560	595	72.50	1,227.50	1,600
1000	4' x 4' x 4' deep		1.40	14.286		1,425	810	98.50	2,333.50	2,875
1200	Manholes, precast with iron racks & pulling irons, C.I. frame									
1400	and cover, 4' x 6' x 7' deep	B-13	2	28	Ea.	2,925	1,200	335	4,460	5,425
1600	6' x 8' x 7' deep		1.90	29.474		3,275	1,275	355	4,905	5,925
1800	6' x 10' x 7' deep		1.80	31.111		3,675	1,350	375	5,400	6,500
4200	Underground duct, banks ready for concrete fill, min. of 7.5"									
4400	between conduits, center to center									
4580	PVC, type EB, 1 @ 2" diameter	2 Elec	480	.033	L.F.	.61	1.89		2.50	3.50
4600	2 @ 2" diameter		240	.067		1.22	3.77		4.99	7
4800	4 @ 2" diameter		120	.133		2.44	7.55		9.99	14
4900	1 @ 3" diameter		400	.040		.93	2.26		3.19	4.41
5000	2 @ 3" diameter		200	.080		1.85	4.53		6.38	8.85
5200	4 @ 3" diameter		100	.160		3.70	9.05		12.75	17.60
5300	1 @ 4" diameter		320	.050		1.33	2.83		4.16	5.70
5400	2 @ 4" diameter		160	.100		2.66	5.65		8.31	11.45
5600	4 @ 4" diameter		80	.200		5.30	11.30		16.60	23
5800	6 @ 4" diameter		54	.296		8	16.75		24.75	34
5810	1 @ 5" diameter		260	.062		1.94	3.48		5.42	7.35
5820	2 @ 5" diameter		130	.123		3.89	6.95		10.84	14.75
5840	4 @ 5" diameter		70	.229		7.80	12.95		20.75	28
5860	6 @ 5" diameter		50	.320		11.65	18.10		29.75	40
5870	1 @ 6" diameter		200	.080		2.79	4.53		7.32	9.85
5880	2 @ 6" diameter		100	.160		5.55	9.05		14.60	19.70
5900	4 @ 6" diameter		50	.320		11.15	18.10		29.25	39.50
5920	6 @ 6" diameter		30	.533		16.70	30		46.70	63.50
6200	Rigid galvanized steel, 2 @ 2" diameter		180	.089		17.45	5.05		22.50	27
6400	4 @ 2" diameter		90	.178		35	10.05		45.05	53.50
6800	2 @ 3" diameter		100	.160		28	9.05		37.05	44.50
7000	4 @ 3" diameter		50	.320		56	18.10		74.10	88.50
7200	2 @ 4" diameter		70	.229		41	12.95		53.95	65
7400	4 @ 4" diameter		34	.471		82.50	26.50		109	131
7600	6 @ 4" diameter		22	.727		124	41		165	198
7620	2 @ 5" diameter		60	.267		81.50	15.10		96.60	112
7640	4 @ 5" diameter		30	.533		163	30		193	224
7660	6 @ 5" diameter		18	.889		244	50.50		294.50	345
7680	2 @ 6" diameter		40	.400		110	22.50		132.50	155
7700	4 @ 6" diameter		20	.800		221	45.50		266.50	310
7720	6 @ 6" diameter		14	1.143		330	64.50		394.50	460
7800	For cast-in-place concrete - Add									
7810	Under 1 C.Y.	C-6	16	3	C.Y.	189	122	3.54	314.54	400
7820	1 C.Y. - 5 C.Y.		19.20	2.500		171	102	2.95	275.95	345

For customer support on your Electrical Costs with RSMeans Data, call 800.448.8182.

359

33 71 Electrical Utility Transmission and Distribution

33 71 19 – Electrical Underground Ducts and Manholes

33 71 19.17 Electric and Telephone Underground	Crew	Daily Output	Labor-Hours	Unit	Material	2017 Bare Costs Labor	Equipment	Total	Total Incl O&P
7830	Over 5 C.Y.	C-6	24	2	C.Y.	142	81.50	2.36	225.86	283
7850	For reinforcing rods - Add									
7860	#4 to #7	2 Rodm	1.10	14.545	Ton	940	790		1,730	2,250
7870	#8 to #14	"	1.50	10.667	"	940	580		1,520	1,925
8000	Fittings, PVC type EB, elbow, 2" diameter	1 Elec	16	.500	Ea.	15.65	28.50		44.15	60
8200	3" diameter		14	.571		17.90	32.50		50.40	68
8400	4" diameter		12	.667		38.50	37.50		76	99
8420	5" diameter		10	.800		129	45.50		174.50	210
8440	6" diameter	▼	9	.889		163	50.50		213.50	256
8500	Coupling, 2" diameter					.58			.58	.64
8600	3" diameter					3.17			3.17	3.49
8700	4" diameter					4.13			4.13	4.54
8720	5" diameter					7.20			7.20	7.95
8740	6" diameter					21			21	23.50
8800	Adapter, 2" diameter	1 Elec	26	.308		.85	17.40		18.25	27
9000	3" diameter		20	.400		2.36	22.50		24.86	36.50
9200	4" diameter		16	.500		3.50	28.50		32	46.50
9220	5" diameter		13	.615		8.45	35		43.45	61.50
9240	6" diameter		10	.800		10.95	45.50		56.45	80
9400	End bell, 2" diameter		16	.500		.49	28.50		28.99	43
9600	3" diameter		14	.571		1	32.50		33.50	49.50
9800	4" diameter		12	.667		1.62	37.50		39.12	58.50
9810	5" diameter		10	.800		2.42	45.50		47.92	70.50
9820	6" diameter		8	1		3.42	56.50		59.92	89
9830	5° angle coupling, 2" diameter		26	.308		6.95	17.40		24.35	33.50
9840	3" diameter		20	.400		26.50	22.50		49	63.50
9850	4" diameter		16	.500		17.25	28.50		45.75	61.50
9860	5" diameter		13	.615		14.85	35		49.85	68.50
9870	6" diameter		10	.800		23.50	45.50		69	94
9880	Expansion joint, 2" diameter		16	.500		28.50	28.50		57	74
9890	3" diameter		18	.444		58.50	25		83.50	102
9900	4" diameter		12	.667		90	37.50		127.50	156
9910	5" diameter		10	.800		170	45.50		215.50	254
9920	6" diameter	▼	8	1		176	56.50		232.50	278
9930	Heat bender, 2" diameter					395			395	435
9940	6" diameter					1,225			1,225	1,350
9950	Cement, quart				▼	15.10			15.10	16.60
9960	Nylon polyethylene pull rope, 1/4"	2 Elec	2000	.008	L.F.	.15	.45		.60	.85

33 71 23 – Insulators and Fittings

33 71 23.16 Post Insulators

0010	**POST INSULATORS**									
7400	Insulators, pedestal type	R-11	112	.500	Ea.		27	6.75	33.75	48
7490	See also line 33 71 39.13 1000									

33 71 26 – Transmission and Distribution Equipment

33 71 26.13 Capacitor Banks

0010	**CAPACITOR BANKS**									
1300	Station capacitors									
1350	Synchronous, 13 to 26 kV	R-11	3.11	18.006	MVAR	6,975	975	244	8,194	9,425
1360	46 kV		3.33	16.817		8,900	910	228	10,038	11,400
1370	69 kV		3.81	14.698		8,750	795	199	9,744	11,000
1380	161 kV		6.51	8.602		8,175	465	116	8,756	9,825
1390	500 kV	▼	10.37	5.400	▼	7,100	292	73	7,465	8,350

33 71 Electrical Utility Transmission and Distribution

33 71 26 – Transmission and Distribution Equipment

33 71 26.13 Capacitor Banks

		Crew	Daily Output	Labor-Hours	Unit	Material	2017 Bare Costs Labor	Equipment	Total	Total Incl O&P
1450	Static, 13 to 26 kV	R-11	3.11	18.006	MVAR	5,925	975	244	7,144	8,250
1460	46 kV		3.01	18.605		7,475	1,000	252	8,727	10,000
1470	69 kV		3.81	14.698		7,250	795	199	8,244	9,400
1480	161 kV		6.51	8.602		6,725	465	116	7,306	8,225
1490	500 kV		10.37	5.400		6,150	292	73	6,515	7,300
1600	Voltage regulators, 13 to 26 kV	↓	.75	74.667	Ea.	264,500	4,025	1,000	269,525	298,000

33 71 26.23 Current Transformers

		Crew	Daily Output	Labor-Hours	Unit	Material	2017 Bare Costs Labor	Equipment	Total	Total Incl O&P
0010	**CURRENT TRANSFORMERS**									
4050	Current transformers, 13 to 26 kV	R-11	14	4	Ea.	3,250	216	54	3,520	3,950
4060	46 kV		9.33	6.002		9,500	325	81.50	9,906.50	11,000
4070	69 kV		7	8		9,850	430	108	10,388	11,600
4080	161 kV	↓	1.87	29.947	↓	31,900	1,625	405	33,930	38,000

33 71 26.26 Potential Transformers

		Crew	Daily Output	Labor-Hours	Unit	Material	2017 Bare Costs Labor	Equipment	Total	Total Incl O&P
0010	**POTENTIAL TRANSFORMERS**									
4100	Potential transformers, 13 to 26 kV	R-11	11.20	5	Ea.	4,650	270	67.50	4,987.50	5,600
4110	46 kV		8	7		9,575	380	95	10,050	11,200
4120	69 kV		6.22	9.003		10,100	485	122	10,707	12,100
4130	161 kV		2.24	25		21,900	1,350	340	23,590	26,500
4140	500 kV	↓	1.40	40	↓	65,500	2,150	540	68,190	76,000

33 71 39 – High-Voltage Wiring

33 71 39.13 Overhead High-Voltage Wiring

		Crew	Daily Output	Labor-Hours	Unit	Material	2017 Bare Costs Labor	Equipment	Total	Total Incl O&P
0010	**OVERHEAD HIGH-VOLTAGE WIRING** R337116-60									
0100	Conductors, primary circuits									
0110	Material handling and spotting	R-5	9.78	8.998	W.Mile		445	140	585	830
0120	For river crossing, add		11	8			395	124	519	735
0150	Conductors, per wire, 210 to 636 kcmil		1.96	44.898		11,000	2,225	695	13,920	16,200
0160	795 to 954 kcmil		1.87	47.059		21,900	2,325	730	24,955	28,400
0170	1000 to 1600 kcmil		1.47	59.864		37,600	2,975	930	41,505	46,800
0180	Over 1600 kcmil		1.35	65.185		52,500	3,225	1,000	56,725	64,000
0200	For river crossing, add, 210 to 636 kcmil		1.24	70.968			3,525	1,100	4,625	6,525
0220	795 to 954 kcmil		1.09	80.734			4,000	1,250	5,250	7,425
0230	1000 to 1600 kcmil		.97	90.722			4,500	1,400	5,900	8,350
0240	Over 1600 kcmil	↓	.87	101	↓		5,000	1,575	6,575	9,300
0300	Joints and dead ends	R-8	6	8	Ea.	1,525	400	52.50	1,977.50	2,350
0400	Sagging	R-5	7.33	12.001	W.Mile		595	186	781	1,100
0500	Clipping, per structure, 69 kV	R-10	9.60	5	Ea.		267	63.50	330.50	470
0510	161 kV		5.33	9.006			480	114	594	850
0520	345 to 500 kV	↓	2.53	18.972			1,025	241	1,266	1,800
0600	Make and install jumpers, per structure, 69 kV	R-8	3.20	15		415	755	98.50	1,268.50	1,725
0620	161 kV		1.20	40		825	2,000	262	3,087	4,225
0640	345 to 500 kV	↓	.32	150		1,400	7,525	985	9,910	14,000
0700	Spacers	R-10	68.57	.700		82.50	37.50	8.90	128.90	157
0720	For river crossings, add	"	60	.800	↓		42.50	10.15	52.65	75.50
0800	Installing pulling line (500 kV only)	R-9	1.45	44.138	W.Mile	765	2,075	217	3,057	4,225
0810	Disposal of surplus material, high voltage conductors	R-7	6.96	6.897	Mile		279	26.50	305.50	460
0820	With trailer mounted reel stands	"	13.71	3.501	"		142	13.55	155.55	233
0900	Insulators and hardware, primary circuits									
0920	Material handling and spotting, 69 kV	R-7	480	.100	Ea.		4.04	.39	4.43	6.65
0930	161 kV		685.71	.070			2.83	.27	3.10	4.66
0950	345 to 500 kV	↓	960	.050			2.02	.19	2.21	3.32
1000	Disk insulators, 69 kV	R-5	880	.100		84	4.96	1.55	90.51	102
1020	161 kV	↓	977.78	.090	↓	96	4.46	1.40	101.86	114

For customer support on your Electrical Costs with RSMeans Data, call 800.448.8182.

361

33 71 39.13 Overhead High-Voltage Wiring		Crew	Daily Output	Labor-Hours	Unit	Material	2017 Bare Costs Labor	2017 Bare Costs Equipment	Total	Total Incl O&P
1040	345 to 500 kV	R-5	1100	.080	Ea.	96	3.96	1.24	101.20	113
1060	See Section 33 71 23.16 for pin or pedestal insulator									
1100	Install disk insulator at river crossing, add									
1110	69 kV	R-5	586.67	.150	Ea.		7.45	2.33	9.78	13.80
1120	161 kV		880	.100			4.96	1.55	6.51	9.20
1140	345 to 500 kV	▼	880	.100	▼		4.96	1.55	6.51	9.20
1150	Disposal of surplus material, high voltage insulators	R-7	41.74	1.150	Mile		46.50	4.45	50.95	76.50
1300	Overhead ground wire installation									
1320	Material handling and spotting	R-7	5.65	8.496	W.Mile		345	33	378	565
1340	Overhead ground wire	R-5	1.76	50		3,000	2,475	775	6,250	7,900
1350	At river crossing, add		1.17	75.214	▼		3,725	1,175	4,900	6,925
1360	Disposal of surplus material, grounding wire	▼	41.74	2.108	Mile		104	32.50	136.50	194
1400	Installing conductors, underbuilt circuits									
1420	Material handling and spotting	R-7	5.65	8.496	W.Mile		345	33	378	565
1440	Conductors, per wire, 210 to 636 kcmil	R-5	1.96	44.898		11,000	2,225	695	13,920	16,200
1450	795 to 954 kcmil		1.87	47.059		21,900	2,325	730	24,955	28,400
1460	1000 to 1600 kcmil		1.47	59.864		37,600	2,975	930	41,505	46,800
1470	Over 1600 kcmil	▼	1.35	65.185	▼	52,500	3,225	1,000	56,725	64,000
1500	Joints and dead ends	R-8	6	8	Ea.	1,525	400	52.50	1,977.50	2,350
1550	Sagging	R-5	8.80	10	W.Mile		495	155	650	920
1600	Clipping, per structure, 69 kV	R-10	9.60	5	Ea.		267	63.50	330.50	470
1620	161 kV		5.33	9.006			480	114	594	850
1640	345 to 500 kV	▼	2.53	18.972			1,025	241	1,266	1,800
1700	Making and installing jumpers, per structure, 69 kV	R-8	5.87	8.177		415	410	53.50	878.50	1,125
1720	161 kV		.96	50		825	2,500	330	3,655	5,075
1740	345 to 500 kV	▼	.32	150		1,400	7,525	985	9,910	14,000
1800	Spacers	R-10	96	.500	▼	82.50	26.50	6.35	115.35	138
1810	Disposal of surplus material, conductors & hardware	R-7	6.96	6.897	Mile		279	26.50	305.50	460
2000	Insulators and hardware for underbuilt circuits									
2100	Material handling and spotting	R-7	1200	.040	Ea.		1.62	.15	1.77	2.66
2150	Disk insulators, 69 kV	R-8	600	.080		84	4.01	.52	88.53	99
2160	161 kV		686	.070		96	3.51	.46	99.97	112
2170	345 to 500 kV		800	.060		96	3.01	.39	99.40	111
2180	Disposal of surplus material, insulators & hardware	R-7	41.74	1.150	Mile		46.50	4.45	50.95	76.50
2300	Sectionalizing switches, 69 kV	R-5	1.26	69.841	Ea.	21,700	3,450	1,075	26,225	30,200
2310	161 kV		.80	110		24,500	5,450	1,700	31,650	37,000
2500	Protective devices	▼	5.50	16	▼	7,075	795	248	8,118	9,275
2600	Clearance poles, 8 poles per mile									
2650	In earth, 69 kV	R-5	1.16	75.862	Mile	5,825	3,750	1,175	10,750	13,400
2660	161 kV	"	.64	137		9,575	6,825	2,125	18,525	23,200
2670	345 to 500 kV	R-6	.48	183		11,500	9,075	7,050	27,625	34,100
2800	In rock, 69 kV	R-5	.69	127		5,825	6,325	1,975	14,125	18,100
2820	161 kV	"	.35	251		9,575	12,500	3,900	25,975	33,600
2840	345 to 500 kV	R-6	.24	366	▼	11,500	18,200	14,100	43,800	55,500

33 72 Utility Substations

33 72 26 – Substation Bus Assemblies

33 72 26.13 Aluminum Substation Bus Assemblies

33 72 26.13 Aluminum Substation Bus Assemblies	Crew	Daily Output	Labor-Hours	Unit	Material	2017 Bare Costs Labor	Equipment	Total	Total Incl O&P
0010 **ALUMINUM SUBSTATION BUS ASSEMBLIES**									
7300 Bus	R-11	590	.095	Lb.	3.05	5.15	1.29	9.49	12.45

33 72 33 – Control House Equipment

33 72 33.33 Raceway/Boxes for Utility Substations

	Crew	Daily Output	Labor-Hours	Unit	Material	Labor	Equipment	Total	Total Incl O&P
0010 **RACEWAY/BOXES FOR UTILITY SUBSTATIONS**									
7000 Conduit, conductors, and insulators									
7100 Conduit, metallic	R-11	560	.100	Lb.	2.80	5.40	1.35	9.55	12.70
7110 Non-metallic	"	800	.070	"	8.60	3.78	.95	13.33	16.20
7190 See Section 26 05 33									
7200 Wire and cable	R-11	700	.080	Lb.	9.10	4.32	1.08	14.50	17.70
7290 See Section 26 05 19									

33 72 33.36 Cable Trays for Utility Substations

	Crew	Daily Output	Labor-Hours	Unit	Material	Labor	Equipment	Total	Total Incl O&P
0010 **CABLE TRAYS FOR UTILITY SUBSTATIONS**									
7700 Cable tray	R-11	40	1.400	L.F.	19	75.50	18.95	113.45	156
7790 See Section 26 05 36									

33 72 33.43 Substation Backup Batteries

	Crew	Daily Output	Labor-Hours	Unit	Material	Labor	Equipment	Total	Total Incl O&P
0010 **SUBSTATION BACKUP BATTERIES**									
9120 Battery chargers	R-11	11.20	5	Ea.	3,975	270	67.50	4,312.50	4,850
9200 Control batteries	"	14	4	K.A.H.	91	216	54	361	485

33 72 33.46 Substation Converter Stations

	Crew	Daily Output	Labor-Hours	Unit	Material	Labor	Equipment	Total	Total Incl O&P
0010 **SUBSTATION CONVERTER STATIONS**									
9000 Station service equipment									
9100 Conversion equipment									
9110 Station service transformers	R-11	5.60	10	Ea.	96,000	540	135	96,675	106,500

33 73 Utility Transformers

33 73 23 – Dry-Type Utility Transformers

33 73 23.20 Primary Transformers

	Crew	Daily Output	Labor-Hours	Unit	Material	Labor	Equipment	Total	Total Incl O&P
0010 **PRIMARY TRANSFORMERS**									
1000 Main conversion equipment									
1050 Power transformers, 13 to 26 kV	R-11	1.72	32.558	MVA	25,000	1,750	440	27,190	30,600
1060 46 kV		3.50	16		23,400	865	217	24,482	27,300
1070 69 kV		3.11	18.006		20,000	975	244	21,219	23,700
1080 110 kV		3.29	17.021		19,000	920	230	20,150	22,500
1090 161 kV		4.31	12.993		17,600	700	176	18,476	20,600
1100 500 kV		7	8		17,600	430	108	18,138	20,100
1200 Grounding transformers		3.11	18.006	Ea.	110,500	975	244	111,719	123,000

For customer support on your Electrical Costs with RSMeans Data, call 800.448.8182.

363

33 75 High-Voltage Switchgear and Protection Devices

33 75 13 – Air High-Voltage Circuit Breaker

33 75 13.13 High-Voltage Circuit Breaker, Air

		Crew	Daily Output	Labor-Hours	Unit	Material	2017 Bare Costs Labor	Equipment	Total	Total Incl O&P
0010	**HIGH-VOLTAGE CIRCUIT BREAKER, AIR**									
2100	Air circuit breakers, 13 to 26 kV	R-11	.56	100	Ea.	62,000	5,400	1,350	68,750	77,500
2110	161 kV	"	.24	233	"	266,000	12,600	3,150	281,750	315,000

33 75 16 – Oil High-Voltage Circuit Breaker

33 75 16.13 Oil Circuit Breaker

		Crew	Daily Output	Labor-Hours	Unit	Material	2017 Bare Costs Labor	Equipment	Total	Total Incl O&P
0010	**OIL CIRCUIT BREAKER**									
2000	Power circuit breakers									
2050	Oil circuit breakers, 13 to 26 kV	R-11	1.12	50	Ea.	59,500	2,700	675	62,875	70,500
2060	46 kV		.75	74.667		87,000	4,025	1,000	92,025	102,500
2070	69 kV		.45	124		201,500	6,725	1,675	209,900	233,500
2080	161 kV		.16	350		307,000	18,900	4,750	330,650	371,000
2090	500 kV		.06	933		1,147,000	50,500	12,600	1,210,100	1,351,500

33 75 19 – Gas High-Voltage Circuit Breaker

33 75 19.13 Gas Circuit Breaker

		Crew	Daily Output	Labor-Hours	Unit	Material	2017 Bare Costs Labor	Equipment	Total	Total Incl O&P
0010	**GAS CIRCUIT BREAKER**									
2000	Power circuit breakers									
2150	Gas circuit breakers, 13 to 26 kV	R-11	.56	100	Ea.	232,500	5,400	1,350	239,250	265,500
2160	161 kV		.08	700		305,000	37,800	9,475	352,275	403,000
2170	500 kV		.04	1400		1,073,500	75,500	19,000	1,168,000	1,316,000

33 75 23 – Vacuum High-Voltage Circuit Breaker

33 75 23.13 Vacuum Circuit Breaker

		Crew	Daily Output	Labor-Hours	Unit	Material	2017 Bare Costs Labor	Equipment	Total	Total Incl O&P
0010	**VACUUM CIRCUIT BREAKER**									
2000	Power circuit breakers									
2200	Vacuum circuit breakers, 13 to 26 kV	R-11	.56	100	Ea.	52,500	5,400	1,350	59,250	67,500

33 75 36 – High-Voltage Utility Fuses

33 75 36.13 Fuses

		Crew	Daily Output	Labor-Hours	Unit	Material	2017 Bare Costs Labor	Equipment	Total	Total Incl O&P
0010	**FUSES**									
8000	Protective equipment									
8250	Fuses, 13 to 26 kV	R-11	18.67	2.999	Ea.	2,175	162	40.50	2,377.50	2,675
8260	46 kV		11.20	5		2,475	270	67.50	2,812.50	3,200
8270	69 kV		8	7		2,625	380	95	3,100	3,575
8280	161 kV		4.67	11.991		3,250	650	162	4,062	4,725

33 75 39 – High-Voltage Surge Arresters

33 75 39.13 Surge Arresters

		Crew	Daily Output	Labor-Hours	Unit	Material	2017 Bare Costs Labor	Equipment	Total	Total Incl O&P
0010	**SURGE ARRESTERS**									
8000	Protective equipment									
8050	Lightning arresters, 13 to 26 kV	R-11	18.67	2.999	Ea.	1,625	162	40.50	1,827.50	2,100
8060	46 kV		14	4		4,350	216	54	4,620	5,150
8070	69 kV		11.20	5		5,575	270	67.50	5,912.50	6,625
8080	161 kV		5.60	10		7,750	540	135	8,425	9,500
8090	500 kV		1.40	40		26,400	2,150	540	29,090	32,800

33 75 43 – Shunt Reactors

33 75 43.13 Reactors

		Crew	Daily Output	Labor-Hours	Unit	Material	2017 Bare Costs Labor	Equipment	Total	Total Incl O&P
0010	**REACTORS**									
8000	Protective equipment									
8150	Reactors and resistors, 13 to 26 kV	R-11	28	2	Ea.	3,875	108	27	4,010	4,475
8160	46 kV		4.31	12.993		11,600	700	176	12,476	14,000
8170	69 kV		2.80	20		18,600	1,075	271	19,946	22,400
8180	161 kV		2.24	25		20,900	1,350	340	22,590	25,400

33 75 High-Voltage Switchgear and Protection Devices

33 75 43 – Shunt Reactors

33 75 43.13 Reactors		Crew	Daily Output	Labor-Hours	Unit	Material	2017 Bare Costs Labor	Equipment	Total	Total Incl O&P
0190	500 kV	R-11	.08	700	Ea.	82,000	37,800	9,475	129,275	158,000

33 75 53 – High-Voltage Switches

33 75 53.13 Switches

		Crew	Daily Output	Labor-Hours	Unit	Material	Labor	Equipment	Total	Total Incl O&P
0010	**SWITCHES**									
3000	Disconnecting switches									
3050	Gang operated switches									
3060	Manual operation, 13 to 26 kV	R-11	1.65	33.939	Ea.	14,700	1,825	460	16,985	19,500
3070	46 kV		1.12	50		24,800	2,700	675	28,175	32,100
3080	69 kV		.80	70		27,100	3,775	950	31,825	36,600
3090	161 kV		.56	100		32,600	5,400	1,350	39,350	45,400
3100	500 kV		.14	400		87,500	21,600	5,425	114,525	135,000
3110	Motor operation, 161 kV		.51	109		49,000	5,925	1,475	56,400	64,500
3120	500 kV		.28	200		133,500	10,800	2,700	147,000	166,000
3250	Circuit switches, 161 kV		.41	136		96,000	7,375	1,850	105,225	118,500
3300	Single pole switches									
3350	Disconnecting switches, 13 to 26 kV	R-11	28	2	Ea.	13,200	108	27	13,335	14,700
3360	46 kV		8	7		23,300	380	95	23,775	26,300
3370	69 kV		5.60	10		25,100	540	135	25,775	28,600
3380	161 kV		2.80	20		94,000	1,075	271	95,346	105,000
3390	500 kV		.22	254		266,500	13,800	3,450	283,750	318,000
3450	Grounding switches, 46 kV		5.60	10		34,900	540	135	35,575	39,400
3460	69 kV		3.73	15.013		35,700	810	203	36,713	40,600
3470	161 kV		2.24	25		38,000	1,350	340	39,690	44,200
3480	500 kV		.62	90.323		47,600	4,875	1,225	53,700	61,000

33 79 Site Grounding

33 79 83 – Site Grounding Conductors

33 79 83.13 Grounding Wire, Bar, and Rod

		Crew	Daily Output	Labor-Hours	Unit	Material	Labor	Equipment	Total	Total Incl O&P
0010	**GROUNDING WIRE, BAR, AND ROD**									
7500	Grounding systems	R-11	280	.200	Lb.	11.55	10.80	2.71	25.06	32

33 81 Communications Structures

33 81 13 – Communications Transmission Towers

33 81 13.10 Radio Towers

		Crew	Daily Output	Labor-Hours	Unit	Material	Labor	Equipment	Total	Total Incl O&P
0010	**RADIO TOWERS**									
0020	Guyed, 50' H, 40 lb. sect., 70 MPH basic wind speed	2 Sswk	1	16	Ea.	2,775	870		3,645	4,500
0100	Wind load 90 MPH basic wind speed	"	1	16		3,675	870		4,545	5,475
0300	190' high, 40 lb. section, wind load 70 MPH basic wind speed	K-2	.33	72.727		9,525	3,750	820	14,095	17,500
0400	200' high, 70 lb. section, wind load 90 MPH basic wind speed		.33	72.727		15,800	3,750	820	20,370	24,300
0600	300' high, 70 lb. section, wind load 70 MPH basic wind speed		.20	120		25,300	6,200	1,350	32,850	39,300
0700	270' high, 90 lb. section, wind load 90 MPH basic wind speed		.20	120		27,400	6,200	1,350	34,950	41,600
0800	400' high, 100 lb. section, wind load 70 MPH basic wind speed		.14	171		38,200	8,850	1,925	48,975	58,500
0900	Self-supporting, 60' high, wind load 70 MPH basic wind speed		.80	30		4,500	1,550	340	6,390	7,825
0910	60' high, wind load 90 MPH basic wind speed		.45	53.333		5,250	2,750	600	8,600	10,900
1000	120' high, wind load 70 MPH basic wind speed		.40	60		9,925	3,100	675	13,700	16,700
1200	190' high, wind load 90 MPH basic wind speed		.20	120		28,300	6,200	1,350	35,850	42,600
2000	For states west of Rocky Mountains, add for shipping					10%				

Division Notes

		CREW	DAILY OUTPUT	LABOR-HOURS	UNIT	BARE COSTS				TOTAL INCL O&P
						MAT.	LABOR	EQUIP.	TOTAL	

Estimating Tips
34 11 00 Rail Tracks
This subdivision includes items that may involve either repair of existing or construction of new railroad tracks. Additional preparation work, such as the roadbed earthwork, would be found in Division 31. Additional new construction siding and turnouts are found in Subdivision 34 72. Maintenance of railroads is found under 34 01 23 Operation and Maintenance of Railways.

34 40 00 Traffic Signals
This subdivision includes traffic signal systems. Other traffic control devices such as traffic signs are found in Subdivision 10 14 53 Traffic Signage.

34 70 00 Vehicle Barriers
This subdivision includes security vehicle barriers, guide and guard rails, crash barriers, and delineators. The actual maintenance and construction of concrete and asphalt pavement are found in Division 32.

Reference Numbers
Reference numbers are shown at the beginning of some major classifications. These numbers refer to related items in the Reference Section. The reference information may be an estimating procedure, an alternate pricing method, or technical information.

Note: Not all subdivisions listed here necessarily appear. ■

Did you know?
Our online estimating solution gives you the same access to RSMeans' data with 24/7 access:

■ Quickly locate costs in the searchable database.

■ Build cost lists, estimates, and reports in minutes.

■ Adjust costs to any location in the U.S. and Canada with the click of a button.

Start your free trial today at
www.RSMeansOnline.com

34 43 13.16 Airfield Runway and Taxiway Inset Lighting	Crew	Daily Output	Labor-Hours	Unit	Material	2017 Bare Costs Labor	2017 Bare Costs Equipment	Total	Total Incl O&P
0010 **AIRFIELD RUNWAY AND TAXIWAY INSET LIGHTING**									
0100 Runway centerline, bidir., semi-flush, 200 W, w/shallow insert base	R-22	12.40	3.006	Ea.	1,825	156		1,981	2,250
0110 for mounting in base housing		18.60	2.004		965	104		1,069	1,225
0120 Flush, 200 W, w/shallow insert base		12.40	3.006		1,825	156		1,981	2,225
0130 for mounting in base housing		18.64	2		950	104		1,054	1,200
0140 45 W, for mounting in base housing		18.64	2		950	104		1,054	1,200
0150 Touchdown zone light, unidirectional, 200 W, w/shallow insert base		12.40	3.006		1,675	156		1,831	2,075
0160 115 W		12.40	3.006		1,800	156		1,956	2,200
0170 Bidirectional, 62 W		12.40	3.006		1,700	156		1,856	2,100
0180 Unidirectional, 200 W, for mounting in base housing		18.60	2.004		750	104		854	980
0190 115 W		18.60	2.004		810	104		914	1,050
0200 Bidirectional, 62 W		18.60	2.004		900	104		1,004	1,150
0210 Runway edge & threshold light, bidir., 200 W, for base housing		9.36	3.983		1,000	206		1,206	1,400
0220 300 W		9.36	3.983		1,400	206		1,606	1,850
0230 499 W		7.44	5.011		2,350	260		2,610	2,975
0240 Threshold & approach light, unidir., 200 W, for base housing		9.36	3.983		585	206		791	950
0250 499 W		7.44	5.011		710	260		970	1,175
0260 Runway edge, bidirectional, 2-115 W, for base housing		12.40	3.006		1,550	156		1,706	1,925
0270 2-185 W		12.40	3.006		1,725	156		1,881	2,100
0280 Runway threshold & end, bidir., 2-115 W, for base housing		12.40	3.006		1,700	156		1,856	2,100
0370 45 W, flush, for mounting in base housing		18.64	2		835	104		939	1,075
0380 115 W		18.64	2		850	104		954	1,100
0400 Transformer, 45 W		37.20	1.002		183	52		235	279
0410 65 W		37.20	1.002		187	52		239	284
0420 100 W		37.20	1.002		232	52		284	335
0430 200 W, 6.6/6.6 A		37.20	1.002		227	52		279	330
0440 20/6.6 A		24.80	1.503		243	78		321	385
0450 500 W		24.80	1.503		320	78		398	465
0460 Base housing, 24" deep, 12" diameter		18.64	2		515	104		619	720
0470 15" diameter		18.64	2		1,125	104		1,229	1,400
0480 Connection kit for 1 conductor cable		24.80	1.503		36.50	78		114.50	158
0500 Elevated runway marker, high intensity quartz, edge, 115 W		14.88	2.505		410	130		540	650
0510 175 W		14.88	2.505		425	130		555	660
0520 Threshold, 115 W		14.88	2.505		460	130		590	700
0530 Edge, 200 W, w/base and transformer		11.85	3.146		1,150	163		1,313	1,500
0540 Elevated runway light, quartz, runway edge, 45 W		14.88	2.505		242	130		372	460
0550 Threshold, 115 W		14.88	2.505		400	130		530	635
0560 Taxiway, 30 W		14.88	2.505		221	130		351	435
0570 Fixture, 200 W, w/base and transformer		11.85	3.146		1,150	163		1,313	1,525
0580 Elevated threshold marker, quartz, 115 W		14.88	2.505		505	130		635	750
0590 175 W		14.88	2.505		505	130		635	750

34 43 23.16 Airfield Wind Cones

	Crew	Daily Output	Labor-Hours	Unit	Material	2017 Bare Costs Labor	2017 Bare Costs Equipment	Total	Total Incl O&P
0010 **AIRFIELD WIND CONES**									
1200 Wind cone, 12' lighted assembly, rigid, w/obstruction light	R-21	1.36	24.118	Ea.	9,850	1,375	44.50	11,269.50	12,900
1210 Without obstruction light		1.52	21.579		8,250	1,225	40	9,515	10,900
1220 Unlighted assembly, w/obstruction light		1.68	19.524		9,000	1,100	36	10,136	11,600
1230 Without obstruction light		1.84	17.826		8,250	1,000	33	9,283	10,600
1240 Wind cone slip fitter, 2-1/2" pipe		21.84	1.502		109	85	2.78	196.78	250
1250 Wind cone sock, 12' x 3', cotton		6.56	5		595	283	9.25	887.25	1,100
1260 Nylon		6.56	5		605	283	9.25	897.25	1,100

368

For customer support on your Electrical Costs with RSMeans Data, call 800.448.8182.

Estimating Tips

- When estimating costs for the installation of electrical power generation equipment, factors to review include access to the job site, access and setting up at the installation site, required connections, uncrating pads, anchors, leveling, final assembly of the components, and temporary protection from physical damage, such as environmental exposure.

- Be aware of the costs of equipment supports, concrete pads, and vibration isolators. Cross-reference them against other trades' specifications. Also, review site and structural drawings for items that must be included in the estimates.

- It is important to include items that are not documented in the plans and specifications but must be priced. These items include, but are not limited to, testing, dust protection, roof penetration, core drilling concrete floors and walls, patching, cleanup, and final adjustments. Add a contingency or allowance for utility company fees for power hookups, if needed.

- The project size and scope of electrical power generation equipment will have a significant impact on cost. The intent of RSMeans cost data is to provide a benchmark cost so that owners, engineers, and electrical contractors will have a comfortable number with which to start a project. Additionally, there are many websites available to use for research and to obtain a vendor's quote to finalize costs.

Reference Numbers

Reference numbers are shown at the beginning of some major classifications. These numbers refer to related items in the Reference Section. The reference information may be an estimating procedure, an alternate pricing method, or technical information.

Note: Not all subdivisions listed here necessarily appear. ■

Did you know?

Our online estimating solution gives you the same access to RSMeans' data with 24/7 access:

- Quickly locate costs in the searchable database.

- Build cost lists, estimates, and reports in minutes.

- Adjust costs to any location in the U.S. and Canada with the click of a button.

Start your free trial today at
www.RSMeansOnline.com

48 15 Wind Energy Electrical Power Generation Equipment

48 15 13 – Wind Turbines

48 15 13.50 Wind Turbines and Components	Crew	Daily Output	Labor-Hours	Unit	Material	2017 Bare Costs Labor	Equipment	Total	Total Incl O&P
0010 **WIND TURBINES & COMPONENTS**									
0500 Complete system, grid connected									
1000 20 kW, 31' dia, incl. labor & material	G			System				49,900	49,900
1010 Enhanced	G							92,000	92,000
1500 10 kW, 23' dia, incl. labor & material	G							74,000	74,000
2000 2.4 kW, 12' dia, incl. labor & material	G			↓				18,000	18,000
2900 Component system									
3000 Turbine, 400 watt, 3' dia	G	3.41	2.346	Ea.	550	133		683	805
3100 600 watt, 3' dia	G	2.56	3.125		710	177		887	1,050
3200 1000 watt, 9' dia	G	2.05	3.902	↓	1,500	221		1,721	1,975
3400 Mounting hardware									
3500 30' guyed tower kit	G	2 Clab 5.12	3.125	Ea.	410	122		532	640
3505 3' galvanized helical earth screw	G	1 Clab 8	1		49.50	39		88.50	115
3510 Attic mount kit	G	1 Rofc 2.56	3.125		194	135		329	440
3520 Roof mount kit	G	1 Clab 3.41	2.346	↓	320	92		412	490
8900 Equipment									
9100 DC to AC inverter for, 48 V, 4,000 watt	G	1 Elec 2	4	Ea.	2,275	226		2,501	2,850

48 18 Fuel Cell Electrical Power Generation Equipment

48 18 13 – Electrical Power Generation Fuel Cells

48 18 13.10 Fuel Cells

	Crew	Daily Output	Labor-Hours	Unit	Material	2017 Bare Costs Labor	Equipment	Total	Total Incl O&P
0010 **FUEL CELLS**									
2001 Complete system, natural gas, installed, 200 kW	G			System				1,150,000	1,150,000
2002 400 kW	G							2,168,000	2,168,000
2003 600 kW	G							3,060,000	3,060,000
2004 800 kW	G							4,000,000	4,000,000
2005 1000 kW	G			↓				5,005,000	5,005,000
2010 Comm type, for battery charging, uses hydrogen, 100 watt, 12 V	G			Ea.	2,625			2,625	2,875
2020 500 watt, 12 V	G				4,850			4,850	5,325
2030 1000 watt, 48 V	G				8,200			8,200	9,000
2040 Small, for demonstration or battery charging units, 12 V	G				80			80	88
2050 Spare anode set for unit	G				30			30	33
2060 3 watts, uses hydrogen gas	G				320			320	350
2070 6 watts, uses hydrogen gas	G				450			450	495
2080 10 watts, uses hydrogen gas	G			↓	960			960	1,050

Assemblies Section

Table of Contents

How RSMeans Assemblies Data Works

Assemblies estimating provides a fast and reasonably accurate way to develop construction costs. An assembly is the grouping of individual work items, with appropriate quantities, to provide a cost for a major construction component in a convenient unit of measure.

An assemblies estimate is often used during early stages of design development to compare the cost impact of various design alternatives on total building cost.

Assemblies estimates are also used as an efficient tool to verify construction estimates.

Assemblies estimates do not require a completed design or detailed drawings. Instead, they are based on the general size of the structure and other known parameters of the project. The degree of accuracy of an assemblies estimate is generally within +/- 15%.

Most assemblies consist of three major elements: a graphic, the system components, and the cost data itself. The **Graphic** is a visual representation showing the typical appearance of the assembly

① Unique 12-character Identifier

Our assemblies are identified by a **unique 12-character identifier**. The assemblies are numbered using UNIFORMAT II, ASTM Standard E1557. The first 5 characters represent this system to Level 3. The last 7 characters represent further breakdown by in order to arrange items in understandable groups of similar tasks. Line numbers are consistent across all our publications, so a line number in any assemblies data set will always refer to the same item.

② Reference Box

Information is available in the Reference Section to assist the estimator with estimating procedures, alternate pricing methods, and additional technical information.

The **Reference Box** indicates the exact location of this information in the Reference Section. The "R" stands for "reference," and the remaining characters are the line numbers.

③ Narrative Descriptions

Our assemblies descriptions appear in two formats: narrative and table. **Narrative descriptions** are shown in a hierarchical structure to make them readable. In order to read a complete description, read up through the indents to the top of the section. Include everything that is above and to the left that is not contradicted by information below.

D20 Plumbing

D2020 Domestic Water Distribution

Installation includes piping and fittings within 10' of heater. Electric water heaters do not require venting.

1 Kilowatt hour will raise:			
Gallons of Water	Degrees F	Gallons of Water	Degrees F
4.1	100°	6.8	60°
4.5	90°	8.2	50°
5.1	80°	10.0	40°
5.9	70°		

System Components	QUANTITY	UNIT	COST EACH MAT.	COST EACH INST.	COST EACH TOTAL
SYSTEM D2020 210 1780					
ELECTRIC WATER HEATER, RESIDENTIAL, 100°F RISE					
10 GALLON TANK, 7 GPH					
Water heater, residential electric, glass lined tank, 10 gal.	1.000	Ea.	510	325	835
Copper tubing, type L, solder joint, hanger 10' OC 1/2" diam.	30.000	L.F.	116.70	276	392.70
Wrought copper 90° elbow for solder joints 1/2" diam.	4.000	Ea.	5.40	150	155.40
Wrought copper Tee for solder joints, 1/2" diam.	2.000	Ea.	4.60	115	119.60
Union, wrought copper, 1/2" diam.	2.000	Ea.	33.60	79	112.60
Valve, gate, bronze, 125 lb, NRS, soldered 1/2" diam.	2.000	Ea.	121	62	183
Relief valve, bronze, press & temp, self-close, 3/4" IPS	1.000	Ea.	226	26.50	252.50
Wrought copper adapter, CTS to MPT 3/4" IPS	1.000	Ea.	4.74	44	48.74
Copper tubing, type L, solder joints, 3/4" diam.	1.000	L.F.	5.40	9.80	15.20
Wrought copper 90° elbow for solder joints 3/4" diam.	1.000	Ea.	3.03	39.50	42.53
TOTAL			1,030.47	1,126.80	2,157.27

D2020 210	Electric Water Heaters - Residential Systems	COST EACH MAT.	COST EACH INST.	COST EACH TOTAL
1760	Electric water heater, residential, 100°F rise			
1780	10 gallon tank, 7 GPH	1,025	1,125	2,150
1820	20 gallon tank, 7 GPH	1,300	1,200	2,500
1860	30 gallon tank, 7 GPH	1,975	1,250	3,225
1900	40 gallon tank, 8 GPH	2,325	1,375	3,700
1940	52 gallon tank, 10 GPH	2,525	1,400	3,925
1980	66 gallon tank, 13 GPH	3,725	1,600	5,325
2020	80 gallon tank, 16 GPH	4,000	1,675	5,675
2060	120 gallon tank, 23 GPH	5,800	1,950	7,750

② R224000 -20

For supplemental customizable square foot estimating forms, visit: **www.RSMeans.com/2017samples**

in question. It is frequently accompanied by additional explanatory technical information describing the class of items. The **System Components** is a listing of the individual tasks that make up the assembly, including the quantity and unit of measure for each item, along with the cost of material and installation. The **Assemblies**

Data below lists prices for other similar systems with dimensional and/or size variations.

All of our assemblies costs represent the cost for the installing contractor. An allowance for profit has been added to all material, labor, and equipment rental costs. A markup for labor burdens, including workers' compensation, fixed

overhead, and business overhead, is included with installation costs.

The information in RSMeans cost data represents a "national average" cost. This data should be modified to the project location using the **City Cost Indexes** or **Location Factors** tables found in the Reference Section.

D20 Plumbing

D2020 Domestic Water Distribution

Installation includes piping and fittings within 10' of heater. Electric water heaters do not require venting.

1 Kilowatt hour will raise:			
Gallons of Water	Degrees F	Gallons of Water	Degrees F
4.1	100°	6.8	60°
4.5	90°	8.2	50°
5.1	80°	10.0	40°
5.9	70°		

System Components		QUANTITY	UNIT	COST EACH		
				MAT.	INST.	TOTAL
SYSTEM D2020 210 1780						
ELECTRIC WATER HEATER, RESIDENTIAL, 100°F RISE						
10 GALLON TANK, 7 GPH						
Water heater, residential electric, glass lined tank, 10 gal.		1.000	Ea.	510	325	835
Copper tubing, type L, solder joint, hanger 10' OC 1/2" diam.		30.000	L.F.	116.70	276	392.70
Wrought copper 90° elbow for solder joints 1/2" diam.		4.000	Ea.	5.40	150	155.40
Wrought copper Tee for solder joints, 1/2" diam.		2.000	Ea.	4.60	115	119.60
Union, wrought copper, 1/2" diam.		2.000	Ea.	33.60	79	112.60
Valve, gate, bronze, 125 lb, NRS, soldered 1/2" diam.		2.000	Ea.	121	62	183
Relief valve, bronze, press & temp, self-close, 3/4" IPS		1.000	Ea.	226	26.50	252.50
Wrought copper adapter, CTS to MPT 3/4" IPS		1.000	Ea.	4.74	44	48.74
Copper tubing, type L, solder joints, 3/4" diam.		1.000	L.F.	5.40	9.80	15.20
Wrought copper 90° elbow for solder joints 3/4" diam.		1.000	Ea.	3.03	39.50	42.53
TOTAL				1,030.47	1,126.80	2,157.27

D2020 210	Electric Water Heaters - Residential Systems		COST EACH		
			MAT.	INST.	TOTAL
1760	Electric water heater, residential, 100°F rise				
1780	10 gallon tank, 7 GPH		1,025	1,125	2,150
1820	20 gallon tank, 7 GPH	R224000	1,300	1,200	2,500
1860	30 gallon tank, 7 GPH	-20	1,975	1,250	3,225
1900	40 gallon tank, 8 GPH		2,325	1,375	3,700
1940	52 gallon tank, 10 GPH		2,525	1,400	3,925
1980	66 gallon tank, 13 GPH		3,725	1,600	5,325
2020	80 gallon tank, 16 GPH		4,000	1,675	5,675
2060	120 gallon tank, 23 GPH		5,800	1,950	7,750

4 Unit of Measure

All RSMeans assemblies data includes a typical **Unit of Measure** used for estimating that item. For instance, for continuous footings or foundation walls the unit is linear feet (L.F.). For spread footings the unit is each (Ea.). The estimator needs to take special care that the unit in the data matches the unit in the takeoff. Abbreviations and unit conversions can be found in the Reference Section.

5 System Components

System components are listed separately to detail what is included in the development of the total system price.

How RSMeans Assemblies Data Works (Continued)

Sample Estimate

This sample demonstrates the elements of an estimate, including a tally of the RSMeans data lines. Published assemblies costs include all markups for labor burden and profit for the installing contractor. This estimate adds a summary of the markups applied by a general contractor on the installing contractor's work. These figures represent the total cost to the owner. The location factor with RSMeans data is applied at the bottom of the estimate to adjust the cost of the work to a specific location.

Project Name:	Interior Fit-out, ABC Office			
Location:	**Anywhere, USA**	**Date: 1/1/2017**		**STD**
Assembly Number	**Description**	**Qty.**	**Unit**	**Subtotal**
① C1010 124 1200	Wood partition, 2 x 4 @ 16" OC w/5/8" FR gypsum board	560.000	S.F.	$2,788.80
C1020 114 1800	Metal door & frame, flush hollow core, 3'-0" x 7'-0"	2.000	Ea.	$2,540.00
C3010 230 0080	Painting, brushwork, primer & 2 coats	1,120.000	S.F.	$1,400.00
C3020 410 0140	Carpet, tufted, nylon, roll goods, 12' wide, 26 oz	240.000	S.F.	$830.40
C3030 210 6000	Acoustic ceilings, 24" x 48" tile, tee grid suspension	200.000	S.F.	$1,178.00
D5020 125 0560	Receptacles incl plate, box, conduit, wire, 20 A duplex	8.000	Ea.	$2,212.00
D5020 125 0720	Light switch incl plate, box, conduit, wire, 20 A single pole	2.000	Ea.	$543.00
D5020 210 0560	Fluorescent fixtures, recess mounted, 20 per 1000 SF	200.000	S.F.	$2,244.00
	Assembly Subtotal			**$13,736.20**
	Sales Tax @ **②**	5 %		$ 343.41
	General Requirements @ **③**	7 %		$ 961.53
	Subtotal A			**$15,041.14**
	GC Overhead @ **④**	5 %		$ 752.06
	Subtotal B			**$15,793.20**
	GC Profit @ **⑤**	5 %		$ 789.66
	Subtotal C			**$16,582.86**
	Adjusted by Location Factor ⑥	114.7		$ 19,020.54
	Architects Fee @ **⑦**	8 %		$ 1,521.64
	Contingency @ **⑧**	15 %		$ 2,853.08
	Project Total Cost			**$ 23,395.26**

This estimate is based on an interactive spreadsheet.
A copy of this spreadsheet is located at www.RSMeans.com/2017samples.
You are free to download it and adjust it to your methodology.

1 Work Performed

The body of the estimate shows the RSMeans data selected, including line numbers, a brief description of each item, its takeoff quantity and unit, and the total installed cost, including the installing contractor's overhead and profit.

2 Sales Tax

If the work is subject to state or local sales taxes, the amount must be added to the estimate. In a conceptual estimate it can be assumed that one half of the total represents material costs. Therefore, apply the sales tax rate to 50% of the assembly subtotal.

3 General Requirements

This item covers project-wide needs provided by the general contractor. These items vary by project but may include temporary facilities and utilities, security, testing, project cleanup, etc. In assemblies estimates a percentage is used, typically between 5% and 15% of project cost.

4 General Contractor Overhead

This entry represents the general contractor's markup on all work to cover project administration costs.

5 General Contractor Profit

This entry represents the GC's profit on all work performed. The value included here can vary widely by project and is influenced by the GC's perception of the project's financial risk and market conditions.

6 Location Factor

RSMeans published data is based on national average costs. If necessary, adjust the total cost of the project using a location factor from the "Location Factor" table or the "City Cost Indexes" table found in the Reference Section. Use location factors if the work is general, covering the work of multiple trades. If the work is by a single trade (e.g., masonry) use the more specific data found in the City Cost Indexes.

To adjust costs by location factors, multiply the base cost by the factor and divide by 100.

7 Architect's Fee

If appropriate, add the design cost to the project estimate. These fees vary based on project complexity and size. Typical design and engineering fees can be found in the reference section.

8 Contingency

A factor for contingency may be added to any estimate to represent the cost of unknowns that may occur between the time that the estimate is performed and the time the project is constructed. The amount of the allowance will depend on the stage of design at which the estimate is done, and the contractor's assessment of the risk involved.

D2020 Domestic Water Distribution

Installation includes piping and fittings within 10′ of heater. Electric water heaters do not require venting.

1 Kilowatt hour will raise:			
Gallons of Water	Degrees F	Gallons of Water	Degrees F
4.1	100°	6.8	60°
4.5	90°	8.2	50°
5.1	80°	10.0	40°
5.9	70°		

System Components			COST EACH		
	QUANTITY	UNIT	MAT.	INST.	TOTAL
SYSTEM D2020 210 1780					
ELECTRIC WATER HEATER, RESIDENTIAL, 100°F RISE					
10 GALLON TANK, 7 GPH					
Water heater, residential electric, glass lined tank, 10 gal.	1.000	Ea.	510	325	835
Copper tubing, type L, solder joint, hanger 10′ OC 1/2″ diam.	30.000	L.F.	116.70	276	392.70
Wrought copper 90° elbow for solder joints 1/2″ diam.	4.000	Ea.	5.40	150	155.40
Wrought copper Tee for solder joints, 1/2″ diam.	2.000	Ea.	4.60	115	119.60
Union, wrought copper, 1/2″ diam.	2.000	Ea.	33.60	79	112.60
Valve, gate, bronze, 125 lb, NRS, soldered 1/2″ diam.	2.000	Ea.	121	62	183
Relief valve, bronze, press & temp, self-close, 3/4″ IPS	1.000	Ea.	226	26.50	252.50
Wrought copper adapter, CTS to MPT 3/4″ IPS	1.000	Ea.	4.74	44	48.74
Copper tubing, type L, solder joints, 3/4″ diam.	1.000	L.F.	5.40	9.80	15.20
Wrought copper 90° elbow for solder joints 3/4″ diam.	1.000	Ea.	3.03	39.50	42.53
TOTAL			1,030.47	1,126.80	2,157.27

D2020 210	Electric Water Heaters - Residential Systems	COST EACH		
		MAT.	INST.	TOTAL
1760	Electric water heater, residential, 100°F rise			
1780	10 gallon tank, 7 GPH	1,025	1,125	2,150
1820	20 gallon tank, 7 GPH	1,300	1,200	2,500
1860	30 gallon tank, 7 GPH R224000 -20	1,975	1,250	3,225
1900	40 gallon tank, 8 GPH	2,325	1,375	3,700
1940	52 gallon tank, 10 GPH	2,525	1,400	3,925
1980	66 gallon tank, 13 GPH	3,725	1,600	5,325
2020	80 gallon tank, 16 GPH	4,000	1,675	5,675
2060	120 gallon tank, 23 GPH	5,800	1,950	7,750

Systems below include piping and fittings within 10' of heater. Electric water heaters do not require venting.

System Components	QUANTITY	UNIT	COST EACH MAT.	COST EACH INST.	COST EACH TOTAL
SYSTEM D2020 240 1820					
ELECTRIC WATER HEATER, COMMERCIAL, 100°F RISE					
50 GALLON TANK, 9 KW, 37 GPH					
Water heater, commercial, electric, 50 Gal, 9 KW, 37 GPH	1.000	Ea.	8,650	415	9,065
Copper tubing, type L, solder joint, hanger 10' OC, 3/4" diam	34.000	L.F.	183.60	333.20	516.80
Wrought copper 90° elbow for solder joints 3/4" diam	5.000	Ea.	15.15	197.50	212.65
Wrought copper Tee for solder joints, 3/4" diam	2.000	Ea.	11.10	124	135.10
Wrought copper union for soldered joints, 3/4" diam.	2.000	Ea.	42	83	125
Valve, gate, bronze, 125 lb, NRS, soldered 3/4" diam	2.000	Ea.	138	75	213
Relief valve, bronze, press & temp, self-close, 3/4" IPS	1.000	Ea.	226	26.50	252.50
Wrought copper adapter, copper tubing to male, 3/4" IPS	1.000	Ea.	4.74	44	48.74
TOTAL			9,270.59	1,298.20	10,568.79

D2020 240	Electric Water Heaters - Commercial Systems		COST EACH MAT.	COST EACH INST.	COST EACH TOTAL
1800	Electric water heater, commercial, 100°F rise				
1820	50 gallon tank, 9 KW 37 GPH		9,275	1,300	10,575
1860	80 gal, 12 KW 49 GPH	R224000 -10	11,800	1,600	13,400
1900	36 KW 147 GPH		16,200	1,725	17,925
1940	120 gal, 36 KW 147 GPH	R224000 -20	17,400	1,875	19,275
1980	150 gal, 120 KW 490 GPH		54,500	2,000	56,500
2020	200 gal, 120 KW 490 GPH		57,000	2,050	59,050
2060	250 gal, 150 KW 615 GPH		63,000	2,400	65,400
2100	300 gal, 180 KW 738 GPH		68,500	2,525	71,025
2140	350 gal, 30 KW 123 GPH		51,000	2,725	53,725
2180	180 KW 738 GPH		71,000	2,725	73,725
2220	500 gal, 30 KW 123 GPH		66,500	3,200	69,700
2260	240 KW 984 GPH		107,500	3,200	110,700
2300	700 gal, 30 KW 123 GPH		80,000	3,675	83,675
2340	300 KW 1230 GPH		119,500	3,675	123,175
2380	1000 gal, 60 KW 245 GPH		96,500	5,100	101,600
2420	480 KW 1970 GPH		157,500	5,100	162,600
2460	1500 gal, 60 KW 245 GPH		141,500	6,300	147,800
2500	480 KW 1970 GPH		195,000	6,300	201,300

D3020 Heat Generating Systems

Small Electric Boiler
System Considerations:
1. Terminal units are fin tube baseboard radiation rated at 720 BTU/hr with 200° water temperature or 820 BTU/hr steam.
2. Primary use being for residential or smaller supplementary areas, the floor levels are based on 7-1/2' ceiling heights.
3. All distribution piping is copper for boilers through 205 MBH. All piping for larger systems is steel pipe.

Boiler   Baseboard Radiation

System Components	QUANTITY	UNIT	COST EACH		
			MAT.	INST.	TOTAL
SYSTEM D3020 102 1120					
SMALL HEATING SYSTEM, HYDRONIC, ELECTRIC BOILER					
1,480 S.F., 61 MBH, STEAM, 1 FLOOR					
Boiler, electric steam, std cntrls, trim, ftngs and valves, 18 KW, 61.4 MBH	1.000	Ea.	5,225	1,870	7,095
Copper tubing type L, solder joint, hanger 10'OC, 1-1/4" diam	160.000	L.F.	2,160	2,056	4,216
Radiation, 3/4" copper tube w/alum fin baseboard pkg 7" high	60.000	L.F.	501	1,410	1,911
Rough in baseboard panel or fin tube with valves & traps	10.000	Set	2,670	7,100	9,770
Pipe covering, calcium silicate w/cover, 1" wall 1-1/4" diam	160.000	L.F.	707.20	1,192	1,899.20
Low water cut-off, quick hookup, in gage glass tappings	1.000	Ea.	305	47	352
TOTAL			11,568.20	13,675	25,243.20
COST PER S.F.			7.82	9.24	17.06

D3020 102	Small Heating Systems, Hydronic, Electric Boilers	COST PER S.F.		
		MAT.	INST.	TOTAL
1100	Small heating systems, hydronic, electric boilers			
1120	Steam, 1 floor, 1480 S.F., 61 M.B.H.	7.84	9.26	17.10
1160	3,000 S.F., 123 M.B.H.	6	8.10	14.10
1200	5,000 S.F., 205 M.B.H.	5.10	7.50	12.60
1240	2 floors, 12,400 S.F., 512 M.B.H.	3.94	7.45	11.39
1280	3 floors, 24,800 S.F., 1023 M.B.H.	4.59	7.35	11.94
1320	34,750 S.F., 1,433 M.B.H.	4.20	7.15	11.35
1360	Hot water, 1 floor, 1,000 S.F., 41 M.B.H.	12.90	5.10	18
1400	2,500 S.F., 103 M.B.H.	9.15	9.25	18.40
1440	2 floors, 4,850 S.F., 205 M.B.H.	8.90	11.10	20
1480	3 floors, 9,700 S.F., 410 M.B.H.	9.05	11.50	20.55

D3020 Heat Generating Systems

Boiler   **Unit Heater**

Large Electric Boiler System Considerations:

1. Terminal units are all unit heaters of the same size. Quantities are varied to accommodate total requirements.
2. All air is circulated through the heaters a minimum of three times per hour.
3. As the capacities are adequate for commercial use, floor levels are based on 10' ceiling heights.
4. All distribution piping is black steel pipe.

System Components	QUANTITY	UNIT	COST EACH		
			MAT.	INST.	TOTAL
SYSTEM D3020 104 1240					
LARGE HEATING SYSTEM, HYDRONIC, ELECTRIC BOILER					
9,280 S.F., 135 KW, 461 MBH, 1 FLOOR					
Boiler, electric hot water, std ctrls, trim, ftngs, valves, 135 KW, 461 MBH	1.000	Ea.	12,225	4,050	16,275
Expansion tank, painted steel, 60 Gal capacity ASME	1.000	Ea.	4,800	225	5,025
Circulating pump, Cl, close cpld, 50 GPM, 2 HP, 2" pipe conn	1.000	Ea.	3,175	450	3,625
Unit heater, 1 speed propeller, horizontal, 200° EWT, 72.7 MBH	7.000	Ea.	6,405	1,722	8,127
Unit heater piping hookup with controls	7.000	Set	5,600	11,200	16,800
Pipe, steel, black, schedule 40, welded, 2-1/2" diam	380.000	L.F.	6,498	11,346.80	17,844.80
Pipe covering, calcium silicate w/cover, 1" wall, 2-1/2" diam	380.000	L.F.	2,090	2,926	5,016
TOTAL			40,793	31,919.80	72,712.80
COST PER S.F.			4.40	3.44	7.84

D3020 104	Large Heating Systems, Hydronic, Electric Boilers	COST PER S.F.		
		MAT.	INST.	TOTAL
1230	Large heating systems, hydronic, electric boilers			
1240	9,280 S.F., 135 K.W., 461 M.B.H., 1 floor	4.40	3.44	7.84
1280	14,900 S.F., 240 K.W., 820 M.B.H., 2 floors	5.90	5.60	11.50
1320	18,600 S.F., 296 K.W., 1,010 M.B.H., 3 floors	5.85	6.05	11.90
1360	26,100 S.F., 420 K.W., 1,432 M.B.H., 4 floors	5.75	5.95	11.70
1400	39,100 S.F., 666 K.W., 2,273 M.B.H., 4 floors	4.90	4.97	9.87
1440	57,700 S.F., 900 K.W., 3,071 M.B.H., 5 floors	4.68	4.88	9.56
1480	111,700 S.F., 1,800 K.W., 6,148 M.B.H., 6 floors	4.14	4.20	8.34
1520	149,000 S.F., 2,400 K.W., 8,191 M.B.H., 8 floors	4.08	4.18	8.26
1560	223,300 S.F., 3,600 K.W., 12,283 M.B.H., 14 floors	4.36	4.75	9.11

381

D4090 Other Fire Protection Systems

General: Automatic fire protection (suppression) systems other than water sprinklers may be desired for special environments, high risk areas, isolated locations or unusual hazards. Some typical applications would include:

Paint dip tanks
Securities vaults
Electronic data processing
Tape and data storage
Transformer rooms
Spray booths
Petroleum storage
High rack storage

Piping and wiring costs are dependent on the individual application and must be added to the component costs shown below.

All areas are assumed to be open.

D4090 910	Fire Suppression Unit Components	COST EACH		
		MAT.	INST.	TOTAL
0020	Detectors with brackets			
0040	Fixed temperature heat detector	56.50	97	153.50
0060	Rate of temperature rise detector	56.50	85	141.50
0080	Ion detector (smoke) detector	143	109	252
0200	Extinguisher agent			
0240	200 lb FM200, container	8,625	335	8,960
0280	75 lb carbon dioxide cylinder	1,400	224	1,624
0320	Dispersion nozzle			
0340	FM200 1-1/2" dispersion nozzle	101	53.50	154.50
0380	Carbon dioxide 3" x 5" dispersion nozzle	73.50	41.50	115
0420	Control station			
0440	Single zone control station with batteries	385	680	1,065
0470	Multizone (4) control station with batteries	835	1,350	2,185
0490				
0500	Electric mechanical release	207	355	562
0520				
0550	Manual pull station	66	124	190
0570				
0640	Battery standby power 10" x 10" x 17"	455	170	625
0700				
0740	Bell signalling device	143	85	228

D4090 920	FM200 Systems	COST PER C.F.		
		MAT.	INST.	TOTAL
0820	Average FM200 system, minimum			1.94
0840	Maximum			3.85

D5010 Electrical Service/Distribution

System Components	QUANTITY	UNIT	COST PER L.F.		
			MAT.	INST.	TOTAL
SYSTEM D5010 110 0200					
HIGH VOLTAGE CABLE, NEUTRAL AND CONDUIT INCLUDED, COPPER #2, 5 kV					
Shielded cable, no splice/termn, copper, XLP shielding, 5 kV, #2	.030	C.L.F.	8.64	10.20	18.84
Wire, 600 volt, type THW, copper, stranded, #8	.010	C.L.F.	.36	.85	1.21
Rigid galv steel conduit to 15' H, 2" diam, w/term, ftng & support	1.000	L.F.	11.30	15.10	26.40
TOTAL			20.30	26.15	46.45

D5010 110	High Voltage Shielded Conductors	COST PER L.F.		
		MAT.	INST.	TOTAL
0200	High voltage cable, neutral & conduit included, copper #2, 5 kV	20.50	26	46.50
0240	Copper #1, 5 kV	25.50	30.50	56
0280	15 kV	25.50	30.50	56
0320	Copper 1/0, 5 kV	28.50	38.50	67
0360	15 kV	30	38.50	68.50
0400	25 kV	34	39.50	73.50
0440	35 kV	36	40	76
0480	Copper 2/0, 5 kV	31.50	39.50	71
0520	15 kV	32	39.50	71.50
0560	25 kV	36.50	40.50	77
0600	35 kV	43	45	88
0640	Copper 4/0, 5 kV	41.50	45.50	87
0680	15 kV	42	45.50	87.50
0720	25 kV	46	46	92
0760	35 kV	49.50	47	96.50
0800	Copper 250 kcmil, 5 kV	45	46	91
0840	15 kV	44	46	90
0880	25 kV	52	47	99
0920	35 kV	57.50	51	108.50
0960	Copper 350 kcmil, 5 kV	55	51	106
1000	15 kV	53.50	51	104.50
1040	25 kV	60.50	52.50	113
1080	35 kV	63.50	54	117.50
1120	Copper 500 kcmil, 5 kV	84.50	64	148.50
1160	15 kV	83.50	64	147.50
1200	25 kV	90.50	65.50	156
1240	35 kV	94	67.50	161.50

System Components	QUANTITY	UNIT	COST EACH		
			MAT.	INST.	TOTAL
SYSTEM D5010 120 0220					
SERVICE INSTALLATION, INCLUDES BREAKERS, METERING, 20' CONDUIT & WIRE					
3 PHASE, 4 WIRE, 60 A					
Wire, 600 volt, copper type XHHW, stranded #6	.600	C.L.F.	33.60	62.40	96
Rigid galvanized steel conduit, 3/4" including fittings	20.000	L.F.	103	170	273
Service entrance cap, 3/4" diameter	1.000	Ea.	6.55	52	58.55
Conduit LB fitting with cover, 3/4" diameter	1.000	Ea.	12.25	52	64.25
Meter socket, three phase, 100 A	1.000	Ea.	118	242	360
Safety switches, heavy duty, 240 volt, 3 pole NEMA 1 fusible, 60 amp	1.000	Ea.	192	295	487
Grounding, wire ground bare armored, #8-1 conductor	.200	C.L.F.	15.30	68	83.30
Grounding, clamp, bronze, 3/4" diameter	1.000	Ea.	6.50	21	27.50
Grounding, rod, copper clad, 8' long, 3/4" diameter	1.000	Ea.	37.50	128	165.50
Wireway w/fittings, 2-1/2" x 2-1/2"	1.000	L.F.	11.90	15.10	27
TOTAL			536.60	1,105.50	1,642.10

D5010 120	Overhead Electric Service, 3 Phase - 4 Wire	COST EACH		
		MAT.	INST.	TOTAL
0200	Service installation, includes breakers, metering, 20' conduit & wire			
0220	3 phase, 4 wire, 120/208 volts, 60 A	535	1,100	1,635
0240	100 A	735	1,250	1,985
0245	100 A w/circuit breaker	1,500	1,550	3,050
0280	200 A	1,300	1,725	3,025
0285	200 A w/circuit breaker	2,900	2,175	5,075
0320	400 A	2,600	3,450	6,050
0325	400 A w/circuit breaker	5,600	4,300	9,900
0360	600 A	4,300	5,075	9,375
0365	600 A, w/switchboard	8,750	6,425	15,175
0400	800 A	6,650	6,075	12,725
0405	800 A, w/switchboard	11,100	7,625	18,725
0440	1000 A	8,125	7,500	15,625
0445	1000 A, w/switchboard	13,500	9,200	22,700
0480	1200 A	10,700	8,550	19,250
0485	1200 A, w/groundfault switchboard	33,800	10,600	44,400
0520	1600 A	13,500	11,200	24,700
0525	1600 A, w/groundfault switchboard	38,600	13,400	52,000

D50 Electrical

D5010 Electrical Service/Distribution

D5010 120	Overhead Electric Service, 3 Phase - 4 Wire	COST EACH		
		MAT.	INST.	TOTAL
0560	2000 A	17,000	13,600	31,200
0565	2000 A, w/groundfault switchboard	46,000	16,800	62,800
0610	1 phase, 3 wire, 120/240 volts, 100 A (no safety switch)	182	610	792
0615	100 A w/load center	350	1,175	1,525
0620	200 A	420	840	1,260
0625	200 A w/load center	790	1,775	2,565

385

Safety Switch

Meter and service equipment

Underground service conductor

Ground rod

System Components			COST EACH		
	QUANTITY	UNIT	MAT.	INST.	TOTAL
SYSTEM D5010 130 1000					
2000 AMP UNDERGROUND ELECTRIC SERVICE WITH GROUNDFAULT SWITCHBOARD					
INCLUDING EXCAVATION, BACKFILL AND COMPACTION					
Excavate Trench	44.440	B.C.Y.		311.97	311.97
4 inch conduit bank	108.000	L.F.	950.40	2,700	3,650.40
4 inch fitting	8.000	Ea.	340	452	792
4 inch bells	4.000	Ea.	7.12	226	233.12
Concrete material	16.580	C.Y.	2,155.40		2,155.40
Concrete placement	16.580	C.Y.		423.12	423.12
Backfill trench	33.710	L.C.Y.		103.83	103.83
Compact fill material in trench	25.930	E.C.Y.		134.57	134.57
Dispose of excess fill material on-site	24.070	L.C.Y.		297.02	297.02
500 kcmil power cable	18.000	C.L.F.	18,450	7,650	26,100
Wire, 600 volt, type THW, copper, stranded, 1/0	6.000	C.L.F.	1,440	1,236	2,676
Saw cutting, concrete walls, plain, per inch of depth	64.000	L.F.	3.20	508.16	511.36
Meter centers and sockets, single pos, 4 terminal, 400 amp	5.000	Ea.	4,450	2,000	6,450
Safety switch, 400 amp	5.000	Ea.	6,750	3,775	10,525
Ground rod clamp	6.000	Ea.	39	126	165
Wireway	1.000	L.F.	11.90	15.10	27
600 volt stranded copper wire, 1/0	1.200	C.L.F.	288	247.20	535.20
Flexible metallic conduit	120.000	L.F.	48	508.80	556.80
Ground rod	6.000	Ea.	336	1,020	1,356
TOTAL			35,269.02	21,734.77	57,003.79

D5010 130	Underground Electric Service	COST EACH		
		MAT.	INST.	TOTAL
0950	Underground electric service including excavation, backfill and compaction			
1000	3 phase, 4 wire, 277/480 volts, 2000 A	35,300	21,800	57,100
1050	2000 A w/groundfault switch	62,500	24,200	86,700
1100	1600 A	27,900	17,500	45,400
1150	1600 A w/groundfault switchboard	53,000	19,700	72,700
1200	1200 A	21,400	13,900	35,300
1250	1200 A w/groundfault switchboard	44,500	16,000	60,500
1400	800 A	15,100	11,500	26,600

D5010 Electrical Service/Distribution

D5010 130	Underground Electric Service	COST EACH		
		MAT.	INST.	TOTAL
1450	800 A w/switchboard	19,500	13,100	32,600
1500	600 A	10,200	10,600	20,800
1550	600 A w/switchboard	14,700	12,000	26,700
1600	1 phase, 3 wire, 120/240 volts, 200 A	3,225	3,650	6,875
1650	200 A w/load center	3,600	4,600	8,200
1700	100 A	2,300	2,975	5,275
1750	100 A w/load center	2,675	3,925	6,600

For customer support on your Electrical Costs with RSMeans Data, call 800.448.8182.

D5010 Electrical Service/Distribution

System Components	QUANTITY	UNIT	COST PER L.F.		
			MAT.	INST.	TOTAL
SYSTEM D5010 230 0200					
FEEDERS, INCLUDING STEEL CONDUIT & WIRE, 60 A					
Rigid galvanized steel conduit, 3/4", including fittings	1.000	L.F.	5.15	8.50	13.65
Wire 600 volt, type XHHW copper stranded #6	.030	C.L.F.	1.68	3.12	4.80
Wire 600 volt, type XHHW copper stranded #8	.010	C.L.F.	.34	.85	1.19
TOTAL			7.17	12.47	19.64

D5010 230	Feeder Installation	COST PER L.F.		
		MAT.	INST.	TOTAL
0200	Feeder installation 600 V, including RGS conduit and XHHW wire, 60 A	7.15	12.45	19.60
0240	100 A	9.15	16.25	25.40
0280	200 A	23	24.50	47.50
0320	400 A	45.50	49	94.50
0360	600 A	75	79.50	154.50
0400	800 A	97	94.50	191.50
0440	1000 A	122	124	246
0480	1200 A	150	159	309
0520	1600 A	194	189	383
0560	2000 A	244	249	493
1200	Branch installation 600 V, including EMT conduit and THW wire, 15 A	1.12	6.05	7.17
1240	20 A	1.31	6.45	7.76
1280	30 A	1.64	6.70	8.34
1320	50 A	3.25	9.30	12.55
1360	65 A	4	9.85	13.85
1400	85 A	6.10	11.50	17.60
1440	100 A	6.75	11.75	18.50
1480	130 A	10.10	13.70	23.80
1520	150 A	12.50	15.70	28.20
1560	200 A	17	17.90	34.90

System Components	QUANTITY	UNIT	COST EACH		
			MAT.	INST.	TOTAL
SYSTEM D5010 240 0240					
SWITCHGEAR INSTALLATION, INCL SWBD, PANELS & CIRC BREAKERS, 600 A					
Switchboards, 120/208 V, 600 amp	1.000	Ea.	4,450	1,350	5,800
Aluminum bus bars, 120/208 V, 600 amp	1.000	Ea.	1,575	1,350	2,925
Feeder section, circuit breakers, KA frame, 70 to 225 amp	1.000	Ea.	1,700	212	1,912
Feeder section, circuit breakers, LA frame, 125 to 400 amp	1.000	Ea.	4,575	295	4,870
TOTAL			12,300	3,207	15,507

D5010 240	Switchgear	COST PER EACH		
		MAT.	INST.	TOTAL
0190	Switchgear installation, including switchboard, panels, & circuit breaker			
0200	120/208 V, 3 phase, 400 A	9,100	2,875	11,975
0240	600 A	12,300	3,200	15,500
0280	800 A	14,900	3,725	18,625
0300	1000 A	18,500	4,125	22,625
0320	1200 A	19,500	4,650	24,150
0360	1600 A	31,700	5,375	37,075
0400	2000 A	38,300	5,875	44,175
0500	277/480 V, 3 phase, 400 A	12,500	5,325	17,825
0520	600 A	17,200	6,125	23,325
0540	800 A	18,900	6,825	25,725
0560	1000 A	24,200	7,525	31,725
0580	1200 A	26,400	8,400	34,800
0600	1600 A	39,100	9,250	48,350
0620	2000 A	49,300	10,300	59,600

System Components	QUANTITY	UNIT	COST EACH		
			MAT.	INST.	TOTAL
SYSTEM D5010 250 1020					
PANELBOARD INSTALLATION, INCLUDES PANELBOARD, CONDUCTOR, & CONDUIT					
Conduit, galvanized steel, 1-1/4"dia.	37.000	L.F.	207.20	418.10	625.30
Panelboards, NQOD, 4 wire, 120/208 volts, 100 amp main, 24 circuits	1.000	Ea.	1,675	1,450	3,125
Wire, 600 volt, type THW, copper, stranded, #3	1.480	C.L.F.	171.68	201.28	372.96
TOTAL			2,053.88	2,069.38	4,123.26

D5010 250	Panelboard	COST EACH		
		MAT.	INST.	TOTAL
0900	Panelboards, NQOD, 4 wire, 120/208 volts w/conductor & conduit			
1000	100 A, 0 stories, 0' horizontal	1,675	1,450	3,125
1020	1 stories, 25' horizontal	2,050	2,075	4,125
1040	5 stories, 50' horizontal	2,800	3,300	6,100
1060	10 stories, 75' horizontal	3,675	4,725	8,400
1080	225A, 0 stories, 0' horizontal	3,025	1,875	4,900
2000	1 stories, 25' horizontal	4,150	3,000	7,150
2020	5 stories, 50' horizontal	6,325	5,200	11,525
2040	10 stories, 75' horizontal	8,900	7,775	16,675
2060	400A, 0 stories, 0' horizontal	4,425	2,825	7,250
2080	1 stories, 25' horizontal	6,175	4,650	10,825
3000	5 stories, 50' horizontal	9,625	8,225	17,850
3020	10 stories, 75' horizontal	18,500	16,100	34,600
3040	600 A, 0 stories, 0' horizontal	6,550	3,400	9,950
3060	1 stories, 25' horizontal	9,475	6,350	15,825
3080	5 stories, 50' horizontal	15,200	12,100	27,300
4000	10 stories, 75' horizontal	30,800	23,900	54,700
4010	Panelboards, NEHB, 4 wire, 277/480 volts w/conductor, conduit, & safety switch			
4020	100 A, 0 stories, 0' horizontal, includes safety switch	3,150	1,975	5,125
4040	1 stories, 25' horizontal	3,525	2,600	6,125
4060	5 stories, 50' horizontal	4,275	3,825	8,100
4080	10 stories, 75' horizontal	5,150	5,250	10,400
5000	225 A, 0 stories, 0' horizontal	4,700	2,400	7,100
5020	1 stories, 25' horizontal	5,825	3,525	9,350
5040	5 stories, 50' horizontal	8,025	5,725	13,750
5060	10 stories, 75' horizontal	10,600	8,275	18,875

For customer support on your Electrical Costs with RSMeans Data, call 800.448.8182.

D50 Electrical

D5010 Electrical Service/Distribution

D5010 250	Panelboard	COST EACH		
		MAT.	INST.	TOTAL
5080	400 A, 0 stories, 0' horizontal	7,550	3,700	11,250
6000	1 stories, 25' horizontal	9,300	5,525	14,825
6020	5 stories, 50' horizontal	12,700	9,100	21,800
6040	10 stories, 75' horizontal	21,600	16,900	38,500
6060	600 A, 0 stories, 0' horizontal	11,600	4,700	16,300
6080	1 stories, 25' horizontal	14,500	7,650	22,150
7000	5 stories, 50' horizontal	20,300	13,400	33,700
7020	10 stories, 75' horizontal	35,900	25,200	61,100

D5020 Lighting and Branch Wiring

Duplex Receptacle

System Components			COST PER S.F.		
	QUANTITY	UNIT	MAT.	INST.	TOTAL
SYSTEM D5020 110 0200					
RECEPTACLES INCL. PLATE, BOX, CONDUIT, WIRE & TRANS. WHEN REQUIRED					
2.5 PER 1000 S.F., .3 WATTS PER S.F.					
Steel intermediate conduit, (IMC) 1/2" diam	167.000	L.F.	.40	1.14	1.54
Wire 600V type THWN-THHN, copper solid #12	3.340	C.L.F.	.04	.21	.25
Wiring device, receptacle, duplex, 120V grounded, 15 amp	2.500	Ea.		.04	.04
Wall plate, 1 gang, brown plastic	2.500	Ea.		.02	.02
Steel outlet box 4" square	2.500	Ea.	.01	.09	.10
Steel outlet box 4" plaster rings	2.500	Ea.	.01	.03	.04
TOTAL			.46	1.53	1.99

D5020 110	Receptacle (by Wattage)	COST PER S.F.		
		MAT.	INST.	TOTAL
0190	Receptacles include plate, box, conduit, wire & transformer when required			
0200	2.5 per 1000 S.F., .3 watts per S.F.	.46	1.53	1.99
0240	With transformer	.55	1.61	2.16
0280	4 per 1000 S.F., .5 watts per S.F.	.52	1.77	2.29
0320	With transformer	.67	1.89	2.56
0360	5 per 1000 S.F., .6 watts per S.F.	.15	.68	.83
0400	With transformer	.79	2.23	3.02
0440	8 per 1000 S.F., .9 watts per S.F.	.64	2.31	2.95
0480	With transformer	.93	2.55	3.48
0520	10 per 1000 S.F., 1.2 watts per S.F.	.65	2.52	3.17
0560	With transformer	1.01	2.82	3.83
0600	16.5 per 1000 S.F., 2.0 watts per S.F.	.78	3.12	3.90
0640	With transformer	1.38	3.62	5
0680	20 per 1000 S.F., 2.4 watts per S.F.	.81	3.41	4.22
0720	With transformer	1.54	4.01	5.55

Underfloor Receptacle System

Description: Table D5020 115 includes installed costs of raceways and copper wire from panel to and including receptacle.

National Electrical Code prohibits use of undercarpet system in residential, school or hospital buildings. Can only be used with carpet squares.

Low density = (1) Outlet per 259 S.F. of floor area.

High density = (1) Outlet per 127 S.F. of floor area.

System Components	QUANTITY	UNIT	COST PER S.F.		
			MAT.	INST.	TOTAL
SYSTEM D5020 115 0200					
RECEPTACLE SYSTEMS, UNDERFLOOR DUCT, 5' ON CENTER, LOW DENSITY					
Underfloor duct 3-1/8" x 7/8" w/insert 24" on center	.190	L.F.	4.18	1.84	6.02
Underfloor duct junction box, single duct, 3-1/8"	.003	Ea.	1.47	.51	1.98
Underfloor junction box carpet pan	.003	Ea.	1.25	.03	1.28
Underfloor duct outlet, high tension receptacle	.004	Ea.	.48	.34	.82
Wire 600V type THWN-THHN copper solid #12	.010	C.L.F.	.12	.62	.74
Vertical elbow for underfloor duct, 3-1/8", included					
Underfloor duct conduit adapter, 2" x 1-1/4", included					
TOTAL			7.50	3.34	10.84

D5020 115	Receptacles, Floor	COST PER S.F.		
		MAT.	INST.	TOTAL
0200	Receptacle systems, underfloor duct, 5' on center, low density	7.50	3.34	10.84
0240	High density	8.10	4.29	12.39
0280	7' on center, low density	5.95	2.87	8.82
0320	High density	6.50	3.82	10.32
0400	Poke thru fittings, low density	1.25	1.63	2.88
0440	High density	2.50	3.26	5.76
0520	Telepoles, using Romex, low density	1.19	1	2.19
0560	High density	2.37	2	4.37
0600	Using EMT, low density	1.23	1.32	2.55
0640	High density	2.49	2.64	5.13
0720	Conduit system with floor boxes, low density	1.18	1.13	2.31
0760	High density	2.38	2.28	4.66
0840	Undercarpet power system, 3 conductor with 5 conductor feeder, low density	1.57	.40	1.97
0880	High density	3.11	.84	3.95

D50 Electrical

D5020 Lighting and Branch Wiring

Duplex Receptacle

Wall Switch

System Components	QUANTITY	UNIT	COST PER S.F.		
			MAT.	INST.	TOTAL
SYSTEM D5020 120 0520					
RECEPTACLES AND WALL SWITCHES					
4 RECEPTACLES PER 400 S.F.					
Steel intermediate conduit, (IMC), 1/2″ diam	.220	L.F.	.53	1.50	2.03
Wire, 600 volt, type THWN-THHN, copper, solid #12	.005	C.L.F.	.06	.31	.37
Steel outlet box 4″ square	.010	Ea.	.03	.34	.37
Steel outlet box, 4″ square, plaster rings	.010	Ea.	.02	.11	.13
Receptacle, duplex, 120 volt grounded, 15 amp	.010	Ea.	.01	.17	.18
Wall plate, 1 gang, brown plastic	.010	Ea.		.09	.09
TOTAL			.65	2.52	3.17

D5020 120	Receptacles & Wall Switches	COST PER S.F.		
		MAT.	INST.	TOTAL
0520	Receptacles and wall switches, 400 S.F., 4 receptacles	.65	2.52	3.17
0560	6 receptacles	.73	2.92	3.65
0600	8 receptacles	.78	3.39	4.17
0640	1 switch	.13	.56	.69
0680	600 S.F., 6 receptacles	.65	2.52	3.17
0720	8 receptacles	.71	2.84	3.55
0760	10 receptacles	.76	3.18	3.94
0800	2 switches	.19	.74	.93
0840	1000 S.F., 10 receptacles	.64	2.51	3.15
0880	12 receptacles	.66	2.63	3.29
0920	14 receptacles	.70	2.86	3.56
0960	2 switches	.09	.40	.49
1000	1600 S.F., 12 receptacles	.59	2.22	2.81
1040	14 receptacles	.62	2.43	3.05
1080	16 receptacles	.64	2.51	3.15
1120	4 switches	.12	.47	.59
1160	2000 S.F., 14 receptacles	.61	2.28	2.89
1200	16 receptacles	.61	2.29	2.90
1240	18 receptacles	.62	2.43	3.05
1280	4 switches	.09	.40	.49
1320	3000 S.F., 12 receptacles	.50	1.75	2.25
1360	18 receptacles	.59	2.14	2.73
1400	24 receptacles	.61	2.29	2.90
1440	6 switches	.09	.40	.49
1480	3600 S.F., 20 receptacles	.57	2.07	2.64
1520	24 receptacles	.58	2.15	2.73
1560	28 receptacles	.60	2.22	2.82
1600	8 switches	.10	.46	.56
1640	4000 S.F., 16 receptacles	.50	1.75	2.25
1680	24 receptacles	.59	2.14	2.73
1720	30 receptacles	.59	2.22	2.81
1760	8 switches	.09	.40	.49
1800	5000 S.F., 20 receptacles	.50	1.75	2.25
1840	26 receptacles	.59	2.07	2.66
1880	30 receptacles	.59	2.14	2.73
1920	10 switches	.09	.40	.49

D5020 Lighting and Branch Wiring

Duplex Receptacle

Wall Switch

System Components	QUANTITY	UNIT	COST PER EACH		
			MAT.	INST.	TOTAL
SYSTEM D5020 125 0520					
RECEPTACLES AND WALL SWITCHES, RECEPTICLE DUPLEX 120 V GROUNDED, 15 A					
Electric metallic tubing conduit, (EMT), 3/4" diam	22.000	L.F.	23.76	114.40	138.16
Wire, 600 volt, type THWN-THHN, copper, solid #12	.630	C.L.F.	7.40	38.75	46.15
Steel outlet box 4" square	1.000	Ea.	3.17	34	37.17
Steel outlet box, 4" square, plaster rings	1.000	Ea.	2.24	10.60	12.84
Receptacle, duplex, 120 volt grounded, 15 amp	1.000	Ea.	1.39	16.95	18.34
Wall plate, 1 gang, brown plastic	1.000	Ea.	.42	8.50	8.92
TOTAL			38.38	223.20	261.58

D5020 125	Receptacles & Switches by Each	COST PER EACH		
		MAT.	INST.	TOTAL
0460	Receptacles & Switches, with box, plate, 3/4" EMT conduit & wire			
0520	Receptacle duplex 120 V grounded, 15 A	38.50	223	261.50
0560	20 A	45.50	231	276.50
0600	Receptacle duplex ground fault interrupting, 15 A	52	231	283
0640	20 A	81	231	312
0680	Toggle switch single, 15 A	37.50	223	260.50
0720	20 A	40.50	231	271.50
0760	3 way switch, 15 A	39	236	275
0800	20 A	41	244	285
0840	4 way switch, 15 A	45.50	251	296.50
0880	20 A	84	268	352

D5020 Lighting and Branch Wiring

Description: Table D5020 130 includes the cost for switch, plate, box, conduit in slab or EMT exposed and copper wire. Add 20% for exposed conduit.

No power required for switches.

Federal energy guidelines recommend the maximum lighting area controlled per switch shall not exceed 1000 S.F. and that areas over 500 S.F. shall be so controlled that total illumination can be reduced by at least 50%.

System Components	QUANTITY	UNIT	COST PER S.F.		
			MAT.	INST.	TOTAL
SYSTEM D5020 130 0360					
WALL SWITCHES, 5.0 PER 1000 S.F.					
Steel, intermediate conduit (IMC), 1/2" diameter	88.000	L.F.	.21	.60	.81
Wire, 600V type THWN-THHN, copper solid #12	1.710	C.L.F.	.02	.11	.13
Toggle switch, single pole, 15 amp	5.000	Ea.		.08	.08
Wall plate, 1 gang, brown plastic	5.000	Ea.		.04	.04
Steel outlet box 4" plaster rings	5.000	Ea.	.02	.17	.19
Plaster rings	5.000	Ea.	.01	.05	.06
TOTAL			.26	1.05	1.31

D5020 130	Wall Switch by Sq. Ft.	COST PER S.F.		
		MAT.	INST.	TOTAL
0200	Wall switches, 1.0 per 1000 S.F.	.05	.25	.30
0240	1.2 per 1000 S.F.	.07	.27	.34
0280	2.0 per 1000 S.F.	.10	.39	.49
0320	2.5 per 1000 S.F.	.12	.50	.62
0360	5.0 per 1000 S.F.	.26	1.05	1.31
0400	10.0 per 1000 S.F.	.53	2.14	2.67

System D5020 135 includes all wiring and connections.

System Components	QUANTITY	UNIT	COST PER S.F.		
			MAT.	INST.	TOTAL
SYSTEM D5020 135 0200					
MISCELLANEOUS POWER, TO .5 WATTS					
Steel intermediate conduit, (IMC) 1/2" diam	15.000	L.F.	.04	.10	.14
Wire 600V type THWN-THHN, copper solid #12	.325	C.L.F.		.02	.02
TOTAL			.04	.12	.16

D5020 135	Miscellaneous Power	COST PER S.F.		
		MAT.	INST.	TOTAL
0200	Miscellaneous power, to .5 watts	.04	.12	.16
0240	.8 watts	.06	.17	.23
0280	1 watt	.08	.24	.32
0320	1.2 watts	.09	.26	.35
0360	1.5 watts	.11	.32	.43
0400	1.8 watts	.12	.36	.48
0440	2 watts	.14	.44	.58
0480	2.5 watts	.18	.54	.72
0520	3 watts	.21	.64	.85

System D5020 140 includes all wiring and connections for central air conditioning units.

System Components	QUANTITY	UNIT	COST PER S.F.		
			MAT.	INST.	TOTAL
SYSTEM D5020 140 0200					
CENTRAL AIR CONDITIONING POWER, 1 WATT					
Steel intermediate conduit, 1/2" diam.	.030	L.F.	.07	.20	.27
Wire 600V type THWN-THHN, copper solid #12	.001	C.L.F.	.01	.06	.07
TOTAL			.08	.26	.34

D5020 140	Central A. C. Power (by Wattage)	COST PER S.F.		
		MAT.	INST.	TOTAL
0200	Central air conditioning power, 1 watt	.08	.26	.34
0220	2 watts	.10	.30	.40
0240	3 watts	.20	.46	.66
0280	4 watts	.20	.45	.65
0320	6 watts	.35	.61	.96
0360	8 watts	.45	.66	1.11
0400	10 watts	.64	.76	1.40

D50 Electrical

D5020 Lighting and Branch Wiring

System D5020 145 includes installed cost of motor wiring using 50' of rigid conduit and copper wire. **Cost and setting of motor not included.**

System Components			COST EACH		
	QUANTITY	UNIT	MAT.	INST.	TOTAL
SYSTEM D5020 145 0200					
MOTOR INST., SINGLE PHASE, 115V, TO AND INCLUDING 1/3 HP MOTOR SIZE					
Wire 600V type THWN-THHN, copper solid #12	1.250	C.L.F.	14.69	76.88	91.57
Steel intermediate conduit, (IMC) 1/2" diam.	50.000	L.F.	121	340	461
Magnetic FVNR, 115V, 1/3 HP, size 00 starter	1.000	Ea.	184	170	354
Safety switch, fused, heavy duty, 240V 2P 30 amp	1.000	Ea.	88	194	282
Safety switch, non fused, heavy duty, 600V, 3 phase, 30 A	1.000	Ea.	109	212	321
Flexible metallic conduit, Greenfield 1/2" diam.	1.500	L.F.	.44	5.09	5.53
Connectors for flexible metallic conduit Greenfield 1/2" diam.	1.000	Ea.	1.86	8.50	10.36
Coupling for Greenfield to conduit 1/2" diam. flexible metalic conduit	1.000	Ea.	.95	13.55	14.50
Fuse cartridge nonrenewable, 250V 30 amp	1.000	Ea.	2.64	13.55	16.19
TOTAL			522.58	1,033.57	1,556.15

D5020 145	Motor Installation	COST EACH		
		MAT.	INST.	TOTAL
0200	Motor installation, single phase, 115V, 1/3 HP motor size	525	1,025	1,550
0240	1 HP motor size	545	1,025	1,570
0280	2 HP motor size	590	1,100	1,690
0320	3 HP motor size	665	1,125	1,790
0360	230V, 1 HP motor size	525	1,050	1,575
0400	2 HP motor size	565	1,050	1,615
0440	3 HP motor size	630	1,125	1,755
0520	Three phase, 200V, 1-1/2 HP motor size	605	1,150	1,755
0560	3 HP motor size	750	1,250	2,000
0600	5 HP motor size	715	1,400	2,115
0640	7-1/2 HP motor size	735	1,425	2,160
0680	10 HP motor size	1,100	1,775	2,875
0720	15 HP motor size	1,500	1,975	3,475
0760	20 HP motor size	1,925	2,275	4,200
0800	25 HP motor size	1,950	2,300	4,250
0840	30 HP motor size	3,025	2,700	5,725
0880	40 HP motor size	3,750	3,175	6,925
0920	50 HP motor size	6,575	3,700	10,275
0960	60 HP motor size	6,850	3,925	10,775
1000	75 HP motor size	8,575	4,475	13,050
1040	100 HP motor size	26,000	5,300	31,300
1080	125 HP motor size	26,100	5,800	31,900
1120	150 HP motor size	30,600	6,825	37,425
1160	200 HP motor size	31,500	8,075	39,575
1240	230V, 1-1/2 HP motor size	580	1,125	1,705
1280	3 HP motor size	725	1,225	1,950
1320	5 HP motor size	690	1,375	2,065
1360	7-1/2 HP motor size	690	1,375	2,065
1400	10 HP motor size	1,025	1,675	2,700
1440	15 HP motor size	1,175	1,850	3,025
1480	20 HP motor size	1,825	2,225	4,050
1520	25 HP motor size	1,925	2,275	4,200

D5020 Lighting and Branch Wiring

D5020 145	Motor Installation	COST EACH		
		MAT.	INST.	TOTAL
1560	30 HP motor size	1,925	2,300	4,225
1600	40 HP motor size	3,700	3,100	6,800
1640	50 HP motor size	3,975	3,275	7,250
1680	60 HP motor size	6,575	3,725	10,300
1720	75 HP motor size	7,900	4,225	12,125
1760	100 HP motor size	9,250	4,700	13,950
1800	125 HP motor size	26,500	5,475	31,975
1840	150 HP motor size	28,200	6,200	34,400
1880	200 HP motor size	29,400	6,875	36,275
1960	460V, 2 HP motor size	720	1,150	1,870
2000	5 HP motor size	870	1,250	2,120
2040	10 HP motor size	795	1,375	2,170
2080	15 HP motor size	1,050	1,575	2,625
2120	20 HP motor size	1,100	1,700	2,800
2160	25 HP motor size	1,175	1,775	2,950
2200	30 HP motor size	1,500	1,925	3,425
2240	40 HP motor size	1,925	2,050	3,975
2280	50 HP motor size	2,175	2,275	4,450
2320	60 HP motor size	3,225	2,675	5,900
2360	75 HP motor size	3,850	2,950	6,800
2400	100 HP motor size	4,300	3,300	7,600
2440	125 HP motor size	6,900	3,725	10,625
2480	150 HP motor size	8,700	4,175	12,875
2520	200 HP motor size	10,100	4,725	14,825
2600	575V, 2 HP motor size	720	1,150	1,870
2640	5 HP motor size	870	1,250	2,120
2680	10 HP motor size	795	1,375	2,170
2720	20 HP motor size	1,050	1,575	2,625
2760	25 HP motor size	1,100	1,700	2,800
2800	30 HP motor size	1,500	1,925	3,425
2840	50 HP motor size	1,625	2,000	3,625
2880	60 HP motor size	3,200	2,650	5,850
2920	75 HP motor size	3,225	2,675	5,900
2960	100 HP motor size	3,850	2,950	6,800
3000	125 HP motor size	6,800	3,675	10,475
3040	150 HP motor size	6,900	3,725	10,625
3080	200 HP motor size	8,725	4,250	12,975

D5020 Lighting and Branch Wiring

System Components	QUANTITY	UNIT	COST PER L.F.		
			MAT.	INST.	TOTAL
SYSTEM D5020 155 0200					
MOTOR FEEDER SYSTEMS, SINGLE PHASE, UP TO 115V, 1HP OR 230V, 2HP					
Steel intermediate conduit, (IMC) 1/2" diam	1.000	L.F.	2.42	6.80	9.22
Wire 600V type THWN-THHN, copper solid #12	.020	C.L.F.	.24	1.23	1.47
TOTAL			2.66	8.03	10.69

D5020 155	Motor Feeder	COST PER L.F.		
		MAT.	INST.	TOTAL
0200	Motor feeder systems, single phase, feed up to 115V 1HP or 230V 2 HP	2.66	8.05	10.71
0240	115V 2HP, 230V 3HP	2.79	8.15	10.94
0280	115V 3HP	3.04	8.50	11.54
0360	Three phase, feed to 200V 3HP, 230V 5HP, 460V 10HP, 575V 10HP	2.77	8.65	11.42
0440	200V 5HP, 230V 7.5HP, 460V 15HP, 575V 20HP	2.97	8.85	11.82
0520	200V 10HP, 230V 10HP, 460V 30HP, 575V 30HP	3.35	9.35	12.70
0600	200V 15HP, 230V 15HP, 460V 40HP, 575V 50HP	4.62	10.65	15.27
0680	200V 20HP, 230V 25HP, 460V 50HP, 575V 60HP	6.60	13.55	20.15
0760	200V 25HP, 230V 30HP, 460V 60HP, 575V 75HP	7.40	13.80	21.20
0840	200V 30HP	8.15	14.25	22.40
0920	230V 40HP, 460V 75HP, 575V 100HP	10.40	15.55	25.95
1000	200V 40HP	11.85	16.65	28.50
1080	230V 50HP, 460V 100HP, 575V 125HP	14.45	18.30	32.75
1160	200V 50HP, 230V 60HP, 460V 125HP, 575V 150HP	16.50	19.45	35.95
1240	200V 60HP, 460V 150HP	20.50	23	43.50
1320	230V 75HP, 575V 200HP	23	24	47
1400	200V 75HP	25.50	24	49.50
1480	230V 100HP, 460V 200HP	35	28	63
1560	200V 100HP	48	35.50	83.50
1640	230V 125HP	48	35.50	83.50
1720	200V 125HP, 230V 150HP	53.50	44	97.50
1800	200V 150HP	64	47.50	111.50
1880	200V 200HP	80.50	50.50	131
1960	230V 200HP	70	52.50	122.50

Starters are full voltage, type NEMA 1 for general purpose indoor application with motor overload protection and include mounting and wire connections.

System Components	QUANTITY	UNIT	COST EACH		
			MAT.	INST.	TOTAL
SYSTEM D5020 160 0200					
MAGNETIC STARTER, SIZE 00 TO 1/3 HP, 1 PHASE 115V OR 1 HP 230V					
Magnetic starter, size 00, to 1/3 HP, 1 phase, 115V or 1 HP 230V	1.000	Ea.	184	170	354
TOTAL			184	170	354

D5020 160	Magnetic Starter	COST EACH		
		MAT.	INST.	TOTAL
0200	Magnetic starter, size 00, to 1/3 HP, 1 phase, 115V or 1 HP 230V	184	170	354
0280	Size 00, to 1-1/2 HP, 3 phase, 200-230V or 2 HP 460-575V	202	194	396
0360	Size 0, to 1 HP, 1 phase, 115V or 2 HP 230V	205	170	375
0440	Size 0, to 3 HP, 3 phase, 200-230V or 5 HP 460-575V	350	295	645
0520	Size 1, to 2 HP, 1 phase, 115V or 3 HP 230V	236	226	462
0600	Size 1, to 7-1/2 HP, 3 phase, 200-230V or 10 HP 460-575V	275	425	700
0680	Size 2, to 10 HP, 3 phase, 200V, 15 HP-230V or 25 HP 460-575V	515	615	1,130
0760	Size 3, to 25 HP, 3 phase, 200V, 30 HP-230V or 50 HP 460-575V	845	755	1,600
0840	Size 4, to 40 HP, 3 phase, 200V, 50 HP-230V or 100 HP 460-575V	1,875	1,125	3,000
0920	Size 5, to 75 HP, 3 phase, 200V, 100 HP-230V or 200 HP 460-575V	4,375	1,500	5,875
1000	Size 6, to 150 HP, 3 phase, 200V, 200 HP-230V or 400 HP 460-575V	20,200	1,700	21,900

D5020 Lighting and Branch Wiring

Safety switches are type NEMA 1 for general purpose indoor application, and include time delay fuses, insulation and wire terminations.

System Components	QUANTITY	UNIT	COST EACH		
			MAT.	INST.	TOTAL
SYSTEM D5020 165 0200					
SAFETY SWITCH, 30A FUSED, 1 PHASE, 115V OR 230V					
Safety switch fused, hvy duty, 240V 2p 30 amp	1.000	Ea.	88	194	282
Fuse, dual element time delay 250V, 30 amp	2.000	Ea.	21.90	27.10	49
TOTAL			109.90	221.10	331

D5020 165	Safety Switches	COST EACH		
		MAT.	INST.	TOTAL
0200	Safety switch, 30 A fused, 1 phase, 2 HP 115 V or 3 HP, 230 V	110	221	331
0280	3 phase, 5 HP, 200 V or 7 1/2 HP, 230 V	147	253	400
0360	15 HP, 460 V or 20 HP, 575 V	264	263	527
0440	60 A fused, 3 phase, 15 HP 200 V or 15 HP 230 V	230	335	565
0520	30 HP 460 V or 40 HP 575 V	340	345	685
0600	100 A fused, 3 phase, 20 HP 200 V or 25 HP 230 V	395	405	800
0680	50 HP 460 V or 60 HP 575 V	650	410	1,060
0760	200 A fused, 3 phase, 50 HP 200 V or 60 HP 230 V	740	575	1,315
0840	125 HP 460 V or 150 HP 575 V	1,050	590	1,640
0920	400 A fused, 3 phase, 100 HP 200 V or 125 HP 230 V	1,725	825	2,550
1000	250 HP 460 V or 350 HP 575 V	2,525	840	3,365
1020	600 A fused, 3 phase, 150 HP 200 V or 200 HP 230 V	3,750	1,200	4,950
1040	400 HP 460 V	3,850	1,225	5,075

Straight Connector

Angle Connector

Flexible Conduit

Table below includes costs for the flexible conduit. Not included are wire terminations and testing motor for correct rotation.

System Components	QUANTITY	UNIT	COST EACH		
			MAT.	INST.	TOTAL
SYSTEM D5020 170 0200					
MOTOR CONNECTIONS, SINGLE PHASE, 115V/230V UP TO 1 HP					
Motor connection, flexible conduit & fittings, 1 HP motor 115V	1.000	Ea.	5.40	85	90.40
TOTAL			5.40	85	90.40

D5020 170	Motor Connections	COST EACH		
		MAT.	INST.	TOTAL
0200	Motor connections, single phase, 115/230V, up to 1 HP	5.40	85	90.40
0240	Up to 3 HP	11.75	104	115.75
0280	Three phase, 200/230/460/575V, up to 3 HP	6.85	100	106.85
0320	Up to 5 HP	5.55	124	129.55
0360	Up to 7-1/2 HP	8.85	147	155.85
0400	Up to 10 HP	18.95	162	180.95
0440	Up to 15 HP	18.95	206	224.95
0480	Up to 25 HP	25	251	276
0520	Up to 50 HP	52.50	310	362.50
0560	Up to 100 HP	118	450	568

For customer support on your Electrical Costs with RSMeans Data, call 800.448.8182.

D5020 Lighting and Branch Wiring

Manual Starter

Magnetic Starter

Induction Motor

For 230/460 Volt A.C., 3 phase, 60 cycle ball bearing squirrel cage induction motors, NEMA Class B standard line. Installation included.

No conduit, wire, or terminations included.

System Components	QUANTITY	UNIT	COST EACH		
			MAT.	INST.	TOTAL
SYSTEM D5020 175 0220					
MOTOR, DRIPPROOF CLASS B INSULATION, 1.15 SERVICE FACTOR, WITH STARTER					
1 H.P., 1200 RPM WITH MANUAL STARTER					
Motor, dripproof, class B insul, 1.15 serv fact, 1200 RPM, 1 HP	1.000	Ea.	520	151	671
Motor starter, manual, 3 phase, 1 HP motor	1.000	Ea.	228	194	422
TOTAL			748	345	1,093

D5020 175	Motor & Starter	COST EACH		
		MAT.	INST.	TOTAL
0190	Motor, dripproof, premium efficient, 1.15 service factor			
0200	1 HP, 1200 RPM, motor only	520	151	671
0220	With manual starter	750	345	1,095
0240	With magnetic starter	720	345	1,065
0260	1800 RPM, motor only	320	151	471
0280	With manual starter	550	345	895
0300	With magnetic starter	520	345	865
0320	2 HP, 1200 RPM, motor only	710	151	861
0340	With manual starter	940	345	1,285
0360	With magnetic starter	1,050	445	1,495
0380	1800 RPM, motor only	385	151	536
0400	With manual starter	615	345	960
0420	With magnetic starter	735	445	1,180
0440	3600 RPM, motor only	640	151	791
0460	With manual starter	870	345	1,215
0480	With magnetic starter	990	445	1,435
0500	3 HP, 1200 RPM, motor only	790	151	941
0520	With manual starter	1,025	345	1,370
0540	With magnetic starter	1,150	445	1,595
0560	1800 RPM, motor only	765	151	916
0580	With manual starter	995	345	1,340
0600	With magnetic starter	1,125	445	1,570
0620	3600 RPM, motor only	660	151	811
0640	With manual starter	890	345	1,235
0660	With magnetic starter	1,000	445	1,445
0680	5 HP, 1200 RPM, motor only	1,025	151	1,176
0700	With manual starter	1,300	490	1,790
0720	With magnetic starter	1,300	575	1,875
0740	1800 RPM, motor only	680	151	831
0760	With manual starter	950	490	1,440
0780	With magnetic starter	955	575	1,530
0800	3600 RPM, motor only	575	151	726

D5020 Lighting and Branch Wiring

D5020 175	Motor & Starter	COST EACH		
		MAT.	INST.	TOTAL
0820	With manual starter	845	490	1,335
0840	With magnetic starter	850	575	1,425
0860	7.5 HP, 1800 RPM, motor only	1,025	162	1,187
0880	With manual starter	1,300	500	1,800
0900	With magnetic starter	1,550	775	2,325
0920	10 HP, 1800 RPM, motor only	1,275	170	1,445
0940	With manual starter	1,550	510	2,060
0960	With magnetic starter	1,800	785	2,585
0980	15 HP, 1800 RPM, motor only	1,775	212	1,987
1000	With magnetic starter	2,300	825	3,125
1040	20 HP, 1800 RPM, motor only	2,150	261	2,411
1060	With magnetic starter	3,000	1,025	4,025
1100	25 HP, 1800 RPM, motor only	2,800	271	3,071
1120	With magnetic starter	3,650	1,025	4,675
1160	30 HP, 1800 RPM, motor only	3,075	283	3,358
1180	With magnetic starter	3,925	1,050	4,975
1220	40 HP, 1800 RPM, motor only	4,000	340	4,340
1240	With magnetic starter	5,875	1,475	7,350
1280	50 HP, 1800 RPM, motor only	4,075	425	4,500
1300	With magnetic starter	5,950	1,550	7,500
1340	60 HP, 1800 RPM, motor only	4,500	485	4,985
1360	With magnetic starter	8,875	1,975	10,850
1400	75 HP, 1800 RPM, motor only	5,275	565	5,840
1420	With magnetic starter	9,650	2,075	11,725
1460	100 HP, 1800 RPM, motor only	6,775	755	7,530
1480	With magnetic starter	11,200	2,250	13,450
1520	125 HP, 1800 RPM, motor only	7,075	970	8,045
1540	With magnetic starter	27,300	2,675	29,975
1580	150 HP, 1800 RPM, motor only	10,800	1,125	11,925
1600	With magnetic starter	31,000	2,825	33,825
1640	200 HP, 1800 RPM, motor only	13,100	1,350	14,450
1660	With magnetic starter	33,300	3,050	36,350
1680	Totally encl, premium efficient, 1.0 ser. fac., 1HP, 1200 RPM, motor only	530	151	681
1700	With manual starter	760	345	1,105
1720	With magnetic starter	730	345	1,075
1740	1800 RPM, motor only	615	151	766
1760	With manual starter	845	345	1,190
1780	With magnetic starter	815	345	1,160
1800	2 HP, 1200 RPM, motor only	600	151	751
1820	With manual starter	830	345	1,175
1840	With magnetic starter	950	445	1,395
1860	1800 RPM, motor only	775	151	926
1880	With manual starter	1,000	345	1,345
1900	With magnetic starter	1,125	445	1,570
1920	3600 RPM, motor only	480	151	631
1940	With manual starter	710	345	1,055
1960	With magnetic starter	830	445	1,275
1980	3 HP, 1200 RPM, motor only	870	151	1,021
2000	With manual starter	1,100	345	1,445
2020	With magnetic starter	1,225	445	1,670
2040	1800 RPM, motor only	700	151	851
2060	With manual starter	930	345	1,275
2080	With magnetic starter	1,050	445	1,495
2100	3600 RPM, motor only	640	151	791
2120	With manual starter	870	345	1,215
2140	With magnetic starter	990	445	1,435
2160	5 HP, 1200 RPM, motor only	1,025	151	1,176
2180	With manual starter	1,300	490	1,790

D5020 Lighting and Branch Wiring

D5020 175	Motor & Starter	COST EACH		
		MAT.	INST.	TOTAL
2200	With magnetic starter	1,300	575	1,875
2220	1800 RPM, motor only	820	151	971
2240	With manual starter	1,100	490	1,590
2260	With magnetic starter	1,100	575	1,675
2280	3600 RPM, motor only	745	151	896
2300	With manual starter	1,025	490	1,515
2320	With magnetic starter	1,025	575	1,600
2340	7.5 HP, 1800 RPM, motor only	1,075	162	1,237
2360	With manual starter	1,350	500	1,850
2380	With magnetic starter	1,600	775	2,375
2400	10 HP, 1800 RPM, motor only	1,500	170	1,670
2420	With manual starter	1,775	510	2,285
2440	With magnetic starter	2,025	785	2,810
2460	15 HP, 1800 RPM, motor only	1,800	212	2,012
2480	With magnetic starter	2,325	825	3,150
2500	20 HP, 1800 RPM, motor only	2,450	261	2,711
2520	With magnetic starter	3,300	1,025	4,325
2540	25 HP, 1800 RPM, motor only	3,500	271	3,771
2560	With magnetic starter	4,350	1,025	5,375
2580	30 HP, 1800 RPM, motor only	3,450	283	3,733
2600	With magnetic starter	4,300	1,050	5,350
2620	40 HP, 1800 RPM, motor only	4,225	340	4,565
2640	With magnetic starter	6,100	1,475	7,575
2660	50 HP, 1800 RPM, motor only	4,550	425	4,975
2680	With magnetic starter	6,425	1,550	7,975
2700	60 HP, 1800 RPM, motor only	6,175	485	6,660
2720	With magnetic starter	10,600	1,975	12,575
2740	75 HP, 1800 RPM, motor only	8,025	565	8,590
2760	With magnetic starter	12,400	2,075	14,475
2780	100 HP, 1800 RPM, motor only	9,475	755	10,230
2800	With magnetic starter	13,900	2,250	16,150
2820	125 HP, 1800 RPM, motor only	12,300	970	13,270
2840	With magnetic starter	32,500	2,675	35,175
2860	150 HP, 1800 RPM, motor only	14,500	1,125	15,625
2880	With magnetic starter	34,700	2,825	37,525
2900	200 HP, 1800 RPM, motor only	18,200	1,350	19,550
2920	With magnetic starter	38,400	3,050	41,450

General: The cost of the lighting portion of the electrical costs is dependent upon:

1. The footcandle requirement of the proposed building.
2. The type of fixtures required.
3. The ceiling heights of the building.
4. Reflectance value of ceilings, walls and floors.
5. Fixture efficiencies and spacing vs. mounting height ratios.

Footcandle Requirements: See Table D5020-204 for Footcandle and Watts per S.F. determination.

Table D5020-201   IESNA* Recommended Illumination Levels in Footcandles

Commercial Buildings			Industrial Buildings		
Type	Description	Footcandles	Type	Description	Footcandles
Bank	Lobby	50	Assembly Areas	Rough bench & machine work	50
	Customer Areas	70		Medium bench & machine work	100
	Teller Stations	150		Fine bench & machine work	500
	Accounting Areas	150	Inspection Areas	Ordinary	50
Offices	Routine Work	100		Difficult	100
	Accounting	150		Highly Difficult	200
	Drafting	200	Material Handling	Loading	20
	Corridors, Halls, Washrooms	30		Stock Picking	30
Schools	Reading or Writing	70		Packing, Wrapping	50
	Drafting, Labs, Shops	100	Stairways	Service Areas	20
	Libraries	70	Washrooms	Service Areas	20
	Auditoriums, Assembly	15	Storage Areas	Inactive	5
	Auditoriums, Exhibition	30		Active, Rough, Bulky	10
Stores	Circulation Areas	30		Active, Medium	20
	Stock Rooms	30		Active, Fine	50
	Merchandise Areas, Service	100	Garages	Active Traffic Areas	20
	Self-Service Areas	200		Service & Repair	100

*IESNA - Illuminating Engineering Society of North America

Table D5020-202 General Lighting Loads by Occupancies

Type of Occupancy	Unit Load per S.F. (Watts)
Armories and Auditoriums	1
Banks	5
Barber Shops and Beauty Parlors	3
Churches	1
Clubs	2
Court Rooms	2
*Dwelling Units	3
Garages — Commercial (storage)	½
Hospitals	2
*Hotels and Motels, including apartment houses without provisions for cooking by tenants	2
Industrial Commercial (Loft) Buildings	2
Lodge Rooms	1½
Office Buildings	5
Restaurants	2
Schools	3
Stores	3
Warehouses (storage)	¼
*In any of the above occupancies except one-family dwellings and individual dwelling units of multi-family dwellings:	
Assembly Halls and Auditoriums	1
Halls, Corridors, Closets	½
Storage Spaces	¼

Table D5020-203 Lighting Limit (Connected Load) for Listed Occupancies: New Building Proposed Energy Conservation Guideline

Type of Use	Maximum Watts per S.F.
Interior	3.00
Category A: Classrooms, office areas, automotive mechanical areas, museums, conference rooms, drafting rooms, clerical areas, laboratories, merchandising areas, kitchens, examining rooms, book stacks, athletic facilities.	
Category B: Auditoriums, waiting areas, spectator areas, restrooms, dining areas, transportation terminals, working corridors in prisons and hospitals, book storage areas, active inventory storage, hospital bedrooms, hotel and motel bedrooms, enclosed shopping mall concourse areas, stairways.	1.00
Category C: Corridors, lobbies, elevators, inactive storage areas.	0.50
Category D: Indoor parking.	0.25
Exterior	
Category E: Building perimeter: wall-wash, facade, canopy.	5.00 (per linear foot)
Category F: Outdoor parking.	0.10

Table D5020-204 Procedure for Calculating Footcandles and Watts Per Square Foot

1. Initial footcandles = No. of fixtures × lamps per fixture × lumens per lamp × coefficient of utilization ÷ square feet
2. Maintained footcandles = initial footcandles × maintenance factor
3. Watts per square foot = No. of fixtures × lamps × (lamp watts + ballast watts) ÷ square feet

Example: To find footcandles and watts per S.F. for an office 20′ x 20′ with 11 fluorescent fixtures each having 4–40 watt C.W. lamps.

Based on good reflectance and clean conditions:

Lumens per lamp = 40 watt cool white at 3150 lumens per lamp

Coefficient of utilization = .42 (varies from .62 for light colored areas to .27 for dark)

Maintenance factor = .75 (varies from .80 for clean areas with good maintenance to .50 for poor)

Ballast loss = 8 watts per lamp (Varies with manufacturer. See manufacturers' catalog.)

1. Initial footcandles:

$$\frac{11 \times 4 \times 3150 \times .42}{400} = \frac{58,212}{400} = 145 \text{ footcandles}$$

2. Maintained footcandles:

$$145 \times .75 = 109 \text{ footcandles}$$

3. Watts per S.F.

$$\frac{11 \times 4\,(40 + 8)}{400} = \frac{2,112}{400} = 5.3 \text{ watts per S.F.}$$

Table D5020-205 Approximate Watts Per Square Foot for Popular Fixture Types

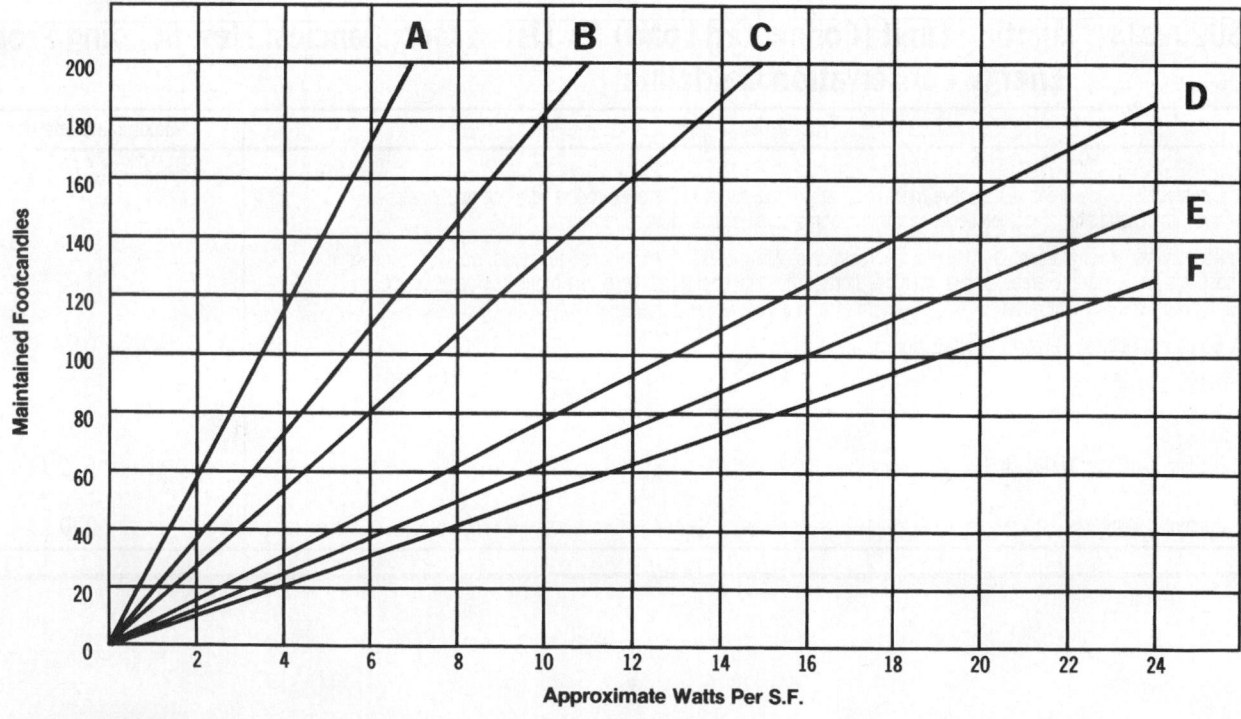

Due to the many variables involved, use for preliminary estimating only:
  a. Fluorescent – industrial System D5020 208
  b. Fluorescent – lens unit System D5020 208 Fixture types B & C
  c. Fluorescent – louvered unit
  d. Incandescent – open reflector System D5020 214, Type D
  e. Incandescent – lens unit System D5020 214, Type A
  f. Incandescent – down light System D5020 214, Type B

D5020 Lighting and Branch Wiring

A. Strip Fixture

C. Recessed

B. Surface Mounted

D. Pendent Mounted

Design Assumptions:

1. A 100 footcandle average maintained level of illumination.
2. Ceiling heights range from 9' to 11'.
3. Average reflectance values are assumed for ceilings, walls and floors.
4. Cool white (CW) fluorescent lamps with 3150 lumens for 40 watt lamps and 6300 lumens for 8' slimline lamps.
5. Four 40 watt lamps per 4' fixture and two 8' lamps per 8' fixture.
6. Average fixture efficiency values and spacing to mounting height ratios.
7. Installation labor is average U.S. rate as of January 1.

System Components	QUANTITY	UNIT	COST PER S.F.		
			MAT.	INST.	TOTAL
SYSTEM D5020 208 0520					
FLUORESCENT FIXTURES MOUNTED 9'-11" ABOVE FLOOR, 100 FC					
TYPE A, 8 FIXTURES PER 400 S.F.					
Conduit, steel intermediate, 1/2" diam.	.185	L.F.	.45	1.26	1.71
Wire, 600V, type THWN-THHN, copper, solid, #12	.004	C.L.F.	.04	.23	.27
Fluorescent strip fixture 8' long, surface mounted, two 75W SL	.020	Ea.	1.46	2.18	3.64
Steel outlet box 4" concrete	.020	Ea.	.23	.68	.91
Steel outlet box plate with stud, 4" concrete	.020	Ea.	.15	.17	.32
Fixture hangers, flexible, 1/2" diameter, 4" long	.040	Ea.	.72	2.26	2.98
Fixture whip, THHN wire, three #12, 3/8" Greenfield	.040	Ea.	.41	.84	1.25
TOTAL			3.46	7.62	11.08

D5020 208	Fluorescent Fixtures (by Type)	COST PER S.F.		
		MAT.	INST.	TOTAL
0520	Fluorescent fixtures, type A, 8 fixtures per 400 S.F.	3.46	7.60	11.06
0560	11 fixtures per 600 S.F.	3.16	6.95	10.11
0600	17 fixtures per 1000 S.F.	2.95	6.45	9.40
0640	23 fixtures per 1600 S.F.	2.46	5.45	7.91
0680	28 fixtures per 2000 S.F.	2.43	5.35	7.78
0720	41 fixtures per 3000 S.F.	2.39	5.25	7.64
0800	53 fixtures per 4000 S.F.	2.30	5.05	7.35
0840	64 fixtures per 5000 S.F.	2.26	4.94	7.20
0880	Type B, 11 fixtures per 400 S.F.	5.30	10.85	16.15
0920	15 fixtures per 600 S.F.	4.79	9.80	14.59
0960	24 fixtures per 1000 S.F.	4.62	9.45	14.07
1000	35 fixtures per 1600 S.F.	4.20	8.60	12.80
1040	42 fixtures per 2000 S.F.	4.01	8.20	12.21
1080	61 fixtures per 3000 S.F.	3.85	7.90	11.75
1160	80 fixtures per 4000 S.F.	2.80	5.05	7.85
1200	98 fixtures per 5000 S.F.	3.78	7.70	11.48
1240	Type C, 11 fixtures per 400 S.F.	4.60	11.30	15.90
1280	14 fixtures per 600 S.F.	3.85	9.45	13.30
1320	23 fixtures per 1000 S.F.	3.81	9.35	13.16
1360	34 fixtures per 1600 S.F.	3.53	8.65	12.18
1400	43 fixtures per 2000 S.F.	3.63	8.85	12.48
1440	63 fixtures per 3000 S.F.	3.49	8.55	12.04
1520	81 fixtures per 4000 S.F.	3.35	8.25	11.60
1560	101 fixtures per 5000 S.F.	3.32	8.15	11.47
1600	Type D, 8 fixtures per 400 S.F.	4.16	8.50	12.66
1640	12 fixtures per 600 S.F.	4.16	8.50	12.66
1680	19 fixtures per 1000 S.F.	3.96	8.10	12.06
1720	27 fixtures per 1600 S.F.	3.55	7.20	10.75
1760	34 fixtures per 2000 S.F.	3.55	7.25	10.80
1800	48 fixtures per 3000 S.F.	3.34	6.80	10.14
1880	64 fixtures per 4000 S.F.	3.34	6.80	10.14
1920	79 fixtures per 5000 S.F.	3.32	6.80	10.12

For customer support on your Electrical Costs with RSMeans Data, call 800.448.8182.

Type C. Recessed, mounted on grid ceiling suspension system, 2' x 4', four 40 watt lamps, acrylic prismatic diffusers.

5.3 watts per S.F. for 100 footcandles.

3 watts per S.F. for 57 footcandles.

System Components	QUANTITY	UNIT	COST PER S.F. MAT.	COST PER S.F. INST.	COST PER S.F. TOTAL
SYSTEM D5020 210 0200					
FLUORESCENT FIXTURES RECESS MOUNTED IN CEILING					
1 WATT PER S.F., 20 FC, 5 FIXTURES PER 1000 S.F.					
Steel intermediate conduit, (IMC) 1/2" diam.	.128	L.F.	.31	.87	1.18
Wire, 600 volt, type THW, copper, solid, #12	.003	C.L.F.	.04	.18	.22
Fluorescent fixture, recessed, 2'x 4', four 40W, w/lens, for grid ceiling	.005	Ea.	.34	.72	1.06
Steel outlet box 4" square	.005	Ea.	.06	.17	.23
Fixture whip, Greenfield w/#12 THHN wire	.005	Ea.	.04	.04	.08
TOTAL			.79	1.98	2.77

D5020 210	Fluorescent Fixtures (by Wattage)	COST PER S.F. MAT.	COST PER S.F. INST.	COST PER S.F. TOTAL
0190	Fluorescent fixtures recess mounted in ceiling			
0195	T12, standard 40 watt lamps			
0200	1 watt per S.F., 20 FC, 5 fixtures @40 watts per 1000 S.F.	.79	1.98	2.77
0240	2 watt per S.F., 40 FC, 10 fixtures @40 watt per 1000 S.F.	1.57	3.92	5.49
0280	3 watt per S.F., 60 FC, 15 fixtures @40 watt per 1000 S.F	2.33	5.90	8.23
0320	4 watt per S.F., 80 FC, 20 fixtures @40 watt per 1000 S.F.	3.11	7.85	10.96
0400	5 watt per S.F., 100 FC, 25 fixtures @40 watt per 1000 S.F.	3.89	9.80	13.69
0450	T8, energy saver 32 watt lamps			
0500	0.8 watt per S.F., 20 FC, 5 fixtures @32 watt per 1000 S.F.	.86	1.98	2.84
0520	1.6 watt per S.F., 40 FC, 10 fixtures @32 watt per 1000 S.F.	1.70	3.92	5.62
0540	2.4 watt per S.F., 60 FC, 15 fixtures @ 32 watt per 1000 S.F	2.52	5.90	8.42
0560	3.2 watt per S.F., 80 FC, 20 fixtures @32 watt per 1000 S.F.	3.37	7.85	11.22
0580	4 watt per S.F., 100 FC, 25 fixtures @32 watt per 1000 S.F.	4.22	9.80	14.02

D5020 Lighting and Branch Wiring

Type A. Recessed wide distribution reflector with flat glass lens 150 W.

Maximum spacing = 1.2 x mounting height.

13 watts per S.F. for 100 footcandles.

Type C. Recessed PAR–38 flood lamp with concentric louver 150 W.

Maximum spacing = 0.5 x mounting height.

19 watts per S.F. for 100 footcandles.

Type B. Recessed reflector down light with baffles 150 W.

Maximum spacing = 0.8 x mounting height.

18 watts per S.F. for 100 footcandles.

Type D. Recessed R–40 flood lamp with reflector skirt.

Maximum spacing = 0.7 x mounting height.

15 watts per S.F. for 100 footcandles.

System Components	QUANTITY	UNIT	COST PER S.F.		
			MAT.	INST.	TOTAL
SYSTEM D5020 214 0400					
INCANDESCENT FIXTURE RECESS MOUNTED, 100 FC					
TYPE A, 34 FIXTURES PER 400 S.F.					
Steel intermediate conduit, (IMC) 1/2″ diam	1.060	L.F.	2.57	7.21	9.78
Wire, 600V, type THWN-THHN, copper, solid, #12	.033	C.L.F.	.39	2.03	2.42
Steel outlet box 4″ square	.085	Ea.	.98	2.89	3.87
Fixture whip, Greenfield w/#12 THHN wire	.085	Ea.	.64	.72	1.36
Incandescent fixture, recessed, w/lens, prewired, square trim, 200W	.085	Ea.	9.10	8.59	17.69
TOTAL			13.68	21.44	35.12

D5020 214	Incandescent Fixture (by Type)	COST PER S.F.		
		MAT.	INST.	TOTAL
0380	Incandescent fixture recess mounted, 100 FC			
0400	Type A, 34 fixtures per 400 S.F.	13.70	21.50	35.20
0440	49 fixtures per 600 S.F.	13.30	21	34.30
0480	63 fixtures per 800 S.F.	13	21	34
0520	90 fixtures per 1200 S.F.	12.55	20.50	33.05
0560	116 fixtures per 1600 S.F.	12.30	20	32.30
0600	143 fixtures per 2000 S.F.	12.20	20	32.20
0640	Type B, 47 fixtures per 400 S.F.	12.80	27	39.80
0680	66 fixtures per 600 S.F.	12.30	26.50	38.80
0720	88 fixtures per 800 S.F.	12.30	26.50	38.80
0760	127 fixtures per 1200 S.F.	12.10	26	38.10
0800	160 fixtures per 1600 S.F.	11.90	26	37.90
0840	206 fixtures per 2000 S.F.	11.85	26	37.85
0880	Type C, 51 fixtures per 400 S.F.	17.40	28.50	45.90
0920	74 fixtures per 600 S.F.	16.95	28	44.95
0960	97 fixtures per 800 S.F.	16.75	27.50	44.25
1000	142 fixtures per 1200 S.F.	16.50	27.50	44
1040	186 fixtures per 1600 S.F.	16.30	27	43.30
1080	230 fixtures per 2000 S.F.	16.25	27	43.25
1120	Type D, 39 fixtures per 400 S.F.	16.30	22.50	38.80
1160	57 fixtures per 600 S.F.	15.90	22	37.90
1200	75 fixtures per 800 S.F.	15.80	22	37.80
1240	109 fixtures per 1200 S.F.	15.45	22	37.45
1280	143 fixtures per 1600 S.F.	15.20	21.50	36.70
1320	176 fixtures per 2000 S.F.	15.05	21.50	36.55

Type A. Recessed, wide distribution reflector with flat glass lens.

150 watt inside frost—2500 lumens per lamp.

PS–25 extended service lamp.

Maximum spacing = 1.2 x mounting height.

13 watts per S.F. for 100 footcandles.

System Components	QUANTITY	UNIT	COST PER S.F.		
			MAT.	INST.	TOTAL
SYSTEM D5020 216 0200					
INCANDESCENT FIXTURE RECESS MOUNTED, TYPE A					
1 WATT PER S.F., 8 FC, 6 FIXT PER 1000 S.F.					
Steel intermediate conduit, (IMC) 1/2" diam	.091	L.F.	.22	.62	.84
Wire, 600V, type THWN-THHN, copper, solid, #12	.002	C.L.F.	.02	.12	.14
Incandescent fixture, recessed, w/lens, prewired, square trim, 200W	.006	Ea.	.64	.61	1.25
Steel outlet box 4" square	.006	Ea.	.07	.20	.27
Fixture whip, Greenfield w/#12 THHN wire	.006	Ea.	.05	.05	.10
TOTAL			1	1.60	2.60

D5020 216	Incandescent Fixture (by Wattage)	COST PER S.F.		
		MAT.	INST.	TOTAL
0190	Incandescent fixture recess mounted, type A			
0200	1 watt per S.F., 8 FC, 6 fixtures per 1000 S.F.	1	1.60	2.60
0240	2 watt per S.F., 16 FC, 12 fixtures per 1000 S.F.	2	3.21	5.21
0280	3 watt per S.F., 24 FC, 18 fixtures, per 1000 S.F.	3	4.75	7.75
0320	4 watt per S.F., 32 FC, 24 fixtures per 1000 S.F.	3.99	6.35	10.34
0400	5 watt per S.F., 40 FC, 30 fixtures per 1000 S.F.	5	7.95	12.95

D5020 Lighting and Branch Wiring

High Bay Fluorescent Fixtures
Four T5 HO/54 watt lamps

System Components	QUANTITY	UNIT	COST PER S.F.		
			MAT.	INST.	TOTAL
SYSTEM D5020 218 0200					
FLUORESCENT HIGH BAY FIXTURE, 4 LAMP, 8'-10' ABOVE WORK PLANE					
0.5 WATT/S.F., 29 FC, 2 FIXTURES/1000 S.F.					
Steel intermediate conduit, (IMC) 1/2" diam	.100	L.F.	.24	.68	.92
Wire, 600V, type THWN-THHN, copper, solid, #10	.002	C.L.F.	.04	.14	.18
Steel outlet box 4" concrete	.002	Ea.	.02	.07	.09
Steel outlet box plate with stud, 4" concrete	.002	Ea.	.02	.02	.04
Flourescent , hi bay, 4 lamp, T-5 fixture	.002	Ea.	.54	.30	.84
TOTAL			.86	1.21	2.07

D5020 218	Fluorescent Fixture, High Bay, 8'-10' (by Wattage)	COST PER S.F.		
		MAT.	INST.	TOTAL
0190	Fluorescent high bay-4 lamp fixture, 8'-10' above work plane			
0200	.5 watt/SF, 29 FC, 2 fixtures per 1000 S.F.	.86	1.21	2.07
0400	1 watt/SF, 59 FC, 4 fixtures per 1000 S.F.	1.67	2.31	3.98
0600	1.5 watt/SF, 103 FC, 7 fixtures per 1000 S.F.	2.77	3.61	6.38
0800	2 watt/SF, 133 FC, 9 fixtures per 1000 S.F.	3.61	4.77	8.38
1000	2.5 watt/SF, 162 FC, 11 fixtures per 1000 S.F.	4.46	5.90	10.36

HIGH BAY FIXTURES

B. Metal halide 400 watt

C. High pressure sodium 400 watt

E. Metal halide 1000 watt

F. High pressure sodium 1000 watt

G. Metal halide 1000 watt
  125,000 lumen lamp

System Components	QUANTITY	UNIT	COST PER S.F.		
			MAT.	INST.	TOTAL
SYSTEM D5020 220 0880					
HIGH INTENSITY DISCHARGE FIXTURE, 8'-10' ABOVE WORK PLANE, 100 FC					
TYPE B, 8 FIXTURES PER 900 S.F.					
Steel intermediate conduit, (IMC) 1/2" diam	.460	L.F.	1.11	3.13	4.24
Wire, 600V, type THWN-THHN, copper, solid, #10	.009	C.L.F.	.17	.61	.78
Steel outlet box 4" concrete	.009	Ea.	.10	.31	.41
Steel outlet box plate with stud 4" concrete	.009	Ea.	.07	.08	.15
Metal halide, hi bay, aluminum reflector, 400 W lamp	.009	Ea.	4.10	2.66	6.76
TOTAL			5.55	6.79	12.34

D5020 220	H.I.D. Fixture, High Bay, 8'-10' (by Type)	COST PER S.F.		
		MAT.	INST.	TOTAL
0500	High intensity discharge fixture, 8'-10' above work plane, 100 FC			
0880	Type B, 8 fixtures per 900 S.F.	5.55	6.80	12.35
0920	15 fixtures per 1800 S.F.	5.10	6.50	11.60
0960	24 fixtures per 3000 S.F.	5.10	6.50	11.60
1000	31 fixtures per 4000 S.F.	5.10	6.50	11.60
1040	38 fixtures per 5000 S.F.	5.10	6.50	11.60
1080	60 fixtures per 8000 S.F.	5.10	6.50	11.60
1120	72 fixtures per 10000 S.F.	4.58	6.05	10.63
1160	115 fixtures per 16000 S.F.	4.58	6.05	10.63
1200	230 fixtures per 32000 S.F.	4.58	6.05	10.63
1240	Type C, 4 fixtures per 900 S.F.	2.70	4.14	6.84
1280	8 fixtures per 1800 S.F.	2.70	4.16	6.86
1320	13 fixtures per 3000 S.F.	2.70	4.14	6.84
1360	17 fixtures per 4000 S.F.	2.70	4.14	6.84
1400	21 fixtures per 5000 S.F.	2.60	3.80	6.40
1440	33 fixtures per 8000 S.F.	2.58	3.73	6.31
1480	40 fixtures per 10000 S.F.	2.50	3.53	6.03
1520	63 fixtures per 16000 S.F.	2.50	3.53	6.03
1560	126 fixtures per 32000 S.F.	2.50	3.53	6.03

D5020 Lighting and Branch Wiring

HIGH BAY FIXTURES

B. Metal halide 400 watt

C. High pressure sodium 400 watt

E. Metal halide 1000 watt

F. High pressure sodium 1000 watt

G. Metal halide 1000 watt
125,000 lumen lamp

System Components	QUANTITY	UNIT	COST PER S.F.		
			MAT.	INST.	TOTAL
SYSTEM D5020 222 0240					
HIGH INTENSITY DISCHARGE FIXTURE, 8'-10' ABOVE WORK PLANE					
1 WATT/S.F., TYPE B, 29 FC, 2 FIXTURES/1000 S.F.					
Steel intermediate conduit, (IMC) 1/2" diam	.100	L.F.	.24	.68	.92
Wire, 600V, type THWN-THHN, copper, solid, #10	.002	C.L.F.	.04	.14	.18
Steel outlet box 4" concrete	.002	Ea.	.02	.07	.09
Steel outlet box plate with stud, 4" concrete	.002	Ea.	.02	.02	.04
Metal halide, hi bay, aluminum reflector, 400 W lamp	.002	Ea.	.91	.59	1.50
TOTAL			1.23	1.50	2.73

D5020 222	H.I.D. Fixture, High Bay, 8'-10' (by Wattage)	COST PER S.F.		
		MAT.	INST.	TOTAL
0190	High intensity discharge fixture, 8'-10' above work plane			
0240	1 watt/S.F., type B, 29 FC, 2 fixtures/1000 S.F.	1.23	1.50	2.73
0280	Type C, 54 FC, 2 fixtures/1000 S.F.	1.04	1.14	2.18
0400	2 watt/S.F., type B, 59 FC, 4 fixtures/1000 S.F.	2.42	2.88	5.30
0440	Type C, 108 FC, 4 fixtures/1000 S.F.	2.05	2.20	4.25
0560	3 watt/S.F., type B, 103 FC, 7 fixtures/1000 S.F.	4.08	4.62	8.70
0600	Type C, 189 FC, 6 fixtures/1000 S.F.	3.23	2.84	6.07
0720	4 watt/S.F., type B, 133 FC, 9 fixtures/1000 S.F.	5.30	6.05	11.35
0760	Type C, 243 FC, 9 fixtures/1000 S.F.	4.58	4.91	9.49
0880	5 watt/S.F., type B, 162 FC, 11 fixtures/1000 S.F.	6.50	7.50	14
0920	Type C, 297 FC, 11 fixtures/1000 S.F.	5.65	6.05	11.70

D5020 Lighting and Branch Wiring

HIGH BAY FIXTURES

B. Metal halide 400 watt

C. High pressure sodium 400 watt

E. Metal halide 1000 watt

F. High pressure sodium 1000 watt

G. Metal halide 1000 watt
   125,000 lumen lamp

System Components	QUANTITY	UNIT	COST PER S.F.		
			MAT.	INST.	TOTAL
SYSTEM D5020 224 1240					
HIGH INTENSITY DISCHARGE FIXTURE, 16′ ABOVE WORK PLANE, 100 FC					
TYPE C, 5 FIXTURES PER 900 S.F.					
Steel intermediate conduit, (IMC) 1/2″ diam	.260	L.F.	.63	1.77	2.40
Wire, 600V, type THWN-THHN, copper, solid, #10	.007	C.L.F.	.13	.48	.61
Steel outlet box 4″ concrete	.006	Ea.	.07	.20	.27
Steel outlet box plate with stud, 4″ concrete	.006	Ea.	.05	.05	.10
High pressure sodium, hi bay, aluminum reflector, 400 W lamp	.006	Ea.	2.52	1.77	4.29
TOTAL			3.40	4.27	7.67

D5020 224	H.I.D. Fixture, High Bay, 16′ (by Type)	COST PER S.F.		
		MAT.	INST.	TOTAL
0510	High intensity discharge fixture, 16′ above work plane, 100 FC			
1240	Type C, 5 fixtures per 900 S.F.	3.40	4.27	7.67
1280	9 fixtures per 1800 S.F.	3.15	4.47	7.62
1320	15 fixtures per 3000 S.F.	3.15	4.47	7.62
1360	18 fixtures per 4000 S.F.	2.98	4	6.98
1400	22 fixtures per 5000 S.F.	2.98	4	6.98
1440	36 fixtures per 8000 S.F.	2.98	4	6.98
1480	42 fixtures per 10,000 S.F.	2.71	4.13	6.84
1520	65 fixtures per 16,000 S.F.	2.71	4.13	6.84
1600	Type G, 4 fixtures per 900 S.F.	4.48	6.75	11.23
1640	6 fixtures per 1800 S.F.	3.76	6.30	10.06
1720	9 fixtures per 4000 S.F.	3.18	6.15	9.33
1760	11 fixtures per 5000 S.F.	3.18	6.15	9.33
1840	21 fixtures per 10,000 S.F.	2.96	5.55	8.51
1880	33 fixtures per 16,000 S.F.	2.96	5.55	8.51

D5020 Lighting and Branch Wiring

HIGH BAY FIXTURES

B. Metal halide 400 watt

C. High pressure sodium 400 watt

E. Metal halide 1000 watt

F. High pressure sodium 1000 watt

G. Metal halide 1000 watt
125,000 lumen lamp

System Components			COST PER S.F.		
	QUANTITY	UNIT	MAT.	INST.	TOTAL
SYSTEM D5020 226 0240					
HIGH INTENSITY DISCHARGE FIXTURE, 16' ABOVE WORK PLANE					
1 WATT/S.F., TYPE E, 42 FC, 1 FIXTURE/1000 S.F.					
Steel intermediate conduit, (IMC) 1/2" diam	.160	L.F.	.39	1.09	1.48
Wire, 600V, type THWN-THHN, copper, solid, #10	.003	C.L.F.	.06	.20	.26
Steel outlet box 4" concrete	.001	Ea.	.01	.03	.04
Steel outlet box plate with stud, 4" concrete	.001	Ea.	.01	.01	.02
Metal halide, hi bay, aluminum reflector, 1000 W lamp	.001	Ea.	.66	.34	1
TOTAL			1.13	1.67	2.80

D5020 226	H.I.D. Fixture, High Bay, 16' (by Wattage)	COST PER S.F.		
		MAT.	INST.	TOTAL
0190	High intensity discharge fixture, 16' above work plane			
0240	1 watt/S.F., type E, 42 FC, 1 fixture/1000 S.F.	1.13	1.67	2.80
0280	Type G, 52 FC, 1 fixture/1000 S.F.	1.13	1.67	2.80
0320	Type C, 54 FC, 2 fixture/1000 S.F.	1.29	1.87	3.16
0440	2 watt/S.F., type E, 84 FC, 2 fixture/1000 S.F.	2.25	3.43	5.68
0480	Type G, 105 FC, 2 fixture/1000 S.F.	2.25	3.43	5.68
0520	Type C, 108 FC, 4 fixture/1000 S.F.	2.58	3.75	6.33
0640	3 watt/S.F., type E, 126 FC, 3 fixture/1000 S.F.	3.36	5.10	8.46
0680	Type G, 157 FC, 3 fixture/1000 S.F.	3.36	5.10	8.46
0720	Type C, 162 FC, 6 fixture/1000 S.F.	3.87	5.60	9.47
0840	4 watt/S.F., type E, 168 FC, 4 fixture/1000 S.F.	4.51	6.85	11.36
0880	Type G, 210 FC, 4 fixture/1000 S.F.	4.51	6.85	11.36
0920	Type C, 243 FC, 9 fixture/1000 S.F.	5.60	7.85	13.45
1040	5 watt/S.F., type E, 210 FC, 5 fixture/1000 S.F.	5.65	8.50	14.15
1080	Type G, 262 FC, 5 fixture/1000 S.F.	5.65	8.50	14.15
1120	Type C, 297 FC, 11 fixture/1000 S.F.	6.90	9.70	16.60

D5020 Lighting and Branch Wiring

HIGH BAY FIXTURES

B. Metal halide 400 watt

C. High pressure sodium 400 watt

E. Metal halide 1000 watt

F. High pressure sodium 1000 watt

G. Metal halide 1000 watt
   125,000 lumen lamp

System Components			COST PER S.F.		
	QUANTITY	UNIT	MAT.	INST.	TOTAL
SYSTEM D5020 228 1240					
HIGH INTENSITY DISCHARGE FIXTURE, 20′ ABOVE WORK PLANE, 100 FC					
TYPE C, 6 FIXTURES PER 900 S.F.					
Steel intermediate conduit, (IMC) 1/2″ diam	.350	L.F.	.85	2.38	3.23
Wire, 600V, type THWN-THHN, copper, solid, #10.	.011	C.L.F.	.20	.75	.95
Steel outlet box 4″ concrete	.007	Ea.	.08	.24	.32
Steel outlet box plate with stud, 4″ concrete	.007	Ea.	.05	.06	.11
High pressure sodium, hi bay, aluminum reflector, 400 W lamp	.007	Ea.	2.94	2.07	5.01
TOTAL			4.12	5.50	9.62

D5020 228	H.I.D. Fixture, High Bay, 20′ (by Type)	COST PER S.F.		
		MAT.	INST.	TOTAL
0510	High intensity discharge fixture 20′ above work plane, 100 FC			
1240	Type C, 6 fixtures per 900 S.F.	4.12	5.50	9.62
1280	10 fixtures per 1800 S.F.	3.69	5.15	8.84
1320	16 fixtures per 3000 S.F.	3.29	4.96	8.25
1360	20 fixtures per 4000 S.F.	3.29	4.96	8.25
1400	24 fixtures per 5000 S.F.	3.29	4.96	8.25
1440	38 fixtures per 8000 S.F.	3.22	4.75	7.97
1520	68 fixtures per 16000 S.F.	3.07	5.25	8.32
1560	132 fixtures per 32000 S.F.	3.07	5.25	8.32
1600	Type G, 4 fixtures per 900 S.F.	4.41	6.65	11.06
1640	6 fixtures per 1800 S.F.	3.75	6.30	10.05
1680	7 fixtures per 3000 S.F.	3.68	6.10	9.78
1720	10 fixtures per 4000 S.F.	3.66	6.05	9.71
1760	11 fixtures per 5000 S.F.	3.28	6.50	9.78
1800	18 fixtures per 8000 S.F.	3.28	6.50	9.78
1840	22 fixtures per 10000 S.F.	3.28	6.50	9.78
1880	34 fixtures per 16000 S.F.	3.20	6.25	9.45
1920	66 fixtures per 32000 S.F.	3.01	5.75	8.76

D5020 Lighting and Branch Wiring

HIGH BAY FIXTURES

B. Metal halide 400 watt

C. High pressure sodium 400 watt

E. Metal halide 1000 watt

F. High pressure sodium 1000 watt

G. Metal halide 1000 watt
   125,000 lumen lamp

System Components	QUANTITY	UNIT	COST PER S.F.		
			MAT.	INST.	TOTAL
SYSTEM D5020 230 0240					
HIGH INTENSITY DISCHARGE FIXTURE, 20' ABOVE WORK PLANE					
1 WATT/S.F., TYPE E, 40 FC, 1 FIXTURE 1000 S.F.					
Steel intermediate conduit, (IMC) 1/2" diam	.160	L.F.	.39	1.09	1.48
Wire, 600V, type THWN-THHN, copper, solid, #10	.005	C.L.F.	.09	.34	.43
Steel outlet box 4" concrete	.001	Ea.	.01	.03	.04
Steel outlet box plate with stud, 4" concrete	.001	Ea.	.01	.01	.02
Metal halide, hi bay, aluminum reflector, 1000 W lamp	.001	Ea.	.66	.34	1
TOTAL			1.16	1.81	2.97

D5020 230	H.I.D. Fixture, High Bay, 20' (by Wattage)	COST PER S.F.		
		MAT.	INST.	TOTAL
0190	High intensity discharge fixture, 20' above work plane			
0240	1 watt/S.F., type E, 40 FC, 1 fixture/1000 S.F.	1.16	1.81	2.97
0280	Type G, 50 FC, 1 fixture/1000 S.F.	1.16	1.81	2.97
0320	Type C, 52 FC, 2 fixtures/1000 S.F.	1.35	2.09	3.44
0440	2 watt/S.F., type E, 81 FC, 2 fixtures/1000 S.F.	2.30	3.63	5.93
0480	Type G, 101 FC, 2 fixtures/1000 S.F.	2.30	3.63	5.93
0520	Type C, 104 FC, 4 fixtures/1000 S.F.	2.69	4.11	6.80
0640	3 watt/S.F., type E, 121 FC, 3 fixtures/1000 S.F.	3.46	5.45	8.91
0680	Type G, 151 FC, 3 fixtures/1000 S.F.	3.46	5.45	8.91
0720	Type C, 155 FC, 6 fixtures/1000 S.F.	4.05	6.20	10.25
0840	4 watt/S.F., type E, 161 FC, 4 fixtures/1000 S.F.	4.62	7.25	11.87
0880	Type G, 202 FC, 4 fixtures/1000 S.F.	4.62	7.25	11.87
0920	Type C, 233 FC, 9 fixtures/1000 S.F.	5.80	8.55	14.35
1040	5 watt/S.F., type E, 202 FC, 5 fixtures/1000 S.F.	5.80	9.05	14.85
1080	Type G, 252 FC, 5 fixtures/1000 S.F.	5.80	9.05	14.85
1120	Type C, 285 FC, 11 fixtures/1000 S.F.	7.15	10.65	17.80

D5020 Lighting and Branch Wiring

HIGH BAY FIXTURES

B. Metal halide 400 watt

C. High pressure sodium 400 watt

E. Metal halide 1000 watt

F. High pressure sodium 1000 watt

G. Metal halide 1000 watt
125,000 lumen lamp

System Components	QUANTITY	UNIT	COST PER S.F.		
			MAT.	INST.	TOTAL
SYSTEM D5020 232 1240					
HIGH INTENSITY DISCHARGE FIXTURE, 30' ABOVE WORK PLANE, 100 FC					
TYPE F, 4 FIXTURES PER 900 S.F.					
Steel intermediate conduit, (IMC) 1/2" diam	.580	L.F.	1.40	3.94	5.34
Wire, 600V, type THWN-THHN, copper, solid, #10	.018	C.L.F.	.33	1.22	1.55
Steel outlet box 4" concrete	.004	Ea.	.05	.14	.19
Steel outlet box plate with stud, 4" concrete	.004	Ea.	.03	.03	.06
High pressure sodium, hi bay, aluminum, 1000 W lamp	.004	Ea.	2.42	1.36	3.78
TOTAL			4.23	6.69	10.92

D5020 232	H.I.D. Fixture, High Bay, 30' (by Type)	COST PER S.F.		
		MAT.	INST.	TOTAL
0510	High intensity discharge fixture, 30' above work plane, 100 FC			
1240	Type F, 4 fixtures per 900 S.F.	4.23	6.70	10.93
1280	6 fixtures per 1800 S.F.	3.63	6.40	10.03
1320	8 fixtures per 3000 S.F.	3.63	6.40	10.03
1360	9 fixtures per 4000 S.F.	3.03	6.05	9.08
1400	10 fixtures per 5000 S.F.	3.03	6.05	9.08
1440	17 fixtures per 8000 S.F.	3.03	6.05	9.08
1480	18 fixtures per 10,000 S.F.	2.86	5.60	8.46
1520	27 fixtures per 16,000 S.F.	2.86	5.60	8.46
1560	52 fixtures per 32000 S.F.	2.84	5.55	8.39
1600	Type G, 4 fixtures per 900 S.F.	4.58	7.10	11.68
1640	6 fixtures per 1800 S.F.	3.81	6.45	10.26
1680	9 fixtures per 3000 S.F.	3.73	6.25	9.98
1720	11 fixtures per 4000 S.F.	3.66	6.05	9.71
1760	13 fixtures per 5000 S.F.	3.66	6.05	9.71
1800	21 fixtures per 8000 S.F.	3.66	6.05	9.71
1840	23 fixtures per 10,000 S.F.	3.19	6.40	9.59
1880	36 fixtures per 16,000 S.F.	3.19	6.40	9.59
1920	70 fixtures per 32,000 S.F.	3.19	6.40	9.59

HIGH BAY FIXTURES

B. Metal halide 400 watt

C. High pressure sodium 400 watt

E. Metal halide 1000 watt

F. High pressure sodium 1000 watt

G. Metal halide 1000 watt
125,000 lumen lamp

System Components	QUANTITY	UNIT	COST PER S.F.		
			MAT.	INST.	TOTAL
SYSTEM D5020 234 0240					
HIGH INTENSITY DISCHARGE FIXTURE, 30' ABOVE WORK PLANE					
1 WATT/S.F., TYPE E, 37 FC, 1 FIXTURE/1000 S.F.					
Steel intermediate conduit, (IMC) 1/2" diam	.196	L.F.	.47	1.33	1.80
Wire, 600V type THWN-THHN, copper, solid, #10	.006	C.L.F.	.11	.41	.52
Steel outlet box 4" concrete	.001	Ea.	.01	.03	.04
Steel outlet box plate with stud, 4" concrete	.001	Ea.	.01	.01	.02
Metal halide, hi bay, aluminum reflector, 1000 W lamp	.001	Ea.	.66	.34	1
TOTAL			1.26	2.12	3.38

D5020 234	H.I.D. Fixture, High Bay, 30' (by Wattage)	COST PER S.F.		
		MAT.	INST.	TOTAL
0190	High intensity discharge fixture, 30' above work plane			
0240	1 watt/S.F., type E, 37 FC, 1 fixture/1000 S.F.	1.26	2.12	3.38
0280	Type G, 45 FC., 1 fixture/1000 S.F.	1.26	2.12	3.38
0320	Type F, 50 FC, 1 fixture/1000 S.F.	1.06	1.66	2.72
0440	2 watt/S.F., type E, 74 FC, 2 fixtures/1000 S.F.	2.52	4.26	6.78
0480	Type G, 92 FC, 2 fixtures/1000 S.F.	2.52	4.26	6.78
0520	Type F, 100 FC, 2 fixtures/1000 S.F.	2.14	3.39	5.53
0640	3 watt/S.F., type E, 110 FC, 3 fixtures/1000 S.F.	3.79	6.45	10.24
0680	Type G, 138 FC, 3 fixtures/1000 S.F.	3.79	6.45	10.24
0720	Type F, 150 FC, 3 fixtures/1000 S.F.	3.18	5.05	8.23
0840	4 watt/S.F., type E, 148 FC, 4 fixtures/1000 S.F.	5.05	8.55	13.60
0880	Type G, 185 FC, 4 fixtures/1000 S.F.	5.05	8.55	13.60
0920	Type F, 200 FC, 4 fixtures/1000 S.F.	4.26	6.80	11.06
1040	5 watt/S.F., type E, 185 FC, 5 fixtures/1000 S.F.	6.30	10.70	17
1080	Type G, 230 FC, 5 fixtures/1000 S.F.	6.30	10.70	17
1120	Type F, 250 FC, 5 fixtures/1000 S.F.	5.30	8.45	13.75

LOW BAY FIXTURES

J. Metal halide 250 watt

K. High pressure sodium 150 watt

System Components	QUANTITY	UNIT	COST PER S.F.		
			MAT.	INST.	TOTAL
SYSTEM D5020 236 0920					
HIGH INTENSITY DISCHARGE FIXTURE, 8'-10' ABOVE WORK PLANE, 50 FC					
TYPE J, 13 FIXTURES PER 1800 S.F.					
Steel intermediate conduit, (IMC) 1/2" diam	.550	L.F.	1.33	3.74	5.07
Wire, 600V, type THWN-THHN, copper, solid, #10	.012	C.L.F.	.22	.82	1.04
Steel outlet box 4" concrete	.007	Ea.	.08	.24	.32
Steel outlet box plate with stud, 4" concrete	.007	Ea.	.05	.06	.11
Metal halide, lo bay, aluminum reflector, 250 W DX lamp	.007	Ea.	2.80	1.48	4.28
TOTAL			4.48	6.34	10.82

D5020 236	H.I.D. Fixture, Low Bay, 8'-10' (by Type)	COST PER S.F.		
		MAT.	INST.	TOTAL
0510	High intensity discharge fixture, 8'-10' above work plane, 50 FC			
0880	Type J, 7 fixtures per 900 S.F.	4.83	6.40	11.23
0920	13 fixtures per 1800 S.F.	4.48	6.35	10.83
0960	21 fixtures per 3000 S.F.	4.48	6.35	10.83
1000	28 fixtures per 4000 S.F.	4.48	6.35	10.83
1040	35 fixtures per 5000 S.F.	4.48	6.35	10.83
1120	62 fixtures per 10,000 S.F.	4.07	6.10	10.17
1160	99 fixtures per 16,000 S.F.	4.07	6.10	10.17
1200	199 fixtures per 32,000 S.F.	4.07	6.10	10.17
1240	Type K, 9 fixtures per 900 S.F.	4.80	5.45	10.25
1280	16 fixtures per 1800 S.F.	4.43	5.30	9.73
1320	26 fixtures per 3000 S.F.	4.41	5.20	9.61
1360	31 fixtures per 4000 S.F.	4.08	5.10	9.18
1400	39 fixtures per 5000 S.F.	4.08	5.10	9.18
1440	62 fixtures per 8000 S.F.	4.08	5.10	9.18
1480	78 fixtures per 10,000 S.F.	4.08	5.10	9.18
1520	124 fixtures per 16,000 S.F.	4.03	4.97	9
1560	248 fixtures per 32,000 S.F.	3.93	5.50	9.43

D5020 Lighting and Branch Wiring

LOW BAY FIXTURES

J. Metal halide 250 watt

K. High pressure sodium 150 watt

System Components	QUANTITY	UNIT	COST PER S.F.		
			MAT.	INST.	TOTAL
SYSTEM D5020 238 0240					
HIGH INTENSITY DISCHARGE FIXTURE, 8'-10' ABOVE WORK PLANE					
1 WATT/S.F., TYPE J, 30 FC, 4 FIXTURES/1000 S.F.					
Steel intermediate conduit, (IMC) 1/2" diam	.280	L.F.	.68	1.90	2.58
Wire, 600V, type THWN-THHN, copper, solid, #10	.008	C.L.F.	.15	.54	.69
Steel outlet box 4" concrete	.004	Ea.	.05	.14	.19
Steel outlet box plate with stud, 4" concrete	.004	Ea.	.03	.03	.06
Metal halide, lo bay, aluminum reflector, 250 W DX lamp	.004	Ea.	1.60	.85	2.45
TOTAL			2.51	3.46	5.97

D5020 238	H.I.D. Fixture, Low Bay, 8'-10' (by Wattage)	COST PER S.F.		
		MAT.	INST.	TOTAL
0190	High intensity discharge fixture, 8'-10' above work plane			
0240	1 watt/S.F., type J, 30 FC, 4 fixtures/1000 S.F.	2.51	3.46	5.97
0280	Type K, 29 FC, 5 fixtures/1000 S.F.	2.52	3.11	5.63
0400	2 watt/S.F., type J, 52 FC, 7 fixtures/1000 S.F.	4.46	6.35	10.81
0440	Type K, 63 FC, 11 fixtures/1000 S.F.	5.45	6.55	12
0560	3 watt/S.F., type J, 81 FC, 11 fixtures/1000 S.F.	6.90	9.55	16.45
0600	Type K, 92 FC, 16 fixtures/1000 S.F.	7.95	9.65	17.60
0720	4 watt/S.F., type J, 103 FC, 14 fixtures/1000 S.F.	8.90	12.65	21.55
0760	Type K, 127 FC, 22 fixtures/1000 S.F.	10.85	13.10	23.95
0880	5 watt/S.F., type J, 133 FC, 18 fixtures/1000 S.F.	11.35	15.95	27.30
0920	Type K, 155 FC, 27 fixtures/1000 S.F.	13.35	16.20	29.55

LOW BAY FIXTURES

J. Metal halide 250 watt

K. High pressure sodium 150 watt

System Components	QUANTITY	UNIT	COST PER S.F.		
			MAT.	INST.	TOTAL
SYSTEM D5020 240 0880					
HIGH INTENSITY DISCHARGE FIXTURE, 16′ ABOVE WORK PLANE, 50 FC					
TYPE J, 9 FIXTURES PER 900 S.F.					
Steel intermediate conduit, (IMC) 1/2″ diam	.630	L.F.	1.52	4.28	5.80
Wire, 600V type, THWN-THHN, copper, solid, #10	.012	C.L.F.	.22	.82	1.04
Steel outlet box 4″ concrete	.010	Ea.	.12	.34	.46
Steel outlet box plate with stud, 4″ concrete	.010	Ea.	.08	.09	.17
Metal halide, lo bay, aluminum reflector, 250 W DX lamp	.010	Ea.	4	2.12	6.12
TOTAL			5.94	7.65	13.59

D5020 240	H.I.D. Fixture, Low Bay, 16′ (by Type)	COST PER S.F.		
		MAT.	INST.	TOTAL
0510	High intensity discharge fixture, 16′ above work plane, 50 FC			
0880	Type J, 9 fixtures per 900 S.F.	5.95	7.65	13.60
0920	14 fixtures per 1800 S.F.	5.10	7.20	12.30
0960	24 fixtures per 3000 S.F.	5.15	7.35	12.50
1000	32 fixtures per 4000 S.F.	5.15	7.35	12.50
1040	35 fixtures per 5000 S.F.	4.77	7.15	11.92
1080	56 fixtures per 8000 S.F.	4.77	7.15	11.92
1120	70 fixtures per 10,000 S.F.	4.76	7.15	11.91
1160	111 fixtures per 16,000 S.F.	4.76	7.15	11.91
1200	222 fixtures per 32,000 S.F.	4.76	7.15	11.91
1240	Type K, 11 fixtures per 900 S.F.	5.95	7.15	13.10
1280	20 fixtures per 1800 S.F.	5.50	6.60	12.10
1320	29 fixtures per 3000 S.F.	5.15	6.50	11.65
1360	39 fixtures per 4000 S.F.	5.10	6.45	11.55
1400	44 fixtures per 5000 S.F.	4.77	6.30	11.07
1440	62 fixtures per 8000 S.F.	4.77	6.30	11.07
1480	87 fixtures per 10,000 S.F.	4.77	6.30	11.07
1520	138 fixtures per 16,000 S.F.	4.77	6.30	11.07

D5020 Lighting and Branch Wiring

LOW BAY FIXTURES

J. Metal halide 250 watt

K. High pressure sodium 150 watt

System Components	QUANTITY	UNIT	COST PER S.F.		
			MAT.	INST.	TOTAL
SYSTEM D5020 242 0240					
HIGH INTENSITY DISCHARGE FIXTURE, 16' ABOVE WORK PLANE					
1 WATT/S.F., TYPE J, 28 FC, 4 FIXTURES/1000 S.F.					
Steel intermediate conduit, (IMC) 1/2" diam	.328	L.F.	.79	2.23	3.02
Wire, 600V, type THWN-THHN, copper, solid, #10	.010	C.L.F.	.18	.68	.86
Steel outlet box 4" concrete	.004	Ea.	.05	.14	.19
Steel outlet box plate with stud, 4" concrete	.004	Ea.	.03	.03	.06
Metal halide, lo bay, aluminum reflector, 250 W DX lamp	.004	Ea.	1.60	.85	2.45
TOTAL			2.65	3.93	6.58

D5020 242	H.I.D. Fixture, Low Bay, 16' (by Wattage)	COST PER S.F.		
		MAT.	INST.	TOTAL
0190	High intensity discharge fixture, mounted 16' above work plane			
0240	1 watt/S.F., type J, 28 FC, 4 fixt./1000 S.F.	2.65	3.93	6.58
0280	Type K, 27 FC, 5 fixt./1000 S.F.	2.95	4.40	7.35
0400	2 watt/S.F., type J, 48 FC, 7 fixt/1000 S.F.	4.89	7.60	12.49
0440	Type K, 58 FC, 11 fixt/1000 S.F.	6.25	9	15.25
0560	3 watt/S.F., type J, 75 FC, 11 fixt/1000 S.F.	7.55	11.50	19.05
0600	Type K, 85 FC, 16 fixt/1000 S.F.	9.20	13.40	22.60
0720	4 watt/S.F., type J, 95 FC, 14 fixt/1000 S.F.	9.80	15.20	25
0760	Type K, 117 FC, 22 fixt/1000 S.F.	12.50	18	30.50
0880	5 watt/S.F., type J, 122 FC, 18 fixt/1000 S.F.	12.45	19.15	31.60
0920	Type K, 143 FC, 27 fixt/1000 S.F.	15.45	22.50	37.95

D5020 Lighting and Branch Wiring

Daylight Dimming System

System Components	QUANTITY	UNIT	COST PER S.F.		
			MAT.	INST.	TOTAL
SYSTEM D5020 290 0800					
DAYLIGHT DIMMING CONTROL SYSTEM					
5 FIXTURES PER 1000 S.F.					
Tray cable, type TC, copper #16-4 conductor	.300	C.L.F.	.01	.03	.04
Wire, 600 volt, type THWN-THHN, copper, solid, #12	.320	C.L.F.		.02	.02
Conduit (EMT) , to 10' H, incl 2 termn,2 elb&11 bm clp per 100', 3/4"	10.000	L.F.	.01	.05	.06
Cabinet, hinged, steel, NEMA 1, 12"W x 12"H x 4"D	.200	Ea.	.01	.02	.03
Lighting control module	.200	Ea.	.07	.07	.14
Dimmable ballast three-lamp	5.000	Ea.	.72	.49	1.21
Daylight level sensor, wall mounted, on/off or dimming	.200	Ea.	.03	.02	.05
Automatic wall switches	.200	Ea.	.02	.01	.03
Remote power pack	.100	Ea.		.01	.01
TOTAL			.87	.72	1.59

D5020 290	Daylight Dimming System	COST PER S.F.		
		MAT.	INST.	TOTAL
0500	Daylight Dimming System (no fixtures or fixture power)			
0800	5 fixtures per 1000 S.F.	.87	.72	1.59
1000	10 fixtures per 1000 S.F.	1.72	1.36	3.08
2000	12 fixtures per 1000 S.F.	2.07	1.60	3.67
3000	15 fixtures per 1000 S.F.	2.58	1.99	4.57
4000	20 fixtures per 1000 S.F.	3.43	2.63	6.06
5000	25 fixtures per 1000 S.F.	4.29	3.27	7.56
6000	50 fixtures per 1000 S.F.	8.55	6.50	15.05

D5020 Lighting and Branch Wiring

Lighting AC Control System

System Components	QUANTITY	UNIT	COST PER S.F.		
			MAT.	INST.	TOTAL
SYSTEM D5020 295 0800					
LIGHTING ON/OFF CONTROL SYSTEM					
5 FIXTURES PER 1000 S.F.					
Tray cable, type TC, copper #16-4 conductor	.600	C.L.F.	.03	.06	.09
Wire, 600 volt, type THWN-THHN, copper, solid, #12	.320	C.L.F.		.02	.02
Conduit (EMT) , to 10' H, incl 2 termn,2 elb&11 bm clp per 100', 3/4"	10.000	L.F.	.01	.05	.06
Cabinet, hinged, steel, NEMA 1, 12"W x 12"H x 4"D	.400	Ea.	.01	.05	.06
Relays, 120 V or 277 V standard	.800	Ea.	.04	.05	.09
24 hour dial with reserve power	.400	Ea.	.27	.08	.35
Lighting control module	.200	Ea.	.07	.07	.14
Occupancy sensors, passive infrared ceiling mounted	.400	Ea.	.03	.04	.07
Automatic wall switches	.400	Ea.	.03	.01	.04
Remote power pack	.200	Ea.	.01	.01	.02
TOTAL			.50	.44	.94

D5020 295	Lighting On/Off Control System	COST PER S.F.		
		MAT.	INST.	TOTAL
0500	Includes occupancy and time switching (no fixtures or fixture power)			
0800	5 fixtures per 1000 SF	.50	.44	.94
1000	10 fixtures per 1000 S.F.	.57	.51	1.08
2000	12 fixtures per 1000 S.F.	.68	.57	1.25
3000	15 fixtures per 1000 S.F.	.85	.70	1.55
4000	20 fixtures per 1000 S.F.	1.13	.91	2.04
5000	25 fixtures per 1000 S.F.	1.42	1.12	2.54
6000	50 fixtures per 1000 S.F.	2.82	2.19	5.01

Description: System below includes telephone fitting installed. Does not include cable.

When poke thru fittings and telepoles are used for power, they can also be used for telephones at a negligible additional cost.

System Components	QUANTITY	UNIT	COST PER S.F.		
			MAT.	INST.	TOTAL
SYSTEM D5030 310 0200					
TELEPHONE SYSTEMS, UNDERFLOOR DUCT, 5' ON CENTER, LOW DENSITY					
Underfloor duct 7-1/4" w/insert 2' O.C. 1-3/8" x 7-1/4" super duct	.190	L.F.	7.22	2.57	9.79
Vertical elbow for underfloor superduct, 7-1/4", included					
Underfloor duct conduit adapter, 2" x 1-1/4", included					
Underfloor duct junction box, single duct, 7-1/4" x 3 1/8"	.003	Ea.	1.85	.51	2.36
Underfloor junction box carpet pan	.003	Ea.	1.25	.03	1.28
Underfloor duct outlet, low tension	.004	Ea.	.46	.34	.80
TOTAL			10.78	3.45	14.23

D5030 310	Telephone Systems	COST PER S.F.		
		MAT.	INST.	TOTAL
0200	Telephone systems, underfloor duct, 5' on center, low density	10.80	3.45	14.25
0240	5' on center, high density	11.25	3.79	15.04
0280	7' on center, low density	8.60	2.87	11.47
0320	7' on center, high density	9.05	3.21	12.26
0400	Poke thru fittings, low density	1.18	1.23	2.41
0440	High density	2.36	2.45	4.81
0520	Telepoles, low density	1.15	.73	1.88
0560	High density	2.30	1.46	3.76
0640	Conduit system with floor boxes, low density	1.53	1.20	2.73
0680	High density	3.04	2.38	5.42
1020	Telephone wiring for offices & laboratories, 8 jacks/M.S.F.	.36	1.86	2.22

D5030 810	Security & Detection Systems	COST EACH		
		MAT.	INST.	TOTAL
0200	Security system, head end equipment	29,800	4,525	34,325
0240	Security system, door/window contact biased, box, conduit & cable	245	510	755
0280	Security system, door/window contact balanced, box, conduit & cable	251	510	761
0440	Security system, proximity card reader, box, conduit & cable	445	680	1,125
1600	Card control entrance system, to 6 zone, including hardware for 100 doors	44,900	31,400	76,300

Sound System Includes AM–FM antenna, outlets, rigid conduit, and copper wire.
Fire Detection System Includes pull stations, signals, smoke and heat detectors, rigid conduit, and copper wire.
Intercom System Includes master and remote stations, rigid conduit, and copper wire.
Master Clock System Includes clocks, bells, rigid conduit, and copper wire.
Master TV Antenna Includes antenna, VHF–UHF reception and distribution, rigid conduit, and copper wire.

System Components	QUANTITY	UNIT	COST EACH		
			MAT.	INST.	TOTAL
SYSTEM D5030 910 0220					
SOUND SYSTEM, INCLUDES OUTLETS, BOXES, CONDUIT & WIRE					
Steel intermediate conduit, (IMC) 1/2" diam	1200.000	L.F.	2,904	8,160	11,064
Wire sound shielded w/drain, #22-2 conductor	15.500	C.L.F.	237.93	1,317.50	1,555.43
Sound system speakers ceiling or wall	12.000	Ea.	1,728	1,020	2,748
Sound system volume control	12.000	Ea.	684	1,020	1,704
Sound system amplifier, 250 Watts	1.000	Ea.	1,575	680	2,255
Sound system antenna, AM FM	1.000	Ea.	166	170	336
Sound system monitor panel	1.000	Ea.	475	170	645
Sound system cabinet	1.000	Ea.	1,025	680	1,705
Steel outlet box 4" square	12.000	Ea.	38.04	408	446.04
Steel outlet box 4" plaster rings	12.000	Ea.	26.88	127.20	154.08
TOTAL			8,859.85	13,752.70	22,612.55

D5030 910	Communication & Alarm Systems	COST PER EACH		
		MAT.	INST.	TOTAL
0200	Communication & alarm systems, includes outlets, boxes, conduit & wire			
0210	Sound system, 6 outlets	6,200	8,600	14,800
0220	12 outlets	8,850	13,800	22,650
0240	30 outlets	15,400	26,000	41,400
0280	100 outlets	46,600	87,000	133,600
0320	Fire detection systems, non-addressable, 12 detectors	3,825	7,125	10,950
0360	25 detectors	6,775	12,000	18,775
0400	50 detectors	13,300	23,800	37,100
0440	100 detectors	24,900	43,400	68,300
0450	Addressable type, 12 detectors	5,275	7,175	12,450
0452	25 detectors	9,550	12,100	21,650
0454	50 detectors	18,400	23,900	42,300
0456	100 detectors	35,600	43,800	79,400
0458	Fire alarm control panel, 8 zone, excluding wire and conduit	945	1,350	2,295
0459	12 zone	2,375	2,025	4,400
0460	Fire alarm command center, addressable without voice, excl. wire & conduit	4,975	1,175	6,150
0462	Addressable with voice	10,500	1,875	12,375
0480	Intercom systems, 6 stations	4,300	5,875	10,175
0520	12 stations	8,375	11,700	20,075
0560	25 stations	14,300	22,500	36,800
0600	50 stations	27,700	42,400	70,100
0640	100 stations	54,500	82,500	137,000
0680	Master clock systems, 6 rooms	5,400	9,575	14,975
0720	12 rooms	8,725	16,300	25,025
0760	20 rooms	12,200	23,100	35,300
0800	30 rooms	20,300	42,600	62,900

D50 Electrical

D5030 Communications and Security

D5030 910	Communication & Alarm Systems	COST PER EACH		
		MAT.	INST.	TOTAL
0840	50 rooms	33,300	72,000	105,300
0880	100 rooms	65,000	142,500	207,500
0920	Master TV antenna systems, 6 outlets	2,875	6,075	8,950
0960	12 outlets	5,375	11,300	16,675
1000	30 outlets	13,000	26,200	39,200
1040	100 outlets	43,400	85,500	128,900

D5030 920	Data Communication	COST PER M.S.F.		
		MAT.	INST.	TOTAL
0100	Data communication system, incl data/voice outlets, boxes, conduit & cable			
0102	Data and voice system, 2 data/voice outlets per 1000 S.F.	136	500	636
0104	4 data/voice outlets per 1000 S.F.	257	990	1,247
0106	6 data/voice outlets per 1000 S.F.	365	1,450	1,815
0110	8 data/voice outlets per 1000 S.F.	470	1,925	2,395

Description: System below tabulates the installed cost for generators by kW. Included in costs are battery, charger, muffler, and transfer switch.

No conduit, wire, or terminations included.

System Components	QUANTITY	UNIT	COST PER kW		
			MAT.	INST.	TOTAL
SYSTEM D5090 210 0200					
GENERATOR SET, INCL. BATTERY, CHARGER, MUFFLER & TRANSFER SWITCH					
GAS/GASOLINE OPER., 3 PHASE, 4 WIRE, 277/480V, 7.5 kW					
Generator set, gas or gasoline operated, 3 ph 4 W, 277/480 V, 7.5 kW	.133	Ea.	1,256.67	297.73	1,554.40
TOTAL			1,256.67	297.73	1,554.40

D5090 210	Generators (by kW)	COST PER kW		
		MAT.	INST.	TOTAL
0190	Generator sets, include battery, charger, muffler & transfer switch			
0200	Gas/gasoline operated, 3 phase, 4 wire, 277/480 volt, 7.5 kW	1,250	298	1,548
0240	11.5 kW	1,150	228	1,378
0280	20 kW	785	147	932
0320	35 kW	535	96.50	631.50
0360	80 kW	385	115	500
0400	100 kW	335	112	447
0440	125 kW	550	106	656
0480	185 kW	490	80	570
0560	Diesel engine with fuel tank, 30 kW	405	112	517
0600	50 kW	440	88	528
0640	75 kW	340	70.50	410.50
0680	100 kW	305	60	365
0720	125 kW	258	51	309
0760	150 kW	276	47.50	323.50
0800	175 kW	263	42.50	305.50
0840	200 kW	249	38.50	287.50
0880	250 kW	214	32	246
0920	300 kW	188	28.50	216.50
0960	350 kW	184	26.50	210.50
1000	400 kW	198	24.50	222.50
1040	500 kW	201	20.50	221.50
1200	750 kW	216	13	229
1400	1000 kW	205	13.70	218.70

PV power system, stand alone, AC and DC loads

System Components			COST EACH		
	QUANTITY	UNIT	MAT.	INST.	TOTAL
SYSTEM D5090 420 0100					
PHOTOVOLTAIC POWER SYSTEM, STAND ALONE					
Alternative energy sources, photovoltaic module, 75 watt, 17 volts	12.000	Ea.	5,460	1,020	6,480
PV rack system, roof, penetrating surface mount, on wood framing, 1 panel	12.000	Ea.	738	1,332	2,070
DC to AC inverter for, 24 V, 2,500 watt	1.000	Ea.	1,650	170	1,820
PV components, combiner box, 10 lug, NEMA 3R enclosure	1.000	Ea.	297	170	467
Alternative energy sources, PV components, fuse, 15 A for combiner box	10.000	Ea.	235	169.50	404.50
Battery charger controller w/temperature sensor	1.000	Ea.	540	170	710
Digital readout panel, displays hours, volts, amps, etc.	1.000	Ea.	222	170	392
Deep cycle solar battery, 6 V, 180 Ah (C/20)	4.000	Ea.	1,320	340	1,660
Battery interconnection, 15" AWG #2/0, sealed w/copper ring lugs	3.000	Ea.	59.70	127.50	187.20
Battery interconn, 24" AWG #2/0, sealed w/copper ring lugs	2.000	Ea.	52	85	137
Battery interconn, 60" AWG #2/0, sealed w/copper ring lugs	2.000	Ea.	130	85	215
Batt temp computer probe, RJ11 jack, 15' cord	1.000	Ea.	24.50	42.50	67
System disconnect, DC 175 amp circuit breaker	1.000	Ea.	203	85	288
Conduit box for inverter	1.000	Ea.	69	85	154
Low voltage disconnect	1.000	Ea.	63	85	148
Vented battery enclosure, wood	1.000	Ea.	248	300	548
Grounding, rod, copper clad, 8' long, 5/8" diameter	1.000	Ea.	21.50	123	144.50
Grounding, clamp, bronze, 5/8" dia	1.000	Ea.	4.93	21	25.93
Bare copper wire, stranded, #8	1.000	C.L.F.	28	61.50	89.50
Wire, 600 volt, type THW, copper, stranded, #12	3.600	C.L.F.	49.68	221.40	271.08
Wire, 600 volt, type THW, copper, stranded, #10	1.050	C.L.F.	23.10	71.40	94.50
Cond to 10' H,incl 2 termn,2 elb&11 bm CLP per 100',galv stl,1/2" dia	120.000	L.F.	330	906	1,236
Conduit,to 10' H,incl 2 termn,2 elb&11 bm clp per 100',(EMT), 1" dia	30.000	L.F.	54.30	177	231.30
Lightning surge suppressor	1.000	Ea.	56	21	77
General duty 240 volt, 2 pole, nonfusible, NEMA 3R, 60 amp	1.000	Ea.	196	295	491
Load centers, 3 wire, 120/240V, 100 amp main lugs, indoor, 8 circuits	2.000	Ea.	276	970	1,246
Circuit breaker, Plug-in, 120/240 volt, to 60 amp, 1 pole	5.000	Ea.	54.50	282.50	337
Fuses, dual element, time delay, 250 volt, 50 amp	2.000	Ea.	25.10	27.10	52.20
TOTAL			12,430.31	7,613.40	20,043.71

D5090 Other Electrical Systems

D5090 420	Photovoltaic Power System, Stand Alone	COST EACH		
		MAT.	INST.	TOTAL
0050	24 V capacity, 900 W (~102 SF)			
0100	Roof mounted, on wood framing	12,400	7,625	20,025
0150	with standoff	12,600	7,625	20,225
0200	Ground placement, ballast, fixed	17,300	8,175	25,475
0250	Adjustable	17,600	8,175	25,775
0300	Top of pole, passive tracking	17,400	8,175	25,575
0350	1.8 kW (~204 SF)			
0400	Roof mounted, on wood framing	20,300	12,100	32,400
0450	with standoff	20,500	12,100	32,600
0500	Ground placement, ballast, fixed	29,200	11,400	40,600
0550	Adjustable	29,800	11,400	41,200
0600	Top of pole, passive tracking	30,300	11,400	41,700
0650	3.2 kW (~408 SF)			
0700	Roof mounted, on wood framing	36,300	20,800	57,100
0750	with standoff	36,800	20,800	57,600
0800	Ground placement, ballast, fixed	53,000	17,700	70,700
0850	Adjustable	54,500	17,700	72,200
0900	Top of pole, passive tracking	55,500	17,600	73,100

For customer support on your Electrical Costs with RSMeans Data, call 800.448.8182.

Photovoltaic Modules →

Photovoltaic power system, grid connected 10 kW

Combiner Box

DC Disconnect

Inverter

AC Disconnect

Isolation Transformer

Utility Connection

System Components	QUANTITY	UNIT	COST EACH		
			MAT.	INST.	TOTAL
SYSTEM D5090 430 0100					
PHOTOVOLTAIC POWER SYSTEM, GRID CONNECTED 10 kW					
Photovoltaic module, 150 watt, 33 volts	60.000	Ea.	26,100	5,100	31,200
PV rack system, roof, non-penetrating ballast, 1 panel	60.000	Ea.	64,500	2,400	66,900
DC to AC inverter for, 24 V, 4,000 watt	3.000	Ea.	8,325	1,020	9,345
Combiner box 10 lug, NEMA 3R	1.000	Ea.	297	170	467
15 amp fuses	10.000	Ea.	235	169.50	404.50
Safety switch, 60 amp	1.000	Ea.	320	310	630
Safety switch, 100 amp	1.000	Ea.	600	375	975
Utility connection, 3 pole breaker	1.000	Ea.	253	109	362
Fuse, 60 A	3.000	Ea.	38.40	40.65	79.05
Fuse, 100 A	3.000	Ea.	93	50.85	143.85
10 kVA isolation tranformer	1.000	Ea.	1,875	850	2,725
EMT Conduit w/fittings & support	1.000	L.F.	325.80	1,062	1,387.80
RGS Conduit w/fittings & support	267.000	L.F.	2,095.95	2,790.15	4,886.10
Enclosure 24" x 24" x 10", NEMA 4	1.000	Ea.	5,400	1,350	6,750
Wire, 600 volt, type THWN-THHN, copper, stranded, #6	8.000	C.L.F.	424	832	1,256
Wire, 600 volt, copper type XLPE-USE(RHW), stranded, #12	18.000	C.L.F.	357.30	1,107	1,464.30
Grounding, bare copper wire stranded, 4/0	2.000	C.L.F.	750	476	1,226
Grounding, exothermic weld, 4/0 wire to building steel	4.000	Ea.	45.20	388	433.20
Grounding, brazed connections, #6 wire	2.000	Ea.	36.30	113	149.30
Insulated ground wire, copper, #6	.400	C.L.F.	21.20	41.60	62.80
TOTAL			112,092.15	18,754.75	130,846.90

D5090 430	Photovoltaic Power System, Grid Connected	COST EACH		
		MAT.	INST.	TOTAL
0050	10 kW			
0100	Roof mounted, non-penetrating ballast	112,000	18,800	130,800
0200	Penetrating surface mount, on steel framing	51,500	30,600	82,100
0300	on wood framing	51,500	23,000	74,500
0400	with standoff	52,000	23,100	75,100
0500	Ground placement, ballast, fixed	72,000	18,700	90,700
0600	adjustable	73,500	18,700	92,200
0700	Top of pole, passive tracking	74,000	19,200	93,200
1050	20 kW			
1100	Roof mounted, non-penetrating ballast	216,500	31,400	247,900
1200	Penetrating surface mount, on steel framing	95,000	55,000	150,000
1300	on wood framing	95,000	39,900	134,900
1400	with standoff	96,000	39,900	135,900
1500	Ground placement, ballast, fixed	136,000	30,200	166,200
1600	adjustable	139,000	30,200	169,200
1700	Top of pole, passive tracking	139,500	31,200	170,700

D5090 Other Electrical Systems

System Components	QUANTITY	UNIT	COST EACH		
			MAT.	INST.	TOTAL
SYSTEM D5090 480 1100					
ELECTRICAL, SINGLE PHASE, 1 METER					
#18 twisted shielded pair in 1/2" EMT conduit	.050	C.L.F.	8.20	11.30	19.50
Wire, 600 volt, type THW, copper, solid, #12	.150	C.L.F.	1.76	9.23	10.99
Conduit (EMT) , to 10' H, incl 2 termn,2 elb&11 bm clp per 100', 3/4"	5.000	L.F.	5.40	26	31.40
Outlet boxes, pressed steel, handy box	1.000	Ea.	2.70	25	27.70
Outlet boxes, pressed steel, handy box, covers, device	1.000	Ea.	.96	10.60	11.56
Wiring devices, receptacle, duplex, 120 volt, ground, 20 amp	1.000	Ea.	8.70	25	33.70
Single phase, 277 volt, 200 amp	1.000	Ea.	450	77.50	527.50
Data recorder, 8 meters	1.000	Ea.	1,750	62	1,812
Software package, per meter, premium	1.000	Ea.	750		750
TOTAL			2,977.72	246.63	3,224.35

D5090 480	Energy Monitoring Systems	COST EACH		
		MAT.	INST.	TOTAL
1000	Electrical			
1100	Single phase, 1 meter	2,975	247	3,222
1110	4 meters	7,375	1,875	9,250
1120	8 meters	14,800	3,850	18,650
1200	Three phase, 1 meter	3,400	315	3,715
1210	5 meters	11,200	2,925	14,125
1220	10 meters	22,800	5,975	28,775
1230	25 meters	54,000	11,900	65,900
2000	Mechanical			
2100	BTU, 1 meter	3,750	910	4,660
2110	w/1 duct sensor	3,950	1,125	5,075
2120	& 1 space sensor	4,475	1,275	5,750
2130	& 5 space sensors	6,575	1,875	8,450
2140	& 10 space sensors	11,900	2,650	14,550
2200	BTU, 3 meters	7,725	2,600	10,325
2210	w/3 duct sensors	8,350	3,250	11,600
2220	& 3 space sensors	9,925	3,700	13,625
2230	& 15 space sensors	16,200	5,500	21,700
2240	& 30 space sensors	26,800	7,800	34,600
9000	Front end display	530	133	663
9100	Computer workstation	1,475	1,750	3,225

D5090 Other Electrical Systems

Low Density and Medium Density Baseboard Radiation

The costs shown in Table below are based on the following system considerations:

1. The heat loss per square foot is based on approximately 34 BTU/hr. per S.F. of floor or 10 watts per S.F. of floor.
2. Baseboard radiation is based on the low watt density type rated 187 watts per L.F. and the medium density type rated 250 watts per L.F.
3. Thermostat is not included.
4. Wiring costs include branch circuit wiring.

System Components	QUANTITY	UNIT	COST PER S.F.		
			MAT.	INST.	TOTAL
SYSTEM D5090 510 1000					
ELECTRIC BASEBOARD RADIATION, LOW DENSITY, 900 S.F., 31 MBH, 9 kW					
Electric baseboard radiator, 5' long 935 watt	.011	Ea.	.52	1.31	1.83
Steel intermediate conduit, (IMC) 1/2" diam	.170	L.F.	.41	1.16	1.57
Wire 600 volt, type THW, copper, solid, #12	.005	C.L.F.	.06	.31	.37
TOTAL			.99	2.78	3.77

D5090 510	Electric Baseboard Radiation (Low Density)	COST PER S.F.		
		MAT.	INST.	TOTAL
1000	Electric baseboard radiation, low density, 900 S.F., 31 MBH, 9 kW	.99	2.78	3.77
1200	1500 S.F., 51 MBH, 15 kW	.97	2.71	3.68
1400	2100 S.F., 72 MBH, 21 kW	.87	2.43	3.30
1600	3000 S.F., 102 MBH, 30 kW	.79	2.21	3
2000	Medium density, 900 S.F., 31 MBH, 9 kW	.89	2.54	3.43
2200	1500 S.F., 51 MBH, 15 kW	.87	2.47	3.34
2400	2100 S.F., 72 MBH, 21 kW	.82	2.31	3.13
2600	3000 S.F., 102 MBH, 30 kW	.75	2.09	2.84

D5090 Other Electrical Systems

Commercial Duty Baseboard Radiation
The costs shown in Table below are
based on the following system
considerations:

1. The heat loss per square foot is based
   on approximately 41 BTU/hr. per
   S.F. of floor or 12 watts per S.F.
2. The baseboard radiation is of the
   commercial duty type rated 250
   watts per L.F. served by 277 volt,
   single phase power.
3. Thermostat is not included.
4. Wiring costs include branch circuit
   wiring.

System Components	QUANTITY	UNIT	COST PER S.F. MAT.	COST PER S.F. INST.	COST PER S.F. TOTAL
SYSTEM D5090 520 1000					
ELECTRIC BASEBOARD RADIATION, MEDIUM DENSITY, 1230 S.F., 51 MBH, 15 kW					
Electric baseboard radiator, 5' long	.013	Ea.	.61	1.55	2.16
Steel intermediate conduit, (IMC) 1/2" diam	.154	L.F.	.37	1.05	1.42
Wire 600 volt, type THW, copper, solid, #12	.004	C.L.F.	.05	.25	.30
TOTAL			1.03	2.85	3.88

D5090 520	Electric Baseboard Radiation (Medium Density)	COST PER S.F. MAT.	COST PER S.F. INST.	COST PER S.F. TOTAL
1000	Electric baseboard radiation, medium density, 1230 SF, 51 MBH, 15 kW	1.03	2.85	3.88
1200	2500 S.F. floor area, 106 MBH, 31 kW	.96	2.67	3.63
1400	3700 S.F. floor area, 157 MBH, 46 kW	.93	2.59	3.52
1600	4800 S.F. floor area, 201 MBH, 59 kW	.87	2.40	3.27
1800	11,300 S.F. floor area, 464 MBH, 136 kW	.81	2.19	3
2000	30,000 S.F. floor area, 1229 MBH, 360 kW	.79	2.14	2.93

G10 Site Preparation

G1030 Site Earthwork

Trenching Systems are shown on a cost per linear foot basis. The systems include: excavation; backfill and removal of spoil; and compaction for various depths and trench bottom widths. The backfill has been reduced to accommodate a pipe of suitable diameter and bedding.

The slope for trench sides varies from none to 1:1.

The Expanded System Listing shows Trenching Systems that range from 2' to 12' in width. Depths range from 2' to 25'.

System Components			COST PER L.F.		
	QUANTITY	UNIT	EQUIP.	LABOR	TOTAL
SYSTEM G1030 805 1310					
TRENCHING COMMON EARTH, NO SLOPE, 2' WIDE, 2' DP, 3/8 C.Y. BUCKET					
Excavation, trench, hyd. backhoe, track mtd., 3/8 C.Y. bucket	.148	B.C.Y.	.40	1.11	1.51
Backfill and load spoil, from stockpile	.153	L.C.Y.	.13	.34	.47
Compaction by vibrating plate, 6" lifts, 4 passes	.118	E.C.Y.	.03	.40	.43
Remove excess spoil, 8 C.Y. dump truck, 2 mile roundtrip	.040	L.C.Y.	.14	.18	.32
TOTAL			.70	2.03	2.73

G1030 805	Trenching Common Earth	COST PER L.F.		
		EQUIP.	LABOR	TOTAL
1310	Trenching, common earth, no slope, 2' wide, 2' deep, 3/8 C.Y. bucket	.70	2.03	2.73
1320	3' deep, 3/8 C.Y. bucket	1.01	3.07	4.08
1330	4' deep, 3/8 C.Y. bucket	1.31	4.08	5.39
1340	6' deep, 3/8 C.Y. bucket	1.67	5.30	6.97
1350	8' deep, 1/2 C.Y. bucket	2.23	7.05	9.28
1360	10' deep, 1 C.Y. bucket	3.54	8.40	11.94
1400	4' wide, 2' deep, 3/8 C.Y. bucket	1.59	4.05	5.64
1410	3' deep, 3/8 C.Y. bucket	2.19	6.10	8.29
1420	4' deep, 1/2 C.Y. bucket	2.53	6.85	9.38
1430	6' deep, 1/2 C.Y. bucket	4.13	11	15.13
1440	8' deep, 1/2 C.Y. bucket	6.75	14.25	21
1450	10' deep, 1 C.Y. bucket	8.15	17.65	25.80
1460	12' deep, 1 C.Y. bucket	10.55	22.50	33.05
1470	15' deep, 1-1/2 C.Y. bucket	9.20	20	29.20
1480	18' deep, 2-1/2 C.Y. bucket	13	28	41
1520	6' wide, 6' deep, 5/8 C.Y. bucket w/trench box	8.65	16.40	25.05
1530	8' deep, 3/4 C.Y. bucket	11.45	21.50	32.95
1540	10' deep, 1 C.Y. bucket	11.45	22.50	33.95
1550	12' deep, 1-1/2 C.Y. bucket	12.10	24	36.10
1560	16' deep, 2-1/2 C.Y. bucket	16.70	30	46.70
1570	20' deep, 3-1/2 C.Y. bucket	22	35.50	57.50
1580	24' deep, 3-1/2 C.Y. bucket	26	43	69
1640	8' wide, 12' deep, 1-1/2 C.Y. bucket w/trench box	16.85	30.50	47.35
1650	15' deep, 1-1/2 C.Y. bucket	22	40	62
1660	18' deep, 2-1/2 C.Y. bucket	24	40	64
1680	24' deep, 3-1/2 C.Y. bucket	35.50	55.50	91
1730	10' wide, 20' deep, 3-1/2 C.Y. bucket w/trench box	28.50	53	81.50
1740	24' deep, 3-1/2 C.Y. bucket	42.50	63.50	106
1780	12' wide, 20' deep, 3-1/2 C.Y. bucket w/trench box	45	67	112
1790	25' deep, bucket	55.50	85.50	141
1800	1/2 to 1 slope, 2' wide, 2' deep, 3/8 C.Y. bucket	1.01	3.07	4.08
1810	3' deep, 3/8 C.Y. bucket	1.68	5.35	7.03

G1030 Site Earthwork

G1030 805	Trenching Common Earth	COST PER L.F.		
		EQUIP.	LABOR	TOTAL
1820	4' deep, 3/8 C.Y. bucket	2.52	8.20	10.72
1840	6' deep, 3/8 C.Y. bucket	4.04	13.30	17.34
1860	8' deep, 1/2 C.Y. bucket	6.40	21	27.40
1880	10' deep, 1 C.Y. bucket	12.20	29.50	41.70
2300	4' wide, 2' deep, 3/8 C.Y. bucket	1.89	5.05	6.94
2310	3' deep, 3/8 C.Y. bucket	2.86	8.40	11.26
2320	4' deep, 1/2 C.Y. bucket	3.59	10.35	13.94
2340	6' deep, 1/2 C.Y. bucket	6.95	19.50	26.45
2360	8' deep, 1/2 C.Y. bucket	13.10	28.50	41.60
2380	10' deep, 1 C.Y. bucket	18.15	40.50	58.65
2400	12' deep, 1 C.Y. bucket	24.50	54.50	79
2430	15' deep, 1-1/2 C.Y. bucket	26	58.50	84.50
2460	18' deep, 2-1/2 C.Y. bucket	46	91.50	137.50
2840	6' wide, 6' deep, 5/8 C.Y. bucket w/trench box	12.80	24.50	37.30
2860	8' deep, 3/4 C.Y. bucket	18.55	36.50	55.05
2880	10' deep, 1 C.Y. bucket	18.20	37	55.20
2900	12' deep, 1-1/2 C.Y. bucket	23	48.50	71.50
2940	16' deep, 2-1/2 C.Y. bucket	38	71	109
2980	20' deep, 3-1/2 C.Y. bucket	55	96	151
3020	24' deep, 3-1/2 C.Y. bucket	78	131	209
3100	8' wide, 12' deep, 1-1/2 C.Y. bucket w/trench box	28.50	55.50	84
3120	15' deep, 1-1/2 C.Y. bucket	41	80.50	121.50
3140	18' deep, 2-1/2 C.Y. bucket	52.50	95.50	148
3180	24' deep, 3-1/2 C.Y. bucket	87	144	231
3270	10' wide, 20' deep, 3-1/2 C.Y. bucket w/trench box	56	111	167
3280	24' deep, 3-1/2 C.Y. bucket	96	157	253
3370	12' wide, 20' deep, 3-1/2 C.Y. bucket w/trench box	81	128	209
3380	25' deep, 3-1/2 C.Y. bucket	112	183	295
3500	1 to 1 slope, 2' wide, 2' deep, 3/8 C.Y. bucket	1.31	4.08	5.39
3520	3' deep, 3/8 C.Y. bucket	3.66	9.30	12.96
3540	4' deep, 3/8 C.Y. bucket	3.71	12.30	16.01
3560	6' deep, 1/2 C.Y. bucket	4.04	13.30	17.34
3580	8' deep, 1/2 C.Y. bucket	8	26.50	34.50
3600	10' deep, 1 C.Y. bucket	21	51	72
3800	4' wide, 2' deep, 3/8 C.Y. bucket	2.19	6.10	8.29
3820	3' deep, 3/8 C.Y. bucket	3.54	10.70	14.24
3840	4' deep, 1/2 C.Y. bucket	4.64	13.90	18.54
3860	6' deep, 1/2 C.Y. bucket	9.80	28	37.80
3880	8' deep, 1/2 C.Y. bucket	19.50	43.50	63
3900	10' deep, 1 C.Y. bucket	28	63	91
3920	12' deep, 1 C.Y. bucket	41.50	91	132.50
3940	15' deep, 1-1/2 C.Y. bucket	43	97	140
3960	18' deep, 2-1/2 C.Y. bucket	63	126	189
4030	6' wide, 6' deep, 5/8 C.Y. bucket w/trench box	16.80	32.50	49.30
4040	8' deep, 3/4 C.Y. bucket	24.50	45	69.50
4050	10' deep, 1 C.Y. bucket	26.50	54.50	81
4060	12' deep, 1-1/2 C.Y. bucket	35.50	74	109.50
4070	16' deep, 2-1/2 C.Y. bucket	60	113	173
4080	20' deep, 3-1/2 C.Y. bucket	89	156	245
4090	24' deep, 3-1/2 C.Y. bucket	130	220	350
4500	8' wide, 12' deep, 1-1/2 C.Y. bucket w/trench box	40	80.50	120.50
4550	15' deep, 1-1/2 C.Y. bucket	60.50	121	181.50
4600	18' deep, 2-1/2 C.Y. bucket	80	148	228
4650	24' deep, 3-1/2 C.Y. bucket	139	232	371
4800	10' wide, 20' deep, 3-1/2 C.Y. bucket w/trench box	83.50	168	251.50
4850	24' deep, 3-1/2 C.Y. bucket	148	245	393
4950	12' wide, 20' deep, 3-1/2 C.Y. bucket w/trench box	117	190	307
4980	25' deep, 3-1/2 C.Y. bucket	168	277	445

443

For customer support on your Electrical Costs with RSMeans Data, call 800.448.8182.

G1030 Site Earthwork

Trenching Systems are shown on a cost per linear foot basis. The systems include: excavation; backfill and removal of spoil; and compaction for various depths and trench bottom widths. The backfill has been reduced to accommodate a pipe of suitable diameter and bedding.

The slope for trench sides varies from none to 1:1.

The Expanded System Listing shows Trenching Systems that range from 2' to 12' in width. Depths range from 2' to 25'.

System Components	QUANTITY	UNIT	COST PER L.F. EQUIP.	COST PER L.F. LABOR	COST PER L.F. TOTAL
SYSTEM G1030 806 1310					
TRENCHING LOAM & SANDY CLAY, NO SLOPE, 2' WIDE, 2' DP, 3/8 C.Y. BUCKET					
Excavation, trench, hyd. backhoe, track mtd., 3/8 C.Y. bucket	.148	B.C.Y.	.37	1.03	1.40
Backfill and load spoil, from stockpile	.165	L.C.Y.	.14	.37	.51
Compaction by vibrating plate 18" wide, 6" lifts, 4 passes	.118	E.C.Y.	.03	.40	.43
Remove excess spoil, 8 C.Y. dump truck, 2 mile roundtrip	.042	L.C.Y.	.15	.19	.34
TOTAL			.69	1.99	2.68

G1030 806	Trenching Loam & Sandy Clay	COST PER L.F. EQUIP.	COST PER L.F. LABOR	COST PER L.F. TOTAL
1310	Trenching, loam & sandy clay, no slope, 2' wide, 2' deep, 3/8 C.Y. bucket	.69	1.99	2.68
1320	3' deep, 3/8 C.Y. bucket	1.09	3.28	4.37
1330	4' deep, 3/8 C.Y. bucket	1.28	3.99	5.25
1340	6' deep, 3/8 C.Y. bucket	1.85	4.76	6.60
1350	8' deep, 1/2 C.Y. bucket	2.45	6.30	8.75
1360	10' deep, 1 C.Y. bucket	2.67	6.70	9.35
1400	4' wide, 2' deep, 3/8 C.Y. bucket	1.59	3.98	5.55
1410	3' deep, 3/8 C.Y. bucket	2.18	6	8.20
1420	4' deep, 1/2 C.Y. bucket	2.52	6.70	9.20
1430	6' deep, 1/2 C.Y. bucket	4.49	9.90	14.40
1440	8' deep, 1/2 C.Y. bucket	6.60	14	20.50
1450	10' deep, 1 C.Y. bucket	6.45	14.30	21
1460	12' deep, 1 C.Y. bucket	8.10	17.85	26
1470	15' deep, 1-1/2 C.Y. bucket	9.60	21	30.50
1480	18' deep, 2-1/2 C.Y. bucket	11.40	23	34.50
1520	6' wide, 6' deep, 5/8 C.Y. bucket w/trench box	8.40	16.15	24.50
1530	8' deep, 3/4 C.Y. bucket	11.10	21	32
1540	10' deep, 1 C.Y. bucket	10.55	21.50	32
1550	12' deep, 1-1/2 C.Y. bucket	11.85	24	36
1560	16' deep, 2-1/2 C.Y. bucket	16.35	30.50	47
1570	20' deep, 3-1/2 C.Y. bucket	20.50	35.50	56
1580	24' deep, 3-1/2 C.Y. bucket	25.50	43.50	69
1640	8' wide, 12' deep, 1-1/4 C.Y. bucket w/trench box	16.65	30.50	47
1650	15' deep, 1-1/2 C.Y. bucket	20.50	39	59.50
1660	18' deep, 2-1/2 C.Y. bucket	25	43.50	68.50
1680	24' deep, 3-1/2 C.Y. bucket	34.50	56.50	91
1730	10' wide, 20' deep, 3-1/2 C.Y. bucket w/trench box	34.50	56.50	91
1740	24' deep, 3-1/2 C.Y. bucket	43.50	69.50	113
1780	12' wide, 20' deep, 3-1/2 C.Y. bucket w/trench box	42	67	109
1790	25' deep, 3-1/2 C.Y. bucket	54.50	86.50	141
1800	1/2:1 slope, 2' wide, 2' deep, 3/8 C.Y. bucket	.98	2.99	3.97
1810	3' deep, 3/8 C.Y. bucket	1.64	5.25	6.90
1820	4' deep, 3/8 C.Y. bucket	2.46	8	10.45
1840	6' deep, 3/8 C.Y. bucket	4.45	11.90	16.35

G1030 Site Earthwork

G1030 806	Trenching Loam & Sandy Clay	COST PER L.F.		
		EQUIP.	LABOR	TOTAL
1860	8' deep, 1/2 C.Y. bucket	7.10	19	26
1880	10' deep, 1 C.Y. bucket	9.15	24	33
2300	4' wide, 2' deep, 3/8 C.Y. bucket	1.88	4.97	6.85
2310	3' deep, 3/8 C.Y. bucket	2.83	8.25	11.10
2320	4' deep, 1/2 C.Y. bucket	3.56	10.15	13.70
2340	6' deep, 1/2 C.Y. bucket	7.55	17.55	25
2360	8' deep, 1/2 C.Y. bucket	12.75	28.50	41.50
2380	10' deep, 1 C.Y. bucket	14.20	33	47
2400	12' deep, 1 C.Y. bucket	24	54.50	78.50
2430	15' deep, 1-1/2 C.Y. bucket	27	60.50	87.50
2460	18' deep, 2-1/2 C.Y. bucket	45	92.50	138
2840	6' wide, 6' deep, 5/8 C.Y. bucket w/trench box	12.25	24.50	37
2860	8' deep, 3/4 C.Y. bucket	17.90	35.50	53.50
2880	10' deep, 1 C.Y. bucket	18.95	40	59
2900	12' deep, 1-1/2 C.Y. bucket	23	49	72
2940	16' deep, 2-1/2 C.Y. bucket	37.50	72	110
2980	20' deep, 3-1/2 C.Y. bucket	53.50	97.50	151
3020	24' deep, 3-1/2 C.Y. bucket	75.50	133	209
3100	8' wide, 12' deep, 1-1/2 C.Y. bucket w/trench box	28	55.50	83.50
3120	15' deep, 1-1/2 C.Y. bucket	38	78	116
3140	18' deep, 2-1/2 C.Y. bucket	51.50	96.50	148
3180	24' deep, 3-1/2 C.Y. bucket	84.50	146	231
3270	10' wide, 20' deep, 3-1/2 C.Y. bucket w/trench box	68	118	186
3280	24' deep, 3-1/2 C.Y. bucket	93.50	159	253
3320	12' wide, 20' deep, 3-1/2 C.Y. bucket w/trench box	75	129	204
3380	25' deep, 3-1/2 C.Y. bucket w/trench box	102	173	275
3500	1:1 slope, 2' wide, 2' deep, 3/8 C.Y. bucket	1.28	3.99	5.25
3520	3' deep, 3/8 C.Y. bucket	2.30	7.50	9.80
3540	4' deep, 3/8 C.Y. bucket	3.61	12	15.60
3560	6' deep, 1/2 C.Y. bucket	4.45	11.90	16.35
3580	8' deep, 1/2 C.Y. bucket	11.70	31.50	43
3600	10' deep, 1 C.Y. bucket	15.60	41	56.50
3800	4' wide, 2' deep, 3/8 C.Y. bucket	2.18	6	8.20
3820	3' deep, 1/2 C.Y. bucket	3.49	10.50	14
3840	4' deep, 1/2 C.Y. bucket	4.59	13.65	18.25
3860	6' deep, 1/2 C.Y. bucket	10.65	25	35.50
3880	8' deep, 1/2 C.Y. bucket	18.95	42.50	61.50
3900	10' deep, 1 C.Y. bucket	22	51.50	73.50
3920	12' deep, 1 C.Y. bucket	31.50	73	105
3940	15' deep, 1-1/2 C.Y. bucket	44.50	101	146
3960	18' deep, 2-1/2 C.Y. bucket	62	128	190
4030	6' wide, 6' deep, 5/8 C.Y. bucket w/trench box	16.10	32.50	48.50
4040	8' deep, 3/4 C.Y. bucket	24.50	50.50	75
4050	10' deep, 1 C.Y. bucket	27.50	59	86.50
4060	12' deep, 1-1/2 C.Y. bucket	34.50	74	109
4070	16' deep, 2-1/2 C.Y. bucket	58.50	114	173
4080	20' deep, 3-1/2 C.Y. bucket	86.50	159	246
4090	24' deep, 3-1/2 C.Y. bucket	126	223	350
4500	8' wide, 12' deep, 1-1/4 C.Y. bucket w/trench box	39.50	80.50	120
4550	15' deep, 1-1/2 C.Y. bucket	56	117	173
4600	18' deep, 2-1/2 C.Y. bucket	78	149	227
4650	24' deep, 3-1/2 C.Y. bucket	135	236	370
4800	10' wide, 20' deep, 3-1/2 C.Y. bucket w/trench box	101	180	281
4850	24' deep, 3-1/2 C.Y. bucket	144	249	395
4950	12' wide, 20' deep, 3-1/2 C.Y. bucket w/trench box	108	190	298
4980	25' deep, 3-1/2 C.Y. bucket	163	281	445

G10 Site Preparation

G1030 Site Earthwork

Trenching Systems are shown on a cost per linear foot basis. The systems include: excavation; backfill and removal of spoil; and compaction for various depths and trench bottom widths. The backfill has been reduced to accommodate a pipe of suitable diameter and bedding.

The slope for trench sides varies from none to 1:1.

The Expanded System Listing shows Trenching Systems that range from 2' to 12' in width. Depths range from 2' to 25'.

System Components	QUANTITY	UNIT	COST PER L.F.		
			EQUIP.	LABOR	TOTAL
SYSTEM G1030 807 1310					
TRENCHING SAND & GRAVEL, NO SLOPE, 2' WIDE, 2' DEEP, 3/8 C.Y. BUCKET					
Excavation, trench, hyd. backhoe, track mtd., 3/8 C.Y. bucket	.148	B.C.Y.	.36	1.01	1.37
Backfill and load spoil, from stockpile	.140	L.C.Y.	.12	.31	.43
Compaction by vibrating plate 18" wide, 6" lifts, 4 passes	.118	E.C.Y.	.03	.40	.43
Remove excess spoil, 8 C.Y. dump truck, 2 mile roundtrip	.035	L.C.Y.	.13	.16	.29
TOTAL			.64	1.88	2.52

G1030 807	Trenching Sand & Gravel	COST PER L.F.		
		EQUIP.	LABOR	TOTAL
1310	Trenching, sand & gravel, no slope, 2' wide, 2' deep, 3/8 C.Y. bucket	.64	1.88	2.52
1320	3' deep, 3/8 C.Y. bucket	1.03	3.15	4.18
1330	4' deep, 3/8 C.Y. bucket	1.19	3.80	4.99
1340	6' deep, 3/8 C.Y. bucket	1.75	4.53	6.30
1350	8' deep, 1/2 C.Y. bucket	2.32	6	8.30
1360	10' deep, 1 C.Y. bucket	2.49	6.30	8.80
1400	4' wide, 2' deep, 3/8 C.Y. bucket	1.44	3.75	5.20
1410	3' deep, 3/8 C.Y. bucket	1.99	5.65	7.65
1420	4' deep, 1/2 C.Y. bucket	2.31	6.35	8.65
1430	6' deep, 1/2 C.Y. bucket	4.25	9.45	13.70
1440	8' deep, 1/2 C.Y. bucket	6.20	13.30	19.50
1450	10' deep, 1 C.Y. bucket	6.10	13.55	19.65
1460	12' deep, 1 C.Y. bucket	7.65	16.85	24.50
1470	15' deep, 1-1/2 C.Y. bucket	9.05	19.60	28.50
1480	18' deep, 2-1/2 C.Y. bucket	10.75	21.50	32.50
1520	6' wide, 6' deep, 5/8 C.Y. bucket w/trench box	7.90	15.25	23
1530	8' deep, 3/4 C.Y. bucket	10.50	20	30.50
1540	10' deep, 1 C.Y. bucket	9.95	20	30
1550	12' deep, 1-1/2 C.Y. bucket	11.15	22.50	33.50
1560	16' deep, 2 C.Y. bucket	15.55	28.50	44
1570	20' deep, 3-1/2 C.Y. bucket	19.15	33.50	52.50
1580	24' deep, 3-1/2 C.Y. bucket	24	41	65
1640	8' wide, 12' deep, 1-1/2 C.Y. bucket w/trench box	15.60	28.50	44
1650	15' deep, 1-1/2 C.Y. bucket	19	36.50	55.50
1660	18' deep, 2-1/2 C.Y. bucket	23.50	41	64.50
1680	24' deep, 3-1/2 C.Y. bucket	32.50	53	85.50
1730	10' wide, 20' deep, 3-1/2 C.Y. bucket w/trench box	32.50	53	85.50
1740	24' deep, 3-1/2 C.Y. bucket	41	65.50	107
1780	12' wide, 20' deep, 3-1/2 C.Y. bucket w/trench box	39.50	62.50	102
1790	25' deep, 3-1/2 C.Y. bucket	51	81	132
1800	1/2:1 slope, 2' wide, 2' deep, 3/8 C.Y. bucket	.92	2.84	3.76
1810	3' deep, 3/8 C.Y. bucket	1.53	4.99	6.50
1820	4' deep, 3/8 C.Y. bucket	2.30	7.60	9.90
1840	6' deep, 3/8 C.Y. bucket	4.24	11.35	15.60

G1030 Site Earthwork

G1030 807	Trenching Sand & Gravel	COST PER L.F.		
		EQUIP.	LABOR	TOTAL
1860	8' deep, 1/2 C.Y. bucket	6.75	18.15	25
1880	10' deep, 1 C.Y. bucket	8.55	22.50	31
2300	4' wide, 2' deep, 3/8 C.Y. bucket	1.72	4.71	6.45
2310	3' deep, 3/8 C.Y. bucket	2.61	7.80	10.40
2320	4' deep, 1/2 C.Y. bucket	3.27	9.65	12.90
2340	6' deep, 1/2 C.Y. bucket	7.20	16.80	24
2360	8' deep, 1/2 C.Y. bucket	12.10	27	39
2380	10' deep, 1 C.Y. bucket	13.45	31	44.50
2400	12' deep, 1 C.Y. bucket	22.50	51.50	74
2430	15' deep, 1-1/2 C.Y. bucket	25.50	57.50	83
2460	18' deep, 2-1/2 C.Y. bucket	42.50	87	130
2840	6' wide, 6' deep, 5/8 C.Y. bucket w/trench box	11.60	23	34.50
2860	8' deep, 3/4 C.Y. bucket	17	34	51
2880	10' deep, 1 C.Y. bucket	17.90	38	56
2900	12' deep, 1-1/2 C.Y. bucket	22	46.50	68.50
2940	16' deep, 2 C.Y. bucket	35.50	68	104
2980	20' deep, 3-1/2 C.Y. bucket	50.50	91.50	142
3020	24' deep, 3-1/2 C.Y. bucket	71.50	125	197
3100	8' wide, 12' deep, 1-1/4 C.Y. bucket w/trench box	26.50	52.50	79
3120	15' deep, 1-1/2 C.Y. bucket	36	73.50	110
3140	18' deep, 2-1/2 C.Y. bucket	48.50	91	140
3180	24' deep, 3-1/2 C.Y. bucket	80	137	217
3270	10' wide, 20' deep, 3-1/2 C.Y. bucket w/trench box	64	111	175
3280	24' deep, 3-1/2 C.Y. bucket	88.50	150	239
3370	12' wide, 20' deep, 3-1/2 C.Y. bucket w/trench box	71.50	123	195
3380	25' deep, 3-1/2 C.Y. bucket	103	173	276
3500	1:1 slope, 2' wide, 2' deep, 3/8 C.Y. bucket	1.99	4.76	6.75
3520	3' deep, 3/8 C.Y. bucket	2.16	7.15	9.30
3540	4' deep, 3/8 C.Y. bucket	3.39	11.45	14.85
3560	6' deep, 3/8 C.Y. bucket	4.24	11.35	15.60
3580	8' deep, 1/2 C.Y. bucket	11.15	30.50	41.50
3600	10' deep, 1 C.Y. bucket	14.65	38.50	53
3800	4' wide, 2' deep, 3/8 C.Y. bucket	1.99	5.65	7.65
3820	3' deep, 3/8 C.Y. bucket	3.23	9.95	13.20
3840	4' deep, 1/2 C.Y. bucket	4.24	13	17.25
3860	6' deep, 1/2 C.Y. bucket	10.15	24	34
3880	8' deep, 1/2 C.Y. bucket	17.95	40.50	58.50
3900	10' deep, 1 C.Y. bucket	21	48.50	69.50
3920	12' deep, 1 C.Y. bucket	30	69	99
3940	15' deep, 1-1/2 C.Y. bucket	42.50	95	138
3960	18' deep, 2-1/2 C.Y. bucket	58.50	120	179
4030	6' wide, 6' deep, 5/8 C.Y. bucket w/trench box	15.25	31	46.50
4040	8' deep, 3/4 C.Y. bucket	23.50	48	71.50
4050	10' deep, 1 C.Y. bucket	26	56	82
4060	12' deep, 1-1/2 C.Y. bucket	32.50	70	103
4070	16' deep, 2 C.Y. bucket	56	108	164
4080	20' deep, 3-1/2 C.Y. bucket	82	149	231
4090	24' deep, 3-1/2 C.Y. bucket	119	209	330
4500	8' wide, 12' deep, 1-1/2 C.Y. bucket w/trench box	37	76.50	114
4550	15' deep, 1-1/2 C.Y. bucket	52.50	111	164
4600	18' deep, 2-1/2 C.Y. bucket	74	141	215
4650	24' deep, 3-1/2 C.Y. bucket	128	221	350
4800	10' wide, 20' deep, 3-1/2 C.Y. bucket w/trench box	95.50	169	265
4850	24' deep, 3-1/2 C.Y. bucket	136	234	370
4950	12' wide, 20' deep, 3-1/2 C.Y. bucket w/trench box	102	178	280
4980	25' deep, 3-1/2 C.Y. bucket	155	264	420

447

For customer support on your Electrical Costs with RSMeans Data, call 800.448.8182.

GROUND SURFACE

BACKFILL

CONCRETE

CONDUIT SUPPORTS

CONDUIT

BEDDING (NATURAL)

UNDERGROUND ELECTRICAL CONDUIT

System Components	QUANTITY	UNIT	COST EACH		
			MAT.	INST.	TOTAL
SYSTEM G4010 312 1000					
2000 AMP UNDERGROUND SERVICE INCLUDING COMMON EARTH EXCAVATION,					
CONCRETE, BACKFILL AND COMPACTION					
Excavate Trench	44.440	B.C.Y.		311.97	311.97
4 inch conduit bank	108.000	L.F.	950.40	2,700	3,650.40
4 inch fitting	8.000	Ea.	340	452	792
4 inch bells	4.000	Ea.	7.12	226	233.12
Concrete material	16.580	C.Y.	2,155.40		2,155.40
Concrete placement	16.580	C.Y.		423.12	423.12
Backfill trench	33.710	L.C.Y.		103.83	103.83
Compact fill material in trench	25.930	E.C.Y.		134.57	134.57
Dispose of excess fill material on-site	24.070	L.C.Y.		297.02	297.02
500 kcmil power cable	18.000	C.L.F.	18,450	7,650	26,100
Wire, 600 volt stranded copper wire, type THW, 1/0	6.000	C.L.F.	1,440	1,236	2,676
TOTAL			23,342.92	13,534.51	36,877.43

G4010 312	Underground Power Feed	COST EACH		
		MAT.	INST.	TOTAL
0900	Underground electrical			
0950	Including common earth excavation, concrete, backfill and compaction			
1000	2000 Amp service, 100' length, 4' depth	23,300	13,600	36,900
1100	1600 Amp service	18,200	10,500	28,700
1200	1200 Amp service	14,300	8,675	22,975
1300	1000 Amp service	11,700	7,950	19,650
1400	800 Amp service	10,200	7,425	17,625
1500	600 Amp service	7,675	6,900	14,575

System Components	QUANTITY	UNIT	COST L.F. MAT.	COST L.F. INST.	COST L.F. TOTAL
SYSTEM G4010 320 1012					
UNDERGROUND ELECTRICAL CONDUIT, 2″ DIAMETER, INCLUDING EXCAVATION,					
CONCRETE, BEDDING, BACKFILL AND COMPACTION					
Excavate Trench	.150	B.C.Y.		1.05	1.05
Base spacer	.200	Ea.	.26	2.42	2.68
Conduit	1.000	L.F.	1.39	3.77	5.16
Concrete material	.050	C.Y.	6.50		6.50
Concrete placement	.050	C.Y.		1.28	1.28
Backfill trench	.120	L.C.Y.		.37	.37
Compact fill material in trench	.100	E.C.Y.		.52	.52
Dispose of excess fill material on-site	.120	L.C.Y.		1.48	1.48
Marking tape	.010	C.L.F.	.39	.03	.42
TOTAL			8.54	10.92	19.46

G4010 320	Underground Electrical Conduit	COST L.F. MAT.	COST L.F. INST.	COST L.F. TOTAL
0950	Underground electrical conduit, including common earth excavation,			
0952	Concrete, bedding, backfill and compaction			
1012	2″ dia. Schedule 40 PVC, 2′ deep	8.55	10.90	19.45
1014	4′ deep	8.55	15.65	24.20
1016	6′ deep	8.55	20	28.55
1022	2 @ 2″ dia. Schedule 40 PVC, 2′ deep	10.20	17.10	27.30
1024	4′ deep	10.20	22	32.20
1026	6′ deep	10.20	26	36.20
1032	3 @ 2″ dia. Schedule 40 PVC, 2′ deep	11.85	23.50	35.35
1034	4′ deep	11.85	28	39.85
1036	6′ deep	11.85	32.50	44.35
1042	4 @ 2″ dia. Schedule 40 PVC, 2′ deep	16.05	29	45.05
1044	4′ deep	16.05	34	50.05
1046	6′ deep	16.05	38.50	54.55

G4010 Electrical Distribution

G4010 320	Underground Electrical Conduit	COST L.F.		
		MAT.	INST.	TOTAL
1062	6 @ 2" dia. Schedule 40 PVC, 2' deep	19.35	41.50	60.85
1064	4' deep	19.35	46.50	65.85
1066	6' deep	19.35	50.50	69.85
1082	8 @ 2" dia. Schedule 40 PVC, 2' deep	22.50	53.50	76
1084	4' deep	22.50	58.50	81
1086	6' deep	22.50	62.50	85
1092	9 @ 2" dia. Schedule 40 PVC, 2' deep	24.50	59.50	84
1094	4' deep	27	64	91
1096	6' deep	27	68.50	95.50
1212	3" dia. Schedule 40 PVC, 2' deep	11.15	13.35	24.50
1214	4' deep	11.15	18.15	29.30
1216	6' deep	11.15	22.50	33.65
1222	2 @ 3" dia. Schedule 40 PVC, 2' deep	12.85	21.50	34.35
1224	4' deep	12.85	26.50	39.35
1226	6' deep	12.85	31	43.85
1232	3 @ 3" dia. Schedule 40 PVC, 2' deep	15.80	30.50	46.30
1234	4' deep	15.80	35	50.80
1236	6' deep	15.80	39.50	55.30
1242	4 @ 3" dia. Schedule 40 PVC, 2' deep	22.50	39	61.50
1244	4' deep	22.50	43.50	66
1246	6' deep	22.50	48	70.50
1262	6 @ 3" dia. Schedule 40 PVC, 2' deep	27.50	56	83.50
1264	4' deep	27.50	60.50	88
1266	6' deep	27.50	65	92.50
1282	8 @ 3" dia. Schedule 40 PVC, 2' deep	33.50	73.50	107
1284	4' deep	33.50	78.50	112
1286	6' deep	33.50	83	116.50
1292	9 @ 3" dia. Schedule 40 PVC, 2' deep	39	83	122
1294	4' deep	40	86.50	126.50
1296	6' deep	40	91	131
1312	4" dia. Schedule 40 PVC, 2' deep	12.25	16.40	28.65
1314	4' deep	12.25	21	33.25
1316	6' deep	12.25	25.50	37.75
1322	2 @ 4" dia. Schedule 40 PVC, 2' deep	16.25	28	44.25
1324	4' deep	16.25	33	49.25
1326	6' deep	16.25	37.50	53.75
1332	3 @ 4" dia. Schedule 40 PVC, 2' deep	19	40	59
1334	4' deep	19	44.50	63.50
1336	6' deep	19	49	68
1342	4 @ 4" dia. Schedule 40 PVC, 2' deep	28	52	80
1344	4' deep	28	56.50	84.50
1346	6' deep	28	61	89
1362	6 @ 4" dia. Schedule 40 PVC, 2' deep	35	75.50	110.50
1364	4' deep	35	79.50	114.50
1366	6' deep	35	84.50	119.50
1382	8 @ 4" dia. Schedule 40 PVC, 2' deep	44.50	99.50	144
1384	4' deep	44.50	104	148.50
1386	6' deep	44.50	110	154.50
1392	9 @ 4" dia. Schedule 40 PVC, 2' deep	49.50	112	161.50
1394	4' deep	49.50	115	164.50
1396	6' deep	49.50	119	168.50
1412	5" dia. Schedule 40 PVC, 2' deep	13.90	19.55	33.45
1414	4' deep	13.90	24.50	38.40
1416	6' deep	13.90	28.50	42.40
1422	2 @ 5" dia. Schedule 40 PVC, 2' deep	19.65	34.50	54.15
1424	4' deep	19.65	39.50	59.15
1426	6' deep	19.65	43.50	63.15
1432	3 @ 5" dia. Schedule 40 PVC, 2' deep	25.50	49.50	75

G4010 Electrical Distribution

G4010 320	Underground Electrical Conduit	COST L.F.		
		MAT.	INST.	TOTAL
1434	4' deep	25.50	54.50	80
1436	6' deep	25.50	59.50	85
1442	4 @ 5" dia. Schedule 40 PVC, 2' deep	35	64	99
1444	4' deep	35	69	104
1446	6' deep	35	73.50	108.50
1462	6 @ 5" dia. Schedule 40 PVC, 2' deep	45.50	94	139.50
1464	4' deep	45.50	98.50	144
1466	6' deep	45.50	104	149.50
1482	8 @ 5" dia. Schedule 40 PVC, 2' deep	59.50	125	184.50
1484	4' deep	59.50	132	191.50
1486	6' deep	59.50	138	197.50
1492	9 @ 5" dia. Schedule 40 PVC, 2' deep	66.50	141	207.50
1494	4' deep	66.50	144	210.50
1496	6' deep	66.50	148	214.50
1512	6" dia. Schedule 40 PVC, 2' deep	17.10	24	41.10
1514	4' deep	17.10	28	45.10
1516	6' deep	17.10	33	50.10
1522	2 @ 6" dia. Schedule 40 PVC, 2' deep	23.50	42.50	66
1524	4' deep	23.50	47	70.50
1526	6' deep	23.50	52	75.50
1532	3 @ 6" dia. Schedule 40 PVC, 2' deep	32.50	62.50	95
1534	4' deep	32.50	68	100.50
1536	6' deep	32.50	74	106.50
1542	4 @ 6" dia. Schedule 40 PVC, 2' deep	42.50	80	122.50
1544	4' deep	42.50	85	127.50
1546	6' deep	42.50	89	131.50
1562	6 @ 6" dia. Schedule 40 PVC, 2' deep	59.50	119	178.50
1564	4' deep	59.50	124	183.50
1566	6' deep	59.50	130	189.50
1582	8 @ 6" dia. Schedule 40 PVC, 2' deep	78.50	159	237.50
1584	4' deep	78.50	166	244.50
1586	6' deep	78.50	173	251.50
1592	9 @ 6" dia. Schedule 40 PVC, 2' deep	87.50	178	265.50
1594	4' deep	87.50	181	268.50
1596	6' deep	87.50	187	274.50

The Site Lighting System includes the complete unit from foundation to electrical fixtures. Each system includes: excavation; concrete base; backfill by hand; compaction with a plate compacter; pole of specified material; all fixtures; and lamps.

The Expanded System Listing shows Site Lighting Systems that use one of two types of lamps: high pressure sodium; and metal halide. Systems are listed for 400-watt and 1000-watt lamps. Pole height varies from 20' to 40'. There are four types of poles possibly listed: aluminum, fiberglass, steel and wood.

System Components	QUANTITY	UNIT	COST EACH		
			MAT.	INST.	TOTAL
SYSTEM G4020 110 5820					
SITE LIGHTING, METAL HALIDE, 400 WATT, ALUMINUM POLE, 20' HIGH					
Excavating, by hand, pits to 6' deep, heavy soil	2.368	C.Y.		284.16	284.16
Concrete in place incl. forms and reinf. stl. spread footings under 1 CY	.465	C.Y.	93	134.44	227.44
Backfill	1.903	C.Y.		82.78	82.78
Compact, vibrating plate	1.903	C.Y.		11.17	11.17
Aluminum light pole, 20', no concrete base	1.000	Ea.	1,075	637.50	1,712.50
Road area luminaire wire	.300	C.L.F.	9.30	25.50	34.80
Roadway area luminaire, metal halide 400 W	1.000	Ea.	665	310	975
TOTAL			1,842.30	1,485.55	3,327.85

G4020 110	Site Lighting	COST EACH		
		MAT.	INST.	TOTAL
2320	Site lighting, high pressure sodium, 400 watt, aluminum pole, 20' high	1,875	1,475	3,350
2340	30' high	2,850	1,825	4,675
2360	40' high	3,375	2,350	5,725
2520	Fiberglass pole, 20' high	1,600	1,325	2,925
2540	30' high	1,825	1,625	3,450
2560	40' high	2,675	2,075	4,750
2720	Steel pole, 20' high	1,925	1,550	3,475
2740	30' high	2,325	1,925	4,250
2760	40' high	2,875	2,525	5,400
2920	Wood pole, 20' high	1,025	1,450	2,475
2940	30' high	1,225	1,825	3,050
2960	40' high	1,575	2,225	3,800
3120	1000 watt, aluminum pole, 20' high	1,950	1,500	3,450
3140	30' high	2,950	1,850	4,800
3160	40' high	3,475	2,375	5,850
3320	Fiberglass pole, 20' high	1,700	1,350	3,050
3340	30' high	1,925	1,650	3,575
3360	40' high	2,775	2,100	4,875
3420	Steel pole, 20' high	2,000	1,575	3,575
3440	30' high	2,425	1,950	4,375

G4020 Site Lighting

G4020 110	Site Lighting	COST EACH		
		MAT.	INST.	TOTAL
3460	40' high	2,975	2,550	5,525
3520	Wood pole, 20' high	1,125	1,475	2,600
3540	30' high	1,325	1,850	3,175
3560	40' high	1,675	2,275	3,950
5820	Metal halide, 400 watt, aluminum pole, 20' high	1,850	1,475	3,325
5840	30' high	2,825	1,825	4,650
5860	40' high	3,350	2,350	5,700
6120	Fiberglass pole, 20' high	1,575	1,325	2,900
6140	30' high	1,800	1,625	3,425
6160	40' high	2,650	2,075	4,725
6320	Steel pole, 20' high	1,900	1,550	3,450
6340	30' high	2,300	1,925	4,225
6360	40' high	2,850	2,525	5,375
7620	1000 watt, aluminum pole, 20' high	1,925	1,500	3,425
7640	30' high	2,900	1,850	4,750
7660	40' high	3,425	2,375	5,800
7900	Fiberglass pole, 20' high	1,650	1,350	3,000
7920	30' high	1,875	1,650	3,525
7940	40' high	2,725	2,100	4,825
8120	Steel pole, 20' high	1,975	1,575	3,550
8140	30' high	2,375	1,950	4,325
8160	40' high	2,925	2,550	5,475

G4020 Site Lighting

Table G4020 210 Procedure for Calculating Floodlights Required for Various Footcandles
Poles should not be spaced more than 4 times the fixture mounting height for good light distribution.

Estimating Chart
Select Lamp type.

Determine total square feet.

Chart will show quantity of fixtures to provide 1 footcandle initial, at intersection of lines. Multiply fixture quantity by desired footcandle level.

Chart based on use of wide beam luminaires in an area whose dimensions are large compared to mounting height and is approximate only.

To maintain 1 footcandle over a large area use these watts per square foot:

Incandescent	0.15
Metal Halide	0.032
Mercury Vapor	0.05
High Pressure Sodium	0.024

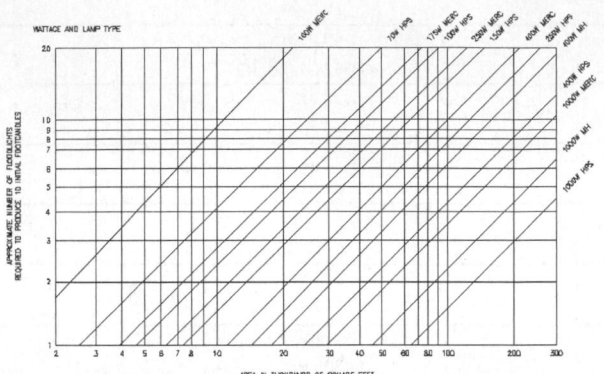

System Components	QUANTITY	UNIT	COST EACH		
			MAT.	INST.	TOTAL
SYSTEM G4020 210 0200					
LIGHT POLES, ALUMINUM, 20' HIGH, 1 ARM BRACKET					
Aluminum light pole, 20', no concrete base	1.000	Ea.	1,075	637.50	1,712.50
Bracket arm for Aluminum light pole	1.000	Ea.	138	85	223
Excavation by hand, pits to 6' deep, heavy soil or clay	2.368	C.Y.		284.16	284.16
Footing, concrete incl forms, reinforcing, spread, under 1 C.Y.	.465	C.Y.	93	134.44	227.44
Backfill by hand	1.903	C.Y.		82.78	82.78
Compaction vibrating plate	1.903	C.Y.		11.17	11.17
TOTAL			1,306	1,235.05	2,541.05

G4020 210	Light Pole (Installed)	COST EACH		
		MAT.	INST.	TOTAL
0200	Light pole, aluminum, 20' high, 1 arm bracket	1,300	1,225	2,525
0240	2 arm brackets	1,450	1,225	2,675
0280	3 arm brackets	1,575	1,275	2,850
0320	4 arm brackets	1,725	1,275	3,000
0360	30' high, 1 arm bracket	2,275	1,550	3,825
0400	2 arm brackets	2,425	1,550	3,975
0440	3 arm brackets	2,550	1,600	4,150
0480	4 arm brackets	2,700	1,600	4,300
0680	40' high, 1 arm bracket	2,800	2,075	4,875
0720	2 arm brackets	2,950	2,075	5,025
0760	3 arm brackets	3,075	2,125	5,200
0800	4 arm brackets	3,225	2,125	5,350
0840	Steel, 20' high, 1 arm bracket	1,425	1,300	2,725
0880	2 arm brackets	1,550	1,300	2,850
0920	3 arm brackets	1,475	1,350	2,825
0960	4 arm brackets	1,575	1,350	2,925
1000	30' high, 1 arm bracket	1,825	1,675	3,500
1040	2 arm brackets	1,925	1,675	3,600
1080	3 arm brackets	1,875	1,700	3,575
1120	4 arm brackets	1,975	1,700	3,675
1320	40' high, 1 arm bracket	2,375	2,250	4,625
1360	2 arm brackets	2,475	2,250	4,725
1400	3 arm brackets	2,400	2,300	4,700
1440	4 arm brackets	2,525	2,300	4,825

Reference Section

All the reference information is in one section, making it easy to find what you need to know ... and easy to use the data set on a daily basis. This section is visually identified by a vertical black bar on the page edges.

In this Reference Section, we've included Equipment Rental Costs, a listing of rental and operating costs; Crew Listings, a full listing of all crews, equipment, and their costs; Historical Cost Indexes for cost comparisons over time; City Cost Indexes and Location Factors for adjusting costs to the region you are in; Reference Tables, where you will find explanations, estimating information and procedures, or technical data; and an explanation of all the Abbreviations in the data set.

Table of Contents

Estimating Tips

- This section contains the average costs to rent and operate hundreds of pieces of construction equipment. This is useful information when estimating the time and material requirements of any particular operation in order to establish a unit or total cost. Bare equipment costs shown on a unit cost line include not only rental, but also operating costs for equipment under normal use.

Rental Costs

- Equipment rental rates are obtained from the following industry sources throughout North America: contractors, suppliers, dealers, manufacturers, and distributors.

- Rental rates vary throughout the country, with larger cities generally having lower rates. Lease plans for new equipment are available for periods in excess of six months, with a percentage of payments applying toward purchase.

- Monthly rental rates vary from 2% to 5% of the purchase price of the equipment depending on the anticipated life of the equipment and its wearing parts.

- Weekly rental rates are about 1/3 of the monthly rates, and daily rental rates are about 1/3 of the weekly rate.

- Rental rates can also be treated as reimbursement costs for contractor-owned equipment. Owned equipment costs include depreciation, loan payments, interest, taxes, insurance, storage, and major repairs.

Operating Costs

- The operating costs include parts and labor for routine servicing, such as the repair and replacement of pumps, filters, and worn lines. Normal operating expendables, such as fuel, lubricants, tires, and electricity (where applicable), are also included.

- Extraordinary operating expendables with highly variable wear patterns, such as diamond bits and blades, are excluded. These costs can be found as material costs in the Unit Price section.

- The hourly operating costs listed do not include the operator's wages.

Equipment Cost/Day

- Any power equipment required by a crew is shown in the Crew Listings with a daily cost.

- This daily cost of equipment needed by a crew includes both the rental cost and the operating cost and is based on dividing the weekly rental rate by 5 (number of working days in the week), and then adding the hourly operating cost times 8 (the number of hours in a day). This "Equipment Cost/Day" is shown in the far right column of the Equipment Rental section.

- If equipment is needed for only one or two days, it is best to develop your own cost by including components for daily rent and hourly operating costs. This is important when the listed Crew for a task does not contain the equipment needed, such as a crane for lifting mechanical heating/cooling equipment up onto a roof.

- If the quantity of work is less than the crew's Daily Output shown for a Unit Price line item that includes a bare unit equipment cost, the recommendation is to estimate one day's rental cost and operating cost for equipment shown in the Crew Listing for that line item.

Mobilization, Demobilization Costs

- The cost to move construction equipment from an equipment yard or rental company to the job site and back again is not included in equipment rental costs listed in the Reference Section, nor in the bare equipment cost of any unit price line item, nor in any equipment costs shown in the Crew Listings.

- Mobilization (to the site) and demobilization (from the site) costs can be found in the Unit Price section.

- If a piece of equipment is already at the job site, it is not appropriate to utilize mobilization, demobilization costs again in an estimate. ∎

Did you know?

Our online estimating solution gives you the same access to RSMeans' data with 24/7 access:

- Quickly locate costs in the searchable database.
- Build cost lists, estimates, and reports in minutes.
- Adjust costs to any location in the U.S. and Canada with the click of a button.

Start your free trial today at
www.RSMeansOnline.com

01 54 33 | Equipment Rental

			UNIT	HOURLY OPER. COST	RENT PER DAY	RENT PER WEEK	RENT PER MONTH	EQUIPMENT COST/DAY	
10	0010	**CONCRETE EQUIPMENT RENTAL** without operators	R015433 -10						**10**
	0200	Bucket, concrete lightweight, 1/2 C.Y.	Ea.	.80	23.50	70	210	20.40	
	0300	1 C.Y.		.90	28	84	252	24	
	0400	1-1/2 C.Y.		1.15	38.50	115	345	32.20	
	0500	2 C.Y.		1.25	45	135	405	37	
	0580	8 C.Y.		6.15	258	775	2,325	204.20	
	0600	Cart, concrete, self-propelled, operator walking, 10 C.F.		3.00	56.50	170	510	58	
	0700	Operator riding, 18 C.F.		4.95	95	285	855	96.60	
	0800	Conveyer for concrete, portable, gas, 16" wide, 26' long		11.35	125	375	1,125	165.80	
	0900	46' long		11.70	150	450	1,350	183.60	
	1000	56' long		11.85	158	475	1,425	189.80	
	1100	Core drill, electric, 2-1/2 H.P., 1" to 8" bit diameter		1.83	67.50	203	610	55.25	
	1150	11 H.P., 8" to 18" cores		5.45	118	355	1,075	114.60	
	1200	Finisher, concrete floor, gas, riding trowel, 96" wide		10.99	147	440	1,325	175.90	
	1300	Gas, walk-behind, 3 blade, 36" trowel		1.85	20.50	62	186	27.20	
	1400	4 blade, 48" trowel		3.62	27.50	83	249	45.55	
	1500	Float, hand-operated (Bull float), 48" wide		.08	13.35	40	120	8.65	
	1570	Curb builder, 14 H.P., gas, single screw		14.35	263	790	2,375	272.80	
	1590	Double screw		15.30	320	955	2,875	313.40	
	1600	Floor grinder, concrete and terrazzo, electric, 22" path		2.69	167	500	1,500	121.50	
	1700	Edger, concrete, electric, 7" path		1.03	51.50	155	465	39.25	
	1750	Vacuum pick-up system for floor grinders, wet/dry		1.48	81.50	245	735	60.85	
	1800	Mixer, powered, mortar and concrete, gas, 6 C.F., 18 H.P.		7.85	120	360	1,075	134.80	
	1900	10 C.F., 25 H.P.		9.70	145	435	1,300	164.60	
	2000	16 C.F.		10.00	167	500	1,500	180	
	2100	Concrete, stationary, tilt drum, 2 C.Y.		7.00	235	705	2,125	197	
	2120	Pump, concrete, truck mounted, 4" line, 80' boom		28.30	965	2,900	8,700	806.40	
	2140	5" line, 110' boom		35.55	1,325	4,010	12,000	1,086	
	2160	Mud jack, 50 C.F. per hr.		6.60	133	400	1,200	132.80	
	2180	225 C.F. per hr.		8.80	152	455	1,375	161.40	
	2190	Shotcrete pump rig, 12 C.Y./hr.		13.90	232	695	2,075	250.20	
	2200	35 C.Y./hr.		15.90	248	745	2,225	276.20	
	2600	Saw, concrete, manual, gas, 18 H.P.		5.90	45	135	405	74.20	
	2650	Self-propelled, gas, 30 H.P.		11.45	103	310	930	153.60	
	2675	V-groove crack chaser, manual, gas, 6 H.P.		2.00	17.65	53	159	26.60	
	2700	Vibrators, concrete, electric, 60 cycle, 2 H.P.		.46	8.65	26	78	8.90	
	2800	3 H.P.		.59	11.65	35	105	11.70	
	2900	Gas engine, 5 H.P.		1.75	16.35	49	147	23.80	
	3000	8 H.P.		2.38	15.35	46	138	28.25	
	3050	Vibrating screed, gas engine, 8 H.P.		2.47	74.50	223	670	64.35	
	3120	Concrete transit mixer, 6 x 4, 250 H.P., 8 C.Y., rear discharge		57.25	580	1,745	5,225	807	
	3200	Front discharge		67.15	715	2,145	6,425	966.20	
	3300	6 x 6, 285 H.P., 12 C.Y., rear discharge		66.20	675	2,030	6,100	935.60	
	3400	Front discharge		69.15	715	2,145	6,425	982.20	
20	0010	**EARTHWORK EQUIPMENT RENTAL** without operators	R015433 -10						**20**
	0040	Aggregate spreader, push type, 8' to 12' wide	Ea.	2.75	25.50	77	231	37.40	
	0045	Tailgate type, 8' wide		2.65	32.50	98	294	40.80	
	0055	Earth auger, truck mounted, for fence & sign posts, utility poles		17.05	445	1,335	4,000	403.40	
	0060	For borings and monitoring wells		43.80	720	2,155	6,475	781.40	
	0070	Portable, trailer mounted		2.77	33.50	100	300	42.15	
	0075	Truck mounted, for caissons, water wells		89.45	3,100	9,285	27,900	2,573	
	0080	Horizontal boring machine, 12" to 36" diameter, 45 H.P.		22.60	207	620	1,850	304.80	
	0090	12" to 48" diameter, 65 H.P.		31.15	360	1,080	3,250	465.20	
	0095	Auger, for fence posts, gas engine, hand held		.51	6.35	19	57	7.90	
	0100	Excavator, diesel hydraulic, crawler mounted, 1/2 C.Y. cap.		23.45	425	1,280	3,850	443.60	
	0120	5/8 C.Y. capacity		31.75	600	1,800	5,400	614	
	0140	3/4 C.Y. capacity		34.90	660	1,975	5,925	674.20	
	0150	1 C.Y. capacity		46.40	710	2,135	6,400	798.20	

01 54 33 | Equipment Rental

		UNIT	HOURLY OPER. COST	RENT PER DAY	RENT PER WEEK	RENT PER MONTH	EQUIPMENT COST/DAY	
20	0200	1-1/2 C.Y. capacity	Ea.	54.75	880	2,635	7,900	965	20
	0300	2 C.Y. capacity		61.90	1,050	3,140	9,425	1,123	
	0320	2-1/2 C.Y. capacity		94.70	1,300	3,890	11,700	1,536	
	0325	3-1/2 C.Y. capacity		134.25	2,200	6,635	19,900	2,401	
	0330	4-1/2 C.Y. capacity		166.65	2,925	8,755	26,300	3,084	
	0335	6 C.Y. capacity		214.30	3,125	9,410	28,200	3,596	
	0340	7 C.Y. capacity		216.45	3,275	9,830	29,500	3,698	
	0342	Excavator attachments, bucket thumbs		3.25	247	740	2,225	174	
	0345	Grapples		2.80	195	585	1,750	139.40	
	0346	Hydraulic hammer for boom mounting, 4000 ft lb.		12.55	355	1,060	3,175	312.40	
	0347	5000 ft lb.		14.65	430	1,295	3,875	376.20	
	0348	8000 ft lb.		21.60	635	1,900	5,700	552.80	
	0349	12,000 ft lb.		23.65	755	2,270	6,800	643.20	
	0350	Gradall type, truck mounted, 3 ton @ 15' radius, 5/8 C.Y.		52.50	815	2,450	7,350	910	
	0370	1 C.Y. capacity		61.90	1,075	3,245	9,725	1,144	
	0400	Backhoe-loader, 40 to 45 H.P., 5/8 C.Y. capacity		14.25	257	770	2,300	268	
	0450	45 H.P. to 60 H.P., 3/4 C.Y. capacity		22.15	315	945	2,825	366.20	
	0460	80 H.P., 1-1/4 C.Y. capacity		23.55	345	1,030	3,100	394.40	
	0470	112 H.P., 1-1/2 C.Y. capacity		37.45	650	1,945	5,825	688.60	
	0482	Backhoe-loader attachment, compactor, 20,000 lb.		5.90	143	430	1,300	133.20	
	0485	Hydraulic hammer, 750 ft lb.		3.35	98.50	295	885	85.80	
	0486	Hydraulic hammer, 1200 ft lb.		6.40	218	655	1,975	182.20	
	0500	Brush chipper, gas engine, 6" cutter head, 35 H.P.		9.90	107	320	960	143.20	
	0550	Diesel engine, 12" cutter head, 130 H.P.		26.30	325	970	2,900	404.40	
	0600	15" cutter head, 165 H.P.		32.05	390	1,170	3,500	490.40	
	0750	Bucket, clamshell, general purpose, 3/8 C.Y.		1.30	38.50	115	345	33.40	
	0800	1/2 C.Y.		1.40	45	135	405	38.20	
	0850	3/4 C.Y.		1.55	55	165	495	45.40	
	0900	1 C.Y.		1.60	60	180	540	48.80	
	0950	1-1/2 C.Y.		2.60	81.50	245	735	69.80	
	1000	2 C.Y.		2.75	90	270	810	76	
	1010	Bucket, dragline, medium duty, 1/2 C.Y.		.75	23.50	70	210	20	
	1020	3/4 C.Y.		.75	24.50	74	222	20.80	
	1030	1 C.Y.		.80	26.50	80	240	22.40	
	1040	1-1/2 C.Y.		1.25	40	120	360	34	
	1050	2 C.Y.		1.30	45	135	405	37.40	
	1070	3 C.Y.		2.00	63.50	190	570	54	
	1200	Compactor, manually guided 2-drum vibratory smooth roller, 7.5 H.P.		7.10	210	630	1,900	182.80	
	1250	Rammer/tamper, gas, 8"		2.75	46.50	140	420	50	
	1260	15"		3.10	53.50	160	480	56.80	
	1300	Vibratory plate, gas, 18" plate, 3000 lb. blow		2.30	25.50	76	228	33.60	
	1350	21" plate, 5000 lb. blow		2.85	33.50	100	300	42.80	
	1370	Curb builder/extruder, 14 H.P., gas, single screw		14.35	263	790	2,375	272.80	
	1390	Double screw		15.30	320	955	2,875	313.40	
	1500	Disc harrow attachment, for tractor		.46	76.50	230	690	49.70	
	1810	Feller buncher, shearing & accumulating trees, 100 H.P.		45.65	780	2,340	7,025	833.20	
	1860	Grader, self-propelled, 25,000 lb.		38.80	750	2,245	6,725	759.40	
	1910	30,000 lb.		39.30	605	1,820	5,450	678.40	
	1920	40,000 lb.		64.30	1,225	3,670	11,000	1,248	
	1930	55,000 lb.		78.85	1,825	5,455	16,400	1,722	
	1950	Hammer, pavement breaker, self-propelled, diesel, 1000 to 1250 lb.		30.65	400	1,200	3,600	485.20	
	2000	1300 to 1500 lb.		45.98	800	2,400	7,200	847.85	
	2050	Pile driving hammer, steam or air, 4150 ft lb. @ 225 bpm		11.25	550	1,645	4,925	419	
	2100	8750 ft lb. @ 145 bpm		13.75	765	2,300	6,900	570	
	2150	15,000 ft lb. @ 60 bpm		14.10	820	2,465	7,400	605.80	
	2200	24,450 ft lb. @ 111 bpm		15.15	910	2,730	8,200	667.20	
	2250	Leads, 60' high for pile driving hammers up to 20,000 ft lb.		3.40	81.50	244	730	76	
	2300	90' high for hammers over 20,000 ft lb.		5.10	142	426	1,275	126	

01 54 33 | Equipment Rental

		UNIT	HOURLY OPER. COST	RENT PER DAY	RENT PER WEEK	RENT PER MONTH	EQUIPMENT COST/DAY
2350	Diesel type hammer, 22,400 ft lb.	Ea.	19.00	450	1,345	4,025	421
2400	41,300 ft lb.		28.25	580	1,740	5,225	574
2450	141,000 ft lb.		45.65	915	2,750	8,250	915.20
2500	Vib. elec. hammer/extractor, 200 kW diesel generator, 34 H.P.		50.30	675	2,025	6,075	807.40
2550	80 H.P.		90.70	970	2,915	8,750	1,309
2600	150 H.P.		170.95	1,875	5,630	16,900	2,494
2800	Log chipper, up to 22" diameter, 600 H.P.		57.85	650	1,950	5,850	852.80
2850	Logger, for skidding & stacking logs, 150 H.P.		48.90	800	2,400	7,200	871.20
2860	Mulcher, diesel powered, trailer mounted		21.75	215	645	1,925	303
2900	Rake, spring tooth, with tractor		16.89	350	1,045	3,125	344.10
3000	Roller, vibratory, tandem, smooth drum, 20 H.P.		7.80	150	450	1,350	152.40
3050	35 H.P.		10.20	260	780	2,350	237.60
3100	Towed type vibratory compactor, smooth drum, 50 H.P.		25.30	375	1,125	3,375	427.40
3150	Sheepsfoot, 50 H.P.		26.25	400	1,205	3,625	451
3170	Landfill compactor, 220 H.P.		76.55	1,625	4,860	14,600	1,584
3200	Pneumatic tire roller, 80 H.P.		14.10	405	1,215	3,650	355.80
3250	120 H.P.		21.30	685	2,050	6,150	580.40
3300	Sheepsfoot vibratory roller, 240 H.P.		67.40	1,250	3,785	11,400	1,296
3320	340 H.P.		90.85	1,875	5,590	16,800	1,845
3350	Smooth drum vibratory roller, 75 H.P.		23.80	690	2,075	6,225	605.40
3400	125 H.P.		28.75	755	2,270	6,800	684
3410	Rotary mower, brush, 60", with tractor		21.35	325	975	2,925	365.80
3420	Rototiller, walk-behind, gas, 5 H.P.		1.50	44	132	395	38.40
3422	8 H.P.		2.59	80	240	720	68.70
3440	Scrapers, towed type, 7 C.Y. capacity		5.90	117	350	1,050	117.20
3450	10 C.Y. capacity		6.70	158	475	1,425	148.60
3500	15 C.Y. capacity		7.20	183	550	1,650	167.60
3525	Self-propelled, single engine, 14 C.Y. capacity		141.45	2,150	6,485	19,500	2,429
3550	Dual engine, 21 C.Y. capacity		164.55	2,450	7,340	22,000	2,784
3600	31 C.Y. capacity		217.70	3,400	10,170	30,500	3,776
3640	44 C.Y. capacity		267.35	4,300	12,865	38,600	4,712
3650	Elevating type, single engine, 11 C.Y. capacity		67.70	1,075	3,250	9,750	1,192
3700	22 C.Y. capacity		129.45	2,425	7,270	21,800	2,490
3710	Screening plant, 110 H.P. w/5' x 10' screen		19.53	385	1,155	3,475	387.25
3720	5' x 16' screen		24.83	500	1,495	4,475	497.65
3850	Shovel, crawler-mounted, front-loading, 7 C.Y. capacity		240.65	3,625	10,910	32,700	4,107
3855	12 C.Y. capacity		391.30	5,025	15,110	45,300	6,152
3860	Shovel/backhoe bucket, 1/2 C.Y.		2.50	68.50	205	615	61
3870	3/4 C.Y.		2.60	75	225	675	65.80
3880	1 C.Y.		2.70	85	255	765	72.60
3890	1-1/2 C.Y.		2.80	98.50	295	885	81.40
3910	3 C.Y.		3.15	132	395	1,175	104.20
3950	Stump chipper, 18" deep, 30 H.P.		6.79	215	646	1,950	183.50
4110	Dozer, crawler, torque converter, diesel 80 H.P.		27.95	410	1,225	3,675	468.60
4150	105 H.P.		34.25	555	1,670	5,000	608
4200	140 H.P.		48.40	765	2,300	6,900	847.20
4260	200 H.P.		72.10	1,350	4,035	12,100	1,384
4310	300 H.P.		95.10	1,900	5,695	17,100	1,900
4360	410 H.P.		125.20	2,275	6,830	20,500	2,368
4370	500 H.P.		160.05	3,425	10,310	30,900	3,342
4380	700 H.P.		264.25	5,175	15,520	46,600	5,218
4400	Loader, crawler, torque conv., diesel, 1-1/2 C.Y., 80 H.P.		32.65	510	1,535	4,600	568.20
4450	1-1/2 to 1-3/4 C.Y., 95 H.P.		33.60	655	1,970	5,900	662.80
4510	1-3/4 to 2-1/4 C.Y., 130 H.P.		53.20	920	2,760	8,275	977.60
4530	2-1/2 to 3-1/4 C.Y., 190 H.P.		65.10	1,275	3,800	11,400	1,281
4560	3-1/2 to 5 C.Y., 275 H.P.		82.45	1,450	4,340	13,000	1,528
4610	Front end loader, 4WD, articulated frame, diesel, 1 to 1-1/4 C.Y., 70 H.P.		18.85	270	810	2,425	312.80
4620	1-1/2 to 1-3/4 C.Y., 95 H.P.		23.25	293	880	2,650	362

01 54 33 | Equipment Rental

		UNIT	HOURLY OPER. COST	RENT PER DAY	RENT PER WEEK	RENT PER MONTH	EQUIPMENT COST/DAY	
20	4650	1-3/4 to 2 C.Y., 130 H.P.	Ea.	24.90	370	1,105	3,325	420.20	**20**
	4710	2-1/2 to 3-1/2 C.Y., 145 H.P.		35.40	455	1,365	4,100	556.20	
	4730	3 to 4-1/2 C.Y., 185 H.P.		40.70	555	1,660	4,975	657.60	
	4760	5-1/4 to 5-3/4 C.Y., 270 H.P.		63.35	955	2,870	8,600	1,081	
	4810	7 to 9 C.Y., 475 H.P.		108.10	1,825	5,510	16,500	1,967	
	4870	9 to 11 C.Y., 620 H.P.		154.85	3,300	9,925	29,800	3,224	
	4880	Skid-steer loader, wheeled, 10 C.F., 30 H.P. gas		9.75	155	465	1,400	171	
	4890	1 C.Y., 78 H.P., diesel		18.80	265	795	2,375	309.40	
	4892	Skid-steer attachment, auger		.40	66.50	200	600	43.20	
	4893	Backhoe		.65	108	325	975	70.20	
	4894	Broom		.79	131	393	1,175	84.90	
	4895	Forks		.19	31.50	95	285	20.50	
	4896	Grapple		.55	92.50	277	830	59.80	
	4897	Concrete hammer		1.07	178	535	1,600	115.55	
	4898	Tree spade		1.03	172	515	1,550	111.25	
	4899	Trencher		.51	85.50	256	770	55.30	
	4900	Trencher, chain, boom type, gas, operator walking, 12 H.P.		4.45	46.50	140	420	63.60	
	4910	Operator riding, 40 H.P.		18.65	293	880	2,650	325.20	
	5000	Wheel type, diesel, 4' deep, 12" wide		80.25	860	2,575	7,725	1,157	
	5100	6' deep, 20" wide		90.50	2,000	6,030	18,100	1,930	
	5150	Chain type, diesel, 5' deep, 8" wide		27.70	400	1,195	3,575	460.60	
	5200	Diesel, 8' deep, 16" wide		116.95	2,550	7,620	22,900	2,460	
	5202	Rock trencher, wheel type, 6" wide x 18" deep		38.00	740	2,225	6,675	749	
	5206	Chain type, 18" wide x 7' deep		109.44	2,950	8,845	26,500	2,645	
	5210	Tree spade, self-propelled		11.28	267	800	2,400	250.25	
	5250	Truck, dump, 2-axle, 12 ton, 8 C.Y. payload, 220 H.P.		31.00	238	715	2,150	391	
	5300	Three axle dump, 16 ton, 12 C.Y. payload, 400 H.P.		54.70	340	1,025	3,075	642.60	
	5310	Four axle dump, 25 ton, 18 C.Y. payload, 450 H.P.		64.70	495	1,490	4,475	815.60	
	5350	Dump trailer only, rear dump, 16 1/2 C.Y.		5.50	140	420	1,250	128	
	5400	20 C.Y.		5.95	158	475	1,425	142.60	
	5450	Flatbed, single axle, 1-1/2 ton rating		22.05	68.50	205	615	217.40	
	5500	3 ton rating		26.40	98.50	295	885	270.20	
	5550	Off highway rear dump, 25 ton capacity		72.20	1,500	4,490	13,500	1,476	
	5600	35 ton capacity		78.15	1,500	4,535	13,600	1,532	
	5610	50 ton capacity		101.00	2,000	5,990	18,000	2,006	
	5620	65 ton capacity		104.00	2,050	6,160	18,500	2,064	
	5630	100 ton capacity		141.00	3,050	9,120	27,400	2,952	
	6000	Vibratory plow, 25 H.P., walking		7.45	63.50	190	570	97.60	
40	0010	**GENERAL EQUIPMENT RENTAL** without operators							**40**
	0020	Aerial lift, scissor type, to 20' high, 1200 lb. capacity, electric [R015433 -10]	Ea.	3.15	55	165	495	58.20	
	0030	To 30' high, 1200 lb. capacity		3.60	71.50	215	645	71.80	
	0040	Over 30' high, 1500 lb. capacity		4.90	130	390	1,175	117.20	
	0070	Articulating boom, to 45' high, 500 lb. capacity, diesel [R015433 -15]		10.05	277	830	2,500	246.40	
	0075	To 60' high, 500 lb. capacity		14.05	485	1,460	4,375	404.40	
	0080	To 80' high, 500 lb. capacity		16.90	585	1,760	5,275	487.20	
	0085	To 125' high, 500 lb. capacity		20.40	690	2,075	6,225	578.20	
	0100	Telescoping boom to 40' high, 500 lb. capacity, diesel		11.85	325	970	2,900	288.80	
	0105	To 45' high, 500 lb. capacity		12.60	330	995	2,975	299.80	
	0110	To 60' high, 500 lb. capacity		16.25	545	1,630	4,900	456	
	0115	To 80' high, 500 lb. capacity		22.45	645	1,930	5,800	565.60	
	0120	To 100' high, 500 lb. capacity		26.35	795	2,385	7,150	687.80	
	0125	To 120' high, 500 lb. capacity		29.80	940	2,815	8,450	801.40	
	0195	Air compressor, portable, 6.5 CFM, electric		.88	13.65	41	123	15.25	
	0196	Gasoline		.65	20.50	62	186	17.60	
	0200	Towed type, gas engine, 60 CFM		12.00	51.50	155	465	127	
	0300	160 CFM		13.95	53.50	160	480	143.60	
	0400	Diesel engine, rotary screw, 250 CFM		13.90	117	350	1,050	181.20	
	0500	365 CFM		18.75	143	430	1,300	236	

For customer support on your Electrical Costs with RSMeans Data, call 800.448.8182.

461

01 54 33 | Equipment Rental

	UNIT	HOURLY OPER. COST	RENT PER DAY	RENT PER WEEK	RENT PER MONTH	EQUIPMENT COST/DAY
0550	450 CFM	Ea.	23.80	178	535	1,600	297.40
0600	600 CFM		41.75	247	740	2,225	482
0700	750 CFM	↓	41.90	255	765	2,300	488.20
0800	For silenced models, small sizes, add to rent		3%	5%	5%	5%	
0900	Large sizes, add to rent		5%	7%	7%	7%	
0930	Air tools, breaker, pavement, 60 lb.	Ea.	.50	10.35	31	93	10.20
0940	80 lb.		.55	10.65	32	96	10.80
0950	Drills, hand (jackhammer), 65 lb.		.60	18.35	55	165	15.80
0960	Track or wagon, swing boom, 4" drifter		56.05	945	2,840	8,525	1,016
0970	5" drifter		65.70	1,150	3,425	10,300	1,211
0975	Track mounted quarry drill, 6" diameter drill		109.15	1,725	5,145	15,400	1,902
0980	Dust control per drill		1.03	25.50	77	231	23.65
0990	Hammer, chipping, 12 lb.		.60	26	78	234	20.40
1000	Hose, air with couplings, 50' long, 3/4" diameter		.03	5	15	45	3.25
1100	1" diameter		.04	6.35	19	57	4.10
1200	1-1/2" diameter		.05	9	27	81	5.80
1300	2" diameter		.07	12	36	108	7.75
1400	2-1/2" diameter		.11	19	57	171	12.30
1410	3" diameter		.14	23	69	207	14.90
1450	Drill, steel, 7/8" x 2'		.05	8.65	26	78	5.60
1460	7/8" x 6'		.05	9	27	81	5.80
1520	Moil points		.02	3.67	11	33	2.35
1525	Pneumatic nailer w/accessories		.49	32.50	97	291	23.30
1530	Sheeting driver for 60 lb. breaker		.04	6	18	54	3.90
1540	For 90 lb. breaker		.12	8	24	72	5.75
1550	Spade, 25 lb.		.50	7.35	22	66	8.40
1560	Tamper, single, 35 lb.		.55	36.50	109	325	26.20
1570	Triple, 140 lb.		.82	54.50	164	490	39.35
1580	Wrenches, impact, air powered, up to 3/4" bolt		.40	13	39	117	11
1590	Up to 1-1/4" bolt		.50	24.50	73	219	18.60
1600	Barricades, barrels, reflectorized, 1 to 99 barrels		.03	4.60	13.80	41.50	3
1610	100 to 200 barrels		.02	3.53	10.60	32	2.30
1620	Barrels with flashers, 1 to 99 barrels		.03	5.25	15.80	47.50	3.40
1630	100 to 200 barrels		.03	4.20	12.60	38	2.75
1640	Barrels with steady burn type C lights		.04	7	21	63	4.50
1650	Illuminated board, trailer mounted, with generator		3.45	130	390	1,175	105.60
1670	Portable barricade, stock, with flashers, 1 to 6 units		.03	5.25	15.80	47.50	3.40
1680	25 to 50 units		.03	4.90	14.70	44	3.20
1685	Butt fusion machine, wheeled, 1.5 HP electric, 2" - 8" diameter pipe		2.63	167	500	1,500	121.05
1690	Tracked, 20 HP diesel, 4"-12" diameter pipe		10.89	545	1,640	4,925	415.10
1695	83 HP diesel, 8" - 24" diameter pipe		47.24	2,400	7,215	21,600	1,821
1700	Carts, brick, hand powered, 1000 lb. capacity		.47	78.50	235	705	50.75
1800	Gas engine, 1500 lb., 7-1/2' lift		3.55	115	345	1,025	97.40
1822	Dehumidifier, medium, 6 lb./hr., 150 CFM		1.11	69.50	209	625	50.70
1824	Large, 18 lb./hr., 600 CFM		2.12	133	398	1,200	96.55
1830	Distributor, asphalt, trailer mounted, 2000 gal., 38 H.P. diesel		10.25	360	1,075	3,225	297
1840	3000 gal., 38 H.P. diesel		11.80	390	1,165	3,500	327.40
1850	Drill, rotary hammer, electric		1.06	27	81	243	24.70
1860	Carbide bit, 1-1/2" diameter, add to electric rotary hammer		.03	4.67	14	42	3.05
1865	Rotary, crawler, 250 H.P.		142.30	2,300	6,925	20,800	2,523
1870	Emulsion sprayer, 65 gal., 5 H.P. gas engine		2.75	104	312	935	84.40
1880	200 gal., 5 H.P. engine		7.35	173	520	1,550	162.80
1900	Floor auto-scrubbing machine, walk-behind, 28" path		5.03	325	980	2,950	236.25
1930	Floodlight, mercury vapor, or quartz, on tripod, 1000 watt		.45	21.50	64	192	16.40
1940	2000 watt		.85	43	129	385	32.60
1950	Floodlights, trailer mounted with generator, 1 - 300 watt light		3.60	73.50	220	660	72.80
1960	2 - 1000 watt lights		4.70	98.50	295	885	96.60
2000	4 - 300 watt lights	↓	4.45	93.50	280	840	91.60

01 54 33	Equipment Rental	UNIT	HOURLY OPER. COST	RENT PER DAY	RENT PER WEEK	RENT PER MONTH	EQUIPMENT COST/DAY	
40	2005	Foam spray rig, incl. box trailer, compressor, generator, proportioner	Ea.	28.70	520	1,565	4,700	542.60	**40**
	2015	Forklift, pneumatic tire, rough terr, straight mast, 5000 lb, 12' lift, gas		22.35	212	635	1,900	305.80	
	2025	8000 lb, 12' lift		26.00	285	855	2,575	379	
	2030	5000 lb, 12' lift, diesel		17.40	238	715	2,150	282.20	
	2035	8000 lb, 12' lift, diesel		18.45	270	810	2,425	309.60	
	2045	All terrain, telescoping boom, diesel, 5000 lb, 10' reach, 19' lift		18.25	330	985	2,950	343	
	2055	6600 lb, 29' reach, 42' lift		22.25	385	1,155	3,475	409	
	2065	10,000 lb, 31' reach, 45' lift		26.20	520	1,555	4,675	520.60	
	2070	Cushion tire, smooth floor, gas, 5000 lb capacity		9.55	83.50	250	750	126.40	
	2075	8000 lb capacity		13.65	103	310	930	171.20	
	2085	Diesel, 5000 lb capacity		8.75	90	270	810	124	
	2090	12,000 lb capacity		13.55	142	425	1,275	193.40	
	2095	20,000 lb capacity		19.75	178	535	1,600	265	
	2100	Generator, electric, gas engine, 1.5 kW to 3 kW		3.15	12.65	38	114	32.80	
	2200	5 kW		4.10	16	48	144	42.40	
	2300	10 kW		7.70	36.50	110	330	83.60	
	2400	25 kW		8.75	90	270	810	124	
	2500	Diesel engine, 20 kW		10.05	78.50	235	705	127.40	
	2600	50 kW		19.15	105	315	945	216.20	
	2700	100 kW		35.30	142	425	1,275	367.40	
	2800	250 kW		69.45	268	805	2,425	716.60	
	2850	Hammer, hydraulic, for mounting on boom, to 500 ft lb.		2.60	76.50	230	690	66.80	
	2860	1000 ft lb.		4.54	128	385	1,150	113.30	
	2900	Heaters, space, oil or electric, 50 MBH		1.39	8	24	72	15.90	
	3000	100 MBH		2.52	10.65	32	96	26.55	
	3100	300 MBH		7.36	38.50	115	345	81.90	
	3150	500 MBH		11.95	45	135	405	122.60	
	3200	Hose, water, suction with coupling, 20' long, 2" diameter		.02	3	9	27	1.95	
	3210	3" diameter		.03	4.67	14	42	3.05	
	3220	4" diameter		.03	5.35	16	48	3.45	
	3230	6" diameter		.11	18.35	55	165	11.90	
	3240	8" diameter		.34	56	168	505	36.30	
	3250	Discharge hose with coupling, 50' long, 2" diameter		.01	1.33	4	12	.90	
	3260	3" diameter		.02	2.67	8	24	1.75	
	3270	4" diameter		.02	3.67	11	33	2.35	
	3280	6" diameter		.06	9.65	29	87	6.30	
	3290	8" diameter		.18	30	90	270	19.45	
	3295	Insulation blower		.78	6.35	19	57	10.05	
	3300	Ladders, extension type, 16' to 36' long		.14	22.50	68	204	14.70	
	3400	40' to 60' long		.19	31	93	279	20.10	
	3405	Lance for cutting concrete		2.13	55.50	167	500	50.45	
	3407	Lawn mower, rotary, 22", 5 H.P.		1.35	33.50	101	305	31	
	3408	48" self-propelled		2.90	95	285	855	80.20	
	3410	Level, electronic, automatic, with tripod and leveling rod		.87	57.50	173	520	41.55	
	3430	Laser type, for pipe and sewer line and grade		.73	48.50	145	435	34.85	
	3440	Rotating beam for interior control		.80	53	159	475	38.20	
	3460	Builder's optical transit, with tripod and rod		.09	14.65	44	132	9.50	
	3500	Light towers, towable, with diesel generator, 2000 watt		4.45	93.50	280	840	91.60	
	3600	4000 watt		4.70	98.50	295	885	96.60	
	3700	Mixer, powered, plaster and mortar, 6 C.F., 7 H.P.		2.30	20	60	180	30.40	
	3800	10 C.F., 9 H.P.		2.45	32.50	98	294	39.20	
	3850	Nailer, pneumatic		.49	32.50	97	291	23.30	
	3900	Paint sprayers complete, 8 CFM		1.06	70.50	211	635	50.70	
	4000	17 CFM		1.89	126	378	1,125	90.70	
	4020	Pavers, bituminous, rubber tires, 8' wide, 50 H.P., diesel		30.50	540	1,615	4,850	567	
	4030	10' wide, 150 H.P.		97.10	1,950	5,875	17,600	1,952	
	4050	Crawler, 8' wide, 100 H.P., diesel		85.85	2,050	6,165	18,500	1,920	
	4060	10' wide, 150 H.P.		104.85	2,425	7,290	21,900	2,297	

		UNIT	HOURLY OPER. COST	RENT PER DAY	RENT PER WEEK	RENT PER MONTH	EQUIPMENT COST/DAY	
40	4070	Concrete paver, 12' to 24' wide, 250 H.P.	Ea.	96.45	1,575	4,730	14,200	1,718	40
	4080	Placer-spreader-trimmer, 24' wide, 300 H.P.		133.20	2,300	6,934	20,800	2,452	
	4100	Pump, centrifugal gas pump, 1-1/2" diam., 65 GPM		3.75	50	150	450	60	
	4200	2" diameter, 130 GPM		5.00	60	180	540	76	
	4300	3" diameter, 250 GPM		5.20	61.50	185	555	78.60	
	4400	6" diameter, 1500 GPM		25.80	198	595	1,775	325.40	
	4500	Submersible electric pump, 1-1/4" diameter, 55 GPM		.41	17.65	53	159	13.90	
	4600	1-1/2" diameter, 83 GPM		.45	20.50	61	183	15.80	
	4700	2" diameter, 120 GPM		1.54	25.50	76	228	27.50	
	4800	3" diameter, 300 GPM		2.78	45	135	405	49.25	
	4900	4" diameter, 560 GPM		14.43	172	515	1,550	218.45	
	5000	6" diameter, 1590 GPM		21.57	227	680	2,050	308.55	
	5100	Diaphragm pump, gas, single, 1-1/2" diameter		1.06	52	156	470	39.70	
	5200	2" diameter		4.00	65	195	585	71	
	5300	3" diameter		4.00	65	195	585	71	
	5400	Double, 4" diameter		5.90	112	335	1,000	114.20	
	5450	Pressure washer 5 GPM, 3000 psi		4.25	53.50	160	480	66	
	5460	7 GPM, 3000 psi		5.50	63.50	190	570	82	
	5500	Trash pump, self-priming, gas, 2" diameter		4.00	22.50	67	201	45.40	
	5600	Diesel, 4" diameter		7.65	96.50	290	870	119.20	
	5650	Diesel, 6" diameter		20.65	172	515	1,550	268.20	
	5655	Grout Pump		24.05	275	825	2,475	357.40	
	5700	Salamanders, L.P. gas fired, 100,000 Btu		2.72	13.65	41	123	29.95	
	5705	50,000 Btu		1.59	10.65	32	96	19.10	
	5720	Sandblaster, portable, open top, 3 C.F. capacity		.60	27.50	83	249	21.40	
	5730	6 C.F. capacity		.95	41.50	125	375	32.60	
	5740	Accessories for above		.13	22.50	67	201	14.45	
	5750	Sander, floor		.89	23.50	71	213	21.30	
	5760	Edger		.53	16	48	144	13.85	
	5800	Saw, chain, gas engine, 18" long		2.00	22.50	67	201	29.40	
	5900	Hydraulic powered, 36" long		.75	65	195	585	45	
	5950	60" long		.75	66.50	200	600	46	
	6000	Masonry, table mounted, 14" diameter, 5 H.P.		1.32	56.50	170	510	44.55	
	6050	Portable cut-off, 8 H.P.		2.15	35	105	315	38.20	
	6100	Circular, hand held, electric, 7-1/4" diameter		.23	4.67	14	42	4.65	
	6200	12" diameter		.23	8.35	25	75	6.85	
	6250	Wall saw, w/hydraulic power, 10 H.P.		8.30	61.50	185	555	103.40	
	6275	Shot blaster, walk-behind, 20" wide		4.80	305	910	2,725	220.40	
	6280	Sidewalk broom, walk-behind		2.21	74.50	224	670	62.50	
	6300	Steam cleaner, 100 gallons per hour		3.40	80	240	720	75.20	
	6310	200 gallons per hour		4.60	98.50	295	885	95.80	
	6340	Tar Kettle/Pot, 400 gallons		14.21	76.50	230	690	159.70	
	6350	Torch, cutting, acetylene-oxygen, 150' hose, excludes gases		.30	16	48	144	12	
	6360	Hourly operating cost includes tips and gas		21.00				168	
	6410	Toilet, portable chemical		.13	21.50	65	195	14.05	
	6420	Recycle flush type		.16	26.50	79	237	17.10	
	6430	Toilet, fresh water flush, garden hose,		.19	31.50	95	285	20.50	
	6440	Hoisted, non-flush, for high rise		.15	25.50	77	231	16.60	
	6465	Tractor, farm with attachment		20.65	335	1,010	3,025	367.20	
	6480	Trailers, platform, flush deck, 2 axle, 3 ton capacity		1.50	20	60	180	24	
	6500	25 ton capacity		6.05	133	400	1,200	128.40	
	6600	40 ton capacity		7.75	188	565	1,700	175	
	6700	3 axle, 50 ton capacity		8.40	208	625	1,875	192.20	
	6800	75 ton capacity		10.65	275	825	2,475	250.20	
	6810	Trailer mounted cable reel for high voltage line work		5.68	270	811	2,425	207.65	
	6820	Trailer mounted cable tensioning rig		11.27	535	1,610	4,825	412.15	
	6830	Cable pulling rig		71.16	3,000	9,030	27,100	2,375	
	6850	Portable cable/wire puller, 8000 lb max pulling capacity		3.71	167	502	1,500	130.10	

01 54 33 | Equipment Rental

			UNIT	HOURLY OPER. COST	RENT PER DAY	RENT PER WEEK	RENT PER MONTH	EQUIPMENT COST/DAY	
40	6900	Water tank trailer, engine driven discharge, 5000 gallons	Ea.	7.00	145	435	1,300	143	**40**
	6925	10,000 gallons		9.55	200	600	1,800	196.40	
	6950	Water truck, off highway, 6000 gallons		82.10	785	2,350	7,050	1,127	
	7010	Tram car for high voltage line work, powered, 2 conductor		6.64	147	440	1,325	141.10	
	7020	Transit (builder's level) with tripod		.09	14.65	44	132	9.50	
	7030	Trench box, 3000 lb., 6' x 8'		.56	93.50	280	840	60.50	
	7040	7200 lb., 6' x 20'		.75	125	375	1,125	81	
	7050	8000 lb., 8' x 16'		1.08	180	540	1,625	116.65	
	7060	9500 lb., 8' x 20'		1.21	201	603	1,800	130.30	
	7065	11,000 lb., 8' x 24'		1.27	211	633	1,900	136.75	
	7070	12,000 lb., 10' x 20'		1.50	251	752	2,250	162.40	
	7100	Truck, pickup, 3/4 ton, 2 wheel drive		11.80	58.50	175	525	129.40	
	7200	4 wheel drive		12.00	73.50	220	660	140	
	7250	Crew carrier, 9 passenger		16.70	86.50	260	780	185.60	
	7290	Flat bed truck, 20,000 lb. GVW		19.50	127	380	1,150	232	
	7300	Tractor, 4 x 2, 220 H.P.		27.20	198	595	1,775	336.60	
	7410	330 H.P.		40.20	273	820	2,450	485.60	
	7500	6 x 4, 380 H.P.		46.10	320	955	2,875	559.80	
	7600	450 H.P.		56.10	385	1,155	3,475	679.80	
	7610	Tractor, with A frame, boom and winch, 225 H.P.		30.10	278	835	2,500	407.80	
	7620	Vacuum truck, hazardous material, 2500 gallons		12.20	293	880	2,650	273.60	
	7625	5,000 gallons		12.65	410	1,230	3,700	347.20	
	7650	Vacuum, HEPA, 16 gallon, wet/dry		.84	19	57	171	18.10	
	7655	55 gallon, wet/dry		.82	28.50	86	258	23.75	
	7660	Water tank, portable		.16	26.50	80	240	17.30	
	7690	Sewer/catch basin vacuum, 14 C.Y., 1500 gallons		16.99	615	1,850	5,550	505.90	
	7700	Welder, electric, 200 amp		3.81	17.35	52	156	40.90	
	7800	300 amp		5.67	21.50	64	192	58.15	
	7900	Gas engine, 200 amp		12.30	26.50	80	240	114.40	
	8000	300 amp		14.10	28.50	85	255	129.80	
	8100	Wheelbarrow, any size		.08	12.65	38	114	8.25	
	8200	Wrecking ball, 4000 lb.		2.35	70	210	630	60.80	
50	0010	**HIGHWAY EQUIPMENT RENTAL** without operators							**50**
	0050	Asphalt batch plant, portable drum mixer, 100 ton/hr.	Ea.	80.67	1,500	4,535	13,600	1,552	
	0060	200 ton/hr.		92.19	1,600	4,810	14,400	1,700	
	0070	300 ton/hr.		109.71	1,875	5,660	17,000	2,010	
	0100	Backhoe attachment, long stick, up to 185 H.P., 10.5' long		.36	24	72	216	17.30	
	0140	Up to 250 H.P., 12' long		.40	26.50	79	237	19	
	0180	Over 250 H.P., 15' long		.55	36.50	109	325	26.20	
	0200	Special dipper arm, up to 100 H.P., 32' long		1.12	74.50	223	670	53.55	
	0240	Over 100 H.P., 33' long		1.39	92.50	278	835	66.70	
	0280	Catch basin/sewer cleaning truck, 3 ton, 9 C.Y., 1000 gal.		38.00	390	1,175	3,525	539	
	0300	Concrete batch plant, portable, electric, 200 C.Y./hr.		23.11	525	1,570	4,700	498.90	
	0520	Grader/dozer attachment, ripper/scarifier, rear mounted, up to 135 H.P.		3.00	60	180	540	60	
	0540	Up to 180 H.P.		3.95	90	270	810	85.60	
	0580	Up to 250 H.P.		5.60	142	425	1,275	129.80	
	0700	Pvmt. removal bucket, for hyd. excavator, up to 90 H.P.		1.95	53.50	160	480	47.60	
	0740	Up to 200 H.P.		2.10	68.50	205	615	57.80	
	0780	Over 200 H.P.		2.30	86.50	260	780	70.40	
	0900	Aggregate spreader, self-propelled, 187 H.P.		50.25	690	2,075	6,225	817	
	1000	Chemical spreader, 3 C.Y.		3.15	43.50	130	390	51.20	
	1900	Hammermill, traveling, 250 H.P.		66.08	2,175	6,490	19,500	1,827	
	2000	Horizontal borer, 3" diameter, 13 H.P. gas driven		5.65	58.50	175	525	80.20	
	2150	Horizontal directional drill, 20,000 lb. thrust, 78 H.P. diesel		28.20	710	2,130	6,400	651.60	
	2160	30,000 lb. thrust, 115 H.P.		34.75	1,075	3,255	9,775	929	
	2170	50,000 lb. thrust, 170 H.P.		49.65	1,375	4,160	12,500	1,229	
	2190	Mud trailer for HDD, 1500 gallons, 175 H.P., gas		27.45	153	460	1,375	311.60	
	2200	Hydromulcher, diesel, 3000 gallon, for truck mounting		21.10	248	745	2,225	317.80	

Note: R015433 -10 (reference box at row 0010)

01 54 33 | Equipment Rental

		UNIT	HOURLY OPER. COST	RENT PER DAY	RENT PER WEEK	RENT PER MONTH	EQUIPMENT COST/DAY	
50	2300	Gas, 600 gallon	Ea.	7.80	100	300	900	122.40	**50**
	2400	Joint & crack cleaner, walk behind, 25 H.P.		3.45	50	150	450	57.60	
	2500	Filler, trailer mounted, 400 gallons, 20 H.P.		9.10	212	635	1,900	199.80	
	3000	Paint striper, self-propelled, 40 gallon, 22 H.P.		6.90	157	470	1,400	149.20	
	3100	120 gallon, 120 H.P.		20.55	400	1,195	3,575	403.40	
	3200	Post drivers, 6″ I-Beam frame, for truck mounting		16.90	385	1,150	3,450	365.20	
	3400	Road sweeper, self-propelled, 8′ wide, 90 H.P.		39.10	645	1,940	5,825	700.80	
	3450	Road sweeper, vacuum assisted, 4 C.Y., 220 gallons		68.85	630	1,885	5,650	927.80	
	4000	Road mixer, self-propelled, 130 H.P.		44.90	840	2,520	7,550	863.20	
	4100	310 H.P.		76.55	2,225	6,650	20,000	1,942	
	4220	Cold mix paver, incl. pug mill and bitumen tank, 165 H.P.		92.95	2,500	7,535	22,600	2,251	
	4240	Pavement brush, towed		3.25	93.50	280	840	82	
	4250	Paver, asphalt, wheel or crawler, 130 H.P., diesel		92.60	2,500	7,470	22,400	2,235	
	4300	Paver, road widener, gas, 1′ to 6′, 67 H.P.		46.00	945	2,830	8,500	934	
	4400	Diesel, 2′ to 14′, 88 H.P.		57.45	1,125	3,385	10,200	1,137	
	4600	Slipform pavers, curb and gutter, 2 track, 75 H.P.		62.00	1,175	3,490	10,500	1,194	
	4700	4 track, 165 H.P.		40.30	800	2,400	7,200	802.40	
	4800	Median barrier, 215 H.P.		63.25	1,225	3,695	11,100	1,245	
	4901	Trailer, low bed, 75 ton capacity		10.80	260	780	2,350	242.40	
	5000	Road planer, walk behind, 10″ cutting width, 10 H.P.		3.30	33.50	100	300	46.40	
	5100	Self-propelled, 12″ cutting width, 64 H.P.		8.95	113	340	1,025	139.60	
	5120	Traffic line remover, metal ball blaster, truck mounted, 115 H.P.		46.35	840	2,515	7,550	873.80	
	5140	Grinder, truck mounted, 115 H.P.		51.30	900	2,705	8,125	951.40	
	5160	Walk-behind, 11 H.P.		3.75	53.50	160	480	62	
	5200	Pavement profiler, 4′ to 6′ wide, 450 H.P.		225.65	3,500	10,525	31,600	3,910	
	5300	8′ to 10′ wide, 750 H.P.		349.00	4,600	13,805	41,400	5,553	
	5400	Roadway plate, steel, 1″ x 8′ x 20′		.08	14	42	126	9.05	
	5600	Stabilizer, self-propelled, 150 H.P.		43.90	715	2,150	6,450	781.20	
	5700	310 H.P.		83.60	1,975	5,960	17,900	1,861	
	5800	Striper, truck mounted, 120 gallon paint, 460 H.P.		55.20	490	1,465	4,400	734.60	
	5900	Thermal paint heating kettle, 115 gallons		7.26	25.50	77	231	73.50	
	6000	Tar kettle, 330 gallon, trailer mounted		10.97	58.50	175	525	122.75	
	7000	Tunnel locomotive, diesel, 8 to 12 ton		29.80	610	1,835	5,500	605.40	
	7005	Electric, 10 ton		26.90	700	2,105	6,325	636.20	
	7010	Muck cars, 1/2 C.Y. capacity		2.10	25.50	76	228	32	
	7020	1 C.Y. capacity		2.30	33.50	100	300	38.40	
	7030	2 C.Y. capacity		2.45	40	120	360	43.60	
	7040	Side dump, 2 C.Y. capacity		2.65	46.50	140	420	49.20	
	7050	3 C.Y. capacity		3.60	53.50	160	480	60.80	
	7060	5 C.Y. capacity		5.15	68.50	205	615	82.20	
	7100	Ventilating blower for tunnel, 7-1/2 H.P.		2.08	53.50	160	480	48.65	
	7110	10 H.P.		2.26	55	165	495	51.10	
	7120	20 H.P.		3.58	71.50	215	645	71.65	
	7140	40 H.P.		5.75	102	305	915	107	
	7160	60 H.P.		8.83	158	475	1,425	165.65	
	7175	75 H.P.		11.60	218	655	1,975	223.80	
	7180	200 H.P.		23.76	315	950	2,850	380.10	
	7800	Windrow loader, elevating		53.10	1,375	4,145	12,400	1,254	
60	0010	**LIFTING AND HOISTING EQUIPMENT RENTAL** without operators							**60**
	0150	Crane, flatbed mounted, 3 ton capacity	Ea.	14.60	218	655	1,975	247.80	
	0200	Crane, climbing, 106′ jib, 6000 lb. capacity, 410 fpm		40.06	1,725	5,160	15,500	1,352	
	0300	101′ jib, 10,250 lb. capacity, 270 fpm		46.96	2,175	6,540	19,600	1,684	
	0500	Tower, static, 130′ high, 106′ jib, 6200 lb. capacity at 400 fpm		44.06	1,975	5,960	17,900	1,544	
	0600	Crawler mounted, lattice boom, 1/2 C.Y., 15 tons at 12′ radius		37.97	755	2,270	6,800	757.75	
	0700	3/4 C.Y., 20 tons at 12′ radius		50.63	945	2,835	8,500	972.05	
	0800	1 C.Y., 25 tons at 12′ radius		67.50	1,250	3,780	11,300	1,296	
	0900	1-1/2 C.Y., 40 tons at 12′ radius		67.95	1,275	3,845	11,500	1,313	
	1000	2 C.Y., 50 tons at 12′ radius		80.20	1,725	5,168	15,500	1,675	

R015433 -10

R312316 -45

01 54 33 | Equipment Rental

		UNIT	HOURLY OPER. COST	RENT PER DAY	RENT PER WEEK	RENT PER MONTH	EQUIPMENT COST/DAY	
60								**60**
1100	3 C.Y., 75 tons at 12' radius	Ea.	77.65	1,700	5,120	15,400	1,645	
1200	100 ton capacity, 60' boom		88.00	1,825	5,500	16,500	1,804	
1300	165 ton capacity, 60' boom		108.25	2,275	6,825	20,500	2,231	
1400	200 ton capacity, 70' boom		143.85	2,900	8,730	26,200	2,897	
1500	350 ton capacity, 80' boom		187.45	4,200	12,600	37,800	4,020	
1600	Truck mounted, lattice boom, 6 x 4, 20 tons at 10' radius		39.35	1,275	3,800	11,400	1,075	
1700	25 tons at 10' radius		42.61	1,375	4,135	12,400	1,168	
1800	8 x 4, 30 tons at 10' radius		45.99	1,475	4,400	13,200	1,248	
1900	40 tons at 12' radius		48.87	1,525	4,600	13,800	1,311	
2000	60 tons at 15' radius		54.26	1,625	4,870	14,600	1,408	
2050	82 tons at 15' radius		60.22	1,725	5,200	15,600	1,522	
2100	90 tons at 15' radius		67.15	1,900	5,670	17,000	1,671	
2200	115 tons at 15' radius		75.69	2,100	6,335	19,000	1,873	
2300	150 tons at 18' radius		83.25	2,225	6,670	20,000	2,000	
2350	165 tons at 18' radius		88.09	2,350	7,070	21,200	2,119	
2400	Truck mounted, hydraulic, 12 ton capacity		35.35	485	1,450	4,350	572.80	
2500	25 ton capacity		40.60	580	1,745	5,225	673.80	
2550	33 ton capacity		49.70	775	2,330	7,000	863.60	
2560	40 ton capacity		55.05	915	2,745	8,225	989.40	
2600	55 ton capacity		63.75	945	2,830	8,500	1,076	
2700	80 ton capacity		83.75	1,575	4,730	14,200	1,616	
2720	100 ton capacity		93.00	1,700	5,085	15,300	1,761	
2740	120 ton capacity		107.35	1,825	5,495	16,500	1,958	
2760	150 ton capacity		113.30	2,225	6,700	20,100	2,246	
2800	Self-propelled, 4 x 4, with telescoping boom, 5 ton		15.50	253	760	2,275	276	
2900	12-1/2 ton capacity		26.95	365	1,100	3,300	435.60	
3000	15 ton capacity		36.50	455	1,365	4,100	565	
3050	20 ton capacity		29.85	525	1,575	4,725	553.80	
3100	25 ton capacity		31.20	595	1,780	5,350	605.60	
3150	40 ton capacity		47.40	660	1,985	5,950	776.20	
3200	Derricks, guy, 20 ton capacity, 60' boom, 75' mast		22.29	420	1,263	3,800	430.90	
3300	100' boom, 115' mast		35.37	725	2,170	6,500	716.95	
3400	Stiffleg, 20 ton capacity, 70' boom, 37' mast		24.93	545	1,640	4,925	527.45	
3500	100' boom, 47' mast		38.59	875	2,630	7,900	834.70	
3550	Helicopter, small, lift to 1250 lb. maximum, w/pilot		94.10	3,400	10,200	30,600	2,793	
3600	Hoists, chain type, overhead, manual, 3/4 ton		.15	.33	1	3	1.40	
3900	10 ton		.75	6.65	20	60	10	
4000	Hoist and tower, 5000 lb. cap., portable electric, 40' high		5.06	242	727	2,175	185.90	
4100	For each added 10' section, add		.11	19	57	171	12.30	
4200	Hoist and single tubular tower, 5000 lb. electric, 100' high		6.86	340	1,016	3,050	258.10	
4300	For each added 6'-6" section, add		.20	33	99	297	21.40	
4400	Hoist and double tubular tower, 5000 lb., 100' high		7.38	375	1,119	3,350	282.85	
4500	For each added 6'-6" section, add		.22	36.50	109	325	23.55	
4550	Hoist and tower, mast type, 6000 lb., 100' high		7.94	385	1,160	3,475	295.50	
4570	For each added 10' section, add		.13	22.50	67	201	14.45	
4600	Hoist and tower, personnel, electric, 2000 lb., 100' @ 125 fpm		16.88	1,025	3,090	9,275	753.05	
4700	3000 lb., 100' @ 200 fpm		19.28	1,175	3,500	10,500	854.25	
4800	3000 lb., 150' @ 300 fpm		21.38	1,300	3,920	11,800	955.05	
4900	4000 lb., 100' @ 300 fpm		22.14	1,325	4,000	12,000	977.10	
5000	6000 lb., 100' @ 275 fpm		23.80	1,400	4,190	12,600	1,028	
5100	For added heights up to 500', add	L.F.	.01	1.67	5	15	1.10	
5200	Jacks, hydraulic, 20 ton	Ea.	.05	2	6	18	1.60	
5500	100 ton		.40	12	36	108	10.40	
6100	Jacks, hydraulic, climbing w/50' jackrods, control console, 30 ton cap.		2.09	139	418	1,250	100.30	
6150	For each added 10' jackrod section, add		.05	3.33	10	30	2.40	
6300	50 ton capacity		3.36	224	672	2,025	161.30	
6350	For each added 10' jackrod section, add		.06	4	12	36	2.90	
6500	125 ton capacity		8.75	585	1,750	5,250	420	

For customer support on your Electrical Costs with RSMeans Data, call 800.448.8182.

467

01 54 33 | Equipment Rental

		UNIT	HOURLY OPER. COST	RENT PER DAY	RENT PER WEEK	RENT PER MONTH	EQUIPMENT COST/DAY	
60	6550	For each added 10' jackrod section, add	Ea.	.60	39.50	119	355	28.60	60
	6600	Cable jack, 10 ton capacity with 200' cable		1.75	117	350	1,050	84	
	6650	For each added 50' of cable, add	▼	.21	14	42	126	10.10	
70	0010	**WELLPOINT EQUIPMENT RENTAL** without operators							70
	0020	Based on 2 months rental	R015433 -10						
	0100	Combination jetting & wellpoint pump, 60 H.P. diesel	Ea.	15.32	345	1,036	3,100	329.75	
	0200	High pressure gas jet pump, 200 H.P., 300 psi	"	33.10	295	885	2,650	441.80	
	0300	Discharge pipe, 8" diameter	L.F.	.01	.56	1.68	5.05	.40	
	0350	12" diameter		.01	.83	2.48	7.45	.60	
	0400	Header pipe, flows up to 150 GPM, 4" diameter		.01	.51	1.53	4.59	.40	
	0500	400 GPM, 6" diameter		.01	.60	1.79	5.35	.45	
	0600	800 GPM, 8" diameter		.01	.83	2.48	7.45	.60	
	0700	1500 GPM, 10" diameter		.01	.87	2.61	7.85	.60	
	0800	2500 GPM, 12" diameter		.02	1.64	4.93	14.80	1.15	
	0900	4500 GPM, 16" diameter		.03	2.10	6.31	18.95	1.50	
	0950	For quick coupling aluminum and plastic pipe, add	▼	.03	2.18	6.54	19.60	1.55	
	1100	Wellpoint, 25' long, with fittings & riser pipe, 1-1/2" or 2" diameter	Ea.	.07	4.35	13.05	39	3.15	
	1200	Wellpoint pump, diesel powered, 4" suction, 20 H.P.		6.87	199	597	1,800	174.35	
	1300	6" suction, 30 H.P.		9.22	247	741	2,225	221.95	
	1400	8" suction, 40 H.P.		12.49	340	1,016	3,050	303.10	
	1500	10" suction, 75 H.P.		18.40	395	1,187	3,550	384.60	
	1600	12" suction, 100 H.P.		26.68	630	1,890	5,675	591.45	
	1700	12" suction, 175 H.P.	▼	38.17	695	2,090	6,275	723.35	
80	0010	**MARINE EQUIPMENT RENTAL** without operators							80
	0200	Barge, 400 Ton, 30' wide x 90' long	R015433 -10 Ea.	17.65	1,100	3,265	9,800	794.20	
	0240	800 Ton, 45' wide x 90' long		21.40	1,325	3,980	11,900	967.20	
	2000	Tugboat, diesel, 100 H.P.		35.00	220	660	1,975	412	
	2040	250 H.P.		71.15	395	1,190	3,575	807.20	
	2080	380 H.P.		145.20	1,200	3,575	10,700	1,877	
	3000	Small work boat, gas, 16-foot, 50 H.P.		14.75	61.50	185	555	155	
	4000	Large, diesel, 48-foot, 200 H.P.	▼	84.45	1,275	3,815	11,400	1,439	

| Crew No. | | Bare Costs | | Incl. Subs O&P | | Cost Per Labor-Hour | |

Crew A-1	Hr.	Daily	Hr.	Daily	Bare Costs	Incl. O&P
1 Building Laborer	$39.15	$313.20	$60.00	$480.00	$39.15	$60.00
1 Concrete Saw, Gas Manual		74.20		81.62	9.28	10.20
8 L.H., Daily Totals		$387.40		$561.62	$48.42	$70.20

Crew A-1A	Hr.	Daily	Hr.	Daily	Bare Costs	Incl. O&P
1 Skilled Worker	$51.45	$411.60	$79.20	$633.60	$51.45	$79.20
1 Shot Blaster, 20"		220.40		242.44	27.55	30.31
8 L.H., Daily Totals		$632.00		$876.04	$79.00	$109.51

Crew A-1B	Hr.	Daily	Hr.	Daily	Bare Costs	Incl. O&P
1 Building Laborer	$39.15	$313.20	$60.00	$480.00	$39.15	$60.00
1 Concrete Saw		153.60		168.96	19.20	21.12
8 L.H., Daily Totals		$466.80		$648.96	$58.35	$81.12

Crew A-1C	Hr.	Daily	Hr.	Daily	Bare Costs	Incl. O&P
1 Building Laborer	$39.15	$313.20	$60.00	$480.00	$39.15	$60.00
1 Chain Saw, Gas, 18"		29.40		32.34	3.67	4.04
8 L.H., Daily Totals		$342.60		$512.34	$42.83	$64.04

Crew A-1D	Hr.	Daily	Hr.	Daily	Bare Costs	Incl. O&P
1 Building Laborer	$39.15	$313.20	$60.00	$480.00	$39.15	$60.00
1 Vibrating Plate, Gas, 18"		33.60		36.96	4.20	4.62
8 L.H., Daily Totals		$346.80		$516.96	$43.35	$64.62

Crew A-1E	Hr.	Daily	Hr.	Daily	Bare Costs	Incl. O&P
1 Building Laborer	$39.15	$313.20	$60.00	$480.00	$39.15	$60.00
1 Vibrating Plate, Gas, 21"		42.80		47.08	5.35	5.88
8 L.H., Daily Totals		$356.00		$527.08	$44.50	$65.89

Crew A-1F	Hr.	Daily	Hr.	Daily	Bare Costs	Incl. O&P
1 Building Laborer	$39.15	$313.20	$60.00	$480.00	$39.15	$60.00
1 Rammer/Tamper, Gas, 8"		50.00		55.00	6.25	6.88
8 L.H., Daily Totals		$363.20		$535.00	$45.40	$66.88

Crew A-1G	Hr.	Daily	Hr.	Daily	Bare Costs	Incl. O&P
1 Building Laborer	$39.15	$313.20	$60.00	$480.00	$39.15	$60.00
1 Rammer/Tamper, Gas, 15"		56.80		62.48	7.10	7.81
8 L.H., Daily Totals		$370.00		$542.48	$46.25	$67.81

Crew A-1H	Hr.	Daily	Hr.	Daily	Bare Costs	Incl. O&P
1 Building Laborer	$39.15	$313.20	$60.00	$480.00	$39.15	$60.00
1 Exterior Steam Cleaner		75.20		82.72	9.40	10.34
8 L.H., Daily Totals		$388.40		$562.72	$48.55	$70.34

Crew A-1J	Hr.	Daily	Hr.	Daily	Bare Costs	Incl. O&P
1 Building Laborer	$39.15	$313.20	$60.00	$480.00	$39.15	$60.00
1 Cultivator, Walk-Behind, 5 H.P.		38.40		42.24	4.80	5.28
8 L.H., Daily Totals		$351.60		$522.24	$43.95	$65.28

Crew A-1K	Hr.	Daily	Hr.	Daily	Bare Costs	Incl. O&P
1 Building Laborer	$39.15	$313.20	$60.00	$480.00	$39.15	$60.00
1 Cultivator, Walk-Behind, 8 H.P.		68.70		75.57	8.59	9.45
8 L.H., Daily Totals		$381.90		$555.57	$47.74	$69.45

Crew A-1M	Hr.	Daily	Hr.	Daily	Bare Costs	Incl. O&P
1 Building Laborer	$39.15	$313.20	$60.00	$480.00	$39.15	$60.00
1 Snow Blower, Walk-Behind		62.50		68.75	7.81	8.59
8 L.H., Daily Totals		$375.70		$548.75	$46.96	$68.59

Crew A-2	Hr.	Daily	Hr.	Daily	Bare Costs	Incl. O&P
2 Laborers	$39.15	$626.40	$60.00	$960.00	$40.82	$62.20
1 Truck Driver (light)	44.15	353.20	66.60	532.80		
1 Flatbed Truck, Gas, 1.5 Ton		217.40		239.14	9.06	9.96
24 L.H., Daily Totals		$1197.00		$1731.94	$49.88	$72.16

Crew A-2A	Hr.	Daily	Hr.	Daily	Bare Costs	Incl. O&P
2 Laborers	$39.15	$626.40	$60.00	$960.00	$40.82	$62.20
1 Truck Driver (light)	44.15	353.20	66.60	532.80		
1 Flatbed Truck, Gas, 1.5 Ton		217.40		239.14		
1 Concrete Saw		153.60		168.96	15.46	17.00
24 L.H., Daily Totals		$1350.60		$1900.90	$56.27	$79.20

Crew A-2B	Hr.	Daily	Hr.	Daily	Bare Costs	Incl. O&P
1 Truck Driver (light)	$44.15	$353.20	$66.60	$532.80	$44.15	$66.60
1 Flatbed Truck, Gas, 1.5 Ton		217.40		239.14	27.18	29.89
8 L.H., Daily Totals		$570.60		$771.94	$71.33	$96.49

Crew A-3A	Hr.	Daily	Hr.	Daily	Bare Costs	Incl. O&P
1 Equip. Oper. (light)	$51.00	$408.00	$77.15	$617.20	$51.00	$77.15
1 Pickup Truck, 4x4, 3/4 Ton		140.00		154.00	17.50	19.25
8 L.H., Daily Totals		$548.00		$771.20	$68.50	$96.40

Crew A-3B	Hr.	Daily	Hr.	Daily	Bare Costs	Incl. O&P
1 Equip. Oper. (medium)	$53.55	$428.40	$81.00	$648.00	$49.55	$74.85
1 Truck Driver (heavy)	45.55	364.40	68.70	549.60		
1 Dump Truck, 12 C.Y., 400 H.P.		642.60		706.86		
1 F.E. Loader, W.M., 2.5 C.Y.		556.20		611.82	74.92	82.42
16 L.H., Daily Totals		$1991.60		$2516.28	$124.47	$157.27

Crew A-3C	Hr.	Daily	Hr.	Daily	Bare Costs	Incl. O&P
1 Equip. Oper. (light)	$51.00	$408.00	$77.15	$617.20	$51.00	$77.15
1 Loader, Skid Steer, 78 H.P.		309.40		340.34	38.67	42.54
8 L.H., Daily Totals		$717.40		$957.54	$89.67	$119.69

Crew A-3D	Hr.	Daily	Hr.	Daily	Bare Costs	Incl. O&P
1 Truck Driver (light)	$44.15	$353.20	$66.60	$532.80	$44.15	$66.60
1 Pickup Truck, 4x4, 3/4 Ton		140.00		154.00		
1 Flatbed Trailer, 25 Ton		128.40		141.24	33.55	36.91
8 L.H., Daily Totals		$621.60		$828.04	$77.70	$103.51

Crew A-3E	Hr.	Daily	Hr.	Daily	Bare Costs	Incl. O&P
1 Equip. Oper. (crane)	$55.70	$445.60	$84.25	$674.00	$50.63	$76.47
1 Truck Driver (heavy)	45.55	364.40	68.70	549.60		
1 Pickup Truck, 4x4, 3/4 Ton		140.00		154.00	8.75	9.63
16 L.H., Daily Totals		$950.00		$1377.60	$59.38	$86.10

Crew A-3F	Hr.	Daily	Hr.	Daily	Bare Costs	Incl. O&P
1 Equip. Oper. (crane)	$55.70	$445.60	$84.25	$674.00	$50.63	$76.47
1 Truck Driver (heavy)	45.55	364.40	68.70	549.60		
1 Pickup Truck, 4x4, 3/4 Ton		140.00		154.00		
1 Truck Tractor, 6x4, 380 H.P.		559.80		615.78		
1 Lowbed Trailer, 75 Ton		242.40		266.64	58.89	64.78
16 L.H., Daily Totals		$1752.20		$2260.02	$109.51	$141.25

Crew No.	Bare Costs		Incl. Subs O&P		Cost Per Labor-Hour	
Crew A-3G	Hr.	Daily	Hr.	Daily	Bare Costs	Incl. O&P
1 Equip. Oper. (crane)	$55.70	$445.60	$84.25	$674.00	$50.63	$76.47
1 Truck Driver (heavy)	45.55	364.40	68.70	549.60		
1 Pickup Truck, 4x4, 3/4 Ton		140.00		154.00		
1 Truck Tractor, 6x4, 450 H.P.		679.80		747.78		
1 Lowbed Trailer, 75 Ton		242.40		266.64	66.39	73.03
16 L.H., Daily Totals		$1872.20		$2392.02	$117.01	$149.50
Crew A-3H	Hr.	Daily	Hr.	Daily	Bare Costs	Incl. O&P
1 Equip. Oper. (crane)	$55.70	$445.60	$84.25	$674.00	$55.70	$84.25
1 Hyd. Crane, 12 Ton (Daily)		767.80		844.58	95.97	105.57
8 L.H., Daily Totals		$1213.40		$1518.58	$151.68	$189.82
Crew A-3I	Hr.	Daily	Hr.	Daily	Bare Costs	Incl. O&P
1 Equip. Oper. (crane)	$55.70	$445.60	$84.25	$674.00	$55.70	$84.25
1 Hyd. Crane, 25 Ton (Daily)		904.80		995.28	113.10	124.41
8 L.H., Daily Totals		$1350.40		$1669.28	$168.80	$208.66
Crew A-3J	Hr.	Daily	Hr.	Daily	Bare Costs	Incl. O&P
1 Equip. Oper. (crane)	$55.70	$445.60	$84.25	$674.00	$55.70	$84.25
1 Hyd. Crane, 40 Ton (Daily)		1354.00		1489.40	169.25	186.18
8 L.H., Daily Totals		$1799.60		$2163.40	$224.95	$270.43
Crew A-3K	Hr.	Daily	Hr.	Daily	Bare Costs	Incl. O&P
1 Equip. Oper. (crane)	$55.70	$445.60	$84.25	$674.00	$51.85	$78.42
1 Equip. Oper. (oiler)	48.00	384.00	72.60	580.80		
1 Hyd. Crane, 55 Ton (Daily)		1455.00		1600.50		
1 P/U Truck, 3/4 Ton (Daily)		154.40		169.84	100.59	110.65
16 L.H., Daily Totals		$2439.00		$3025.14	$152.44	$189.07
Crew A-3L	Hr.	Daily	Hr.	Daily	Bare Costs	Incl. O&P
1 Equip. Oper. (crane)	$55.70	$445.60	$84.25	$674.00	$51.85	$78.42
1 Equip. Oper. (oiler)	48.00	384.00	72.60	580.80		
1 Hyd. Crane, 80 Ton (Daily)		2245.00		2469.50		
1 P/U Truck, 3/4 Ton (Daily)		154.40		169.84	149.96	164.96
16 L.H., Daily Totals		$3229.00		$3894.14	$201.81	$243.38
Crew A-3M	Hr.	Daily	Hr.	Daily	Bare Costs	Incl. O&P
1 Equip. Oper. (crane)	$55.70	$445.60	$84.25	$674.00	$51.85	$78.42
1 Equip. Oper. (oiler)	48.00	384.00	72.60	580.80		
1 Hyd. Crane, 100 Ton (Daily)		2439.00		2682.90		
1 P/U Truck, 3/4 Ton (Daily)		154.40		169.84	162.09	178.30
16 L.H., Daily Totals		$3423.00		$4107.54	$213.94	$256.72
Crew A-3N	Hr.	Daily	Hr.	Daily	Bare Costs	Incl. O&P
1 Equip. Oper. (crane)	$55.70	$445.60	$84.25	$674.00	$55.70	$84.25
1 Tower Crane (monthly)		1166.00		1282.60	145.75	160.32
8 L.H., Daily Totals		$1611.60		$1956.60	$201.45	$244.57
Crew A-3P	Hr.	Daily	Hr.	Daily	Bare Costs	Incl. O&P
1 Equip. Oper. (light)	$51.00	$408.00	$77.15	$617.20	$51.00	$77.15
1 A.T. Forklift, 31' reach, 45' lift		520.60		572.66	65.08	71.58
8 L.H., Daily Totals		$928.60		$1189.86	$116.08	$148.73
Crew A-3Q	Hr.	Daily	Hr.	Daily	Bare Costs	Incl. O&P
1 Equip. Oper. (light)	$51.00	$408.00	$77.15	$617.20	$51.00	$77.15
1 Pickup Truck, 4x4, 3/4 Ton		140.00		154.00		
1 Flatbed Trailer, 3 Ton		24.00		26.40	20.50	22.55
8 L.H., Daily Totals		$572.00		$797.60	$71.50	$99.70

Crew No.	Bare Costs		Incl. Subs O&P		Cost Per Labor-Hour	
Crew A-3R	Hr.	Daily	Hr.	Daily	Bare Costs	Incl. O&P
1 Equip. Oper. (light)	$51.00	$408.00	$77.15	$617.20	$51.00	$77.15
1 Forklift, Smooth Floor, 8,000 Lb.		171.20		188.32	21.40	23.54
8 L.H., Daily Totals		$579.20		$805.52	$72.40	$100.69
Crew A-4	Hr.	Daily	Hr.	Daily	Bare Costs	Incl. O&P
2 Carpenters	$49.25	$788.00	$75.45	$1207.20	$46.73	$71.28
1 Painter, Ordinary	41.70	333.60	62.95	503.60		
24 L.H., Daily Totals		$1121.60		$1710.80	$46.73	$71.28
Crew A-5	Hr.	Daily	Hr.	Daily	Bare Costs	Incl. O&P
2 Laborers	$39.15	$626.40	$60.00	$960.00	$39.71	$60.73
.25 Truck Driver (light)	44.15	88.30	66.60	133.20		
.25 Flatbed Truck, Gas, 1.5 Ton		54.35		59.78	3.02	3.32
18 L.H., Daily Totals		$769.05		$1152.98	$42.73	$64.05
Crew A-6	Hr.	Daily	Hr.	Daily	Bare Costs	Incl. O&P
1 Instrument Man	$51.45	$411.60	$79.20	$633.60	$49.63	$75.97
1 Rodman/Chainman	47.80	382.40	72.75	582.00		
1 Level, Electronic		41.55		45.70	2.60	2.86
16 L.H., Daily Totals		$835.55		$1261.31	$52.22	$78.83
Crew A-7	Hr.	Daily	Hr.	Daily	Bare Costs	Incl. O&P
1 Chief of Party	$62.70	$501.60	$95.25	$762.00	$53.98	$82.40
1 Instrument Man	51.45	411.60	79.20	633.60		
1 Rodman/Chainman	47.80	382.40	72.75	582.00		
1 Level, Electronic		41.55		45.70	1.73	1.90
24 L.H., Daily Totals		$1337.15		$2023.31	$55.71	$84.30
Crew A-8	Hr.	Daily	Hr.	Daily	Bare Costs	Incl. O&P
1 Chief of Party	$62.70	$501.60	$95.25	$762.00	$52.44	$79.99
1 Instrument Man	51.45	411.60	79.20	633.60		
2 Rodmen/Chainmen	47.80	764.80	72.75	1164.00		
1 Level, Electronic		41.55		45.70	1.30	1.43
32 L.H., Daily Totals		$1719.55		$2605.30	$53.74	$81.42
Crew A-9	Hr.	Daily	Hr.	Daily	Bare Costs	Incl. O&P
1 Asbestos Foreman	$55.55	$444.40	$86.30	$690.40	$55.11	$85.64
7 Asbestos Workers	55.05	3082.80	85.55	4790.80		
64 L.H., Daily Totals		$3527.20		$5481.20	$55.11	$85.64
Crew A-10A	Hr.	Daily	Hr.	Daily	Bare Costs	Incl. O&P
1 Asbestos Foreman	$55.55	$444.40	$86.30	$690.40	$55.22	$85.80
2 Asbestos Workers	55.05	880.80	85.55	1368.80		
24 L.H., Daily Totals		$1325.20		$2059.20	$55.22	$85.80
Crew A-10B	Hr.	Daily	Hr.	Daily	Bare Costs	Incl. O&P
1 Asbestos Foreman	$55.55	$444.40	$86.30	$690.40	$55.17	$85.74
3 Asbestos Workers	55.05	1321.20	85.55	2053.20		
32 L.H., Daily Totals		$1765.60		$2743.60	$55.17	$85.74
Crew A-10C	Hr.	Daily	Hr.	Daily	Bare Costs	Incl. O&P
3 Asbestos Workers	$55.05	$1321.20	$85.55	$2053.20	$55.05	$85.55
1 Flatbed Truck, Gas, 1.5 Ton		217.40		239.14	9.06	9.96
24 L.H., Daily Totals		$1538.60		$2292.34	$64.11	$95.51

Crew A-10D	Hr.	Daily	Hr.	Daily	Bare Costs	Incl. O&P
2 Asbestos Workers	$55.05	$880.80	$85.55	$1368.80	$53.45	$81.99
1 Equip. Oper. (crane)	55.70	445.60	84.25	674.00		
1 Equip. Oper. (oiler)	48.00	384.00	72.60	580.80		
1 Hydraulic Crane, 33 Ton		863.60		949.96	26.99	29.69
32 L.H., Daily Totals		$2574.00		$3573.56	$80.44	$111.67

Crew A-11	Hr.	Daily	Hr.	Daily	Bare Costs	Incl. O&P
1 Asbestos Foreman	$55.55	$444.40	$86.30	$690.40	$55.11	$85.64
7 Asbestos Workers	55.05	3082.80	85.55	4790.80		
2 Chip Hammers, 12 Lb., Elec.		40.80		44.88	.64	.70
64 L.H., Daily Totals		$3568.00		$5526.08	$55.75	$86.35

Crew A-12	Hr.	Daily	Hr.	Daily	Bare Costs	Incl. O&P
1 Asbestos Foreman	$55.55	$444.40	$86.30	$690.40	$55.11	$85.64
7 Asbestos Workers	55.05	3082.80	85.55	4790.80		
1 Trk-Mtd Vac, 14 CY, 1500 Gal.		505.90		556.49		
1 Flatbed Truck, 20,000 GVW		232.00		255.20	11.53	12.68
64 L.H., Daily Totals		$4265.10		$6292.89	$66.64	$98.33

Crew A-13	Hr.	Daily	Hr.	Daily	Bare Costs	Incl. O&P
1 Equip. Oper. (light)	$51.00	$408.00	$77.15	$617.20	$51.00	$77.15
1 Trk-Mtd Vac, 14 CY, 1500 Gal.		505.90		556.49		
1 Flatbed Truck, 20,000 GVW		232.00		255.20	92.24	101.46
8 L.H., Daily Totals		$1145.90		$1428.89	$143.24	$178.61

Crew B-1	Hr.	Daily	Hr.	Daily	Bare Costs	Incl. O&P
1 Labor Foreman (outside)	$41.15	$329.20	$63.05	$504.40	$39.82	$61.02
2 Laborers	39.15	626.40	60.00	960.00		
24 L.H., Daily Totals		$955.60		$1464.40	$39.82	$61.02

Crew B-1A	Hr.	Daily	Hr.	Daily	Bare Costs	Incl. O&P
1 Labor Foreman (outside)	$41.15	$329.20	$63.05	$504.40	$39.82	$61.02
2 Laborers	39.15	626.40	60.00	960.00		
2 Cutting Torches		24.00		26.40		
2 Sets of Gases		336.00		369.60	15.00	16.50
24 L.H., Daily Totals		$1315.60		$1860.40	$54.82	$77.52

Crew B-1B	Hr.	Daily	Hr.	Daily	Bare Costs	Incl. O&P
1 Labor Foreman (outside)	$41.15	$329.20	$63.05	$504.40	$43.79	$66.83
2 Laborers	39.15	626.40	60.00	960.00		
1 Equip. Oper. (crane)	55.70	445.60	84.25	674.00		
2 Cutting Torches		24.00		26.40		
2 Sets of Gases		336.00		369.60		
1 Hyd. Crane, 12 Ton		572.80		630.08	29.15	32.06
32 L.H., Daily Totals		$2334.00		$3164.48	$72.94	$98.89

Crew B-1C	Hr.	Daily	Hr.	Daily	Bare Costs	Incl. O&P
1 Labor Foreman (outside)	$41.15	$329.20	$63.05	$504.40	$39.82	$61.02
2 Laborers	39.15	626.40	60.00	960.00		
1 Telescoping Boom Lift, to 60'		456.00		501.60	19.00	20.90
24 L.H., Daily Totals		$1411.60		$1966.00	$58.82	$81.92

Crew B-1D	Hr.	Daily	Hr.	Daily	Bare Costs	Incl. O&P
2 Laborers	$39.15	$626.40	$60.00	$960.00	$39.15	$60.00
1 Small Work Boat, Gas, 50 H.P.		155.00		170.50		
1 Pressure Washer, 7 GPM		82.00		90.20	14.81	16.29
16 L.H., Daily Totals		$863.40		$1220.70	$53.96	$76.29

Crew B-1E	Hr.	Daily	Hr.	Daily	Bare Costs	Incl. O&P
1 Labor Foreman (outside)	$41.15	$329.20	$63.05	$504.40	$39.65	$60.70
3 Laborers	39.15	939.60	60.00	1440.00		
1 Work Boat, Diesel, 200 H.P.		1439.00		1582.90		
2 Pressure Washers, 7 GPM		164.00		180.40	50.09	55.10
32 L.H., Daily Totals		$2871.80		$3707.70	$89.74	$115.87

Crew B-1F	Hr.	Daily	Hr.	Daily	Bare Costs	Incl. O&P
2 Skilled Workers	$51.45	$823.20	$79.20	$1267.20	$47.35	$72.80
1 Laborer	39.15	313.20	60.00	480.00		
1 Small Work Boat, Gas, 50 H.P.		155.00		170.50		
1 Pressure Washer, 7 GPM		82.00		90.20	9.88	10.86
24 L.H., Daily Totals		$1373.40		$2007.90	$57.23	$83.66

Crew B-1G	Hr.	Daily	Hr.	Daily	Bare Costs	Incl. O&P
2 Laborers	$39.15	$626.40	$60.00	$960.00	$39.15	$60.00
1 Small Work Boat, Gas, 50 H.P.		155.00		170.50	9.69	10.66
16 L.H., Daily Totals		$781.40		$1130.50	$48.84	$70.66

Crew B-1H	Hr.	Daily	Hr.	Daily	Bare Costs	Incl. O&P
2 Skilled Workers	$51.45	$823.20	$79.20	$1267.20	$47.35	$72.80
1 Laborer	39.15	313.20	60.00	480.00		
1 Small Work Boat, Gas, 50 H.P.		155.00		170.50	6.46	7.10
24 L.H., Daily Totals		$1291.40		$1917.70	$53.81	$79.90

Crew B-1J	Hr.	Daily	Hr.	Daily	Bare Costs	Incl. O&P
1 Labor Foreman (inside)	$39.65	$317.20	$60.75	$486.00	$39.40	$60.38
1 Laborer	39.15	313.20	60.00	480.00		
16 L.H., Daily Totals		$630.40		$966.00	$39.40	$60.38

Crew B-1K	Hr.	Daily	Hr.	Daily	Bare Costs	Incl. O&P
1 Carpenter Foreman (inside)	$49.75	$398.00	$76.20	$609.60	$49.50	$75.83
1 Carpenter	49.25	394.00	75.45	603.60		
16 L.H., Daily Totals		$792.00		$1213.20	$49.50	$75.83

Crew B-2	Hr.	Daily	Hr.	Daily	Bare Costs	Incl. O&P
1 Labor Foreman (outside)	$41.15	$329.20	$63.05	$504.40	$39.55	$60.61
4 Laborers	39.15	1252.80	60.00	1920.00		
40 L.H., Daily Totals		$1582.00		$2424.40	$39.55	$60.61

Crew B-2A	Hr.	Daily	Hr.	Daily	Bare Costs	Incl. O&P
1 Labor Foreman (outside)	$41.15	$329.20	$63.05	$504.40	$39.82	$61.02
2 Laborers	39.15	626.40	60.00	960.00		
1 Telescoping Boom Lift, to 60'		456.00		501.60	19.00	20.90
24 L.H., Daily Totals		$1411.60		$1966.00	$58.82	$81.92

Crew B-3	Hr.	Daily	Hr.	Daily	Bare Costs	Incl. O&P
1 Labor Foreman (outside)	$41.15	$329.20	$63.05	$504.40	$44.02	$66.91
2 Laborers	39.15	626.40	60.00	960.00		
1 Equip. Oper. (medium)	53.55	428.40	81.00	648.00		
2 Truck Drivers (heavy)	45.55	728.80	68.70	1099.20		
1 Crawler Loader, 3 C.Y.		1281.00		1409.10		
2 Dump Trucks, 12 C.Y., 400 H.P.		1285.20		1413.72	53.46	58.81
48 L.H., Daily Totals		$4679.00		$6034.42	$97.48	$125.72

Crew B-3A	Hr.	Daily	Hr.	Daily	Bare Costs	Incl. O&P
4 Laborers	$39.15	$1252.80	$60.00	$1920.00	$42.03	$64.20
1 Equip. Oper. (medium)	53.55	428.40	81.00	648.00		
1 Hyd. Excavator, 1.5 C.Y.		965.00		1061.50	24.13	26.54
40 L.H., Daily Totals		$2646.20		$3629.50	$66.16	$90.74

Crews - Standard

Crew No.	Bare Costs		Incl. Subs O&P		Cost Per Labor-Hour	
Crew B-3B	Hr.	Daily	Hr.	Daily	Bare Costs	Incl. O&P
2 Laborers	$39.15	$626.40	$60.00	$960.00	$44.35	$67.42
1 Equip. Oper. (medium)	53.55	428.40	81.00	648.00		
1 Truck Driver (heavy)	45.55	364.40	68.70	549.60		
1 Backhoe Loader, 80 H.P.		394.40		433.84		
1 Dump Truck, 12 C.Y., 400 H.P.		642.60		706.86	32.41	35.65
32 L.H., Daily Totals		$2456.20		$3298.30	$76.76	$103.07
Crew B-3C	Hr.	Daily	Hr.	Daily	Bare Costs	Incl. O&P
3 Laborers	$39.15	$939.60	$60.00	$1440.00	$42.75	$65.25
1 Equip. Oper. (medium)	53.55	428.40	81.00	648.00		
1 Crawler Loader, 4 C.Y.		1528.00		1680.80	47.75	52.52
32 L.H., Daily Totals		$2896.00		$3768.80	$90.50	$117.78
Crew B-4	Hr.	Daily	Hr.	Daily	Bare Costs	Incl. O&P
1 Labor Foreman (outside)	$41.15	$329.20	$63.05	$504.40	$40.55	$61.96
4 Laborers	39.15	1252.80	60.00	1920.00		
1 Truck Driver (heavy)	45.55	364.40	68.70	549.60		
1 Truck Tractor, 220 H.P.		336.60		370.26		
1 Flatbed Trailer, 40 Ton		175.00		192.50	10.66	11.72
48 L.H., Daily Totals		$2458.00		$3536.76	$51.21	$73.68
Crew B-5	Hr.	Daily	Hr.	Daily	Bare Costs	Incl. O&P
1 Labor Foreman (outside)	$41.15	$329.20	$63.05	$504.40	$43.55	$66.44
4 Laborers	39.15	1252.80	60.00	1920.00		
2 Equip. Oper. (medium)	53.55	856.80	81.00	1296.00		
1 Air Compressor, 250 cfm		181.20		199.32		
2 Breakers, Pavement, 60 lb.		20.40		22.44		
2 -50' Air Hoses, 1.5"		11.60		12.76		
1 Crawler Loader, 3 C.Y.		1281.00		1409.10	26.68	29.35
56 L.H., Daily Totals		$3933.00		$5364.02	$70.23	$95.79
Crew B-5A	Hr.	Daily	Hr.	Daily	Bare Costs	Incl. O&P
1 Labor Foreman (outside)	$41.15	$329.20	$63.05	$504.40	$43.77	$66.63
6 Laborers	39.15	1879.20	60.00	2880.00		
2 Equip. Oper. (medium)	53.55	856.80	81.00	1296.00		
1 Equip. Oper. (light)	51.00	408.00	77.15	617.20		
2 Truck Drivers (heavy)	45.55	728.80	68.70	1099.20		
1 Air Compressor, 365 cfm		236.00		259.60		
2 Breakers, Pavement, 60 lb.		20.40		22.44		
8 -50' Air Hoses, 1"		32.80		36.08		
2 Dump Trucks, 8 C.Y., 220 H.P.		782.00		860.20	11.16	12.27
96 L.H., Daily Totals		$5273.20		$7575.12	$54.93	$78.91
Crew B-5B	Hr.	Daily	Hr.	Daily	Bare Costs	Incl. O&P
1 Powderman	$51.45	$411.60	$79.20	$633.60	$49.20	$74.55
2 Equip. Oper. (medium)	53.55	856.80	81.00	1296.00		
3 Truck Drivers (heavy)	45.55	1093.20	68.70	1648.80		
1 F.E. Loader, W.M., 2.5 C.Y.		556.20		611.82		
3 Dump Trucks, 12 C.Y., 400 H.P.		1927.80		2120.58		
1 Air Compressor, 365 CFM		236.00		259.60	56.67	62.33
48 L.H., Daily Totals		$5081.60		$6570.40	$105.87	$136.88

Crew No.	Bare Costs		Incl. Subs O&P		Cost Per Labor-Hour	
Crew B-5C	Hr.	Daily	Hr.	Daily	Bare Costs	Incl. O&P
3 Laborers	$39.15	$939.60	$60.00	$1440.00	$45.73	$69.41
1 Equip. Oper. (medium)	53.55	428.40	81.00	648.00		
2 Truck Drivers (heavy)	45.55	728.80	68.70	1099.20		
1 Equip. Oper. (crane)	55.70	445.60	84.25	674.00		
1 Equip. Oper. (oiler)	48.00	384.00	72.60	580.80		
2 Dump Trucks, 12 C.Y., 400 H.P.		1285.20		1413.72		
1 Crawler Loader, 4 C.Y.		1528.00		1680.80		
1 S.P. Crane, 4x4, 25 Ton		605.60		666.16	53.42	58.76
64 L.H., Daily Totals		$6345.20		$8202.68	$99.14	$128.17
Crew B-5D	Hr.	Daily	Hr.	Daily	Bare Costs	Incl. O&P
1 Labor Foreman (outside)	$41.15	$329.20	$63.05	$504.40	$43.80	$66.72
4 Laborers	39.15	1252.80	60.00	1920.00		
2 Equip. Oper. (medium)	53.55	856.80	81.00	1296.00		
1 Truck Driver (heavy)	45.55	364.40	68.70	549.60		
1 Air Compressor, 250 cfm		181.20		199.32		
2 Breakers, Pavement, 60 lb.		20.40		22.44		
2 -50' Air Hoses, 1.5"		11.60		12.76		
1 Crawler Loader, 3 C.Y.		1281.00		1409.10		
1 Dump Truck, 12 C.Y., 400 H.P.		642.60		706.86	33.39	36.73
64 L.H., Daily Totals		$4940.00		$6620.48	$77.19	$103.45
Crew B-6	Hr.	Daily	Hr.	Daily	Bare Costs	Incl. O&P
2 Laborers	$39.15	$626.40	$60.00	$960.00	$43.10	$65.72
1 Equip. Oper. (light)	51.00	408.00	77.15	617.20		
1 Backhoe Loader, 48 H.P.		366.20		402.82	15.26	16.78
24 L.H., Daily Totals		$1400.60		$1980.02	$58.36	$82.50
Crew B-6A	Hr.	Daily	Hr.	Daily	Bare Costs	Incl. O&P
.5 Labor Foreman (outside)	$41.15	$164.60	$63.05	$252.20	$45.31	$69.01
1 Laborer	39.15	313.20	60.00	480.00		
1 Equip. Oper. (medium)	53.55	428.40	81.00	648.00		
1 Vacuum Truck, 5000 Gal.		347.20		381.92	17.36	19.10
20 L.H., Daily Totals		$1253.40		$1762.12	$62.67	$88.11
Crew B-6B	Hr.	Daily	Hr.	Daily	Bare Costs	Incl. O&P
2 Labor Foremen (outside)	$41.15	$658.40	$63.05	$1008.80	$39.82	$61.02
4 Laborers	39.15	1252.80	60.00	1920.00		
1 S.P. Crane, 4x4, 5 Ton		276.00		303.60		
1 Flatbed Truck, Gas, 1.5 Ton		217.40		239.14		
1 Butt Fusion Mach., 4"-12" diam.		415.10		456.61	18.93	20.82
48 L.H., Daily Totals		$2819.70		$3928.15	$58.74	$81.84
Crew B-6C	Hr.	Daily	Hr.	Daily	Bare Costs	Incl. O&P
2 Labor Foremen (outside)	$41.15	$658.40	$63.05	$1008.80	$39.82	$61.02
4 Laborers	39.15	1252.80	60.00	1920.00		
1 S.P. Crane, 4x4, 12 Ton		435.60		479.16		
1 Flatbed Truck, Gas, 3 Ton		270.20		297.22		
1 Butt Fusion Mach., 8"-24" diam.		1821.00		2003.10	52.64	57.91
48 L.H., Daily Totals		$4438.00		$5708.28	$92.46	$118.92
Crew B-7	Hr.	Daily	Hr.	Daily	Bare Costs	Incl. O&P
1 Labor Foreman (outside)	$41.15	$329.20	$63.05	$504.40	$41.88	$64.01
4 Laborers	39.15	1252.80	60.00	1920.00		
1 Equip. Oper. (medium)	53.55	428.40	81.00	648.00		
1 Brush Chipper, 12", 130 H.P.		404.40		444.84		
1 Crawler Loader, 3 C.Y.		1281.00		1409.10		
2 Chain Saws, Gas, 36" Long		90.00		99.00	36.99	40.69
48 L.H., Daily Totals		$3785.80		$5025.34	$78.87	$104.69

Crew No.	Bare Costs		Incl. Subs O&P		Cost Per Labor-Hour	

Crew B-7A	Hr.	Daily	Hr.	Daily	Bare Costs	Incl. O&P
2 Laborers	$39.15	$626.40	$60.00	$960.00	$43.10	$65.72
1 Equip. Oper. (light)	51.00	408.00	77.15	617.20		
1 Rake w/Tractor		344.10		378.51		
2 Chain Saws, Gas, 18"		58.80		64.68	16.79	18.47
24 L.H., Daily Totals		$1437.30		$2020.39	$59.89	$84.18

Crew B-7B	Hr.	Daily	Hr.	Daily	Bare Costs	Incl. O&P
1 Labor Foreman (outside)	$41.15	$329.20	$63.05	$504.40	$42.41	$64.68
4 Laborers	39.15	1252.80	60.00	1920.00		
1 Equip. Oper. (medium)	53.55	428.40	81.00	648.00		
1 Truck Driver (heavy)	45.55	364.40	68.70	549.60		
1 Brush Chipper, 12", 130 H.P.		404.40		444.84		
1 Crawler Loader, 3 C.Y.		1281.00		1409.10		
2 Chain Saws, Gas, 36" Long		90.00		99.00		
1 Dump Truck, 8 C.Y., 220 H.P.		391.00		430.10	38.69	42.55
56 L.H., Daily Totals		$4541.20		$6005.04	$81.09	$107.23

Crew B-7C	Hr.	Daily	Hr.	Daily	Bare Costs	Incl. O&P
1 Labor Foreman (outside)	$41.15	$329.20	$63.05	$504.40	$42.41	$64.68
4 Laborers	39.15	1252.80	60.00	1920.00		
1 Equip. Oper. (medium)	53.55	428.40	81.00	648.00		
1 Truck Driver (heavy)	45.55	364.40	68.70	549.60		
1 Brush Chipper, 12", 130 H.P.		404.40		444.84		
1 Crawler Loader, 3 C.Y.		1281.00		1409.10		
2 Chain Saws, Gas, 36" Long		90.00		99.00		
1 Dump Truck, 12 C.Y., 400 H.P.		642.60		706.86	43.18	47.50
56 L.H., Daily Totals		$4792.80		$6281.80	$85.59	$112.18

Crew B-8	Hr.	Daily	Hr.	Daily	Bare Costs	Incl. O&P
1 Labor Foreman (outside)	$41.15	$329.20	$63.05	$504.40	$45.71	$69.38
2 Laborers	39.15	626.40	60.00	960.00		
2 Equip. Oper. (medium)	53.55	856.80	81.00	1296.00		
1 Equip. Oper. (oiler)	48.00	384.00	72.60	580.80		
2 Truck Drivers (heavy)	45.55	728.80	68.70	1099.20		
1 Hyd. Crane, 25 Ton		673.80		741.18		
1 Crawler Loader, 3 C.Y.		1281.00		1409.10		
2 Dump Trucks, 12 C.Y., 400 H.P.		1285.20		1413.72	50.63	55.69
64 L.H., Daily Totals		$6165.20		$8004.40	$96.33	$125.07

Crew B-9	Hr.	Daily	Hr.	Daily	Bare Costs	Incl. O&P
1 Labor Foreman (outside)	$41.15	$329.20	$63.05	$504.40	$39.55	$60.61
4 Laborers	39.15	1252.80	60.00	1920.00		
1 Air Compressor, 250 cfm		181.20		199.32		
2 Breakers, Pavement, 60 lb.		20.40		22.44		
2 -50' Air Hoses, 1.5"		11.60		12.76	5.33	5.86
40 L.H., Daily Totals		$1795.20		$2658.92	$44.88	$66.47

Crew B-9A	Hr.	Daily	Hr.	Daily	Bare Costs	Incl. O&P
2 Laborers	$39.15	$626.40	$60.00	$960.00	$41.28	$62.90
1 Truck Driver (heavy)	45.55	364.40	68.70	549.60		
1 Water Tank Trailer, 5000 Gal.		143.00		157.30		
1 Truck Tractor, 220 H.P.		336.60		370.26		
2 -50' Discharge Hoses, 3"		3.50		3.85	20.13	22.14
24 L.H., Daily Totals		$1473.90		$2041.01	$61.41	$85.04

Crew B-9B	Hr.	Daily	Hr.	Daily	Bare Costs	Incl. O&P
2 Laborers	$39.15	$626.40	$60.00	$960.00	$41.28	$62.90
1 Truck Driver (heavy)	45.55	364.40	68.70	549.60		
2 -50' Discharge Hoses, 3"		3.50		3.85		
1 Water Tank Trailer, 5000 Gal.		143.00		157.30		
1 Truck Tractor, 220 H.P.		336.60		370.26		
1 Pressure Washer		66.00		72.60	22.88	25.17
24 L.H., Daily Totals		$1539.90		$2113.61	$64.16	$88.07

Crew B-9D	Hr.	Daily	Hr.	Daily	Bare Costs	Incl. O&P
1 Labor Foreman (outside)	$41.15	$329.20	$63.05	$504.40	$39.55	$60.61
4 Common Laborers	39.15	1252.80	60.00	1920.00		
1 Air Compressor, 250 cfm		181.20		199.32		
2 -50' Air Hoses, 1.5"		11.60		12.76		
2 Air Powered Tampers		52.40		57.64	6.13	6.74
40 L.H., Daily Totals		$1827.20		$2694.12	$45.68	$67.35

Crew B-10	Hr.	Daily	Hr.	Daily	Bare Costs	Incl. O&P
1 Equip. Oper. (medium)	$53.55	$428.40	$81.00	$648.00	$48.75	$74.00
.5 Laborer	39.15	156.60	60.00	240.00		
12 L.H., Daily Totals		$585.00		$888.00	$48.75	$74.00

Crew B-10A	Hr.	Daily	Hr.	Daily	Bare Costs	Incl. O&P
1 Equip. Oper. (medium)	$53.55	$428.40	$81.00	$648.00	$48.75	$74.00
.5 Laborer	39.15	156.60	60.00	240.00		
1 Roller, 2-Drum, W.B., 7.5 H.P.		182.80		201.08	15.23	16.76
12 L.H., Daily Totals		$767.80		$1089.08	$63.98	$90.76

Crew B-10B	Hr.	Daily	Hr.	Daily	Bare Costs	Incl. O&P
1 Equip. Oper. (medium)	$53.55	$428.40	$81.00	$648.00	$48.75	$74.00
.5 Laborer	39.15	156.60	60.00	240.00		
1 Dozer, 200 H.P.		1384.00		1522.40	115.33	126.87
12 L.H., Daily Totals		$1969.00		$2410.40	$164.08	$200.87

Crew B-10C	Hr.	Daily	Hr.	Daily	Bare Costs	Incl. O&P
1 Equip. Oper. (medium)	$53.55	$428.40	$81.00	$648.00	$48.75	$74.00
.5 Laborer	39.15	156.60	60.00	240.00		
1 Dozer, 200 H.P.		1384.00		1522.40		
1 Vibratory Roller, Towed, 23 Ton		427.40		470.14	150.95	166.04
12 L.H., Daily Totals		$2396.40		$2880.54	$199.70	$240.04

Crew B-10D	Hr.	Daily	Hr.	Daily	Bare Costs	Incl. O&P
1 Equip. Oper. (medium)	$53.55	$428.40	$81.00	$648.00	$48.75	$74.00
.5 Laborer	39.15	156.60	60.00	240.00		
1 Dozer, 200 H.P.		1384.00		1522.40		
1 Sheepsft. Roller, Towed		451.00		496.10	152.92	168.21
12 L.H., Daily Totals		$2420.00		$2906.50	$201.67	$242.21

Crew B-10E	Hr.	Daily	Hr.	Daily	Bare Costs	Incl. O&P
1 Equip. Oper. (medium)	$53.55	$428.40	$81.00	$648.00	$48.75	$74.00
.5 Laborer	39.15	156.60	60.00	240.00		
1 Tandem Roller, 5 Ton		152.40		167.64	12.70	13.97
12 L.H., Daily Totals		$737.40		$1055.64	$61.45	$87.97

Crew B-10F	Hr.	Daily	Hr.	Daily	Bare Costs	Incl. O&P
1 Equip. Oper. (medium)	$53.55	$428.40	$81.00	$648.00	$48.75	$74.00
.5 Laborer	39.15	156.60	60.00	240.00		
1 Tandem Roller, 10 Ton		237.60		261.36	19.80	21.78
12 L.H., Daily Totals		$822.60		$1149.36	$68.55	$95.78

For customer support on your Electrical Costs with RSMeans Data, call 800.448.8182.

473

Crew No.	Bare Costs		Incl. Subs O&P		Cost Per Labor-Hour	

Crew B-10G

	Hr.	Daily	Hr.	Daily	Bare Costs	Incl. O&P
1 Equip. Oper. (medium)	$53.55	$428.40	$81.00	$648.00	$48.75	$74.00
.5 Laborer	39.15	156.60	60.00	240.00		
1 Sheepsfoot Roller, 240 H.P.		1296.00		1425.60	108.00	118.80
12 L.H., Daily Totals		$1881.00		$2313.60	$156.75	$192.80

Crew B-10H

	Hr.	Daily	Hr.	Daily	Bare Costs	Incl. O&P
1 Equip. Oper. (medium)	$53.55	$428.40	$81.00	$648.00	$48.75	$74.00
.5 Laborer	39.15	156.60	60.00	240.00		
1 Diaphragm Water Pump, 2"		71.00		78.10		
1 -20' Suction Hose, 2"		1.95		2.15		
2 -50' Discharge Hoses, 2"		1.80		1.98	6.23	6.85
12 L.H., Daily Totals		$659.75		$970.23	$54.98	$80.85

Crew B-10I

	Hr.	Daily	Hr.	Daily	Bare Costs	Incl. O&P
1 Equip. Oper. (medium)	$53.55	$428.40	$81.00	$648.00	$48.75	$74.00
.5 Laborer	39.15	156.60	60.00	240.00		
1 Diaphragm Water Pump, 4"		114.20		125.62		
1 -20' Suction Hose, 4"		3.45		3.79		
2 -50' Discharge Hoses, 4"		4.70		5.17	10.20	11.22
12 L.H., Daily Totals		$707.35		$1022.59	$58.95	$85.22

Crew B-10J

	Hr.	Daily	Hr.	Daily	Bare Costs	Incl. O&P
1 Equip. Oper. (medium)	$53.55	$428.40	$81.00	$648.00	$48.75	$74.00
.5 Laborer	39.15	156.60	60.00	240.00		
1 Centrifugal Water Pump, 3"		78.60		86.46		
1 -20' Suction Hose, 3"		3.05		3.36		
2 -50' Discharge Hoses, 3"		3.50		3.85	7.10	7.81
12 L.H., Daily Totals		$670.15		$981.66	$55.85	$81.81

Crew B-10K

	Hr.	Daily	Hr.	Daily	Bare Costs	Incl. O&P
1 Equip. Oper. (medium)	$53.55	$428.40	$81.00	$648.00	$48.75	$74.00
.5 Laborer	39.15	156.60	60.00	240.00		
1 Centr. Water Pump, 6"		325.40		357.94		
1 -20' Suction Hose, 6"		11.90		13.09		
2 -50' Discharge Hoses, 6"		12.60		13.86	29.16	32.07
12 L.H., Daily Totals		$934.90		$1272.89	$77.91	$106.07

Crew B-10L

	Hr.	Daily	Hr.	Daily	Bare Costs	Incl. O&P
1 Equip. Oper. (medium)	$53.55	$428.40	$81.00	$648.00	$48.75	$74.00
.5 Laborer	39.15	156.60	60.00	240.00		
1 Dozer, 80 H.P.		468.60		515.46	39.05	42.95
12 L.H., Daily Totals		$1053.60		$1403.46	$87.80	$116.96

Crew B-10M

	Hr.	Daily	Hr.	Daily	Bare Costs	Incl. O&P
1 Equip. Oper. (medium)	$53.55	$428.40	$81.00	$648.00	$48.75	$74.00
.5 Laborer	39.15	156.60	60.00	240.00		
1 Dozer, 300 H.P.		1900.00		2090.00	158.33	174.17
12 L.H., Daily Totals		$2485.00		$2978.00	$207.08	$248.17

Crew B-10N

	Hr.	Daily	Hr.	Daily	Bare Costs	Incl. O&P
1 Equip. Oper. (medium)	$53.55	$428.40	$81.00	$648.00	$48.75	$74.00
.5 Laborer	39.15	156.60	60.00	240.00		
1 F.E. Loader, T.M., 1.5 C.Y.		568.20		625.02	47.35	52.09
12 L.H., Daily Totals		$1153.20		$1513.02	$96.10	$126.08

Crew B-10O

	Hr.	Daily	Hr.	Daily	Bare Costs	Incl. O&P
1 Equip. Oper. (medium)	$53.55	$428.40	$81.00	$648.00	$48.75	$74.00
.5 Laborer	39.15	156.60	60.00	240.00		
1 F.E. Loader, T.M., 2.25 C.Y.		977.60		1075.36	81.47	89.61
12 L.H., Daily Totals		$1562.60		$1963.36	$130.22	$163.61

Crew B-10P

	Hr.	Daily	Hr.	Daily	Bare Costs	Incl. O&P
1 Equip. Oper. (medium)	$53.55	$428.40	$81.00	$648.00	$48.75	$74.00
.5 Laborer	39.15	156.60	60.00	240.00		
1 Crawler Loader, 3 C.Y.		1281.00		1409.10	106.75	117.43
12 L.H., Daily Totals		$1866.00		$2297.10	$155.50	$191.43

Crew B-10Q

	Hr.	Daily	Hr.	Daily	Bare Costs	Incl. O&P
1 Equip. Oper. (medium)	$53.55	$428.40	$81.00	$648.00	$48.75	$74.00
.5 Laborer	39.15	156.60	60.00	240.00		
1 Crawler Loader, 4 C.Y.		1528.00		1680.80	127.33	140.07
12 L.H., Daily Totals		$2113.00		$2568.80	$176.08	$214.07

Crew B-10R

	Hr.	Daily	Hr.	Daily	Bare Costs	Incl. O&P
1 Equip. Oper. (medium)	$53.55	$428.40	$81.00	$648.00	$48.75	$74.00
.5 Laborer	39.15	156.60	60.00	240.00		
1 F.E. Loader, W.M., 1 C.Y.		312.80		344.08	26.07	28.67
12 L.H., Daily Totals		$897.80		$1232.08	$74.82	$102.67

Crew B-10S

	Hr.	Daily	Hr.	Daily	Bare Costs	Incl. O&P
1 Equip. Oper. (medium)	$53.55	$428.40	$81.00	$648.00	$48.75	$74.00
.5 Laborer	39.15	156.60	60.00	240.00		
1 F.E. Loader, W.M., 1.5 C.Y.		362.00		398.20	30.17	33.18
12 L.H., Daily Totals		$947.00		$1286.20	$78.92	$107.18

Crew B-10T

	Hr.	Daily	Hr.	Daily	Bare Costs	Incl. O&P
1 Equip. Oper. (medium)	$53.55	$428.40	$81.00	$648.00	$48.75	$74.00
.5 Laborer	39.15	156.60	60.00	240.00		
1 F.E. Loader, W.M., 2.5 C.Y.		556.20		611.82	46.35	50.98
12 L.H., Daily Totals		$1141.20		$1499.82	$95.10	$124.99

Crew B-10U

	Hr.	Daily	Hr.	Daily	Bare Costs	Incl. O&P
1 Equip. Oper. (medium)	$53.55	$428.40	$81.00	$648.00	$48.75	$74.00
.5 Laborer	39.15	156.60	60.00	240.00		
1 F.E. Loader, W.M., 5.5 C.Y.		1081.00		1189.10	90.08	99.09
12 L.H., Daily Totals		$1666.00		$2077.10	$138.83	$173.09

Crew B-10V

	Hr.	Daily	Hr.	Daily	Bare Costs	Incl. O&P
1 Equip. Oper. (medium)	$53.55	$428.40	$81.00	$648.00	$48.75	$74.00
.5 Laborer	39.15	156.60	60.00	240.00		
1 Dozer, 700 H.P.		5218.00		5739.80	434.83	478.32
12 L.H., Daily Totals		$5803.00		$6627.80	$483.58	$552.32

Crew B-10W

	Hr.	Daily	Hr.	Daily	Bare Costs	Incl. O&P
1 Equip. Oper. (medium)	$53.55	$428.40	$81.00	$648.00	$48.75	$74.00
.5 Laborer	39.15	156.60	60.00	240.00		
1 Dozer, 105 H.P.		608.00		668.80	50.67	55.73
12 L.H., Daily Totals		$1193.00		$1556.80	$99.42	$129.73

Crew B-10X

	Hr.	Daily	Hr.	Daily	Bare Costs	Incl. O&P
1 Equip. Oper. (medium)	$53.55	$428.40	$81.00	$648.00	$48.75	$74.00
.5 Laborer	39.15	156.60	60.00	240.00		
1 Dozer, 410 H.P.		2368.00		2604.80	197.33	217.07
12 L.H., Daily Totals		$2953.00		$3492.80	$246.08	$291.07

Crew B-10Y

	Hr.	Daily	Hr.	Daily	Bare Costs	Incl. O&P
1 Equip. Oper. (medium)	$53.55	$428.40	$81.00	$648.00	$48.75	$74.00
.5 Laborer	39.15	156.60	60.00	240.00		
1 Vibr. Roller, Towed, 12 Ton		605.40		665.94	50.45	55.49
12 L.H., Daily Totals		$1190.40		$1553.94	$99.20	$129.50

Crews - Standard

Crew B-11A

	Bare Hr.	Bare Daily	Incl. Subs O&P Hr.	Incl. Subs O&P Daily	Cost Per Labor-Hour Bare Costs	Cost Per Labor-Hour Incl. O&P
1 Equipment Oper. (med.)	$53.55	$428.40	$81.00	$648.00	$46.35	$70.50
1 Laborer	39.15	313.20	60.00	480.00		
1 Dozer, 200 H.P.		1384.00		1522.40	86.50	95.15
16 L.H., Daily Totals		$2125.60		$2650.40	$132.85	$165.65

Crew B-11B

	Bare Hr.	Bare Daily	Incl. Subs O&P Hr.	Incl. Subs O&P Daily	Bare Costs	Incl. O&P
1 Equipment Oper. (light)	$51.00	$408.00	$77.15	$617.20	$45.08	$68.58
1 Laborer	39.15	313.20	60.00	480.00		
1 Air Powered Tamper		26.20		28.82		
1 Air Compressor, 365 cfm		236.00		259.60		
2 -50' Air Hoses, 1.5"		11.60		12.76	17.11	18.82
16 L.H., Daily Totals		$995.00		$1398.38	$62.19	$87.40

Crew B-11C

	Bare Hr.	Bare Daily	Incl. Subs O&P Hr.	Incl. Subs O&P Daily	Bare Costs	Incl. O&P
1 Equipment Oper. (med.)	$53.55	$428.40	$81.00	$648.00	$46.35	$70.50
1 Laborer	39.15	313.20	60.00	480.00		
1 Backhoe Loader, 48 H.P.		366.20		402.82	22.89	25.18
16 L.H., Daily Totals		$1107.80		$1530.82	$69.24	$95.68

Crew B-11J

	Bare Hr.	Bare Daily	Incl. Subs O&P Hr.	Incl. Subs O&P Daily	Bare Costs	Incl. O&P
1 Equipment Oper. (med.)	$53.55	$428.40	$81.00	$648.00	$46.35	$70.50
1 Laborer	39.15	313.20	60.00	480.00		
1 Grader, 30,000 Lbs.		678.40		746.24		
1 Ripper, Beam & 1 Shank		85.60		94.16	47.75	52.52
16 L.H., Daily Totals		$1505.60		$1968.40	$94.10	$123.03

Crew B-11K

	Bare Hr.	Bare Daily	Incl. Subs O&P Hr.	Incl. Subs O&P Daily	Bare Costs	Incl. O&P
1 Equipment Oper. (med.)	$53.55	$428.40	$81.00	$648.00	$46.35	$70.50
1 Laborer	39.15	313.20	60.00	480.00		
1 Trencher, Chain Type, 8' D		2460.00		2706.00	153.75	169.13
16 L.H., Daily Totals		$3201.60		$3834.00	$200.10	$239.63

Crew B-11L

	Bare Hr.	Bare Daily	Incl. Subs O&P Hr.	Incl. Subs O&P Daily	Bare Costs	Incl. O&P
1 Equipment Oper. (med.)	$53.55	$428.40	$81.00	$648.00	$46.35	$70.50
1 Laborer	39.15	313.20	60.00	480.00		
1 Grader, 30,000 Lbs.		678.40		746.24	42.40	46.64
16 L.H., Daily Totals		$1420.00		$1874.24	$88.75	$117.14

Crew B-11M

	Bare Hr.	Bare Daily	Incl. Subs O&P Hr.	Incl. Subs O&P Daily	Bare Costs	Incl. O&P
1 Equipment Oper. (med.)	$53.55	$428.40	$81.00	$648.00	$46.35	$70.50
1 Laborer	39.15	313.20	60.00	480.00		
1 Backhoe Loader, 80 H.P.		394.40		433.84	24.65	27.11
16 L.H., Daily Totals		$1136.00		$1561.84	$71.00	$97.61

Crew B-11N

	Bare Hr.	Bare Daily	Incl. Subs O&P Hr.	Incl. Subs O&P Daily	Bare Costs	Incl. O&P
1 Labor Foreman (outside)	$41.15	$329.20	$63.05	$504.40	$46.84	$70.81
2 Equipment Operators (med.)	53.55	856.80	81.00	1296.00		
6 Truck Drivers (heavy)	45.55	2186.40	68.70	3297.60		
1 F.E. Loader, W.M., 5.5 C.Y.		1081.00		1189.10		
1 Dozer, 410 H.P.		2368.00		2604.80		
6 Dump Trucks, Off Hwy., 50 Ton		12036.00		13239.60	215.07	236.58
72 L.H., Daily Totals		$18857.40		$22131.50	$261.91	$307.38

Crew B-11Q

	Bare Hr.	Bare Daily	Incl. Subs O&P Hr.	Incl. Subs O&P Daily	Bare Costs	Incl. O&P
1 Equipment Operator (med.)	$53.55	$428.40	$81.00	$648.00	$48.75	$74.00
.5 Laborer	39.15	156.60	60.00	240.00		
1 Dozer, 140 H.P.		847.20		931.92	70.60	77.66
12 L.H., Daily Totals		$1432.20		$1819.92	$119.35	$151.66

Crew B-11R

	Bare Hr.	Bare Daily	Incl. Subs O&P Hr.	Incl. Subs O&P Daily	Bare Costs	Incl. O&P
1 Equipment Operator (med.)	$53.55	$428.40	$81.00	$648.00	$48.75	$74.00
.5 Laborer	39.15	156.60	60.00	240.00		
1 Dozer, 200 H.P.		1384.00		1522.40	115.33	126.87
12 L.H., Daily Totals		$1969.00		$2410.40	$164.08	$200.87

Crew B-11S

	Bare Hr.	Bare Daily	Incl. Subs O&P Hr.	Incl. Subs O&P Daily	Bare Costs	Incl. O&P
1 Equipment Operator (med.)	$53.55	$428.40	$81.00	$648.00	$48.75	$74.00
.5 Laborer	39.15	156.60	60.00	240.00		
1 Dozer, 300 H.P.		1900.00		2090.00		
1 Ripper, Beam & 1 Shank		85.60		94.16	165.47	182.01
12 L.H., Daily Totals		$2570.60		$3072.16	$214.22	$256.01

Crew B-11T

	Bare Hr.	Bare Daily	Incl. Subs O&P Hr.	Incl. Subs O&P Daily	Bare Costs	Incl. O&P
1 Equipment Operator (med.)	$53.55	$428.40	$81.00	$648.00	$48.75	$74.00
.5 Laborer	39.15	156.60	60.00	240.00		
1 Dozer, 410 H.P.		2368.00		2604.80		
1 Ripper, Beam & 2 Shanks		129.80		142.78	208.15	228.97
12 L.H., Daily Totals		$3082.80		$3635.58	$256.90	$302.96

Crew B-11U

	Bare Hr.	Bare Daily	Incl. Subs O&P Hr.	Incl. Subs O&P Daily	Bare Costs	Incl. O&P
1 Equipment Operator (med.)	$53.55	$428.40	$81.00	$648.00	$48.75	$74.00
.5 Laborer	39.15	156.60	60.00	240.00		
1 Dozer, 520 H.P.		3342.00		3676.20	278.50	306.35
12 L.H., Daily Totals		$3927.00		$4564.20	$327.25	$380.35

Crew B-11V

	Bare Hr.	Bare Daily	Incl. Subs O&P Hr.	Incl. Subs O&P Daily	Bare Costs	Incl. O&P
3 Laborers	$39.15	$939.60	$60.00	$1440.00	$39.15	$60.00
1 Roller, 2-Drum, W.B., 7.5 H.P.		182.80		201.08	7.62	8.38
24 L.H., Daily Totals		$1122.40		$1641.08	$46.77	$68.38

Crew B-11W

	Bare Hr.	Bare Daily	Incl. Subs O&P Hr.	Incl. Subs O&P Daily	Bare Costs	Incl. O&P
1 Equipment Operator (med.)	$53.55	$428.40	$81.00	$648.00	$45.68	$69.00
1 Common Laborer	39.15	313.20	60.00	480.00		
10 Truck Drivers (heavy)	45.55	3644.00	68.70	5496.00		
1 Dozer, 200 H.P.		1384.00		1522.40		
1 Vibratory Roller, Towed, 23 Ton		427.40		470.14		
10 Dump Trucks, 8 C.Y., 220 H.P.		3910.00		4301.00	59.60	65.56
96 L.H., Daily Totals		$10107.00		$12917.54	$105.28	$134.56

Crew B-11Y

	Bare Hr.	Bare Daily	Incl. Subs O&P Hr.	Incl. Subs O&P Daily	Bare Costs	Incl. O&P
1 Labor Foreman (outside)	$41.15	$329.20	$63.05	$504.40	$44.17	$67.34
5 Common Laborers	39.15	1566.00	60.00	2400.00		
3 Equipment Operators (med.)	53.55	1285.20	81.00	1944.00		
1 Dozer, 80 H.P.		468.60		515.46		
2 Rollers, 2-Drum, W.B., 7.5 H.P.		365.60		402.16		
4 Vibrating Plates, Gas, 21"		171.20		188.32	13.96	15.36
72 L.H., Daily Totals		$4185.80		$5954.34	$58.14	$82.70

Crew B-12A

	Bare Hr.	Bare Daily	Incl. Subs O&P Hr.	Incl. Subs O&P Daily	Bare Costs	Incl. O&P
1 Equip. Oper. (crane)	$55.70	$445.60	$84.25	$674.00	$47.42	$72.13
1 Laborer	39.15	313.20	60.00	480.00		
1 Hyd. Excavator, 1 C.Y.		798.20		878.02	49.89	54.88
16 L.H., Daily Totals		$1557.00		$2032.02	$97.31	$127.00

Crew B-12B

	Bare Hr.	Bare Daily	Incl. Subs O&P Hr.	Incl. Subs O&P Daily	Bare Costs	Incl. O&P
1 Equip. Oper. (crane)	$55.70	$445.60	$84.25	$674.00	$47.42	$72.13
1 Laborer	39.15	313.20	60.00	480.00		
1 Hyd. Excavator, 1.5 C.Y.		965.00		1061.50	60.31	66.34
16 L.H., Daily Totals		$1723.80		$2215.50	$107.74	$138.47

Crew No.	Bare Costs Hr.	Daily	Incl. Subs O&P Hr.	Daily	Cost Per Labor-Hour Bare Costs	Incl. O&P
Crew B-12C	Hr.	Daily	Hr.	Daily	Bare Costs	Incl. O&P
1 Equip. Oper. (crane)	$55.70	$445.60	$84.25	$674.00	$47.42	$72.13
1 Laborer	39.15	313.20	60.00	480.00		
1 Hyd. Excavator, 2 C.Y.		1123.00		1235.30	70.19	77.21
16 L.H., Daily Totals		$1881.80		$2389.30	$117.61	$149.33

Crew No.	Hr.	Daily	Hr.	Daily	Bare Costs	Incl. O&P
Crew B-12D	Hr.	Daily	Hr.	Daily	Bare Costs	Incl. O&P
1 Equip. Oper. (crane)	$55.70	$445.60	$84.25	$674.00	$47.42	$72.13
1 Laborer	39.15	313.20	60.00	480.00		
1 Hyd. Excavator, 3.5 C.Y.		2401.00		2641.10	150.06	165.07
16 L.H., Daily Totals		$3159.80		$3795.10	$197.49	$237.19

Crew No.	Hr.	Daily	Hr.	Daily	Bare Costs	Incl. O&P
Crew B-12E	Hr.	Daily	Hr.	Daily	Bare Costs	Incl. O&P
1 Equip. Oper. (crane)	$55.70	$445.60	$84.25	$674.00	$47.42	$72.13
1 Laborer	39.15	313.20	60.00	480.00		
1 Hyd. Excavator, .5 C.Y.		443.60		487.96	27.73	30.50
16 L.H., Daily Totals		$1202.40		$1641.96	$75.15	$102.62

Crew No.	Hr.	Daily	Hr.	Daily	Bare Costs	Incl. O&P
Crew B-12F	Hr.	Daily	Hr.	Daily	Bare Costs	Incl. O&P
1 Equip. Oper. (crane)	$55.70	$445.60	$84.25	$674.00	$47.42	$72.13
1 Laborer	.39.15	313.20	60.00	480.00		
1 Hyd. Excavator, .75 C.Y.		674.20		741.62	42.14	46.35
16 L.H., Daily Totals		$1433.00		$1895.62	$89.56	$118.48

Crew No.	Hr.	Daily	Hr.	Daily	Bare Costs	Incl. O&P
Crew B-12G	Hr.	Daily	Hr.	Daily	Bare Costs	Incl. O&P
1 Equip. Oper. (crane)	$55.70	$445.60	$84.25	$674.00	$47.42	$72.13
1 Laborer	39.15	313.20	60.00	480.00		
1 Crawler Crane, 15 Ton		757.75		833.52		
1 Clamshell Bucket, .5 C.Y.		38.20		42.02	49.75	54.72
16 L.H., Daily Totals		$1554.75		$2029.55	$97.17	$126.85

Crew No.	Hr.	Daily	Hr.	Daily	Bare Costs	Incl. O&P
Crew B-12H	Hr.	Daily	Hr.	Daily	Bare Costs	Incl. O&P
1 Equip. Oper. (crane)	$55.70	$445.60	$84.25	$674.00	$47.42	$72.13
1 Laborer	39.15	313.20	60.00	480.00		
1 Crawler Crane, 25 Ton		1296.00		1425.60		
1 Clamshell Bucket, 1 C.Y.		48.80		53.68	84.05	92.45
16 L.H., Daily Totals		$2103.60		$2633.28	$131.47	$164.58

Crew No.	Hr.	Daily	Hr.	Daily	Bare Costs	Incl. O&P
Crew B-12I	Hr.	Daily	Hr.	Daily	Bare Costs	Incl. O&P
1 Equip. Oper. (crane)	$55.70	$445.60	$84.25	$674.00	$47.42	$72.13
1 Laborer	39.15	313.20	60.00	480.00		
1 Crawler Crane, 20 Ton		972.05		1069.26		
1 Dragline Bucket, .75 C.Y.		20.80		22.88	62.05	68.26
16 L.H., Daily Totals		$1751.65		$2246.14	$109.48	$140.38

Crew No.	Hr.	Daily	Hr.	Daily	Bare Costs	Incl. O&P
Crew B-12J	Hr.	Daily	Hr.	Daily	Bare Costs	Incl. O&P
1 Equip. Oper. (crane)	$55.70	$445.60	$84.25	$674.00	$47.42	$72.13
1 Laborer	39.15	313.20	60.00	480.00		
1 Gradall, 5/8 C.Y.		910.00		1001.00	56.88	62.56
16 L.H., Daily Totals		$1668.80		$2155.00	$104.30	$134.69

Crew No.	Hr.	Daily	Hr.	Daily	Bare Costs	Incl. O&P
Crew B-12K	Hr.	Daily	Hr.	Daily	Bare Costs	Incl. O&P
1 Equip. Oper. (crane)	$55.70	$445.60	$84.25	$674.00	$47.42	$72.13
1 Laborer	39.15	313.20	60.00	480.00		
1 Gradall, 3 Ton, 1 C.Y.		1144.00		1258.40	71.50	78.65
16 L.H., Daily Totals		$1902.80		$2412.40	$118.93	$150.78

Crew No.	Hr.	Daily	Hr.	Daily	Bare Costs	Incl. O&P
Crew B-12L	Hr.	Daily	Hr.	Daily	Bare Costs	Incl. O&P
1 Equip. Oper. (crane)	$55.70	$445.60	$84.25	$674.00	$47.42	$72.13
1 Laborer	39.15	313.20	60.00	480.00		
1 Crawler Crane, 15 Ton		757.75		833.52		
1 F.E. Attachment, .5 C.Y.		61.00		67.10	51.17	56.29
16 L.H., Daily Totals		$1577.55		$2054.63	$98.60	$128.41

Crew No.	Hr.	Daily	Hr.	Daily	Bare Costs	Incl. O&P
Crew B-12M	Hr.	Daily	Hr.	Daily	Bare Costs	Incl. O&P
1 Equip. Oper. (crane)	$55.70	$445.60	$84.25	$674.00	$47.42	$72.13
1 Laborer	39.15	313.20	60.00	480.00		
1 Crawler Crane, 20 Ton		972.05		1069.26		
1 F.E. Attachment, .75 C.Y.		65.80		72.38	64.87	71.35
16 L.H., Daily Totals		$1796.65		$2295.64	$112.29	$143.48

Crew No.	Hr.	Daily	Hr.	Daily	Bare Costs	Incl. O&P
Crew B-12N	Hr.	Daily	Hr.	Daily	Bare Costs	Incl. O&P
1 Equip. Oper. (crane)	$55.70	$445.60	$84.25	$674.00	$47.42	$72.13
1 Laborer	39.15	313.20	60.00	480.00		
1 Crawler Crane, 25 Ton		1296.00		1425.60		
1 F.E. Attachment, 1 C.Y.		72.60		79.86	85.54	94.09
16 L.H., Daily Totals		$2127.40		$2659.46	$132.96	$166.22

Crew No.	Hr.	Daily	Hr.	Daily	Bare Costs	Incl. O&P
Crew B-12O	Hr.	Daily	Hr.	Daily	Bare Costs	Incl. O&P
1 Equip. Oper. (crane)	$55.70	$445.60	$84.25	$674.00	$47.42	$72.13
1 Laborer	39.15	313.20	60.00	480.00		
1 Crawler Crane, 40 Ton		1313.00		1444.30		
1 F.E. Attachment, 1.5 C.Y.		81.40		89.54	87.15	95.86
16 L.H., Daily Totals		$2153.20		$2687.84	$134.57	$167.99

Crew No.	Hr.	Daily	Hr.	Daily	Bare Costs	Incl. O&P
Crew B-12P	Hr.	Daily	Hr.	Daily	Bare Costs	Incl. O&P
1 Equip. Oper. (crane)	$55.70	$445.60	$84.25	$674.00	$47.42	$72.13
1 Laborer	39.15	313.20	60.00	480.00		
1 Crawler Crane, 40 Ton		1313.00		1444.30		
1 Dragline Bucket, 1.5 C.Y.		34.00		37.40	84.19	92.61
16 L.H., Daily Totals		$2105.80		$2635.70	$131.61	$164.73

Crew No.	Hr.	Daily	Hr.	Daily	Bare Costs	Incl. O&P
Crew B-12Q	Hr.	Daily	Hr.	Daily	Bare Costs	Incl. O&P
1 Equip. Oper. (crane)	$55.70	$445.60	$84.25	$674.00	$47.42	$72.13
1 Laborer	39.15	313.20	60.00	480.00		
1 Hyd. Excavator, 5/8 C.Y.		614.00		675.40	38.38	42.21
16 L.H., Daily Totals		$1372.80		$1829.40	$85.80	$114.34

Crew No.	Hr.	Daily	Hr.	Daily	Bare Costs	Incl. O&P
Crew B-12S	Hr.	Daily	Hr.	Daily	Bare Costs	Incl. O&P
1 Equip. Oper. (crane)	$55.70	$445.60	$84.25	$674.00	$47.42	$72.13
1 Laborer	39.15	313.20	60.00	480.00		
1 Hyd. Excavator, 2.5 C.Y.		1536.00		1689.60	96.00	105.60
16 L.H., Daily Totals		$2294.80		$2843.60	$143.43	$177.72

Crew No.	Hr.	Daily	Hr.	Daily	Bare Costs	Incl. O&P
Crew B-12T	Hr.	Daily	Hr.	Daily	Bare Costs	Incl. O&P
1 Equip. Oper. (crane)	$55.70	$445.60	$84.25	$674.00	$47.42	$72.13
1 Laborer	39.15	313.20	60.00	480.00		
1 Crawler Crane, 75 Ton		1645.00		1809.50		
1 F.E. Attachment, 3 C.Y.		104.20		114.62	109.33	120.26
16 L.H., Daily Totals		$2508.00		$3078.12	$156.75	$192.38

Crew No.	Hr.	Daily	Hr.	Daily	Bare Costs	Incl. O&P
Crew B-12V	Hr.	Daily	Hr.	Daily	Bare Costs	Incl. O&P
1 Equip. Oper. (crane)	$55.70	$445.60	$84.25	$674.00	$47.42	$72.13
1 Laborer	39.15	313.20	60.00	480.00		
1 Crawler Crane, 75 Ton		1645.00		1809.50		
1 Dragline Bucket, 3 C.Y.		54.00		59.40	106.19	116.81
16 L.H., Daily Totals		$2457.80		$3022.90	$153.61	$188.93

Crew No.	Bare Costs		Incl. Subs O&P		Cost Per Labor-Hour	
Crew B-12Y	**Hr.**	**Daily**	**Hr.**	**Daily**	Bare Costs	Incl. O&P
1 Equip. Oper. (crane)	$55.70	$445.60	$84.25	$674.00	$44.67	$68.08
2 Laborers	39.15	626.40	60.00	960.00		
1 Hyd. Excavator, 3.5 C.Y.		2401.00		2641.10	100.04	110.05
24 L.H., Daily Totals		$3473.00		$4275.10	$144.71	$178.13
Crew B-12Z	**Hr.**	**Daily**	**Hr.**	**Daily**	Bare Costs	Incl. O&P
1 Equip. Oper. (crane)	$55.70	$445.60	$84.25	$674.00	$44.67	$68.08
2 Laborers	39.15	626.40	60.00	960.00		
1 Hyd. Excavator, 2.5 C.Y.		1536.00		1689.60	64.00	70.40
24 L.H., Daily Totals		$2608.00		$3323.60	$108.67	$138.48
Crew B-13	**Hr.**	**Daily**	**Hr.**	**Daily**	Bare Costs	Incl. O&P
1 Labor Foreman (outside)	$41.15	$329.20	$63.05	$504.40	$43.06	$65.70
4 Laborers	39.15	1252.80	60.00	1920.00		
1 Equip. Oper. (crane)	55.70	445.60	84.25	674.00		
1 Equip. Oper. (oiler)	48.00	384.00	72.60	580.80		
1 Hyd. Crane, 25 Ton		673.80		741.18	12.03	13.24
56 L.H., Daily Totals		$3085.40		$4420.38	$55.10	$78.94
Crew B-13A	**Hr.**	**Daily**	**Hr.**	**Daily**	Bare Costs	Incl. O&P
1 Labor Foreman (outside)	$41.15	$329.20	$63.05	$504.40	$45.38	$68.92
2 Laborers	39.15	626.40	60.00	960.00		
2 Equipment Operators (med.)	53.55	856.80	81.00	1296.00		
2 Truck Drivers (heavy)	45.55	728.80	68.70	1099.20		
1 Crawler Crane, 75 Ton		1645.00		1809.50		
1 Crawler Loader, 4 C.Y.		1528.00		1680.80		
2 Dump Trucks, 8 C.Y., 220 H.P.		782.00		860.20	70.63	77.69
56 L.H., Daily Totals		$6496.20		$8210.10	$116.00	$146.61
Crew B-13B	**Hr.**	**Daily**	**Hr.**	**Daily**	Bare Costs	Incl. O&P
1 Labor Foreman (outside)	$41.15	$329.20	$63.05	$504.40	$43.06	$65.70
4 Laborers	39.15	1252.80	60.00	1920.00		
1 Equip. Oper. (crane)	55.70	445.60	84.25	674.00		
1 Equip. Oper. (oiler)	48.00	384.00	72.60	580.80		
1 Hyd. Crane, 55 Ton		1076.00		1183.60	19.21	21.14
56 L.H., Daily Totals		$3487.60		$4862.80	$62.28	$86.84
Crew B-13C	**Hr.**	**Daily**	**Hr.**	**Daily**	Bare Costs	Incl. O&P
1 Labor Foreman (outside)	$41.15	$329.20	$63.05	$504.40	$43.06	$65.70
4 Laborers	39.15	1252.80	60.00	1920.00		
1 Equip. Oper. (crane)	55.70	445.60	84.25	674.00		
1 Equip. Oper. (oiler)	48.00	384.00	72.60	580.80		
1 Crawler Crane, 100 Ton		1804.00		1984.40	32.21	35.44
56 L.H., Daily Totals		$4215.60		$5663.60	$75.28	$101.14
Crew B-13D	**Hr.**	**Daily**	**Hr.**	**Daily**	Bare Costs	Incl. O&P
1 Laborer	$39.15	$313.20	$60.00	$480.00	$47.42	$72.13
1 Equip. Oper. (crane)	55.70	445.60	84.25	674.00		
1 Hyd. Excavator, 1 C.Y.		798.20		878.02		
1 Trench Box		81.00		89.10	54.95	60.45
16 L.H., Daily Totals		$1638.00		$2121.12	$102.38	$132.57
Crew B-13E	**Hr.**	**Daily**	**Hr.**	**Daily**	Bare Costs	Incl. O&P
1 Laborer	$39.15	$313.20	$60.00	$480.00	$47.42	$72.13
1 Equip. Oper. (crane)	55.70	445.60	84.25	674.00		
1 Hyd. Excavator, 1.5 C.Y.		965.00		1061.50		
1 Trench Box		81.00		89.10	65.38	71.91
16 L.H., Daily Totals		$1804.80		$2304.60	$112.80	$144.04

Crew No.	Bare Costs		Incl. Subs O&P		Cost Per Labor-Hour	
Crew B-13F	**Hr.**	**Daily**	**Hr.**	**Daily**	Bare Costs	Incl. O&P
1 Laborer	$39.15	$313.20	$60.00	$480.00	$47.42	$72.13
1 Equip. Oper. (crane)	55.70	445.60	84.25	674.00		
1 Hyd. Excavator, 3.5 C.Y.		2401.00		2641.10		
1 Trench Box		81.00		89.10	155.13	170.64
16 L.H., Daily Totals		$3240.80		$3884.20	$202.55	$242.76
Crew B-13G	**Hr.**	**Daily**	**Hr.**	**Daily**	Bare Costs	Incl. O&P
1 Laborer	$39.15	$313.20	$60.00	$480.00	$47.42	$72.13
1 Equip. Oper. (crane)	55.70	445.60	84.25	674.00		
1 Hyd. Excavator, .75 C.Y.		674.20		741.62		
1 Trench Box		81.00		89.10	47.20	51.92
16 L.H., Daily Totals		$1514.00		$1984.72	$94.63	$124.05
Crew B-13H	**Hr.**	**Daily**	**Hr.**	**Daily**	Bare Costs	Incl. O&P
1 Laborer	$39.15	$313.20	$60.00	$480.00	$47.42	$72.13
1 Equip. Oper. (crane)	55.70	445.60	84.25	674.00		
1 Gradall, 5/8 C.Y.		910.00		1001.00		
1 Trench Box		81.00		89.10	61.94	68.13
16 L.H., Daily Totals		$1749.80		$2244.10	$109.36	$140.26
Crew B-13I	**Hr.**	**Daily**	**Hr.**	**Daily**	Bare Costs	Incl. O&P
1 Laborer	$39.15	$313.20	$60.00	$480.00	$47.42	$72.13
1 Equip. Oper. (crane)	55.70	445.60	84.25	674.00		
1 Gradall, 3 Ton, 1 C.Y.		1144.00		1258.40		
1 Trench Box		81.00		89.10	76.56	84.22
16 L.H., Daily Totals		$1983.80		$2501.50	$123.99	$156.34
Crew B-13J	**Hr.**	**Daily**	**Hr.**	**Daily**	Bare Costs	Incl. O&P
1 Laborer	$39.15	$313.20	$60.00	$480.00	$47.42	$72.13
1 Equip. Oper. (crane)	55.70	445.60	84.25	674.00		
1 Hyd. Excavator, 2.5 C.Y.		1536.00		1689.60		
1 Trench Box		81.00		89.10	101.06	111.17
16 L.H., Daily Totals		$2375.80		$2932.70	$148.49	$183.29
Crew B-13K	**Hr.**	**Daily**	**Hr.**	**Daily**	Bare Costs	Incl. O&P
2 Equip. Opers. (crane)	$55.70	$891.20	$84.25	$1348.00	$55.70	$84.25
1 Hyd. Excavator, .75 C.Y.		674.20		741.62		
1 Hyd. Hammer, 4000 ft-lb		312.40		343.64		
1 Hyd. Excavator, .75 C.Y.		674.20		741.62	103.80	114.18
16 L.H., Daily Totals		$2552.00		$3174.88	$159.50	$198.43
Crew B-13L	**Hr.**	**Daily**	**Hr.**	**Daily**	Bare Costs	Incl. O&P
2 Equip. Opers. (crane)	$55.70	$891.20	$84.25	$1348.00	$55.70	$84.25
1 Hyd. Excavator, 1.5 C.Y.		965.00		1061.50		
1 Hyd. Hammer, 5000 ft-lb		376.20		413.82		
1 Hyd. Excavator, .75 C.Y.		674.20		741.62	125.96	138.56
16 L.H., Daily Totals		$2906.60		$3564.94	$181.66	$222.81
Crew B-13M	**Hr.**	**Daily**	**Hr.**	**Daily**	Bare Costs	Incl. O&P
2 Equip. Opers. (crane)	$55.70	$891.20	$84.25	$1348.00	$55.70	$84.25
1 Hyd. Excavator, 2.5 C.Y.		1536.00		1689.60		
1 Hyd. Hammer, 8000 ft-lb		552.80		608.08		
1 Hyd. Excavator, 1.5 C.Y.		965.00		1061.50	190.86	209.95
16 L.H., Daily Totals		$3945.00		$4707.18	$246.56	$294.20

| Crew No. | Bare Costs | | Incl. Subs O&P | | Cost Per Labor-Hour | |

Crew B-13N

Crew B-13N	Hr.	Daily	Hr.	Daily	Bare Costs	Incl. O&P
2 Equip. Opers. (crane)	$55.70	$891.20	$84.25	$1348.00	$55.70	$84.25
1 Hyd. Excavator, 3.5 C.Y.		2401.00		2641.10		
1 Hyd. Hammer, 12,000 ft-lb		643.20		707.52		
1 Hyd. Excavator, 1.5 C.Y.		965.00		1061.50	250.57	275.63
16 L.H., Daily Totals		$4900.40		$5758.12	$306.27	$359.88

Crew B-14

Crew B-14	Hr.	Daily	Hr.	Daily	Bare Costs	Incl. O&P
1 Labor Foreman (outside)	$41.15	$329.20	$63.05	$504.40	$41.46	$63.37
4 Laborers	39.15	1252.80	60.00	1920.00		
1 Equip. Oper. (light)	51.00	408.00	77.15	617.20		
1 Backhoe Loader, 48 H.P.		366.20		402.82	7.63	8.39
48 L.H., Daily Totals		$2356.20		$3444.42	$49.09	$71.76

Crew B-14A

Crew B-14A	Hr.	Daily	Hr.	Daily	Bare Costs	Incl. O&P
1 Equip. Oper. (crane)	$55.70	$445.60	$84.25	$674.00	$50.18	$76.17
.5 Laborer	39.15	156.60	60.00	240.00		
1 Hyd. Excavator, 4.5 C.Y.		3084.00		3392.40	257.00	282.70
12 L.H., Daily Totals		$3686.20		$4306.40	$307.18	$358.87

Crew B-14B

Crew B-14B	Hr.	Daily	Hr.	Daily	Bare Costs	Incl. O&P
1 Equip. Oper. (crane)	$55.70	$445.60	$84.25	$674.00	$50.18	$76.17
.5 Laborer	39.15	156.60	60.00	240.00		
1 Hyd. Excavator, 6 C.Y.		3596.00		3955.60	299.67	329.63
12 L.H., Daily Totals		$4198.20		$4869.60	$349.85	$405.80

Crew B-14C

Crew B-14C	Hr.	Daily	Hr.	Daily	Bare Costs	Incl. O&P
1 Equip. Oper. (crane)	$55.70	$445.60	$84.25	$674.00	$50.18	$76.17
.5 Laborer	39.15	156.60	60.00	240.00		
1 Hyd. Excavator, 7 C.Y.		3698.00		4067.80	308.17	338.98
12 L.H., Daily Totals		$4300.20		$4981.80	$358.35	$415.15

Crew B-14F

Crew B-14F	Hr.	Daily	Hr.	Daily	Bare Costs	Incl. O&P
1 Equip. Oper. (crane)	$55.70	$445.60	$84.25	$674.00	$50.18	$76.17
.5 Laborer	39.15	156.60	60.00	240.00		
1 Hyd. Shovel, 7 C.Y.		4107.00		4517.70	342.25	376.48
12 L.H., Daily Totals		$4709.20		$5431.70	$392.43	$452.64

Crew B-14G

Crew B-14G	Hr.	Daily	Hr.	Daily	Bare Costs	Incl. O&P
1 Equip. Oper. (crane)	$55.70	$445.60	$84.25	$674.00	$50.18	$76.17
.5 Laborer	39.15	156.60	60.00	240.00		
1 Hyd. Shovel, 12 C.Y.		6152.00		6767.20	512.67	563.93
12 L.H., Daily Totals		$6754.20		$7681.20	$562.85	$640.10

Crew B-14J

Crew B-14J	Hr.	Daily	Hr.	Daily	Bare Costs	Incl. O&P
1 Equip. Oper. (medium)	$53.55	$428.40	$81.00	$648.00	$48.75	$74.00
.5 Laborer	39.15	156.60	60.00	240.00		
1 F.E. Loader, 8 C.Y.		1967.00		2163.70	163.92	180.31
12 L.H., Daily Totals		$2552.00		$3051.70	$212.67	$254.31

Crew B-14K

Crew B-14K	Hr.	Daily	Hr.	Daily	Bare Costs	Incl. O&P
1 Equip. Oper. (medium)	$53.55	$428.40	$81.00	$648.00	$48.75	$74.00
.5 Laborer	39.15	156.60	60.00	240.00		
1 F.E. Loader, 10 C.Y.		3224.00		3546.40	268.67	295.53
12 L.H., Daily Totals		$3809.00		$4434.40	$317.42	$369.53

Crew B-15

Crew B-15	Hr.	Daily	Hr.	Daily	Bare Costs	Incl. O&P
1 Equipment Oper. (med.)	$53.55	$428.40	$81.00	$648.00	$46.92	$70.97
.5 Laborer	39.15	156.60	60.00	240.00		
2 Truck Drivers (heavy)	45.55	728.80	68.70	1099.20		
2 Dump Trucks, 12 C.Y., 400 H.P.		1285.20		1413.72		
1 Dozer, 200 H.P.		1384.00		1522.40	95.33	104.86
28 L.H., Daily Totals		$3983.00		$4923.32	$142.25	$175.83

Crew B-16

Crew B-16	Hr.	Daily	Hr.	Daily	Bare Costs	Incl. O&P
1 Labor Foreman (outside)	$41.15	$329.20	$63.05	$504.40	$41.25	$62.94
2 Laborers	39.15	626.40	60.00	960.00		
1 Truck Driver (heavy)	45.55	364.40	68.70	549.60		
1 Dump Truck, 12 C.Y., 400 H.P.		642.60		706.86	20.08	22.09
32 L.H., Daily Totals		$1962.60		$2720.86	$61.33	$85.03

Crew B-17

Crew B-17	Hr.	Daily	Hr.	Daily	Bare Costs	Incl. O&P
2 Laborers	$39.15	$626.40	$60.00	$960.00	$43.71	$66.46
1 Equip. Oper. (light)	51.00	408.00	77.15	617.20		
1 Truck Driver (heavy)	45.55	364.40	68.70	549.60		
1 Backhoe Loader, 48 H.P.		366.20		402.82		
1 Dump Truck, 8 C.Y., 220 H.P.		391.00		430.10	23.66	26.03
32 L.H., Daily Totals		$2156.00		$2959.72	$67.38	$92.49

Crew B-17A

Crew B-17A	Hr.	Daily	Hr.	Daily	Bare Costs	Incl. O&P
2 Labor Foremen (outside)	$41.15	$658.40	$63.05	$1008.80	$42.21	$64.75
6 Laborers	39.15	1879.20	60.00	2880.00		
1 Skilled Worker Foreman (out)	53.45	427.60	82.25	658.00		
1 Skilled Worker	51.45	411.60	79.20	633.60		
80 L.H., Daily Totals		$3376.80		$5180.40	$42.21	$64.75

Crew B-17B

Crew B-17B	Hr.	Daily	Hr.	Daily	Bare Costs	Incl. O&P
2 Laborers	$39.15	$626.40	$60.00	$960.00	$43.71	$66.46
1 Equip. Oper. (light)	51.00	408.00	77.15	617.20		
1 Truck Driver (heavy)	45.55	364.40	68.70	549.60		
1 Backhoe Loader, 48 H.P.		366.20		402.82		
1 Dump Truck, 12 C.Y., 400 H.P.		642.60		706.86	31.52	34.68
32 L.H., Daily Totals		$2407.60		$3236.48	$75.24	$101.14

Crew B-18

Crew B-18	Hr.	Daily	Hr.	Daily	Bare Costs	Incl. O&P
1 Labor Foreman (outside)	$41.15	$329.20	$63.05	$504.40	$39.82	$61.02
2 Laborers	39.15	626.40	60.00	960.00		
1 Vibrating Plate, Gas, 21"		42.80		47.08	1.78	1.96
24 L.H., Daily Totals		$998.40		$1511.48	$41.60	$62.98

Crew B-19

Crew B-19	Hr.	Daily	Hr.	Daily	Bare Costs	Incl. O&P
1 Pile Driver Foreman (outside)	$51.50	$412.00	$81.80	$654.40	$51.11	$79.66
4 Pile Drivers	49.50	1584.00	78.60	2515.20		
2 Equip. Oper. (crane)	55.70	891.20	84.25	1348.00		
1 Equip. Oper. (oiler)	48.00	384.00	72.60	580.80		
1 Crawler Crane, 40 Ton		1313.00		1444.30		
1 Lead, 90' High		126.00		138.60		
1 Hammer, Diesel, 22k ft-lb		421.00		463.10	29.06	31.97
64 L.H., Daily Totals		$5131.20		$7144.40	$80.17	$111.63

Crew No.	Bare Costs		Incl. Subs O&P		Cost Per Labor-Hour	

Crew B-19A	Hr.	Daily	Hr.	Daily	Bare Costs	Incl. O&P
1 Pile Driver Foreman (outside)	$51.50	$412.00	$81.80	$654.40	$51.11	$79.66
4 Pile Drivers	49.50	1584.00	78.60	2515.20		
2 Equip. Oper. (crane)	55.70	891.20	84.25	1348.00		
1 Equip. Oper. (oiler)	48.00	384.00	72.60	580.80		
1 Crawler Crane, 75 Ton		1645.00		1809.50		
1 Lead, 90' high		126.00		138.60		
1 Hammer, Diesel, 41k ft-lb		574.00		631.40	36.64	40.30
64 L.H., Daily Totals		$5616.20		$7677.90	$87.75	$119.97

Crew B-19B	Hr.	Daily	Hr.	Daily	Bare Costs	Incl. O&P
1 Pile Driver Foreman (outside)	$51.50	$412.00	$81.80	$654.40	$51.11	$79.66
4 Pile Drivers	49.50	1584.00	78.60	2515.20		
2 Equip. Oper. (crane)	55.70	891.20	84.25	1348.00		
1 Equip. Oper. (oiler)	48.00	384.00	72.60	580.80		
1 Crawler Crane, 40 Ton		1313.00		1444.30		
1 Lead, 90' High		126.00		138.60		
1 Hammer, Diesel, 22k ft-lb		421.00		463.10		
1 Barge, 400 Ton		794.20		873.62	41.47	45.62
64 L.H., Daily Totals		$5925.40		$8018.02	$92.58	$125.28

Crew B-19C	Hr.	Daily	Hr.	Daily	Bare Costs	Incl. O&P
1 Pile Driver Foreman (outside)	$51.50	$412.00	$81.80	$654.40	$51.11	$79.66
4 Pile Drivers	49.50	1584.00	78.60	2515.20		
2 Equip. Oper. (crane)	55.70	891.20	84.25	1348.00		
1 Equip. Oper. (oiler)	48.00	384.00	72.60	580.80		
1 Crawler Crane, 75 Ton		1645.00		1809.50		
1 Lead, 90' High		126.00		138.60		
1 Hammer, Diesel, 41k ft-lb		574.00		631.40		
1 Barge, 400 Ton		794.20		873.62	49.05	53.95
64 L.H., Daily Totals		$6410.40		$8551.52	$100.16	$133.62

Crew B-20	Hr.	Daily	Hr.	Daily	Bare Costs	Incl. O&P
1 Labor Foreman (outside)	$41.15	$329.20	$63.05	$504.40	$43.92	$67.42
1 Skilled Worker	51.45	411.60	79.20	633.60		
1 Laborer	39.15	313.20	60.00	480.00		
24 L.H., Daily Totals		$1054.00		$1618.00	$43.92	$67.42

Crew B-20A	Hr.	Daily	Hr.	Daily	Bare Costs	Incl. O&P
1 Labor Foreman (outside)	$41.15	$329.20	$63.05	$504.40	$47.89	$72.72
1 Laborer	39.15	313.20	60.00	480.00		
1 Plumber	61.80	494.40	93.25	746.00		
1 Plumber Apprentice	49.45	395.60	74.60	596.80		
32 L.H., Daily Totals		$1532.40		$2327.20	$47.89	$72.72

Crew B-21	Hr.	Daily	Hr.	Daily	Bare Costs	Incl. O&P
1 Labor Foreman (outside)	$41.15	$329.20	$63.05	$504.40	$45.60	$69.82
1 Skilled Worker	51.45	411.60	79.20	633.60		
1 Laborer	39.15	313.20	60.00	480.00		
.5 Equip. Oper. (crane)	55.70	222.80	84.25	337.00		
.5 S.P. Crane, 4x4, 5 Ton		138.00		151.80	4.93	5.42
28 L.H., Daily Totals		$1414.80		$2106.80	$50.53	$75.24

Crew B-21A	Hr.	Daily	Hr.	Daily	Bare Costs	Incl. O&P
1 Labor Foreman (outside)	$41.15	$329.20	$63.05	$504.40	$49.45	$75.03
1 Laborer	39.15	313.20	60.00	480.00		
1 Plumber	61.80	494.40	93.25	746.00		
1 Plumber Apprentice	49.45	395.60	74.60	596.80		
1 Equip. Oper. (crane)	55.70	445.60	84.25	674.00		
1 S.P. Crane, 4x4, 12 Ton		435.60		479.16	10.89	11.98
40 L.H., Daily Totals		$2413.60		$3480.36	$60.34	$87.01

Crew B-21B	Hr.	Daily	Hr.	Daily	Bare Costs	Incl. O&P
1 Labor Foreman (outside)	$41.15	$329.20	$63.05	$504.40	$42.86	$65.46
3 Laborers	39.15	939.60	60.00	1440.00		
1 Equip. Oper. (crane)	55.70	445.60	84.25	674.00		
1 Hyd. Crane, 12 Ton		572.80		630.08	14.32	15.75
40 L.H., Daily Totals		$2287.20		$3248.48	$57.18	$81.21

Crew B-21C	Hr.	Daily	Hr.	Daily	Bare Costs	Incl. O&P
1 Labor Foreman (outside)	$41.15	$329.20	$63.05	$504.40	$43.06	$65.70
4 Laborers	39.15	1252.80	60.00	1920.00		
1 Equip. Oper. (crane)	55.70	445.60	84.25	674.00		
1 Equip. Oper. (oiler)	48.00	384.00	72.60	580.80		
2 Cutting Torches		24.00		26.40		
2 Sets of Gases		336.00		369.60		
1 Lattice Boom Crane, 90 Ton		1671.00		1838.10	36.27	39.89
56 L.H., Daily Totals		$4442.60		$5913.30	$79.33	$105.59

Crew B-22	Hr.	Daily	Hr.	Daily	Bare Costs	Incl. O&P
1 Labor Foreman (outside)	$41.15	$329.20	$63.05	$504.40	$46.27	$70.78
1 Skilled Worker	51.45	411.60	79.20	633.60		
1 Laborer	39.15	313.20	60.00	480.00		
.75 Equip. Oper. (crane)	55.70	334.20	84.25	505.50		
.75 S.P. Crane, 4x4, 5 Ton		207.00		227.70	6.90	7.59
30 L.H., Daily Totals		$1595.20		$2351.20	$53.17	$78.37

Crew B-22A	Hr.	Daily	Hr.	Daily	Bare Costs	Incl. O&P
1 Labor Foreman (outside)	$41.15	$329.20	$63.05	$504.40	$45.32	$69.30
1 Skilled Worker	51.45	411.60	79.20	633.60		
2 Laborers	39.15	626.40	60.00	960.00		
1 Equipment Operator, Crane	55.70	445.60	84.25	674.00		
1 S.P. Crane, 4x4, 5 Ton		276.00		303.60		
1 Butt Fusion Mach., 4"-12" diam.		415.10		456.61	17.28	19.01
40 L.H., Daily Totals		$2503.90		$3532.21	$62.60	$88.31

Crew B-22B	Hr.	Daily	Hr.	Daily	Bare Costs	Incl. O&P
1 Labor Foreman (outside)	$41.15	$329.20	$63.05	$504.40	$45.32	$69.30
1 Skilled Worker	51.45	411.60	79.20	633.60		
2 Laborers	39.15	626.40	60.00	960.00		
1 Equip. Oper. (crane)	55.70	445.60	84.25	674.00		
1 S.P. Crane, 4x4, 5 Ton		276.00		303.60		
1 Butt Fusion Mach., 8"-24" diam.		1821.00		2003.10	52.42	57.67
40 L.H., Daily Totals		$3909.80		$5078.70	$97.75	$126.97

Crew B-22C	Hr.	Daily	Hr.	Daily	Bare Costs	Incl. O&P
1 Skilled Worker	$51.45	$411.60	$79.20	$633.60	$45.30	$69.60
1 Laborer	39.15	313.20	60.00	480.00		
1 Butt Fusion Mach., 2"-8" diam.		121.05		133.16	7.57	8.32
16 L.H., Daily Totals		$845.85		$1246.76	$52.87	$77.92

Crew B-23	Hr.	Daily	Hr.	Daily	Bare Costs	Incl. O&P
1 Labor Foreman (outside)	$41.15	$329.20	$63.05	$504.40	$39.55	$60.61
4 Laborers	39.15	1252.80	60.00	1920.00		
1 Drill Rig, Truck-Mounted		2573.00		2830.30		
1 Flatbed Truck, Gas, 3 Ton		270.20		297.22	71.08	78.19
40 L.H., Daily Totals		$4425.20		$5551.92	$110.63	$138.80

479

For customer support on your Electrical Costs with RSMeans Data, call 800.448.8182.

Crew No.	Bare Costs		Incl. Subs O&P		Cost Per Labor-Hour	

Crew B-23A	Hr.	Daily	Hr.	Daily	Bare Costs	Incl. O&P
1 Labor Foreman (outside)	$41.15	$329.20	$63.05	$504.40	$44.62	$68.02
1 Laborer	39.15	313.20	60.00	480.00		
1 Equip. Oper. (medium)	53.55	428.40	81.00	648.00		
1 Drill Rig, Truck-Mounted		2573.00		2830.30		
1 Pickup Truck, 3/4 Ton		129.40		142.34	112.60	123.86
24 L.H., Daily Totals		$3773.20		$4605.04	$157.22	$191.88

Crew B-23B	Hr.	Daily	Hr.	Daily	Bare Costs	Incl. O&P
1 Labor Foreman (outside)	$41.15	$329.20	$63.05	$504.40	$44.62	$68.02
1 Laborer	39.15	313.20	60.00	480.00		
1 Equip. Oper. (medium)	53.55	428.40	81.00	648.00		
1 Drill Rig, Truck-Mounted		2573.00		2830.30		
1 Pickup Truck, 3/4 Ton		129.40		142.34		
1 Centr. Water Pump, 6"		325.40		357.94	126.16	138.77
24 L.H., Daily Totals		$4098.60		$4962.98	$170.78	$206.79

Crew B-24	Hr.	Daily	Hr.	Daily	Bare Costs	Incl. O&P
1 Cement Finisher	$46.80	$374.40	$69.60	$556.80	$45.07	$68.35
1 Laborer	39.15	313.20	60.00	480.00		
1 Carpenter	49.25	394.00	75.45	603.60		
24 L.H., Daily Totals		$1081.60		$1640.40	$45.07	$68.35

Crew B-25	Hr.	Daily	Hr.	Daily	Bare Costs	Incl. O&P
1 Labor Foreman (outside)	$41.15	$329.20	$63.05	$504.40	$43.26	$66.00
7 Laborers	39.15	2192.40	60.00	3360.00		
3 Equip. Oper. (medium)	53.55	1285.20	81.00	1944.00		
1 Asphalt Paver, 130 H.P.		2235.00		2458.50		
1 Tandem Roller, 10 Ton		237.60		261.36		
1 Roller, Pneum. Whl., 12 Ton		355.80		391.38	32.14	35.35
88 L.H., Daily Totals		$6635.20		$8919.64	$75.40	$101.36

Crew B-25B	Hr.	Daily	Hr.	Daily	Bare Costs	Incl. O&P
1 Labor Foreman (outside)	$41.15	$329.20	$63.05	$504.40	$44.12	$67.25
7 Laborers	39.15	2192.40	60.00	3360.00		
4 Equip. Oper. (medium)	53.55	1713.60	81.00	2592.00		
1 Asphalt Paver, 130 H.P.		2235.00		2458.50		
2 Tandem Rollers, 10 Ton		475.20		522.72		
1 Roller, Pneum. Whl., 12 Ton		355.80		391.38	31.94	35.13
96 L.H., Daily Totals		$7301.20		$9829.00	$76.05	$102.39

Crew B-25C	Hr.	Daily	Hr.	Daily	Bare Costs	Incl. O&P
1 Labor Foreman (outside)	$41.15	$329.20	$63.05	$504.40	$44.28	$67.51
3 Laborers	39.15	939.60	60.00	1440.00		
2 Equip. Oper. (medium)	53.55	856.80	81.00	1296.00		
1 Asphalt Paver, 130 H.P.		2235.00		2458.50		
1 Tandem Roller, 10 Ton		237.60		261.36	51.51	56.66
48 L.H., Daily Totals		$4598.20		$5960.26	$95.80	$124.17

Crew B-25D	Hr.	Daily	Hr.	Daily	Bare Costs	Incl. O&P
1 Labor Foreman (outside)	$41.15	$329.20	$63.05	$504.40	$44.49	$67.80
3 Laborers	39.15	939.60	60.00	1440.00		
2.125 Equip. Oper. (medium)	53.55	910.35	81.00	1377.00		
.125 Truck Driver (heavy)	45.55	45.55	68.70	68.70		
.125 Truck Tractor, 6x4, 380 H.P.		69.97		76.97		
.125 Dist. Tanker, 3000 Gallon		40.92		45.02		
1 Asphalt Paver, 130 H.P.		2235.00		2458.50		
1 Tandem Roller, 10 Ton		237.60		261.36	51.67	56.84
50 L.H., Daily Totals		$4808.20		$6231.95	$96.16	$124.64

Crew B-25E	Hr.	Daily	Hr.	Daily	Bare Costs	Incl. O&P
1 Labor Foreman (outside)	$41.15	$329.20	$63.05	$504.40	$44.69	$68.07
3 Laborers	39.15	939.60	60.00	1440.00		
2.250 Equip. Oper. (medium)	53.55	963.90	81.00	1458.00		
.25 Truck Driver (heavy)	45.55	91.10	68.70	137.40		
.25 Truck Tractor, 6x4, 380 H.P.		139.95		153.94		
.25 Dist. Tanker, 3000 Gallon		81.85		90.03		
1 Asphalt Paver, 130 H.P.		2235.00		2458.50		
1 Tandem Roller, 10 Ton		237.60		261.36	51.82	57.00
52 L.H., Daily Totals		$5018.20		$6503.64	$96.50	$125.07

Crew B-26	Hr.	Daily	Hr.	Daily	Bare Costs	Incl. O&P
1 Labor Foreman (outside)	$41.15	$329.20	$63.05	$504.40	$44.02	$67.12
6 Laborers	39.15	1879.20	60.00	2880.00		
2 Equip. Oper. (medium)	53.55	856.80	81.00	1296.00		
1 Rodman (reinf.)	54.30	434.40	83.70	669.60		
1 Cement Finisher	46.80	374.40	69.60	556.80		
1 Grader, 30,000 Lbs.		678.40		746.24		
1 Paving Mach. & Equip.		2452.00		2697.20	35.57	39.13
88 L.H., Daily Totals		$7004.40		$9350.24	$79.60	$106.25

Crew B-26A	Hr.	Daily	Hr.	Daily	Bare Costs	Incl. O&P
1 Labor Foreman (outside)	$41.15	$329.20	$63.05	$504.40	$44.02	$67.12
6 Laborers	39.15	1879.20	60.00	2880.00		
2 Equip. Oper. (medium)	53.55	856.80	81.00	1296.00		
1 Rodman (reinf.)	54.30	434.40	83.70	669.60		
1 Cement Finisher	46.80	374.40	69.60	556.80		
1 Grader, 30,000 Lbs.		678.40		746.24		
1 Paving Mach. & Equip.		2452.00		2697.20		
1 Concrete Saw		153.60		168.96	37.32	41.05
88 L.H., Daily Totals		$7158.00		$9519.20	$81.34	$108.17

Crew B-26B	Hr.	Daily	Hr.	Daily	Bare Costs	Incl. O&P
1 Labor Foreman (outside)	$41.15	$329.20	$63.05	$504.40	$44.82	$68.28
6 Laborers	39.15	1879.20	60.00	2880.00		
3 Equip. Oper. (medium)	53.55	1285.20	81.00	1944.00		
1 Rodman (reinf.)	54.30	434.40	83.70	669.60		
1 Cement Finisher	46.80	374.40	69.60	556.80		
1 Grader, 30,000 Lbs.		678.40		746.24		
1 Paving Mach. & Equip.		2452.00		2697.20		
1 Concrete Pump, 110' Boom		1086.00		1194.60	43.92	48.31
96 L.H., Daily Totals		$8518.80		$11192.84	$88.74	$116.59

Crew B-26C	Hr.	Daily	Hr.	Daily	Bare Costs	Incl. O&P
1 Labor Foreman (outside)	$41.15	$329.20	$63.05	$504.40	$43.07	$65.73
6 Laborers	39.15	1879.20	60.00	2880.00		
1 Equip. Oper. (medium)	53.55	428.40	81.00	648.00		
1 Rodman (reinf.)	54.30	434.40	83.70	669.60		
1 Cement Finisher	46.80	374.40	69.60	556.80		
1 Paving Mach. & Equip.		2452.00		2697.20		
1 Concrete Saw		153.60		168.96	32.57	35.83
80 L.H., Daily Totals		$6051.20		$8124.96	$75.64	$101.56

Crew B-27	Hr.	Daily	Hr.	Daily	Bare Costs	Incl. O&P
1 Labor Foreman (outside)	$41.15	$329.20	$63.05	$504.40	$39.65	$60.76
3 Laborers	39.15	939.60	60.00	1440.00		
1 Berm Machine		313.40		344.74	9.79	10.77
32 L.H., Daily Totals		$1582.20		$2289.14	$49.44	$71.54

Crews - Standard

Crew B-28

Crew B-28	Hr.	Daily	Hr.	Daily	Bare Costs	Incl. O&P
2 Carpenters	$49.25	$788.00	$75.45	$1207.20	$46.88	$70.30
1 Laborer	39.15	313.20	60.00	480.00		
24 L.H., Daily Totals		$1101.20		$1687.20	$45.88	$70.30

Crew B-29

Crew B-29	Hr.	Daily	Hr.	Daily	Bare Costs	Incl. O&P
1 Labor Foreman (outside)	$41.15	$329.20	$63.05	$504.40	$43.06	$65.70
4 Laborers	39.15	1252.80	60.00	1920.00		
1 Equip. Oper. (crane)	55.70	445.60	84.25	674.00		
1 Equip. Oper. (oiler)	48.00	384.00	72.60	580.80		
1 Gradall, 5/8 C.Y.		910.00		1001.00	16.25	17.88
56 L.H., Daily Totals		$3321.60		$4680.20	$59.31	$83.58

Crew B-30

Crew B-30	Hr.	Daily	Hr.	Daily	Bare Costs	Incl. O&P
1 Equip. Oper. (medium)	$53.55	$428.40	$81.00	$648.00	$48.22	$72.80
2 Truck Drivers (heavy)	45.55	728.80	68.70	1099.20		
1 Hyd. Excavator, 1.5 C.Y.		965.00		1061.50		
2 Dump Trucks, 12 C.Y., 400 H.P.		1285.20		1413.72	93.76	103.13
24 L.H., Daily Totals		$3407.40		$4222.42	$141.97	$175.93

Crew B-31

Crew B-31	Hr.	Daily	Hr.	Daily	Bare Costs	Incl. O&P
1 Labor Foreman (outside)	$41.15	$329.20	$63.05	$504.40	$41.57	$63.70
3 Laborers	39.15	939.60	60.00	1440.00		
1 Carpenter	49.25	394.00	75.45	603.60		
1 Air Compressor, 250 cfm		181.20		199.32		
1 Sheeting Driver		5.75		6.33		
2 -50' Air Hoses, 1.5"		11.60		12.76	4.96	5.46
40 L.H., Daily Totals		$1861.35		$2766.41	$46.53	$69.16

Crew B-32

Crew B-32	Hr.	Daily	Hr.	Daily	Bare Costs	Incl. O&P
1 Laborer	$39.15	$313.20	$60.00	$480.00	$49.95	$75.75
3 Equip. Oper. (medium)	53.55	1285.20	81.00	1944.00		
1 Grader, 30,000 Lbs.		678.40		746.24		
1 Tandem Roller, 10 Ton		237.60		261.36		
1 Dozer, 200 H.P.		1384.00		1522.40	71.88	79.06
32 L.H., Daily Totals		$3898.40		$4954.00	$121.83	$154.81

Crew B-32A

Crew B-32A	Hr.	Daily	Hr.	Daily	Bare Costs	Incl. O&P
1 Laborer	$39.15	$313.20	$60.00	$480.00	$48.75	$74.00
2 Equip. Oper. (medium)	53.55	856.80	81.00	1296.00		
1 Grader, 30,000 Lbs.		678.40		746.24		
1 Roller, Vibratory, 25 Ton		684.00		752.40	56.77	62.44
24 L.H., Daily Totals		$2532.40		$3274.64	$105.52	$136.44

Crew B-32B

Crew B-32B	Hr.	Daily	Hr.	Daily	Bare Costs	Incl. O&P
1 Laborer	$39.15	$313.20	$60.00	$480.00	$48.75	$74.00
2 Equip. Oper. (medium)	53.55	856.80	81.00	1296.00		
1 Dozer, 200 H.P.		1384.00		1522.40		
1 Roller, Vibratory, 25 Ton		684.00		752.40	86.17	94.78
24 L.H., Daily Totals		$3238.00		$4050.80	$134.92	$168.78

Crew B-32C

Crew B-32C	Hr.	Daily	Hr.	Daily	Bare Costs	Incl. O&P
1 Labor Foreman (outside)	$41.15	$329.20	$63.05	$504.40	$46.68	$71.01
2 Laborers	39.15	626.40	60.00	960.00		
3 Equip. Oper. (medium)	53.55	1285.20	81.00	1944.00		
1 Grader, 30,000 Lbs.		678.40		746.24		
1 Tandem Roller, 10 Ton		237.60		261.36		
1 Dozer, 200 H.P.		1384.00		1522.40	47.92	52.71
48 L.H., Daily Totals		$4540.80		$5938.40	$94.60	$123.72

Crew B-33A

Crew B-33A	Hr.	Daily	Hr.	Daily	Bare Costs	Incl. O&P
1 Equip. Oper. (medium)	$53.55	$428.40	$81.00	$648.00	$49.44	$75.00
.5 Laborer	39.15	156.60	60.00	240.00		
.25 Equip. Oper. (medium)	53.55	107.10	81.00	162.00		
1 Scraper, Towed, 7 C.Y.		117.20		128.92		
1.25 Dozers, 300 H.P.		2375.00		2612.50	178.01	195.82
14 L.H., Daily Totals		$3184.30		$3791.42	$227.45	$270.82

Crew B-33B

Crew B-33B	Hr.	Daily	Hr.	Daily	Bare Costs	Incl. O&P
1 Equip. Oper. (medium)	$53.55	$428.40	$81.00	$648.00	$49.44	$75.00
.5 Laborer	39.15	156.60	60.00	240.00		
.25 Equip. Oper. (medium)	53.55	107.10	81.00	162.00		
1 Scraper, Towed, 10 C.Y.		148.60		163.46		
1.25 Dozers, 300 H.P.		2375.00		2612.50	180.26	198.28
14 L.H., Daily Totals		$3215.70		$3825.96	$229.69	$273.28

Crew B-33C

Crew B-33C	Hr.	Daily	Hr.	Daily	Bare Costs	Incl. O&P
1 Equip. Oper. (medium)	$53.55	$428.40	$81.00	$648.00	$49.44	$75.00
.5 Laborer	39.15	156.60	60.00	240.00		
.25 Equip. Oper. (medium)	53.55	107.10	81.00	162.00		
1 Scraper, Towed, 15 C.Y.		167.60		184.36		
1.25 Dozers, 300 H.P.		2375.00		2612.50	181.61	199.78
14 L.H., Daily Totals		$3234.70		$3846.86	$231.05	$274.78

Crew B-33D

Crew B-33D	Hr.	Daily	Hr.	Daily	Bare Costs	Incl. O&P
1 Equip. Oper. (medium)	$53.55	$428.40	$81.00	$648.00	$49.44	$75.00
.5 Laborer	39.15	156.60	60.00	240.00		
.25 Equip. Oper. (medium)	53.55	107.10	81.00	162.00		
1 S.P. Scraper, 14 C.Y.		2429.00		2671.90		
.25 Dozer, 300 H.P.		475.00		522.50	207.43	228.17
14 L.H., Daily Totals		$3596.10		$4244.40	$256.86	$303.17

Crew B-33E

Crew B-33E	Hr.	Daily	Hr.	Daily	Bare Costs	Incl. O&P
1 Equip. Oper. (medium)	$53.55	$428.40	$81.00	$648.00	$49.44	$75.00
.5 Laborer	39.15	156.60	60.00	240.00		
.25 Equip. Oper. (medium)	53.55	107.10	81.00	162.00		
1 S.P. Scraper, 21 C.Y.		2784.00		3062.40		
.25 Dozer, 300 H.P.		475.00		522.50	232.79	256.06
14 L.H., Daily Totals		$3951.10		$4634.90	$282.22	$331.06

Crew B-33F

Crew B-33F	Hr.	Daily	Hr.	Daily	Bare Costs	Incl. O&P
1 Equip. Oper. (medium)	$53.55	$428.40	$81.00	$648.00	$49.44	$75.00
.5 Laborer	39.15	156.60	60.00	240.00		
.25 Equip. Oper. (medium)	53.55	107.10	81.00	162.00		
1 Elev. Scraper, 11 C.Y.		1192.00		1311.20		
.25 Dozer, 300 H.P.		475.00		522.50	119.07	130.98
14 L.H., Daily Totals		$2359.10		$2883.70	$168.51	$205.98

Crew B-33G

Crew B-33G	Hr.	Daily	Hr.	Daily	Bare Costs	Incl. O&P
1 Equip. Oper. (medium)	$53.55	$428.40	$81.00	$648.00	$49.44	$75.00
.5 Laborer	39.15	156.60	60.00	240.00		
.25 Equip. Oper. (medium)	53.55	107.10	81.00	162.00		
1 Elev. Scraper, 22 C.Y.		2490.00		2739.00		
.25 Dozer, 300 H.P.		475.00		522.50	211.79	232.96
14 L.H., Daily Totals		$3657.10		$4311.50	$261.22	$307.96

Crew No.	Bare Costs Hr.	Bare Costs Daily	Incl. Subs O&P Hr.	Incl. Subs O&P Daily	Cost Per Labor-Hour Bare Costs	Cost Per Labor-Hour Incl. O&P
Crew B-33H	Hr.	Daily	Hr.	Daily	Bare Costs	Incl. O&P
.5 Laborer	$39.15	$156.60	$60.00	$240.00	$49.44	$75.00
1 Equipment Operator (med.)	53.55	428.40	81.00	648.00		
.25 Equipment Operator (med.)	53.55	107.10	81.00	162.00		
1 S.P. Scraper, 44 C.Y.		4712.00		5183.20		
.25 Dozer, 410 H.P.		592.00		651.20	378.86	416.74
14 L.H., Daily Totals		$5996.10		$6884.40	$428.29	$491.74
Crew B-33J	Hr.	Daily	Hr.	Daily	Bare Costs	Incl. O&P
1 Equipment Operator (med.)	$53.55	$428.40	$81.00	$648.00	$53.55	$81.00
1 S.P. Scraper, 14 C.Y.		2429.00		2671.90	303.63	333.99
8 L.H., Daily Totals		$2857.40		$3319.90	$357.18	$414.99
Crew B-33K	Hr.	Daily	Hr.	Daily	Bare Costs	Incl. O&P
1 Equipment Operator (med.)	$53.55	$428.40	$81.00	$648.00	$49.44	$75.00
.25 Equipment Operator (med.)	53.55	107.10	81.00	162.00		
.5 Laborer	39.15	156.60	60.00	240.00		
1 S.P. Scraper, 31 C.Y.		3776.00		4153.60		
.25 Dozer, 410 H.P.		592.00		651.20	312.00	343.20
14 L.H., Daily Totals		$5060.10		$5854.80	$361.44	$418.20
Crew B-34A	Hr.	Daily	Hr.	Daily	Bare Costs	Incl. O&P
1 Truck Driver (heavy)	$45.55	$364.40	$68.70	$549.60	$45.55	$68.70
1 Dump Truck, 8 C.Y., 220 H.P.		391.00		430.10	48.88	53.76
8 L.H., Daily Totals		$755.40		$979.70	$94.42	$122.46
Crew B-34B	Hr.	Daily	Hr.	Daily	Bare Costs	Incl. O&P
1 Truck Driver (heavy)	$45.55	$364.40	$68.70	$549.60	$45.55	$68.70
1 Dump Truck, 12 C.Y., 400 H.P.		642.60		706.86	80.33	88.36
8 L.H., Daily Totals		$1007.00		$1256.46	$125.88	$157.06
Crew B-34C	Hr.	Daily	Hr.	Daily	Bare Costs	Incl. O&P
1 Truck Driver (heavy)	$45.55	$364.40	$68.70	$549.60	$45.55	$68.70
1 Truck Tractor, 6x4, 380 H.P.		559.80		615.78		
1 Dump Trailer, 16.5 C.Y.		128.00		140.80	85.97	94.57
8 L.H., Daily Totals		$1052.20		$1306.18	$131.53	$163.27
Crew B-34D	Hr.	Daily	Hr.	Daily	Bare Costs	Incl. O&P
1 Truck Driver (heavy)	$45.55	$364.40	$68.70	$549.60	$45.55	$68.70
1 Truck Tractor, 6x4, 380 H.P.		559.80		615.78		
1 Dump Trailer, 20 C.Y.		142.60		156.86	87.80	96.58
8 L.H., Daily Totals		$1066.80		$1322.24	$133.35	$165.28
Crew B-34E	Hr.	Daily	Hr.	Daily	Bare Costs	Incl. O&P
1 Truck Driver (heavy)	$45.55	$364.40	$68.70	$549.60	$45.55	$68.70
1 Dump Truck, Off Hwy., 25 Ton		1476.00		1623.60	184.50	202.95
8 L.H., Daily Totals		$1840.40		$2173.20	$230.05	$271.65
Crew B-34F	Hr.	Daily	Hr.	Daily	Bare Costs	Incl. O&P
1 Truck Driver (heavy)	$45.55	$364.40	$68.70	$549.60	$45.55	$68.70
1 Dump Truck, Off Hwy., 35 Ton		1532.00		1685.20	191.50	210.65
8 L.H., Daily Totals		$1896.40		$2234.80	$237.05	$279.35
Crew B-34G	Hr.	Daily	Hr.	Daily	Bare Costs	Incl. O&P
1 Truck Driver (heavy)	$45.55	$364.40	$68.70	$549.60	$45.55	$68.70
1 Dump Truck, Off Hwy., 50 Ton		2006.00		2206.60	250.75	275.82
8 L.H., Daily Totals		$2370.40		$2756.20	$296.30	$344.52

Crew No.	Bare Costs Hr.	Bare Costs Daily	Incl. Subs O&P Hr.	Incl. Subs O&P Daily	Cost Per Labor-Hour Bare Costs	Cost Per Labor-Hour Incl. O&P
Crew B-34H	Hr.	Daily	Hr.	Daily	Bare Costs	Incl. O&P
1 Truck Driver (heavy)	$45.55	$364.40	$68.70	$549.60	$45.55	$68.70
1 Dump Truck, Off Hwy., 65 Ton		2064.00		2270.40	258.00	283.80
8 L.H., Daily Totals		$2428.40		$2820.00	$303.55	$352.50
Crew B-34I	Hr.	Daily	Hr.	Daily	Bare Costs	Incl. O&P
1 Truck Driver (heavy)	$45.55	$364.40	$68.70	$549.60	$45.55	$68.70
1 Dump Truck, 18 C.Y., 450 H.P.		815.60		897.16	101.95	112.15
8 L.H., Daily Totals		$1180.00		$1446.76	$147.50	$180.85
Crew B-34J	Hr.	Daily	Hr.	Daily	Bare Costs	Incl. O&P
1 Truck Driver (heavy)	$45.55	$364.40	$68.70	$549.60	$45.55	$68.70
1 Dump Truck, Off Hwy., 100 Ton		2952.00		3247.20	369.00	405.90
8 L.H., Daily Totals		$3316.40		$3796.80	$414.55	$474.60
Crew B-34K	Hr.	Daily	Hr.	Daily	Bare Costs	Incl. O&P
1 Truck Driver (heavy)	$45.55	$364.40	$68.70	$549.60	$45.55	$68.70
1 Truck Tractor, 6x4, 450 H.P.		679.80		747.78		
1 Lowbed Trailer, 75 Ton		242.40		266.64	115.28	126.80
8 L.H., Daily Totals		$1286.60		$1564.02	$160.82	$195.50
Crew B-34L	Hr.	Daily	Hr.	Daily	Bare Costs	Incl. O&P
1 Equip. Oper. (light)	$51.00	$408.00	$77.15	$617.20	$51.00	$77.15
1 Flatbed Truck, Gas, 1.5 Ton		217.40		239.14	27.18	29.89
8 L.H., Daily Totals		$625.40		$856.34	$78.17	$107.04
Crew B-34M	Hr.	Daily	Hr.	Daily	Bare Costs	Incl. O&P
1 Equip. Oper. (light)	$51.00	$408.00	$77.15	$617.20	$51.00	$77.15
1 Flatbed Truck, Gas, 3 Ton		270.20		297.22	33.77	37.15
8 L.H., Daily Totals		$678.20		$914.42	$84.78	$114.30
Crew B-34N	Hr.	Daily	Hr.	Daily	Bare Costs	Incl. O&P
1 Truck Driver (heavy)	$45.55	$364.40	$68.70	$549.60	$49.55	$74.85
1 Equip. Oper. (medium)	53.55	428.40	81.00	648.00		
1 Truck Tractor, 6x4, 380 H.P.		559.80		615.78		
1 Flatbed Trailer, 40 Ton		175.00		192.50	45.92	50.52
16 L.H., Daily Totals		$1527.60		$2005.88	$95.47	$125.37
Crew B-34P	Hr.	Daily	Hr.	Daily	Bare Costs	Incl. O&P
1 Pipe Fitter	$62.25	$498.00	$93.95	$751.60	$53.32	$80.52
1 Truck Driver (light)	44.15	353.20	66.60	532.80		
1 Equip. Oper. (medium)	53.55	428.40	81.00	648.00		
1 Flatbed Truck, Gas, 3 Ton		270.20		297.22		
1 Backhoe Loader, 48 H.P.		366.20		402.82	26.52	29.17
24 L.H., Daily Totals		$1916.00		$2632.44	$79.83	$109.69
Crew B-34Q	Hr.	Daily	Hr.	Daily	Bare Costs	Incl. O&P
1 Pipe Fitter	$62.25	$498.00	$93.95	$751.60	$54.03	$81.60
1 Truck Driver (light)	44.15	353.20	66.60	532.80		
1 Equip. Oper. (crane)	55.70	445.60	84.25	674.00		
1 Flatbed Trailer, 25 Ton		128.40		141.24		
1 Dump Truck, 8 C.Y., 220 H.P.		391.00		430.10		
1 Hyd. Crane, 25 Ton		673.80		741.18	49.72	54.69
24 L.H., Daily Totals		$2490.00		$3270.92	$103.75	$136.29

Crew No.	Bare Costs		Incl. Subs O&P		Cost Per Labor-Hour	

Crew R-34R	Hr.	Daily	Hr.	Daily	Bare Costs	Incl. O&P
1 Pipe Fitter	$62.25	$498.00	$93.95	$751.60	$54.03	$81.60
1 Truck Driver (light)	44.15	353.20	66.60	532.80		
1 Equip. Oper. (crane)	55.70	445.60	84.25	674.00		
1 Flatbed Trailer, 25 Ton		128.40		141.24		
1 Dump Truck, 8 C.Y., 220 H.P.		391.00		430.10		
1 Hyd. Crane, 25 Ton		673.80		741.18		
1 Hyd. Excavator, 1 C.Y.		798.20		878.02	82.97	91.27
24 L.H., Daily Totals		$3288.20		$4148.94	$137.01	$172.87

Crew B-34S	Hr.	Daily	Hr.	Daily	Bare Costs	Incl. O&P
2 Pipe Fitters	$62.25	$996.00	$93.95	$1503.20	$56.44	$85.21
1 Truck Driver (heavy)	45.55	364.40	68.70	549.60		
1 Equip. Oper. (crane)	55.70	445.60	84.25	674.00		
1 Flatbed Trailer, 40 Ton		175.00		192.50		
1 Truck Tractor, 6x4, 380 H.P.		559.80		615.78		
1 Hyd. Crane, 80 Ton		1616.00		1777.60		
1 Hyd. Excavator, 2 C.Y.		1123.00		1235.30	108.56	119.41
32 L.H., Daily Totals		$5279.80		$6547.98	$164.99	$204.62

Crew B-34T	Hr.	Daily	Hr.	Daily	Bare Costs	Incl. O&P
2 Pipe Fitters	$62.25	$996.00	$93.95	$1503.20	$56.44	$85.21
1 Truck Driver (heavy)	45.55	364.40	68.70	549.60		
1 Equip. Oper. (crane)	55.70	445.60	84.25	674.00		
1 Flatbed Trailer, 40 Ton		175.00		192.50		
1 Truck Tractor, 6x4, 380 H.P.		559.80		615.78		
1 Hyd. Crane, 80 Ton		1616.00		1777.60	73.46	80.81
32 L.H., Daily Totals		$4156.80		$5312.68	$129.90	$166.02

Crew B-34U	Hr.	Daily	Hr.	Daily	Bare Costs	Incl. O&P
1 Truck Driver (heavy)	$45.55	$364.40	$68.70	$549.60	$48.27	$72.92
1 Equip. Oper. (light)	51.00	408.00	77.15	617.20		
1 Truck Tractor, 220 H.P.		336.60		370.26		
1 Flatbed Trailer, 25 Ton		128.40		141.24	29.06	31.97
16 L.H., Daily Totals		$1237.40		$1678.30	$77.34	$104.89

Crew B-34V	Hr.	Daily	Hr.	Daily	Bare Costs	Incl. O&P
1 Truck Driver (heavy)	$45.55	$364.40	$68.70	$549.60	$50.75	$76.70
1 Equip. Oper. (crane)	55.70	445.60	84.25	674.00		
1 Equip. Oper. (light)	51.00	408.00	77.15	617.20		
1 Truck Tractor, 6x4, 450 H.P.		679.80		747.78		
1 Equipment Trailer, 50 Ton		192.20		211.42		
1 Pickup Truck, 4x4, 3/4 Ton		140.00		154.00	42.17	46.38
24 L.H., Daily Totals		$2230.00		$2954.00	$92.92	$123.08

Crew B-34W	Hr.	Daily	Hr.	Daily	Bare Costs	Incl. O&P
5 Truck Drivers (heavy)	$45.55	$1822.00	$68.70	$2748.00	$48.24	$72.94
2 Equip. Opers. (crane)	55.70	891.20	84.25	1348.00		
1 Equip. Oper. (mechanic)	55.85	446.80	84.50	676.00		
1 Laborer	39.15	313.20	60.00	480.00		
4 Truck Tractors, 6x4, 380 H.P.		2239.20		2463.12		
2 Equipment Trailers, 50 Ton		384.40		422.84		
2 Flatbed Trailers, 40 Ton		350.00		385.00		
1 Pickup Truck, 4x4, 3/4 Ton		140.00		154.00		
1 S.P. Crane, 4x4, 20 Ton		553.80		609.18	50.94	56.03
72 L.H., Daily Totals		$7140.60		$9286.14	$99.17	$128.97

Crew B-35	Hr.	Daily	Hr.	Daily	Bare Costs	Incl. O&P
1 Labor Foreman (outside)	$41.15	$329.20	$63.05	$504.40	$49.54	$75.39
1 Skilled Worker	51.45	411.60	79.20	633.60		
1 Welder (plumber)	61.80	494.40	93.25	746.00		
1 Laborer	39.15	313.20	60.00	480.00		
1 Equip. Oper. (crane)	55.70	445.60	84.25	674.00		
1 Equip. Oper. (oiler)	48.00	384.00	72.60	580.80		
1 Welder, Electric, 300 amp		58.15		63.97		
1 Hyd. Excavator, .75 C.Y.		674.20		741.62	15.26	16.78
48 L.H., Daily Totals		$3110.35		$4424.39	$64.80	$92.17

Crew B-35A	Hr.	Daily	Hr.	Daily	Bare Costs	Incl. O&P
1 Labor Foreman (outside)	$41.15	$329.20	$63.05	$504.40	$48.06	$73.19
2 Laborers	39.15	626.40	60.00	960.00		
1 Skilled Worker	51.45	411.60	79.20	633.60		
1 Welder (plumber)	61.80	494.40	93.25	746.00		
1 Equip. Oper. (crane)	55.70	445.60	84.25	674.00		
1 Equip. Oper. (oiler)	48.00	384.00	72.60	580.80		
1 Welder, Gas Engine, 300 amp		129.80		142.78		
1 Crawler Crane, 75 Ton		1645.00		1809.50	31.69	34.86
56 L.H., Daily Totals		$4466.00		$6051.08	$79.75	$108.06

Crew B-36	Hr.	Daily	Hr.	Daily	Bare Costs	Incl. O&P
1 Labor Foreman (outside)	$41.15	$329.20	$63.05	$504.40	$45.31	$69.01
2 Laborers	39.15	626.40	60.00	960.00		
2 Equip. Oper. (medium)	53.55	856.80	81.00	1296.00		
1 Dozer, 200 H.P.		1384.00		1522.40		
1 Aggregate Spreader		37.40		41.14		
1 Tandem Roller, 10 Ton		237.60		261.36	41.48	45.62
40 L.H., Daily Totals		$3471.40		$4585.30	$86.78	$114.63

Crew B-36A	Hr.	Daily	Hr.	Daily	Bare Costs	Incl. O&P
1 Labor Foreman (outside)	$41.15	$329.20	$63.05	$504.40	$47.66	$72.44
2 Laborers	39.15	626.40	60.00	960.00		
4 Equip. Oper. (medium)	53.55	1713.60	81.00	2592.00		
1 Dozer, 200 H.P.		1384.00		1522.40		
1 Aggregate Spreader		37.40		41.14		
1 Tandem Roller, 10 Ton		237.60		261.36		
1 Roller, Pneum. Whl., 12 Ton		355.80		391.38	35.98	39.58
56 L.H., Daily Totals		$4684.00		$6272.68	$83.64	$112.01

Crew B-36B	Hr.	Daily	Hr.	Daily	Bare Costs	Incl. O&P
1 Labor Foreman (outside)	$41.15	$329.20	$63.05	$504.40	$47.40	$71.97
2 Laborers	39.15	626.40	60.00	960.00		
4 Equip. Oper. (medium)	53.55	1713.60	81.00	2592.00		
1 Truck Driver (heavy)	45.55	364.40	68.70	549.60		
1 Grader, 30,000 Lbs.		678.40		746.24		
1 F.E. Loader, Crl. 1.5 C.Y.		662.80		729.08		
1 Dozer, 300 H.P.		1900.00		2090.00		
1 Roller, Vibratory, 25 Ton		684.00		752.40		
1 Truck Tractor, 6x4, 450 H.P.		679.80		747.78		
1 Water Tank Trailer, 5000 Gal.		143.00		157.30	74.19	81.61
64 L.H., Daily Totals		$7781.60		$9828.80	$121.59	$153.58

For customer support on your Electrical Costs with RSMeans Data, call 800.448.8182.

483

Crews - Standard

Crew No.	Bare Costs		Incl. Subs O&P		Cost Per Labor-Hour	

Crew B-36C

	Hr.	Daily	Hr.	Daily	Bare Costs	Incl. O&P
1 Labor Foreman (outside)	$41.15	$329.20	$63.05	$504.40	$49.47	$74.95
3 Equip. Oper. (medium)	53.55	1285.20	81.00	1944.00		
1 Truck Driver (heavy)	45.55	364.40	68.70	549.60		
1 Grader, 30,000 Lbs.		678.40		746.24		
1 Dozer, 300 H.P.		1900.00		2090.00		
1 Roller, Vibratory, 25 Ton		684.00		752.40		
1 Truck Tractor, 6x4, 450 H.P.		679.80		747.78		
1 Water Tank Trailer, 5000 Gal.		143.00		157.30	102.13	112.34
40 L.H., Daily Totals		$6064.00		$7491.72	$151.60	$187.29

Crew B-36D

	Hr.	Daily	Hr.	Daily	Bare Costs	Incl. O&P
1 Labor Foreman (outside)	$41.15	$329.20	$63.05	$504.40	$50.45	$76.51
3 Equip. Oper. (medium)	53.55	1285.20	81.00	1944.00		
1 Grader, 30,000 Lbs.		678.40		746.24		
1 Dozer, 300 H.P.		1900.00		2090.00		
1 Roller, Vibratory, 25 Ton		684.00		752.40	101.95	112.15
32 L.H., Daily Totals		$4876.80		$6037.04	$152.40	$188.66

Crew B-37

	Hr.	Daily	Hr.	Daily	Bare Costs	Incl. O&P
1 Labor Foreman (outside)	$41.15	$329.20	$63.05	$504.40	$41.46	$63.37
4 Laborers	39.15	1252.80	60.00	1920.00		
1 Equip. Oper. (light)	51.00	408.00	77.15	617.20		
1 Tandem Roller, 5 Ton		152.40		167.64	3.17	3.49
48 L.H., Daily Totals		$2142.40		$3209.24	$44.63	$66.86

Crew B-37A

	Hr.	Daily	Hr.	Daily	Bare Costs	Incl. O&P
2 Laborers	$39.15	$626.40	$60.00	$960.00	$40.82	$62.20
1 Truck Driver (light)	44.15	353.20	66.60	532.80		
1 Flatbed Truck, Gas, 1.5 Ton		217.40		239.14		
1 Tar Kettle, T.M.		122.75		135.03	14.17	15.59
24 L.H., Daily Totals		$1319.75		$1866.96	$54.99	$77.79

Crew B-37B

	Hr.	Daily	Hr.	Daily	Bare Costs	Incl. O&P
3 Laborers	$39.15	$939.60	$60.00	$1440.00	$40.40	$61.65
1 Truck Driver (light)	44.15	353.20	66.60	532.80		
1 Flatbed Truck, Gas, 1.5 Ton		217.40		239.14		
1 Tar Kettle, T.M.		122.75		135.03	10.63	11.69
32 L.H., Daily Totals		$1632.95		$2346.97	$51.03	$73.34

Crew B-37C

	Hr.	Daily	Hr.	Daily	Bare Costs	Incl. O&P
2 Laborers	$39.15	$626.40	$60.00	$960.00	$41.65	$63.30
2 Truck Drivers (light)	44.15	706.40	66.60	1065.60		
2 Flatbed Trucks, Gas, 1.5 Ton		434.80		478.28		
1 Tar Kettle, T.M.		122.75		135.03	17.42	19.17
32 L.H., Daily Totals		$1890.35		$2638.91	$59.07	$82.47

Crew B-37D

	Hr.	Daily	Hr.	Daily	Bare Costs	Incl. O&P
1 Laborer	$39.15	$313.20	$60.00	$480.00	$41.65	$63.30
1 Truck Driver (light)	44.15	353.20	66.60	532.80		
1 Pickup Truck, 3/4 Ton		129.40		142.34	8.09	8.90
16 L.H., Daily Totals		$795.80		$1155.14	$49.74	$72.20

Crew B-37E

	Hr.	Daily	Hr.	Daily	Bare Costs	Incl. O&P
3 Laborers	$39.15	$939.60	$60.00	$1440.00	$44.33	$67.34
1 Equip. Oper. (light)	51.00	408.00	77.15	617.20		
1 Equip. Oper. (medium)	53.55	428.40	81.00	648.00		
2 Truck Drivers (light)	44.15	706.40	66.60	1065.60		
4 Barrels w/ Flasher		13.60		14.96		
1 Concrete Saw		153.60		168.96		
1 Rotary Hammer Drill		24.70		27.17		
1 Hammer Drill Bit		3.05		3.36		
1 Loader, Skid Steer, 30 H.P.		171.00		188.10		
1 Conc. Hammer Attach.		115.55		127.11		
1 Vibrating Plate, Gas, 18"		33.60		36.96		
2 Flatbed Trucks, Gas, 1.5 Ton		434.80		478.28	16.96	18.66
56 L.H., Daily Totals		$3432.30		$4815.69	$61.29	$85.99

Crew B-37F

	Hr.	Daily	Hr.	Daily	Bare Costs	Incl. O&P
3 Laborers	$39.15	$939.60	$60.00	$1440.00	$40.40	$61.65
1 Truck Driver (light)	44.15	353.20	66.60	532.80		
4 Barrels w/ Flasher		13.60		14.96		
1 Concrete Mixer, 10 C.F.		164.60		181.06		
1 Air Compressor, 60 cfm		127.00		139.70		
1 -50' Air Hose, 3/4"		3.25		3.58		
1 Spade (Chipper)		8.40		9.24		
1 Flatbed Truck, Gas, 1.5 Ton		217.40		239.14	16.70	18.36
32 L.H., Daily Totals		$1827.05		$2560.47	$57.10	$80.01

Crew B-37G

	Hr.	Daily	Hr.	Daily	Bare Costs	Incl. O&P
1 Labor Foreman (outside)	$41.15	$329.20	$63.05	$504.40	$41.46	$63.37
4 Laborers	39.15	1252.80	60.00	1920.00		
1 Equip. Oper. (light)	51.00	408.00	77.15	617.20		
1 Berm Machine		313.40		344.74		
1 Tandem Roller, 5 Ton		152.40		167.64	9.70	10.67
48 L.H., Daily Totals		$2455.80		$3553.98	$51.16	$74.04

Crew B-37H

	Hr.	Daily	Hr.	Daily	Bare Costs	Incl. O&P
1 Labor Foreman (outside)	$41.15	$329.20	$63.05	$504.40	$41.46	$63.37
4 Laborers	39.15	1252.80	60.00	1920.00		
1 Equip. Oper. (light)	51.00	408.00	77.15	617.20		
1 Tandem Roller, 5 Ton		152.40		167.64		
1 Flatbed Truck, Gas, 1.5 Ton		217.40		239.14		
1 Tar Kettle, T.M.		122.75		135.03	10.26	11.29
48 L.H., Daily Totals		$2482.55		$3583.41	$51.72	$74.65

Crew B-37I

	Hr.	Daily	Hr.	Daily	Bare Costs	Incl. O&P
3 Laborers	$39.15	$939.60	$60.00	$1440.00	$44.33	$67.34
1 Equip. Oper. (light)	51.00	408.00	77.15	617.20		
1 Equip. Oper. (medium)	53.55	428.40	81.00	648.00		
2 Truck Drivers (light)	44.15	706.40	66.60	1065.60		
4 Barrels w/ Flasher		13.60		14.96		
1 Concrete Saw		153.60		168.96		
1 Rotary Hammer Drill		24.70		27.17		
1 Hammer Drill Bit		3.05		3.36		
1 Air Compressor, 60 cfm		127.00		139.70		
1 -50' Air Hose, 3/4"		3.25		3.58		
1 Spade (Chipper)		8.40		9.24		
1 Loader, Skid Steer, 30 H.P.		171.00		188.10		
1 Conc. Hammer Attach.		115.55		127.11		
1 Concrete Mixer, 10 C.F.		164.60		181.06		
1 Vibrating Plate, Gas, 18"		33.60		36.96		
2 Flatbed Trucks, Gas, 1.5 Ton		434.80		478.28	22.38	24.62
56 L.H., Daily Totals		$3735.55		$5149.27	$66.71	$91.95

For customer support on your Electrical Costs with RSMeans Data, call 800.448.8182.

Crew No.	Bare Costs		Incl. Subs O&P		Cost Per Labor-Hour	

Crew B-37J

	Hr.	Daily	Hr.	Daily	Bare Costs	Incl. O&P
1 Labor Foreman (outside)	$41.15	$329.20	$63.05	$504.40	$41.46	$63.37
4 Laborers	39.15	1252.80	60.00	1920.00		
1 Equip. Oper. (light)	51.00	408.00	77.15	617.20		
1 Air Compressor, 60 cfm		127.00		139.70		
1 -50' Air Hose, 3/4"		3.25		3.58		
2 Concrete Mixers, 10 C.F.		329.20		362.12		
2 Flatbed Trucks, Gas, 1.5 Ton		434.80		478.28		
1 Shot Blaster, 20"		220.40		242.44	23.22	25.54
48 L.H., Daily Totals		$3104.65		$4267.72	$64.68	$88.91

Crew B-37K

	Hr.	Daily	Hr.	Daily	Bare Costs	Incl. O&P
1 Labor Foreman (outside)	$41.15	$329.20	$63.05	$504.40	$41.46	$63.37
4 Laborers	39.15	1252.80	60.00	1920.00		
1 Equip. Oper. (light)	51.00	408.00	77.15	617.20		
1 Air Compressor, 60 cfm		127.00		139.70		
1 -50' Air Hose, 3/4"		3.25		3.58		
2 Flatbed Trucks, Gas, 1.5 Ton		434.80		478.28		
1 Shot Blaster, 20"		220.40		242.44	16.36	18.00
48 L.H., Daily Totals		$2775.45		$3905.59	$57.82	$81.37

Crew B-38

	Hr.	Daily	Hr.	Daily	Bare Costs	Incl. O&P
1 Labor Foreman (outside)	$41.15	$329.20	$63.05	$504.40	$44.80	$68.24
2 Laborers	39.15	626.40	60.00	960.00		
1 Equip. Oper. (light)	51.00	408.00	77.15	617.20		
1 Equip. Oper. (medium)	53.55	428.40	81.00	648.00		
1 Backhoe Loader, 48 H.P.		366.20		402.82		
1 Hyd. Hammer (1200 lb.)		182.20		200.42		
1 F.E. Loader, W.M., 4 C.Y.		657.60		723.36		
1 Pvmt. Rem. Bucket		57.80		63.58	31.59	34.75
40 L.H., Daily Totals		$3055.80		$4119.78	$76.39	$102.99

Crew B-39

	Hr.	Daily	Hr.	Daily	Bare Costs	Incl. O&P
1 Labor Foreman (outside)	$41.15	$329.20	$63.05	$504.40	$41.46	$63.37
4 Laborers	39.15	1252.80	60.00	1920.00		
1 Equip. Oper. (light)	51.00	408.00	77.15	617.20		
1 Air Compressor, 250 cfm		181.20		199.32		
2 Breakers, Pavement, 60 lb.		20.40		22.44		
2 -50' Air Hoses, 1.5"		11.60		12.76	4.44	4.89
48 L.H., Daily Totals		$2203.20		$3276.12	$45.90	$68.25

Crew B-40

	Hr.	Daily	Hr.	Daily	Bare Costs	Incl. O&P
1 Pile Driver Foreman (outside)	$51.50	$412.00	$81.80	$654.40	$51.11	$79.66
4 Pile Drivers	49.50	1584.00	78.60	2515.20		
2 Equip. Oper. (crane)	55.70	891.20	84.25	1348.00		
1 Equip. Oper. (oiler)	48.00	384.00	72.60	580.80		
1 Crawler Crane, 40 Ton		1313.00		1444.30		
1 Vibratory Hammer & Gen.		2494.00		2743.40	59.48	65.43
64 L.H., Daily Totals		$7078.20		$9286.10	$110.60	$145.10

Crew B-40B

	Hr.	Daily	Hr.	Daily	Bare Costs	Incl. O&P
1 Labor Foreman (outside)	$41.15	$329.20	$63.05	$504.40	$43.72	$66.65
3 Laborers	39.15	939.60	60.00	1440.00		
1 Equip. Oper. (crane)	55.70	445.60	84.25	674.00		
1 Equip. Oper. (oiler)	48.00	384.00	72.60	580.80		
1 Lattice Boom Crane, 40 Ton		1311.00		1442.10	27.31	30.04
48 L.H., Daily Totals		$3409.40		$4641.30	$71.03	$96.69

Crew B-41

	Hr.	Daily	Hr.	Daily	Bare Costs	Incl. O&P
1 Labor Foreman (outside)	$41.15	$329.20	$63.05	$504.40	$40.67	$62.23
4 Laborers	39.15	1252.80	60.00	1920.00		
.25 Equip. Oper. (crane)	55.70	111.40	84.25	168.50		
.25 Equip. Oper. (oiler)	48.00	96.00	72.60	145.20		
.25 Crawler Crane, 40 Ton		328.25		361.07	7.46	8.21
44 L.H., Daily Totals		$2117.65		$3099.18	$48.13	$70.44

Crew B-42

	Hr.	Daily	Hr.	Daily	Bare Costs	Incl. O&P
1 Labor Foreman (outside)	$41.15	$329.20	$63.05	$504.40	$44.47	$68.80
4 Laborers	39.15	1252.80	60.00	1920.00		
1 Equip. Oper. (crane)	55.70	445.60	84.25	674.00		
1 Equip. Oper. (oiler)	48.00	384.00	72.60	580.80		
1 Welder	54.30	434.40	90.50	724.00		
1 Hyd. Crane, 25 Ton		673.80		741.18		
1 Welder, Gas Engine, 300 amp		129.80		142.78		
1 Horz. Boring Csg. Mch.		465.20		511.72	19.82	21.81
64 L.H., Daily Totals		$4114.80		$5798.88	$64.29	$90.61

Crew B-43

	Hr.	Daily	Hr.	Daily	Bare Costs	Incl. O&P
1 Labor Foreman (outside)	$41.15	$329.20	$63.05	$504.40	$43.72	$66.65
3 Laborers	39.15	939.60	60.00	1440.00		
1 Equip. Oper. (crane)	55.70	445.60	84.25	674.00		
1 Equip. Oper. (oiler)	48.00	384.00	72.60	580.80		
1 Drill Rig, Truck-Mounted		2573.00		2830.30	53.60	58.96
48 L.H., Daily Totals		$4671.40		$6029.50	$97.32	$125.61

Crew B-44

	Hr.	Daily	Hr.	Daily	Bare Costs	Incl. O&P
1 Pile Driver Foreman (outside)	$51.50	$412.00	$81.80	$654.40	$50.01	$78.09
4 Pile Drivers	49.50	1584.00	78.60	2515.20		
2 Equip. Oper. (crane)	55.70	891.20	84.25	1348.00		
1 Laborer	39.15	313.20	60.00	480.00		
1 Crawler Crane, 40 Ton		1313.00		1444.30		
1 Lead, 60' High		76.00		83.60		
1 Hammer, Diesel, 15K ft.-lbs.		605.80		666.38	31.17	34.29
64 L.H., Daily Totals		$5195.20		$7191.88	$81.18	$112.37

Crew B-45

	Hr.	Daily	Hr.	Daily	Bare Costs	Incl. O&P
1 Equip. Oper. (medium)	$53.55	$428.40	$81.00	$648.00	$49.55	$74.85
1 Truck Driver (heavy)	45.55	364.40	68.70	549.60		
1 Dist. Tanker, 3000 Gallon		327.40		360.14		
1 Truck Tractor, 6x4, 380 H.P.		559.80		615.78	55.45	60.99
16 L.H., Daily Totals		$1680.00		$2173.52	$105.00	$135.85

Crew B-46

	Hr.	Daily	Hr.	Daily	Bare Costs	Incl. O&P
1 Pile Driver Foreman (outside)	$51.50	$412.00	$81.80	$654.40	$44.66	$69.83
2 Pile Drivers	49.50	792.00	78.60	1257.60		
3 Laborers	39.15	939.60	60.00	1440.00		
1 Chain Saw, Gas, 36" Long		45.00		49.50	.94	1.03
48 L.H., Daily Totals		$2188.60		$3401.50	$45.60	$70.86

Crew B-47

	Hr.	Daily	Hr.	Daily	Bare Costs	Incl. O&P
1 Blast Foreman (outside)	$41.15	$329.20	$63.05	$504.40	$43.77	$66.73
1 Driller	39.15	313.20	60.00	480.00		
1 Equip. Oper. (light)	51.00	408.00	77.15	617.20		
1 Air Track Drill, 4"		1016.00		1117.60		
1 Air Compressor, 600 cfm		482.00		530.20		
2 -50' Air Hoses, 3"		29.80		32.78	63.66	70.02
24 L.H., Daily Totals		$2578.20		$3282.18	$107.43	$136.76

| Crew No. | Bare Costs | | Incl. Subs O&P | | Cost Per Labor-Hour | |

Crew B-47A

	Hr.	Daily	Hr.	Daily	Bare Costs	Incl. O&P
1 Drilling Foreman (outside)	$41.15	$329.20	$63.05	$504.40	$48.28	$73.30
1 Equip. Oper. (heavy)	55.70	445.60	84.25	674.00		
1 Equip. Oper. (oiler)	48.00	384.00	72.60	580.80		
1 Air Track Drill, 5"		1211.00		1332.10	50.46	55.50
24 L.H., Daily Totals		$2369.80		$3091.30	$98.74	$128.80

Crew B-47C

	Hr.	Daily	Hr.	Daily	Bare Costs	Incl. O&P
1 Laborer	$39.15	$313.20	$60.00	$480.00	$45.08	$68.58
1 Equip. Oper. (light)	51.00	408.00	77.15	617.20		
1 Air Compressor, 750 cfm		488.20		537.02		
2 -50' Air Hoses, 3"		29.80		32.78		
1 Air Track Drill, 4"		1016.00		1117.60	95.88	105.46
16 L.H., Daily Totals		$2255.20		$2784.60	$140.95	$174.04

Crew B-47E

	Hr.	Daily	Hr.	Daily	Bare Costs	Incl. O&P
1 Labor Foreman (outside)	$41.15	$329.20	$63.05	$504.40	$39.65	$60.76
3 Laborers	39.15	939.60	60.00	1440.00		
1 Flatbed Truck, Gas, 3 Ton		270.20		297.22	8.44	9.29
32 L.H., Daily Totals		$1539.00		$2241.62	$48.09	$70.05

Crew B-47G

	Hr.	Daily	Hr.	Daily	Bare Costs	Incl. O&P
1 Labor Foreman (outside)	$41.15	$329.20	$63.05	$504.40	$42.61	$65.05
2 Laborers	39.15	626.40	60.00	960.00		
1 Equip. Oper. (light)	51.00	408.00	77.15	617.20		
1 Air Track Drill, 4"		1016.00		1117.60		
1 Air Compressor, 600 cfm		482.00		530.20		
2 -50' Air Hoses, 3"		29.80		32.78		
1 Gunite Pump Rig		357.40		393.14	58.91	64.80
32 L.H., Daily Totals		$3248.80		$4155.32	$101.53	$129.85

Crew B-47H

	Hr.	Daily	Hr.	Daily	Bare Costs	Incl. O&P
1 Skilled Worker Foreman (out)	$53.45	$427.60	$82.25	$658.00	$51.95	$79.96
3 Skilled Workers	51.45	1234.80	79.20	1900.80		
1 Flatbed Truck, Gas, 3 Ton		270.20		297.22	8.44	9.29
32 L.H., Daily Totals		$1932.60		$2856.02	$60.39	$89.25

Crew B-48

	Hr.	Daily	Hr.	Daily	Bare Costs	Incl. O&P
1 Labor Foreman (outside)	$41.15	$329.20	$63.05	$504.40	$44.76	$68.15
3 Laborers	39.15	939.60	60.00	1440.00		
1 Equip. Oper. (crane)	55.70	445.60	84.25	674.00		
1 Equip. Oper. (oiler)	48.00	384.00	72.60	580.80		
1 Equip. Oper. (light)	51.00	408.00	77.15	617.20		
1 Centr. Water Pump, 6"		325.40		357.94		
1 -20' Suction Hose, 6"		11.90		13.09		
1 -50' Discharge Hose, 6"		6.30		6.93		
1 Drill Rig, Truck-Mounted		2573.00		2830.30	52.08	57.29
56 L.H., Daily Totals		$5423.00		$7024.66	$96.84	$125.44

Crew B-49

	Hr.	Daily	Hr.	Daily	Bare Costs	Incl. O&P
1 Labor Foreman (outside)	$41.15	$329.20	$63.05	$504.40	$46.91	$71.92
3 Laborers	39.15	939.60	60.00	1440.00		
2 Equip. Oper. (crane)	55.70	891.20	84.25	1348.00		
2 Equip. Oper. (oilers)	48.00	768.00	72.60	1161.60		
1 Equip. Oper. (light)	51.00	408.00	77.15	617.20		
2 Pile Drivers	49.50	792.00	78.60	1257.60		
1 Hyd. Crane, 25 Ton		673.80		741.18		
1 Centr. Water Pump, 6"		325.40		357.94		
1 -20' Suction Hose, 6"		11.90		13.09		
1 -50' Discharge Hose, 6"		6.30		6.93		
1 Drill Rig, Truck-Mounted		2573.00		2830.30	40.80	44.88
88 L.H., Daily Totals		$7718.40		$10278.24	$87.71	$116.80

| Crew No. | Bare Costs | | Incl. Subs O&P | | Cost Per Labor-Hour | |

Crew B-50

	Hr.	Daily	Hr.	Daily	Bare Costs	Incl. O&P
2 Pile Driver Foremen (outside)	$51.50	$824.00	$81.80	$1308.80	$48.35	$75.45
6 Pile Drivers	49.50	2376.00	78.60	3772.80		
2 Equip. Oper. (crane)	55.70	891.20	84.25	1348.00		
1 Equip. Oper. (oiler)	48.00	384.00	72.60	580.80		
3 Laborers	39.15	939.60	60.00	1440.00		
1 Crawler Crane, 40 Ton		1313.00		1444.30		
1 Lead, 60' High		76.00		83.60		
1 Hammer, Diesel, 15K ft.-lbs.		605.80		666.38		
1 Air Compressor, 600 cfm		482.00		530.20		
2 -50' Air Hoses, 3"		29.80		32.78		
1 Chain Saw, Gas, 36" Long		45.00		49.50	22.78	25.06
112 L.H., Daily Totals		$7966.40		$11257.16	$71.13	$100.51

Crew B-51

	Hr.	Daily	Hr.	Daily	Bare Costs	Incl. O&P
1 Labor Foreman (outside)	$41.15	$329.20	$63.05	$504.40	$40.32	$61.61
4 Laborers	39.15	1252.80	60.00	1920.00		
1 Truck Driver (light)	44.15	353.20	66.60	532.80		
1 Flatbed Truck, Gas, 1.5 Ton		217.40		239.14	4.53	4.98
48 L.H., Daily Totals		$2152.60		$3196.34	$44.85	$66.59

Crew B-52

	Hr.	Daily	Hr.	Daily	Bare Costs	Incl. O&P
1 Carpenter Foreman (outside)	$51.25	$410.00	$78.50	$628.00	$45.52	$69.41
1 Carpenter	49.25	394.00	75.45	603.60		
3 Laborers	39.15	939.60	60.00	1440.00		
1 Cement Finisher	46.80	374.40	69.60	556.80		
.5 Rodman (reinf.)	54.30	217.20	83.70	334.80		
.5 Equip. Oper. (medium)	53.55	214.20	81.00	324.00		
.5 Crawler Loader, 3 C.Y.		640.50		704.55	11.44	12.58
56 L.H., Daily Totals		$3189.90		$4591.75	$56.96	$82.00

Crew B-53

	Hr.	Daily	Hr.	Daily	Bare Costs	Incl. O&P
1 Equip. Oper. (light)	$51.00	$408.00	$77.15	$617.20	$51.00	$77.15
1 Trencher, Chain, 12 H.P.		63.60		69.96	7.95	8.74
8 L.H., Daily Totals		$471.60		$687.16	$58.95	$85.89

Crew B-54

	Hr.	Daily	Hr.	Daily	Bare Costs	Incl. O&P
1 Equip. Oper. (light)	$51.00	$408.00	$77.15	$617.20	$51.00	$77.15
1 Trencher, Chain, 40 H.P.		325.20		357.72	40.65	44.72
8 L.H., Daily Totals		$733.20		$974.92	$91.65	$121.86

Crew B-54A

	Hr.	Daily	Hr.	Daily	Bare Costs	Incl. O&P
.17 Labor Foreman (outside)	$41.15	$55.96	$63.05	$85.75	$51.75	$78.39
1 Equipment Operator (med.)	53.55	428.40	81.00	648.00		
1 Wheel Trencher, 67 H.P.		1157.00		1272.70	123.61	135.97
9.36 L.H., Daily Totals		$1641.36		$2006.45	$175.36	$214.36

Crew B-54B

	Hr.	Daily	Hr.	Daily	Bare Costs	Incl. O&P
.25 Labor Foreman (outside)	$41.15	$82.30	$63.05	$126.10	$51.07	$77.41
1 Equipment Operator (med.)	53.55	428.40	81.00	648.00		
1 Wheel Trencher, 150 H.P.		1930.00		2123.00	193.00	212.30
10 L.H., Daily Totals		$2440.70		$2897.10	$244.07	$289.71

Crew B-54C

	Hr.	Daily	Hr.	Daily	Bare Costs	Incl. O&P
1 Laborer	$39.15	$313.20	$60.00	$480.00	$46.35	$70.50
1 Equipment Operator (med.)	53.55	428.40	81.00	648.00		
1 Wheel Trencher, 67 H.P.		1157.00		1272.70	72.31	79.54
16 L.H., Daily Totals		$1898.60		$2400.70	$118.66	$150.04

Crew No.	Bare Costs Hr.	Bare Costs Daily	Incl. Subs O&P Hr.	Incl. Subs O&P Daily	Cost Per Labor-Hour Bare Costs	Cost Per Labor-Hour Incl. O&P
Crew B-54D	Hr.	Daily	Hr.	Daily	Bare Costs	Incl. O&P
1 Laborer	$39.15	$313.20	$60.00	$480.00	$46.35	$70.50
1 Equipment Operator (med.)	53.55	428.40	81.00	648.00		
1 Rock Trencher, 6" Width		749.00		823.90	46.81	51.49
16 L.H., Daily Totals		$1490.60		$1951.90	$93.16	$121.99
Crew B-54E	Hr.	Daily	Hr.	Daily	Bare Costs	Incl. O&P
1 Laborer	$39.15	$313.20	$60.00	$480.00	$46.35	$70.50
1 Equipment Operator (med.)	53.55	428.40	81.00	648.00		
1 Rock Trencher, 18" Width		2645.00		2909.50	165.31	181.84
16 L.H., Daily Totals		$3386.60		$4037.50	$211.66	$252.34
Crew B-55	Hr.	Daily	Hr.	Daily	Bare Costs	Incl. O&P
2 Laborers	$39.15	$626.40	$60.00	$960.00	$40.82	$62.20
1 Truck Driver (light)	44.15	353.20	66.60	532.80		
1 Truck-Mounted Earth Auger		781.40		859.54		
1 Flatbed Truck, Gas, 3 Ton		270.20		297.22	43.82	48.20
24 L.H., Daily Totals		$2031.20		$2649.56	$84.63	$110.40
Crew B-56	Hr.	Daily	Hr.	Daily	Bare Costs	Incl. O&P
1 Laborer	$39.15	$313.20	$60.00	$480.00	$45.08	$68.58
1 Equip. Oper. (light)	51.00	408.00	77.15	617.20		
1 Air Track Drill, 4"		1016.00		1117.60		
1 Air Compressor, 600 cfm		482.00		530.20		
1 -50' Air Hose, 3"		14.90		16.39	94.56	104.01
16 L.H., Daily Totals		$2234.10		$2761.39	$139.63	$172.59
Crew B-57	Hr.	Daily	Hr.	Daily	Bare Costs	Incl. O&P
1 Labor Foreman (outside)	$41.15	$329.20	$63.05	$504.40	$45.69	$69.51
2 Laborers	39.15	626.40	60.00	960.00		
1 Equip. Oper. (crane)	55.70	445.60	84.25	674.00		
1 Equip. Oper. (light)	51.00	408.00	77.15	617.20		
1 Equip. Oper. (oiler)	48.00	384.00	72.60	580.80		
1 Crawler Crane, 25 Ton		1296.00		1425.60		
1 Clamshell Bucket, 1 C.Y.		48.80		53.68		
1 Centr. Water Pump, 6"		325.40		357.94		
1 -20' Suction Hose, 6"		11.90		13.09		
20 -50' Discharge Hoses, 6"		126.00		138.60	37.67	41.44
48 L.H., Daily Totals		$4001.30		$5325.31	$83.36	$110.94
Crew B-58	Hr.	Daily	Hr.	Daily	Bare Costs	Incl. O&P
2 Laborers	$39.15	$626.40	$60.00	$960.00	$43.10	$65.72
1 Equip. Oper. (light)	51.00	408.00	77.15	617.20		
1 Backhoe Loader, 48 H.P.		366.20		402.82		
1 Small Helicopter, w/ Pilot		2793.00		3072.30	131.63	144.80
24 L.H., Daily Totals		$4193.60		$5052.32	$174.73	$210.51
Crew B-59	Hr.	Daily	Hr.	Daily	Bare Costs	Incl. O&P
1 Truck Driver (heavy)	$45.55	$364.40	$68.70	$549.60	$45.55	$68.70
1 Truck Tractor, 220 H.P.		336.60		370.26		
1 Water Tank Trailer, 5000 Gal.		143.00		157.30	59.95	65.94
8 L.H., Daily Totals		$844.00		$1077.16	$105.50	$134.65
Crew B-59A	Hr.	Daily	Hr.	Daily	Bare Costs	Incl. O&P
2 Laborers	$39.15	$626.40	$60.00	$960.00	$41.28	$62.90
1 Truck Driver (heavy)	45.55	364.40	68.70	549.60		
1 Water Tank Trailer, 5000 Gal.		143.00		157.30		
1 Truck Tractor, 220 H.P.		336.60		370.26	19.98	21.98
24 L.H., Daily Totals		$1470.40		$2037.16	$61.27	$84.88

Crew No.	Bare Costs Hr.	Bare Costs Daily	Incl. Subs O&P Hr.	Incl. Subs O&P Daily	Cost Per Labor-Hour Bare Costs	Cost Per Labor-Hour Incl. O&P
Crew B-60	Hr.	Daily	Hr.	Daily	Bare Costs	Incl. O&P
1 Labor Foreman (outside)	$41.15	$329.20	$63.05	$504.40	$46.45	$70.60
2 Laborers	39.15	626.40	60.00	960.00		
1 Equip. Oper. (crane)	55.70	445.60	84.25	674.00		
2 Equip. Oper. (light)	51.00	816.00	77.15	1234.40		
1 Equip. Oper. (oiler)	48.00	384.00	72.60	580.80		
1 Crawler Crane, 40 Ton		1313.00		1444.30		
1 Lead, 60' High		76.00		83.60		
1 Hammer, Diesel, 15K ft.-lbs.		605.80		666.38		
1 Backhoe Loader, 48 H.P.		366.20		402.82	42.16	46.38
56 L.H., Daily Totals		$4962.20		$6550.70	$88.61	$116.98
Crew B-61	Hr.	Daily	Hr.	Daily	Bare Costs	Incl. O&P
1 Labor Foreman (outside)	$41.15	$329.20	$63.05	$504.40	$41.92	$64.04
3 Laborers	39.15	939.60	60.00	1440.00		
1 Equip. Oper. (light)	51.00	408.00	77.15	617.20		
1 Cement Mixer, 2 C.Y.		197.00		216.70		
1 Air Compressor, 160 cfm		143.60		157.96	8.52	9.37
40 L.H., Daily Totals		$2017.40		$2936.26	$50.44	$73.41
Crew B-62	Hr.	Daily	Hr.	Daily	Bare Costs	Incl. O&P
2 Laborers	$39.15	$626.40	$60.00	$960.00	$43.10	$65.72
1 Equip. Oper. (light)	51.00	408.00	77.15	617.20		
1 Loader, Skid Steer, 30 H.P.		171.00		188.10	7.13	7.84
24 L.H., Daily Totals		$1205.40		$1765.30	$50.23	$73.55
Crew B-62A	Hr.	Daily	Hr.	Daily	Bare Costs	Incl. O&P
2 Laborers	$39.15	$626.40	$60.00	$960.00	$43.10	$65.72
1 Equip. Oper. (light)	51.00	408.00	77.15	617.20		
1 Loader, Skid Steer, 30 H.P.		171.00		188.10		
1 Trencher Attachment		55.30		60.83	9.43	10.37
24 L.H., Daily Totals		$1260.70		$1826.13	$52.53	$76.09
Crew B-63	Hr.	Daily	Hr.	Daily	Bare Costs	Incl. O&P
4 Laborers	$39.15	$1252.80	$60.00	$1920.00	$41.52	$63.43
1 Equip. Oper. (light)	51.00	408.00	77.15	617.20		
1 Loader, Skid Steer, 30 H.P.		171.00		188.10	4.28	4.70
40 L.H., Daily Totals		$1831.80		$2725.30	$45.80	$68.13
Crew B-63B	Hr.	Daily	Hr.	Daily	Bare Costs	Incl. O&P
1 Labor Foreman (inside)	$39.65	$317.20	$60.75	$486.00	$42.24	$64.47
2 Laborers	39.15	626.40	60.00	960.00		
1 Equip. Oper. (light)	51.00	408.00	77.15	617.20		
1 Loader, Skid Steer, 78 H.P.		309.40		340.34	9.67	10.64
32 L.H., Daily Totals		$1661.00		$2403.54	$51.91	$75.11
Crew B-64	Hr.	Daily	Hr.	Daily	Bare Costs	Incl. O&P
1 Laborer	$39.15	$313.20	$60.00	$480.00	$41.65	$63.30
1 Truck Driver (light)	44.15	353.20	66.60	532.80		
1 Power Mulcher (small)		143.20		157.52		
1 Flatbed Truck, Gas, 1.5 Ton		217.40		239.14	22.54	24.79
16 L.H., Daily Totals		$1027.00		$1409.46	$64.19	$88.09
Crew B-65	Hr.	Daily	Hr.	Daily	Bare Costs	Incl. O&P
1 Laborer	$39.15	$313.20	$60.00	$480.00	$41.65	$63.30
1 Truck Driver (light)	44.15	353.20	66.60	532.80		
1 Power Mulcher (Large)		303.00		333.30		
1 Flatbed Truck, Gas, 1.5 Ton		217.40		239.14	32.52	35.78
16 L.H., Daily Totals		$1186.80		$1585.24	$74.17	$99.08

Crew No.	Bare Costs		Incl. Subs O&P		Cost Per Labor-Hour	
Crew B-66	Hr.	Daily	Hr.	Daily	Bare Costs	Incl. O&P
1 Equip. Oper. (light)	$51.00	$408.00	$77.15	$617.20	$51.00	$77.15
1 Loader-Backhoe, 40 H.P.		268.00		294.80	33.50	36.85
8 L.H., Daily Totals		$676.00		$912.00	$84.50	$114.00
Crew B-67	Hr.	Daily	Hr.	Daily	Bare Costs	Incl. O&P
1 Millwright	$51.55	$412.40	$75.50	$604.00	$51.27	$76.33
1 Equip. Oper. (light)	51.00	408.00	77.15	617.20		
1 R.T. Forklift, 5,000 Lb., diesel		282.20		310.42	17.64	19.40
16 L.H., Daily Totals		$1102.60		$1531.62	$68.91	$95.73
Crew B-67B	Hr.	Daily	Hr.	Daily	Bare Costs	Incl. O&P
1 Millwright Foreman (inside)	$52.05	$416.40	$76.25	$610.00	$51.80	$75.88
1 Millwright	51.55	412.40	75.50	604.00		
16 L.H., Daily Totals		$828.80		$1214.00	$51.80	$75.88
Crew B-68	Hr.	Daily	Hr.	Daily	Bare Costs	Incl. O&P
2 Millwrights	$51.55	$824.80	$75.50	$1208.00	$51.37	$76.05
1 Equip. Oper. (light)	51.00	408.00	77.15	617.20		
1 R.T. Forklift, 5,000 Lb., diesel		282.20		310.42	11.76	12.93
24 L.H., Daily Totals		$1515.00		$2135.62	$63.13	$88.98
Crew B-68A	Hr.	Daily	Hr.	Daily	Bare Costs	Incl. O&P
1 Millwright Foreman (inside)	$52.05	$416.40	$76.25	$610.00	$51.72	$75.75
2 Millwrights	51.55	824.80	75.50	1208.00		
1 Forklift, Smooth Floor, 8,000 Lb.		171.20		188.32	7.13	7.85
24 L.H., Daily Totals		$1412.40		$2006.32	$58.85	$83.60
Crew B-68B	Hr.	Daily	Hr.	Daily	Bare Costs	Incl. O&P
1 Millwright Foreman (inside)	$52.05	$416.40	$76.25	$610.00	$55.99	$83.34
2 Millwrights	51.55	824.80	75.50	1208.00		
2 Electricians	56.60	905.60	84.80	1356.80		
2 Plumbers	61.80	988.80	93.25	1492.00		
1 R.T. Forklift, 5,000 Lb., gas		305.80		336.38	5.46	6.01
56 L.H., Daily Totals		$3441.40		$5003.18	$61.45	$89.34
Crew B-68C	Hr.	Daily	Hr.	Daily	Bare Costs	Incl. O&P
1 Millwright Foreman (inside)	$52.05	$416.40	$76.25	$610.00	$55.50	$82.45
1 Millwright	51.55	412.40	75.50	604.00		
1 Electrician	56.60	452.80	84.80	678.40		
1 Plumber	61.80	494.40	93.25	746.00		
1 R.T. Forklift, 5,000 Lb., gas		305.80		336.38	9.56	10.51
32 L.H., Daily Totals		$2081.80		$2974.78	$65.06	$92.96
Crew B-68D	Hr.	Daily	Hr.	Daily	Bare Costs	Incl. O&P
1 Labor Foreman (inside)	$39.65	$317.20	$60.75	$486.00	$43.27	$65.97
1 Laborer	39.15	313.20	60.00	480.00		
1 Equip. Oper. (light)	51.00	408.00	77.15	617.20		
1 R.T. Forklift, 5,000 Lb., gas		305.80		336.38	12.74	14.02
24 L.H., Daily Totals		$1344.20		$1919.58	$56.01	$79.98
Crew B-68E	Hr.	Daily	Hr.	Daily	Bare Costs	Incl. O&P
1 Struc. Steel Foreman (inside)	$54.80	$438.40	$91.35	$730.80	$54.40	$90.67
3 Struc. Steel Workers	54.30	1303.20	90.50	2172.00		
1 Welder	54.30	434.40	90.50	724.00		
1 Forklift, Smooth Floor, 8,000 Lb.		171.20		188.32	4.28	4.71
40 L.H., Daily Totals		$2347.20		$3815.12	$58.68	$95.38

Crew No.	Bare Costs		Incl. Subs O&P		Cost Per Labor-Hour	
Crew B-68F	Hr.	Daily	Hr.	Daily	Bare Costs	Incl. O&P
1 Skilled Worker Foreman (out)	$53.45	$427.60	$82.25	$658.00	$52.12	$80.22
2 Skilled Workers	51.45	823.20	79.20	1267.20		
1 R.T. Forklift, 5,000 Lb., gas		305.80		336.38	12.74	14.02
24 L.H., Daily Totals		$1556.60		$2261.58	$64.86	$94.23
Crew B-68G	Hr.	Daily	Hr.	Daily	Bare Costs	Incl. O&P
2 Structural Steel Workers	$54.30	$868.80	$90.50	$1448.00	$54.30	$90.50
1 R.T. Forklift, 5,000 Lb., gas		305.80		336.38	19.11	21.02
16 L.H., Daily Totals		$1174.60		$1784.38	$73.41	$111.52
Crew B-69	Hr.	Daily	Hr.	Daily	Bare Costs	Incl. O&P
1 Labor Foreman (outside)	$41.15	$329.20	$63.05	$504.40	$43.72	$66.65
3 Laborers	39.15	939.60	60.00	1440.00		
1 Equip. Oper. (crane)	55.70	445.60	84.25	674.00		
1 Equip. Oper. (oiler)	48.00	384.00	72.60	580.80		
1 Hyd. Crane, 80 Ton		1616.00		1777.60	33.67	37.03
48 L.H., Daily Totals		$3714.40		$4976.80	$77.38	$103.68
Crew B-69A	Hr.	Daily	Hr.	Daily	Bare Costs	Incl. O&P
1 Labor Foreman (outside)	$41.15	$329.20	$63.05	$504.40	$43.16	$65.61
3 Laborers	39.15	939.60	60.00	1440.00		
1 Equip. Oper. (medium)	53.55	428.40	81.00	648.00		
1 Concrete Finisher	46.80	374.40	69.60	556.80		
1 Curb/Gutter Paver, 2-Track		1194.00		1313.40	24.88	27.36
48 L.H., Daily Totals		$3265.60		$4462.60	$68.03	$92.97
Crew B-69B	Hr.	Daily	Hr.	Daily	Bare Costs	Incl. O&P
1 Labor Foreman (outside)	$41.15	$329.20	$63.05	$504.40	$43.16	$65.61
3 Laborers	39.15	939.60	60.00	1440.00		
1 Equip. Oper. (medium)	53.55	428.40	81.00	648.00		
1 Cement Finisher	46.80	374.40	69.60	556.80		
1 Curb/Gutter Paver, 4-Track		802.40		882.64	16.72	18.39
48 L.H., Daily Totals		$2874.00		$4031.84	$59.88	$84.00
Crew B-70	Hr.	Daily	Hr.	Daily	Bare Costs	Incl. O&P
1 Labor Foreman (outside)	$41.15	$329.20	$63.05	$504.40	$45.61	$69.44
3 Laborers	39.15	939.60	60.00	1440.00		
3 Equip. Oper. (medium)	53.55	1285.20	81.00	1944.00		
1 Grader, 30,000 Lbs.		678.40		746.24		
1 Ripper, Beam & 1 Shank		85.60		94.16		
1 Road Sweeper, S.P., 8' wide		700.80		770.88		
1 F.E. Loader, W.M., 1.5 C.Y.		362.00		398.20	32.62	35.88
56 L.H., Daily Totals		$4380.80		$5897.88	$78.23	$105.32
Crew B-70A	Hr.	Daily	Hr.	Daily	Bare Costs	Incl. O&P
1 Laborer	$39.15	$313.20	$60.00	$480.00	$50.67	$76.80
4 Equip. Oper. (medium)	53.55	1713.60	81.00	2592.00		
1 Grader, 40,000 Lbs.		1248.00		1372.80		
1 F.E. Loader, W.M., 2.5 C.Y.		556.20		611.82		
1 Dozer, 80 H.P.		468.60		515.46		
1 Roller, Pneum. Whl., 12 Ton		355.80		391.38	65.72	72.29
40 L.H., Daily Totals		$4655.40		$5963.46	$116.39	$149.09
Crew B-71	Hr.	Daily	Hr.	Daily	Bare Costs	Incl. O&P
1 Labor Foreman (outside)	$41.15	$329.20	$63.05	$504.40	$45.61	$69.44
3 Laborers	39.15	939.60	60.00	1440.00		
3 Equip. Oper. (medium)	53.55	1285.20	81.00	1944.00		
1 Pvmt. Profiler, 750 H.P.		5553.00		6108.30		
1 Road Sweeper, S.P., 8' wide		700.80		770.88		
1 F.E. Loader, W.M., 1.5 C.Y.		362.00		398.20	118.14	129.95
56 L.H., Daily Totals		$9169.80		$11165.78	$163.75	$199.39

Crew B-72

	Bare Costs		Incl. Subs O&P		Cost Per Labor-Hour	
Crew No.	Hr.	Daily	Hr.	Daily	Bare Costs	Incl. O&P
1 Labor Foreman (outside)	$41.15	$329.20	$63.05	$504.40	$48.60	$70.00
3 Laborers	39.15	939.60	60.00	1440.00		
4 Equip. Oper. (medium)	53.55	1713.60	81.00	2592.00		
1 Pvmt. Profiler, 750 H.P.		5553.00		6108.30		
1 Hammermill, 250 H.P.		1827.00		2009.70		
1 Windrow Loader		1254.00		1379.40		
1 Mix Paver, 165 H.P.		2251.00		2476.10		
1 Roller, Pneum. Whl., 12 Ton		355.80		391.38	175.64	193.20
64 L.H., Daily Totals		$14223.20		$16901.28	$222.24	$264.08

Crew B-73

	Bare Costs		Incl. Subs O&P		Cost Per Labor-Hour	
Crew No.	Hr.	Daily	Hr.	Daily	Bare Costs	Incl. O&P
1 Labor Foreman (outside)	$41.15	$329.20	$63.05	$504.40	$48.40	$73.51
2 Laborers	39.15	626.40	60.00	960.00		
5 Equip. Oper. (medium)	53.55	2142.00	81.00	3240.00		
1 Road Mixer, 310 H.P.		1942.00		2136.20		
1 Tandem Roller, 10 Ton		237.60		261.36		
1 Hammermill, 250 H.P.		1827.00		2009.70		
1 Grader, 30,000 Lbs.		678.40		746.24		
.5 F.E. Loader, W.M., 1.5 C.Y.		181.00		199.10		
.5 Truck Tractor, 220 H.P.		168.30		185.13		
.5 Water Tank Trailer, 5000 Gal.		71.50		78.65	79.78	87.76
64 L.H., Daily Totals		$8203.40		$10320.78	$128.18	$161.26

Crew B-74

	Bare Costs		Incl. Subs O&P		Cost Per Labor-Hour	
Crew No.	Hr.	Daily	Hr.	Daily	Bare Costs	Incl. O&P
1 Labor Foreman (outside)	$41.15	$329.20	$63.05	$504.40	$48.20	$73.06
1 Laborer	39.15	313.20	60.00	480.00		
4 Equip. Oper. (medium)	53.55	1713.60	81.00	2592.00		
2 Truck Drivers (heavy)	45.55	728.80	68.70	1099.20		
1 Grader, 30,000 Lbs.		678.40		746.24		
1 Ripper, Beam & 1 Shank		85.60		94.16		
2 Stabilizers, 310 H.P.		3722.00		4094.20		
1 Flatbed Truck, Gas, 3 Ton		270.20		297.22		
1 Chem. Spreader, Towed		51.20		56.32		
1 Roller, Vibratory, 25 Ton		684.00		752.40		
1 Water Tank Trailer, 5000 Gal.		143.00		157.30		
1 Truck Tractor, 220 H.P.		336.60		370.26	93.30	102.63
64 L.H., Daily Totals		$9055.80		$11243.70	$141.50	$175.68

Crew B-75

	Bare Costs		Incl. Subs O&P		Cost Per Labor-Hour	
Crew No.	Hr.	Daily	Hr.	Daily	Bare Costs	Incl. O&P
1 Labor Foreman (outside)	$41.15	$329.20	$63.05	$504.40	$48.58	$73.68
1 Laborer	39.15	313.20	60.00	480.00		
4 Equip. Oper. (medium)	53.55	1713.60	81.00	2592.00		
1 Truck Driver (heavy)	45.55	364.40	68.70	549.60		
1 Grader, 30,000 Lbs.		678.40		746.24		
1 Ripper, Beam & 1 Shank		85.60		94.16		
2 Stabilizers, 310 H.P.		3722.00		4094.20		
1 Dist. Tanker, 3000 Gallon		327.40		360.14		
1 Truck Tractor, 6x4, 380 H.P.		559.80		615.78		
1 Roller, Vibratory, 25 Ton		684.00		752.40	108.16	118.98
56 L.H., Daily Totals		$8777.60		$10788.92	$156.74	$192.66

Crew B-76

	Bare Costs		Incl. Subs O&P		Cost Per Labor-Hour	
Crew No.	Hr.	Daily	Hr.	Daily	Bare Costs	Incl. O&P
1 Dock Builder Foreman (outside)	$51.50	$412.00	$81.80	$654.40	$50.93	$79.54
5 Dock Builders	49.50	1980.00	78.60	3144.00		
2 Equip. Oper. (crane)	55.70	891.20	84.25	1348.00		
1 Equip. Oper. (oiler)	48.00	384.00	72.60	580.80		
1 Crawler Crane, 50 Ton		1675.00		1842.50		
1 Barge, 400 Ton		794.20		873.62		
1 Hammer, Diesel, 15K ft.-lbs.		605.80		666.38		
1 Lead, 60' High		76.00		83.60		
1 Air Compressor, 600 cfm		482.00		530.20		
2 -50' Air Hoses, 3"		29.80		32.78	50.87	55.96
72 L.H., Daily Totals		$7330.00		$9756.28	$101.81	$135.50

Crew B-76A

	Bare Costs		Incl. Subs O&P		Cost Per Labor-Hour	
Crew No.	Hr.	Daily	Hr.	Daily	Bare Costs	Incl. O&P
1 Labor Foreman (outside)	$41.15	$329.20	$63.05	$504.40	$42.58	$64.99
5 Laborers	39.15	1566.00	60.00	2400.00		
1 Equip. Oper. (crane)	55.70	445.60	84.25	674.00		
1 Equip. Oper. (oiler)	48.00	384.00	72.60	580.80		
1 Crawler Crane, 50 Ton		1675.00		1842.50		
1 Barge, 400 Ton		794.20		873.62	38.58	42.44
64 L.H., Daily Totals		$5194.00		$6875.32	$81.16	$107.43

Crew B-77

	Bare Costs		Incl. Subs O&P		Cost Per Labor-Hour	
Crew No.	Hr.	Daily	Hr.	Daily	Bare Costs	Incl. O&P
1 Labor Foreman (outside)	$41.15	$329.20	$63.05	$504.40	$40.55	$61.93
3 Laborers	39.15	939.60	60.00	1440.00		
1 Truck Driver (light)	44.15	353.20	66.60	532.80		
1 Crack Cleaner, 25 H.P.		57.60		63.36		
1 Crack Filler, Trailer Mtd.		199.80		219.78		
1 Flatbed Truck, Gas, 3 Ton		270.20		297.22	13.19	14.51
40 L.H., Daily Totals		$2149.60		$3057.56	$53.74	$76.44

Crew B-78

	Bare Costs		Incl. Subs O&P		Cost Per Labor-Hour	
Crew No.	Hr.	Daily	Hr.	Daily	Bare Costs	Incl. O&P
1 Labor Foreman (outside)	$41.15	$329.20	$63.05	$504.40	$40.32	$61.61
4 Laborers	39.15	1252.80	60.00	1920.00		
1 Truck Driver (light)	44.15	353.20	66.60	532.80		
1 Paint Striper, S.P., 40 Gallon		149.20		164.12		
1 Flatbed Truck, Gas, 3 Ton		270.20		297.22		
1 Pickup Truck, 3/4 Ton		129.40		142.34	11.43	12.58
48 L.H., Daily Totals		$2484.00		$3560.88	$51.75	$74.19

Crew B-78A

	Bare Costs		Incl. Subs O&P		Cost Per Labor-Hour	
Crew No.	Hr.	Daily	Hr.	Daily	Bare Costs	Incl. O&P
1 Equip. Oper. (light)	$51.00	$408.00	$77.15	$617.20	$51.00	$77.15
1 Line Rem. (Metal Balls) 115 H.P.		873.80		961.18	109.22	120.15
8 L.H., Daily Totals		$1281.80		$1578.38	$160.22	$197.30

Crew B-78B

	Bare Costs		Incl. Subs O&P		Cost Per Labor-Hour	
Crew No.	Hr.	Daily	Hr.	Daily	Bare Costs	Incl. O&P
2 Laborers	$39.15	$626.40	$60.00	$960.00	$40.47	$61.91
.25 Equip. Oper. (light)	51.00	102.00	77.15	154.30		
1 Pickup Truck, 3/4 Ton		129.40		142.34		
1 Line Rem.,11 H.P.,Walk Behind		62.00		68.20		
.25 Road Sweeper, S.P., 8' wide		175.20		192.72	20.37	22.40
18 L.H., Daily Totals		$1095.00		$1517.56	$60.83	$84.31

Crew B-78C

	Bare Costs		Incl. Subs O&P		Cost Per Labor-Hour	
Crew No.	Hr.	Daily	Hr.	Daily	Bare Costs	Incl. O&P
1 Labor Foreman (outside)	$41.15	$329.20	$63.05	$504.40	$40.32	$61.61
4 Laborers	39.15	1252.80	60.00	1920.00		
1 Truck Driver (light)	44.15	353.20	66.60	532.80		
1 Paint Striper, T.M., 120 Gal.		734.60		808.06		
1 Flatbed Truck, Gas, 3 Ton		270.20		297.22		
1 Pickup Truck, 3/4 Ton		129.40		142.34	23.63	25.99
48 L.H., Daily Totals		$3069.40		$4204.82	$63.95	$87.60

Crew No.	Bare Costs		Incl. Subs O&P		Cost Per Labor-Hour	

Crew B-78D

Crew B-78D	Hr.	Daily	Hr.	Daily	Bare Costs	Incl. O&P
2 Labor Foremen (outside)	$41.15	$658.40	$63.05	$1008.80	$40.05	$61.27
7 Laborers	39.15	2192.40	60.00	3360.00		
1 Truck Driver (light)	44.15	353.20	66.60	532.80		
1 Paint Striper, T.M., 120 Gal.		734.60		808.06		
1 Flatbed Truck, Gas, 3 Ton		270.20		297.22		
3 Pickup Trucks, 3/4 Ton		388.20		427.02		
1 Air Compressor, 60 cfm		127.00		139.70		
1 -50' Air Hose, 3/4"		3.25		3.58		
1 Breaker, Pavement, 60 lb.		10.20		11.22	19.17	21.08
80 L.H., Daily Totals		$4737.45		$6588.40	$59.22	$82.35

Crew B-78E

Crew B-78E	Hr.	Daily	Hr.	Daily	Bare Costs	Incl. O&P
2 Labor Foremen (outside)	$41.15	$658.40	$63.05	$1008.80	$39.90	$61.06
9 Laborers	39.15	2818.80	60.00	4320.00		
1 Truck Driver (light)	44.15	353.20	66.60	532.80		
1 Paint Striper, T.M., 120 Gal.		734.60		808.06		
1 Flatbed Truck, Gas, 3 Ton		270.20		297.22		
4 Pickup Trucks, 3/4 Ton		517.60		569.36		
2 Air Compressors, 60 cfm		254.00		279.40		
2 -50' Air Hoses, 3/4"		6.50		7.15		
2 Breakers, Pavement, 60 lb.		20.40		22.44	18.78	20.66
96 L.H., Daily Totals		$5633.70		$7845.23	$58.68	$81.72

Crew B-78F

Crew B-78F	Hr.	Daily	Hr.	Daily	Bare Costs	Incl. O&P
2 Labor Foremen (outside)	$41.15	$658.40	$63.05	$1008.80	$39.79	$60.91
11 Laborers	39.15	3445.20	60.00	5280.00		
1 Truck Driver (light)	44.15	353.20	66.60	532.80		
1 Paint Striper, T.M., 120 Gal.		734.60		808.06		
1 Flatbed Truck, Gas, 3 Ton		270.20		297.22		
7 Pickup Trucks, 3/4 Ton		905.80		996.38		
3 Air Compressors, 60 cfm		381.00		419.10		
3 -50' Air Hoses, 3/4"		9.75		10.73		
3 Breakers, Pavement, 60 lb.		30.60		33.66	20.82	22.90
112 L.H., Daily Totals		$6788.75		$9386.75	$60.61	$83.81

Crew B-79

Crew B-79	Hr.	Daily	Hr.	Daily	Bare Costs	Incl. O&P
1 Labor Foreman (outside)	$41.15	$329.20	$63.05	$504.40	$40.55	$61.93
3 Laborers	39.15	939.60	60.00	1440.00		
1 Truck Driver (light)	44.15	353.20	66.60	532.80		
1 Paint Striper, T.M., 120 Gal.		734.60		808.06		
1 Heating Kettle, 115 Gallon		73.50		80.85		
1 Flatbed Truck, Gas, 3 Ton		270.20		297.22		
2 Pickup Trucks, 3/4 Ton		258.80		284.68	33.43	36.77
40 L.H., Daily Totals		$2959.10		$3948.01	$73.98	$98.70

Crew B-79A

Crew B-79A	Hr.	Daily	Hr.	Daily	Bare Costs	Incl. O&P
1.5 Equip. Oper. (light)	$51.00	$612.00	$77.15	$925.80	$51.00	$77.15
.5 Line Remov. (Grinder) 115 H.P.		475.70		523.27		
1 Line Rem. (Metal Balls) 115 H.P.		873.80		961.18	112.46	123.70
12 L.H., Daily Totals		$1961.50		$2410.25	$163.46	$200.85

Crew B-79B

Crew B-79B	Hr.	Daily	Hr.	Daily	Bare Costs	Incl. O&P
1 Laborer	$39.15	$313.20	$60.00	$480.00	$39.15	$60.00
1 Set of Gases		168.00		184.80	21.00	23.10
8 L.H., Daily Totals		$481.20		$664.80	$60.15	$83.10

Crew B-79C

Crew B-79C	Hr.	Daily	Hr.	Daily	Bare Costs	Incl. O&P
1 Labor Foreman (outside)	$41.15	$329.20	$63.05	$504.40	$40.15	$61.38
5 Laborers	39.15	1566.00	60.00	2400.00		
1 Truck Driver (light)	44.15	353.20	66.60	532.80		
1 Paint Striper, T.M., 120 Gal.		734.60		808.06		
1 Heating Kettle, 115 Gallon		73.50		80.85		
1 Flatbed Truck, Gas, 3 Ton		270.20		297.22		
3 Pickup Trucks, 3/4 Ton		388.20		427.02		
1 Air Compressor, 60 cfm		127.00		139.70		
1 -50' Air Hose, 3/4"		3.25		3.58		
1 Breaker, Pavement, 60 lb.		10.20		11.22	28.70	31.57
56 L.H., Daily Totals		$3855.35		$5204.85	$68.85	$92.94

Crew B-79D

Crew B-79D	Hr.	Daily	Hr.	Daily	Bare Costs	Incl. O&P
2 Labor Foremen (outside)	$41.15	$658.40	$63.05	$1008.80	$40.27	$61.59
5 Laborers	39.15	1566.00	60.00	2400.00		
1 Truck Driver (light)	44.15	353.20	66.60	532.80		
1 Paint Striper, T.M., 120 Gal.		734.60		808.06		
1 Heating Kettle, 115 Gallon		73.50		80.85		
1 Flatbed Truck, Gas, 3 Ton		270.20		297.22		
4 Pickup Trucks, 3/4 Ton		517.60		569.36		
1 Air Compressor, 60 cfm		127.00		139.70		
1 -50' Air Hose, 3/4"		3.25		3.58		
1 Breaker, Pavement, 60 lb.		10.20		11.22	27.13	29.84
64 L.H., Daily Totals		$4313.95		$5851.59	$67.41	$91.43

Crew B-79E

Crew B-79E	Hr.	Daily	Hr.	Daily	Bare Costs	Incl. O&P
2 Labor Foremen (outside)	$41.15	$658.40	$63.05	$1008.80	$40.05	$61.27
7 Laborers	39.15	2192.40	60.00	3360.00		
1 Truck Driver (light)	44.15	353.20	66.60	532.80		
1 Paint Striper, T.M., 120 Gal.		734.60		808.06		
1 Heating Kettle, 115 Gallon		73.50		80.85		
1 Flatbed Truck, Gas, 3 Ton		270.20		297.22		
5 Pickup Trucks, 3/4 Ton		647.00		711.70		
2 Air Compressors, 60 cfm		254.00		279.40		
2 -50' Air Hoses, 3/4"		6.50		7.15		
2 Breakers, Pavement, 60 lb.		20.40		22.44	25.08	27.59
80 L.H., Daily Totals		$5210.20		$7108.42	$65.13	$88.86

Crew B-80

Crew B-80	Hr.	Daily	Hr.	Daily	Bare Costs	Incl. O&P
1 Labor Foreman (outside)	$41.15	$329.20	$63.05	$504.40	$43.86	$66.70
1 Laborer	39.15	313.20	60.00	480.00		
1 Truck Driver (light)	44.15	353.20	66.60	532.80		
1 Equip. Oper. (light)	51.00	408.00	77.15	617.20		
1 Flatbed Truck, Gas, 3 Ton		270.20		297.22		
1 Earth Auger, Truck-Mtd.		403.40		443.74	21.05	23.16
32 L.H., Daily Totals		$2077.20		$2875.36	$64.91	$89.86

Crew B-80A

Crew B-80A	Hr.	Daily	Hr.	Daily	Bare Costs	Incl. O&P
3 Laborers	$39.15	$939.60	$60.00	$1440.00	$39.15	$60.00
1 Flatbed Truck, Gas, 3 Ton		270.20		297.22	11.26	12.38
24 L.H., Daily Totals		$1209.80		$1737.22	$50.41	$72.38

Crew B-80B

Crew B-80B	Hr.	Daily	Hr.	Daily	Bare Costs	Incl. O&P
3 Laborers	$39.15	$939.60	$60.00	$1440.00	$42.11	$64.29
1 Equip. Oper. (light)	51.00	408.00	77.15	617.20		
1 Crane, Flatbed Mounted, 3 Ton		247.80		272.58	7.74	8.52
32 L.H., Daily Totals		$1595.40		$2329.78	$49.86	$72.81

Crew B-80C

Crew No.	Bare Costs Hr.	Daily	Incl. Subs O&P Hr.	Daily	Cost Per Labor-Hour Bare Costs	Incl. O&P
2 Laborers	$39.15	$626.40	$60.00	$960.00	$40.82	$62.20
1 Truck Driver (light)	44.15	353.20	66.60	532.80		
1 Flatbed Truck, Gas, 1.5 Ton		217.40		239.14		
1 Manual Fence Post Auger, Gas		7.90		8.69	9.39	10.33
24 L.H., Daily Totals		$1204.90		$1740.63	$50.20	$72.53

Crew B-81

Crew No.	Bare Costs Hr.	Daily	Incl. Subs O&P Hr.	Daily	Cost Per Labor-Hour Bare Costs	Incl. O&P
1 Laborer	$39.15	$313.20	$60.00	$480.00	$46.08	$69.90
1 Equip. Oper. (medium)	53.55	428.40	81.00	648.00		
1 Truck Driver (heavy)	45.55	364.40	68.70	549.60		
1 Hydromulcher, T.M., 3000 Gal.		317.80		349.58		
1 Truck Tractor, 220 H.P.		336.60		370.26	27.27	29.99
24 L.H., Daily Totals		$1760.40		$2397.44	$73.35	$99.89

Crew B-81A

Crew No.	Bare Costs Hr.	Daily	Incl. Subs O&P Hr.	Daily	Cost Per Labor-Hour Bare Costs	Incl. O&P
1 Laborer	$39.15	$313.20	$60.00	$480.00	$41.65	$63.30
1 Truck Driver (light)	44.15	353.20	66.60	532.80		
1 Hydromulcher, T.M., 600 Gal.		122.40		134.64		
1 Flatbed Truck, Gas, 3 Ton		270.20		297.22	24.54	26.99
16 L.H., Daily Totals		$1059.00		$1444.66	$66.19	$90.29

Crew B-82

Crew No.	Bare Costs Hr.	Daily	Incl. Subs O&P Hr.	Daily	Cost Per Labor-Hour Bare Costs	Incl. O&P
1 Laborer	$39.15	$313.20	$60.00	$480.00	$45.08	$68.58
1 Equip. Oper. (light)	51.00	408.00	77.15	617.20		
1 Horiz. Borer, 6 H.P.		80.20		88.22	5.01	5.51
16 L.H., Daily Totals		$801.40		$1185.42	$50.09	$74.09

Crew B-82A

Crew No.	Bare Costs Hr.	Daily	Incl. Subs O&P Hr.	Daily	Cost Per Labor-Hour Bare Costs	Incl. O&P
2 Laborers	$39.15	$626.40	$60.00	$960.00	$45.08	$68.58
2 Equip. Opers. (light)	51.00	816.00	77.15	1234.40		
2 Dump Truck, 8 C.Y., 220 H.P.		782.00		860.20		
1 Flatbed Trailer, 25 Ton		128.40		141.24		
1 Horiz. Dir. Drill, 20k lb. Thrust		651.60		716.76		
1 Mud Trailer for HDD, 1500 Gal.		311.60		342.76		
1 Pickup Truck, 4x4, 3/4 Ton		140.00		154.00		
1 Flatbed Trailer, 3 Ton		24.00		26.40		
1 Loader, Skid Steer, 78 H.P.		309.40		340.34	73.34	80.68
32 L.H., Daily Totals		$3789.40		$4776.10	$118.42	$149.25

Crew B-82B

Crew No.	Bare Costs Hr.	Daily	Incl. Subs O&P Hr.	Daily	Cost Per Labor-Hour Bare Costs	Incl. O&P
2 Laborers	$39.15	$626.40	$60.00	$960.00	$45.08	$68.58
2 Equip. Opers. (light)	51.00	816.00	77.15	1234.40		
2 Dump Truck, 8 C.Y., 220 H.P.		782.00		860.20		
1 Flatbed Trailer, 25 Ton		128.40		141.24		
1 Horiz. Dir. Drill, 30k lb. Thrust		929.00		1021.90		
1 Mud Trailer for HDD, 1500 Gal.		311.60		342.76		
1 Pickup Truck, 4x4, 3/4 Ton		140.00		154.00		
1 Flatbed Trailer, 3 Ton		24.00		26.40		
1 Loader, Skid Steer, 78 H.P.		309.40		340.34	82.01	90.21
32 L.H., Daily Totals		$4066.80		$5081.24	$127.09	$158.79

Crew B-82C

Crew No.	Bare Costs Hr.	Daily	Incl. Subs O&P Hr.	Daily	Cost Per Labor-Hour Bare Costs	Incl. O&P
2 Laborers	$39.15	$626.40	$60.00	$960.00	$45.08	$68.58
2 Equip. Opers. (light)	51.00	816.00	77.15	1234.40		
2 Dump Truck, 8 C.Y., 220 H.P.		782.00		860.20		
1 Flatbed Trailer, 25 Ton		128.40		141.24		
1 Horiz. Dir. Drill, 50k lb. Thrust		1229.00		1351.90		
1 Mud Trailer for HDD, 1500 Gal.		311.60		342.76		
1 Pickup Truck, 4x4, 3/4 Ton		140.00		154.00		
1 Flatbed Trailer, 3 Ton		24.00		26.40		
1 Loader, Skid Steer, 78 H.P.		309.40		340.34	91.39	100.53
32 L.H., Daily Totals		$4366.80		$5411.24	$136.46	$169.10

Crew B-82D

Crew No.	Bare Costs Hr.	Daily	Incl. Subs O&P Hr.	Daily	Cost Per Labor-Hour Bare Costs	Incl. O&P
1 Equip. Oper. (light)	$51.00	$408.00	$77.15	$617.20	$51.00	$77.15
1 Mud Trailer for HDD, 1500 Gal.		311.60		342.76	38.95	42.84
8 L.H., Daily Totals		$719.60		$959.96	$89.95	$120.00

Crew B-83

Crew No.	Bare Costs Hr.	Daily	Incl. Subs O&P Hr.	Daily	Cost Per Labor-Hour Bare Costs	Incl. O&P
1 Tugboat Captain	$53.55	$428.40	$81.00	$648.00	$46.35	$70.50
1 Tugboat Hand	39.15	313.20	60.00	480.00		
1 Tugboat, 250 H.P.		807.20		887.92	50.45	55.49
16 L.H., Daily Totals		$1548.80		$2015.92	$96.80	$126.00

Crew B-84

Crew No.	Bare Costs Hr.	Daily	Incl. Subs O&P Hr.	Daily	Cost Per Labor-Hour Bare Costs	Incl. O&P
1 Equip. Oper. (medium)	$53.55	$428.40	$81.00	$648.00	$53.55	$81.00
1 Rotary Mower/Tractor		365.80		402.38	45.73	50.30
8 L.H., Daily Totals		$794.20		$1050.38	$99.28	$131.30

Crew B-85

Crew No.	Bare Costs Hr.	Daily	Incl. Subs O&P Hr.	Daily	Cost Per Labor-Hour Bare Costs	Incl. O&P
3 Laborers	$39.15	$939.60	$60.00	$1440.00	$43.31	$65.94
1 Equip. Oper. (medium)	53.55	428.40	81.00	648.00		
1 Truck Driver (heavy)	45.55	364.40	68.70	549.60		
1 Telescoping Boom Lift, to 80'		565.60		622.16		
1 Brush Chipper, 12", 130 H.P.		404.40		444.84		
1 Pruning Saw, Rotary		6.85		7.54	24.42	26.86
40 L.H., Daily Totals		$2709.25		$3712.14	$67.73	$92.80

Crew B-86

Crew No.	Bare Costs Hr.	Daily	Incl. Subs O&P Hr.	Daily	Cost Per Labor-Hour Bare Costs	Incl. O&P
1 Equip. Oper. (medium)	$53.55	$428.40	$81.00	$648.00	$53.55	$81.00
1 Stump Chipper, S.P.		183.50		201.85	22.94	25.23
8 L.H., Daily Totals		$611.90		$849.85	$76.49	$106.23

Crew B-86A

Crew No.	Bare Costs Hr.	Daily	Incl. Subs O&P Hr.	Daily	Cost Per Labor-Hour Bare Costs	Incl. O&P
1 Equip. Oper. (medium)	$53.55	$428.40	$81.00	$648.00	$53.55	$81.00
1 Grader, 30,000 Lbs.		678.40		746.24	84.80	93.28
8 L.H., Daily Totals		$1106.80		$1394.24	$138.35	$174.28

Crew B-86B

Crew No.	Bare Costs Hr.	Daily	Incl. Subs O&P Hr.	Daily	Cost Per Labor-Hour Bare Costs	Incl. O&P
1 Equip. Oper. (medium)	$53.55	$428.40	$81.00	$648.00	$53.55	$81.00
1 Dozer, 200 H.P.		1384.00		1522.40	173.00	190.30
8 L.H., Daily Totals		$1812.40		$2170.40	$226.55	$271.30

Crew B-87

Crew No.	Bare Costs Hr.	Daily	Incl. Subs O&P Hr.	Daily	Cost Per Labor-Hour Bare Costs	Incl. O&P
1 Laborer	$39.15	$313.20	$60.00	$480.00	$50.67	$76.80
4 Equip. Oper. (medium)	53.55	1713.60	81.00	2592.00		
2 Feller Bunchers, 100 H.P.		1666.40		1833.04		
1 Log Chipper, 22" Tree		852.80		938.08		
1 Dozer, 105 H.P.		608.00		668.80		
1 Chain Saw, Gas, 36" Long		45.00		49.50	79.31	87.24
40 L.H., Daily Totals		$5199.00		$6561.42	$129.97	$164.04

Crew No.	Bare Costs Hr.	Daily	Incl. Subs O&P Hr.	Daily	Cost Per Labor-Hour Bare Costs	Incl. O&P
Crew B-88	Hr.	Daily	Hr.	Daily	Bare Costs	Incl. O&P
1 Laborer	$39.15	$313.20	$60.00	$480.00	$51.49	$78.00
6 Equip. Oper. (medium)	53.55	2570.40	81.00	3888.00		
2 Feller Bunchers, 100 H.P.		1666.40		1833.04		
1 Log Chipper, 22" Tree		852.80		938.08		
2 Log Skidders, 50 H.P.		1742.40		1916.64		
1 Dozer, 105 H.P.		608.00		668.80		
1 Chain Saw, Gas, 36" Long		45.00		49.50	87.76	96.54
56 L.H., Daily Totals		$7798.20		$9774.06	$139.25	$174.54

Crew B-89	Hr.	Daily	Hr.	Daily	Bare Costs	Incl. O&P
1 Equip. Oper. (light)	$51.00	$408.00	$77.15	$617.20	$47.58	$71.88
1 Truck Driver (light)	44.15	353.20	66.60	532.80		
1 Flatbed Truck, Gas, 3 Ton		270.20		297.22		
1 Concrete Saw		153.60		168.96		
1 Water Tank, 65 Gal.		17.30		19.03	27.57	30.33
16 L.H., Daily Totals		$1202.30		$1635.21	$75.14	$102.20

Crew B-89A	Hr.	Daily	Hr.	Daily	Bare Costs	Incl. O&P
1 Skilled Worker	$51.45	$411.60	$79.20	$633.60	$45.30	$69.60
1 Laborer	39.15	313.20	60.00	480.00		
1 Core Drill (Large)		114.60		126.06	7.16	7.88
16 L.H., Daily Totals		$839.40		$1239.66	$52.46	$77.48

Crew B-89B	Hr.	Daily	Hr.	Daily	Bare Costs	Incl. O&P
1 Equip. Oper. (light)	$51.00	$408.00	$77.15	$617.20	$47.58	$71.88
1 Truck Driver (light)	44.15	353.20	66.60	532.80		
1 Wall Saw, Hydraulic, 10 H.P.		103.40		113.74		
1 Generator, Diesel, 100 kW		367.40		404.14		
1 Water Tank, 65 Gal.		17.30		19.03		
1 Flatbed Truck, Gas, 3 Ton		270.20		297.22	47.39	52.13
16 L.H., Daily Totals		$1519.50		$1984.13	$94.97	$124.01

Crew B-90	Hr.	Daily	Hr.	Daily	Bare Costs	Incl. O&P
1 Labor Foreman (outside)	$41.15	$329.20	$63.05	$504.40	$43.96	$66.84
3 Laborers	39.15	939.60	60.00	1440.00		
2 Equip. Oper. (light)	51.00	816.00	77.15	1234.40		
2 Truck Drivers (heavy)	45.55	728.80	68.70	1099.20		
1 Road Mixer, 310 H.P.		1942.00		2136.20		
1 Dist. Truck, 2000 Gal.		297.00		326.70	34.98	38.48
64 L.H., Daily Totals		$5052.60		$6740.90	$78.95	$105.33

Crew B-90A	Hr.	Daily	Hr.	Daily	Bare Costs	Incl. O&P
1 Labor Foreman (outside)	$41.15	$329.20	$63.05	$504.40	$47.66	$72.44
2 Laborers	39.15	626.40	60.00	960.00		
4 Equip. Oper. (medium)	53.55	1713.60	81.00	2592.00		
2 Graders, 30,000 Lbs.		1356.80		1492.48		
1 Tandem Roller, 10 Ton		237.60		261.36		
1 Roller, Pneum. Whl., 12 Ton		355.80		391.38	34.83	38.31
56 L.H., Daily Totals		$4619.40		$6201.62	$82.49	$110.74

Crew B-90B	Hr.	Daily	Hr.	Daily	Bare Costs	Incl. O&P
1 Labor Foreman (outside)	$41.15	$329.20	$63.05	$504.40	$46.68	$71.01
2 Laborers	39.15	626.40	60.00	960.00		
3 Equip. Oper. (medium)	53.55	1285.20	81.00	1944.00		
1 Roller, Pneum. Whl., 12 Ton		355.80		391.38		
1 Road Mixer, 310 H.P.		1942.00		2136.20	47.87	52.66
48 L.H., Daily Totals		$4538.60		$5935.98	$94.55	$123.67

Crew B-90C	Hr.	Daily	Hr.	Daily	Bare Costs	Incl. O&P
1 Labor Foreman (outside)	$41.15	$329.20	$63.05	$504.40	$45.00	$68.38
4 Laborers	39.15	1252.80	60.00	1920.00		
3 Equip. Oper. (medium)	53.55	1285.20	81.00	1944.00		
3 Truck Drivers (heavy)	45.55	1093.20	68.70	1648.80		
3 Road Mixers, 310 H.P.		5826.00		6408.60	66.20	72.83
88 L.H., Daily Totals		$9786.40		$12425.80	$111.21	$141.20

Crew B-90D	Hr.	Daily	Hr.	Daily	Bare Costs	Incl. O&P
1 Labor Foreman (outside)	$41.15	$329.20	$63.05	$504.40	$44.10	$67.09
6 Laborers	39.15	1879.20	60.00	2880.00		
3 Equip. Oper. (medium)	53.55	1285.20	81.00	1944.00		
3 Truck Drivers (heavy)	45.55	1093.20	68.70	1648.80		
3 Road Mixers, 310 H.P.		5826.00		6408.60	56.02	61.62
104 L.H., Daily Totals		$10412.80		$13385.80	$100.12	$128.71

Crew B-90E	Hr.	Daily	Hr.	Daily	Bare Costs	Incl. O&P
1 Labor Foreman (outside)	$41.15	$329.20	$63.05	$504.40	$44.88	$68.31
4 Laborers	39.15	1252.80	60.00	1920.00		
3 Equip. Oper. (medium)	53.55	1285.20	81.00	1944.00		
1 Truck Driver (heavy)	45.55	364.40	68.70	549.60		
1 Road Mixer, 310 H.P.		1942.00		2136.20	26.97	29.67
72 L.H., Daily Totals		$5173.60		$7054.20	$71.86	$97.97

Crew B-91	Hr.	Daily	Hr.	Daily	Bare Costs	Incl. O&P
1 Labor Foreman (outside)	$41.15	$329.20	$63.05	$504.40	$47.40	$71.97
2 Laborers	39.15	626.40	60.00	960.00		
4 Equip. Oper. (medium)	53.55	1713.60	81.00	2592.00		
1 Truck Driver (heavy)	45.55	364.40	68.70	549.60		
1 Dist. Tanker, 3000 Gallon		327.40		360.14		
1 Truck Tractor, 6x4, 380 H.P.		559.80		615.78		
1 Aggreg. Spreader, S.P.		817.00		898.70		
1 Roller, Pneum. Whl., 12 Ton		355.80		391.38		
1 Tandem Roller, 10 Ton		237.60		261.36	35.90	39.49
64 L.H., Daily Totals		$5331.20		$7133.36	$83.30	$111.46

Crew B-91B	Hr.	Daily	Hr.	Daily	Bare Costs	Incl. O&P
1 Laborer	$39.15	$313.20	$60.00	$480.00	$46.35	$70.50
1 Equipment Oper. (med.)	53.55	428.40	81.00	648.00		
1 Road Sweeper, Vac. Assist.		927.80		1020.58	57.99	63.79
16 L.H., Daily Totals		$1669.40		$2148.58	$104.34	$134.29

Crew B-91C	Hr.	Daily	Hr.	Daily	Bare Costs	Incl. O&P
1 Laborer	$39.15	$313.20	$60.00	$480.00	$41.65	$63.30
1 Truck Driver (light)	44.15	353.20	66.60	532.80		
1 Catch Basin Cleaning Truck		539.00		592.90	33.69	37.06
16 L.H., Daily Totals		$1205.40		$1605.70	$75.34	$100.36

Crew B-91D	Hr.	Daily	Hr.	Daily	Bare Costs	Incl. O&P
1 Labor Foreman (outside)	$41.15	$329.20	$63.05	$504.40	$45.83	$69.65
5 Laborers	39.15	1566.00	60.00	2400.00		
5 Equip. Oper. (medium)	53.55	2142.00	81.00	3240.00		
2 Truck Drivers (heavy)	45.55	728.80	68.70	1099.20		
1 Aggreg. Spreader, S.P.		817.00		898.70		
2 Truck Tractors, 6x4, 380 H.P.		1119.60		1231.56		
2 Dist. Tankers, 3000 Gallon		654.80		720.28		
2 Pavement Brushes, Towed		164.00		180.40		
2 Rollers Pneum. Whl., 12 Ton		711.60		782.76	33.34	36.67
104 L.H., Daily Totals		$8233.00		$11057.30	$79.16	$106.32

Crews - Standard

Crew No.	Bare Costs Hr.	Bare Costs Daily	Incl. Subs O&P Hr.	Incl. Subs O&P Daily	Cost Per Labor-Hour Bare Costs	Cost Per Labor-Hour Incl. O&P
Crew B-92						
1 Labor Foreman (outside)	$41.15	$329.20	$63.05	$504.40	$39.65	$60.76
3 Laborers	39.15	939.60	60.00	1440.00		
1 Crack Cleaner, 25 H.P.		57.60		63.36		
1 Air Compressor, 60 cfm		127.00		139.70		
1 Tar Kettle, T.M.		122.75		135.03		
1 Flatbed Truck, Gas, 3 Ton		270.20		297.22	18.05	19.85
32 L.H., Daily Totals		$1846.35		$2579.70	$57.70	$80.62
Crew B-93						
1 Equip. Oper. (medium)	$53.55	$428.40	$81.00	$648.00	$53.55	$81.00
1 Feller Buncher, 100 H.P.		833.20		916.52	104.15	114.57
8 L.H., Daily Totals		$1261.60		$1564.52	$157.70	$195.57
Crew B-94A						
1 Laborer	$39.15	$313.20	$60.00	$480.00	$39.15	$60.00
1 Diaphragm Water Pump, 2"		71.00		78.10		
1 -20' Suction Hose, 2"		1.95		2.15		
2 -50' Discharge Hoses, 2"		1.80		1.98	9.34	10.28
8 L.H., Daily Totals		$387.95		$562.23	$48.49	$70.28
Crew B-94B						
1 Laborer	$39.15	$313.20	$60.00	$480.00	$39.15	$60.00
1 Diaphragm Water Pump, 4"		114.20		125.62		
1 -20' Suction Hose, 4"		3.45		3.79		
2 -50' Discharge Hoses, 4"		4.70		5.17	15.29	16.82
8 L.H., Daily Totals		$435.55		$614.59	$54.44	$76.82
Crew B-94C						
1 Laborer	$39.15	$313.20	$60.00	$480.00	$39.15	$60.00
1 Centrifugal Water Pump, 3"		78.60		86.46		
1 -20' Suction Hose, 3"		3.05		3.36		
2 -50' Discharge Hoses, 3"		3.50		3.85	10.64	11.71
8 L.H., Daily Totals		$398.35		$573.66	$49.79	$71.71
Crew B-94D						
1 Laborer	$39.15	$313.20	$60.00	$480.00	$39.15	$60.00
1 Centr. Water Pump, 6"		325.40		357.94		
1 -20' Suction Hose, 6"		11.90		13.09		
2 -50' Discharge Hoses, 6"		12.60		13.86	43.74	48.11
8 L.H., Daily Totals		$663.10		$864.89	$82.89	$108.11
Crew C-1						
3 Carpenters	$49.25	$1182.00	$75.45	$1810.80	$46.73	$71.59
1 Laborer	39.15	313.20	60.00	480.00		
32 L.H., Daily Totals		$1495.20		$2290.80	$46.73	$71.59
Crew C-2						
1 Carpenter Foreman (outside)	$51.25	$410.00	$78.50	$628.00	$47.90	$73.38
4 Carpenters	49.25	1576.00	75.45	2414.40		
1 Laborer	39.15	313.20	60.00	480.00		
48 L.H., Daily Totals		$2299.20		$3522.40	$47.90	$73.38
Crew C-2A						
1 Carpenter Foreman (outside)	$51.25	$410.00	$78.50	$628.00	$47.49	$72.41
3 Carpenters	49.25	1182.00	75.45	1810.80		
1 Cement Finisher	46.80	374.40	69.60	556.80		
1 Laborer	39.15	313.20	60.00	480.00		
48 L.H., Daily Totals		$2279.60		$3475.60	$47.49	$72.41

Crew No.	Bare Costs Hr.	Bare Costs Daily	Incl. Subs O&P Hr.	Incl. Subs O&P Daily	Cost Per Labor-Hour Bare Costs	Cost Per Labor-Hour Incl. O&P
Crew C-3						
1 Rodman Foreman (outside)	$56.30	$450.40	$86.75	$694.00	$50.35	$77.34
4 Rodmen (reinf.)	54.30	1737.60	83.70	2678.40		
1 Equip. Oper. (light)	51.00	408.00	77.15	617.20		
2 Laborers	39.15	626.40	60.00	960.00		
3 Stressing Equipment		31.20		34.32		
.5 Grouting Equipment		80.70		88.77	1.75	1.92
64 L.H., Daily Totals		$3334.30		$5072.69	$52.10	$79.26
Crew C-4						
1 Rodman Foreman (outside)	$56.30	$450.40	$86.75	$694.00	$54.80	$84.46
3 Rodmen (reinf.)	54.30	1303.20	83.70	2008.80		
3 Stressing Equipment		31.20		34.32	.97	1.07
32 L.H., Daily Totals		$1784.80		$2737.12	$55.77	$85.53
Crew C-4A						
2 Rodmen (reinf.)	$54.30	$868.80	$83.70	$1339.20	$54.30	$83.70
4 Stressing Equipment		41.60		45.76	2.60	2.86
16 L.H., Daily Totals		$910.40		$1384.96	$56.90	$86.56
Crew C-5						
1 Rodman Foreman (outside)	$56.30	$450.40	$86.75	$694.00	$53.89	$82.63
4 Rodmen (reinf.)	54.30	1737.60	83.70	2678.40		
1 Equip. Oper. (crane)	55.70	445.60	84.25	674.00		
1 Equip. Oper. (oiler)	48.00	384.00	72.60	580.80		
1 Hyd. Crane, 25 Ton		673.80		741.18	12.03	13.24
56 L.H., Daily Totals		$3691.40		$5368.38	$65.92	$95.86
Crew C-6						
1 Labor Foreman (outside)	$41.15	$329.20	$63.05	$504.40	$40.76	$62.11
4 Laborers	39.15	1252.80	60.00	1920.00		
1 Cement Finisher	46.80	374.40	69.60	556.80		
2 Gas Engine Vibrators		56.50		62.15	1.18	1.29
48 L.H., Daily Totals		$2012.90		$3043.35	$41.94	$63.40
Crew C-7						
1 Labor Foreman (outside)	$41.15	$329.20	$63.05	$504.40	$42.81	$65.14
5 Laborers	39.15	1566.00	60.00	2400.00		
1 Cement Finisher	46.80	374.40	69.60	556.80		
1 Equip. Oper. (medium)	53.55	428.40	81.00	648.00		
1 Equip. Oper. (oiler)	48.00	384.00	72.60	580.80		
2 Gas Engine Vibrators		56.50		62.15		
1 Concrete Bucket, 1 C.Y.		24.00		26.40		
1 Hyd. Crane, 55 Ton		1076.00		1183.60	16.06	17.67
72 L.H., Daily Totals		$4238.50		$5962.15	$58.87	$82.81
Crew C-7A						
1 Labor Foreman (outside)	$41.15	$329.20	$63.05	$504.40	$41.00	$62.56
5 Laborers	39.15	1566.00	60.00	2400.00		
2 Truck Drivers (heavy)	45.55	728.80	68.70	1099.20		
2 Conc. Transit Mixers		1964.40		2160.84	30.69	33.76
64 L.H., Daily Totals		$4588.40		$6164.44	$71.69	$96.32
Crew C-7B						
1 Labor Foreman (outside)	$41.15	$329.20	$63.05	$504.40	$42.58	$64.99
5 Laborers	39.15	1566.00	60.00	2400.00		
1 Equipment Operator, Crane	55.70	445.60	84.25	674.00		
1 Equipment Oiler	48.00	384.00	72.60	580.80		
1 Conc. Bucket, 2 C.Y.		37.00		40.70		
1 Lattice Boom Crane, 165 Ton		2119.00		2330.90	33.69	37.06
64 L.H., Daily Totals		$4880.80		$6530.80	$76.26	$102.04

For customer support on your Electrical Costs with RSMeans Data, call 800.448.8182.

493

Crew No.	Bare Costs		Incl. Subs O&P		Cost Per Labor-Hour	

Crew C-7C	Hr.	Daily	Hr.	Daily	Bare Costs	Incl. O&P
1 Labor Foreman (outside)	$41.15	$329.20	$63.05	$504.40	$43.00	$65.63
5 Laborers	39.15	1566.00	60.00	2400.00		
2 Equipment Operators (med.)	53.55	856.80	81.00	1296.00		
2 F.E. Loaders, W.M., 4 C.Y.		1315.20		1446.72	20.55	22.61
64 L.H., Daily Totals		$4067.20		$5647.12	$63.55	$88.24

Crew C-7D	Hr.	Daily	Hr.	Daily	Bare Costs	Incl. O&P
1 Labor Foreman (outside)	$41.15	$329.20	$63.05	$504.40	$41.49	$63.44
5 Laborers	39.15	1566.00	60.00	2400.00		
1 Equip. Oper. (medium)	53.55	428.40	81.00	648.00		
1 Concrete Conveyer		189.80		208.78	3.39	3.73
56 L.H., Daily Totals		$2513.40		$3761.18	$44.88	$67.16

Crew C-8	Hr.	Daily	Hr.	Daily	Bare Costs	Incl. O&P
1 Labor Foreman (outside)	$41.15	$329.20	$63.05	$504.40	$43.68	$66.18
3 Laborers	39.15	939.60	60.00	1440.00		
2 Cement Finishers	46.80	748.80	69.60	1113.60		
1 Equip. Oper. (medium)	53.55	428.40	81.00	648.00		
1 Concrete Pump (Small)		806.40		887.04	14.40	15.84
56 L.H., Daily Totals		$3252.40		$4593.04	$58.08	$82.02

Crew C-8A	Hr.	Daily	Hr.	Daily	Bare Costs	Incl. O&P
1 Labor Foreman (outside)	$41.15	$329.20	$63.05	$504.40	$42.03	$63.71
3 Laborers	39.15	939.60	60.00	1440.00		
2 Cement Finishers	46.80	748.80	69.60	1113.60		
48 L.H., Daily Totals		$2017.60		$3058.00	$42.03	$63.71

Crew C-8B	Hr.	Daily	Hr.	Daily	Bare Costs	Incl. O&P
1 Labor Foreman (outside)	$41.15	$329.20	$63.05	$504.40	$42.43	$64.81
3 Laborers	39.15	939.60	60.00	1440.00		
1 Equip. Oper. (medium)	53.55	428.40	81.00	648.00		
1 Vibrating Power Screed		64.35		70.78		
1 Roller, Vibratory, 25 Ton		684.00		752.40		
1 Dozer, 200 H.P.		1384.00		1522.40	53.31	58.64
40 L.H., Daily Totals		$3829.55		$4937.98	$95.74	$123.45

Crew C-8C	Hr.	Daily	Hr.	Daily	Bare Costs	Incl. O&P
1 Labor Foreman (outside)	$41.15	$329.20	$63.05	$504.40	$43.16	$65.61
3 Laborers	39.15	939.60	60.00	1440.00		
1 Cement Finisher	46.80	374.40	69.60	556.80		
1 Equip. Oper. (medium)	53.55	428.40	81.00	648.00		
1 Shotcrete Rig, 12 C.Y./hr		250.20		275.22		
1 Air Compressor, 160 cfm		143.60		157.96		
4 -50' Air Hoses, 1"		16.40		18.04		
4 -50' Air Hoses, 2"		31.00		34.10	9.19	10.11
48 L.H., Daily Totals		$2512.80		$3634.52	$52.35	$75.72

Crew C-8D	Hr.	Daily	Hr.	Daily	Bare Costs	Incl. O&P
1 Labor Foreman (outside)	$41.15	$329.20	$63.05	$504.40	$44.52	$67.45
1 Laborer	39.15	313.20	60.00	480.00		
1 Cement Finisher	46.80	374.40	69.60	556.80		
1 Equipment Oper. (light)	51.00	408.00	77.15	617.20		
1 Air Compressor, 250 cfm		181.20		199.32		
2 -50' Air Hoses, 1"		8.20		9.02	5.92	6.51
32 L.H., Daily Totals		$1614.20		$2366.74	$50.44	$73.96

Crew C-8E	Hr.	Daily	Hr.	Daily	Bare Costs	Incl. O&P
1 Labor Foreman (outside)	$41.15	$329.20	$63.05	$504.40	$42.73	$64.97
3 Laborers	39.15	939.60	60.00	1440.00		
1 Cement Finisher	46.80	374.40	69.60	556.80		
1 Equipment Oper. (light)	51.00	408.00	77.15	617.20		
1 Shotcrete Rig, 35 C.Y./hr		276.20		303.82		
1 Air Compressor, 250 cfm		181.20		199.32		
4 -50' Air Hoses, 1"		16.40		18.04		
4 -50' Air Hoses, 2"		31.00		34.10	10.52	11.57
48 L.H., Daily Totals		$2556.00		$3673.68	$53.25	$76.53

Crew C-10	Hr.	Daily	Hr.	Daily	Bare Costs	Incl. O&P
1 Laborer	$39.15	$313.20	$60.00	$480.00	$44.25	$66.40
2 Cement Finishers	46.80	748.80	69.60	1113.60		
24 L.H., Daily Totals		$1062.00		$1593.60	$44.25	$66.40

Crew C-10B	Hr.	Daily	Hr.	Daily	Bare Costs	Incl. O&P
3 Laborers	$39.15	$939.60	$60.00	$1440.00	$42.21	$63.84
2 Cement Finishers	46.80	748.80	69.60	1113.60		
1 Concrete Mixer, 10 C.F.		164.60		181.06		
2 Trowels, 48" Walk-Behind		91.10		100.21	6.39	7.03
40 L.H., Daily Totals		$1944.10		$2834.87	$48.60	$70.87

Crew C-10C	Hr.	Daily	Hr.	Daily	Bare Costs	Incl. O&P
1 Laborer	$39.15	$313.20	$60.00	$480.00	$44.25	$66.40
2 Cement Finishers	46.80	748.80	69.60	1113.60		
1 Trowel, 48" Walk-Behind		45.55		50.10	1.90	2.09
24 L.H., Daily Totals		$1107.55		$1643.70	$46.15	$68.49

Crew C-10D	Hr.	Daily	Hr.	Daily	Bare Costs	Incl. O&P
1 Laborer	$39.15	$313.20	$60.00	$480.00	$44.25	$66.40
2 Cement Finishers	46.80	748.80	69.60	1113.60		
1 Vibrating Power Screed		64.35		70.78		
1 Trowel, 48" Walk-Behind		45.55		50.10	4.58	5.04
24 L.H., Daily Totals		$1171.90		$1714.49	$48.83	$71.44

Crew C-10E	Hr.	Daily	Hr.	Daily	Bare Costs	Incl. O&P
1 Laborer	$39.15	$313.20	$60.00	$480.00	$44.25	$66.40
2 Cement Finishers	46.80	748.80	69.60	1113.60		
1 Vibrating Power Screed		64.35		70.78		
1 Cement Trowel, 96" Ride-On		175.90		193.49	10.01	11.01
24 L.H., Daily Totals		$1302.25		$1857.88	$54.26	$77.41

Crew C-10F	Hr.	Daily	Hr.	Daily	Bare Costs	Incl. O&P
1 Laborer	$39.15	$313.20	$60.00	$480.00	$44.25	$66.40
2 Cement Finishers	46.80	748.80	69.60	1113.60		
1 Telescoping Boom Lift, to 60'		456.00		501.60	19.00	20.90
24 L.H., Daily Totals		$1518.00		$2095.20	$63.25	$87.30

Crew C-11	Hr.	Daily	Hr.	Daily	Bare Costs	Incl. O&P
1 Struc. Steel Foreman (outside)	$56.30	$450.40	$93.85	$750.80	$53.98	$88.19
6 Struc. Steel Workers	54.30	2606.40	90.50	4344.00		
1 Equip. Oper. (crane)	55.70	445.60	84.25	674.00		
1 Equip. Oper. (oiler)	48.00	384.00	72.60	580.80		
1 Lattice Boom Crane, 150 Ton		2000.00		2200.00	27.78	30.56
72 L.H., Daily Totals		$5886.40		$8549.60	$81.76	$118.74

Crew No.	Bare Costs		Incl. Subs O&P		Cost Per Labor-Hour	

Crew C-12

	Hr.	Daily	Hr.	Daily	Bare Costs	Incl. O&P
1 Carpenter Foreman (outside)	$51.25	$410.00	$78.50	$628.00	$48.98	$74.85
3 Carpenters	49.25	1182.00	75.45	1810.80		
1 Laborer	39.15	313.20	60.00	480.00		
1 Equip. Oper. (crane)	55.70	445.60	84.25	674.00		
1 Hyd. Crane, 12 Ton		572.80		630.08	11.93	13.13
48 L.H., Daily Totals		$2923.60		$4222.88	$60.91	$87.98

Crew C-13

	Hr.	Daily	Hr.	Daily	Bare Costs	Incl. O&P
1 Struc. Steel Worker	$54.30	$434.40	$90.50	$724.00	$52.62	$85.48
1 Welder	54.30	434.40	90.50	724.00		
1 Carpenter	49.25	394.00	75.45	603.60		
1 Welder, Gas Engine, 300 amp		129.80		142.78	5.41	5.95
24 L.H., Daily Totals		$1392.60		$2194.38	$58.02	$91.43

Crew C-14

	Hr.	Daily	Hr.	Daily	Bare Costs	Incl. O&P
1 Carpenter Foreman (outside)	$51.25	$410.00	$78.50	$628.00	$48.26	$73.70
5 Carpenters	49.25	1970.00	75.45	3018.00		
4 Laborers	39.15	1252.80	60.00	1920.00		
4 Rodmen (reinf.)	54.30	1737.60	83.70	2678.40		
2 Cement Finishers	46.80	748.80	69.60	1113.60		
1 Equip. Oper. (crane)	55.70	445.60	84.25	674.00		
1 Equip. Oper. (oiler)	48.00	384.00	72.60	580.80		
1 Hyd. Crane, 80 Ton		1616.00		1777.60	11.22	12.34
144 L.H., Daily Totals		$8564.80		$12390.40	$59.48	$86.04

Crew C-14A

	Hr.	Daily	Hr.	Daily	Bare Costs	Incl. O&P
1 Carpenter Foreman (outside)	$51.25	$410.00	$78.50	$628.00	$49.40	$75.64
16 Carpenters	49.25	6304.00	75.45	9657.60		
4 Rodmen (reinf.)	54.30	1737.60	83.70	2678.40		
2 Laborers	39.15	626.40	60.00	960.00		
1 Cement Finisher	46.80	374.40	69.60	556.80		
1 Equip. Oper. (medium)	53.55	428.40	81.00	648.00		
1 Gas Engine Vibrator		28.25		31.07		
1 Concrete Pump (Small)		806.40		887.04	4.17	4.59
200 L.H., Daily Totals		$10715.45		$16046.92	$53.58	$80.23

Crew C-14B

	Hr.	Daily	Hr.	Daily	Bare Costs	Incl. O&P
1 Carpenter Foreman (outside)	$51.25	$410.00	$78.50	$628.00	$49.30	$75.41
16 Carpenters	49.25	6304.00	75.45	9657.60		
4 Rodmen (reinf.)	54.30	1737.60	83.70	2678.40		
2 Laborers	39.15	626.40	60.00	960.00		
2 Cement Finishers	46.80	748.80	69.60	1113.60		
1 Equip. Oper. (medium)	53.55	428.40	81.00	648.00		
1 Gas Engine Vibrator		28.25		31.07		
1 Concrete Pump (Small)		806.40		887.04	4.01	4.41
208 L.H., Daily Totals		$11089.85		$16603.72	$53.32	$79.83

Crew C-14C

	Hr.	Daily	Hr.	Daily	Bare Costs	Incl. O&P
1 Carpenter Foreman (outside)	$51.25	$410.00	$78.50	$628.00	$47.05	$72.01
6 Carpenters	49.25	2364.00	75.45	3621.60		
2 Rodmen (reinf.)	54.30	868.80	83.70	1339.20		
4 Laborers	39.15	1252.80	60.00	1920.00		
1 Cement Finisher	46.80	374.40	69.60	556.80		
1 Gas Engine Vibrator		28.25		31.07	.25	.28
112 L.H., Daily Totals		$5298.25		$8096.68	$47.31	$72.29

Crew C-14D

	Hr.	Daily	Hr.	Daily	Bare Costs	Incl. O&P
1 Carpenter Foreman (outside)	$51.25	$410.00	$78.50	$628.00	$49.00	$74.98
18 Carpenters	49.25	7092.00	75.45	10864.80		
2 Rodmen (reinf.)	54.30	868.80	83.70	1339.20		
2 Laborers	39.15	626.40	60.00	960.00		
1 Cement Finisher	46.80	374.40	69.60	556.80		
1 Equip. Oper. (medium)	53.55	428.40	81.00	648.00		
1 Gas Engine Vibrator		28.25		31.07		
1 Concrete Pump (Small)		806.40		887.04	4.17	4.59
200 L.H., Daily Totals		$10634.65		$15914.92	$53.17	$79.57

Crew C-14E

	Hr.	Daily	Hr.	Daily	Bare Costs	Incl. O&P
1 Carpenter Foreman (outside)	$51.25	$410.00	$78.50	$628.00	$48.29	$73.98
2 Carpenters	49.25	788.00	75.45	1207.20		
4 Rodmen (reinf.)	54.30	1737.60	83.70	2678.40		
3 Laborers	39.15	939.60	60.00	1440.00		
1 Cement Finisher	46.80	374.40	69.60	556.80		
1 Gas Engine Vibrator		28.25		31.07	.32	.35
88 L.H., Daily Totals		$4277.85		$6541.48	$48.61	$74.33

Crew C-14F

	Hr.	Daily	Hr.	Daily	Bare Costs	Incl. O&P
1 Labor Foreman (outside)	$41.15	$329.20	$63.05	$504.40	$44.47	$66.74
2 Laborers	39.15	626.40	60.00	960.00		
6 Cement Finishers	46.80	2246.40	69.60	3340.80		
1 Gas Engine Vibrator		28.25		31.07	.39	.43
72 L.H., Daily Totals		$3230.25		$4836.27	$44.86	$67.17

Crew C-14G

	Hr.	Daily	Hr.	Daily	Bare Costs	Incl. O&P
1 Labor Foreman (outside)	$41.15	$329.20	$63.05	$504.40	$43.81	$65.92
2 Laborers	39.15	626.40	60.00	960.00		
4 Cement Finishers	46.80	1497.60	69.60	2227.20		
1 Gas Engine Vibrator		28.25		31.07	.50	.55
56 L.H., Daily Totals		$2481.45		$3722.68	$44.31	$66.48

Crew C-14H

	Hr.	Daily	Hr.	Daily	Bare Costs	Incl. O&P
1 Carpenter Foreman (outside)	$51.25	$410.00	$78.50	$628.00	$48.33	$73.78
2 Carpenters	49.25	788.00	75.45	1207.20		
1 Rodman (reinf.)	54.30	434.40	83.70	669.60		
1 Laborer	39.15	313.20	60.00	480.00		
1 Cement Finisher	46.80	374.40	69.60	556.80		
1 Gas Engine Vibrator		28.25		31.07	.59	.65
48 L.H., Daily Totals		$2348.25		$3572.68	$48.92	$74.43

Crew C-14L

	Hr.	Daily	Hr.	Daily	Bare Costs	Incl. O&P
1 Carpenter Foreman (outside)	$51.25	$410.00	$78.50	$628.00	$45.85	$70.07
6 Carpenters	49.25	2364.00	75.45	3621.60		
4 Laborers	39.15	1252.80	60.00	1920.00		
1 Cement Finisher	46.80	374.40	69.60	556.80		
1 Gas Engine Vibrator		28.25		31.07	.29	.32
96 L.H., Daily Totals		$4429.45		$6757.48	$46.14	$70.39

Crew C-14M

	Hr.	Daily	Hr.	Daily	Bare Costs	Incl. O&P
1 Carpenter Foreman (outside)	$51.25	$410.00	$78.50	$628.00	$47.84	$72.96
2 Carpenters	49.25	788.00	75.45	1207.20		
1 Rodman (reinf.)	54.30	434.40	83.70	669.60		
2 Laborers	39.15	626.40	60.00	960.00		
1 Cement Finisher	46.80	374.40	69.60	556.80		
1 Equip. Oper. (medium)	53.55	428.40	81.00	648.00		
1 Gas Engine Vibrator		28.25		31.07		
1 Concrete Pump (Small)		806.40		887.04	13.04	14.35
64 L.H., Daily Totals		$3896.25		$5587.72	$60.88	$87.31

Crews - Standard

Crew No.	Bare Costs		Incl. Subs O&P		Cost Per Labor-Hour	
Crew C-15	Hr.	Daily	Hr.	Daily	Bare Costs	Incl. O&P
1 Carpenter Foreman (outside)	$51.25	$410.00	$78.50	$628.00	$46.12	$70.26
2 Carpenters	49.25	788.00	75.45	1207.20		
3 Laborers	39.15	939.60	60.00	1440.00		
2 Cement Finishers	46.80	748.80	69.60	1113.60		
1 Rodman (reinf.)	54.30	434.40	83.70	669.60		
72 L.H., Daily Totals		$3320.80		$5058.40	$46.12	$70.26
Crew C-16	Hr.	Daily	Hr.	Daily	Bare Costs	Incl. O&P
1 Labor Foreman (outside)	$41.15	$329.20	$63.05	$504.40	$43.68	$66.18
3 Laborers	39.15	939.60	60.00	1440.00		
2 Cement Finishers	46.80	748.80	69.60	1113.60		
1 Equip. Oper. (medium)	53.55	428.40	81.00	648.00		
1 Gunite Pump Rig		357.40		393.14		
2 -50' Air Hoses, 3/4"		6.50		7.15		
2 -50' Air Hoses, 2"		15.50		17.05	6.78	7.45
56 L.H., Daily Totals		$2825.40		$4123.34	$50.45	$73.63
Crew C-16A	Hr.	Daily	Hr.	Daily	Bare Costs	Incl. O&P
1 Laborer	$39.15	$313.20	$60.00	$480.00	$46.58	$70.05
2 Cement Finishers	46.80	748.80	69.60	1113.60		
1 Equip. Oper. (medium)	53.55	428.40	81.00	648.00		
1 Gunite Pump Rig		357.40		393.14		
2 -50' Air Hoses, 3/4"		6.50		7.15		
2 -50' Air Hoses, 2"		15.50		17.05		
1 Telescoping Boom Lift, to 60'		456.00		501.60	26.11	28.72
32 L.H., Daily Totals		$2325.80		$3160.54	$72.68	$98.77
Crew C-17	Hr.	Daily	Hr.	Daily	Bare Costs	Incl. O&P
2 Skilled Worker Foremen (out)	$53.45	$855.20	$82.25	$1316.00	$51.85	$79.81
8 Skilled Workers	51.45	3292.80	79.20	5068.80		
80 L.H., Daily Totals		$4148.00		$6384.80	$51.85	$79.81
Crew C-17A	Hr.	Daily	Hr.	Daily	Bare Costs	Incl. O&P
2 Skilled Worker Foremen (out)	$53.45	$855.20	$82.25	$1316.00	$51.90	$79.86
8 Skilled Workers	51.45	3292.80	79.20	5068.80		
.125 Equip. Oper. (crane)	55.70	55.70	84.25	84.25		
.125 Hyd. Crane, 80 Ton		202.00		222.20	2.49	2.74
81 L.H., Daily Totals		$4405.70		$6691.25	$54.39	$82.61
Crew C-17B	Hr.	Daily	Hr.	Daily	Bare Costs	Incl. O&P
2 Skilled Worker Foremen (out)	$53.45	$855.20	$82.25	$1316.00	$51.94	$79.92
8 Skilled Workers	51.45	3292.80	79.20	5068.80		
.25 Equip. Oper. (crane)	55.70	111.40	84.25	168.50		
.25 Hyd. Crane, 80 Ton		404.00		444.40		
.25 Trowel, 48" Walk-Behind		11.39		12.53	5.07	5.57
82 L.H., Daily Totals		$4674.79		$7010.23	$57.01	$85.49
Crew C-17C	Hr.	Daily	Hr.	Daily	Bare Costs	Incl. O&P
2 Skilled Worker Foremen (out)	$53.45	$855.20	$82.25	$1316.00	$51.99	$79.97
8 Skilled Workers	51.45	3292.80	79.20	5068.80		
.375 Equip. Oper. (crane)	55.70	167.10	84.25	252.75		
.375 Hyd. Crane, 80 Ton		606.00		666.60	7.30	8.03
83 L.H., Daily Totals		$4921.10		$7304.15	$59.29	$88.00
Crew C-17D	Hr.	Daily	Hr.	Daily	Bare Costs	Incl. O&P
2 Skilled Worker Foremen (out)	$53.45	$855.20	$82.25	$1316.00	$52.03	$80.02
8 Skilled Workers	51.45	3292.80	79.20	5068.80		
.5 Equip. Oper. (crane)	55.70	222.80	84.25	337.00		
.5 Hyd. Crane, 80 Ton		808.00		888.80	9.62	10.58
84 L.H., Daily Totals		$5178.80		$7610.60	$61.65	$90.60

Crew No.	Bare Costs		Incl. Subs O&P		Cost Per Labor-Hour	
Crew C-17E	Hr.	Daily	Hr.	Daily	Bare Costs	Incl. O&P
2 Skilled Worker Foremen (out)	$53.45	$855.20	$82.25	$1316.00	$51.85	$79.81
8 Skilled Workers	51.45	3292.80	79.20	5068.80		
1 Hyd. Jack with Rods		100.30		110.33	1.25	1.38
80 L.H., Daily Totals		$4248.30		$6495.13	$53.10	$81.19
Crew C-18	Hr.	Daily	Hr.	Daily	Bare Costs	Incl. O&P
.125 Labor Foreman (outside)	$41.15	$41.15	$63.05	$63.05	$39.37	$60.34
1 Laborer	39.15	313.20	60.00	480.00		
1 Concrete Cart, 10 C.F.		58.00		63.80	6.44	7.09
9 L.H., Daily Totals		$412.35		$606.85	$45.82	$67.43
Crew C-19	Hr.	Daily	Hr.	Daily	Bare Costs	Incl. O&P
.125 Labor Foreman (outside)	$41.15	$41.15	$63.05	$63.05	$39.37	$60.34
1 Laborer	39.15	313.20	60.00	480.00		
1 Concrete Cart, 18 C.F.		96.60		106.26	10.73	11.81
9 L.H., Daily Totals		$450.95		$649.31	$50.11	$72.15
Crew C-20	Hr.	Daily	Hr.	Daily	Bare Costs	Incl. O&P
1 Labor Foreman (outside)	$41.15	$329.20	$63.05	$504.40	$42.16	$64.21
5 Laborers	39.15	1566.00	60.00	2400.00		
1 Cement Finisher	46.80	374.40	69.60	556.80		
1 Equip. Oper. (medium)	53.55	428.40	81.00	648.00		
2 Gas Engine Vibrators		56.50		62.15		
1 Concrete Pump (Small)		806.40		887.04	13.48	14.83
64 L.H., Daily Totals		$3560.90		$5058.39	$55.64	$79.04
Crew C-21	Hr.	Daily	Hr.	Daily	Bare Costs	Incl. O&P
1 Labor Foreman (outside)	$41.15	$329.20	$63.05	$504.40	$42.16	$64.21
5 Laborers	39.15	1566.00	60.00	2400.00		
1 Cement Finisher	46.80	374.40	69.60	556.80		
1 Equip. Oper. (medium)	53.55	428.40	81.00	648.00		
2 Gas Engine Vibrators		56.50		62.15		
1 Concrete Conveyer		189.80		208.78	3.85	4.23
64 L.H., Daily Totals		$2944.30		$4380.13	$46.00	$68.44
Crew C-22	Hr.	Daily	Hr.	Daily	Bare Costs	Incl. O&P
1 Rodman Foreman (outside)	$56.30	$450.40	$86.75	$694.00	$54.56	$84.03
4 Rodmen (reinf.)	54.30	1737.60	83.70	2678.40		
.125 Equip. Oper. (crane)	55.70	55.70	84.25	84.25		
.125 Equip. Oper. (oiler)	48.00	48.00	72.60	72.60		
.125 Hyd. Crane, 25 Ton		84.22		92.65	2.01	2.21
42 L.H., Daily Totals		$2375.93		$3621.90	$56.57	$86.24
Crew C-23	Hr.	Daily	Hr.	Daily	Bare Costs	Incl. O&P
2 Skilled Worker Foremen (out)	$53.45	$855.20	$82.25	$1316.00	$51.93	$79.66
6 Skilled Workers	51.45	2469.60	79.20	3801.60		
1 Equip. Oper. (crane)	55.70	445.60	84.25	674.00		
1 Equip. Oper. (oiler)	48.00	384.00	72.60	580.80		
1 Lattice Boom Crane, 90 Ton		1671.00		1838.10	20.89	22.98
80 L.H., Daily Totals		$5825.40		$8210.50	$72.82	$102.63
Crew C-23A	Hr.	Daily	Hr.	Daily	Bare Costs	Incl. O&P
1 Labor Foreman (outside)	$41.15	$329.20	$63.05	$504.40	$44.63	$67.98
2 Laborers	39.15	626.40	60.00	960.00		
1 Equip. Oper. (crane)	55.70	445.60	84.25	674.00		
1 Equip. Oper. (oiler)	48.00	384.00	72.60	580.80		
1 Crawler Crane, 100 Ton		1804.00		1984.40		
3 Conc. Buckets, 8 C.Y.		612.60		673.86	60.41	66.46
40 L.H., Daily Totals		$4201.80		$5377.46	$105.05	$134.44

496

Crew No.	Bare Costs Hr	Bare Costs Daily	Incl. Subs O&P Hr.	Incl. Subs O&P Daily	Cost Per Labor-Hour Bare Costs	Cost Per Labor-Hour Incl. O&P
Crew C-24	Hr	Daily	Hr.	Daily	Bare Costs	Incl. O&P
2 Skilled Worker Foremen (out)	$53.45	$855.20	$82.25	$1316.00	$51.03	$79.66
6 Skilled Workers	51.45	2469.60	79.20	3801.60		
1 Equip. Oper. (crane)	55.70	445.60	84.25	674.00		
1 Equip. Oper. (oiler)	48.00	384.00	72.60	580.80		
1 Lattice Boom Crane, 150 Ton		2000.00		2200.00	25.00	27.50
80 L.H., Daily Totals		$6154.40		$8572.40	$76.93	$107.16

Crew C-25	Hr.	Daily	Hr.	Daily	Bare Costs	Incl. O&P
2 Rodmen (reinf.)	$54.30	$868.80	$83.70	$1339.20	$43.20	$69.13
2 Rodmen Helpers	32.10	513.60	54.55	872.80		
32 L.H., Daily Totals		$1382.40		$2212.00	$43.20	$69.13

Crew C-27	Hr.	Daily	Hr.	Daily	Bare Costs	Incl. O&P
2 Cement Finishers	$46.80	$748.80	$69.60	$1113.60	$46.80	$69.60
1 Concrete Saw		153.60		168.96	9.60	10.56
16 L.H., Daily Totals		$902.40		$1282.56	$56.40	$80.16

Crew C-28	Hr.	Daily	Hr.	Daily	Bare Costs	Incl. O&P
1 Cement Finisher	$46.80	$374.40	$69.60	$556.80	$46.80	$69.60
1 Portable Air Compressor, Gas		17.60		19.36	2.20	2.42
8 L.H., Daily Totals		$392.00		$576.16	$49.00	$72.02

Crew C-29	Hr.	Daily	Hr.	Daily	Bare Costs	Incl. O&P
1 Laborer	$39.15	$313.20	$60.00	$480.00	$39.15	$60.00
1 Pressure Washer		66.00		72.60	8.25	9.07
8 L.H., Daily Totals		$379.20		$552.60	$47.40	$69.08

Crew C-30	Hr.	Daily	Hr.	Daily	Bare Costs	Incl. O&P
1 Laborer	$39.15	$313.20	$60.00	$480.00	$39.15	$60.00
1 Concrete Mixer, 10 C.F.		164.60		181.06	20.57	22.63
8 L.H., Daily Totals		$477.80		$661.06	$59.73	$82.63

Crew C-31	Hr.	Daily	Hr.	Daily	Bare Costs	Incl. O&P
1 Cement Finisher	$46.80	$374.40	$69.60	$556.80	$46.80	$69.60
1 Grout Pump		357.40		393.14	44.67	49.14
8 L.H., Daily Totals		$731.80		$949.94	$91.47	$118.74

Crew C-32	Hr.	Daily	Hr.	Daily	Bare Costs	Incl. O&P
1 Cement Finisher	$46.80	$374.40	$69.60	$556.80	$42.98	$64.80
1 Laborer	39.15	313.20	60.00	480.00		
1 Crack Chaser Saw, Gas, 6 H.P.		26.60		29.26		
1 Vacuum Pick-Up System		60.85		66.94	5.47	6.01
16 L.H., Daily Totals		$775.05		$1132.99	$48.44	$70.81

Crew D-1	Hr.	Daily	Hr.	Daily	Bare Costs	Incl. O&P
1 Bricklayer	$47.75	$382.00	$73.45	$587.60	$43.27	$66.55
1 Bricklayer Helper	38.80	310.40	59.65	477.20		
16 L.H., Daily Totals		$692.40		$1064.80	$43.27	$66.55

Crew D-2	Hr.	Daily	Hr.	Daily	Bare Costs	Incl. O&P
3 Bricklayers	$47.75	$1146.00	$73.45	$1762.80	$44.63	$68.61
2 Bricklayer Helpers	38.80	620.80	59.65	954.40		
.5 Carpenter	49.25	197.00	75.45	301.80		
44 L.H., Daily Totals		$1963.80		$3019.00	$44.63	$68.61

Crew D-3	Hr.	Daily	Hr.	Daily	Bare Costs	Incl. O&P
3 Bricklayers	$47.75	$1146.00	$73.45	$1762.80	$44.41	$68.29
2 Bricklayer Helpers	38.80	620.80	59.65	954.40		
.25 Carpenter	49.25	98.50	75.45	150.90		
42 L.H., Daily Totals		$1865.30		$2868.10	$44.41	$68.29

Crew D-4	Hr.	Daily	Hr.	Daily	Bare Costs	Incl. O&P
1 Bricklayer	$47.75	$382.00	$73.45	$587.60	$44.09	$67.47
2 Bricklayer Helpers	38.80	620.80	59.65	954.40		
1 Equip. Oper. (light)	51.00	408.00	77.15	617.20		
1 Grout Pump, 50 C.F./hr.		132.80		146.08	4.15	4.57
32 L.H., Daily Totals		$1543.60		$2305.28	$48.24	$72.04

Crew D-5	Hr.	Daily	Hr.	Daily	Bare Costs	Incl. O&P
1 Bricklayer	47.75	382.00	73.45	587.60	47.75	73.45
8 L.H., Daily Totals		$382.00		$587.60	$47.75	$73.45

Crew D-6	Hr.	Daily	Hr.	Daily	Bare Costs	Incl. O&P
3 Bricklayers	$47.75	$1146.00	$73.45	$1762.80	$43.51	$66.91
3 Bricklayer Helpers	38.80	931.20	59.65	1431.60		
.25 Carpenter	49.25	98.50	75.45	150.90		
50 L.H., Daily Totals		$2175.70		$3345.30	$43.51	$66.91

Crew D-7	Hr.	Daily	Hr.	Daily	Bare Costs	Incl. O&P
1 Tile Layer	$45.85	$366.80	$68.05	$544.40	$41.08	$60.95
1 Tile Layer Helper	36.30	290.40	53.85	430.80		
16 L.H., Daily Totals		$657.20		$975.20	$41.08	$60.95

Crew D-8	Hr.	Daily	Hr.	Daily	Bare Costs	Incl. O&P
3 Bricklayers	$47.75	$1146.00	$73.45	$1762.80	$44.17	$67.93
2 Bricklayer Helpers	38.80	620.80	59.65	954.40		
40 L.H., Daily Totals		$1766.80		$2717.20	$44.17	$67.93

Crew D-9	Hr.	Daily	Hr.	Daily	Bare Costs	Incl. O&P
3 Bricklayers	$47.75	$1146.00	$73.45	$1762.80	$43.27	$66.55
3 Bricklayer Helpers	38.80	931.20	59.65	1431.60		
48 L.H., Daily Totals		$2077.20		$3194.40	$43.27	$66.55

Crew D-10	Hr.	Daily	Hr.	Daily	Bare Costs	Incl. O&P
1 Bricklayer Foreman (outside)	$49.75	$398.00	$76.50	$612.00	$48.00	$73.46
1 Bricklayer	47.75	382.00	73.45	587.60		
1 Bricklayer Helper	38.80	310.40	59.65	477.20		
1 Equip. Oper. (crane)	55.70	445.60	84.25	674.00		
1 S.P. Crane, 4x4, 12 Ton		435.60		479.16	13.61	14.97
32 L.H., Daily Totals		$1971.60		$2829.96	$61.61	$88.44

Crew D-11	Hr.	Daily	Hr.	Daily	Bare Costs	Incl. O&P
1 Bricklayer Foreman (outside)	$49.75	$398.00	$76.50	$612.00	$45.43	$69.87
1 Bricklayer	47.75	382.00	73.45	587.60		
1 Bricklayer Helper	38.80	310.40	59.65	477.20		
24 L.H., Daily Totals		$1090.40		$1676.80	$45.43	$69.87

Crew D-12	Hr.	Daily	Hr.	Daily	Bare Costs	Incl. O&P
1 Bricklayer Foreman (outside)	$49.75	$398.00	$76.50	$612.00	$43.77	$67.31
1 Bricklayer	47.75	382.00	73.45	587.60		
2 Bricklayer Helpers	38.80	620.80	59.65	954.40		
32 L.H., Daily Totals		$1400.80		$2154.00	$43.77	$67.31

Crew No.	Bare Costs		Incl. Subs O&P		Cost Per Labor-Hour	

Crew D-13

	Hr.	Daily	Hr.	Daily	Bare Costs	Incl. O&P
1 Bricklayer Foreman (outside)	$49.75	$398.00	$76.50	$612.00	$46.67	$71.49
1 Bricklayer	47.75	382.00	73.45	587.60		
2 Bricklayer Helpers	38.80	620.80	59.65	954.40		
1 Carpenter	49.25	394.00	75.45	603.60		
1 Equip. Oper. (crane)	55.70	445.60	84.25	674.00		
1 S.P. Crane, 4x4, 12 Ton		435.60		479.16	9.07	9.98
48 L.H., Daily Totals		$2676.00		$3910.76	$55.75	$81.47

Crew D-14

	Hr.	Daily	Hr.	Daily	Bare Costs	Incl. O&P
3 Bricklayers	$47.75	$1146.00	$73.45	$1762.80	$45.51	$70.00
1 Bricklayer Helper	38.80	310.40	59.65	477.20		
32 L.H., Daily Totals		$1456.40		$2240.00	$45.51	$70.00

Crew E-1

	Hr.	Daily	Hr.	Daily	Bare Costs	Incl. O&P
1 Welder Foreman (outside)	$56.30	$450.40	$93.85	$750.80	$53.87	$87.17
1 Welder	54.30	434.40	90.50	724.00		
1 Equip. Oper. (light)	51.00	408.00	77.15	617.20		
1 Welder, Gas Engine, 300 amp		129.80		142.78	5.41	5.95
24 L.H., Daily Totals		$1422.60		$2234.78	$59.27	$93.12

Crew E-2

	Hr.	Daily	Hr.	Daily	Bare Costs	Incl. O&P
1 Struc. Steel Foreman (outside)	$56.30	$450.40	$93.85	$750.80	$53.89	$87.53
4 Struc. Steel Workers	54.30	1737.60	90.50	2896.00		
1 Equip. Oper. (crane)	55.70	445.60	84.25	674.00		
1 Equip. Oper. (oiler)	48.00	384.00	72.60	580.80		
1 Lattice Boom Crane, 90 Ton		1671.00		1838.10	29.84	32.82
56 L.H., Daily Totals		$4688.60		$6739.70	$83.72	$120.35

Crew E-3

	Hr.	Daily	Hr.	Daily	Bare Costs	Incl. O&P
1 Struc. Steel Foreman (outside)	$56.30	$450.40	$93.85	$750.80	$54.97	$91.62
1 Struc. Steel Worker	54.30	434.40	90.50	724.00		
1 Welder	54.30	434.40	90.50	724.00		
1 Welder, Gas Engine, 300 amp		129.80		142.78	5.41	5.95
24 L.H., Daily Totals		$1449.00		$2341.58	$60.38	$97.57

Crew E-3A

	Hr.	Daily	Hr.	Daily	Bare Costs	Incl. O&P
1 Struc. Steel Foreman (outside)	$56.30	$450.40	$93.85	$750.80	$54.97	$91.62
1 Struc. Steel Worker	54.30	434.40	90.50	724.00		
1 Welder	54.30	434.40	90.50	724.00		
1 Welder, Gas Engine, 300 amp		129.80		142.78		
1 Telescoping Boom Lift, to 40'		288.80		317.68	17.44	19.19
24 L.H., Daily Totals		$1737.80		$2659.26	$72.41	$110.80

Crew E-4

	Hr.	Daily	Hr.	Daily	Bare Costs	Incl. O&P
1 Struc. Steel Foreman (outside)	$56.30	$450.40	$93.85	$750.80	$54.80	$91.34
3 Struc. Steel Workers	54.30	1303.20	90.50	2172.00		
1 Welder, Gas Engine, 300 amp		129.80		142.78	4.06	4.46
32 L.H., Daily Totals		$1883.40		$3065.58	$58.86	$95.80

Crew E-5

	Hr.	Daily	Hr.	Daily	Bare Costs	Incl. O&P
2 Struc. Steel Foremen (outside)	$56.30	$900.80	$93.85	$1501.60	$54.21	$88.75
5 Struc. Steel Workers	54.30	2172.00	90.50	3620.00		
1 Equip. Oper. (crane)	55.70	445.60	84.25	674.00		
1 Welder	54.30	434.40	90.50	724.00		
1 Equip. Oper. (oiler)	48.00	384.00	72.60	580.80		
1 Lattice Boom Crane, 90 Ton		1671.00		1838.10		
1 Welder, Gas Engine, 300 amp		129.80		142.78	22.51	24.76
80 L.H., Daily Totals		$6137.60		$9081.28	$76.72	$113.52

Crew E-6

	Hr.	Daily	Hr.	Daily	Bare Costs	Incl. O&P
3 Struc. Steel Foremen (outside)	$56.30	$1351.20	$93.85	$2252.40	$54.16	$88.78
9 Struc. Steel Workers	54.30	3909.60	90.50	6516.00		
1 Equip. Oper. (crane)	55.70	445.60	84.25	674.00		
1 Welder	54.30	434.40	90.50	724.00		
1 Equip. Oper. (oiler)	48.00	384.00	72.60	580.80		
1 Equip. Oper. (light)	51.00	408.00	77.15	617.20		
1 Lattice Boom Crane, 90 Ton		1671.00		1838.10		
1 Welder, Gas Engine, 300 amp		129.80		142.78		
1 Air Compressor, 160 cfm		143.60		157.96		
2 Impact Wrenches		37.20		40.92	15.48	17.03
128 L.H., Daily Totals		$8914.40		$13544.16	$69.64	$105.81

Crew E-7

	Hr.	Daily	Hr.	Daily	Bare Costs	Incl. O&P
1 Struc. Steel Foreman (outside)	$56.30	$450.40	$93.85	$750.80	$54.21	$88.75
4 Struc. Steel Workers	54.30	1737.60	90.50	2896.00		
1 Equip. Oper. (crane)	55.70	445.60	84.25	674.00		
1 Equip. Oper. (oiler)	48.00	384.00	72.60	580.80		
1 Welder Foreman (outside)	56.30	450.40	93.85	750.80		
2 Welders	54.30	868.80	90.50	1448.00		
1 Lattice Boom Crane, 90 Ton		1671.00		1838.10		
2 Welder, Gas Engine, 300 amp		259.60		285.56	24.13	26.55
80 L.H., Daily Totals		$6267.40		$9224.06	$78.34	$115.30

Crew E-8

	Hr.	Daily	Hr.	Daily	Bare Costs	Incl. O&P
1 Struc. Steel Foreman (outside)	$56.30	$450.40	$93.85	$750.80	$53.98	$88.13
4 Struc. Steel Workers	54.30	1737.60	90.50	2896.00		
1 Welder Foreman (outside)	56.30	450.40	93.85	750.80		
4 Welders	54.30	1737.60	90.50	2896.00		
1 Equip. Oper. (crane)	55.70	445.60	84.25	674.00		
1 Equip. Oper. (oiler)	48.00	384.00	72.60	580.80		
1 Equip. Oper. (light)	51.00	408.00	77.15	617.20		
1 Lattice Boom Crane, 90 Ton		1671.00		1838.10		
4 Welder, Gas Engine, 300 amp		519.20		571.12	21.06	23.17
104 L.H., Daily Totals		$7803.80		$11574.82	$75.04	$111.30

Crew E-9

	Hr.	Daily	Hr.	Daily	Bare Costs	Incl. O&P
2 Struc. Steel Foremen (outside)	$56.30	$900.80	$93.85	$1501.60	$54.16	$88.78
5 Struc. Steel Workers	54.30	2172.00	90.50	3620.00		
1 Welder Foreman (outside)	56.30	450.40	93.85	750.80		
5 Welders	54.30	2172.00	90.50	3620.00		
1 Equip. Oper. (crane)	55.70	445.60	84.25	674.00		
1 Equip. Oper. (oiler)	48.00	384.00	72.60	580.80		
1 Equip. Oper. (light)	51.00	408.00	77.15	617.20		
1 Lattice Boom Crane, 90 Ton		1671.00		1838.10		
5 Welder, Gas Engine, 300 amp		649.00		713.90	18.13	19.94
128 L.H., Daily Totals		$9252.80		$13916.40	$72.29	$108.72

Crew E-10

	Hr.	Daily	Hr.	Daily	Bare Costs	Incl. O&P
1 Welder Foreman (outside)	$56.30	$450.40	$93.85	$750.80	$55.30	$92.17
1 Welder	54.30	434.40	90.50	724.00		
1 Welder, Gas Engine, 300 amp		129.80		142.78		
1 Flatbed Truck, Gas, 3 Ton		270.20		297.22	25.00	27.50
16 L.H., Daily Totals		$1284.80		$1914.80	$80.30	$119.68

Crew E-11

	Hr.	Daily	Hr.	Daily	Bare Costs	Incl. O&P
2 Painters, Struc. Steel	$43.00	$688.00	$72.65	$1162.40	$44.04	$70.61
1 Building Laborer	39.15	313.20	60.00	480.00		
1 Equip. Oper. (light)	51.00	408.00	77.15	617.20		
1 Air Compressor, 250 cfm		181.20		199.32		
1 Sandblaster, Portable, 3 C.F.		21.40		23.54		
1 Set Sand Blasting Accessories		14.45		15.90	6.78	7.46
32 L.H., Daily Totals		$1626.25		$2498.36	$50.82	$78.07

For customer support on your Electrical Costs with RSMeans Data, call 800.448.8182.

Crew No.	Bare Costs		Incl. Subs O&P		Cost Per Labor-Hour	

Crew E-11A

	Hr.	Daily	Hr.	Daily	Bare Costs	Incl. O&P
2 Painters, Struc. Steel	$43.00	$688.00	$72.65	$1162.40	$44.04	$70.61
1 Building Laborer	39.15	313.20	60.00	480.00		
1 Equip. Oper. (light)	51.00	408.00	77.15	617.20		
1 Air Compressor, 250 cfm		181.20		199.32		
1 Sandblaster, Portable, 3 C.F.		21.40		23.54		
1 Set Sand Blasting Accessories		14.45		15.90		
1 Telescoping Boom Lift, to 60'		456.00		501.60	21.03	23.14
32 L.H., Daily Totals		$2082.25		$2999.95	$65.07	$93.75

Crew E-11B

	Hr.	Daily	Hr.	Daily	Bare Costs	Incl. O&P
2 Painters, Struc. Steel	$43.00	$688.00	$72.65	$1162.40	$41.72	$68.43
1 Building Laborer	39.15	313.20	60.00	480.00		
2 Paint Sprayer, 8 C.F.M.		101.40		111.54		
1 Telescoping Boom Lift, to 60'		456.00		501.60	23.23	25.55
24 L.H., Daily Totals		$1558.60		$2255.54	$64.94	$93.98

Crew E-12

	Hr.	Daily	Hr.	Daily	Bare Costs	Incl. O&P
1 Welder Foreman (outside)	$56.30	$450.40	$93.85	$750.80	$53.65	$85.50
1 Equip. Oper. (light)	51.00	408.00	77.15	617.20		
1 Welder, Gas Engine, 300 amp		129.80		142.78	8.11	8.92
16 L.H., Daily Totals		$988.20		$1510.78	$61.76	$94.42

Crew E-13

	Hr.	Daily	Hr.	Daily	Bare Costs	Incl. O&P
1 Welder Foreman (outside)	$56.30	$450.40	$93.85	$750.80	$54.53	$88.28
.5 Equip. Oper. (light)	51.00	204.00	77.15	308.60		
1 Welder, Gas Engine, 300 amp		129.80		142.78	10.82	11.90
12 L.H., Daily Totals		$784.20		$1202.18	$65.35	$100.18

Crew E-14

	Hr.	Daily	Hr.	Daily	Bare Costs	Incl. O&P
1 Welder Foreman (outside)	$56.30	$450.40	$93.85	$750.80	$56.30	$93.85
1 Welder, Gas Engine, 300 amp		129.80		142.78	16.23	17.85
8 L.H., Daily Totals		$580.20		$893.58	$72.53	$111.70

Crew E-16

	Hr.	Daily	Hr.	Daily	Bare Costs	Incl. O&P
1 Welder Foreman (outside)	$56.30	$450.40	$93.85	$750.80	$55.30	$92.17
1 Welder	54.30	434.40	90.50	724.00		
1 Welder, Gas Engine, 300 amp		129.80		142.78	8.11	8.92
16 L.H., Daily Totals		$1014.60		$1617.58	$63.41	$101.10

Crew E-17

	Hr.	Daily	Hr.	Daily	Bare Costs	Incl. O&P
1 Struc. Steel Foreman (outside)	$56.30	$450.40	$93.85	$750.80	$55.30	$92.17
1 Structural Steel Worker	54.30	434.40	90.50	724.00		
16 L.H., Daily Totals		$884.80		$1474.80	$55.30	$92.17

Crew E-18

	Hr.	Daily	Hr.	Daily	Bare Costs	Incl. O&P
1 Struc. Steel Foreman (outside)	$56.30	$450.40	$93.85	$750.80	$54.55	$89.27
3 Structural Steel Workers	54.30	1303.20	90.50	2172.00		
1 Equipment Operator (med.)	53.55	428.40	81.00	648.00		
1 Lattice Boom Crane, 20 Ton		1075.00		1182.50	26.88	29.56
40 L.H., Daily Totals		$3257.00		$4753.30	$81.42	$118.83

Crew E-19

	Hr.	Daily	Hr.	Daily	Bare Costs	Incl. O&P
1 Struc. Steel Foreman (outside)	$56.30	$450.40	$93.85	$750.80	$53.87	$87.17
1 Structural Steel Worker	54.30	434.40	90.50	724.00		
1 Equip. Oper. (light)	51.00	408.00	77.15	617.20		
1 Lattice Boom Crane, 20 Ton		1075.00		1182.50	44.79	49.27
24 L.H., Daily Totals		$2367.80		$3274.50	$98.66	$136.44

Crew E-20

	Hr.	Daily	Hr.	Daily	Bare Costs	Incl. O&P
1 Struc. Steel Foreman (outside)	$56.30	$450.40	$93.85	$750.80	$53.94	$87.90
5 Structural Steel Workers	54.30	2172.00	90.50	3620.00		
1 Equip. Oper. (crane)	55.70	445.60	84.25	674.00		
1 Equip. Oper. (oiler)	48.00	384.00	72.60	580.80		
1 Lattice Boom Crane, 40 Ton		1311.00		1442.10	20.48	22.53
64 L.H., Daily Totals		$4763.00		$7067.70	$74.42	$110.43

Crew E-22

	Hr.	Daily	Hr.	Daily	Bare Costs	Incl. O&P
1 Skilled Worker Foreman (out)	$53.45	$427.60	$82.25	$658.00	$52.12	$80.22
2 Skilled Workers	51.45	823.20	79.20	1267.20		
24 L.H., Daily Totals		$1250.80		$1925.20	$52.12	$80.22

Crew E-24

	Hr.	Daily	Hr.	Daily	Bare Costs	Incl. O&P
3 Structural Steel Workers	$54.30	$1303.20	$90.50	$2172.00	$54.11	$88.13
1 Equipment Operator (med.)	53.55	428.40	81.00	648.00		
1 Hyd. Crane, 25 Ton		673.80		741.18	21.06	23.16
32 L.H., Daily Totals		$2405.40		$3561.18	$75.17	$111.29

Crew E-25

	Hr.	Daily	Hr.	Daily	Bare Costs	Incl. O&P
1 Welder Foreman (outside)	$56.30	$450.40	$93.85	$750.80	$56.30	$93.85
1 Cutting Torch		12.00		13.20	1.50	1.65
8 L.H., Daily Totals		$462.40		$764.00	$57.80	$95.50

Crew E-26

	Hr.	Daily	Hr.	Daily	Bare Costs	Incl. O&P
1 Struc. Steel Foreman (outside)	$56.30	$450.40	$93.85	$750.80	$55.57	$91.25
1 Struc. Steel Worker	54.30	434.40	90.50	724.00		
1 Welder	54.30	434.40	90.50	724.00		
.25 Electrician	56.60	113.20	84.80	169.60		
.25 Plumber	61.80	123.60	93.25	186.50		
1 Welder, Gas Engine, 300 amp		129.80		142.78	4.64	5.10
28 L.H., Daily Totals		$1685.80		$2697.68	$60.21	$96.35

Crew E-27

	Hr.	Daily	Hr.	Daily	Bare Costs	Incl. O&P
1 Struc. Steel Foreman (outside)	$56.30	$450.40	$93.85	$750.80	$53.94	$87.90
5 Struc. Steel Workers	54.30	2172.00	90.50	3620.00		
1 Equip. Oper. (crane)	55.70	445.60	84.25	674.00		
1 Equip. Oper. (oiler)	48.00	384.00	72.60	580.80		
1 Hyd. Crane, 12 Ton		572.80		630.08		
1 Hyd. Crane, 80 Ton		1616.00		1777.60	34.20	37.62
64 L.H., Daily Totals		$5640.80		$8033.28	$88.14	$125.52

Crew F-3

	Hr.	Daily	Hr.	Daily	Bare Costs	Incl. O&P
4 Carpenters	$49.25	$1576.00	$75.45	$2414.40	$50.54	$77.21
1 Equip. Oper. (crane)	55.70	445.60	84.25	674.00		
1 Hyd. Crane, 12 Ton		572.80		630.08	14.32	15.75
40 L.H., Daily Totals		$2594.40		$3718.48	$64.86	$92.96

Crew F-4

	Hr.	Daily	Hr.	Daily	Bare Costs	Incl. O&P
4 Carpenters	$49.25	$1576.00	$75.45	$2414.40	$50.12	$76.44
1 Equip. Oper. (crane)	55.70	445.60	84.25	674.00		
1 Equip. Oper. (oiler)	48.00	384.00	72.60	580.80		
1 Hyd. Crane, 55 Ton		1076.00		1183.60	22.42	24.66
48 L.H., Daily Totals		$3481.60		$4852.80	$72.53	$101.10

Crew F-5

	Hr.	Daily	Hr.	Daily	Bare Costs	Incl. O&P
1 Carpenter Foreman (outside)	$51.25	$410.00	$78.50	$628.00	$49.75	$76.21
3 Carpenters	49.25	1182.00	75.45	1810.80		
32 L.H., Daily Totals		$1592.00		$2438.80	$49.75	$76.21

Crew No.	Bare Costs		Incl. Subs O&P		Cost Per Labor-Hour	

Crew F-6	Hr.	Daily	Hr.	Daily	Bare Costs	Incl. O&P
2 Carpenters	$49.25	$788.00	$75.45	$1207.20	$46.50	$71.03
2 Building Laborers	39.15	626.40	60.00	960.00		
1 Equip. Oper. (crane)	55.70	445.60	84.25	674.00		
1 Hyd. Crane, 12 Ton		572.80		630.08	14.32	15.75
40 L.H., Daily Totals		$2432.80		$3471.28	$60.82	$86.78

Crew F-7	Hr.	Daily	Hr.	Daily	Bare Costs	Incl. O&P
2 Carpenters	$49.25	$788.00	$75.45	$1207.20	$44.20	$67.72
2 Building Laborers	39.15	626.40	60.00	960.00		
32 L.H., Daily Totals		$1414.40		$2167.20	$44.20	$67.72

Crew G-1	Hr.	Daily	Hr.	Daily	Bare Costs	Incl. O&P
1 Roofer Foreman (outside)	$45.15	$361.20	$76.75	$614.00	$40.28	$68.46
4 Roofers Composition	43.15	1380.80	73.35	2347.20		
2 Roofer Helpers	32.10	513.60	54.55	872.80		
1 Application Equipment		183.60		201.96		
1 Tar Kettle/Pot		159.70		175.67		
1 Crew Truck		185.60		204.16	9.44	10.39
56 L.H., Daily Totals		$2784.50		$4415.79	$49.72	$78.85

Crew G-2	Hr.	Daily	Hr.	Daily	Bare Costs	Incl. O&P
1 Plasterer	$45.90	$367.20	$68.85	$550.80	$41.37	$62.48
1 Plasterer Helper	39.05	312.40	58.60	468.80		
1 Building Laborer	39.15	313.20	60.00	480.00		
1 Grout Pump, 50 C.F./hr.		132.80		146.08	5.53	6.09
24 L.H., Daily Totals		$1125.60		$1645.68	$46.90	$68.57

Crew G-2A	Hr.	Daily	Hr.	Daily	Bare Costs	Incl. O&P
1 Roofer Composition	$43.15	$345.20	$73.35	$586.80	$38.13	$62.63
1 Roofer Helper	32.10	256.80	54.55	436.40		
1 Building Laborer	39.15	313.20	60.00	480.00		
1 Foam Spray Rig, Trailer-Mtd.		542.60		596.86		
1 Pickup Truck, 3/4 Ton		129.40		142.34	28.00	30.80
24 L.H., Daily Totals		$1587.20		$2242.40	$66.13	$93.43

Crew G-3	Hr.	Daily	Hr.	Daily	Bare Costs	Incl. O&P
2 Sheet Metal Workers	$58.05	$928.80	$88.85	$1421.60	$48.60	$74.42
2 Building Laborers	39.15	626.40	60.00	960.00		
32 L.H., Daily Totals		$1555.20		$2381.60	$48.60	$74.42

Crew G-4	Hr.	Daily	Hr.	Daily	Bare Costs	Incl. O&P
1 Labor Foreman (outside)	$41.15	$329.20	$63.05	$504.40	$39.82	$61.02
2 Building Laborers	39.15	626.40	60.00	960.00		
1 Flatbed Truck, Gas, 1.5 Ton		217.40		239.14		
1 Air Compressor, 160 cfm		143.60		157.96	15.04	16.55
24 L.H., Daily Totals		$1316.60		$1861.50	$54.86	$77.56

Crew G-5	Hr.	Daily	Hr.	Daily	Bare Costs	Incl. O&P
1 Roofer Foreman (outside)	$45.15	$361.20	$76.75	$614.00	$39.13	$66.51
2 Roofers Composition	43.15	690.40	73.35	1173.60		
2 Roofer Helpers	32.10	513.60	54.55	872.80		
1 Application Equipment		183.60		201.96	4.59	5.05
40 L.H., Daily Totals		$1748.80		$2862.36	$43.72	$71.56

Crew G-6A	Hr.	Daily	Hr.	Daily	Bare Costs	Incl. O&P
2 Roofers Composition	$43.15	$690.40	$73.35	$1173.60	$43.15	$73.35
1 Small Compressor, Electric		15.25		16.77		
2 Pneumatic Nailers		46.60		51.26	3.87	4.25
16 L.H., Daily Totals		$752.25		$1241.64	$47.02	$77.60

Crew G-7	Hr.	Daily	Hr.	Daily	Bare Costs	Incl. O&P
1 Carpenter	$49.25	$394.00	$75.45	$603.60	$49.25	$75.45
1 Small Compressor, Electric		15.25		16.77		
1 Pneumatic Nailer		23.30		25.63	4.82	5.30
8 L.H., Daily Totals		$432.55		$646.01	$54.07	$80.75

Crew H-1	Hr.	Daily	Hr.	Daily	Bare Costs	Incl. O&P
2 Glaziers	$47.80	$764.80	$72.75	$1164.00	$51.05	$81.63
2 Struc. Steel Workers	54.30	868.80	90.50	1448.00		
32 L.H., Daily Totals		$1633.60		$2612.00	$51.05	$81.63

Crew H-2	Hr.	Daily	Hr.	Daily	Bare Costs	Incl. O&P
2 Glaziers	$47.80	$764.80	$72.75	$1164.00	$44.92	$68.50
1 Building Laborer	39.15	313.20	60.00	480.00		
24 L.H., Daily Totals		$1078.00		$1644.00	$44.92	$68.50

Crew H-3	Hr.	Daily	Hr.	Daily	Bare Costs	Incl. O&P
1 Glazier	$47.80	$382.40	$72.75	$582.00	$42.45	$65.15
1 Helper	37.10	296.80	57.55	460.40		
16 L.H., Daily Totals		$679.20		$1042.40	$42.45	$65.15

Crew H-4	Hr.	Daily	Hr.	Daily	Bare Costs	Incl. O&P
1 Carpenter	$49.25	$394.00	$75.45	$603.60	$45.86	$70.16
1 Carpenter Helper	37.10	296.80	57.55	460.40		
.5 Electrician	56.60	226.40	84.80	339.20		
20 L.H., Daily Totals		$917.20		$1403.20	$45.86	$70.16

Crew J-1	Hr.	Daily	Hr.	Daily	Bare Costs	Incl. O&P
3 Plasterers	$45.90	$1101.60	$68.85	$1652.40	$43.16	$64.75
2 Plasterer Helpers	39.05	624.80	58.60	937.60		
1 Mixing Machine, 6 C.F.		134.80		148.28	3.37	3.71
40 L.H., Daily Totals		$1861.20		$2738.28	$46.53	$68.46

Crew J-2	Hr.	Daily	Hr.	Daily	Bare Costs	Incl. O&P
3 Plasterers	$45.90	$1101.60	$68.85	$1652.40	$43.95	$65.78
2 Plasterer Helpers	39.05	624.80	58.60	937.60		
1 Lather	47.90	383.20	70.90	567.20		
1 Mixing Machine, 6 C.F.		134.80		148.28	2.81	3.09
48 L.H., Daily Totals		$2244.40		$3305.48	$46.76	$68.86

Crew J-3	Hr.	Daily	Hr.	Daily	Bare Costs	Incl. O&P
1 Terrazzo Worker	$45.95	$367.60	$68.20	$545.60	$42.38	$62.90
1 Terrazzo Helper	38.80	310.40	57.60	460.80		
1 Floor Grinder, 22" Path		121.50		133.65		
1 Terrazzo Mixer		180.00		198.00	18.84	20.73
16 L.H., Daily Totals		$979.50		$1338.05	$61.22	$83.63

Crew J-4	Hr.	Daily	Hr.	Daily	Bare Costs	Incl. O&P
2 Cement Finishers	$46.80	$748.80	$69.60	$1113.60	$44.25	$66.40
1 Laborer	39.15	313.20	60.00	480.00		
1 Floor Grinder, 22" Path		121.50		133.65		
1 Floor Edger, 7" Path		39.25		43.17		
1 Vacuum Pick-Up System		60.85		66.94	9.23	10.16
24 L.H., Daily Totals		$1283.60		$1837.36	$53.48	$76.56

Crews - Standard

Crew J-4A

Crew J-4A	Hr.	Daily	Hr.	Daily	Bare Costs	Incl. O&P
2 Cement Finishers	$46.80	$748.80	$69.60	$1113.60	$42.98	$64.80
2 Laborers	39.15	626.40	60.00	960.00		
1 Floor Grinder, 22" Path		121.50		133.65		
1 Floor Edger, 7" Path		39.25		43.17		
1 Vacuum Pick-Up System		60.85		66.94		
1 Floor Auto Scrubber		236.25		259.88	14.31	15.74
32 L.H., Daily Totals		$1833.05		$2577.24	$57.28	$80.54

Crew J-4B

Crew J-4B	Hr.	Daily	Hr.	Daily	Bare Costs	Incl. O&P
1 Laborer	$39.15	$313.20	$60.00	$480.00	$39.15	$60.00
1 Floor Auto Scrubber		236.25		259.88	29.53	32.48
8 L.H., Daily Totals		$549.45		$739.88	$68.68	$92.48

Crew J-6

Crew J-6	Hr.	Daily	Hr.	Daily	Bare Costs	Incl. O&P
2 Painters	$41.70	$667.20	$62.95	$1007.20	$43.39	$65.76
1 Building Laborer	39.15	313.20	60.00	480.00		
1 Equip. Oper. (light)	51.00	408.00	77.15	617.20		
1 Air Compressor, 250 cfm		181.20		199.32		
1 Sandblaster, Portable, 3 C.F.		21.40		23.54		
1 Set Sand Blasting Accessories		14.45		15.90	6.78	7.46
32 L.H., Daily Totals		$1605.45		$2343.16	$50.17	$73.22

Crew J-7

Crew J-7	Hr.	Daily	Hr.	Daily	Bare Costs	Incl. O&P
2 Painters	$41.70	$667.20	$62.95	$1007.20	$41.70	$62.95
1 Floor Belt Sander		21.30		23.43		
1 Floor Sanding Edger		13.85		15.23	2.20	2.42
16 L.H., Daily Totals		$702.35		$1045.87	$43.90	$65.37

Crew K-1

Crew K-1	Hr.	Daily	Hr.	Daily	Bare Costs	Incl. O&P
1 Carpenter	$49.25	$394.00	$75.45	$603.60	$46.70	$71.03
1 Truck Driver (light)	44.15	353.20	66.60	532.80		
1 Flatbed Truck, Gas, 3 Ton		270.20		297.22	16.89	18.58
16 L.H., Daily Totals		$1017.40		$1433.62	$63.59	$89.60

Crew K-2

Crew K-2	Hr.	Daily	Hr.	Daily	Bare Costs	Incl. O&P
1 Struc. Steel Foreman (outside)	$56.30	$450.40	$93.85	$750.80	$51.58	$83.65
1 Struc. Steel Worker	54.30	434.40	90.50	724.00		
1 Truck Driver (light)	44.15	353.20	66.60	532.80		
1 Flatbed Truck, Gas, 3 Ton		270.20		297.22	11.26	12.38
24 L.H., Daily Totals		$1508.20		$2304.82	$62.84	$96.03

Crew L-1

Crew L-1	Hr.	Daily	Hr.	Daily	Bare Costs	Incl. O&P
1 Electrician	$56.60	$452.80	$84.80	$678.40	$59.20	$89.03
1 Plumber	61.80	494.40	93.25	746.00		
16 L.H., Daily Totals		$947.20		$1424.40	$59.20	$89.03

Crew L-2

Crew L-2	Hr.	Daily	Hr.	Daily	Bare Costs	Incl. O&P
1 Carpenter	$49.25	$394.00	$75.45	$603.60	$43.17	$66.50
1 Carpenter Helper	37.10	296.80	57.55	460.40		
16 L.H., Daily Totals		$690.80		$1064.00	$43.17	$66.50

Crew L-3

Crew L-3	Hr.	Daily	Hr.	Daily	Bare Costs	Incl. O&P
1 Carpenter	$49.25	$394.00	$75.45	$603.60	$53.29	$81.14
.5 Electrician	56.60	226.40	84.80	339.20		
.5 Sheet Metal Worker	58.05	232.20	88.85	355.40		
16 L.H., Daily Totals		$852.60		$1298.20	$53.29	$81.14

Crew L-3A

Crew L-3A	Hr.	Daily	Hr.	Daily	Bare Costs	Incl. O&P
1 Carpenter Foreman (outside)	$61.25	$410.00	$78.50	$628.00	$53.52	$81.95
.5 Sheet Metal Worker	58.05	232.20	88.85	355.40		
12 L.H., Daily Totals		$642.20		$983.40	$53.52	$81.95

Crew L-4

Crew L-4	Hr.	Daily	Hr.	Daily	Bare Costs	Incl. O&P
2 Skilled Workers	$51.45	$823.20	$79.20	$1267.20	$46.67	$71.98
1 Helper	37.10	296.80	57.55	460.40		
24 L.H., Daily Totals		$1120.00		$1727.60	$46.67	$71.98

Crew L-5

Crew L-5	Hr.	Daily	Hr.	Daily	Bare Costs	Incl. O&P
1 Struc. Steel Foreman (outside)	$56.30	$450.40	$93.85	$750.80	$54.79	$90.09
5 Struc. Steel Workers	54.30	2172.00	90.50	3620.00		
1 Equip. Oper. (crane)	55.70	445.60	84.25	674.00		
1 Hyd. Crane, 25 Ton		673.80		741.18	12.03	13.24
56 L.H., Daily Totals		$3741.80		$5785.98	$66.82	$103.32

Crew L-5A

Crew L-5A	Hr.	Daily	Hr.	Daily	Bare Costs	Incl. O&P
1 Struc. Steel Foreman (outside)	$56.30	$450.40	$93.85	$750.80	$55.15	$89.78
2 Structural Steel Workers	54.30	868.80	90.50	1448.00		
1 Equip. Oper. (crane)	55.70	445.60	84.25	674.00		
1 S.P. Crane, 4x4, 25 Ton		605.60		666.16	18.93	20.82
32 L.H., Daily Totals		$2370.40		$3538.96	$74.08	$110.59

Crew L-5B

Crew L-5B	Hr.	Daily	Hr.	Daily	Bare Costs	Incl. O&P
1 Struc. Steel Foreman (outside)	$56.30	$450.40	$93.85	$750.80	$56.26	$87.69
2 Structural Steel Workers	54.30	868.80	90.50	1448.00		
2 Electricians	56.60	905.60	84.80	1356.80		
2 Steamfitters/Pipefitters	62.25	996.00	93.95	1503.20		
1 Equip. Oper. (crane)	55.70	445.60	84.25	674.00		
1 Equip. Oper. (oiler)	48.00	384.00	72.60	580.80		
1 Hyd. Crane, 80 Ton		1616.00		1777.60	22.44	24.69
72 L.H., Daily Totals		$5666.40		$8091.20	$78.70	$112.38

Crew L-6

Crew L-6	Hr.	Daily	Hr.	Daily	Bare Costs	Incl. O&P
1 Plumber	$61.80	$494.40	$93.25	$746.00	$60.07	$90.43
.5 Electrician	56.60	226.40	84.80	339.20		
12 L.H., Daily Totals		$720.80		$1085.20	$60.07	$90.43

Crew L-7

Crew L-7	Hr.	Daily	Hr.	Daily	Bare Costs	Incl. O&P
2 Carpenters	$49.25	$788.00	$75.45	$1207.20	$47.41	$72.37
1 Building Laborer	39.15	313.20	60.00	480.00		
.5 Electrician	56.60	226.40	84.80	339.20		
28 L.H., Daily Totals		$1327.60		$2026.40	$47.41	$72.37

Crew L-8

Crew L-8	Hr.	Daily	Hr.	Daily	Bare Costs	Incl. O&P
2 Carpenters	$49.25	$788.00	$75.45	$1207.20	$51.76	$79.01
.5 Plumber	61.80	247.20	93.25	373.00		
20 L.H., Daily Totals		$1035.20		$1580.20	$51.76	$79.01

Crew L-9

Crew L-9	Hr.	Daily	Hr.	Daily	Bare Costs	Incl. O&P
1 Labor Foreman (inside)	$39.65	$317.20	$60.75	$486.00	$44.57	$69.70
2 Building Laborers	39.15	626.40	60.00	960.00		
1 Struc. Steel Worker	54.30	434.40	90.50	724.00		
.5 Electrician	56.60	226.40	84.80	339.20		
36 L.H., Daily Totals		$1604.40		$2509.20	$44.57	$69.70

Crews - Standard

Crew No.	Bare Costs Hr.	Daily	Incl. Subs O&P Hr.	Daily	Cost Per Labor-Hour Bare Costs	Incl. O&P
Crew L-10	Hr.	Daily	Hr.	Daily	Bare Costs	Incl. O&P
1 Struc. Steel Foreman (outside)	$56.30	$450.40	$93.85	$750.80	$55.43	$89.53
1 Structural Steel Worker	54.30	434.40	90.50	724.00		
1 Equip. Oper. (crane)	55.70	445.60	84.25	674.00		
1 Hyd. Crane, 12 Ton		572.80		630.08	23.87	26.25
24 L.H., Daily Totals		$1903.20		$2778.88	$79.30	$115.79
Crew L-11	Hr.	Daily	Hr.	Daily	Bare Costs	Incl. O&P
2 Wreckers	$39.15	$626.40	$62.70	$1003.20	$46.25	$71.70
1 Equip. Oper. (crane)	55.70	445.60	84.25	674.00		
1 Equip. Oper. (light)	51.00	408.00	77.15	617.20		
1 Hyd. Excavator, 2.5 C.Y.		1536.00		1689.60		
1 Loader, Skid Steer, 78 H.P.		309.40		340.34	57.67	63.44
32 L.H., Daily Totals		$3325.40		$4324.34	$103.92	$135.14
Crew M-1	Hr.	Daily	Hr.	Daily	Bare Costs	Incl. O&P
3 Elevator Constructors	$81.80	$1963.20	$122.15	$2931.60	$77.71	$116.04
1 Elevator Apprentice	65.45	523.60	97.70	781.60		
5 Hand Tools		50.00		55.00	1.56	1.72
32 L.H., Daily Totals		$2536.80		$3768.20	$79.28	$117.76
Crew M-3	Hr.	Daily	Hr.	Daily	Bare Costs	Incl. O&P
1 Electrician Foreman (outside)	$58.60	$468.80	$87.80	$702.40	$60.80	$91.27
1 Common Laborer	39.15	313.20	60.00	480.00		
.25 Equipment Operator (med.)	53.55	107.10	81.00	162.00		
1 Elevator Constructor	81.80	654.40	122.15	977.20		
1 Elevator Apprentice	65.45	523.60	97.70	781.60		
.25 S.P. Crane, 4x4, 20 Ton		138.45		152.29	4.07	4.48
34 L.H., Daily Totals		$2205.55		$3255.49	$64.87	$95.75
Crew M-4	Hr.	Daily	Hr.	Daily	Bare Costs	Incl. O&P
1 Electrician Foreman (outside)	$58.60	$468.80	$87.80	$702.40	$60.21	$90.41
1 Common Laborer	39.15	313.20	60.00	480.00		
.25 Equipment Operator, Crane	55.70	111.40	84.25	168.50		
.25 Equip. Oper. (oiler)	48.00	96.00	72.60	145.20		
1 Elevator Constructor	81.80	654.40	122.15	977.20		
1 Elevator Apprentice	65.45	523.60	97.70	781.60		
.25 S.P. Crane, 4x4, 40 Ton		194.05		213.46	5.39	5.93
36 L.H., Daily Totals		$2361.45		$3468.36	$65.60	$96.34
Crew Q-1	Hr.	Daily	Hr.	Daily	Bare Costs	Incl. O&P
1 Plumber	$61.80	$494.40	$93.25	$746.00	$55.63	$83.92
1 Plumber Apprentice	49.45	395.60	74.60	596.80		
16 L.H., Daily Totals		$890.00		$1342.80	$55.63	$83.92
Crew Q-1A	Hr.	Daily	Hr.	Daily	Bare Costs	Incl. O&P
.25 Plumber Foreman (outside)	$63.80	$127.60	$96.25	$192.50	$62.20	$93.85
1 Plumber	61.80	494.40	93.25	746.00		
10 L.H., Daily Totals		$622.00		$938.50	$62.20	$93.85
Crew Q-1C	Hr.	Daily	Hr.	Daily	Bare Costs	Incl. O&P
1 Plumber	$61.80	$494.40	$93.25	$746.00	$54.93	$82.95
1 Plumber Apprentice	49.45	395.60	74.60	596.80		
1 Equip. Oper. (medium)	53.55	428.40	81.00	648.00		
1 Trencher, Chain Type, 8' D		2460.00		2706.00	102.50	112.75
24 L.H., Daily Totals		$3778.40		$4696.80	$157.43	$195.70
Crew Q-2	Hr.	Daily	Hr.	Daily	Bare Costs	Incl. O&P
2 Plumbers	$61.80	$988.80	$93.25	$1492.00	$57.68	$87.03
1 Plumber Apprentice	49.45	395.60	74.60	596.80		
24 L.H., Daily Totals		$1384.40		$2088.80	$57.68	$87.03

Crew No.	Bare Costs Hr.	Daily	Incl. Subs O&P Hr.	Daily	Cost Per Labor-Hour Bare Costs	Incl. O&P
Crew Q-3	Hr.	Daily	Hr.	Daily	Bare Costs	Incl. O&P
1 Plumber Foreman (inside)	$62.30	$498.40	$94.00	$752.00	$58.84	$88.78
2 Plumbers	61.80	988.80	93.25	1492.00		
1 Plumber Apprentice	49.45	395.60	74.60	596.80		
32 L.H., Daily Totals		$1882.80		$2840.80	$58.84	$88.78
Crew Q-4	Hr.	Daily	Hr.	Daily	Bare Costs	Incl. O&P
1 Plumber Foreman (inside)	$62.30	$498.40	$94.00	$752.00	$58.84	$88.78
1 Plumber	61.80	494.40	93.25	746.00		
1 Welder (plumber)	61.80	494.40	93.25	746.00		
1 Plumber Apprentice	49.45	395.60	74.60	596.80		
1 Welder, Electric, 300 amp		58.15		63.97	1.82	2.00
32 L.H., Daily Totals		$1940.95		$2904.76	$60.65	$90.77
Crew Q-5	Hr.	Daily	Hr.	Daily	Bare Costs	Incl. O&P
1 Steamfitter	$62.25	$498.00	$93.95	$751.60	$56.02	$84.55
1 Steamfitter Apprentice	49.80	398.40	75.15	601.20		
16 L.H., Daily Totals		$896.40		$1352.80	$56.02	$84.55
Crew Q-6	Hr.	Daily	Hr.	Daily	Bare Costs	Incl. O&P
2 Steamfitters	$62.25	$996.00	$93.95	$1503.20	$58.10	$87.68
1 Steamfitter Apprentice	49.80	398.40	75.15	601.20		
24 L.H., Daily Totals		$1394.40		$2104.40	$58.10	$87.68
Crew Q-7	Hr.	Daily	Hr.	Daily	Bare Costs	Incl. O&P
1 Steamfitter Foreman (inside)	$62.75	$502.00	$94.70	$757.60	$59.26	$89.44
2 Steamfitters	62.25	996.00	93.95	1503.20		
1 Steamfitter Apprentice	49.80	398.40	75.15	601.20		
32 L.H., Daily Totals		$1896.40		$2862.00	$59.26	$89.44
Crew Q-8	Hr.	Daily	Hr.	Daily	Bare Costs	Incl. O&P
1 Steamfitter Foreman (inside)	$62.75	$502.00	$94.70	$757.60	$59.26	$89.44
1 Steamfitter	62.25	498.00	93.95	751.60		
1 Welder (steamfitter)	62.25	498.00	93.95	751.60		
1 Steamfitter Apprentice	49.80	398.40	75.15	601.20		
1 Welder, Electric, 300 amp		58.15		63.97	1.82	2.00
32 L.H., Daily Totals		$1954.55		$2925.97	$61.08	$91.44
Crew Q-9	Hr.	Daily	Hr.	Daily	Bare Costs	Incl. O&P
1 Sheet Metal Worker	$58.05	$464.40	$88.85	$710.80	$52.25	$79.97
1 Sheet Metal Apprentice	46.45	371.60	71.10	568.80		
16 L.H., Daily Totals		$836.00		$1279.60	$52.25	$79.97
Crew Q-10	Hr.	Daily	Hr.	Daily	Bare Costs	Incl. O&P
2 Sheet Metal Workers	$58.05	$928.80	$88.85	$1421.60	$54.18	$82.93
1 Sheet Metal Apprentice	46.45	371.60	71.10	568.80		
24 L.H., Daily Totals		$1300.40		$1990.40	$54.18	$82.93
Crew Q-11	Hr.	Daily	Hr.	Daily	Bare Costs	Incl. O&P
1 Sheet Metal Foreman (inside)	$58.55	$468.40	$89.65	$717.20	$55.27	$84.61
2 Sheet Metal Workers	58.05	928.80	88.85	1421.60		
1 Sheet Metal Apprentice	46.45	371.60	71.10	568.80		
32 L.H., Daily Totals		$1768.80		$2707.60	$55.27	$84.61
Crew Q-12	Hr.	Daily	Hr.	Daily	Bare Costs	Incl. O&P
1 Sprinkler Installer	$59.00	$472.00	$89.35	$714.80	$53.10	$80.40
1 Sprinkler Apprentice	47.20	377.60	71.45	571.60		
16 L.H., Daily Totals		$849.60		$1286.40	$53.10	$80.40

Crew No.	Bare Costs		Incl. Subs O&P		Cost Per Labor-Hour	

Crew Q-13	Hr.	Daily	Hr.	Daily	Bare Costs	Incl. O&P
1 Sprinkler Foreman (inside)	$59.50	$476.00	$90.10	$720.80	$56.17	$85.06
2 Sprinkler Installers	59.00	944.00	89.35	1429.60		
1 Sprinkler Apprentice	47.20	377.60	71.45	571.60		
32 L.H., Daily Totals		$1797.60		$2722.00	$56.17	$85.06

Crew Q-14	Hr.	Daily	Hr.	Daily	Bare Costs	Incl. O&P
1 Asbestos Worker	$55.05	$440.40	$85.55	$684.40	$49.55	$77.00
1 Asbestos Apprentice	44.05	352.40	68.45	547.60		
16 L.H., Daily Totals		$792.80		$1232.00	$49.55	$77.00

Crew Q-15	Hr.	Daily	Hr.	Daily	Bare Costs	Incl. O&P
1 Plumber	$61.80	$494.40	$93.25	$746.00	$55.63	$83.92
1 Plumber Apprentice	49.45	395.60	74.60	596.80		
1 Welder, Electric, 300 amp		58.15		63.97	3.63	4.00
16 L.H., Daily Totals		$948.15		$1406.77	$59.26	$87.92

Crew Q-16	Hr.	Daily	Hr.	Daily	Bare Costs	Incl. O&P
2 Plumbers	$61.80	$988.80	$93.25	$1492.00	$57.68	$87.03
1 Plumber Apprentice	49.45	395.60	74.60	596.80		
1 Welder, Electric, 300 amp		58.15		63.97	2.42	2.67
24 L.H., Daily Totals		$1442.55		$2152.76	$60.11	$89.70

Crew Q-17	Hr.	Daily	Hr.	Daily	Bare Costs	Incl. O&P
1 Steamfitter	$62.25	$498.00	$93.95	$751.60	$56.02	$84.55
1 Steamfitter Apprentice	49.80	398.40	75.15	601.20		
1 Welder, Electric, 300 amp		58.15		63.97	3.63	4.00
16 L.H., Daily Totals		$954.55		$1416.77	$59.66	$88.55

Crew Q-17A	Hr.	Daily	Hr.	Daily	Bare Costs	Incl. O&P
1 Steamfitter	$62.25	$498.00	$93.95	$751.60	$55.92	$84.45
1 Steamfitter Apprentice	49.80	398.40	75.15	601.20		
1 Equip. Oper. (crane)	55.70	445.60	84.25	674.00		
1 Hyd. Crane, 12 Ton		572.80		630.08		
1 Welder, Electric, 300 amp		58.15		63.97	26.29	28.92
24 L.H., Daily Totals		$1972.95		$2720.84	$82.21	$113.37

Crew Q-18	Hr.	Daily	Hr.	Daily	Bare Costs	Incl. O&P
2 Steamfitters	$62.25	$996.00	$93.95	$1503.20	$58.10	$87.68
1 Steamfitter Apprentice	49.80	398.40	75.15	601.20		
1 Welder, Electric, 300 amp		58.15		63.97	2.42	2.67
24 L.H., Daily Totals		$1452.55		$2168.36	$60.52	$90.35

Crew Q-19	Hr.	Daily	Hr.	Daily	Bare Costs	Incl. O&P
1 Steamfitter	$62.25	$498.00	$93.95	$751.60	$56.22	$84.63
1 Steamfitter Apprentice	49.80	398.40	75.15	601.20		
1 Electrician	56.60	452.80	84.80	678.40		
24 L.H., Daily Totals		$1349.20		$2031.20	$56.22	$84.63

Crew Q-20	Hr.	Daily	Hr.	Daily	Bare Costs	Incl. O&P
1 Sheet Metal Worker	$58.05	$464.40	$88.85	$710.80	$53.12	$80.94
1 Sheet Metal Apprentice	46.45	371.60	71.10	568.80		
.5 Electrician	56.60	226.40	84.80	339.20		
20 L.H., Daily Totals		$1062.40		$1618.80	$53.12	$80.94

Crew Q-21	Hr.	Daily	Hr.	Daily	Bare Costs	Incl. O&P
2 Steamfitters	$62.25	$996.00	$93.95	$1503.20	$57.73	$86.96
1 Steamfitter Apprentice	49.80	398.40	75.15	601.20		
1 Electrician	56.60	452.80	84.80	678.40		
32 L.H., Daily Totals		$1847.20		$2782.80	$57.73	$86.96

Crew Q-22	Hr.	Daily	Hr.	Daily	Bare Costs	Incl. O&P
1 Plumber	$61.80	$494.40	$93.25	$746.00	$55.63	$83.92
1 Plumber Apprentice	49.45	395.60	74.60	596.80		
1 Hyd. Crane, 12 Ton		572.80		630.08	35.80	39.38
16 L.H., Daily Totals		$1462.80		$1972.88	$91.42	$123.31

Crew Q-22A	Hr.	Daily	Hr.	Daily	Bare Costs	Incl. O&P
1 Plumber	$61.80	$494.40	$93.25	$746.00	$51.52	$78.03
1 Plumber Apprentice	49.45	395.60	74.60	596.80		
1 Laborer	39.15	313.20	60.00	480.00		
1 Equip. Oper. (crane)	55.70	445.60	84.25	674.00		
1 Hyd. Crane, 12 Ton		572.80		630.08	17.90	19.69
32 L.H., Daily Totals		$2221.60		$3126.88	$69.42	$97.72

Crew Q-23	Hr.	Daily	Hr.	Daily	Bare Costs	Incl. O&P
1 Plumber Foreman (outside)	$63.80	$510.40	$96.25	$770.00	$59.72	$90.17
1 Plumber	61.80	494.40	93.25	746.00		
1 Equip. Oper. (medium)	53.55	428.40	81.00	648.00		
1 Lattice Boom Crane, 20 Ton		1075.00		1182.50	44.79	49.27
24 L.H., Daily Totals		$2508.20		$3346.50	$104.51	$139.44

Crew R-1	Hr.	Daily	Hr.	Daily	Bare Costs	Incl. O&P
1 Electrician Foreman	$57.10	$456.80	$85.55	$684.40	$52.92	$79.28
3 Electricians	56.60	1358.40	84.80	2035.20		
2 Electrician Apprentices	45.30	724.80	67.85	1085.60		
48 L.H., Daily Totals		$2540.00		$3805.20	$52.92	$79.28

Crew R-1A	Hr.	Daily	Hr.	Daily	Bare Costs	Incl. O&P
1 Electrician	$56.60	$452.80	$84.80	$678.40	$50.95	$76.33
1 Electrician Apprentice	45.30	362.40	67.85	542.80		
16 L.H., Daily Totals		$815.20		$1221.20	$50.95	$76.33

Crew R-1B	Hr.	Daily	Hr.	Daily	Bare Costs	Incl. O&P
1 Electrician	$56.60	$452.80	$84.80	$678.40	$49.07	$73.50
2 Electrician Apprentices	45.30	724.80	67.85	1085.60		
24 L.H., Daily Totals		$1177.60		$1764.00	$49.07	$73.50

Crew R-1C	Hr.	Daily	Hr.	Daily	Bare Costs	Incl. O&P
2 Electricians	$56.60	$905.60	$84.80	$1356.80	$50.95	$76.33
2 Electrician Apprentices	45.30	724.80	67.85	1085.60		
1 Portable cable puller, 8000 lb.		130.10		143.11	4.07	4.47
32 L.H., Daily Totals		$1760.50		$2585.51	$55.02	$80.80

Crew R-2	Hr.	Daily	Hr.	Daily	Bare Costs	Incl. O&P
1 Electrician Foreman	$57.10	$456.80	$85.55	$684.40	$53.31	$79.99
3 Electricians	56.60	1358.40	84.80	2035.20		
2 Electrician Apprentices	45.30	724.80	67.85	1085.60		
1 Equip. Oper. (crane)	55.70	445.60	84.25	674.00		
1 S.P. Crane, 4x4, 5 Ton		276.00		303.60	4.93	5.42
56 L.H., Daily Totals		$3261.60		$4782.80	$58.24	$85.41

Crew R-3	Hr.	Daily	Hr.	Daily	Bare Costs	Incl. O&P
1 Electrician Foreman	$57.10	$456.80	$85.55	$684.40	$56.62	$84.99
1 Electrician	56.60	452.80	84.80	678.40		
.5 Equip. Oper. (crane)	55.70	222.80	84.25	337.00		
.5 S.P. Crane, 4x4, 5 Ton		138.00		151.80	6.90	7.59
20 L.H., Daily Totals		$1270.40		$1851.60	$63.52	$92.58

For customer support on your Electrical Costs with RSMeans Data, call 800.448.8182.

503

Crew No.	Bare Costs		Incl. Subs O&P		Cost Per Labor-Hour	

Crew R-4	Hr.	Daily	Hr.	Daily	Bare Costs	Incl. O&P
1 Struc. Steel Foreman (outside)	$56.30	$450.40	$93.85	$750.80	$55.16	$90.03
3 Struc. Steel Workers	54.30	1303.20	90.50	2172.00		
1 Electrician	56.60	452.80	84.80	678.40		
1 Welder, Gas Engine, 300 amp		129.80		142.78	3.25	3.57
40 L.H., Daily Totals		$2336.20		$3743.98	$58.41	$93.60

Crew R-5	Hr.	Daily	Hr.	Daily	Bare Costs	Incl. O&P
1 Electrician Foreman	$57.10	$456.80	$85.55	$684.40	$49.55	$74.96
4 Electrician Linemen	56.60	1811.20	84.80	2713.60		
2 Electrician Operators	56.60	905.60	84.80	1356.80		
4 Electrician Groundmen	37.10	1187.20	57.55	1841.60		
1 Crew Truck		185.60		204.16		
1 Flatbed Truck, 20,000 GVW		232.00		255.20		
1 Pickup Truck, 3/4 Ton		129.40		142.34		
.2 Hyd. Crane, 55 Ton		215.20		236.72		
.2 Hyd. Crane, 12 Ton		114.56		126.02		
.2 Earth Auger, Truck-Mtd.		80.68		88.75		
1 Tractor w/Winch		407.80		448.58	15.51	17.07
88 L.H., Daily Totals		$5726.04		$8098.16	$65.07	$92.02

Crew R-6	Hr.	Daily	Hr.	Daily	Bare Costs	Incl. O&P
1 Electrician Foreman	$57.10	$456.80	$85.55	$684.40	$49.55	$74.96
4 Electrician Linemen	56.60	1811.20	84.80	2713.60		
2 Electrician Operators	56.60	905.60	84.80	1356.80		
4 Electrician Groundmen	37.10	1187.20	57.55	1841.60		
1 Crew Truck		185.60		204.16		
1 Flatbed Truck, 20,000 GVW		232.00		255.20		
1 Pickup Truck, 3/4 Ton		129.40		142.34		
.2 Hyd. Crane, 55 Ton		215.20		236.72		
.2 Hyd. Crane, 12 Ton		114.56		126.02		
.2 Earth Auger, Truck-Mtd.		80.68		88.75		
1 Tractor w/Winch		407.80		448.58		
3 Cable Trailers		622.95		685.25		
.5 Tensioning Rig		206.07		226.68		
.5 Cable Pulling Rig		1187.50		1306.25	38.43	42.27
88 L.H., Daily Totals		$7742.56		$10316.34	$87.98	$117.23

Crew R-7	Hr.	Daily	Hr.	Daily	Bare Costs	Incl. O&P
1 Electrician Foreman	$57.10	$456.80	$85.55	$684.40	$40.43	$62.22
5 Electrician Groundmen	37.10	1484.00	57.55	2302.00		
1 Crew Truck		185.60		204.16	3.87	4.25
48 L.H., Daily Totals		$2126.40		$3190.56	$44.30	$66.47

Crew R-8	Hr.	Daily	Hr.	Daily	Bare Costs	Incl. O&P
1 Electrician Foreman	$57.10	$456.80	$85.55	$684.40	$50.18	$75.84
3 Electrician Linemen	56.60	1358.40	84.80	2035.20		
2 Electrician Groundmen	37.10	593.60	57.55	920.80		
1 Pickup Truck, 3/4 Ton		129.40		142.34		
1 Crew Truck		185.60		204.16	6.56	7.22
48 L.H., Daily Totals		$2723.80		$3986.90	$56.75	$83.06

Crew R-9	Hr.	Daily	Hr.	Daily	Bare Costs	Incl. O&P
1 Electrician Foreman	$57.10	$456.80	$85.55	$684.40	$46.91	$71.27
1 Electrician Lineman	56.60	452.80	84.80	678.40		
2 Electrician Operators	56.60	905.60	84.80	1356.80		
4 Electrician Groundmen	37.10	1187.20	57.55	1841.60		
1 Pickup Truck, 3/4 Ton		129.40		142.34		
1 Crew Truck		185.60		204.16	4.92	5.41
64 L.H., Daily Totals		$3317.40		$4907.70	$51.83	$76.68

Crew R-10	Hr.	Daily	Hr.	Daily	Bare Costs	Incl. O&P
1 Electrician Foreman	$57.10	$456.80	$85.55	$684.40	$53.43	$80.38
4 Electrician Linemen	56.60	1811.20	84.80	2713.60		
1 Electrician Groundman	37.10	296.80	57.55	460.40		
1 Crew Truck		185.60		204.16		
3 Tram Cars		423.30		465.63	12.69	13.95
48 L.H., Daily Totals		$3173.70		$4528.19	$66.12	$94.34

Crew R-11	Hr.	Daily	Hr.	Daily	Bare Costs	Incl. O&P
1 Electrician Foreman	$57.10	$456.80	$85.55	$684.40	$54.05	$81.29
4 Electricians	56.60	1811.20	84.80	2713.60		
1 Equip. Oper. (crane)	55.70	445.60	84.25	674.00		
1 Common Laborer	39.15	313.20	60.00	480.00		
1 Crew Truck		185.60		204.16		
1 Hyd. Crane, 12 Ton		572.80		630.08	13.54	14.90
56 L.H., Daily Totals		$3785.20		$5386.24	$67.59	$96.18

Crew R-12	Hr.	Daily	Hr.	Daily	Bare Costs	Incl. O&P
1 Carpenter Foreman (inside)	$49.75	$398.00	$76.20	$609.60	$46.47	$71.77
4 Carpenters	49.25	1576.00	75.45	2414.40		
4 Common Laborers	39.15	1252.80	60.00	1920.00		
1 Equip. Oper. (medium)	53.55	428.40	81.00	648.00		
1 Steel Worker	54.30	434.40	90.50	724.00		
1 Dozer, 200 H.P.		1384.00		1522.40		
1 Pickup Truck, 3/4 Ton		129.40		142.34	17.20	18.92
88 L.H., Daily Totals		$5603.00		$7980.74	$63.67	$90.69

Crew R-13	Hr.	Daily	Hr.	Daily	Bare Costs	Incl. O&P
1 Electrician Foreman	$57.10	$456.80	$85.55	$684.40	$55.01	$82.59
3 Electricians	56.60	1358.40	84.80	2035.20		
.25 Equip. Oper. (crane)	55.70	111.40	84.25	168.50		
1 Equipment Oiler	48.00	384.00	72.60	580.80		
.25 Hydraulic Crane, 33 Ton		215.90		237.49	5.14	5.65
42 L.H., Daily Totals		$2526.50		$3706.39	$60.15	$88.25

Crew R-15	Hr.	Daily	Hr.	Daily	Bare Costs	Incl. O&P
1 Electrician Foreman	$57.10	$456.80	$85.55	$684.40	$55.75	$83.65
4 Electricians	56.60	1811.20	84.80	2713.60		
1 Equipment Oper. (light)	51.00	408.00	77.15	617.20		
1 Telescoping Boom Lift, to 40'		288.80		317.68	6.02	6.62
48 L.H., Daily Totals		$2964.80		$4332.88	$61.77	$90.27

Crew R-15A	Hr.	Daily	Hr.	Daily	Bare Costs	Incl. O&P
1 Electrician Foreman	$57.10	$456.80	$85.55	$684.40	$49.93	$75.38
2 Electricians	56.60	905.60	84.80	1356.80		
2 Common Laborers	39.15	626.40	60.00	960.00		
1 Equip. Oper. (light)	51.00	408.00	77.15	617.20		
1 Telescoping Boom Lift, to 40'		288.80		317.68	6.02	6.62
48 L.H., Daily Totals		$2685.60		$3936.08	$55.95	$82.00

Crew R-18	Hr.	Daily	Hr.	Daily	Bare Costs	Incl. O&P
.25 Electrician Foreman	$57.10	$114.20	$85.55	$171.10	$49.68	$74.43
1 Electrician	56.60	452.80	84.80	678.40		
2 Electrician Apprentices	45.30	724.80	67.85	1085.60		
26 L.H., Daily Totals		$1291.80		$1935.10	$49.68	$74.43

Crew R-19	Hr.	Daily	Hr.	Daily	Bare Costs	Incl. O&P
.5 Electrician Foreman	$57.10	$228.40	$85.55	$342.20	$56.70	$84.95
2 Electricians	56.60	905.60	84.80	1356.80		
20 L.H., Daily Totals		$1134.00		$1699.00	$56.70	$84.95

Crew No.	Bare Costs		Incl. Subs O & P		Cost Per Labor-Hour	
Crew R-21	Hr.	Daily	Hr.	Daily	Bare Costs	Incl. O&P
1 Electrician Foreman	$57.10	$456.80	$85.55	$684.40	$56.65	$84.89
3 Electricians	56.60	1358.40	84.80	2035.20		
.1 Equip. Oper. (medium)	53.55	42.84	81.00	64.80		
.1 S.P. Crane, 4x4, 25 Ton		60.56		66.62	1.85	2.03
32.8 L.H., Daily Totals		$1918.60		$2851.02	$58.49	$86.92
Crew R-22	Hr.	Daily	Hr.	Daily	Bare Costs	Incl. O&P
.66 Electrician Foreman	$57.10	$301.49	$85.55	$451.70	$51.82	$77.63
2 Electricians	56.60	905.60	84.80	1356.80		
2 Electrician Apprentices	45.30	724.80	67.85	1085.60		
37.28 L.H., Daily Totals		$1931.89		$2894.10	$51.82	$77.63
Crew R-30	Hr.	Daily	Hr.	Daily	Bare Costs	Incl. O&P
.25 Electrician Foreman (outside)	$58.60	$117.20	$87.80	$175.60	$46.02	$69.77
1 Electrician	56.60	452.80	84.80	678.40		
2 Laborers (Semi-Skilled)	39.15	626.40	60.00	960.00		
26 L.H., Daily Totals		$1196.40		$1814.00	$46.02	$69.77
Crew R-31	Hr.	Daily	Hr.	Daily	Bare Costs	Incl. O&P
1 Electrician	$56.60	$452.80	$84.80	$678.40	$56.60	$84.80
1 Core Drill, Electric, 2.5 H.P.		55.25		60.77	6.91	7.60
8 L.H., Daily Totals		$508.05		$739.17	$63.51	$92.40
Crew W-41E	Hr.	Daily	Hr.	Daily	Bare Costs	Incl. O&P
.5 Plumber Foreman (outside)	$63.80	$255.20	$96.25	$385.00	$53.14	$80.55
1 Plumber	61.80	494.40	93.25	746.00		
1 Laborer	39.15	313.20	60.00	480.00		
20 L.H., Daily Totals		$1062.80		$1611.00	$53.14	$80.55

Historical Cost Indexes

The table below lists both the RSMeans® historical cost index based on Jan. 1, 1993 = 100 as well as the computed value of an index based on Jan. 1, 2017 costs. Since the Jan. 1, 2017 figure is estimated, space is left to write in the actual index figures as they become available through the quarterly *RSMeans Construction Cost Indexes*.

To compute the actual index based on Jan. 1, 2017 = 100, divide the historical cost index for a particular year by the actual Jan. 1, 2017 construction cost index. Space has been left to advance the index figures as the year progresses.

Year	Historical Cost Index Jan. 1, 1993 = 100		Current Index Based on Jan. 1, 2017 = 100		Year	Historical Cost Index Jan. 1, 1993 = 100	Current Index Based on Jan. 1, 2017 = 100		Year	Historical Cost Index Jan. 1, 1993 = 100	Current Index Based on Jan. 1, 2017 = 100	
	Est.	Actual	Est.	Actual		Actual	Est.	Actual		Actual	Est.	Actual
Oct 2017*					July 2002	128.7	61.7		July 1984	82.0	39.3	
July 2017*					2001	125.1	60.0		1983	80.2	38.4	
April 2017*					2000	120.9	58.0		1982	76.1	36.5	
Jan 2017*	208.5		100.0	100.0	1999	117.6	56.4		1981	70.0	33.6	
July 2016		207.3	99.4		1998	115.1	55.2		1980	62.9	30.2	
2015		206.2	98.9		1997	112.8	54.1		1979	57.8	27.7	
2014		204.9	98.3		1996	110.2	52.9		1978	53.5	25.7	
2013		201.2	96.5		1995	107.6	51.6		1977	49.5	23.7	
2012		194.6	93.3		1994	104.4	50.1		1976	46.9	22.5	
2011		191.2	91.7		1993	101.7	48.8		1975	44.8	21.5	
2010		183.5	88.0		1992	99.4	47.7		1974	41.4	19.9	
2009		180.1	86.4		1991	96.8	46.4		1973	37.7	18.1	
2008		180.4	86.5		1990	94.3	45.2		1972	34.8	16.7	
2007		169.4	81.2		1989	92.1	44.2		1971	32.1	15.4	
2006		162.0	77.7		1988	89.9	43.1		1970	28.7	13.8	
2005		151.6	72.7		1987	87.7	42.1		1969	26.9	12.9	
2004		143.7	68.9		1986	84.2	40.4		1968	24.9	11.9	
2003		132.0	63.3		1985	82.6	39.6		1967	23.5	11.3	

Adjustments to Costs

The "Historical Cost Index" can be used to convert national average building costs at a particular time to the approximate building costs for some other time.

Example:

Estimate and compare construction costs for different years in the same city.

To estimate the national average construction cost of a building in 1970, knowing that it cost $900,000 in 2017:

INDEX in 1970 = 28.7

INDEX in 2017 = 208.5

Note: The city cost indexes for Canada can be used to convert U.S. national averages to local costs in Canadian dollars.

Example:

To estimate and compare the cost of a building in Toronto, ON in 2017 with the known cost of $600,000 (US$) in New York, NY in 2017:

INDEX Toronto = 110.6

INDEX New York = 134.6

$$\frac{\text{INDEX Toronto}}{\text{INDEX New York}} \times \text{Cost New York} = \text{Cost Toronto}$$

$$\frac{110.6}{134.6} \times \$600,000 = .822 \times \$600,000 = \$493,200$$

The construction cost of the building in Toronto is $493,200 (CN$).

Time Adjustment Using the Historical Cost Indexes:

$$\frac{\text{Index for Year A}}{\text{Index for Year B}} \times \text{Cost in Year B} = \text{Cost in Year A}$$

$$\frac{\text{INDEX 1970}}{\text{INDEX 2017}} \times \text{Cost 2017} = \text{Cost 1970}$$

$$\frac{28.7}{208.5} \times \$900,000 = .138 \times \$900,000 = \$124,200$$

The construction cost of the building in 1970 was $124,200.

*Historical Cost Index updates and other resources are provided on the following website:
http://info.thegordiangroup.com/RSMeans.html

How to Use the City Cost Indexes

What you should know before you begin

RSMeans City Cost Indexes (CCI) are an extremely useful tool for when you want to compare costs from city to city and region to region.

This publication contains average construction cost indexes for 731 U.S. and Canadian cities covering over 930 three-digit zip code locations, as listed directly under each city.

Keep in mind that a City Cost Index number is a percentage ratio of a specific city's cost to the national average cost of the same item at a stated time period.

In other words, these index figures represent relative construction factors (or, if you prefer, multipliers) for material and installation costs, as well as the weighted average for Total In Place costs for each CSI MasterFormat division. Installation costs include both labor and equipment rental costs. When estimating equipment rental rates only for a specific location, use 01 54 33 EQUIPMENT RENTAL COSTS in the Reference Section.

The 30 City Average Index is the average of 30 major U.S. cities and serves as a national average.

Index figures for both material and installation are based on the 30 major city average of 100 and represent the cost relationship as of July 1, 2016. The index for each division is computed from representative material and labor quantities for that division. The weighted average for each city is a weighted total of the components listed above it. It does not include relative productivity between trades or cities.

As changes occur in local material prices, labor rates, and equipment rental rates (including fuel costs), the impact of these changes should be accurately measured by the change in the City Cost Index for each particular city (as compared to the 30 city average).

Therefore, if you know (or have estimated) building costs in one city today, you can easily convert those costs to expected building costs in another city.

In addition, by using the Historical Cost Index, you can easily convert national average building costs at a particular time to the approximate building costs for some other time. The City Cost Indexes can then be applied to calculate the costs for a particular city.

Quick calculations

Location Adjustment Using the City Cost Indexes:

$$\frac{\text{Index for City A}}{\text{Index for City B}} \times \text{Cost in City B} = \text{Cost in City A}$$

**Time Adjustment for the National Average
Using the Historical Cost Index:**

$$\frac{\text{Index for Year A}}{\text{Index for Year B}} \times \text{Cost in Year B} = \text{Cost in Year A}$$

Adjustment from the National Average:

$$\frac{\text{Index for City A}}{100} \times \text{National Average Cost} = \text{Cost in City A}$$

Since each of the other RSMeans data sets contains many different items, any *one* item multiplied by the particular city index may give incorrect results. However, the larger the number of items compiled, the closer the results should be to actual costs for that particular city.

The City Cost Indexes for Canadian cities are calculated using Canadian material and equipment prices and labor rates in Canadian dollars. Therefore, indexes for Canadian cities can be used to convert U.S. national average prices to local costs in Canadian dollars.

How to use this section

1. Compare costs from city to city.

In using the RSMeans Indexes, remember that an index number is not a fixed number but a ratio: It's a percentage ratio of a building component's cost at any stated time to the national average cost of that same component at the same time period. Put in the form of an equation:

$$\frac{\text{Specific City Cost}}{\text{National Average Cost}} \times 100 = \text{City Index Number}$$

Therefore, when making cost comparisons between cities, do not subtract one city's index number from the index number of another city and read the result as a percentage difference. Instead, divide one city's index number by that of the other city. The resulting number may then be used as a multiplier to calculate cost differences from city to city.

The formula used to find cost differences between cities for the purpose of comparison is as follows:

$$\frac{\text{City A Index}}{\text{City B Index}} \times \text{City B Cost (Known)} = \text{City A Cost (Unknown)}$$

In addition, you can use RSMeans CCI to calculate and compare costs division by division between cities using the same basic formula. (Just be sure that you're comparing similar divisions.)

2. Compare a specific city's construction costs with the national average.

When you're studying construction location feasibility, it's advisable to compare a prospective project's cost index with an index of the national average cost.

For example, divide the weighted average index of construction costs of a specific city by that of the 30 City Average, which = 100.

$$\frac{\text{City Index}}{100} = \% \text{ of National Average}$$

As a result, you get a ratio that indicates the relative cost of construction in that city in comparison with the national average.

3. Convert U.S. national average to actual costs in Canadian City.

$$\frac{\text{Index for Canadian City}}{100} \times \text{National Average Cost} = \text{Cost in Canadian City in \$ CAN}$$

4. Adjust construction cost data based on a national average.

When you use a source of construction cost data which is based on a national average (such as RSMeans cost data), it is necessary to adjust those costs to a specific location.

$$\frac{\text{City Index}}{100} \times \frac{\text{Cost Based on}}{\text{National Average Costs}} = \frac{\text{City Cost}}{\text{(Unknown)}}$$

5. When applying the City Cost Indexes to demolition projects, use the appropriate division installation index. For example, for removal of existing doors and windows, use the Division 8 (Openings) index.

What you might like to know about how we developed the Indexes

The information presented in the CCI is organized according to the Construction Specifications Institute (CSI) MasterFormat 2014 classification system.

To create a reliable index, RSMeans researched the building type most often constructed in the United States and Canada. Because it was concluded that no one type of building completely represented the building construction industry, nine different types of buildings were combined to create a composite model.

The exact material, labor, and equipment quantities are based on detailed analyses of these nine building types, and then each quantity is weighted in proportion to expected usage. These various material items, labor hours, and equipment rental rates are thus combined to form a composite building representing as closely as possible the actual usage of materials, labor, and equipment in the North American building construction industry.

The following structures were chosen to make up that composite model:

1. Factory, 1 story
2. Office, 2–4 stories
3. Store, Retail
4. Town Hall, 2–3 stories
5. High School, 2–3 stories
6. Hospital, 4–8 stories
7. Garage, Parking
8. Apartment, 1–3 stories
9. Hotel/Motel, 2–3 stories

For the purposes of ensuring the timeliness of the data, the components of the index for the composite model have been streamlined. They currently consist of:

- specific quantities of 66 commonly used construction materials;
- specific labor-hours for 21 building construction trades; and
- specific days of equipment rental for 6 types of construction equipment (normally used to install the 66 material items by the 21 trades.) Fuel costs and routine maintenance costs are included in the equipment cost.

Material and equipment price quotations are gathered quarterly from cities in the United States and Canada. These prices and the latest negotiated labor wage rates for 21 different building trades are used to compile the quarterly update of the City Cost Index.

The 30 major U.S. cities used to calculate the national average are:

Atlanta, GA	Memphis, TN
Baltimore, MD	Milwaukee, WI
Boston, MA	Minneapolis, MN
Buffalo, NY	Nashville, TN
Chicago, IL	New Orleans, LA
Cincinnati, OH	New York, NY
Cleveland, OH	Philadelphia, PA
Columbus, OH	Phoenix, AZ
Dallas, TX	Pittsburgh, PA
Denver, CO	St. Louis, MO
Detroit, MI	San Antonio, TX
Houston, TX	San Diego, CA
Indianapolis, IN	San Francisco, CA
Kansas City, MO	Seattle, WA
Los Angeles, CA	Washington, DC

What the CCI does not indicate

The weighted average for each city is a total of the divisional components weighted to reflect typical usage. It does not include the productivity variations between trades or cities.

In addition, the CCI does not take into consideration factors such as the following:

- managerial efficiency
- competitive conditions
- automation
- restrictive union practices
- unique local requirements
- regional variations due to specific building codes

Table 1

DIVISION		UNITED STATES 30 CITY AVERAGE			ALABAMA ANNISTON 362			BIRMINGHAM 350 - 352			BUTLER 369			DECATUR 356			DOTHAN 363		
		MAT.	INST.	TOTAL	MAT.	INST.	TOTAL	MAT.	INST.	TOTAL	MAT.	INST.	TOTAL	MAT.	INST.	TOTAL	MAT.	INST.	TOTAL
015433	CONTRACTOR EQUIPMENT		100.0	100.0		106.4	106.4		106.6	106.6		103.9	103.9		106.4	106.4		103.9	103.9
0241, 31 - 34	SITE & INFRASTRUCTURE, DEMOLITION	100.0	100.0	100.0	86.9	94.1	91.9	94.4	94.3	94.4	100.6	89.4	92.8	87.6	93.5	91.7	98.2	89.8	92.4
0310	Concrete Forming & Accessories	100.0	100.0	100.0	90.2	68.6	71.5	94.4	69.1	72.5	86.6	69.1	71.5	97.0	64.3	68.7	95.6	70.5	73.9
0320	Concrete Reinforcing	100.0	100.0	100.0	86.2	72.4	79.2	95.7	72.2	83.7	91.2	71.9	81.4	89.5	67.9	78.5	91.2	71.9	81.4
0330	Cast-in-Place Concrete	100.0	100.0	100.0	88.4	69.0	81.0	97.9	69.3	87.0	86.9	69.3	79.7	96.1	68.5	85.6	93.8	69.4	79.8
03	CONCRETE	100.0	100.0	100.0	93.5	71.1	83.2	93.3	71.4	83.2	94.5	71.4	83.8	93.2	68.2	81.6	93.8	72.1	83.7
04	MASONRY	100.0	100.0	100.0	94.0	73.4	81.3	91.5	68.0	77.0	98.9	73.5	83.2	89.4	72.4	78.9	100.3	73.5	83.8
05	METALS	100.0	100.0	100.0	99.2	96.6	98.4	98.9	96.6	98.2	98.1	97.3	97.9	101.3	94.6	99.3	98.2	97.5	97.9
06	WOOD, PLASTICS & COMPOSITES	100.0	100.0	100.0	89.2	69.2	78.2	94.7	69.2	80.7	84.0	69.2	75.9	102.4	63.4	81.0	95.6	70.8	82.0
07	THERMAL & MOISTURE PROTECTION	100.0	100.0	100.0	95.8	67.0	83.8	99.0	68.3	86.3	95.8	69.8	85.0	97.7	68.7	85.7	95.8	70.4	85.2
08	OPENINGS	100.0	100.0	100.0	95.9	68.4	89.7	103.1	68.4	95.2	96.0	68.3	89.7	108.0	63.8	98.0	96.0	69.1	89.9
0920	Plaster & Gypsum Board	100.0	100.0	100.0	88.0	68.8	75.3	91.0	68.8	76.3	85.1	68.8	74.3	93.9	62.9	73.3	95.3	70.5	78.8
0950, 0980	Ceilings & Acoustic Treatment	100.0	100.0	100.0	75.0	68.8	70.9	83.8	68.8	73.8	75.0	68.8	70.9	80.3	62.9	68.7	75.0	70.5	72.0
0960	Flooring	100.0	100.0	100.0	86.3	82.7	85.3	97.8	74.4	91.0	91.1	82.7	88.6	92.1	82.7	89.3	96.4	82.7	92.4
0970, 0990	Wall Finishes & Painting/Coating	100.0	100.0	100.0	89.3	61.1	72.7	91.0	61.1	73.4	89.3	49.9	66.1	86.5	63.8	73.1	89.3	80.3	84.0
09	FINISHES	100.0	100.0	100.0	81.7	70.9	75.8	89.1	69.3	78.2	84.6	69.7	76.4	85.7	67.6	75.8	87.4	73.9	80.0
COVERS	DIVS. 10 - 14, 25, 28, 41, 43, 44, 46	100.0	100.0	100.0	100.0	74.0	94.1	100.0	85.2	96.7	100.0	81.1	95.7	100.0	73.0	93.9	100.0	74.0	94.1
21, 22, 23	FIRE SUPPRESSION, PLUMBING & HVAC	100.0	100.0	100.0	100.8	52.1	79.2	100.0	62.5	83.4	97.9	67.8	84.6	100.0	66.6	85.2	97.9	66.4	83.9
26, 27, 3370	ELECTRICAL, COMMUNICATIONS & UTIL.	100.0	100.0	100.0	92.6	61.8	76.3	96.7	60.3	77.4	94.5	69.2	81.1	92.4	66.0	78.4	93.4	78.1	85.3
MF2014	WEIGHTED AVERAGE	100.0	100.0	100.0	95.7	70.0	84.3	97.5	71.7	86.1	96.0	74.3	86.4	97.5	72.3	86.3	96.1	75.7	87.1

Table 2

DIVISION		ALABAMA EVERGREEN 364			GADSDEN 359			HUNTSVILLE 357 - 358			JASPER 355			MOBILE 365 - 366			MONTGOMERY 360 - 361		
		MAT.	INST.	TOTAL	MAT.	INST.	TOTAL	MAT.	INST.	TOTAL	MAT.	INST.	TOTAL	MAT.	INST.	TOTAL	MAT.	INST.	TOTAL
015433	CONTRACTOR EQUIPMENT		103.9	103.9		106.4	106.4		106.4	106.4		106.4	106.4		103.9	103.9		103.9	103.9
0241, 31 - 34	SITE & INFRASTRUCTURE, DEMOLITION	101.0	89.4	92.9	93.4	94.1	93.9	87.3	93.9	91.9	93.2	94.1	93.8	93.3	90.5	91.4	91.7	89.6	90.3
0310	Concrete Forming & Accessories	83.2	70.2	72.0	88.8	69.0	71.7	97.0	66.0	70.2	94.2	68.9	72.3	94.7	70.1	73.4	93.7	68.5	71.9
0320	Concrete Reinforcing	91.3	71.9	81.4	95.0	72.2	83.4	89.5	71.7	80.5	89.5	72.5	80.9	88.9	71.4	80.0	96.9	72.0	84.3
0330	Cast-in-Place Concrete	86.2	69.3	79.7	96.1	69.2	85.9	93.6	67.8	83.8	106.5	69.3	92.3	90.3	69.2	82.3	87.4	68.4	80.2
03	CONCRETE	94.9	71.9	84.2	97.7	71.4	85.5	92.0	69.5	81.5	101.2	71.4	87.4	90.2	71.8	81.6	88.3	70.9	80.2
04	MASONRY	98.9	73.5	83.2	87.8	67.7	75.5	90.7	65.4	75.1	85.4	73.7	78.2	97.1	65.4	77.6	94.3	64.0	75.6
05	METALS	98.1	97.2	97.9	99.3	96.6	98.5	101.3	96.2	99.8	99.2	96.8	98.5	100.1	96.5	99.0	98.9	96.5	98.2
06	WOOD, PLASTICS & COMPOSITES	80.5	70.8	75.2	93.2	69.2	80.0	102.4	66.4	82.6	99.6	69.2	82.9	94.2	70.8	81.4	91.5	69.2	79.3
07	THERMAL & MOISTURE PROTECTION	95.8	70.7	85.4	97.9	68.2	85.6	97.7	66.8	84.8	97.9	65.0	84.3	95.4	67.7	83.9	94.1	66.9	82.9
08	OPENINGS	96.0	69.1	89.9	104.4	68.2	96.2	107.7	67.2	98.5	104.3	68.4	96.2	98.8	68.9	92.1	97.0	68.4	90.5
0920	Plaster & Gypsum Board	84.4	70.5	75.1	86.8	68.8	74.8	93.9	65.9	75.3	90.7	68.8	76.2	92.1	70.5	77.7	89.6	68.8	75.8
0950, 0980	Ceilings & Acoustic Treatment	75.0	70.5	72.0	77.8	68.8	71.8	82.2	65.9	71.3	77.8	68.8	71.8	80.3	70.5	73.8	83.6	68.8	73.8
0960	Flooring	88.9	82.7	87.1	88.1	74.4	84.1	92.1	74.4	86.9	90.3	82.7	88.1	96.0	65.3	87.1	94.1	65.3	85.7
0970, 0990	Wall Finishes & Painting/Coating	89.3	49.8	66.1	86.5	61.1	71.6	86.5	63.9	73.2	86.5	61.1	71.6	92.6	48.9	66.9	89.7	61.1	72.9
09	FINISHES	83.9	70.6	76.6	83.5	69.2	75.7	86.1	67.2	75.8	84.6	71.0	77.2	87.5	66.9	76.2	87.0	67.0	76.1
COVERS	DIVS. 10 - 14, 25, 28, 41, 43, 44, 46	100.0	74.0	94.1	100.0	85.2	96.6	100.0	84.1	96.4	100.0	74.9	94.3	100.0	86.2	96.9	100.0	84.8	96.6
21, 22, 23	FIRE SUPPRESSION, PLUMBING & HVAC	97.9	67.8	84.6	102.2	64.1	85.3	100.0	62.8	83.5	102.2	62.5	84.6	99.8	65.1	84.5	99.9	65.7	84.8
26, 27, 3370	ELECTRICAL, COMMUNICATIONS & UTIL.	91.9	69.2	79.9	92.4	60.3	75.4	93.3	65.5	78.6	92.1	60.3	75.2	95.2	58.1	75.5	95.6	78.1	86.3
MF2014	WEIGHTED AVERAGE	95.7	74.3	86.2	97.5	71.9	86.2	97.4	71.5	86.0	97.9	72.1	86.5	96.6	71.2	85.4	95.8	73.6	86.0

Table 3

DIVISION		ALABAMA PHENIX CITY 368			SELMA 367			TUSCALOOSA 354			ALASKA ANCHORAGE 995 - 996			FAIRBANKS 997			JUNEAU 998		
		MAT.	INST.	TOTAL	MAT.	INST.	TOTAL	MAT.	INST.	TOTAL	MAT.	INST.	TOTAL	MAT.	INST.	TOTAL	MAT.	INST.	TOTAL
015433	CONTRACTOR EQUIPMENT		103.9	103.9		103.9	103.9		106.4	106.4		117.0	117.0		117.0	117.0		117.0	117.0
0241, 31 - 34	SITE & INFRASTRUCTURE, DEMOLITION	104.8	89.8	94.3	98.1	89.7	92.3	87.9	94.1	92.2	127.7	132.1	130.8	124.9	132.1	129.9	143.2	132.1	135.4
0310	Concrete Forming & Accessories	90.2	69.2	72.0	87.7	69.2	71.7	97.0	69.1	72.8	126.6	120.4	121.2	133.9	120.5	122.3	132.8	120.4	122.1
0320	Concrete Reinforcing	91.2	66.5	78.7	91.2	72.5	81.7	89.5	72.2	80.7	148.5	117.0	132.5	150.8	117.0	133.6	145.2	117.0	130.9
0330	Cast-in-Place Concrete	86.2	69.3	79.7	86.2	69.3	79.7	97.5	69.2	86.7	114.0	119.0	115.9	119.4	119.3	119.3	126.6	119.0	123.7
03	CONCRETE	97.7	70.5	85.1	93.3	71.5	83.2	93.8	71.4	83.4	122.9	118.5	120.8	114.5	118.7	116.4	127.6	118.5	123.4
04	MASONRY	98.8	73.4	83.2	102.2	73.4	84.5	89.6	67.7	76.1	178.8	122.3	144.0	188.5	122.3	147.8	168.5	122.3	140.1
05	METALS	98.1	95.0	97.2	98.1	97.2	97.8	100.5	96.7	99.4	120.2	104.7	115.5	124.3	104.9	118.4	122.9	104.7	117.3
06	WOOD, PLASTICS & COMPOSITES	88.9	69.1	78.0	86.0	69.2	76.8	102.4	69.2	84.2	114.6	119.4	117.3	129.6	119.4	124.0	124.4	119.4	121.6
07	THERMAL & MOISTURE PROTECTION	96.2	69.7	85.2	95.7	69.8	84.9	97.7	68.2	85.5	166.3	117.1	145.8	181.7	118.2	155.4	187.0	117.1	158.0
08	OPENINGS	95.9	66.8	89.3	95.9	68.4	89.7	107.7	68.4	98.8	126.8	117.4	124.6	135.0	117.7	131.1	127.8	117.4	125.4
0920	Plaster & Gypsum Board	89.3	68.7	75.6	87.4	68.8	75.0	93.9	68.8	77.2	140.1	119.8	126.6	166.9	119.8	135.6	153.0	119.8	130.9
0950, 0980	Ceilings & Acoustic Treatment	75.0	68.7	70.8	75.0	68.8	70.9	82.2	68.8	73.3	123.9	119.8	121.1	127.0	119.8	122.2	136.2	119.8	125.3
0960	Flooring	93.0	82.7	90.0	91.5	82.7	89.0	92.1	74.4	86.9	125.9	123.2	125.1	124.3	123.2	124.0	133.2	123.2	130.3
0970, 0990	Wall Finishes & Painting/Coating	89.3	80.3	84.0	89.3	61.1	72.7	86.5	61.1	71.6	107.1	117.0	112.9	110.3	121.7	117.0	112.8	117.0	115.3
09	FINISHES	86.2	73.0	79.0	84.8	70.9	77.2	86.1	69.2	76.9	126.3	121.1	123.5	129.6	121.6	125.2	132.7	121.1	126.4
COVERS	DIVS. 10 - 14, 25, 28, 41, 43, 44, 46	100.0	85.2	96.6	100.0	74.5	94.2	100.0	85.2	96.6	100.0	110.4	102.4	100.0	110.4	102.4	100.0	110.4	102.4
21, 22, 23	FIRE SUPPRESSION, PLUMBING & HVAC	97.9	66.4	83.9	97.9	66.5	84.0	100.0	66.6	85.2	100.6	105.4	102.7	100.6	109.0	104.3	100.6	105.4	102.8
26, 27, 3370	ELECTRICAL, COMMUNICATIONS & UTIL.	94.0	68.7	80.6	93.1	78.1	85.2	92.9	60.3	75.6	112.9	112.6	112.7	120.2	112.6	116.2	108.1	112.6	110.5
MF2014	WEIGHTED AVERAGE	96.6	74.0	86.6	95.8	75.2	86.7	97.5	72.5	86.4	119.7	115.0	117.6	122.3	115.9	119.4	121.5	115.0	118.6

ALASKA / ARIZONA

DIVISION		KETCHIKAN 999			CHAMBERS 865			FLAGSTAFF 860			GLOBE 855			KINGMAN 864			MESA/TEMPE 852		
		MAT.	INST.	TOTAL	MAT.	INST.	TOTAL	MAT.	INST.	TOTAL	MAT.	INST.	TOTAL	MAT.	INST.	TOTAL	MAT.	INST.	TOTAL
015433	CONTRACTOR EQUIPMENT		117.0	117.0		91.9	91.9		91.9	91.9		92.9	92.9		91.9	91.9		92.9	92.9
0241, 31 - 34	SITE & INFRASTRUCTURE, DEMOLITION	183.3	132.1	147.6	71.7	97.0	89.3	91.2	96.9	95.2	102.9	98.5	99.8	71.6	96.9	89.3	92.7	97.8	96.2
0310	Concrete Forming & Accessories	124.7	120.4	121.0	99.5	70.4	74.3	104.9	67.3	72.4	95.9	70.7	74.1	97.7	70.3	74.0	99.1	70.5	74.4
0320	Concrete Reinforcing	112.9	117.0	115.0	102.8	82.6	92.6	102.7	82.6	92.5	106.7	82.7	94.5	103.0	82.6	92.6	107.4	82.6	94.8
0330	Cast-in-Place Concrete	241.6	119.0	194.9	87.5	70.4	81.0	87.6	70.4	81.0	86.0	70.7	80.2	87.3	70.3	80.8	86.7	70.0	80.3
03	CONCRETE	195.2	118.5	159.6	94.6	72.5	84.3	115.4	71.1	94.8	107.5	72.9	91.5	94.3	72.4	84.1	98.2	72.4	86.3
04	MASONRY	196.3	122.3	150.8	97.6	59.4	74.1	97.7	59.4	74.1	110.2	59.5	79.0	97.6	59.4	74.1	110.4	59.2	78.9
05	METALS	124.5	104.7	118.4	100.7	74.3	92.6	101.2	74.1	92.9	96.1	76.9	90.2	101.4	74.0	93.0	96.4	74.9	89.8
06	WOOD, PLASTICS & COMPOSITES	120.3	119.4	119.8	100.5	72.7	85.3	106.3	68.6	85.6	95.5	72.9	83.1	95.8	72.7	83.1	98.7	72.9	84.5
07	THERMAL & MOISTURE PROTECTION	186.5	117.1	157.7	95.0	73.0	85.9	96.9	71.8	86.5	100.8	73.4	89.4	95.0	73.0	85.9	100.7	71.5	88.6
08	OPENINGS	130.7	117.4	127.6	106.3	70.0	98.0	106.4	72.3	98.7	95.5	70.3	89.8	106.5	72.4	98.7	95.6	72.4	90.4
0920	Plaster & Gypsum Board	155.6	119.8	131.8	88.1	72.1	77.5	91.3	67.9	75.7	88.4	72.1	77.6	81.1	72.1	75.1	90.4	72.1	78.3
0950, 0980	Ceilings & Acoustic Treatment	120.3	119.8	120.0	101.9	72.1	82.1	102.8	67.9	79.5	94.0	72.1	79.5	102.8	72.1	82.4	94.0	72.1	79.5
0960	Flooring	124.3	123.2	124.0	93.7	60.6	84.1	96.1	60.6	85.8	101.2	60.6	89.5	92.4	60.6	83.2	102.9	60.6	90.7
0970, 0990	Wall Finishes & Painting/Coating	110.3	117.0	114.2	91.1	65.2	75.9	91.1	65.2	75.9	96.3	65.2	78.0	91.1	65.2	75.9	96.3	65.2	78.0
09	FINISHES	130.7	121.1	125.4	92.3	67.7	78.8	95.5	65.3	79.0	98.8	67.8	81.9	91.1	67.7	78.3	98.5	67.8	81.7
COVERS	DIVS. 10 - 14, 25, 28, 41, 43, 44, 46	100.0	110.4	102.4	100.0	83.9	96.4	100.0	83.4	96.2	100.0	84.2	96.4	100.0	83.8	96.3	100.0	84.2	96.4
21, 22, 23	FIRE SUPPRESSION, PLUMBING & HVAC	98.6	105.4	101.6	97.6	77.7	88.8	100.2	77.9	90.3	96.5	77.8	88.2	97.6	77.7	88.8	100.1	77.9	90.3
26, 27, 3370	ELECTRICAL, COMMUNICATIONS & UTIL.	120.2	112.6	116.2	103.4	88.5	95.5	102.3	63.9	82.0	98.2	64.0	80.0	103.5	63.9	82.5	95.0	63.9	78.5
MF2014	WEIGHTED AVERAGE	133.4	115.0	125.3	98.3	76.2	88.6	102.3	72.3	89.1	99.3	73.3	87.8	98.3	72.9	87.1	98.4	73.0	87.2

ARIZONA / ARKANSAS

DIVISION		PHOENIX 850,853			PRESCOTT 863			SHOW LOW 859			TUCSON 856 - 857			BATESVILLE 725			CAMDEN 717		
		MAT.	INST.	TOTAL	MAT.	INST.	TOTAL	MAT.	INST.	TOTAL	MAT.	INST.	TOTAL	MAT.	INST.	TOTAL	MAT.	INST.	TOTAL
015433	CONTRACTOR EQUIPMENT		93.8	93.8		91.9	91.9		92.9	92.9		92.9	92.9		93.3	93.3		93.3	93.3
0241, 31 - 34	SITE & INFRASTRUCTURE, DEMOLITION	93.2	98.0	96.5	78.5	96.9	91.3	105.2	97.9	100.1	88.2	97.8	94.9	73.7	91.0	85.8	80.7	91.0	87.9
0310	Concrete Forming & Accessories	100.0	68.0	72.3	101.0	70.4	74.5	103.3	70.5	75.0	99.5	67.7	72.0	84.7	58.5	62.1	82.2	58.5	61.7
0320	Concrete Reinforcing	105.5	82.7	93.9	102.7	82.6	92.5	107.4	82.6	94.8	88.9	82.6	85.7	92.8	66.2	79.3	101.5	65.9	83.4
0330	Cast-in-Place Concrete	86.8	70.2	80.5	87.6	70.3	81.0	86.0	70.0	79.9	89.3	69.9	81.9	70.6	76.3	72.8	80.9	76.3	79.1
03	CONCRETE	97.8	71.4	85.6	100.3	72.4	87.3	110.0	72.4	92.6	96.8	71.1	84.9	76.7	66.9	72.1	83.1	66.8	75.5
04	MASONRY	97.6	59.2	74.0	97.7	59.3	74.1	110.3	59.3	78.9	95.6	59.2	73.2	94.4	43.4	63.0	111.8	37.7	66.1
05	METALS	97.8	75.7	91.0	101.2	73.9	92.9	95.9	75.1	89.5	97.1	74.7	90.3	100.5	74.3	92.5	104.6	73.9	95.2
06	WOOD, PLASTICS & COMPOSITES	99.6	69.4	83.0	101.8	72.9	85.9	103.0	72.9	86.5	99.0	69.3	82.7	93.4	60.0	75.1	93.3	60.0	75.0
07	THERMAL & MOISTURE PROTECTION	99.7	70.1	87.4	95.6	73.2	86.3	101.0	72.9	89.4	101.8	65.1	86.5	103.9	59.7	85.6	96.8	58.1	80.7
08	OPENINGS	97.4	72.8	91.8	106.4	70.3	98.2	94.8	72.4	89.7	92.1	72.7	87.7	99.9	55.4	89.8	102.8	57.3	92.5
0920	Plaster & Gypsum Board	92.5	68.4	76.5	88.3	72.3	77.7	92.4	72.1	78.9	95.3	68.4	77.4	82.0	59.3	66.9	85.1	59.3	68.0
0950, 0980	Ceilings & Acoustic Treatment	101.6	68.4	79.5	101.1	72.3	82.0	94.0	72.1	79.5	94.9	68.4	77.3	84.1	59.3	67.6	79.6	59.3	66.1
0960	Flooring	103.2	60.6	90.8	94.6	60.6	84.8	104.8	65.3	93.3	94.2	60.6	84.4	89.5	54.3	79.3	98.4	36.4	80.5
0970, 0990	Wall Finishes & Painting/Coating	96.3	67.4	79.3	91.1	65.2	75.9	96.3	65.2	78.0	97.4	65.2	78.5	93.7	36.7	60.2	96.4	47.2	67.5
09	FINISHES	100.5	66.0	81.7	92.9	67.8	79.2	100.6	68.6	83.1	96.7	65.7	79.8	80.5	54.9	66.5	83.3	52.7	66.6
COVERS	DIVS. 10 - 14, 25, 28, 41, 43, 44, 46	100.0	84.0	96.4	100.0	83.8	96.3	100.0	84.2	96.4	100.0	83.8	96.3	100.0	68.8	92.9	100.0	68.8	92.9
21, 22, 23	FIRE SUPPRESSION, PLUMBING & HVAC	100.0	77.9	90.2	100.2	77.7	90.3	96.5	77.7	88.2	100.0	71.6	87.5	96.7	51.5	76.7	96.5	57.9	79.4
26, 27, 3370	ELECTRICAL, COMMUNICATIONS & UTIL.	100.4	63.9	81.1	102.0	63.9	81.8	95.3	63.9	78.7	97.2	63.9	79.6	95.9	62.5	78.2	95.2	58.8	75.9
MF2014	WEIGHTED AVERAGE	98.8	72.7	87.3	99.8	72.8	87.9	99.5	73.2	87.9	97.2	71.0	85.6	93.6	60.9	79.1	96.3	60.9	80.7

ARKANSAS

DIVISION		FAYETTEVILLE 727			FORT SMITH 729			HARRISON 726			HOT SPRINGS 719			JONESBORO 724			LITTLE ROCK 720 - 722		
		MAT.	INST.	TOTAL	MAT.	INST.	TOTAL	MAT.	INST.	TOTAL	MAT.	INST.	TOTAL	MAT.	INST.	TOTAL	MAT.	INST.	TOTAL
015433	CONTRACTOR EQUIPMENT		93.3	93.3		93.3	93.3		93.3	93.3		93.3	93.3		118.2	118.2		93.3	93.3
0241, 31 - 34	SITE & INFRASTRUCTURE, DEMOLITION	73.1	91.1	85.6	78.2	91.0	87.2	78.6	91.0	87.3	84.0	91.1	88.9	98.3	109.7	106.3	86.9	91.1	89.8
0310	Concrete Forming & Accessories	80.2	58.7	61.6	99.7	58.4	64.0	89.2	58.4	62.5	79.7	58.6	61.5	88.3	58.7	62.7	93.7	59.3	63.9
0320	Concrete Reinforcing	92.8	60.9	76.6	94.0	63.7	78.6	92.5	66.2	79.1	99.5	66.2	82.6	89.7	66.4	77.8	99.5	67.7	83.4
0330	Cast-in-Place Concrete	70.6	76.4	72.8	80.7	76.1	79.0	78.3	76.2	77.5	82.8	76.4	80.3	76.9	77.7	77.2	78.2	76.6	77.6
03	CONCRETE	76.4	66.1	71.6	83.8	66.3	75.7	83.4	66.8	75.7	86.5	66.9	77.4	80.9	68.5	75.1	84.7	67.6	76.8
04	MASONRY	85.6	42.9	59.3	92.6	48.8	65.6	94.8	44.5	63.8	83.8	43.1	58.7	86.9	40.8	58.5	88.4	68.2	75.9
05	METALS	100.5	73.5	92.3	102.8	73.8	94.0	101.7	74.2	93.3	104.5	74.4	95.3	96.9	89.9	94.8	103.1	76.8	95.1
06	WOOD, PLASTICS & COMPOSITES	89.9	60.0	73.5	109.7	60.0	82.4	99.3	60.0	77.7	90.7	60.0	73.8	97.6	60.4	77.2	96.6	60.0	76.5
07	THERMAL & MOISTURE PROTECTION	104.7	59.5	86.0	105.1	61.1	86.8	104.3	59.9	85.9	97.0	59.6	81.5	109.7	58.9	88.6	99.3	66.5	85.7
08	OPENINGS	99.9	57.3	90.2	101.9	55.9	91.5	100.7	54.2	90.2	102.8	57.2	92.5	105.6	58.5	94.9	98.1	57.4	88.9
0920	Plaster & Gypsum Board	81.4	59.3	66.7	88.3	59.3	69.0	87.3	59.3	68.7	83.8	59.3	67.5	96.1	59.3	71.6	92.7	59.3	70.5
0950, 0980	Ceilings & Acoustic Treatment	84.1	59.3	67.6	85.8	59.3	68.2	85.8	59.3	68.2	79.6	59.3	66.1	88.1	59.3	68.9	90.8	59.3	69.8
0960	Flooring	86.5	53.2	76.8	96.4	53.8	84.0	91.8	54.3	80.9	97.3	53.2	84.5	64.7	48.2	59.9	96.2	71.9	89.2
0970, 0990	Wall Finishes & Painting/Coating	93.7	49.2	67.6	93.7	50.0	68.1	93.7	31.7	57.3	96.4	47.2	67.5	83.0	45.0	60.7	92.0	47.2	65.7
09	FINISHES	79.6	55.8	66.6	84.1	56.5	69.0	82.7	54.2	67.1	83.2	55.8	68.2	78.4	54.6	65.4	87.0	60.0	72.2
COVERS	DIVS. 10 - 14, 25, 28, 41, 43, 44, 46	100.0	68.8	92.9	100.0	79.1	95.3	100.0	69.9	93.2	100.0	68.8	93.0	100.0	67.8	92.7	100.0	79.2	95.3
21, 22, 23	FIRE SUPPRESSION, PLUMBING & HVAC	96.7	62.4	81.5	100.3	48.1	77.2	96.7	49.3	75.7	96.5	52.4	77.0	100.6	50.5	78.5	100.0	52.5	79.0
26, 27, 3370	ELECTRICAL, COMMUNICATIONS & UTIL.	89.8	56.1	71.9	93.2	55.1	73.0	94.5	56.1	74.1	97.4	66.1	80.8	99.0	62.6	79.7	99.9	66.1	82.0
MF2014	WEIGHTED AVERAGE	92.4	62.3	79.1	96.1	60.2	80.2	94.9	59.6	79.3	95.6	61.8	80.7	95.5	63.7	81.5	96.4	65.7	82.8

City Cost Indexes

ARKANSAS / CALIFORNIA

DIVISION		PINE BLUFF 716 MAT.	INST.	TOTAL	RUSSELLVILLE 728 MAT.	INST.	TOTAL	TEXARKANA 718 MAT.	INST.	TOTAL	WEST MEMPHIS 723 MAT.	INST.	TOTAL	ALHAMBRA 917-918 MAT.	INST.	TOTAL	ANAHEIM 928 MAT.	INST.	TOTAL
015433	CONTRACTOR EQUIPMENT		93.3	93.3		93.3	93.3		94.6	94.6		110.2	110.2		97.3	97.3		102.4	102.4
0241, 31 - 34	SITE & INFRASTRUCTURE, DEMOLITION	86.0	91.0	89.5	74.9	91.0	86.2	97.1	92.9	94.2	105.6	109.4	108.2	99.3	110.2	106.9	100.9	110.8	107.8
0310	Concrete Forming & Accessories	79.4	58.8	61.5	85.4	58.3	62.0	85.5	58.5	62.2	94.0	59.0	63.7	120.0	137.3	135.0	106.7	137.6	133.4
0320	Concrete Reinforcing	101.4	66.9	83.9	93.4	66.1	79.5	101.0	66.1	83.3	89.7	62.9	76.1	103.6	126.1	115.0	96.0	125.9	111.2
0330	Cast-in-Place Concrete	82.8	76.3	80.3	74.0	76.2	74.8	90.2	76.3	84.9	87.4	77.7	79.5	87.4	127.8	102.8	88.6	131.5	104.9
03	CONCRETE	87.2	67.1	77.9	79.6	66.7	73.6	85.5	66.9	76.9	87.7	68.0	78.6	99.4	130.7	113.9	99.3	132.2	114.6
04	MASONRY	118.6	54.2	79.0	91.9	41.9	61.1	98.3	42.3	63.8	75.4	40.7	54.1	112.7	143.6	131.7	79.5	138.4	115.8
05	METALS	105.3	75.5	96.2	100.5	74.0	92.4	96.9	74.2	90.0	96.0	89.0	93.9	92.0	109.3	97.3	107.5	111.1	108.6
06	WOOD, PLASTICS & COMPOSITES	90.2	60.0	73.6	94.7	60.0	75.6	97.7	60.0	77.0	103.3	60.4	79.7	98.9	134.4	118.4	99.4	134.8	118.8
07	THERMAL & MOISTURE PROTECTION	97.1	62.2	82.6	105.0	59.2	86.0	97.7	59.3	81.8	110.2	58.8	88.9	100.1	131.4	113.1	106.2	134.2	117.8
08	OPENINGS	104.0	55.7	93.1	99.9	56.5	90.0	109.1	56.5	97.2	103.0	56.8	92.6	91.3	133.3	100.8	107.6	133.5	113.5
0920	Plaster & Gypsum Board	83.5	59.3	67.4	82.0	59.3	66.9	86.5	59.3	68.4	98.4	59.3	72.4	95.5	135.6	122.2	105.7	135.6	125.6
0950, 0980	Ceilings & Acoustic Treatment	79.6	59.3	66.1	84.1	59.3	67.6	83.0	59.3	67.2	86.2	59.3	68.3	108.3	135.6	126.5	109.2	135.6	126.8
0960	Flooring	97.0	53.8	84.4	89.0	54.3	78.9	99.3	45.9	83.8	67.1	48.2	61.6	103.2	116.3	107.0	101.6	116.3	105.8
0970, 0990	Wall Finishes & Painting/Coating	96.4	46.8	67.3	93.7	33.9	58.6	96.4	42.5	64.7	83.0	47.2	62.0	107.4	120.8	115.3	91.8	120.8	108.8
09	FINISHES	83.1	56.4	68.5	80.7	54.5	66.4	85.5	54.0	68.3	79.7	55.1	66.3	103.7	131.5	118.9	99.7	131.8	117.2
COVERS	DIVS. 10 - 14, 25, 28, 41, 43, 44, 46	100.0	79.1	95.3	100.0	68.8	92.9	100.0	68.8	92.9	100.0	69.7	93.1	100.0	117.0	103.8	100.0	117.6	104.0
21, 22, 23	FIRE SUPPRESSION, PLUMBING & HVAC	100.1	50.7	78.3	96.7	51.3	76.6	100.1	56.6	80.9	97.1	65.4	83.1	96.4	125.6	109.3	100.0	130.1	113.3
26, 27, 3370	ELECTRICAL, COMMUNICATIONS & UTIL.	95.3	64.9	79.2	93.2	56.1	73.5	97.3	57.9	76.4	100.6	63.1	80.7	120.7	130.2	125.7	90.7	111.5	101.7
MF2014	WEIGHTED AVERAGE	98.4	62.9	82.7	93.6	59.8	78.7	97.0	61.4	81.3	95.2	66.8	82.6	99.8	127.1	111.8	100.3	125.5	111.4

CALIFORNIA

DIVISION		BAKERSFIELD 932-933 MAT.	INST.	TOTAL	BERKELEY 947 MAT.	INST.	TOTAL	EUREKA 955 MAT.	INST.	TOTAL	FRESNO 936-938 MAT.	INST.	TOTAL	INGLEWOOD 903-905 MAT.	INST.	TOTAL	LONG BEACH 906-908 MAT.	INST.	TOTAL
015433	CONTRACTOR EQUIPMENT		100.3	100.3		104.1	104.1		100.1	100.1		100.3	100.3		99.0	99.0		99.0	99.0
0241, 31 - 34	SITE & INFRASTRUCTURE, DEMOLITION	97.8	108.5	105.3	106.4	110.5	109.2	112.4	107.5	109.0	102.1	107.9	106.2	92.0	106.7	102.3	99.4	106.7	104.5
0310	Concrete Forming & Accessories	104.5	137.3	132.8	116.0	164.4	157.8	115.8	149.5	144.9	104.0	148.7	142.7	108.9	137.6	133.8	103.7	137.7	133.1
0320	Concrete Reinforcing	96.5	125.8	111.4	89.7	127.7	109.0	104.4	127.3	116.0	81.0	126.7	104.2	97.8	126.2	112.2	97.0	126.2	111.8
0330	Cast-in-Place Concrete	87.9	130.5	104.1	114.5	131.9	121.1	96.1	128.1	108.3	95.4	127.6	107.6	84.3	130.5	101.9	95.9	130.5	109.1
03	CONCRETE	90.9	131.6	109.8	105.8	144.5	123.8	110.1	136.5	122.4	95.0	135.8	113.9	93.1	131.8	111.1	103.0	131.9	116.4
04	MASONRY	93.7	137.8	120.9	115.3	157.0	141.0	105.0	153.7	135.0	98.5	146.4	128.0	80.3	143.7	119.3	89.9	143.7	123.0
05	METALS	107.9	110.3	108.6	110.2	114.2	111.4	107.3	113.0	109.0	108.2	111.0	109.1	102.8	111.1	105.4	102.7	111.2	105.3
06	WOOD, PLASTICS & COMPOSITES	91.8	135.6	115.9	106.8	169.8	141.4	113.4	152.3	134.8	103.4	152.3	130.3	99.2	134.9	118.8	93.5	134.9	116.2
07	THERMAL & MOISTURE PROTECTION	100.9	126.6	111.6	103.4	154.5	124.6	109.9	147.0	125.3	92.4	132.2	109.0	101.5	131.5	114.0	101.8	133.2	114.8
08	OPENINGS	95.0	131.1	103.2	95.8	157.1	109.7	106.7	139.3	114.1	96.9	140.6	106.8	93.4	133.5	102.5	93.4	133.5	102.5
0920	Plaster & Gypsum Board	94.0	135.6	121.6	110.3	171.1	150.7	110.9	153.6	139.3	92.8	153.6	133.2	100.9	135.6	124.0	97.3	135.6	122.8
0950, 0980	Ceilings & Acoustic Treatment	96.1	135.6	122.4	99.6	171.1	147.2	113.5	153.6	140.1	92.7	153.6	133.2	104.6	135.6	125.2	104.6	135.6	125.2
0960	Flooring	107.4	116.3	110.0	120.6	130.9	123.6	105.5	130.9	112.9	110.2	109.5	110.0	106.0	116.3	109.0	103.0	116.3	106.9
0970, 0990	Wall Finishes & Painting/Coating	95.1	110.5	104.2	112.8	164.1	142.9	93.2	129.7	114.6	107.3	116.3	112.6	106.7	120.8	115.0	106.7	120.8	115.0
09	FINISHES	95.2	130.7	114.6	109.4	159.9	137.0	104.9	145.6	127.1	97.0	140.3	120.7	104.1	131.7	119.2	103.2	131.7	118.8
COVERS	DIVS. 10 - 14, 25, 28, 41, 43, 44, 46	100.0	114.8	103.3	100.0	130.9	107.0	100.0	127.7	106.3	100.0	126.7	106.2	100.0	117.9	104.1	100.0	117.9	104.1
21, 22, 23	FIRE SUPPRESSION, PLUMBING & HVAC	100.0	123.1	110.2	96.6	156.6	123.1	96.4	123.1	108.2	100.1	124.4	110.9	96.2	123.0	108.0	96.2	125.7	109.2
26, 27, 3370	ELECTRICAL, COMMUNICATIONS & UTIL.	105.3	107.9	106.7	102.4	160.4	133.2	97.2	123.9	111.4	95.6	103.3	99.7	100.5	130.2	116.3	100.2	130.2	116.1
MF2014	WEIGHTED AVERAGE	99.4	122.6	109.6	103.3	147.7	123.0	103.6	130.6	115.5	99.5	126.1	111.3	97.3	126.7	110.3	99.0	127.3	111.5

CALIFORNIA

DIVISION		LOS ANGELES 900-902 MAT.	INST.	TOTAL	MARYSVILLE 959 MAT.	INST.	TOTAL	MODESTO 953 MAT.	INST.	TOTAL	MOJAVE 935 MAT.	INST.	TOTAL	OAKLAND 946 MAT.	INST.	TOTAL	OXNARD 930 MAT.	INST.	TOTAL
015433	CONTRACTOR EQUIPMENT		101.3	101.3		100.1	100.1		100.1	100.1		100.3	100.3		104.1	104.1		99.2	99.2
0241, 31 - 34	SITE & INFRASTRUCTURE, DEMOLITION	99.6	108.8	106.0	108.8	107.5	107.9	103.4	107.6	106.3	95.3	108.5	104.5	111.4	110.5	110.7	102.4	106.5	105.3
0310	Concrete Forming & Accessories	105.7	138.0	133.7	105.5	149.2	143.3	101.9	148.9	142.6	116.2	137.1	134.3	104.8	164.4	156.3	107.3	137.7	133.6
0320	Concrete Reinforcing	98.6	126.1	112.6	104.4	126.6	115.6	108.1	126.5	117.5	96.9	125.8	111.6	91.8	127.7	110.0	95.2	125.8	110.7
0330	Cast-in-Place Concrete	91.0	131.2	106.3	107.4	127.9	115.2	96.2	127.8	108.2	82.5	130.4	100.8	108.6	131.9	117.5	96.0	130.8	109.3
03	CONCRETE	98.6	132.3	114.2	110.9	136.2	122.6	101.6	136.0	117.6	86.9	131.5	107.6	106.2	144.5	124.0	95.1	131.9	112.2
04	MASONRY	95.3	141.6	123.8	105.9	142.4	128.4	103.1	142.4	127.3	96.6	137.8	122.0	122.4	157.0	143.8	99.6	136.4	122.3
05	METALS	109.5	111.7	110.1	106.8	111.9	108.3	103.5	111.6	106.0	105.4	110.2	106.8	105.8	114.2	108.4	103.2	110.7	105.5
06	WOOD, PLASTICS & COMPOSITES	99.3	135.0	118.9	101.0	152.3	129.2	96.7	152.3	127.3	102.5	134.8	120.3	95.6	169.8	136.4	97.7	134.8	118.1
07	THERMAL & MOISTURE PROTECTION	100.9	133.1	114.3	109.4	136.8	120.8	108.9	134.0	119.4	98.2	124.2	109.0	102.1	154.5	123.8	101.5	132.4	114.3
08	OPENINGS	100.5	133.6	108.0	106.0	141.8	114.1	104.7	140.7	112.9	91.6	131.1	100.5	95.9	157.1	109.7	94.3	133.5	103.2
0920	Plaster & Gypsum Board	100.7	135.6	123.9	103.5	153.6	136.8	105.7	153.6	137.5	102.6	135.6	124.5	104.9	171.1	148.9	96.7	135.6	122.6
0950, 0980	Ceilings & Acoustic Treatment	114.8	135.6	128.7	112.6	153.6	139.9	109.2	153.6	138.7	94.1	135.6	121.7	102.3	171.1	148.1	96.5	135.6	122.5
0960	Flooring	103.5	116.3	107.2	101.2	121.5	107.1	101.5	121.3	107.3	111.2	116.3	112.7	114.0	130.9	118.9	102.9	116.3	106.8
0970, 0990	Wall Finishes & Painting/Coating	105.8	120.8	114.6	93.2	134.4	117.4	93.2	127.0	113.0	91.7	109.1	101.9	112.8	164.1	142.9	91.7	115.3	105.6
09	FINISHES	105.5	132.0	120.0	101.9	144.4	125.1	101.1	143.6	124.3	97.3	130.5	115.4	107.6	159.9	136.2	94.7	131.2	114.7
COVERS	DIVS. 10 - 14, 25, 28, 41, 43, 44, 46	100.0	118.3	104.1	100.0	127.7	106.3	100.0	127.6	106.2	100.0	114.8	103.4	100.0	130.9	107.0	100.0	117.8	104.0
21, 22, 23	FIRE SUPPRESSION, PLUMBING & HVAC	100.0	130.2	113.3	96.4	125.7	109.4	100.0	124.3	110.7	96.4	122.5	108.0	100.1	156.6	125.1	100.0	130.1	113.3
26, 27, 3370	ELECTRICAL, COMMUNICATIONS & UTIL.	98.8	129.3	115.0	94.0	121.4	108.5	96.3	106.7	101.9	94.1	110.8	102.9	101.6	160.4	132.8	99.4	113.7	107.0
MF2014	WEIGHTED AVERAGE	101.6	128.2	113.4	102.8	129.2	114.5	101.6	126.6	112.6	96.5	122.7	108.1	103.5	147.7	123.1	98.9	125.1	110.4

511

City Cost Indexes

CALIFORNIA

DIVISION		PALM SPRINGS 922 MAT.	INST.	TOTAL	PALO ALTO 943 MAT.	INST.	TOTAL	PASADENA 910-912 MAT.	INST.	TOTAL	REDDING 960 MAT.	INST.	TOTAL	RICHMOND 948 MAT.	INST.	TOTAL	RIVERSIDE 925 MAT.	INST.	TOTAL
015433	CONTRACTOR EQUIPMENT		101.2	101.2		104.1	104.1		97.3	97.3		100.1	100.1		104.1	104.1		101.2	101.2
0241, 31-34	SITE & INFRASTRUCTURE, DEMOLITION	92.3	108.8	103.8	102.7	110.5	108.1	96.0	110.2	105.9	133.8	107.5	115.5	110.7	110.4	110.5	99.4	108.7	105.9
0310	Concrete Forming & Accessories	103.3	137.6	133.0	103.0	164.3	156.1	108.5	137.3	133.4	108.4	149.2	143.7	118.8	164.1	158.0	107.3	137.6	133.5
0320	Concrete Reinforcing	109.8	126.0	118.0	89.7	127.4	108.9	104.5	126.1	115.5	139.4	126.6	132.9	89.7	127.3	108.8	106.6	125.8	116.4
0330	Cast-in-Place Concrete	84.4	131.5	102.4	96.9	131.9	110.2	82.9	127.8	100.0	115.3	127.9	120.1	111.4	131.7	119.1	91.9	131.4	106.9
03	CONCRETE	93.6	132.2	111.5	95.4	144.5	118.2	94.8	130.7	111.4	122.4	136.2	128.8	108.1	144.3	124.9	99.7	132.1	114.7
04	MASONRY	77.6	140.9	116.6	98.1	151.5	131.0	97.4	143.6	125.8	134.8	142.4	139.5	115.1	151.5	137.5	78.5	138.1	115.2
05	METALS	108.2	111.3	109.2	103.4	113.8	106.6	92.1	109.3	97.4	102.6	111.9	105.4	103.5	113.5	106.5	107.6	111.0	108.7
06	WOOD, PLASTICS & COMPOSITES	94.4	134.8	116.6	93.2	169.8	135.3	85.8	134.4	112.6	111.6	152.3	134.0	110.1	169.8	142.9	99.4	134.8	118.8
07	THERMAL & MOISTURE PROTECTION	105.5	134.9	117.7	101.2	154.6	123.4	99.7	131.4	112.9	135.2	136.8	135.9	101.9	150.6	122.1	106.4	133.2	117.5
08	OPENINGS	103.2	133.5	110.1	95.9	157.1	109.7	91.3	133.3	100.8	119.3	141.8	124.4	95.9	157.1	109.7	106.2	133.5	112.4
0920	Plaster & Gypsum Board	101.0	135.6	124.0	103.3	171.1	148.4	89.2	135.6	120.1	104.9	153.6	137.2	111.8	171.1	151.2	104.9	135.6	125.3
0950, 0980	Ceilings & Acoustic Treatment	105.9	135.6	125.7	100.4	171.1	147.5	108.3	135.6	126.5	137.6	153.6	148.2	100.4	171.1	147.5	113.4	135.6	128.2
0960	Flooring	103.8	122.6	109.2	112.6	130.9	117.9	97.2	116.3	102.7	98.1	121.8	105.0	123.0	130.9	125.3	105.4	116.3	108.5
0970, 0990	Wall Finishes & Painting/Coating	90.2	120.8	108.2	112.8	164.1	142.9	107.4	120.8	115.3	104.0	134.4	121.9	112.8	164.1	142.9	90.2	120.8	108.2
09	FINISHES	98.2	132.8	117.1	106.0	159.9	135.5	100.9	131.5	117.6	107.8	144.5	127.9	110.9	159.9	137.7	101.2	131.8	117.9
COVERS	DIVS. 10-14, 25, 28, 41, 43, 44, 46	100.0	117.6	104.0	100.0	131.0	107.0	100.0	117.0	103.8	100.0	127.7	106.3	100.0	130.9	107.0	100.0	117.6	104.0
21, 22, 23	FIRE SUPPRESSION, PLUMBING & HVAC	96.4	125.5	109.3	96.6	156.3	123.0	96.4	122.9	108.1	100.5	125.7	111.6	96.6	154.7	122.3	100.0	130.1	113.3
26, 27, 3370	ELECTRICAL, COMMUNICATIONS & UTIL.	93.7	113.8	104.4	101.5	169.1	137.4	117.4	130.2	124.2	99.0	121.4	110.9	102.1	139.5	121.9	90.5	110.9	101.3
MF2014	WEIGHTED AVERAGE	98.2	125.1	110.1	99.4	148.3	121.0	97.7	126.5	110.4	109.8	129.2	118.4	102.7	143.7	120.8	100.2	125.2	111.2

CALIFORNIA

DIVISION		SACRAMENTO 942,956-958 MAT.	INST.	TOTAL	SALINAS 939 MAT.	INST.	TOTAL	SAN BERNARDINO 923-924 MAT.	INST.	TOTAL	SAN DIEGO 919-921 MAT.	INST.	TOTAL	SAN FRANCISCO 940-941 MAT.	INST.	TOTAL	SAN JOSE 951 MAT.	INST.	TOTAL
015433	CONTRACTOR EQUIPMENT		102.8	102.8		100.3	100.3		101.2	101.2		98.9	98.9		108.5	108.5		101.9	101.9
0241, 31-34	SITE & INFRASTRUCTURE, DEMOLITION	92.2	116.6	109.2	116.0	108.2	110.5	78.3	108.7	99.5	103.0	104.0	103.8	113.5	111.2	111.9	134.9	102.4	112.2
0310	Concrete Forming & Accessories	103.0	151.7	145.1	110.6	152.1	146.5	111.2	137.5	133.9	108.7	124.4	122.3	104.6	165.3	157.1	108.0	164.2	156.6
0320	Concrete Reinforcing	85.3	126.8	106.4	95.6	127.0	111.6	106.6	125.9	116.4	101.2	125.7	113.6	104.6	127.9	116.4	95.5	127.4	111.7
0330	Cast-in-Place Concrete	91.9	128.8	105.9	94.9	128.2	107.6	63.5	131.4	89.4	90.9	113.7	99.6	111.3	132.8	119.5	111.7	131.2	119.1
03	CONCRETE	97.1	137.4	115.8	104.5	137.7	119.9	73.7	132.1	100.8	100.0	120.1	109.3	109.2	145.7	126.1	107.9	144.5	124.9
04	MASONRY	99.0	145.8	127.8	96.7	148.3	128.4	84.9	139.0	118.2	89.3	130.0	114.4	123.0	158.2	144.7	133.1	151.6	144.5
05	METALS	101.3	107.9	103.3	108.2	112.8	109.6	107.6	111.0	108.6	109.5	110.1	109.7	111.1	120.3	113.9	101.8	118.7	106.9
06	WOOD, PLASTICS & COMPOSITES	89.4	155.7	125.8	102.1	155.5	131.5	104.9	134.8	120.4	99.6	121.5	111.6	95.6	169.9	136.4	109.4	169.5	142.5
07	THERMAL & MOISTURE PROTECTION	111.5	137.8	122.4	98.9	143.6	117.5	104.6	134.4	116.9	104.7	117.8	110.1	103.2	155.0	124.7	105.4	152.1	124.8
08	OPENINGS	109.1	142.5	116.7	95.5	149.2	107.6	103.3	132.8	110.0	98.8	124.6	104.6	100.3	157.1	113.1	96.1	156.9	109.9
0920	Plaster & Gypsum Board	100.6	156.8	138.0	97.6	156.8	137.0	106.3	135.6	125.8	95.9	121.9	113.2	106.9	171.1	149.6	101.8	171.1	147.9
0950, 0980	Ceilings & Acoustic Treatment	100.4	156.8	138.0	94.1	156.8	135.8	109.2	135.6	126.8	115.9	121.9	119.9	108.9	171.1	150.3	108.4	171.1	150.1
0960	Flooring	112.6	121.5	115.2	105.0	130.9	112.5	107.4	116.3	110.0	105.9	116.3	108.9	114.0	130.9	118.9	94.8	130.9	105.3
0970, 0990	Wall Finishes & Painting/Coating	109.4	140.1	127.4	92.6	164.1	134.6	90.2	120.8	108.2	104.0	120.8	113.9	112.8	173.9	148.7	93.5	164.1	134.9
09	FINISHES	104.8	147.1	127.9	96.7	151.2	126.5	99.6	131.8	117.2	106.6	122.1	115.1	109.3	161.1	137.6	100.0	159.7	132.6
COVERS	DIVS. 10-14, 25, 28, 41, 43, 44, 46	100.0	128.5	106.4	100.0	130.9	107.0	100.0	112.4	102.8	100.0	113.9	103.1	100.0	131.2	107.1	100.0	130.4	106.9
21, 22, 23	FIRE SUPPRESSION, PLUMBING & HVAC	100.0	125.6	111.3	96.4	131.8	112.1	96.4	127.3	110.1	100.0	126.3	111.6	100.1	190.7	140.1	100.0	159.5	126.3
26, 27, 3370	ELECTRICAL, COMMUNICATIONS & UTIL.	97.2	111.0	104.5	95.1	123.9	110.4	93.7	111.1	103.0	103.5	102.9	103.2	101.7	172.1	139.0	99.2	168.1	135.8
MF2014	WEIGHTED AVERAGE	101.0	129.1	113.4	100.2	133.2	114.8	95.8	124.5	108.5	102.0	118.1	109.1	105.6	157.7	128.6	103.6	148.6	123.5

CALIFORNIA

DIVISION		SAN LUIS OBISPO 934 MAT.	INST.	TOTAL	SAN MATEO 944 MAT.	INST.	TOTAL	SAN RAFAEL 949 MAT.	INST.	TOTAL	SANTA ANA 926-927 MAT.	INST.	TOTAL	SANTA BARBARA 931 MAT.	INST.	TOTAL	SANTA CRUZ 950 MAT.	INST.	TOTAL
015433	CONTRACTOR EQUIPMENT		100.3	100.3		104.1	104.1		103.3	103.3		101.2	101.2		100.3	100.3		101.9	101.9
0241, 31-34	SITE & INFRASTRUCTURE, DEMOLITION	108.0	108.6	108.4	108.5	110.4	109.9	104.5	116.4	112.8	90.7	108.7	103.3	102.4	108.6	106.7	134.5	102.2	112.0
0310	Concrete Forming & Accessories	118.0	137.6	135.0	109.0	164.3	156.8	113.8	164.3	157.5	111.4	137.5	133.9	108.1	137.7	133.7	108.0	152.4	146.4
0320	Concrete Reinforcing	96.9	125.8	111.6	89.7	127.6	108.9	90.5	127.6	109.3	110.4	126.0	118.3	95.2	125.8	110.7	117.9	127.1	122.6
0330	Cast-in-Place Concrete	102.0	130.6	112.9	107.8	131.8	117.0	125.1	131.0	127.6	81.0	131.4	100.2	95.7	130.7	109.0	111.0	130.1	118.3
03	CONCRETE	102.7	131.8	116.2	104.7	144.5	123.1	127.1	144.0	134.9	91.1	132.1	110.1	95.0	131.9	112.1	110.5	138.8	123.6
04	MASONRY	98.2	136.9	122.1	114.8	154.9	139.5	94.3	154.9	131.6	74.5	141.3	115.6	96.9	136.9	121.6	137.1	148.4	144.1
05	METALS	106.1	110.6	107.5	103.3	114.0	106.6	104.4	110.7	106.3	107.7	111.2	108.7	103.7	110.7	105.8	109.2	117.4	111.8
06	WOOD, PLASTICS & COMPOSITES	104.6	134.8	121.2	100.4	169.8	138.5	96.6	169.5	136.7	104.9	134.8	121.3	97.7	134.8	118.1	109.4	155.6	134.8
07	THERMAL & MOISTURE PROTECTION	99.0	132.1	112.7	101.7	153.7	123.2	106.0	152.9	125.5	105.8	135.0	117.9	98.5	131.5	112.2	104.9	146.0	122.0
08	OPENINGS	93.5	131.1	102.0	95.9	157.1	109.7	106.6	156.9	118.0	102.5	133.5	109.5	95.3	133.7	104.0	97.4	149.3	109.1
0920	Plaster & Gypsum Board	103.6	135.6	124.9	108.2	171.1	150.0	109.9	171.1	150.6	108.0	135.6	126.4	96.7	135.6	122.6	110.4	156.8	141.3
0950, 0980	Ceilings & Acoustic Treatment	94.1	135.6	121.7	94.1	171.1	147.5	107.2	171.1	149.7	109.2	135.6	126.8	96.5	135.6	122.5	110.1	156.8	141.2
0960	Flooring	112.2	116.3	113.4	116.3	130.9	120.5	128.3	130.9	129.1	107.9	116.3	110.3	104.1	116.3	110.0	98.9	130.9	108.2
0970, 0990	Wall Finishes & Painting/Coating	91.7	113.0	104.3	112.8	164.1	142.9	108.8	158.6	138.1	90.2	120.8	108.2	91.7	115.3	105.6	93.7	164.1	135.0
09	FINISHES	98.7	130.8	116.3	108.2	159.9	136.5	111.4	159.1	137.5	101.1	131.7	117.8	95.2	131.2	114.9	102.8	151.3	129.3
COVERS	DIVS. 10-14, 25, 28, 41, 43, 44, 46	100.0	124.8	105.6	100.0	130.9	107.0	100.0	130.2	106.8	100.0	117.6	104.0	100.0	117.8	104.0	100.0	128.4	106.4
21, 22, 23	FIRE SUPPRESSION, PLUMBING & HVAC	96.4	127.4	110.1	96.6	155.7	122.7	96.5	183.8	135.1	96.4	122.1	107.8	100.0	130.1	113.3	100.0	132.2	114.2
26, 27, 3370	ELECTRICAL, COMMUNICATIONS & UTIL.	94.1	113.4	104.3	101.5	160.8	132.9	98.5	123.9	111.9	93.7	112.9	103.9	93.0	112.9	103.6	98.3	123.9	111.9
MF2014	WEIGHTED AVERAGE	99.3	124.7	110.5	101.8	147.3	121.9	104.9	148.2	124.0	97.9	124.1	109.5	98.2	125.2	110.1	105.6	133.6	118.0

CALIFORNIA / COLORADO

DIVISION		SANTA ROSA 954 MAT.	INST.	TOTAL	STOCKTON 952 MAT.	INST.	TOTAL	SUSANVILLE 961 MAT.	INST.	TOTAL	VALLEJO 945 MAT.	INST.	TOTAL	VAN NUYS 913-916 MAT.	INST.	TOTAL	ALAMOSA 811 MAT.	INST.	TOTAL
015433	CONTRACTOR EQUIPMENT		100.7	100.7		100.1	100.1		100.1	100.1		103.0	103.0		97.3	97.3		94.0	94.0
0241, 31-34	SITE & INFRASTRUCTURE, DEMOLITION	105.1	107.5	106.8	103.1	107.6	106.2	142.3	107.5	118.0	93.2	116.4	109.3	113.9	110.2	111.3	141.3	89.6	105.2
0310	Concrete Forming & Accessories	104.3	163.6	155.6	105.9	151.3	145.2	109.6	145.0	140.3	104.2	163.2	155.2	115.5	137.3	134.3	105.3	54.9	61.7
0320	Concrete Reinforcing	105.3	127.7	116.7	108.1	126.6	117.5	139.4	126.6	132.9	91.6	127.5	109.8	104.5	126.1	115.5	111.1	63.3	86.8
0330	Cast-in-Place Concrete	105.5	129.5	114.7	93.7	127.9	106.7	104.9	127.9	113.6	100.0	130.1	111.5	87.4	127.8	102.8	97.6	72.7	88.1
03	CONCRETE	110.8	143.5	125.9	100.7	137.2	117.6	125.0	134.3	129.3	101.9	143.1	121.0	109.8	130.7	119.5	114.1	75.0	90.6
04	MASONRY	103.7	157.1	136.6	103.0	142.4	127.2	133.2	142.4	138.9	71.7	153.8	122.3	112.7	143.6	131.7	132.9	61.7	89.1
05	METALS	108.0	115.0	110.1	103.8	111.7	106.2	101.4	111.8	104.5	104.4	110.0	106.1	91.2	109.3	96.8	103.0	77.0	95.1
06	WOOD, PLASTICS & COMPOSITES	95.8	169.3	136.2	102.1	155.5	131.4	113.3	146.8	131.8	86.7	169.5	132.2	94.0	134.4	116.2	98.4	51.9	72.8
07	THERMAL & MOISTURE PROTECTION	106.3	153.4	125.8	109.4	135.2	120.1	137.0	134.1	135.8	104.1	152.4	124.1	100.8	131.4	113.5	105.9	67.8	90.1
08	OPENINGS	104.2	156.8	116.1	104.7	142.4	113.3	120.2	138.8	124.4	108.5	155.8	119.2	91.2	133.3	100.7	96.7	59.0	88.2
0920	Plaster & Gypsum Board	102.7	171.1	148.2	105.7	156.8	139.7	105.7	148.0	133.8	104.6	171.1	148.8	93.6	135.6	121.5	77.8	50.5	59.6
0950, 0980	Ceilings & Acoustic Treatment	109.2	171.1	150.4	116.8	156.8	143.5	130.1	148.0	142.0	109.1	171.1	150.4	105.7	135.6	125.6	98.5	50.5	66.6
0960	Flooring	104.2	116.0	107.6	101.5	121.3	107.3	98.5	121.5	105.2	122.1	130.9	124.7	100.3	116.3	105.0	112.8	73.1	101.3
0970, 0990	Wall Finishes & Painting/Coating	90.2	158.6	130.4	93.2	130.7	115.2	104.0	134.4	121.9	109.8	158.6	138.5	107.4	120.8	115.3	105.9	62.1	80.2
09	FINISHES	100.2	156.1	130.7	102.7	145.8	126.3	107.6	141.2	126.0	108.0	158.8	135.8	103.2	131.4	118.6	101.3	57.9	77.6
COVERS	DIVS. 10-14, 25, 28, 41, 43, 44, 46	100.0	129.3	106.6	100.0	128.0	106.3	100.0	127.1	106.1	100.0	129.9	106.8	100.0	117.0	103.8	100.0	83.7	96.3
21, 22, 23	FIRE SUPPRESSION, PLUMBING & HVAC	96.4	183.1	134.8	100.0	124.3	110.8	96.9	125.7	109.6	100.1	143.6	119.3	96.4	122.9	108.1	96.4	66.1	83.0
26, 27, 3370	ELECTRICAL, COMMUNICATIONS & UTIL.	94.0	121.4	108.6	96.3	113.7	105.5	99.4	121.4	111.1	94.7	129.4	113.1	117.4	130.2	124.2	98.2	66.8	81.5
MF2014	WEIGHTED AVERAGE	102.3	147.1	122.1	101.7	128.2	113.4	109.5	128.3	117.8	100.5	139.9	117.9	100.9	126.5	112.2	103.9	67.3	87.8

COLORADO

DIVISION		BOULDER 803 MAT.	INST.	TOTAL	COLORADO SPRINGS 808-809 MAT.	INST.	TOTAL	DENVER 800-802 MAT.	INST.	TOTAL	DURANGO 813 MAT.	INST.	TOTAL	FORT COLLINS 805 MAT.	INST.	TOTAL	FORT MORGAN 807 MAT.	INST.	TOTAL
015433	CONTRACTOR EQUIPMENT		96.4	96.4		94.2	94.2		98.3	98.3		94.0	94.0		96.4	96.4		96.4	96.4
0241, 31-34	SITE & INFRASTRUCTURE, DEMOLITION	97.6	97.2	97.3	99.4	92.1	94.3	98.3	101.3	100.4	134.4	89.6	103.1	109.9	97.1	101.0	99.7	96.9	97.7
0310	Concrete Forming & Accessories	106.4	74.5	78.8	96.6	59.0	64.1	103.0	62.7	68.1	111.8	54.9	62.6	103.8	71.7	76.0	106.9	54.6	61.7
0320	Concrete Reinforcing	101.2	64.3	82.5	100.4	65.3	82.6	100.4	65.2	82.6	111.1	63.2	86.8	101.3	64.3	82.5	101.4	63.4	82.1
0330	Cast-in-Place Concrete	109.6	73.4	95.8	112.6	72.3	97.2	106.5	71.9	93.3	112.3	72.7	97.2	123.7	72.0	104.0	107.5	72.0	94.0
03	CONCRETE	111.0	72.7	93.3	115.0	65.6	92.1	108.4	67.0	89.2	115.9	63.6	91.6	122.9	71.0	98.8	109.3	63.1	87.9
04	MASONRY	98.1	66.8	78.9	99.4	64.4	77.9	101.3	64.6	78.7	119.3	61.1	83.5	116.3	64.3	84.3	113.5	64.3	83.2
05	METALS	97.1	76.5	90.8	100.1	77.0	93.0	102.5	76.5	94.5	103.0	77.0	95.1	98.3	76.5	91.6	96.8	76.1	90.5
06	WOOD, PLASTICS & COMPOSITES	109.2	77.0	91.5	99.9	57.6	76.7	107.0	62.2	82.4	107.2	51.9	76.8	106.8	74.5	89.0	109.2	51.4	77.5
07	THERMAL & MOISTURE PROTECTION	100.2	73.5	89.1	100.9	69.9	88.0	99.4	69.7	87.1	105.9	67.6	90.0	100.4	73.9	89.4	100.1	70.0	87.6
08	OPENINGS	100.1	73.0	94.0	104.5	62.6	95.0	105.0	65.1	96.0	103.7	59.0	93.6	100.1	71.6	93.7	100.1	58.7	90.7
0920	Plaster & Gypsum Board	116.0	76.8	89.9	100.0	56.7	71.2	111.9	61.6	78.5	90.3	50.5	63.8	110.4	74.1	86.3	116.0	50.5	72.4
0950, 0980	Ceilings & Acoustic Treatment	85.5	76.8	79.7	93.1	56.7	68.9	96.1	61.6	73.1	98.5	50.5	66.6	85.5	74.1	77.9	85.5	50.5	62.2
0960	Flooring	108.6	73.1	98.3	100.0	73.1	92.2	104.9	73.1	95.7	118.3	73.1	105.2	104.7	73.1	95.6	109.0	73.1	98.6
0970, 0990	Wall Finishes & Painting/Coating	101.0	60.9	77.4	100.7	48.2	69.9	101.0	60.9	77.4	105.9	47.7	71.8	101.0	60.9	77.4	101.0	75.7	86.1
09	FINISHES	102.6	73.0	86.4	99.4	59.5	77.6	102.9	63.7	81.5	103.9	56.3	77.9	101.2	70.9	84.6	102.6	59.0	78.8
COVERS	DIVS. 10-14, 25, 28, 41, 43, 44, 46	100.0	86.3	96.9	100.0	83.5	96.3	100.0	83.8	96.3	100.0	83.7	96.3	100.0	85.2	96.7	100.0	82.9	96.1
21, 22, 23	FIRE SUPPRESSION, PLUMBING & HVAC	96.4	73.2	86.2	100.1	74.8	88.9	99.9	75.6	89.2	96.4	73.4	86.2	100.0	71.9	87.6	96.4	71.9	85.6
26, 27, 3370	ELECTRICAL, COMMUNICATIONS & UTIL.	94.1	79.5	86.3	97.3	76.6	86.3	98.9	81.5	89.7	97.6	63.5	79.5	94.1	79.5	86.3	94.5	77.3	85.4
MF2014	WEIGHTED AVERAGE	99.7	76.0	89.2	102.1	71.8	88.7	102.2	74.2	89.8	104.3	68.2	88.3	103.2	74.8	90.7	100.3	70.9	87.3

COLORADO

DIVISION		GLENWOOD SPRINGS 816 MAT.	INST.	TOTAL	GOLDEN 804 MAT.	INST.	TOTAL	GRAND JUNCTION 815 MAT.	INST.	TOTAL	GREELEY 806 MAT.	INST.	TOTAL	MONTROSE 814 MAT.	INST.	TOTAL	PUEBLO 810 MAT.	INST.	TOTAL
015433	CONTRACTOR EQUIPMENT		97.3	97.3		96.4	96.4		97.3	97.3		96.4	96.4		95.7	95.7		94.0	94.0
0241, 31-34	SITE & INFRASTRUCTURE, DEMOLITION	150.8	97.7	113.8	111.3	97.2	101.5	133.8	97.9	108.8	96.1	97.1	96.8	144.0	93.6	108.9	125.2	89.5	100.3
0310	Concrete Forming & Accessories	102.1	54.6	61.0	99.0	61.1	66.2	110.5	76.3	80.9	101.6	75.9	79.4	101.6	54.8	61.1	107.6	59.1	65.6
0320	Concrete Reinforcing	109.9	63.4	86.3	101.4	64.3	82.6	110.3	64.4	87.0	101.2	64.3	82.5	109.8	63.2	86.2	106.2	65.0	85.3
0330	Cast-in-Place Concrete	97.6	71.5	87.7	107.6	73.4	94.6	108.0	73.1	94.7	103.4	72.0	91.4	97.6	72.1	87.9	96.9	72.5	87.1
03	CONCRETE	119.4	63.0	93.3	121.6	66.7	96.1	112.4	73.5	94.3	105.7	72.9	90.5	110.0	63.3	88.3	102.3	65.6	85.3
04	MASONRY	103.7	64.2	79.4	116.4	66.8	85.9	140.2	67.6	95.5	109.9	64.3	81.8	112.4	61.1	80.8	99.8	60.7	75.7
05	METALS	102.7	76.8	94.8	97.0	76.4	90.7	104.3	77.4	96.0	98.2	76.6	91.6	101.8	76.8	94.1	105.9	77.5	97.2
06	WOOD, PLASTICS & COMPOSITES	93.7	51.6	70.6	101.8	58.9	78.2	104.9	79.5	90.9	104.1	80.1	90.9	94.9	51.8	71.2	100.9	57.9	77.3
07	THERMAL & MOISTURE PROTECTION	105.8	68.5	90.3	101.2	70.0	88.3	104.9	75.4	92.6	99.8	75.8	89.8	106.0	67.6	90.0	104.3	67.4	89.0
08	OPENINGS	102.7	58.8	92.8	100.1	63.1	91.7	103.4	74.3	96.8	100.1	74.5	94.3	103.9	58.9	93.7	98.6	62.8	90.5
0920	Plaster & Gypsum Board	120.3	50.5	73.9	108.1	58.2	74.9	132.4	79.1	97.0	108.7	79.9	89.6	77.2	50.5	59.4	81.9	56.7	65.1
0950, 0980	Ceilings & Acoustic Treatment	97.7	50.5	66.3	85.5	58.2	67.3	97.7	79.1	85.3	85.5	79.9	81.8	98.5	50.5	66.6	106.2	56.7	73.2
0960	Flooring	111.9	73.1	100.7	102.4	73.1	93.9	117.5	73.1	104.7	103.6	73.1	94.8	115.5	73.1	103.2	114.1	73.1	102.2
0970, 0990	Wall Finishes & Painting/Coating	105.9	57.4	77.4	101.0	60.9	77.4	105.9	60.9	79.5	101.0	60.9	77.4	105.9	47.7	71.8	105.9	44.7	70.0
09	FINISHES	107.3	57.1	79.9	101.0	62.4	79.9	108.8	74.5	90.0	99.8	74.2	85.8	102.1	56.2	77.0	102.0	59.4	78.7
COVERS	DIVS. 10-14, 25, 28, 41, 43, 44, 46	100.0	83.0	96.1	100.0	84.3	96.5	100.0	86.8	97.0	100.0	85.8	96.8	100.0	83.3	96.2	100.0	84.2	96.4
21, 22, 23	FIRE SUPPRESSION, PLUMBING & HVAC	96.4	67.3	83.5	96.4	73.2	86.2	99.9	73.6	88.3	100.0	71.9	87.6	96.4	77.8	88.2	99.9	63.3	83.7
26, 27, 3370	ELECTRICAL, COMMUNICATIONS & UTIL.	94.9	63.5	78.3	94.5	79.5	86.5	97.3	54.5	74.6	94.1	79.5	86.3	97.3	51.6	73.1	98.2	66.8	81.5
MF2014	WEIGHTED AVERAGE	104.2	67.8	88.1	102.1	73.0	89.2	106.2	73.2	91.6	100.2	75.7	89.4	103.0	67.7	87.4	101.9	67.4	86.7

For customer support on your Electrical Costs with RSMeans Data, call 800.448.8182.

513

City Cost Indexes

COLORADO / CONNECTICUT

DIVISION		SALIDA 812 MAT.	INST.	TOTAL	BRIDGEPORT 066 MAT.	INST.	TOTAL	BRISTOL 060 MAT.	INST.	TOTAL	HARTFORD 061 MAT.	INST.	TOTAL	MERIDEN 064 MAT.	INST.	TOTAL	NEW BRITAIN 060 MAT.	INST.	TOTAL
015433	CONTRACTOR EQUIPMENT		95.7	95.7		99.8	99.8		99.8	99.8		99.8	99.8		100.2	100.2		99.8	99.8
0241, 31 - 34	SITE & INFRASTRUCTURE, DEMOLITION	134.1	93.6	105.9	102.4	104.0	103.5	101.6	104.0	103.3	97.1	104.0	101.9	99.6	104.8	103.2	101.8	104.0	103.3
0310	Concrete Forming & Accessories	110.4	54.6	62.1	105.3	119.0	117.1	105.3	118.9	117.0	104.2	118.9	116.9	105.0	118.9	117.0	105.8	118.8	117.1
0320	Concrete Reinforcing	109.5	63.2	86.0	115.4	140.1	127.9	115.4	140.0	127.9	110.7	140.0	125.6	115.4	140.0	127.9	115.4	140.0	127.9
0330	Cast-in-Place Concrete	111.8	72.1	96.7	93.1	128.7	106.7	87.2	128.7	103.0	91.4	128.7	105.6	83.9	128.7	101.0	88.6	128.7	103.9
03	CONCRETE	110.7	63.2	88.7	96.3	125.2	109.7	93.4	125.2	108.1	93.5	125.2	108.2	91.8	125.2	107.3	94.1	125.1	108.5
04	MASONRY	141.5	61.7	92.4	115.4	131.2	125.1	106.5	131.2	121.7	105.8	131.2	121.4	106.2	131.2	121.6	108.9	131.2	122.6
05	METALS	101.5	76.6	93.9	93.0	115.9	100.0	93.0	115.8	99.9	97.6	115.8	103.2	90.3	115.8	98.1	89.4	115.7	97.5
06	WOOD, PLASTICS & COMPOSITES	101.9	51.8	74.4	110.6	117.4	114.4	110.6	117.4	114.4	95.3	117.4	107.4	110.6	117.4	114.4	110.6	117.4	114.4
07	THERMAL & MOISTURE PROTECTION	104.8	67.8	89.4	101.1	123.5	110.4	101.2	122.0	109.8	106.4	122.0	112.8	101.2	122.0	109.8	101.2	119.7	108.9
08	OPENINGS	96.8	58.9	88.2	95.7	122.3	101.7	95.7	122.3	101.7	94.0	122.3	100.4	98.0	122.3	103.5	95.7	122.3	101.7
0920	Plaster & Gypsum Board	77.5	50.5	59.5	115.6	117.5	116.8	115.6	117.5	116.8	108.1	117.5	114.3	116.8	117.5	117.2	115.6	117.5	116.8
0950, 0980	Ceilings & Acoustic Treatment	98.5	50.5	66.6	92.7	117.5	109.2	92.7	117.5	109.2	94.9	117.5	109.9	95.8	117.5	110.2	92.7	117.5	109.2
0960	Flooring	121.1	73.1	107.2	92.9	129.4	103.5	92.9	124.7	102.1	96.0	129.4	105.7	92.9	124.7	102.1	92.9	124.7	102.1
0970, 0990	Wall Finishes & Painting/Coating	105.9	47.7	71.8	95.6	128.9	115.2	95.6	127.7	114.4	97.8	127.7	115.4	95.6	128.9	115.2	95.6	127.7	114.4
09	FINISHES	102.7	56.2	77.3	93.8	121.4	108.9	93.9	120.5	108.4	93.8	121.3	108.8	94.7	120.6	108.9	93.9	120.5	108.4
COVERS	DIVS. 10 - 14, 25, 28, 41, 43, 44, 46	100.0	83.3	96.2	100.0	112.6	102.9	100.0	112.6	102.9	100.0	112.6	102.9	100.0	112.6	102.9	100.0	112.6	102.9
21, 22, 23	FIRE SUPPRESSION, PLUMBING & HVAC	96.4	63.5	81.8	100.0	116.0	107.1	100.0	116.0	107.1	100.0	116.0	107.1	96.5	116.0	105.1	100.0	116.0	107.1
26, 27, 3370	ELECTRICAL, COMMUNICATIONS & UTIL.	97.5	62.4	78.9	100.1	109.1	104.9	100.1	109.1	104.9	99.5	109.5	104.8	100.0	108.5	104.5	100.2	109.1	104.9
MF2014	WEIGHTED AVERAGE	103.6	66.2	87.0	98.3	118.0	107.0	97.5	117.8	106.5	97.9	117.9	106.8	96.3	117.7	105.8	97.1	117.7	106.2

CONNECTICUT

DIVISION		NEW HAVEN 065 MAT.	INST.	TOTAL	NEW LONDON 063 MAT.	INST.	TOTAL	NORWALK 068 MAT.	INST.	TOTAL	STAMFORD 069 MAT.	INST.	TOTAL	WATERBURY 067 MAT.	INST.	TOTAL	WILLIMANTIC 062 MAT.	INST.	TOTAL
015433	CONTRACTOR EQUIPMENT		100.2	100.2		100.2	100.2		99.8	99.8		99.8	99.8		99.8	99.8		99.8	99.8
0241, 31 - 34	SITE & INFRASTRUCTURE, DEMOLITION	101.7	104.6	103.7	94.3	104.7	101.5	102.2	104.0	103.5	102.8	104.0	103.7	102.2	104.0	103.5	102.2	103.9	103.4
0310	Concrete Forming & Accessories	105.0	118.9	117.0	105.0	118.9	117.0	105.3	119.3	117.4	105.3	119.3	117.4	105.3	118.9	117.1	105.3	118.9	117.0
0320	Concrete Reinforcing	115.4	140.0	127.9	90.5	140.0	115.6	115.4	140.2	128.0	115.4	140.2	128.0	115.4	140.0	127.9	115.4	140.0	127.9
0330	Cast-in-Place Concrete	90.2	128.7	104.8	76.9	128.7	96.6	91.6	130.1	106.3	93.1	130.1	107.2	93.1	128.7	106.7	87.0	128.7	102.9
03	CONCRETE	107.3	125.2	115.6	82.5	125.2	102.3	95.5	125.9	109.6	96.3	125.9	110.0	96.3	125.2	109.7	93.3	125.2	108.1
04	MASONRY	106.8	131.2	121.8	105.2	131.2	121.2	106.1	132.6	122.4	107.0	132.6	122.7	107.0	131.2	121.9	106.4	131.2	121.7
05	METALS	89.7	115.8	97.6	89.4	115.8	97.4	93.0	116.3	100.1	93.0	116.3	100.1	93.0	115.8	100.0	92.7	115.8	99.8
06	WOOD, PLASTICS & COMPOSITES	110.6	117.4	114.4	110.6	117.4	114.4	110.6	117.4	114.4	110.6	117.4	114.4	110.6	117.4	114.4	110.6	117.4	114.4
07	THERMAL & MOISTURE PROTECTION	101.3	121.3	109.6	101.1	122.0	109.8	101.2	124.1	110.7	101.2	124.1	110.7	101.2	121.3	109.6	101.4	121.9	109.9
08	OPENINGS	95.7	122.3	101.7	98.0	122.3	103.5	95.7	122.3	101.7	95.7	122.3	101.7	95.7	122.3	101.7	98.1	122.3	103.5
0920	Plaster & Gypsum Board	115.6	117.5	116.8	115.6	117.5	116.8	115.6	117.5	116.8	115.6	117.5	116.8	115.6	117.5	116.8	115.6	117.5	116.8
0950, 0980	Ceilings & Acoustic Treatment	92.7	117.5	109.2	90.8	117.5	108.5	92.7	117.5	109.2	92.7	117.5	109.2	92.7	117.5	109.2	90.8	117.5	108.5
0960	Flooring	92.9	129.4	103.5	92.9	129.4	103.5	92.9	124.7	102.1	92.9	124.7	102.1	92.9	129.4	103.5	92.9	128.3	103.2
0970, 0990	Wall Finishes & Painting/Coating	95.6	128.9	115.2	95.6	128.9	115.2	95.6	128.9	115.2	95.6	128.9	115.2	95.6	128.9	115.2	95.6	128.9	115.2
09	FINISHES	93.9	121.4	108.9	93.0	121.4	108.6	93.9	120.6	108.5	93.9	120.6	108.5	93.8	121.4	108.9	93.6	121.2	108.7
COVERS	DIVS. 10 - 14, 25, 28, 41, 43, 44, 46	100.0	112.6	102.9	100.0	112.6	102.9	100.0	112.8	102.9	100.0	112.8	102.9	100.0	112.8	102.9	100.0	112.6	102.9
21, 22, 23	FIRE SUPPRESSION, PLUMBING & HVAC	100.0	116.0	107.1	96.5	116.0	105.1	100.0	116.1	107.1	100.0	116.1	107.1	100.0	116.0	107.1	100.0	116.0	107.1
26, 27, 3370	ELECTRICAL, COMMUNICATIONS & UTIL.	100.0	108.5	104.5	96.8	110.5	104.1	100.1	159.5	131.6	100.1	162.7	133.3	99.6	114.4	107.4	100.1	111.4	106.1
MF2014	WEIGHTED AVERAGE	98.7	117.8	107.1	94.4	118.1	104.9	97.8	125.2	109.9	97.9	125.6	110.2	97.8	118.6	107.0	97.7	118.2	106.8

D.C. / DELAWARE / FLORIDA

DIVISION		WASHINGTON 200 - 205 MAT.	INST.	TOTAL	DOVER 199 MAT.	INST.	TOTAL	NEWARK 197 MAT.	INST.	TOTAL	WILMINGTON 198 MAT.	INST.	TOTAL	DAYTONA BEACH 321 MAT.	INST.	TOTAL	FORT LAUDERDALE 333 MAT.	INST.	TOTAL
015433	CONTRACTOR EQUIPMENT		107.2	107.2		124.1	124.1		124.1	124.1		124.3	124.3		103.9	103.9		96.6	96.6
0241, 31 - 34	SITE & INFRASTRUCTURE, DEMOLITION	105.0	96.0	98.7	104.6	115.6	112.3	104.3	114.4	111.4	103.5	114.8	111.4	100.2	90.2	93.2	92.4	77.4	81.9
0310	Concrete Forming & Accessories	98.5	72.2	75.8	99.3	102.5	102.0	101.0	102.3	102.1	100.0	102.3	102.0	99.9	62.6	67.6	99.3	58.0	63.6
0320	Concrete Reinforcing	99.8	84.4	92.0	100.1	115.3	107.8	98.1	115.3	106.8	100.1	115.3	107.8	89.6	61.7	75.4	83.9	56.5	70.0
0330	Cast-in-Place Concrete	112.2	80.2	100.0	101.7	105.2	103.0	88.6	105.1	94.9	96.3	105.1	99.7	86.0	63.7	78.6	90.7	63.7	80.4
03	CONCRETE	106.9	78.4	93.6	99.0	106.8	102.6	93.4	106.7	99.6	96.4	106.7	101.2	87.4	65.7	77.3	90.2	61.7	77.0
04	MASONRY	104.7	74.9	86.3	102.9	98.4	100.1	104.5	98.4	100.7	103.1	98.4	100.2	91.2	70.5	78.4	96.6	65.7	77.5
05	METALS	98.4	96.9	97.9	98.3	124.9	106.5	99.7	124.8	107.3	98.3	124.8	106.4	101.9	91.1	98.6	99.4	88.5	96.1
06	WOOD, PLASTICS & COMPOSITES	93.1	70.5	80.7	91.1	101.6	96.8	96.6	101.6	99.3	87.5	101.6	95.2	100.8	61.2	79.1	90.6	58.1	72.8
07	THERMAL & MOISTURE PROTECTION	101.4	83.9	94.1	102.2	112.5	106.5	106.2	112.5	108.8	102.6	112.5	106.7	97.8	69.1	85.9	100.8	63.7	85.4
08	OPENINGS	96.9	73.9	91.7	88.0	111.9	93.5	92.1	111.9	96.6	85.7	111.9	91.6	95.5	60.1	87.5	96.3	57.2	87.5
0920	Plaster & Gypsum Board	105.6	69.6	81.7	97.3	101.5	100.1	99.2	101.5	100.8	96.7	101.5	99.9	88.7	60.6	70.0	97.7	57.4	70.9
0950, 0980	Ceilings & Acoustic Treatment	106.3	69.6	81.9	95.9	101.5	99.7	92.5	101.5	98.5	93.4	101.5	98.8	80.6	60.6	67.3	84.6	57.4	66.5
0960	Flooring	95.3	77.1	90.0	93.4	106.0	96.9	91.8	106.0	95.9	93.7	106.0	97.3	103.5	78.7	96.3	100.8	78.7	94.4
0970, 0990	Wall Finishes & Painting/Coating	106.8	76.3	88.9	91.1	112.7	103.8	89.2	112.7	103.0	86.9	112.7	102.1	98.1	61.8	76.8	90.9	64.3	75.3
09	FINISHES	97.2	72.7	83.8	91.1	103.4	97.8	91.0	103.4	97.8	90.5	103.4	97.5	90.9	65.0	76.7	91.4	62.3	75.5
COVERS	DIVS. 10 - 14, 25, 28, 41, 43, 44, 46	100.0	95.6	99.0	100.0	105.9	101.3	100.0	105.9	101.3	100.0	105.9	101.3	100.0	82.5	96.0	100.0	82.0	95.9
21, 22, 23	FIRE SUPPRESSION, PLUMBING & HVAC	100.0	88.4	94.9	100.0	120.5	109.1	100.1	120.5	109.2	100.0	120.5	109.1	99.9	72.5	87.7	99.9	57.6	81.2
26, 27, 3370	ELECTRICAL, COMMUNICATIONS & UTIL.	98.7	101.2	100.0	98.4	113.4	106.3	98.7	113.4	106.5	98.5	113.4	106.4	94.4	63.3	77.9	94.3	68.3	80.5
MF2014	WEIGHTED AVERAGE	100.2	86.1	94.0	97.6	112.1	104.0	97.9	111.9	104.1	97.0	112.0	103.6	96.4	71.8	85.6	96.6	66.4	83.2

FLORIDA

DIVISION		FORT MYERS 339,341			GAINESVILLE 326,344			JACKSONVILLE 320,322			LAKELAND 338			MELBOURNE 329			MIAMI 330 - 332,340		
		MAT.	INST.	TOTAL	MAT.	INST.	TOTAL	MAT.	INST.	TOTAL	MAT.	INST.	TOTAL	MAT.	INST.	TOTAL	MAT.	INST.	TOTAL
015433	CONTRACTOR EQUIPMENT		103.9	103.9		103.9	103.9		103.9	103.9		103.9	103.9		103.9	103.9		96.6	96.6
0241, 31 - 34	SITE & INFRASTRUCTURE, DEMOLITION	103.9	89.8	94.0	107.8	90.0	95.4	100.3	90.0	93.1	105.8	90.0	94.8	106.9	90.1	95.2	93.8	77.4	82.4
0310	Concrete Forming & Accessories	94.9	58.0	63.0	94.8	56.3	61.4	99.6	56.3	62.1	91.0	60.5	64.7	96.0	63.0	67.5	104.1	58.1	64.3
0320	Concrete Reinforcing	84.8	56.5	70.5	95.1	56.4	75.5	89.6	56.4	72.8	86.9	75.7	81.3	90.6	65.1	77.7	90.0	56.5	73.0
0330	Cast-in-Place Concrete	94.6	63.7	82.8	98.8	64.9	85.9	86.8	64.9	78.5	96.7	64.8	84.6	103.7	66.2	89.4	87.6	63.8	78.5
03	CONCRETE	90.8	61.7	77.3	98.1	61.3	81.1	87.8	61.3	76.5	92.5	66.6	80.5	98.6	66.3	83.6	88.4	61.7	76.0
04	MASONRY	90.1	65.7	75.1	104.5	67.6	81.8	90.9	67.6	76.6	106.5	67.3	82.4	88.8	69.6	77.0	96.8	65.7	77.6
05	METALS	101.6	88.5	97.6	100.9	88.9	97.2	100.4	88.9	96.9	101.6	95.7	99.8	110.8	92.3	105.1	99.7	88.6	96.3
06	WOOD, PLASTICS & COMPOSITES	87.5	58.1	71.4	94.8	54.7	72.7	100.8	54.7	75.5	82.7	60.4	70.4	96.4	62.2	77.6	95.9	58.1	75.2
07	THERMAL & MOISTURE PROTECTION	100.6	64.0	85.4	98.1	64.6	84.2	98.0	64.5	84.1	100.6	65.0	85.8	98.3	66.6	85.1	100.5	63.7	85.2
08	OPENINGS	97.6	57.2	88.4	95.0	55.3	86.1	95.5	55.3	86.4	97.5	62.9	89.7	94.7	61.4	87.2	98.3	57.2	89.0
0920	Plaster & Gypsum Board	93.8	57.4	69.6	85.5	53.9	64.5	88.7	53.9	65.6	90.5	59.7	70.1	85.5	61.6	69.6	93.7	57.4	69.6
0950, 0980	Ceilings & Acoustic Treatment	80.1	57.4	65.0	75.0	53.9	61.0	80.6	53.9	62.8	80.1	59.7	66.5	79.8	61.6	67.7	89.7	57.4	68.2
0960	Flooring	97.6	76.9	91.6	100.8	78.3	94.3	103.5	78.7	96.3	95.3	77.0	90.0	101.0	78.7	94.5	99.8	78.7	93.7
0970, 0990	Wall Finishes & Painting/Coating	95.0	64.2	76.9	98.1	61.8	76.8	98.1	64.2	78.2	95.0	64.2	76.9	98.1	81.6	88.4	88.9	64.3	74.4
09	FINISHES	91.0	61.9	75.1	89.2	60.4	73.5	90.9	60.8	74.4	90.0	63.6	75.6	90.0	67.5	77.7	91.7	62.3	75.6
COVERS	DIVS. 10 - 14, 25, 28, 41, 43, 44, 46	100.0	77.0	94.8	100.0	80.8	95.6	100.0	78.9	95.2	100.0	77.8	95.0	100.0	82.3	96.0	100.0	82.0	95.9
21, 22, 23	FIRE SUPPRESSION, PLUMBING & HVAC	97.9	57.6	80.1	98.6	60.9	81.9	99.9	60.9	82.6	97.9	57.8	80.2	99.9	74.9	88.8	99.9	57.9	81.3
26, 27, 3370	ELECTRICAL, COMMUNICATIONS & UTIL.	96.3	59.5	76.8	94.7	59.6	76.1	94.1	64.0	78.1	94.5	65.0	78.9	95.5	62.6	78.0	98.0	71.4	83.9
MF2014	WEIGHTED AVERAGE	96.9	65.9	83.2	98.0	66.7	84.2	96.2	67.3	83.4	97.6	68.8	84.9	99.3	72.7	87.5	97.1	66.9	83.8

FLORIDA

DIVISION		ORLANDO 327 - 328,347			PANAMA CITY 324			PENSACOLA 325			SARASOTA 342			ST. PETERSBURG 337			TALLAHASSEE 323		
		MAT.	INST.	TOTAL	MAT.	INST.	TOTAL	MAT.	INST.	TOTAL	MAT.	INST.	TOTAL	MAT.	INST.	TOTAL	MAT.	INST.	TOTAL
015433	CONTRACTOR EQUIPMENT		103.9	103.9		103.9	103.9		103.9	103.9		103.9	103.9		103.9	103.9		103.9	103.9
0241, 31 - 34	SITE & INFRASTRUCTURE, DEMOLITION	99.0	90.2	92.8	111.1	89.5	96.0	111.5	89.9	96.4	112.5	90.0	96.8	107.4	89.7	95.1	98.3	90.0	92.5
0310	Concrete Forming & Accessories	102.9	63.1	68.4	98.9	43.0	50.5	96.8	66.2	70.4	97.5	60.5	65.5	98.6	59.9	65.1	101.3	56.4	62.4
0320	Concrete Reinforcing	92.8	62.9	77.6	93.6	68.8	81.0	96.0	68.8	82.2	89.8	73.3	81.4	86.9	73.3	80.0	96.8	56.5	76.3
0330	Cast-in-Place Concrete	100.9	66.6	87.8	91.3	60.8	79.7	112.8	65.9	94.9	102.4	64.8	88.1	97.8	62.9	84.5	90.3	64.9	80.6
03	CONCRETE	94.2	66.1	81.1	96.3	56.1	77.7	106.0	68.3	88.5	96.8	66.1	82.6	94.0	65.2	80.7	90.2	61.4	76.8
04	MASONRY	96.5	70.5	80.5	95.5	60.5	74.0	115.9	69.4	87.3	94.3	67.3	77.7	146.7	64.1	95.8	93.3	67.6	77.5
05	METALS	99.8	91.3	97.2	101.7	92.9	99.0	102.7	93.1	99.8	103.5	94.8	100.8	102.4	94.7	100.1	98.9	89.0	95.9
06	WOOD, PLASTICS & COMPOSITES	92.7	62.2	75.9	99.6	40.6	67.2	97.6	67.4	81.1	98.0	60.4	77.3	92.0	61.3	75.1	100.1	54.7	75.1
07	THERMAL & MOISTURE PROTECTION	98.6	70.2	86.4	98.3	58.5	81.8	98.3	67.3	85.4	99.0	65.0	84.9	100.8	63.2	85.2	99.5	64.6	85.0
08	OPENINGS	99.2	60.9	90.6	93.5	50.5	83.7	93.5	65.2	87.1	99.1	62.4	90.8	96.3	62.9	88.7	98.2	55.3	88.5
0920	Plaster & Gypsum Board	96.7	61.6	73.3	87.8	39.4	55.6	95.5	67.0	76.6	95.0	59.7	71.6	96.1	60.7	72.6	96.8	53.9	68.3
0950, 0980	Ceilings & Acoustic Treatment	88.8	61.6	70.7	79.8	39.4	52.9	79.8	67.0	71.3	84.7	59.7	68.1	82.0	60.7	67.8	88.1	53.9	65.3
0960	Flooring	97.7	78.7	92.2	103.0	76.9	95.4	98.6	78.7	92.8	106.0	76.9	97.6	99.6	76.9	93.0	99.2	78.7	93.2
0970, 0990	Wall Finishes & Painting/Coating	96.8	64.2	77.7	98.1	61.8	76.8	98.1	61.8	76.8	98.6	64.2	78.4	95.0	64.3	76.9	95.2	64.2	77.0
09	FINISHES	92.3	65.9	77.8	91.5	50.1	68.9	91.0	68.4	78.7	96.3	63.6	78.5	92.6	63.4	76.6	91.5	60.8	74.7
COVERS	DIVS. 10 - 14, 25, 28, 41, 43, 44, 46	100.0	82.6	96.1	100.0	69.3	93.1	100.0	75.2	94.4	100.0	77.8	95.0	100.0	75.0	94.4	100.0	77.1	94.8
21, 22, 23	FIRE SUPPRESSION, PLUMBING & HVAC	100.0	58.1	81.5	99.9	48.4	77.1	99.9	52.9	79.1	99.8	57.8	81.3	99.9	56.1	80.5	99.9	68.3	85.9
26, 27, 3370	ELECTRICAL, COMMUNICATIONS & UTIL.	98.4	64.3	80.3	93.2	59.6	75.4	96.8	53.6	73.9	96.6	64.0	79.3	94.5	63.8	78.2	99.0	59.6	78.1
MF2014	WEIGHTED AVERAGE	98.1	69.1	85.3	97.7	60.7	81.4	100.4	67.1	85.7	99.4	68.5	85.8	100.6	67.5	86.0	97.2	68.2	84.4

FLORIDA | GEORGIA

DIVISION		TAMPA 335 - 336,346			WEST PALM BEACH 334,349			ALBANY 317,398			ATHENS 306			ATLANTA 300 - 303,399			AUGUSTA 308 - 309		
		MAT.	INST.	TOTAL	MAT.	INST.	TOTAL	MAT.	INST.	TOTAL	MAT.	INST.	TOTAL	MAT.	INST.	TOTAL	MAT.	INST.	TOTAL
015433	CONTRACTOR EQUIPMENT		103.9	103.9		96.6	96.6		97.6	97.6		96.8	96.8		95.8	95.8		96.8	96.8
0241, 31 - 34	SITE & INFRASTRUCTURE, DEMOLITION	107.8	90.2	95.5	89.3	77.4	81.0	100.6	80.3	86.4	101.6	96.9	98.3	98.1	94.8	95.8	94.7	97.2	96.5
0310	Concrete Forming & Accessories	101.8	61.6	67.1	103.0	58.0	64.1	95.3	62.4	66.8	92.4	45.9	52.2	96.3	73.3	76.4	93.5	73.8	76.4
0320	Concrete Reinforcing	83.9	75.7	79.7	86.3	54.2	70.0	90.6	71.7	81.0	94.0	66.2	79.9	93.3	71.0	82.0	94.4	68.2	81.1
0330	Cast-in-Place Concrete	95.6	66.5	84.5	86.2	63.7	77.7	86.8	69.6	80.3	106.7	70.6	93.0	106.7	72.0	93.5	100.8	71.2	89.5
03	CONCRETE	92.7	67.6	81.1	87.0	61.3	75.1	88.7	68.5	79.4	102.5	59.4	82.5	99.9	73.1	87.5	95.1	72.5	84.6
04	MASONRY	97.6	70.2	80.7	96.1	65.7	77.4	93.8	80.8	85.8	80.5	81.1	80.8	94.4	67.8	78.0	94.6	81.5	86.5
05	METALS	101.5	95.7	99.7	98.5	87.7	95.2	100.2	99.6	100.0	96.7	81.4	92.0	97.6	84.6	93.6	96.4	83.1	92.3
06	WOOD, PLASTICS & COMPOSITES	96.0	60.4	76.4	95.6	58.1	75.0	86.1	60.6	72.1	93.3	38.6	63.3	97.2	74.8	84.9	94.8	76.2	84.5
07	THERMAL & MOISTURE PROTECTION	101.0	66.3	86.6	100.6	64.3	85.5	99.8	71.7	88.1	95.8	71.5	85.7	95.6	72.4	86.0	95.5	75.8	87.3
08	OPENINGS	97.5	62.9	89.7	95.9	56.7	87.0	87.9	66.2	83.0	92.5	52.7	83.5	97.9	76.7	93.1	92.5	74.1	88.3
0920	Plaster & Gypsum Board	98.4	59.7	72.7	102.1	57.4	72.4	103.6	60.0	74.6	94.7	37.3	56.5	97.0	74.3	81.9	96.0	75.8	82.6
0950, 0980	Ceilings & Acoustic Treatment	84.6	59.7	68.0	80.1	57.4	65.0	81.3	60.0	67.1	95.0	37.3	56.6	95.0	74.3	81.2	95.9	75.8	82.6
0960	Flooring	100.8	77.0	93.9	102.8	78.7	95.8	103.4	88.5	99.1	98.3	86.8	94.9	99.9	86.8	96.1	98.5	86.8	95.1
0970, 0990	Wall Finishes & Painting/Coating	95.0	64.2	76.9	90.9	61.8	73.8	92.3	95.6	94.2	94.9	95.6	95.3	94.9	95.6	95.3	94.9	76.1	83.9
09	FINISHES	93.8	64.4	77.7	91.4	62.0	75.4	94.8	70.0	81.3	96.2	56.8	74.7	96.6	78.2	86.5	96.0	76.8	85.5
COVERS	DIVS. 10 - 14, 25, 28, 41, 43, 44, 46	100.0	80.9	95.7	100.0	82.0	95.9	100.0	83.8	96.3	100.0	79.1	95.3	100.0	86.1	96.9	100.0	85.4	96.7
21, 22, 23	FIRE SUPPRESSION, PLUMBING & HVAC	99.9	59.3	81.9	97.9	57.4	80.0	99.9	70.2	86.8	96.5	68.7	84.2	100.0	70.5	87.0	100.1	69.6	86.6
26, 27, 3370	ELECTRICAL, COMMUNICATIONS & UTIL.	94.3	63.8	78.1	95.4	68.3	81.0	96.7	63.4	79.1	100.4	69.2	83.9	99.5	72.5	85.2	101.1	67.1	83.1
MF2014	WEIGHTED AVERAGE	98.1	69.7	85.5	95.6	66.2	82.6	96.1	73.8	86.3	96.8	70.0	84.9	98.5	75.9	88.5	97.1	76.1	87.8

For customer support on your Electrical Costs with RSMeans Data, call 800.448.8182.

515

City Cost Indexes

GEORGIA

DIVISION		COLUMBUS 318 - 319			DALTON 307			GAINESVILLE 305			MACON 310 - 312			SAVANNAH 313 - 314			STATESBORO 304		
		MAT.	INST.	TOTAL	MAT.	INST.	TOTAL	MAT.	INST.	TOTAL	MAT.	INST.	TOTAL	MAT.	INST.	TOTAL	MAT.	INST.	TOTAL
015433	CONTRACTOR EQUIPMENT		97.6	97.6		113.0	113.0		96.8	96.8		107.8	107.8		98.5	98.5		100.0	100.0
0241, 31 - 34	SITE & INFRASTRUCTURE, DEMOLITION	100.5	80.5	86.5	101.2	102.6	102.2	101.4	96.9	98.3	102.1	96.1	97.9	100.5	81.9	87.5	102.2	82.8	88.7
0310	Concrete Forming & Accessories	95.3	70.8	74.1	85.2	49.5	54.3	96.0	43.2	50.4	94.9	48.2	54.5	96.5	72.7	75.9	80.0	54.2	57.6
0320	Concrete Reinforcing	90.4	71.8	81.0	93.5	63.3	78.2	93.8	66.1	79.7	91.6	71.8	81.5	97.3	68.3	82.6	93.0	37.0	64.6
0330	Cast-in-Place Concrete	86.5	69.8	80.2	103.6	69.6	90.7	112.2	70.4	96.2	85.3	71.1	79.9	90.2	69.8	82.4	106.5	69.3	92.3
03	CONCRETE	88.5	72.5	81.1	101.7	61.3	83.0	104.3	58.1	82.9	88.1	62.7	76.3	89.9	72.6	81.9	102.0	58.7	81.9
04	MASONRY	93.8	81.1	86.0	81.8	81.0	81.3	89.1	81.1	84.1	106.4	81.2	90.9	88.7	81.4	84.2	83.6	81.0	82.0
05	METALS	99.9	100.5	100.1	97.9	96.3	97.4	96.0	80.8	91.3	95.3	100.3	96.8	96.2	98.2	96.9	101.5	86.3	96.9
06	WOOD, PLASTICS & COMPOSITES	86.1	71.8	78.3	76.7	44.9	59.2	97.0	35.8	63.4	92.9	41.4	64.6	91.8	74.5	82.3	70.6	50.9	59.8
07	THERMAL & MOISTURE PROTECTION	99.7	74.5	89.2	97.8	71.3	86.8	95.7	71.2	85.5	98.1	72.2	87.3	97.3	74.1	87.7	96.4	70.8	85.8
08	OPENINGS	87.9	72.5	84.4	93.3	55.4	84.7	92.4	51.1	83.1	87.6	55.7	80.4	93.4	73.2	88.8	94.3	51.2	84.5
0920	Plaster & Gypsum Board	103.6	71.5	82.2	83.4	43.7	57.0	97.0	34.4	55.4	109.5	40.2	63.5	100.1	74.3	82.9	83.0	50.0	61.1
0950, 0980	Ceilings & Acoustic Treatment	81.3	71.5	74.8	107.3	43.7	65.0	95.0	34.4	54.7	76.4	40.2	52.3	90.6	74.3	79.7	103.6	50.0	67.9
0960	Flooring	103.4	86.8	98.6	99.4	86.2	95.7	99.9	86.8	96.1	81.6	88.9	83.7	98.8	88.9	95.9	117.2	86.8	108.4
0970, 0990	Wall Finishes & Painting/Coating	92.3	95.6	94.2	85.8	74.6	79.3	94.9	95.6	95.3	94.4	74.6	82.8	91.5	80.6	85.1	92.6	74.6	82.1
09	FINISHES	94.7	76.3	84.6	104.9	58.2	79.4	96.8	55.2	74.1	84.1	56.6	69.1	93.4	76.7	84.3	108.4	61.7	82.9
COVERS	DIVS. 10 - 14, 25, 28, 41, 43, 44, 46	100.0	85.0	96.6	100.0	26.8	83.4	100.0	37.6	85.9	100.0	81.8	95.9	100.0	85.0	96.6	100.0	44.0	87.3
21, 22, 23	FIRE SUPPRESSION, PLUMBING & HVAC	100.0	67.6	85.6	96.6	63.7	82.0	96.5	67.4	83.6	100.0	69.9	86.6	100.0	67.6	85.7	97.1	67.1	83.8
26, 27, 3370	ELECTRICAL, COMMUNICATIONS & UTIL.	96.9	72.5	84.0	108.7	67.4	86.8	100.4	72.4	85.6	95.8	63.2	78.5	101.1	74.3	86.9	100.4	57.1	77.4
MF2014	WEIGHTED AVERAGE	96.0	76.5	87.4	98.5	69.5	85.7	97.4	68.3	84.5	94.9	71.8	84.7	96.2	76.8	87.6	98.9	66.9	84.7

GEORGIA / HAWAII / IDAHO

DIVISION		VALDOSTA 316			WAYCROSS 315			HILO 967			HONOLULU 968			STATES & POSS., GUAM 969			BOISE 836 - 837		
		MAT.	INST.	TOTAL	MAT.	INST.	TOTAL	MAT.	INST.	TOTAL	MAT.	INST.	TOTAL	MAT.	INST.	TOTAL	MAT.	INST.	TOTAL
015433	CONTRACTOR EQUIPMENT		97.6	97.6		97.6	97.6		100.7	100.7		100.7	100.7		168.4	168.4		98.8	98.8
0241, 31 - 34	SITE & INFRASTRUCTURE, DEMOLITION	110.0	80.3	89.3	106.8	81.5	89.2	156.2	106.9	121.8	164.8	106.9	124.4	202.8	104.2	134.0	87.6	97.7	94.6
0310	Concrete Forming & Accessories	85.2	43.6	49.2	87.3	67.3	70.0	111.8	121.2	119.9	124.5	121.2	121.6	114.4	55.4	63.4	101.2	81.6	84.2
0320	Concrete Reinforcing	92.5	62.0	77.0	92.5	62.2	77.1	145.1	112.9	128.7	168.8	112.9	140.4	262.3	28.5	143.6	104.8	77.5	90.9
0330	Cast-in-Place Concrete	85.0	69.6	79.1	96.0	69.3	85.8	193.9	121.6	166.4	155.9	121.6	142.9	168.1	102.2	143.0	88.4	85.3	87.2
03	CONCRETE	93.7	58.4	77.3	96.5	68.8	83.7	157.7	118.9	139.7	148.9	118.9	135.0	160.7	68.0	117.7	99.0	82.3	91.3
04	MASONRY	99.3	81.4	88.3	100.2	81.0	88.4	155.9	113.7	129.9	142.4	113.7	124.7	221.4	37.4	108.1	128.3	87.9	103.5
05	METALS	99.4	95.4	98.2	98.5	91.0	96.2	108.7	101.9	106.6	121.3	101.9	115.3	139.9	78.0	121.0	107.4	81.2	99.4
06	WOOD, PLASTICS & COMPOSITES	74.3	35.5	53.0	75.9	68.5	71.8	115.3	122.6	119.3	129.7	122.6	125.8	127.1	58.1	89.2	93.0	80.5	86.1
07	THERMAL & MOISTURE PROTECTION	99.9	69.8	87.4	99.7	72.4	88.4	135.5	116.8	127.7	154.1	116.8	138.6	158.8	62.4	118.8	95.7	84.1	90.9
08	OPENINGS	84.4	49.9	76.6	84.7	65.2	80.3	117.3	118.4	117.5	132.0	118.4	128.9	121.9	46.9	104.9	97.4	74.8	92.3
0920	Plaster & Gypsum Board	95.7	34.2	54.9	95.7	68.1	77.4	108.1	123.0	118.0	152.4	123.0	132.8	216.4	46.0	103.1	92.2	80.0	84.1
0950, 0980	Ceilings & Acoustic Treatment	78.7	34.2	49.1	76.8	68.1	71.0	127.6	123.0	124.5	137.2	123.0	127.7	242.0	46.0	111.6	99.5	80.0	86.5
0960	Flooring	97.1	88.5	94.6	98.3	86.8	95.0	114.8	126.3	118.1	134.4	126.3	132.0	135.3	41.9	108.2	96.6	90.3	94.7
0970, 0990	Wall Finishes & Painting/Coating	92.3	95.6	94.2	92.3	74.6	81.9	99.1	139.8	123.0	107.1	139.8	126.3	104.0	33.6	62.7	96.0	42.1	64.3
09	FINISHES	92.2	55.4	72.1	91.8	72.0	81.0	112.1	124.7	118.9	127.2	124.7	125.8	184.9	51.5	112.0	94.6	79.5	86.3
COVERS	DIVS. 10 - 14, 25, 28, 41, 43, 44, 46	100.0	80.7	95.6	100.0	51.9	89.1	100.0	111.1	102.5	100.0	111.1	102.5	100.0	70.1	93.2	100.0	86.4	96.9
21, 22, 23	FIRE SUPPRESSION, PLUMBING & HVAC	100.0	69.9	86.6	97.7	64.6	83.1	100.5	106.5	103.1	100.5	106.5	103.1	103.7	35.3	73.4	100.0	73.0	88.1
26, 27, 3370	ELECTRICAL, COMMUNICATIONS & UTIL.	95.0	56.0	74.3	99.3	57.1	76.9	105.6	121.2	113.9	107.1	121.2	114.6	152.4	38.9	92.2	97.7	69.5	82.8
MF2014	WEIGHTED AVERAGE	96.2	68.0	83.8	96.3	70.4	84.9	117.7	113.9	116.0	122.0	113.9	118.5	140.4	54.4	102.4	101.1	79.7	91.6

IDAHO / ILLINOIS

DIVISION		COEUR D'ALENE 838			IDAHO FALLS 834			LEWISTON 835			POCATELLO 832			TWIN FALLS 833			BLOOMINGTON 617		
		MAT.	INST.	TOTAL	MAT.	INST.	TOTAL	MAT.	INST.	TOTAL	MAT.	INST.	TOTAL	MAT.	INST.	TOTAL	MAT.	INST.	TOTAL
015433	CONTRACTOR EQUIPMENT		93.4	93.4		98.8	98.8		93.4	93.4		98.8	98.8		98.8	98.8		106.9	106.9
0241, 31 - 34	SITE & INFRASTRUCTURE, DEMOLITION	86.4	91.6	90.0	85.1	97.6	93.8	93.2	92.4	92.7	88.4	97.6	94.8	95.5	97.1	96.6	95.5	101.9	100.0
0310	Concrete Forming & Accessories	112.2	79.1	83.6	95.0	80.0	82.0	117.5	79.8	84.9	101.3	81.3	84.0	102.6	54.3	60.8	85.0	119.6	114.9
0320	Concrete Reinforcing	112.9	92.3	102.5	106.8	77.5	91.9	112.9	92.6	102.6	105.2	77.4	91.1	107.2	77.0	91.9	96.5	103.8	100.2
0330	Cast-in-Place Concrete	95.5	83.4	90.9	84.1	84.1	84.1	99.3	83.9	93.4	90.8	85.2	88.7	93.2	83.9	89.7	95.7	118.5	104.4
03	CONCRETE	105.5	83.1	95.1	90.8	81.1	86.3	109.1	83.6	97.3	98.0	82.1	90.6	106.0	69.4	89.1	95.2	117.1	105.4
04	MASONRY	130.0	81.8	100.3	123.2	85.8	100.2	130.4	85.1	102.5	125.7	87.9	102.5	128.6	85.8	102.2	117.3	124.6	121.8
05	METALS	100.6	86.2	96.2	115.7	81.1	105.1	100.0	86.8	96.0	115.8	80.9	105.1	115.8	80.6	105.1	99.2	125.6	107.2
06	WOOD, PLASTICS & COMPOSITES	98.1	77.7	86.9	87.2	79.6	83.0	103.4	77.7	89.3	93.0	80.5	86.2	94.0	45.3	67.2	86.8	117.6	103.7
07	THERMAL & MOISTURE PROTECTION	149.9	83.6	122.4	94.9	76.6	87.3	150.3	86.7	123.9	95.5	76.7	87.7	96.3	78.9	89.1	98.6	116.5	106.0
08	OPENINGS	114.7	75.2	105.8	100.4	74.3	94.5	108.4	76.4	101.1	98.1	68.3	91.4	101.2	45.8	88.7	94.7	122.2	100.9
0920	Plaster & Gypsum Board	166.2	77.2	107.1	77.4	79.0	78.5	167.9	77.2	107.6	79.2	80.0	79.7	80.9	43.7	56.2	92.8	118.1	109.6
0950, 0980	Ceilings & Acoustic Treatment	130.7	77.2	95.1	99.4	79.0	85.9	130.7	77.2	95.1	106.2	80.0	88.7	101.9	43.7	63.2	86.5	118.1	107.5
0960	Flooring	136.8	79.1	120.1	96.2	90.3	94.5	140.3	89.8	125.6	99.9	90.3	97.1	101.2	90.3	98.0	88.6	122.7	98.5
0970, 0990	Wall Finishes & Painting/Coating	115.1	73.1	90.4	96.0	42.1	64.3	115.1	73.1	90.4	95.9	42.1	64.3	96.0	42.1	64.3	87.5	141.7	119.3
09	FINISHES	159.1	78.2	114.9	91.8	78.4	84.5	160.5	80.6	116.8	95.1	79.5	86.6	95.5	58.3	75.2	88.9	122.8	107.4
COVERS	DIVS. 10 - 14, 25, 28, 41, 43, 44, 46	100.0	97.5	99.4	100.0	87.8	97.2	100.0	97.7	99.5	100.0	86.4	96.9	100.0	84.0	96.4	100.0	107.9	101.8
21, 22, 23	FIRE SUPPRESSION, PLUMBING & HVAC	99.6	81.2	91.4	101.0	70.7	87.6	101.0	84.3	93.6	99.9	73.0	88.0	99.9	69.6	86.5	96.4	106.7	101.0
26, 27, 3370	ELECTRICAL, COMMUNICATIONS & UTIL.	90.6	88.4	89.4	90.3	68.7	78.8	88.6	79.8	83.9	95.3	68.7	81.2	91.7	58.2	73.9	95.1	96.7	95.9
MF2014	WEIGHTED AVERAGE	109.0	83.7	97.8	100.7	78.3	90.8	109.1	84.1	98.1	102.1	79.0	91.9	103.5	70.8	89.1	97.1	113.1	104.2

ILLINOIS

DIVISION		CARBONDALE 629			CENTRALIA 628			CHAMPAIGN 618 - 619			CHICAGO 606 - 608			DECATUR 625			EAST ST. LOUIS 620 - 622		
		MAT.	INST.	TOTAL	MAT.	INST.	TOTAL	MAT.	INST.	TOTAL	MAT.	INST.	TOTAL	MAT.	INST.	TOTAL	MAT.	INST.	TOTAL
015433	CONTRACTOR EQUIPMENT		115.9	115.9		115.9	115.9		107.8	107.8		100.7	100.7		107.8	107.8		115.9	115.9
0241, 31 - 34	SITE & INFRASTRUCTURE, DEMOLITION	96.1	103.0	100.9	96.4	103.7	101.5	104.6	103.0	103.5	98.6	106.3	104.0	92.9	103.0	99.9	98.4	103.8	102.2
0310	Concrete Forming & Accessories	93.3	109.2	107.0	95.0	113.9	111.3	91.6	115.8	112.6	97.8	158.8	150.6	95.5	119.5	116.3	90.7	115.1	111.8
0320	Concrete Reinforcing	95.9	103.7	99.8	95.9	103.9	99.9	96.5	98.6	97.6	100.4	147.7	124.4	94.0	99.3	96.7	95.8	104.1	100.0
0330	Cast-in-Place Concrete	85.4	105.5	93.1	85.9	119.2	98.6	110.9	113.0	111.7	109.7	155.9	127.3	93.3	116.7	102.2	87.3	120.1	99.8
03	CONCRETE	82.7	108.5	94.7	83.2	115.5	98.2	107.8	112.6	110.0	103.3	155.1	127.3	93.3	116.5	103.7	84.2	116.4	99.1
04	MASONRY	79.1	113.6	100.3	79.2	116.2	101.9	142.3	121.3	129.3	103.2	165.8	141.8	74.7	116.6	100.7	79.4	121.1	105.1
05	METALS	98.8	132.5	109.1	98.9	134.8	109.9	99.2	121.4	106.0	95.6	144.3	110.5	102.5	121.0	108.2	99.9	135.3	110.8
06	WOOD, PLASTICS & COMPOSITES	91.2	106.0	99.3	93.6	111.7	103.6	93.2	114.0	104.6	100.0	157.4	131.6	91.5	119.1	106.7	88.7	112.4	101.7
07	THERMAL & MOISTURE PROTECTION	96.0	103.9	99.3	96.0	110.7	102.1	99.3	115.4	106.0	102.4	150.2	122.2	101.8	112.2	106.1	96.0	110.2	101.9
08	OPENINGS	89.5	118.3	96.0	89.5	121.4	96.7	95.3	116.7	100.2	104.2	167.5	118.5	100.7	119.8	105.0	89.6	121.8	96.9
0920	Plaster & Gypsum Board	97.3	106.2	103.2	98.3	112.1	107.5	94.7	114.4	107.8	98.0	159.0	138.5	99.7	119.7	113.0	96.3	112.7	107.2
0950, 0980	Ceilings & Acoustic Treatment	84.9	106.2	99.0	84.9	112.1	103.0	86.5	114.4	105.1	97.0	159.0	138.3	90.8	119.7	110.0	84.9	112.7	103.4
0960	Flooring	114.3	116.7	115.0	115.2	112.4	114.4	92.0	111.1	97.5	91.3	158.7	110.9	102.5	111.7	105.2	113.2	112.4	113.0
0970, 0990	Wall Finishes & Painting/Coating	97.8	106.8	103.1	97.8	93.0	95.0	87.5	101.7	95.9	89.8	162.6	132.5	89.6	113.7	103.8	97.8	111.4	105.8
09	FINISHES	94.1	109.1	102.3	94.6	111.0	103.6	90.9	113.7	103.4	93.6	159.9	129.9	94.0	118.1	107.2	93.8	114.3	105.0
COVERS	DIVS. 10 - 14, 25, 28, 41, 43, 44, 46	100.0	106.6	101.5	100.0	107.4	101.7	100.0	106.7	101.5	100.0	127.3	106.2	100.0	107.3	101.6	100.0	107.9	101.8
21, 22, 23	FIRE SUPPRESSION, PLUMBING & HVAC	96.4	106.9	101.1	96.4	95.1	95.8	96.4	106.1	100.7	100.0	139.7	117.5	100.0	98.4	99.3	100.0	98.7	99.4
26, 27, 3370	ELECTRICAL, COMMUNICATIONS & UTIL.	97.4	110.2	104.2	98.9	108.7	104.1	98.3	96.8	97.5	96.6	139.1	119.1	101.6	92.8	97.0	98.5	103.1	100.9
MF2014	WEIGHTED AVERAGE	93.7	111.0	101.3	93.9	110.4	101.2	100.8	110.2	104.9	99.5	146.0	120.0	97.9	108.6	102.6	94.9	111.5	102.3

ILLINOIS

DIVISION		EFFINGHAM 624			GALESBURG 614			JOLIET 604			KANKAKEE 609			LA SALLE 613			NORTH SUBURBAN 600 - 603		
		MAT.	INST.	TOTAL	MAT.	INST.	TOTAL	MAT.	INST.	TOTAL	MAT.	INST.	TOTAL	MAT.	INST.	TOTAL	MAT.	INST.	TOTAL
015433	CONTRACTOR EQUIPMENT		107.8	107.8		106.9	106.9		98.1	98.1		98.1	98.1		106.9	106.9		98.1	98.1
0241, 31 - 34	SITE & INFRASTRUCTURE, DEMOLITION	96.6	102.0	100.4	98.0	101.5	100.5	98.7	104.2	102.5	92.6	103.5	100.2	97.4	102.5	100.9	97.9	104.2	102.3
0310	Concrete Forming & Accessories	100.2	114.5	112.6	91.5	117.1	113.7	99.6	162.4	154.0	93.1	145.7	138.6	105.7	125.9	123.2	99.0	158.1	150.1
0320	Concrete Reinforcing	97.0	92.9	95.0	96.0	103.7	99.9	100.4	139.8	120.4	101.2	136.3	119.0	96.1	135.2	115.9	100.4	147.6	124.4
0330	Cast-in-Place Concrete	93.0	109.6	99.3	98.5	108.6	102.4	109.6	154.3	126.6	102.2	141.6	117.2	98.4	128.4	109.8	109.7	152.8	126.1
03	CONCRETE	94.1	109.6	101.3	98.2	112.6	104.9	103.4	154.6	127.2	97.2	142.1	118.0	99.0	129.2	113.0	103.4	153.6	126.7
04	MASONRY	83.0	117.0	103.9	117.5	124.6	121.9	106.4	166.2	143.2	102.7	152.7	133.5	117.5	150.6	137.9	103.2	164.5	140.9
05	METALS	99.7	115.5	104.6	99.2	124.7	107.0	93.8	138.5	107.5	93.8	135.9	106.6	99.2	145.2	113.3	94.8	142.2	109.3
06	WOOD, PLASTICS & COMPOSITES	93.8	114.0	104.9	93.1	115.5	105.4	101.6	162.3	135.0	94.8	144.3	122.0	107.7	123.3	116.3	100.0	157.4	131.6
07	THERMAL & MOISTURE PROTECTION	101.3	111.3	105.4	98.8	112.0	104.3	102.3	150.0	122.1	101.4	141.7	118.1	98.9	127.1	110.6	102.6	147.9	121.4
08	OPENINGS	95.4	114.9	99.8	94.7	116.1	99.5	101.7	167.6	116.7	94.8	156.6	108.8	94.7	135.0	103.8	101.8	167.4	116.7
0920	Plaster & Gypsum Board	99.6	114.4	109.4	94.7	116.0	108.9	95.0	164.0	140.9	92.7	145.5	127.8	101.7	124.0	116.5	98.0	159.0	138.5
0950, 0980	Ceilings & Acoustic Treatment	84.9	114.4	104.5	86.5	116.0	106.1	97.0	164.0	141.6	97.0	145.5	129.3	86.5	124.0	111.5	97.0	159.0	138.3
0960	Flooring	103.6	111.1	105.8	91.8	122.7	100.7	91.0	158.7	110.6	87.7	159.7	108.6	98.7	126.0	106.6	91.3	158.7	110.9
0970, 0990	Wall Finishes & Painting/Coating	89.6	111.4	102.4	87.5	101.7	95.9	88.1	181.6	143.0	88.1	141.7	119.6	87.5	141.7	119.3	89.8	162.6	132.5
09	FINISHES	93.1	114.4	104.8	90.3	117.2	105.0	93.1	165.0	132.4	91.4	148.3	122.5	93.3	126.4	111.4	93.6	159.6	129.7
COVERS	DIVS. 10 - 14, 25, 28, 41, 43, 44, 46	100.0	79.7	95.4	100.0	104.8	101.1	100.0	127.9	106.3	100.0	120.5	104.6	100.0	106.3	101.4	100.0	124.3	105.5
21, 22, 23	FIRE SUPPRESSION, PLUMBING & HVAC	96.4	105.3	100.4	96.4	104.1	99.8	100.0	135.5	115.7	96.4	131.1	111.8	96.4	125.2	109.1	99.9	134.6	115.3
26, 27, 3370	ELECTRICAL, COMMUNICATIONS & UTIL.	99.3	110.2	105.1	96.0	88.7	92.1	96.0	130.5	114.3	90.9	129.8	111.5	93.1	129.8	112.6	95.7	135.5	116.8
MF2014	WEIGHTED AVERAGE	96.4	109.5	102.2	97.8	109.4	102.9	99.0	143.9	118.8	95.6	136.3	113.6	99.0	129.1	111.7	99.0	143.5	118.7

ILLINOIS

DIVISION		PEORIA 615 - 616			QUINCY 623			ROCK ISLAND 612			ROCKFORD 610 - 611			SOUTH SUBURBAN 605			SPRINGFIELD 626 - 627		
		MAT.	INST.	TOTAL	MAT.	INST.	TOTAL	MAT.	INST.	TOTAL	MAT.	INST.	TOTAL	MAT.	INST.	TOTAL	MAT.	INST.	TOTAL
015433	CONTRACTOR EQUIPMENT		106.9	106.9		107.8	107.8		106.9	106.9		106.9	106.9		98.1	98.1		107.8	107.8
0241, 31 - 34	SITE & INFRASTRUCTURE, DEMOLITION	98.3	102.0	100.8	95.5	102.5	100.4	96.1	101.0	99.5	97.8	103.0	101.5	97.9	103.9	102.1	96.6	103.0	101.1
0310	Concrete Forming & Accessories	94.4	123.1	119.2	98.0	116.4	113.9	93.0	103.1	101.7	98.8	132.8	128.2	99.0	158.1	150.1	95.9	119.8	116.5
0320	Concrete Reinforcing	93.5	103.8	98.7	96.7	85.2	90.8	96.0	97.0	96.5	88.5	129.9	109.5	100.4	147.6	124.4	97.1	99.8	98.5
0330	Cast-in-Place Concrete	95.5	118.0	104.1	93.1	103.3	97.0	96.4	102.1	98.6	97.8	133.0	111.2	109.7	152.7	126.1	88.5	111.0	97.1
03	CONCRETE	95.4	118.6	106.1	93.8	107.0	99.9	96.1	102.8	99.2	96.1	132.9	113.1	103.4	153.5	126.6	91.5	113.8	101.8
04	MASONRY	116.7	125.4	122.1	106.8	111.8	109.9	117.3	102.3	108.1	90.6	143.6	123.2	103.2	164.5	140.9	85.8	124.3	109.5
05	METALS	101.8	125.6	109.1	99.8	113.7	104.0	99.2	120.0	105.6	101.8	141.5	114.0	94.8	142.2	109.3	100.2	121.7	106.8
06	WOOD, PLASTICS & COMPOSITES	100.6	122.1	112.4	91.4	119.1	106.6	94.6	102.3	98.9	100.5	129.8	116.6	100.0	157.4	131.6	90.8	119.1	106.4
07	THERMAL & MOISTURE PROTECTION	99.5	115.4	106.1	101.3	107.1	103.7	98.7	101.4	99.8	101.9	134.2	115.3	102.6	147.9	121.4	103.8	116.6	109.1
08	OPENINGS	100.7	125.8	106.4	96.2	115.2	100.5	94.7	106.9	97.5	100.7	140.4	109.7	101.8	167.4	116.7	100.3	119.8	104.7
0920	Plaster & Gypsum Board	98.5	122.7	114.6	98.3	119.7	112.5	94.7	102.4	99.9	98.5	130.7	119.9	98.0	159.0	138.5	99.3	119.7	112.8
0950, 0980	Ceilings & Acoustic Treatment	91.6	122.7	112.3	84.9	119.7	108.0	86.5	102.4	97.1	91.6	130.7	117.6	97.0	159.0	138.3	94.6	119.7	111.3
0960	Flooring	95.5	122.7	103.4	102.5	114.7	106.0	93.0	94.6	93.5	95.5	126.0	104.4	91.3	158.7	110.9	105.9	111.7	107.6
0970, 0990	Wall Finishes & Painting/Coating	87.5	141.7	119.3	89.6	113.7	103.8	87.5	101.7	95.9	87.5	149.6	124.0	89.8	162.6	132.5	87.8	113.7	103.0
09	FINISHES	93.0	125.6	110.8	92.6	117.1	106.0	90.6	101.1	96.3	93.0	133.2	115.0	93.6	159.6	129.7	96.6	118.2	108.4
COVERS	DIVS. 10 - 14, 25, 28, 41, 43, 44, 46	100.0	108.7	102.0	100.0	81.5	95.8	100.0	101.0	100.2	100.0	116.5	103.7	100.0	124.3	105.5	100.0	107.3	101.7
21, 22, 23	FIRE SUPPRESSION, PLUMBING & HVAC	100.0	103.1	101.3	96.5	100.3	98.2	96.4	98.9	97.5	100.0	117.3	107.7	99.9	134.6	115.3	100.0	104.0	101.7
26, 27, 3370	ELECTRICAL, COMMUNICATIONS & UTIL.	97.1	99.1	98.2	96.6	82.6	89.2	88.2	96.3	92.5	97.3	132.5	116.0	95.7	135.5	116.8	104.2	91.7	97.6
MF2014	WEIGHTED AVERAGE	99.7	113.4	105.8	97.3	103.9	100.2	96.8	102.4	99.2	98.6	128.9	112.0	99.0	143.5	118.6	98.4	110.4	103.7

For customer support on your Electrical Costs with RSMeans Data, call 800.448.8182.

517

INDIANA

DIVISION		ANDERSON 460 MAT.	INST.	TOTAL	BLOOMINGTON 474 MAT.	INST.	TOTAL	COLUMBUS 472 MAT.	INST.	TOTAL	EVANSVILLE 476-477 MAT.	INST.	TOTAL	FORT WAYNE 467-468 MAT.	INST.	TOTAL	GARY 463-464 MAT.	INST.	TOTAL
015433	CONTRACTOR EQUIPMENT		98.3	98.3		84.6	84.6		84.6	84.6		115.7	115.7		98.3	98.3		98.3	98.3
0241, 31 - 34	SITE & INFRASTRUCTURE, DEMOLITION	98.6	94.6	95.8	87.3	93.3	91.5	83.9	93.1	90.3	92.9	123.7	114.4	99.6	94.3	95.9	99.2	98.2	98.5
0310	Concrete Forming & Accessories	96.1	81.4	83.3	100.6	81.4	84.0	94.6	79.4	81.5	94.0	85.3	86.4	94.2	75.5	78.0	96.1	117.9	114.9
0320	Concrete Reinforcing	96.3	85.8	91.0	91.8	85.4	88.6	92.2	85.4	88.8	100.5	79.3	89.7	96.3	77.8	86.9	96.3	114.2	105.4
0330	Cast-in-Place Concrete	102.1	79.4	93.4	99.0	78.7	91.2	98.5	76.5	90.2	94.6	88.2	92.1	108.5	57.5	93.4	106.7	118.2	111.1
03	CONCRETE	94.4	82.0	88.7	101.1	80.8	91.7	100.4	79.1	90.5	101.3	85.3	93.9	97.4	76.7	87.8	96.7	116.9	106.1
04	MASONRY	91.3	78.3	83.3	93.0	74.2	81.4	92.9	74.1	81.3	88.4	82.6	84.8	94.6	75.4	82.7	92.7	115.4	106.7
05	METALS	96.6	90.6	94.7	100.0	75.4	92.5	100.0	74.7	92.3	92.8	84.2	90.2	96.6	87.4	93.8	96.6	107.4	99.9
06	WOOD, PLASTICS & COMPOSITES	96.5	81.7	88.4	111.0	81.8	94.9	106.1	79.1	91.3	91.7	85.0	88.0	96.3	75.5	84.9	93.9	116.6	106.4
07	THERMAL & MOISTURE PROTECTION	110.6	77.8	97.0	97.0	79.7	89.8	96.4	82.5	90.6	101.3	86.5	95.2	110.4	74.8	95.6	109.1	110.4	109.6
08	OPENINGS	95.2	79.8	91.7	100.9	79.8	96.1	97.0	78.4	92.8	94.8	80.2	91.5	95.2	72.4	90.0	95.2	118.4	100.4
0920	Plaster & Gypsum Board	105.9	81.4	89.6	98.7	82.0	87.6	96.1	79.3	84.9	94.4	84.1	87.6	105.3	75.0	85.2	99.0	117.3	111.2
0950, 0980	Ceilings & Acoustic Treatment	87.2	81.4	83.4	77.3	82.0	80.4	77.3	79.3	78.6	81.1	84.1	83.1	87.2	75.0	79.1	87.2	117.3	107.3
0960	Flooring	98.0	79.5	92.6	102.4	81.5	96.4	97.1	79.5	92.0	96.7	74.5	90.3	98.0	75.7	91.5	98.0	114.1	102.7
0970, 0990	Wall Finishes & Painting/Coating	94.0	70.1	80.0	87.1	80.9	83.5	87.1	81.1	83.6	92.5	88.8	90.3	94.0	71.3	80.7	94.0	121.6	110.2
09	FINISHES	92.7	80.1	85.8	91.7	81.4	86.1	89.7	79.5	84.1	90.3	83.7	86.7	92.4	75.1	82.9	91.6	117.8	105.9
COVERS	DIVS. 10 - 14, 25, 28, 41, 43, 44, 46	100.0	90.8	97.9	100.0	89.7	97.7	100.0	89.4	97.6	100.0	95.8	99.0	100.0	88.3	97.4	100.0	105.6	101.3
21, 22, 23	FIRE SUPPRESSION, PLUMBING & HVAC	100.0	78.1	90.3	99.7	78.3	90.2	96.1	78.1	88.1	100.0	80.2	91.2	100.0	73.7	88.3	100.0	106.9	103.1
26, 27, 3370	ELECTRICAL, COMMUNICATIONS & UTIL.	87.1	88.8	88.0	99.8	89.7	94.5	99.0	88.7	93.6	96.0	88.3	91.9	87.7	78.5	82.8	98.6	115.9	107.8
MF2014	WEIGHTED AVERAGE	96.2	83.3	90.5	98.8	81.6	91.2	97.1	80.8	89.9	96.4	87.1	92.3	96.7	78.4	88.7	97.5	111.8	103.8

INDIANA

DIVISION		INDIANAPOLIS 461-462 MAT.	INST.	TOTAL	KOKOMO 469 MAT.	INST.	TOTAL	LAFAYETTE 479 MAT.	INST.	TOTAL	LAWRENCEBURG 470 MAT.	INST.	TOTAL	MUNCIE 473 MAT.	INST.	TOTAL	NEW ALBANY 471 MAT.	INST.	TOTAL
015433	CONTRACTOR EQUIPMENT		85.6	85.6		98.3	98.3		84.6	84.6		105.2	105.2		96.8	96.8		94.5	94.5
0241, 31 - 34	SITE & INFRASTRUCTURE, DEMOLITION	99.1	93.4	95.1	95.0	94.5	94.7	84.8	93.1	90.6	82.8	109.1	101.2	87.2	93.7	91.7	79.8	95.6	90.8
0310	Concrete Forming & Accessories	97.2	84.5	86.2	99.4	78.3	81.1	92.2	77.7	79.2	91.1	78.2	79.9	92.1	80.8	82.3	89.4	76.6	78.3
0320	Concrete Reinforcing	95.9	85.8	90.7	87.1	85.7	86.4	91.8	85.7	88.7	91.0	77.9	84.4	101.5	85.7	93.5	92.4	80.3	86.3
0330	Cast-in-Place Concrete	96.9	85.2	92.4	101.1	83.5	94.4	99.1	82.5	92.8	92.6	75.8	86.2	104.0	78.5	94.3	95.7	75.5	88.0
03	CONCRETE	96.1	84.3	90.6	91.4	82.0	87.1	100.6	80.2	91.2	93.6	78.0	86.4	99.5	81.5	91.1	99.1	77.2	88.9
04	MASONRY	94.1	79.2	84.9	91.0	77.1	82.4	98.5	78.4	86.1	77.2	74.0	75.2	94.9	78.4	84.7	84.0	68.8	74.7
05	METALS	95.0	73.8	88.5	93.6	90.4	92.3	98.5	75.4	91.4	94.9	86.2	92.2	101.8	90.5	98.3	97.0	82.0	92.4
06	WOOD, PLASTICS & COMPOSITES	95.3	85.0	89.7	99.6	77.2	87.3	103.4	76.0	88.3	90.1	78.0	83.5	105.2	81.2	92.0	91.9	77.2	83.9
07	THERMAL & MOISTURE PROTECTION	102.8	82.0	94.1	109.6	78.6	96.7	96.4	81.0	90.0	102.1	78.6	92.4	99.5	79.1	91.1	88.3	73.1	82.0
08	OPENINGS	100.1	81.6	95.9	90.6	77.3	87.6	95.5	76.7	91.2	96.7	75.1	91.8	94.3	79.5	90.9	94.3	76.7	90.3
0920	Plaster & Gypsum Board	97.5	84.7	89.0	110.5	76.8	88.1	93.7	76.1	82.0	73.3	78.0	76.4	94.4	81.4	85.8	92.1	77.0	82.1
0950, 0980	Ceilings & Acoustic Treatment	92.6	84.7	87.4	87.2	76.8	80.3	73.9	76.1	75.3	84.4	78.0	80.2	77.3	81.4	80.0	81.1	77.0	78.4
0960	Flooring	98.8	79.5	93.2	102.4	87.6	98.0	96.1	79.5	91.3	71.3	79.5	73.6	96.1	79.5	91.3	94.2	57.2	83.5
0970, 0990	Wall Finishes & Painting/Coating	92.9	82.7	86.9	94.0	72.3	81.3	87.1	82.8	84.6	88.0	73.6	79.5	87.1	70.1	77.2	92.5	67.1	77.6
09	FINISHES	93.9	83.5	88.2	94.4	79.2	86.1	88.4	77.9	82.6	80.2	78.0	79.0	88.9	79.5	83.7	89.5	71.8	79.8
COVERS	DIVS. 10 - 14, 25, 28, 41, 43, 44, 46	100.0	91.9	98.2	100.0	90.2	97.8	100.0	89.3	97.6	100.0	87.8	97.3	100.0	89.7	97.7	100.0	86.9	97.0
21, 22, 23	FIRE SUPPRESSION, PLUMBING & HVAC	99.9	80.1	91.1	96.4	79.6	89.0	96.1	78.6	88.4	97.2	73.1	86.5	99.7	77.9	90.1	96.4	77.3	88.0
26, 27, 3370	ELECTRICAL, COMMUNICATIONS & UTIL.	102.9	89.7	95.9	91.6	81.2	86.1	98.5	82.2	89.9	93.9	74.7	83.8	91.8	79.1	85.0	94.5	77.4	85.4
MF2014	WEIGHTED AVERAGE	98.2	83.3	91.6	94.4	82.2	89.0	96.8	80.3	89.0	93.5	79.5	87.3	97.2	81.7	90.4	94.8	77.8	87.3

INDIANA / IOWA

DIVISION		SOUTH BEND 465-466 MAT.	INST.	TOTAL	TERRE HAUTE 478 MAT.	INST.	TOTAL	WASHINGTON 475 MAT.	INST.	TOTAL	BURLINGTON 526 MAT.	INST.	TOTAL	CARROLL 514 MAT.	INST.	TOTAL	CEDAR RAPIDS 522-524 MAT.	INST.	TOTAL
015433	CONTRACTOR EQUIPMENT		110.3	110.3		115.7	115.7		115.7	115.7		102.9	102.9		102.9	102.9		99.6	99.6
0241, 31 - 34	SITE & INFRASTRUCTURE, DEMOLITION	97.4	95.2	95.9	94.7	123.9	115.1	94.6	124.1	115.2	99.3	98.0	98.4	88.1	98.6	95.4	100.5	97.1	98.1
0310	Concrete Forming & Accessories	98.4	81.6	83.8	94.9	82.6	84.3	95.7	83.0	84.7	95.2	84.7	86.1	82.9	82.7	82.7	101.2	86.9	88.8
0320	Concrete Reinforcing	97.1	84.9	90.9	100.5	85.9	93.1	92.9	85.8	89.3	94.6	85.2	89.8	95.3	77.2	86.1	95.3	81.0	88.0
0330	Cast-in-Place Concrete	96.8	82.2	91.2	91.6	83.3	88.4	99.6	88.4	95.4	107.0	58.2	88.4	107.0	59.7	89.0	107.2	84.6	98.6
03	CONCRETE	91.0	84.0	87.7	104.4	83.6	94.7	110.2	85.5	98.8	97.4	76.4	87.7	97.5	74.6	86.2	97.5	85.8	92.1
04	MASONRY	95.1	77.9	84.5	96.3	78.3	85.2	88.5	80.1	83.3	101.4	77.5	86.7	103.1	76.6	86.8	107.2	82.8	92.2
05	METALS	98.9	106.1	101.1	93.6	86.9	91.5	88.1	86.9	87.7	88.7	95.5	90.7	88.7	92.5	89.9	91.0	95.0	92.2
06	WOOD, PLASTICS & COMPOSITES	94.5	81.2	87.2	93.7	82.9	87.8	94.1	81.7	87.3	89.1	83.9	86.3	76.5	87.1	82.3	95.3	87.8	91.2
07	THERMAL & MOISTURE PROTECTION	103.4	82.8	94.9	101.4	81.8	93.3	101.3	85.2	94.6	105.1	81.4	95.3	105.5	74.2	92.5	106.2	85.0	97.4
08	OPENINGS	94.9	79.0	91.3	95.2	80.5	91.9	92.0	80.3	89.4	93.8	86.3	92.1	98.2	82.6	94.7	98.7	83.0	95.1
0920	Plaster & Gypsum Board	93.6	80.9	85.2	94.4	82.0	86.2	94.8	80.8	85.5	109.4	83.6	92.2	104.8	86.8	92.8	113.6	87.8	96.5
0950, 0980	Ceilings & Acoustic Treatment	90.6	80.9	84.1	81.1	82.0	81.7	76.8	80.8	79.4	94.4	83.6	87.2	94.4	86.8	89.3	96.9	87.8	90.8
0960	Flooring	97.7	87.6	94.7	96.7	80.2	91.9	97.6	69.6	89.5	98.7	73.2	91.3	92.6	84.3	90.2	113.0	89.2	106.1
0970, 0990	Wall Finishes & Painting/Coating	96.1	85.9	87.6	92.5	80.2	85.3	96.8	88.8	90.3	98.0	90.8	93.8	98.0	77.6	86.0	99.3	72.4	83.5
09	FINISHES	92.1	83.1	87.2	90.3	81.7	85.6	90.0	80.8	85.0	96.0	83.5	89.2	92.0	83.5	87.4	101.3	86.1	93.0
COVERS	DIVS. 10 - 14, 25, 28, 41, 43, 44, 46	100.0	92.6	98.3	100.0	92.6	98.3	100.0	95.4	99.0	100.0	91.1	98.0	100.0	66.8	92.5	100.0	92.8	98.4
21, 22, 23	FIRE SUPPRESSION, PLUMBING & HVAC	99.9	74.9	88.9	100.0	79.0	90.7	96.4	81.2	89.7	96.7	80.1	89.3	96.7	74.5	86.9	100.2	80.1	91.3
26, 27, 3370	ELECTRICAL, COMMUNICATIONS & UTIL.	97.0	86.5	91.4	94.2	90.1	92.0	94.7	88.3	91.3	101.1	76.1	87.8	101.9	81.4	91.0	98.6	81.7	89.6
MF2014	WEIGHTED AVERAGE	96.9	84.6	91.5	97.2	86.2	92.4	95.5	87.0	91.7	96.2	82.7	90.3	96.0	80.6	89.2	98.6	85.6	92.8

IOWA

DIVISION		COUNCIL BLUFFS 515 MAT.	INST.	TOTAL	CRESTON 508 MAT.	INST.	TOTAL	DAVENPORT 527-528 MAT.	INST.	TOTAL	DECORAH 521 MAT.	INST.	TOTAL	DES MOINES 500-503,509 MAT.	INST.	TOTAL	DUBUQUE 520 MAT.	INST.	TOTAL
015433	CONTRACTOR EQUIPMENT		98.9	98.9		102.9	102.9		102.9	102.9		102.9	102.9		104.9	104.9		98.4	98.4
0241, 31 - 34	SITE & INFRASTRUCTURE, DEMOLITION	103.5	92.9	96.1	94.5	99.7	98.1	99.5	99.6	99.6	97.9	97.6	97.7	100.4	101.3	101.0	98.3	94.3	95.5
0310	Concrete Forming & Accessories	82.3	77.1	77.8	79.7	86.0	85.1	100.7	96.2	96.8	92.8	76.8	79.0	98.0	87.6	89.0	83.7	79.6	80.1
0320	Concrete Reinforcing	97.2	77.6	87.3	95.1	76.7	85.8	95.3	98.4	96.9	94.6	71.7	83.0	99.8	81.7	90.6	94.0	80.4	87.1
0330	Cast-in-Place Concrete	111.5	80.7	99.8	112.3	64.3	94.0	103.3	92.0	99.0	104.1	81.0	95.3	95.5	86.1	91.9	105.0	99.1	102.8
03	CONCRETE	99.9	79.4	90.4	98.9	77.6	89.0	95.6	95.6	95.6	95.4	78.3	87.5	92.1	86.8	89.6	94.4	87.4	91.2
04	MASONRY	108.4	75.7	88.2	104.1	74.9	86.1	103.9	87.2	93.7	123.4	72.0	91.8	91.0	88.3	89.4	108.2	72.2	86.0
05	METALS	96.2	92.5	95.1	92.6	92.1	92.5	91.0	102.8	94.6	88.8	89.8	89.1	98.6	97.0	98.1	89.6	94.1	91.0
06	WOOD, PLASTICS & COMPOSITES	75.5	78.0	76.8	72.3	87.1	80.4	95.4	97.1	96.3	86.3	76.6	81.0	90.1	87.1	88.4	77.0	78.8	78.0
07	THERMAL & MOISTURE PROTECTION	105.5	72.4	91.8	105.7	81.8	95.8	105.6	92.3	100.1	105.3	74.4	92.5	97.4	86.6	92.9	105.8	81.4	95.7
08	OPENINGS	97.7	78.9	93.5	105.2	84.4	100.5	98.7	96.9	98.3	96.8	79.1	92.8	96.1	87.4	94.1	97.8	81.8	94.1
0920	Plaster & Gypsum Board	104.8	77.7	86.8	102.5	86.8	92.1	113.6	97.1	102.6	108.1	76.1	86.8	95.2	86.8	89.6	104.8	78.5	87.3
0950, 0980	Ceilings & Acoustic Treatment	94.4	77.7	83.3	87.2	86.8	87.0	96.9	97.1	97.0	94.4	76.1	82.2	91.5	86.8	88.4	94.4	78.5	83.8
0960	Flooring	91.0	85.1	89.3	83.1	73.2	80.3	101.3	94.3	99.3	98.1	73.2	90.9	92.6	94.3	93.1	103.5	73.2	94.8
0970, 0990	Wall Finishes & Painting/Coating	93.9	64.9	76.9	87.4	79.1	82.5	98.0	96.0	96.8	98.0	86.6	91.3	88.8	86.6	87.5	98.5	88.4	92.6
09	FINISHES	92.7	77.4	84.4	85.6	83.4	84.4	97.8	96.2	97.0	95.6	77.4	85.6	90.3	89.0	89.6	96.6	78.9	86.9
COVERS	DIVS. 10 - 14, 25, 28, 41, 43, 44, 46	100.0	90.3	97.8	100.0	69.5	93.1	100.0	95.7	99.0	100.0	83.5	96.3	100.0	94.1	98.7	100.0	91.3	98.0
21, 22, 23	FIRE SUPPRESSION, PLUMBING & HVAC	100.2	74.4	88.8	96.4	82.4	90.2	100.2	92.4	96.8	96.7	73.9	86.6	99.8	83.4	92.6	100.2	75.0	89.0
26, 27, 3370	ELECTRICAL, COMMUNICATIONS & UTIL.	104.1	81.9	92.4	92.6	81.4	86.6	96.7	92.7	94.6	98.6	51.2	73.5	103.9	83.4	93.0	102.6	77.7	89.4
MF2014	WEIGHTED AVERAGE	99.4	80.4	91.0	96.5	82.9	90.5	97.6	94.7	96.3	97.1	75.5	87.6	97.3	88.4	93.3	97.7	81.5	90.5

IOWA

DIVISION		FORT DODGE 505 MAT.	INST.	TOTAL	MASON CITY 504 MAT.	INST.	TOTAL	OTTUMWA 525 MAT.	INST.	TOTAL	SHENANDOAH 516 MAT.	INST.	TOTAL	SIBLEY 512 MAT.	INST.	TOTAL	SIOUX CITY 510-511 MAT.	INST.	TOTAL
015433	CONTRACTOR EQUIPMENT		102.9	102.9		102.9	102.9		98.4	98.4		98.9	98.9		102.9	102.9		102.9	102.9
0241, 31 - 34	SITE & INFRASTRUCTURE, DEMOLITION	103.2	96.4	98.4	103.3	97.5	99.3	98.8	92.1	94.1	102.1	94.2	96.6	109.5	97.7	101.2	111.1	98.6	102.4
0310	Concrete Forming & Accessories	80.3	77.2	77.6	84.4	76.5	77.6	90.7	76.9	78.8	84.0	59.5	62.8	84.4	39.9	45.9	101.2	74.4	78.0
0320	Concrete Reinforcing	95.1	67.6	81.2	95.0	76.6	85.7	94.6	85.2	89.8	97.2	68.0	82.4	97.2	62.5	79.6	95.3	91.2	93.2
0330	Cast-in-Place Concrete	105.4	44.1	82.0	105.4	75.9	94.1	107.7	67.7	92.5	107.8	80.6	97.4	105.6	58.8	87.8	106.3	55.5	87.0
03	CONCRETE	94.3	65.0	80.7	94.5	77.3	86.5	97.0	76.2	87.3	97.3	69.7	84.5	96.3	52.5	76.0	96.9	71.9	85.3
04	MASONRY	102.9	53.4	72.4	116.6	70.7	88.3	104.7	56.9	75.3	108.0	75.7	88.1	127.3	53.7	82.0	101.1	66.9	80.0
05	METALS	92.7	86.2	90.7	92.8	91.9	92.5	88.6	95.0	90.6	95.2	88.4	93.1	88.9	85.3	87.8	91.0	97.7	93.0
06	WOOD, PLASTICS & COMPOSITES	72.7	87.1	80.6	76.5	76.6	76.6	83.7	83.7	83.7	77.0	54.4	64.6	77.7	36.8	55.3	95.3	75.6	84.5
07	THERMAL & MOISTURE PROTECTION	105.0	68.3	89.8	104.5	74.8	92.1	106.0	71.2	91.6	104.8	68.3	89.7	105.1	55.2	84.4	105.6	69.8	90.7
08	OPENINGS	99.2	70.2	92.6	91.5	80.5	89.0	98.2	82.8	94.7	89.3	59.8	82.7	94.9	42.3	83.0	98.7	77.7	93.9
0920	Plaster & Gypsum Board	102.5	86.8	92.1	102.5	76.1	84.9	105.8	83.6	91.0	104.8	53.5	70.7	104.8	35.2	58.5	113.6	75.1	88.0
0950, 0980	Ceilings & Acoustic Treatment	87.2	86.8	87.0	87.2	76.1	79.8	94.4	83.6	87.2	94.4	53.5	67.2	94.4	35.2	55.0	96.9	75.1	82.4
0960	Flooring	84.4	73.2	81.2	86.4	73.2	82.6	106.8	73.2	97.1	91.8	78.3	87.9	93.5	73.2	87.7	101.4	73.2	93.2
0970, 0990	Wall Finishes & Painting/Coating	87.4	86.6	86.9	87.4	86.6	86.9	98.5	86.6	91.5	93.9	64.9	76.9	98.0	60.9	76.2	98.0	65.7	79.0
09	FINISHES	87.4	78.8	82.7	88.0	77.0	82.0	97.8	77.8	86.8	92.8	62.3	76.1	95.3	46.7	68.7	99.4	73.2	85.1
COVERS	DIVS. 10 - 14, 25, 28, 41, 43, 44, 46	100.0	83.3	96.2	100.0	87.9	97.3	100.0	89.3	96.3	100.0	63.5	91.7	100.0	76.9	94.8	100.0	89.6	97.6
21, 22, 23	FIRE SUPPRESSION, PLUMBING & HVAC	96.4	71.3	85.3	96.4	80.3	89.3	96.7	73.4	86.4	96.7	87.9	92.8	96.7	67.8	83.9	100.2	78.5	90.6
26, 27, 3370	ELECTRICAL, COMMUNICATIONS & UTIL.	99.1	75.2	86.4	98.2	51.2	73.2	100.9	74.7	87.0	98.6	81.3	89.4	98.6	51.2	73.5	98.6	74.5	85.8
MF2014	WEIGHTED AVERAGE	96.2	73.9	86.4	96.1	76.9	87.6	96.9	77.1	88.2	96.6	77.7	88.3	97.4	61.8	81.7	98.3	78.6	89.6

IOWA / KANSAS

DIVISION		SPENCER 513 MAT.	INST.	TOTAL	WATERLOO 506-507 MAT.	INST.	TOTAL	BELLEVILLE 669 MAT.	INST.	TOTAL	COLBY 677 MAT.	INST.	TOTAL	DODGE CITY 678 MAT.	INST.	TOTAL	EMPORIA 668 MAT.	INST.	TOTAL
015433	CONTRACTOR EQUIPMENT		102.9	102.9		102.9	102.9		108.8	108.8		108.8	108.8		108.8	108.8		106.9	106.9
0241, 31 - 34	SITE & INFRASTRUCTURE, DEMOLITION	109.5	96.3	100.3	108.5	97.3	100.7	108.7	98.5	101.6	108.3	99.2	101.9	110.7	98.1	101.9	100.8	95.9	97.4
0310	Concrete Forming & Accessories	90.6	39.7	46.6	96.3	57.4	62.7	97.1	56.7	63.0	103.3	60.5	66.3	96.3	61.9	66.6	87.9	70.0	72.4
0320	Concrete Reinforcing	97.2	63.6	80.2	95.8	80.7	88.1	97.4	57.1	77.0	96.9	57.1	76.7	94.5	57.5	75.4	96.1	57.7	76.6
0330	Cast-in-Place Concrete	105.6	69.7	92.0	112.9	77.7	99.5	114.0	89.2	104.5	107.6	93.1	102.1	109.4	92.7	103.0	110.2	93.3	103.7
03	CONCRETE	96.6	56.3	78.0	100.3	70.1	86.3	111.8	70.2	92.5	107.6	72.8	91.5	108.9	73.2	92.4	104.2	77.2	91.7
04	MASONRY	127.3	53.7	82.0	103.7	78.1	87.9	93.0	57.0	70.8	103.2	63.0	78.5	113.7	61.8	81.8	99.0	71.2	81.8
05	METALS	88.8	85.6	87.9	95.0	94.1	94.7	101.2	85.1	96.3	101.6	85.9	96.8	103.0	84.4	97.3	100.9	86.7	96.6
06	WOOD, PLASTICS & COMPOSITES	83.5	36.8	57.9	89.6	49.5	67.6	98.5	55.3	74.7	107.4	55.8	79.1	99.4	58.2	76.8	89.8	68.0	77.9
07	THERMAL & MOISTURE PROTECTION	106.1	55.9	85.2	104.7	76.5	93.0	97.3	65.0	83.9	98.4	67.6	85.6	98.4	67.2	85.4	95.5	80.3	89.2
08	OPENINGS	106.2	42.6	91.8	91.9	62.8	85.3	98.4	59.5	89.6	103.6	59.8	93.7	103.6	57.0	93.0	96.3	65.0	89.2
0920	Plaster & Gypsum Board	105.8	35.2	58.9	111.0	48.2	69.3	95.4	54.1	67.9	100.6	54.6	70.0	95.0	57.1	69.8	92.7	67.2	75.8
0950, 0980	Ceilings & Acoustic Treatment	94.4	35.2	55.0	89.7	48.2	62.1	81.5	54.1	63.2	78.9	54.6	62.8	78.9	57.1	64.4	81.5	67.2	72.0
0960	Flooring	96.5	73.2	89.7	91.8	83.6	89.4	94.5	69.8	87.4	92.5	69.8	85.9	88.5	69.8	83.1	89.5	69.8	83.8
0970, 0990	Wall Finishes & Painting/Coating	98.0	60.9	76.2	87.4	86.6	86.9	87.5	82.6	84.6	95.0	82.6	87.7	95.0	82.6	87.7	87.5	82.6	84.6
09	FINISHES	96.3	45.4	68.5	91.6	63.7	76.3	89.1	61.6	74.0	88.7	63.5	74.9	86.9	64.9	74.9	86.2	70.7	77.7
COVERS	DIVS. 10 - 14, 25, 28, 41, 43, 44, 46	100.0	76.9	94.8	100.0	88.5	97.4	100.0	87.9	97.3	100.0	90.2	97.8	100.0	90.5	97.8	100.0	91.5	98.1
21, 22, 23	FIRE SUPPRESSION, PLUMBING & HVAC	96.7	71.4	85.5	100.0	79.4	90.9	96.3	71.3	85.3	96.4	69.6	84.6	100.0	70.5	86.9	96.3	76.3	87.5
26, 27, 3370	ELECTRICAL, COMMUNICATIONS & UTIL.	100.4	51.2	74.3	94.6	61.8	77.2	99.3	68.0	82.7	99.1	75.7	86.7	96.0	71.1	82.8	96.6	71.9	83.5
MF2014	WEIGHTED AVERAGE	99.1	62.9	83.1	97.5	75.5	87.8	99.5	71.1	86.9	100.2	73.3	88.3	101.4	72.6	88.7	97.7	77.1	88.6

For customer support on your Electrical Costs with RSMeans Data, call 800.448.8182.

519

KANSAS

DIVISION		FORT SCOTT 667			HAYS 676			HUTCHINSON 675			INDEPENDENCE 673			KANSAS CITY 660 - 662			LIBERAL 679		
		MAT.	INST.	TOTAL	MAT.	INST.	TOTAL	MAT.	INST.	TOTAL	MAT.	INST.	TOTAL	MAT.	INST.	TOTAL	MAT.	INST.	TOTAL
015433	CONTRACTOR EQUIPMENT		107.8	107.8		108.8	108.8		108.8	108.8		108.8	108.8		105.3	105.3		108.8	108.8
0241, 31 - 34	SITE & INFRASTRUCTURE, DEMOLITION	97.6	95.9	96.5	113.7	98.7	103.3	92.7	99.2	97.2	112.0	99.2	103.1	92.0	96.0	94.8	113.2	98.7	103.1
0310	Concrete Forming & Accessories	105.5	84.0	86.9	100.7	59.7	65.2	90.7	57.2	61.8	112.4	72.2	77.7	102.0	99.2	99.6	96.8	49.6	56.0
0320	Concrete Reinforcing	95.4	93.5	94.5	94.5	57.1	75.5	93.9	57.0	75.5	93.9	65.6	79.5	92.6	102.2	97.4	95.8	57.0	76.1
0330	Cast-in-Place Concrete	102.2	88.1	96.8	84.9	89.4	86.6	78.6	92.7	84.0	109.9	93.0	103.5	87.5	100.3	92.4	84.9	89.0	86.4
03	CONCRETE	99.6	87.9	94.2	99.8	71.2	86.5	82.6	71.1	77.3	110.1	79.4	95.9	91.9	100.6	95.9	101.7	66.4	85.4
04	MASONRY	100.4	57.8	74.2	112.9	57.1	78.5	103.3	61.8	77.8	100.3	66.8	79.6	101.1	98.7	99.6	111.6	55.4	77.0
05	METALS	100.9	98.3	100.1	101.2	85.6	96.4	101.0	84.5	95.9	100.9	87.4	96.8	109.1	106.1	108.2	101.5	84.4	96.3
06	WOOD, PLASTICS & COMPOSITES	108.5	91.0	98.9	104.2	58.2	78.9	94.4	51.7	70.9	117.7	71.2	92.1	104.4	99.4	101.7	100.0	44.7	69.6
07	THERMAL & MOISTURE PROTECTION	96.4	75.6	87.8	98.7	65.3	84.9	97.2	66.5	84.5	98.4	79.8	90.7	96.1	98.7	97.2	98.9	62.8	83.9
08	OPENINGS	96.3	86.0	93.9	103.5	57.0	93.0	103.5	53.5	92.2	101.3	65.4	93.2	97.6	97.6	97.6	103.6	49.6	91.4
0920	Plaster & Gypsum Board	97.7	90.7	93.1	97.9	57.1	70.8	94.0	50.4	65.0	107.5	70.4	82.8	95.6	99.4	96.7	95.6	43.2	60.8
0950, 0980	Ceilings & Acoustic Treatment	81.5	90.7	87.6	78.9	57.1	64.4	78.9	50.4	60.0	78.9	70.4	73.3	81.5	99.4	93.4	78.9	43.2	55.2
0960	Flooring	104.5	69.6	94.4	91.2	69.8	85.0	85.5	69.8	80.9	97.0	69.6	89.0	84.1	98.2	88.2	88.8	50.0	83.3
0970, 0990	Wall Finishes & Painting/Coating	89.2	82.6	85.3	95.0	82.6	87.7	95.0	82.6	87.7	95.0	82.6	87.7	94.7	99.2	97.4	95.0	82.6	87.7
09	FINISHES	91.6	82.4	86.5	88.5	63.3	74.7	84.3	61.1	71.6	91.2	73.0	81.3	86.6	99.3	93.5	87.7	55.4	70.1
COVERS	DIVS. 10 - 14, 25, 28, 41, 43, 44, 46	100.0	91.0	98.0	100.0	88.3	97.3	100.0	89.7	97.7	100.0	91.9	98.2	100.0	98.4	99.6	100.0	86.8	97.0
21, 22, 23	FIRE SUPPRESSION, PLUMBING & HVAC	96.3	69.4	84.4	96.4	67.2	83.5	96.4	70.5	85.0	96.4	73.1	86.1	99.8	97.4	98.8	96.4	68.6	84.1
26, 27, 3370	ELECTRICAL, COMMUNICATIONS & UTIL.	95.8	71.9	83.1	98.0	66.1	81.1	93.1	66.1	78.8	95.3	71.9	82.9	101.5	95.6	98.4	96.0	71.1	82.8
MF2014	WEIGHTED AVERAGE	97.7	79.3	89.6	99.7	70.3	86.7	95.5	71.0	84.7	100.0	76.9	89.8	99.0	98.8	98.9	99.6	68.8	86.0

DIVISION		KANSAS									KENTUCKY								
		SALINA 674			TOPEKA 664 - 666			WICHITA 670 - 672			ASHLAND 411 - 412			BOWLING GREEN 421 - 422			CAMPTON 413 - 414		
		MAT.	INST.	TOTAL	MAT.	INST.	TOTAL	MAT.	INST.	TOTAL	MAT.	INST.	TOTAL	MAT.	INST.	TOTAL	MAT.	INST.	TOTAL
015433	CONTRACTOR EQUIPMENT		108.8	108.8		106.9	106.9		108.8	108.8		101.8	101.8		94.5	94.5		101.1	101.1
0241, 31 - 34	SITE & INFRASTRUCTURE, DEMOLITION	101.2	98.7	99.5	95.4	95.2	95.3	97.2	101.1	99.9	115.2	84.0	93.4	79.9	95.5	90.8	88.9	96.8	94.4
0310	Concrete Forming & Accessories	92.6	57.8	62.5	98.9	68.3	72.4	98.5	61.5	66.5	87.1	94.5	93.5	85.7	79.6	80.4	89.0	75.3	77.1
0320	Concrete Reinforcing	93.9	57.2	75.3	92.1	104.1	98.2	92.1	80.5	86.2	93.9	95.5	94.7	91.1	78.1	84.5	92.0	94.3	93.2
0330	Cast-in-Place Concrete	95.0	89.5	92.9	91.9	86.7	89.9	88.9	98.4	92.5	87.0	97.2	90.9	86.4	73.1	81.3	96.3	71.1	86.7
03	CONCRETE	96.2	70.4	84.2	93.5	82.3	88.3	92.0	79.1	86.0	94.8	96.8	95.7	93.3	77.5	86.0	96.9	77.7	88.0
04	MASONRY	129.3	57.1	84.8	94.7	60.8	73.8	100.4	71.5	82.6	95.4	93.5	94.2	97.6	72.1	81.9	94.1	59.0	72.5
05	METALS	102.8	85.8	97.6	105.2	103.4	104.6	105.2	93.0	101.4	96.0	110.7	100.5	97.7	84.6	93.7	97.0	90.9	95.1
06	WOOD, PLASTICS & COMPOSITES	95.9	55.3	73.6	99.9	71.0	84.0	101.3	51.7	74.0	74.5	92.9	84.6	87.0	79.9	83.1	85.6	80.0	82.5
07	THERMAL & MOISTURE PROTECTION	97.9	65.0	84.2	100.2	75.8	90.1	97.3	69.9	85.9	92.4	92.0	92.3	88.3	80.7	85.1	101.4	71.0	88.8
08	OPENINGS	103.5	55.4	92.6	103.8	77.4	97.8	107.0	58.7	96.0	93.6	93.3	93.5	94.3	81.2	91.3	95.6	82.9	92.7
0920	Plaster & Gypsum Board	94.0	54.1	67.5	95.7	70.2	78.8	93.4	50.4	64.8	61.6	92.9	82.4	88.2	79.7	82.6	88.2	79.0	82.1
0950, 0980	Ceilings & Acoustic Treatment	78.9	54.1	62.4	87.0	70.2	75.8	82.8	50.4	61.2	76.3	92.9	87.4	81.1	79.7	80.2	81.1	79.0	79.7
0960	Flooring	87.0	69.8	82.0	95.7	69.8	88.2	98.1	69.8	89.9	76.7	98.6	83.1	92.0	78.7	88.2	94.1	37.5	77.7
0970, 0990	Wall Finishes & Painting/Coating	95.0	82.6	87.7	92.0	75.3	82.2	95.3	71.0	81.1	94.7	94.0	94.3	92.5	89.9	91.0	92.5	57.4	71.9
09	FINISHES	85.5	61.6	72.4	91.1	68.5	78.8	90.6	62.3	75.1	77.5	95.4	87.3	88.1	80.5	84.0	88.9	66.2	76.5
COVERS	DIVS. 10 - 14, 25, 28, 41, 43, 44, 46	100.0	86.4	96.9	100.0	83.0	96.2	100.0	91.5	98.1	100.0	83.5	96.3	100.0	89.8	97.7	100.0	49.5	88.6
21, 22, 23	FIRE SUPPRESSION, PLUMBING & HVAC	100.0	69.2	86.4	100.0	70.9	87.1	99.8	77.7	90.0	96.2	87.5	92.3	100.0	79.2	90.8	96.4	75.9	87.4
26, 27, 3370	ELECTRICAL, COMMUNICATIONS & UTIL.	95.7	74.3	84.4	100.2	71.9	85.2	99.9	74.3	86.3	92.2	95.7	94.0	94.8	79.2	86.5	92.1	95.6	94.0
MF2014	WEIGHTED AVERAGE	100.2	71.4	87.5	99.4	77.0	89.5	99.9	77.2	89.8	94.3	93.7	94.0	95.0	80.7	88.9	95.5	78.3	87.9

KENTUCKY

DIVISION		CORBIN 407 - 409			COVINGTON 410			ELIZABETHTOWN 427			FRANKFORT 406			HAZARD 417 - 418			HENDERSON 424		
		MAT.	INST.	TOTAL	MAT.	INST.	TOTAL	MAT.	INST.	TOTAL	MAT.	INST.	TOTAL	MAT.	INST.	TOTAL	MAT.	INST.	TOTAL
015433	CONTRACTOR EQUIPMENT		101.1	101.1		105.2	105.2		94.5	94.5		101.1	101.1		101.1	101.1		115.7	115.7
0241, 31 - 34	SITE & INFRASTRUCTURE, DEMOLITION	91.1	97.3	95.4	84.3	109.3	101.7	74.3	95.2	88.9	88.9	97.6	94.9	86.6	98.0	94.5	82.7	123.1	110.9
0310	Concrete Forming & Accessories	84.5	73.9	75.3	84.4	73.3	74.8	80.4	77.4	77.8	94.1	75.7	77.9	85.5	75.7	77.0	92.1	80.9	82.4
0320	Concrete Reinforcing	102.2	62.6	82.1	90.6	80.2	85.3	91.6	81.1	86.3	107.6	81.0	94.1	92.4	62.8	77.4	91.2	78.2	84.6
0330	Cast-in-Place Concrete	88.5	75.5	83.5	92.2	76.8	86.3	78.1	70.4	75.2	87.6	77.4	83.7	92.6	73.9	85.5	76.3	89.3	81.3
03	CONCRETE	89.6	73.1	82.0	95.2	76.8	86.7	85.2	76.2	81.0	91.9	77.6	85.3	93.7	73.4	84.2	90.3	83.6	87.2
04	MASONRY	91.5	64.1	74.6	109.2	76.3	88.9	81.0	66.5	72.1	87.0	70.5	76.9	92.8	61.2	73.3	101.2	78.7	87.4
05	METALS	96.7	78.9	91.3	94.8	93.2	94.3	96.8	86.0	93.5	99.6	86.4	95.6	97.0	79.2	91.5	87.9	84.9	87.0
06	WOOD, PLASTICS & COMPOSITES	72.4	74.6	73.6	83.8	70.0	76.2	82.6	79.9	81.1	86.5	74.6	79.9	82.8	80.0	81.3	89.5	79.6	84.0
07	THERMAL & MOISTURE PROTECTION	106.1	73.3	92.5	102.4	79.8	93.0	87.7	72.7	81.5	104.0	75.5	92.2	101.3	72.9	89.5	100.7	80.5	92.3
08	OPENINGS	89.5	62.4	83.4	97.6	76.0	92.7	94.3	79.0	90.8	93.0	77.4	89.5	96.0	75.1	91.2	92.4	79.8	89.6
0920	Plaster & Gypsum Board	93.1	73.4	80.0	70.8	79.7	70.1	87.5	79.7	82.4	93.6	73.4	80.2	87.5	79.0	81.9	91.2	78.5	82.8
0950, 0980	Ceilings & Acoustic Treatment	77.6	73.4	74.8	83.6	69.7	74.4	81.1	79.7	80.2	86.1	73.4	77.7	81.1	79.0	79.7	76.8	78.5	78.0
0960	Flooring	90.8	37.5	75.3	68.8	82.9	72.9	89.3	78.2	86.1	96.7	49.5	83.0	92.3	38.2	76.6	95.7	79.0	90.9
0970, 0990	Wall Finishes & Painting/Coating	94.2	66.0	77.6	88.0	73.4	79.4	92.5	69.0	78.7	96.6	72.6	82.5	92.5	57.4	71.9	92.5	91.3	91.8
09	FINISHES	85.5	66.0	74.8	79.1	74.4	76.6	86.9	76.5	81.2	89.9	70.0	79.1	88.1	66.9	76.5	88.2	81.8	84.7
COVERS	DIVS. 10 - 14, 25, 28, 41, 43, 44, 46	100.0	88.6	97.4	100.0	89.5	97.6	100.0	75.1	94.4	100.0	60.1	91.0	100.0	50.3	88.8	100.0	59.5	90.8
21, 22, 23	FIRE SUPPRESSION, PLUMBING & HVAC	96.5	74.9	86.9	97.2	78.4	88.9	96.6	75.8	87.4	100.1	77.6	90.1	96.4	76.4	87.6	96.6	79.4	89.0
26, 27, 3370	ELECTRICAL, COMMUNICATIONS & UTIL.	91.2	95.6	93.5	96.0	76.5	85.6	91.9	79.2	85.2	100.1	77.5	88.1	92.1	95.6	94.0	94.2	77.8	85.5
MF2014	WEIGHTED AVERAGE	93.5	77.3	86.3	95.5	81.1	89.2	92.2	78.0	85.9	96.4	77.7	88.1	94.9	76.9	87.0	93.2	83.3	88.8

For customer support on your Electrical Costs with RSMeans Data, call 800.448.8182.

City Cost Indexes

KENTUCKY

DIVISION		LEXINGTON 403 - 405			LOUISVILLE 400 - 402			OWENSBORO 423			PADUCAH 420			PIKEVILLE 415 - 416			SOMERSET 425 - 426		
		MAT.	INST.	TOTAL	MAT.	INST.	TOTAL	MAT.	INST.	TOTAL	MAT.	INST.	TOTAL	MAT.	INST.	TOTAL	MAT.	INST.	TOTAL
015433	CONTRACTOR EQUIPMENT		101.1	101.1		94.5	94.5		115.7	115.7		115.7	115.7		101.8	101.8		101.1	101.1
0241, 31 - 34	SITE & INFRASTRUCTURE, DEMOLITION	93.1	99.2	97.4	87.8	95.4	93.1	92.9	123.7	114.4	85.5	122.9	111.6	126.7	83.0	96.2	79.3	97.4	91.9
0310	Concrete Forming & Accessories	96.0	76.3	78.9	94.7	78.7	80.8	90.5	80.6	81.9	88.5	83.6	84.3	96.1	80.5	82.6	86.5	74.3	76.0
0320	Concrete Reinforcing	112.2	83.7	97.8	107.6	83.7	95.5	91.2	80.4	85.7	91.8	81.7	86.7	94.5	55.3	74.9	91.6	62.9	77.0
0330	Cast-in-Place Concrete	90.5	80.7	86.8	87.7	72.0	81.7	89.0	88.2	88.7	81.3	85.4	82.9	95.7	92.4	94.4	76.3	93.2	82.8
03	CONCRETE	92.7	79.6	86.6	92.0	77.6	85.3	102.5	83.5	93.7	94.9	84.1	89.9	108.6	88.8	99.4	80.2	79.4	79.8
04	MASONRY	89.7	73.4	79.6	87.9	70.2	77.0	93.4	76.1	82.8	96.1	80.9	86.8	92.6	85.8	88.4	87.7	67.1	75.0
05	METALS	99.3	87.8	95.8	100.4	86.4	96.1	89.3	87.0	88.6	86.5	87.0	86.6	96.0	109.5	100.1	96.9	79.5	91.6
06	WOOD, PLASTICS & COMPOSITES	86.3	74.6	79.9	86.6	79.9	82.9	87.5	79.6	83.1	85.3	84.8	85.0	83.1	79.4	81.1	83.3	74.6	78.5
07	THERMAL & MOISTURE PROTECTION	106.4	77.3	94.3	103.4	74.3	91.3	101.3	79.9	92.5	100.7	84.7	94.1	93.2	83.2	89.0	100.7	74.3	89.7
08	OPENINGS	89.8	77.0	86.9	83.8	79.0	82.7	92.4	80.4	89.7	91.7	83.9	90.0	94.2	78.3	90.6	95.0	68.8	89.1
0920	Plaster & Gypsum Board	102.5	73.4	83.2	94.0	79.7	84.5	89.9	78.5	82.3	88.9	83.9	85.6	64.2	79.0	74.0	87.5	73.4	78.2
0950, 0980	Ceilings & Acoustic Treatment	81.0	73.4	76.0	89.0	79.7	82.8	76.8	78.5	78.0	76.8	83.9	81.5	76.3	79.0	78.1	81.1	73.4	76.0
0960	Flooring	96.0	60.9	85.8	95.9	78.2	90.8	95.1	78.7	90.3	94.0	54.0	82.4	81.1	98.6	86.2	92.6	37.5	76.6
0970, 0990	Wall Finishes & Painting/Coating	94.2	71.1	80.6	95.9	69.0	80.1	92.5	91.3	91.8	92.5	77.9	83.9	94.7	71.2	80.9	92.5	69.0	78.7
09	FINISHES	89.1	72.2	79.9	90.3	77.7	83.4	88.4	81.1	84.4	87.6	77.6	82.1	80.1	83.1	81.7	87.5	66.3	75.9
COVERS	DIVS. 10 - 14, 25, 28, 41, 43, 44, 46	100.0	91.8	98.1	100.0	89.3	97.6	100.0	96.6	99.3	100.0	56.8	90.2	100.0	49.8	88.6	100.0	88.6	97.4
21, 22, 23	FIRE SUPPRESSION, PLUMBING & HVAC	100.1	77.8	90.2	100.1	78.5	90.6	100.0	80.4	91.3	96.6	80.3	89.4	96.2	83.2	90.4	96.6	75.2	87.1
26, 27, 3370	ELECTRICAL, COMMUNICATIONS & UTIL.	93.9	79.2	86.1	99.8	79.2	88.9	94.3	77.8	85.5	96.6	78.6	87.1	95.2	68.5	81.0	92.6	95.6	94.2
MF2014	WEIGHTED AVERAGE	95.7	80.0	88.8	95.5	79.9	88.6	95.5	84.6	90.7	93.4	83.8	89.1	96.8	83.3	90.8	92.7	78.9	86.6

LOUISIANA

DIVISION		ALEXANDRIA 713 - 714			BATON ROUGE 707 - 708			HAMMOND 704			LAFAYETTE 705			LAKE CHARLES 706			MONROE 712		
		MAT.	INST.	TOTAL	MAT.	INST.	TOTAL	MAT.	INST.	TOTAL	MAT.	INST.	TOTAL	MAT.	INST.	TOTAL	MAT.	INST.	TOTAL
015433	CONTRACTOR EQUIPMENT		94.6	94.6		92.6	92.6		93.1	93.1		93.1	93.1		92.6	92.6		94.6	94.6
0241, 31 - 34	SITE & INFRASTRUCTURE, DEMOLITION	103.5	93.3	96.4	102.3	92.2	95.2	99.7	91.6	94.0	100.7	93.6	95.7	101.4	92.9	95.5	103.5	93.3	96.4
0310	Concrete Forming & Accessories	81.3	63.2	65.7	96.7	75.3	78.2	79.0	58.7	61.4	96.7	69.2	72.9	97.6	68.5	72.5	80.9	62.5	65.0
0320	Concrete Reinforcing	102.9	64.5	83.4	91.8	54.4	72.8	90.9	54.2	72.3	92.2	54.5	73.1	92.2	54.6	73.1	101.7	64.0	82.6
0330	Cast-in-Place Concrete	94.3	67.2	84.0	94.2	76.9	87.6	92.6	66.7	82.7	92.1	67.7	82.8	97.0	69.7	86.6	94.3	68.0	84.3
03	CONCRETE	90.9	65.6	79.1	91.9	72.5	82.9	90.0	61.4	76.8	91.0	66.5	79.7	93.4	67.0	81.2	90.7	65.4	79.0
04	MASONRY	116.2	63.6	83.8	88.8	63.6	73.3	94.4	56.5	71.1	94.4	62.2	74.6	93.8	65.6	76.4	110.7	55.9	76.9
05	METALS	95.7	75.4	89.5	99.9	70.3	90.8	89.6	69.3	83.4	88.9	70.2	83.2	88.9	70.6	83.3	95.6	74.4	89.1
06	WOOD, PLASTICS & COMPOSITES	93.2	62.3	76.3	103.2	77.4	89.1	87.1	58.6	71.5	106.9	71.4	87.4	105.2	68.4	85.0	92.6	62.3	76.0
07	THERMAL & MOISTURE PROTECTION	98.2	68.0	85.7	97.8	70.0	86.3	97.2	64.9	83.8	97.7	68.3	85.5	97.4	69.3	85.7	98.2	65.5	84.6
08	OPENINGS	110.7	65.3	100.4	102.2	70.7	95.1	97.3	57.3	88.2	101.0	58.0	91.2	101.0	65.2	92.9	110.7	58.5	98.9
0920	Plaster & Gypsum Board	84.0	61.7	69.1	99.6	77.2	84.7	99.4	57.8	71.8	107.2	71.0	83.1	107.2	67.9	81.1	83.7	61.7	69.0
0950, 0980	Ceilings & Acoustic Treatment	80.4	61.7	67.9	95.6	77.2	83.4	97.9	57.8	71.3	96.3	71.0	79.4	97.2	67.9	77.7	80.4	61.7	67.9
0960	Flooring	97.3	64.5	87.8	93.2	60.1	83.6	91.7	58.6	82.1	100.7	64.5	90.2	100.7	66.9	90.9	96.8	52.4	83.9
0970, 0990	Wall Finishes & Painting/Coating	96.4	61.0	75.6	92.6	74.7	82.1	100.1	42.9	66.5	100.1	51.4	71.5	100.1	79.2	87.8	96.4	66.3	78.7
09	FINISHES	84.5	62.9	72.7	89.3	73.0	80.4	92.8	56.6	73.0	96.2	66.8	80.1	96.3	69.4	81.6	84.3	60.8	71.5
COVERS	DIVS. 10 - 14, 25, 28, 41, 43, 44, 46	100.0	80.7	95.6	100.0	87.4	97.1	100.0	80.1	95.5	100.0	85.4	96.7	100.0	86.2	96.9	100.0	82.2	96.0
21, 22, 23	FIRE SUPPRESSION, PLUMBING & HVAC	100.1	63.7	84.0	100.0	65.0	84.5	96.6	61.7	81.2	100.2	63.1	83.8	100.2	64.9	84.6	100.1	55.9	80.6
26, 27, 3370	ELECTRICAL, COMMUNICATIONS & UTIL.	94.2	66.6	79.6	98.8	60.2	78.3	93.3	72.4	82.2	94.5	64.0	78.3	94.0	66.4	79.4	96.1	60.1	77.0
MF2014	WEIGHTED AVERAGE	98.3	68.3	85.1	97.7	70.0	85.5	94.2	65.4	81.5	96.0	67.2	83.6	96.3	69.6	84.5	98.2	64.3	83.2

LOUISIANA / MAINE

DIVISION		NEW ORLEANS 700 - 701			SHREVEPORT 710 - 711			THIBODAUX 703			AUGUSTA 043			BANGOR 044			BATH 045		
		MAT.	INST.	TOTAL	MAT.	INST.	TOTAL	MAT.	INST.	TOTAL	MAT.	INST.	TOTAL	MAT.	INST.	TOTAL	MAT.	INST.	TOTAL
015433	CONTRACTOR EQUIPMENT		87.6	87.6		94.6	94.6		93.1	93.1		99.8	99.8		99.8	99.8		99.8	99.8
0241, 31 - 34	SITE & INFRASTRUCTURE, DEMOLITION	99.3	94.2	95.7	105.8	92.7	96.6	102.0	93.6	96.2	91.5	99.3	96.9	94.6	99.6	98.1	92.5	99.3	97.2
0310	Concrete Forming & Accessories	97.3	70.5	74.2	95.1	45.6	52.3	91.1	68.7	71.7	100.9	72.7	76.5	94.4	78.3	80.5	90.1	72.9	75.3
0320	Concrete Reinforcing	91.8	54.5	72.9	103.1	54.1	78.3	90.9	52.8	71.6	101.0	79.8	90.2	90.9	81.1	85.9	89.9	81.0	85.4
0330	Cast-in-Place Concrete	95.4	69.8	85.6	97.3	62.9	84.2	99.4	54.6	82.3	92.1	102.7	96.1	74.4	110.3	88.1	74.4	102.8	85.2
03	CONCRETE	96.0	67.3	82.7	94.4	54.4	75.8	95.1	61.5	79.5	93.2	85.1	89.4	86.3	90.4	88.2	86.3	85.4	85.9
04	MASONRY	99.2	61.8	76.2	99.9	49.0	68.6	118.1	55.7	79.7	104.9	54.6	73.9	120.7	89.5	101.5	128.0	75.3	95.5
05	METALS	98.8	62.4	87.6	99.9	71.0	91.1	89.6	68.9	83.3	97.7	90.2	95.4	87.9	92.3	89.3	86.4	91.9	88.1
06	WOOD, PLASTICS & COMPOSITES	100.8	73.0	85.5	100.1	44.1	69.3	94.4	70.8	81.4	95.3	76.8	85.1	98.2	76.8	86.4	92.8	76.8	84.0
07	THERMAL & MOISTURE PROTECTION	93.6	68.9	83.4	95.8	60.0	81.0	97.2	66.3	84.4	103.7	64.4	87.4	100.7	82.9	93.3	100.7	70.8	88.3
08	OPENINGS	103.1	65.9	94.7	108.0	43.4	93.4	101.9	60.4	92.5	102.9	80.6	97.8	98.2	80.2	94.1	98.2	80.6	94.2
0920	Plaster & Gypsum Board	97.4	72.5	80.9	93.4	42.9	59.8	100.7	70.4	80.6	111.4	75.7	87.7	112.7	75.7	88.1	108.5	75.7	86.7
0950, 0980	Ceilings & Acoustic Treatment	102.5	72.5	82.5	85.4	42.9	57.1	97.9	70.4	79.6	96.9	75.7	82.8	84.0	75.7	78.5	83.1	75.7	78.2
0960	Flooring	103.5	64.5	92.2	101.6	56.2	88.4	98.0	40.4	81.3	94.2	48.5	81.0	90.4	102.2	93.9	88.6	48.5	77.0
0970, 0990	Wall Finishes & Painting/Coating	102.0	63.1	79.1	88.6	39.6	59.8	101.3	44.0	67.7	93.7	92.7	93.1	94.0	43.6	64.4	94.0	92.7	93.3
09	FINISHES	100.4	68.9	83.2	88.8	45.7	65.3	95.1	60.9	76.4	93.0	69.2	80.0	90.1	78.6	83.8	88.7	69.3	78.1
COVERS	DIVS. 10 - 14, 25, 28, 41, 43, 44, 46	100.0	85.7	96.8	100.0	80.5	95.6	100.0	85.6	96.8	100.0	98.8	99.7	100.0	103.2	100.7	100.0	98.8	99.7
21, 22, 23	FIRE SUPPRESSION, PLUMBING & HVAC	100.1	64.6	84.4	99.9	58.7	81.7	96.6	62.8	81.7	99.9	62.2	83.2	100.1	68.9	86.3	96.6	62.2	81.4
26, 27, 3370	ELECTRICAL, COMMUNICATIONS & UTIL.	96.7	72.3	83.8	101.5	66.2	82.8	92.1	70.6	80.7	100.7	78.8	89.1	99.2	74.7	86.2	97.2	78.8	87.4
MF2014	WEIGHTED AVERAGE	99.1	69.3	86.0	99.4	60.2	82.1	96.8	66.5	83.4	98.6	75.3	88.3	96.1	82.5	90.1	95.0	77.8	87.4

City Cost Indexes

MAINE

DIVISION		HOULTON 047 MAT.	INST.	TOTAL	KITTERY 039 MAT.	INST.	TOTAL	LEWISTON 042 MAT.	INST.	TOTAL	MACHIAS 046 MAT.	INST.	TOTAL	PORTLAND 040-041 MAT.	INST.	TOTAL	ROCKLAND 048 MAT.	INST.	TOTAL
015433	CONTRACTOR EQUIPMENT		99.8	99.8		99.8	99.8		99.8	99.8		99.8	99.8		99.8	99.8		99.8	99.8
0241, 31 - 34	SITE & INFRASTRUCTURE, DEMOLITION	94.4	100.1	98.4	83.7	99.4	94.6	92.1	99.6	97.3	93.8	100.1	98.2	92.1	99.6	97.3	90.2	100.1	97.1
0310	Concrete Forming & Accessories	98.4	77.6	80.4	90.3	73.5	75.8	100.3	78.3	81.3	95.3	77.6	80.0	101.6	78.3	81.4	96.4	77.6	80.1
0320	Concrete Reinforcing	90.9	79.5	85.1	86.6	81.1	83.8	111.7	81.1	96.2	90.9	79.5	85.1	101.0	81.1	90.9	90.9	79.5	85.1
0330	Cast-in-Place Concrete	74.4	110.1	88.0	73.7	103.3	85.0	75.9	110.3	89.0	74.4	110.0	88.0	92.1	110.3	99.1	75.9	110.0	88.9
03	CONCRETE	87.2	89.9	88.4	81.8	85.9	83.7	86.6	90.5	88.4	86.7	89.8	88.1	92.5	90.5	91.5	84.3	89.8	86.8
04	MASONRY	102.4	63.0	78.1	117.7	76.0	92.0	103.0	89.5	94.7	102.4	63.0	78.1	108.5	89.5	96.8	95.8	63.0	75.6
05	METALS	86.6	89.8	87.6	83.0	92.2	85.8	91.2	92.3	91.5	86.7	89.8	87.6	97.8	92.3	96.1	86.5	89.8	87.5
06	WOOD, PLASTICS & COMPOSITES	102.1	76.8	88.2	96.1	76.8	85.5	104.0	76.8	89.0	99.1	76.8	86.8	95.4	76.8	85.2	99.9	76.8	87.2
07	THERMAL & MOISTURE PROTECTION	100.8	70.3	88.1	101.7	70.3	88.7	100.5	82.9	93.2	100.7	69.5	87.8	103.9	82.9	95.2	100.4	69.5	87.6
08	OPENINGS	98.3	80.6	94.2	97.5	84.4	94.5	101.5	80.2	96.7	98.3	80.6	94.3	102.1	80.2	97.2	98.2	80.6	94.2
0920	Plaster & Gypsum Board	115.1	75.7	88.9	104.8	75.7	85.4	118.0	75.7	89.9	113.4	75.7	88.3	111.9	75.7	87.8	113.4	75.7	88.3
0950, 0980	Ceilings & Acoustic Treatment	83.1	75.7	78.2	95.8	75.7	82.4	92.5	75.7	81.3	83.1	75.7	78.2	95.1	75.7	82.2	83.1	75.7	78.2
0960	Flooring	91.8	45.4	78.3	90.4	50.6	78.9	93.4	102.2	96.0	90.9	45.3	77.7	95.0	102.2	97.1	91.3	45.4	78.0
0970, 0990	Wall Finishes & Painting/Coating	94.0	92.7	93.3	87.9	106.8	99.0	94.0	43.6	64.4	94.0	92.7	93.3	96.6	43.6	65.5	94.0	92.7	93.3
09	FINISHES	90.6	72.0	80.4	90.1	71.3	79.9	93.0	78.6	85.1	90.1	72.0	80.2	93.8	78.6	85.5	89.8	72.0	80.1
COVERS	DIVS. 10 - 14, 25, 28, 41, 43, 44, 46	100.0	103.2	100.7	100.0	99.1	99.8	100.0	103.2	100.7	100.0	103.2	100.7	100.0	103.2	100.7	100.0	103.2	100.7
21, 22, 23	FIRE SUPPRESSION, PLUMBING & HVAC	96.6	68.9	84.3	96.5	72.5	85.9	100.1	69.0	86.3	96.6	68.9	84.3	99.9	69.0	86.2	96.6	68.9	84.3
26, 27, 3370	ELECTRICAL, COMMUNICATIONS & UTIL.	101.2	78.8	89.3	94.6	78.8	86.2	101.3	78.8	89.3	101.2	78.8	89.3	103.3	78.8	90.3	101.2	78.8	89.3
MF2014	WEIGHTED AVERAGE	94.6	78.9	87.7	93.0	80.6	87.5	96.6	83.1	90.6	94.4	78.9	87.6	99.0	83.1	92.0	93.7	78.9	87.1

MAINE / MARYLAND

DIVISION		WATERVILLE 049 MAT.	INST.	TOTAL	ANNAPOLIS 214 MAT.	INST.	TOTAL	BALTIMORE 210-212 MAT.	INST.	TOTAL	COLLEGE PARK 207-208 MAT.	INST.	TOTAL	CUMBERLAND 215 MAT.	INST.	TOTAL	EASTON 216 MAT.	INST.	TOTAL
015433	CONTRACTOR EQUIPMENT		99.8	99.8		107.0	107.0		106.1	106.1		112.7	112.7		107.0	107.0		107.0	107.0
0241, 31 - 34	SITE & INFRASTRUCTURE, DEMOLITION	94.2	99.3	97.7	105.2	95.2	98.2	103.7	98.5	100.0	102.0	99.6	100.4	96.5	96.0	96.2	103.8	92.3	95.8
0310	Concrete Forming & Accessories	89.6	72.7	75.0	101.7	77.8	81.0	98.7	78.1	80.9	85.4	72.9	74.5	92.5	87.1	87.8	90.4	75.4	77.4
0320	Concrete Reinforcing	90.9	79.8	85.2	98.4	90.9	94.6	101.0	90.9	95.9	99.8	87.6	93.6	89.0	85.7	87.3	88.3	87.2	87.7
0330	Cast-in-Place Concrete	74.4	102.7	85.2	114.9	75.7	99.9	112.0	77.2	98.8	113.3	75.1	98.7	95.6	82.2	90.5	106.1	68.8	91.9
03	CONCRETE	87.7	85.1	86.5	102.6	80.9	92.5	107.4	81.1	95.2	106.7	78.2	93.5	91.7	86.4	89.2	100.0	76.6	89.1
04	MASONRY	113.1	54.6	77.1	101.8	72.0	83.5	108.2	72.1	86.0	119.7	69.9	89.0	104.9	90.8	96.2	119.4	41.7	71.5
05	METALS	86.6	90.2	87.7	98.3	106.2	100.7	97.4	101.0	98.5	85.4	110.5	93.1	94.3	105.0	97.5	94.5	99.9	96.2
06	WOOD, PLASTICS & COMPOSITES	92.3	76.8	83.8	95.6	79.8	86.9	98.1	80.0	88.2	79.1	73.9	76.3	88.5	86.6	87.4	86.6	83.4	84.8
07	THERMAL & MOISTURE PROTECTION	100.8	64.4	85.7	103.8	81.1	94.4	101.4	81.8	93.2	101.6	80.9	93.0	100.3	82.1	92.8	100.5	71.6	88.5
08	OPENINGS	98.3	80.6	94.2	99.3	88.1	96.8	98.2	88.2	95.9	91.5	81.1	89.1	98.3	89.3	96.2	96.5	78.1	92.4
0920	Plaster & Gypsum Board	108.5	75.7	86.7	102.3	79.5	87.1	102.8	79.5	87.3	97.4	73.3	81.4	103.7	86.4	92.2	103.7	83.2	90.1
0950, 0980	Ceilings & Acoustic Treatment	83.1	75.7	78.2	90.7	79.5	83.2	107.1	79.5	88.7	97.8	73.3	81.5	99.2	86.4	90.7	99.2	83.2	88.5
0960	Flooring	88.3	48.5	76.8	91.1	79.8	87.8	95.4	79.8	90.9	88.5	78.0	85.5	88.6	96.5	90.9	87.7	47.9	76.2
0970, 0990	Wall Finishes & Painting/Coating	94.0	92.7	93.3	90.5	75.7	81.8	104.0	75.7	87.4	106.8	75.7	88.5	99.2	92.6	95.3	99.2	75.7	85.4
09	FINISHES	88.8	69.2	78.1	89.0	77.6	82.8	100.6	77.8	88.1	92.2	73.4	81.9	94.3	89.8	91.8	94.5	71.5	81.9
COVERS	DIVS. 10 - 14, 25, 28, 41, 43, 44, 46	100.0	98.6	99.7	100.0	88.3	97.4	100.0	88.9	97.5	100.0	83.8	96.3	100.0	92.9	98.4	100.0	73.0	93.9
21, 22, 23	FIRE SUPPRESSION, PLUMBING & HVAC	96.6	62.2	81.4	100.0	82.8	92.4	100.0	82.9	92.4	96.6	82.8	90.5	96.3	73.4	86.2	96.3	76.4	87.5
26, 27, 3370	ELECTRICAL, COMMUNICATIONS & UTIL.	101.2	78.8	89.3	99.0	92.4	95.5	98.8	92.4	95.4	98.3	101.2	99.8	96.5	82.1	88.9	95.9	65.8	79.9
MF2014	WEIGHTED AVERAGE	94.9	75.3	86.3	99.2	85.6	93.2	100.7	85.5	94.0	96.8	86.0	92.0	96.3	86.6	92.0	98.0	74.2	87.5

MARYLAND / MASSACHUSETTS

DIVISION		ELKTON 219 MAT.	INST.	TOTAL	HAGERSTOWN 217 MAT.	INST.	TOTAL	SALISBURY 218 MAT.	INST.	TOTAL	SILVER SPRING 209 MAT.	INST.	TOTAL	WALDORF 206 MAT.	INST.	TOTAL	BOSTON 020-022, 024 MAT.	INST.	TOTAL
015433	CONTRACTOR EQUIPMENT		107.0	107.0		107.0	107.0		107.0	107.0		104.0	104.0		104.0	104.0		103.5	103.5
0241, 31 - 34	SITE & INFRASTRUCTURE, DEMOLITION	90.4	94.9	93.5	94.6	96.1	95.6	103.8	92.4	95.8	89.9	91.2	90.8	96.2	90.9	92.5	100.8	104.0	103.1
0310	Concrete Forming & Accessories	96.5	92.9	93.4	91.5	82.2	83.4	104.8	53.5	60.4	94.1	71.1	74.2	101.5	69.4	73.8	102.6	140.3	135.2
0320	Concrete Reinforcing	88.3	113.5	101.1	89.0	85.7	87.3	88.3	67.1	77.5	98.6	87.5	92.9	99.2	87.5	93.3	103.3	146.7	125.4
0330	Cast-in-Place Concrete	85.9	75.0	81.8	91.0	82.3	87.7	106.1	64.0	91.2	116.0	78.1	101.6	129.9	75.4	109.1	97.1	141.0	113.8
03	CONCRETE	84.3	91.4	87.6	88.0	84.2	86.2	100.8	62.6	83.1	104.7	78.2	92.4	115.6	76.5	97.4	99.6	140.9	118.8
04	MASONRY	103.3	58.8	75.9	110.5	90.8	98.4	119.1	45.9	74.0	119.2	75.0	92.0	101.9	70.1	82.3	105.5	149.1	132.4
05	METALS	94.6	113.8	100.4	94.4	105.0	97.6	94.6	92.6	93.9	89.6	106.1	94.7	89.6	106.3	94.7	96.6	131.7	107.3
06	WOOD, PLASTICS & COMPOSITES	93.5	101.2	97.7	87.8	79.8	83.4	103.4	55.5	77.0	85.4	69.7	76.7	92.1	69.7	79.8	104.5	141.2	124.6
07	THERMAL & MOISTURE PROTECTION	100.0	79.8	91.6	100.7	87.3	95.1	100.7	69.0	87.6	105.2	87.9	98.1	105.8	85.7	97.4	99.7	137.8	115.5
08	OPENINGS	96.5	101.7	97.7	96.5	82.4	93.3	96.8	64.2	89.4	84.2	78.2	82.8	84.8	78.8	83.4	99.9	145.1	110.1
0920	Plaster & Gypsum Board	107.3	101.5	103.5	103.7	79.5	87.6	114.3	54.5	74.5	103.0	69.7	80.9	106.0	69.7	81.9	103.5	142.0	129.1
0950, 0980	Ceilings & Acoustic Treatment	99.2	101.5	100.7	100.1	79.5	86.4	99.2	54.5	69.5	106.3	69.7	81.9	106.3	69.7	81.9	100.6	142.0	128.6
0960	Flooring	90.2	54.3	79.8	88.2	96.5	90.6	94.1	60.0	84.2	94.4	78.0	89.6	97.9	78.0	92.1	97.9	161.0	116.2
0970, 0990	Wall Finishes & Painting/Coating	99.2	75.7	85.4	99.2	75.7	85.4	99.2	75.7	85.4	114.7	75.7	91.8	114.7	75.7	91.8	101.8	156.9	134.2
09	FINISHES	94.9	85.5	89.8	94.2	83.9	88.6	97.9	56.6	75.3	93.0	71.2	81.1	94.8	70.7	81.6	100.4	146.8	125.8
COVERS	DIVS. 10 - 14, 25, 28, 41, 43, 44, 46	100.0	59.8	90.9	100.0	92.2	98.2	100.0	82.1	96.0	100.0	83.3	96.2	100.0	83.8	96.3	100.0	117.2	103.9
21, 22, 23	FIRE SUPPRESSION, PLUMBING & HVAC	96.3	81.3	89.7	99.9	87.3	94.3	96.3	74.0	86.5	96.6	85.1	91.5	96.6	82.4	90.3	100.1	126.4	111.7
26, 27, 3370	ELECTRICAL, COMMUNICATIONS & UTIL.	97.7	91.5	94.4	96.3	82.1	88.8	94.7	65.1	79.0	95.7	101.2	98.6	93.3	101.2	97.5	101.3	129.4	116.2
MF2014	WEIGHTED AVERAGE	95.2	86.8	91.5	96.6	88.3	92.9	98.4	68.8	85.4	96.0	85.6	91.4	96.7	84.2	91.2	99.9	133.4	114.7

MASSACHUSETTS

	DIVISION	BROCKTON 023			BUZZARDS BAY 025			FALL RIVER 027			FITCHBURG 014			FRAMINGHAM 017			GREENFIELD 013		
		MAT.	INST.	TOTAL	MAT.	INST.	TOTAL	MAT.	INST.	TOTAL	MAT.	INST.	TOTAL	MAT.	INST.	TOTAL	MAT.	INST.	TOTAL
015433	CONTRACTOR EQUIPMENT		102.4	102.4		102.4	102.4		103.3	103.3		99.8	99.8		101.7	101.7		99.8	99.8
0241, 31 - 34	SITE & INFRASTRUCTURE, DEMOLITION	94.5	104.5	101.5	84.8	104.5	98.5	93.5	104.6	101.2	85.2	104.4	98.6	81.9	104.2	97.5	88.8	103.4	98.9
0310	Concrete Forming & Accessories	100.7	126.4	123.0	98.2	126.0	122.3	100.7	126.3	122.8	94.8	126.2	122.0	102.6	126.5	123.3	93.1	112.1	109.5
0320	Concrete Reinforcing	102.6	146.0	124.6	82.3	123.1	103.0	102.6	123.2	113.0	86.3	145.6	116.4	86.3	146.3	116.8	90.0	119.7	105.1
0330	Cast-in-Place Concrete	91.5	137.5	109.0	76.1	137.3	99.4	88.5	137.8	107.3	79.5	137.4	101.6	79.5	137.6	101.6	81.7	126.2	98.7
03	CONCRETE	95.0	133.2	112.7	80.5	128.9	102.9	93.6	129.2	110.1	79.5	132.8	104.2	82.1	133.3	105.8	82.9	117.9	99.1
04	MASONRY	102.6	133.6	121.7	95.5	141.3	123.7	103.3	141.3	126.7	103.3	137.8	124.6	110.1	138.4	127.5	108.2	122.4	117.0
05	METALS	93.1	128.1	103.8	88.1	118.8	97.5	93.1	119.2	101.1	90.6	124.8	101.1	90.6	128.4	102.2	92.9	110.7	98.4
06	WOOD, PLASTICS & COMPOSITES	103.8	126.0	116.0	100.9	126.0	114.7	103.8	126.3	116.2	100.5	126.0	114.6	106.7	125.8	117.2	98.6	110.5	105.1
07	THERMAL & MOISTURE PROTECTION	100.5	129.6	112.6	99.4	129.2	111.7	100.3	128.5	112.0	99.7	125.7	110.5	99.8	130.8	112.7	99.8	112.0	104.8
08	OPENINGS	99.6	134.0	107.4	95.4	124.0	101.9	99.6	124.2	105.1	100.4	133.8	108.0	91.2	133.9	100.8	100.8	114.9	104.0
0920	Plaster & Gypsum Board	91.7	126.3	114.7	87.8	126.3	113.4	91.7	126.3	114.7	108.3	126.3	120.3	111.0	126.3	121.2	109.3	110.3	110.0
0950, 0980	Ceilings & Acoustic Treatment	104.9	126.3	119.1	91.5	126.3	114.7	104.9	126.3	119.1	90.4	126.3	114.3	90.4	126.3	114.3	98.9	110.3	106.5
0960	Flooring	95.1	161.0	114.2	92.9	161.0	112.6	94.1	161.0	113.5	91.5	161.0	111.7	93.4	161.0	113.0	90.7	133.3	103.1
0970, 0990	Wall Finishes & Painting/Coating	93.9	140.0	120.9	93.9	140.0	120.9	93.9	140.0	120.9	90.7	140.0	119.6	91.6	140.0	120.0	90.7	116.4	105.8
09	FINISHES	94.5	134.9	116.6	90.0	134.9	114.5	94.3	135.1	116.5	89.8	134.9	114.4	90.5	134.7	114.7	91.7	116.7	105.4
COVERS	DIVS. 10 - 14, 25, 28, 41, 43, 44, 46	100.0	114.0	103.2	100.0	114.0	103.2	100.0	114.6	103.3	100.0	108.6	102.0	100.0	113.6	103.1	100.0	106.0	101.4
21, 22, 23	FIRE SUPPRESSION, PLUMBING & HVAC	100.3	107.6	103.6	96.8	107.4	101.5	100.3	107.4	103.5	96.9	108.1	102.1	96.9	121.6	107.9	96.9	100.5	98.5
26, 27, 3370	ELECTRICAL, COMMUNICATIONS & UTIL.	99.8	103.0	101.5	97.0	103.0	100.2	99.7	103.0	101.4	100.0	100.7	100.4	96.6	122.2	110.2	100.0	97.7	98.8
MF2014	WEIGHTED AVERAGE	97.8	120.3	107.7	92.6	119.2	104.3	97.6	119.3	107.2	94.2	120.0	105.6	93.5	126.5	108.1	95.5	109.1	101.5

MASSACHUSETTS

	DIVISION	HYANNIS 026			LAWRENCE 019			LOWELL 018			NEW BEDFORD 027			PITTSFIELD 012			SPRINGFIELD 010 - 011		
		MAT.	INST.	TOTAL	MAT.	INST.	TOTAL	MAT.	INST.	TOTAL	MAT.	INST.	TOTAL	MAT.	INST.	TOTAL	MAT.	INST.	TOTAL
015433	CONTRACTOR EQUIPMENT		102.4	102.4		102.4	102.4		99.8	99.8		103.3	103.3		99.8	99.8		99.8	99.8
0241, 31 - 34	SITE & INFRASTRUCTURE, DEMOLITION	90.9	104.5	100.4	94.0	104.5	101.3	92.9	104.4	100.9	92.0	104.6	100.8	93.9	103.0	100.2	93.3	103.4	100.3
0310	Concrete Forming & Accessories	92.4	126.0	121.5	103.9	126.9	123.8	100.2	126.8	123.2	100.7	126.3	122.8	100.2	109.7	108.5	100.4	112.1	110.5
0320	Concrete Reinforcing	82.3	123.1	103.0	106.8	138.0	122.6	107.7	137.8	123.0	102.6	123.2	113.0	89.4	121.9	105.9	107.7	119.7	113.8
0330	Cast-in-Place Concrete	83.5	137.3	104.0	92.0	137.6	109.4	83.7	137.6	104.2	78.0	137.8	100.8	91.3	118.3	101.6	87.1	126.2	102.0
03	CONCRETE	86.5	128.9	106.2	95.9	132.0	112.7	87.9	131.7	108.2	88.5	129.2	107.4	89.1	114.5	100.9	89.5	117.9	102.7
04	MASONRY	101.5	141.3	126.0	116.1	141.3	131.6	102.2	137.8	124.1	101.5	141.3	126.0	102.8	116.5	111.2	102.4	122.4	114.7
05	METALS	89.6	118.8	98.5	93.3	125.6	103.2	93.3	122.1	102.1	93.1	119.2	101.1	93.1	111.5	98.7	95.9	110.7	100.4
06	WOOD, PLASTICS & COMPOSITES	94.5	126.0	111.8	106.9	126.0	117.4	106.4	126.0	117.2	103.8	126.3	116.2	106.4	110.5	108.6	106.4	110.5	108.6
07	THERMAL & MOISTURE PROTECTION	99.9	129.2	112.0	100.4	131.8	113.4	100.2	130.8	112.9	100.3	128.5	112.0	100.3	108.6	103.7	100.2	112.0	105.1
08	OPENINGS	95.9	124.0	102.3	95.0	131.6	103.3	101.9	131.6	108.6	99.6	124.2	105.1	101.9	115.5	105.0	101.9	114.9	104.8
0920	Plaster & Gypsum Board	83.5	126.3	112.0	113.6	126.3	122.0	113.6	126.3	122.0	91.7	126.3	114.7	113.6	110.3	111.4	113.6	110.3	111.4
0950, 0980	Ceilings & Acoustic Treatment	98.1	126.3	116.9	100.8	126.3	117.8	100.8	126.3	117.8	104.9	126.3	119.1	100.8	110.3	107.1	100.8	110.3	107.1
0960	Flooring	90.1	161.0	110.7	93.8	161.0	113.3	93.8	161.0	113.3	94.1	161.0	113.5	94.3	133.3	105.6	93.3	133.3	104.9
0970, 0990	Wall Finishes & Painting/Coating	93.9	140.0	120.9	90.8	140.0	119.7	90.7	140.0	119.6	93.9	140.0	120.9	90.7	116.4	105.8	91.9	116.4	106.3
09	FINISHES	90.3	134.9	114.6	93.8	134.9	116.3	93.8	134.9	116.2	94.1	135.1	116.5	94.0	115.2	105.6	93.7	116.7	106.3
COVERS	DIVS. 10 - 14, 25, 28, 41, 43, 44, 46	100.0	114.0	103.2	100.0	114.1	103.2	100.0	114.1	103.2	100.0	114.6	103.3	100.0	104.0	100.9	100.0	106.0	101.4
21, 22, 23	FIRE SUPPRESSION, PLUMBING & HVAC	100.3	107.4	103.4	100.1	124.1	110.7	100.1	124.1	110.7	100.3	107.4	103.5	100.1	97.5	98.9	100.1	100.5	100.3
26, 27, 3370	ELECTRICAL, COMMUNICATIONS & UTIL.	97.4	103.0	100.4	99.1	127.6	114.2	99.6	122.1	111.5	100.6	103.0	101.8	99.6	97.7	98.6	99.6	97.7	98.6
MF2014	WEIGHTED AVERAGE	94.9	119.2	105.6	97.9	127.6	111.1	97.0	126.1	109.9	96.9	119.3	106.8	97.2	107.1	101.6	97.7	109.1	102.7

	DIVISION	MASSACHUSETTS WORCESTER 015 - 016			MICHIGAN ANN ARBOR 481			BATTLE CREEK 490			BAY CITY 487			DEARBORN 481			DETROIT 482		
		MAT.	INST.	TOTAL	MAT.	INST.	TOTAL	MAT.	INST.	TOTAL	MAT.	INST.	TOTAL	MAT.	INST.	TOTAL	MAT.	INST.	TOTAL
015433	CONTRACTOR EQUIPMENT		99.8	99.8		114.1	114.1		100.4	100.4		114.1	114.1		114.1	114.1		95.9	95.9
0241, 31 - 34	SITE & INFRASTRUCTURE, DEMOLITION	93.3	104.4	101.0	82.3	97.9	93.2	93.4	86.0	88.3	73.7	96.9	89.9	82.0	98.0	93.2	97.6	99.8	99.2
0310	Concrete Forming & Accessories	100.8	126.2	122.8	98.2	108.5	107.1	98.4	80.6	83.0	98.3	84.4	86.3	98.1	109.4	107.9	100.8	109.3	108.2
0320	Concrete Reinforcing	107.7	145.6	127.0	97.6	105.4	101.6	94.8	79.2	86.9	97.6	104.6	101.2	97.6	105.5	101.6	99.4	105.4	102.5
0330	Cast-in-Place Concrete	86.6	137.4	105.9	87.7	102.7	93.4	84.9	94.1	88.4	83.9	87.2	85.2	85.8	104.0	92.7	102.4	105.8	104.1
03	CONCRETE	89.3	132.7	109.4	90.7	106.8	98.1	88.2	84.7	86.6	88.9	90.4	89.6	89.7	107.6	98.0	102.4	105.8	104.0
04	MASONRY	102.0	137.8	124.1	99.4	101.4	100.6	99.2	80.9	87.9	99.0	82.4	88.8	99.2	103.7	102.0	95.0	103.7	100.4
05	METALS	96.0	124.7	104.8	99.3	118.0	105.1	103.5	81.8	96.9	99.9	114.8	104.5	99.4	118.1	105.1	98.7	94.3	97.4
06	WOOD, PLASTICS & COMPOSITES	106.9	126.0	117.4	91.4	110.6	101.9	89.4	79.2	83.8	91.4	84.7	87.7	91.4	110.6	101.9	97.9	110.5	104.9
07	THERMAL & MOISTURE PROTECTION	100.2	125.7	110.8	103.7	103.3	103.5	100.2	79.2	91.5	101.1	86.8	95.2	102.0	107.3	104.2	101.3	107.1	103.7
08	OPENINGS	101.9	133.8	109.1	96.8	104.5	98.5	91.9	77.1	88.6	96.8	88.8	95.0	96.8	104.5	98.5	98.8	104.5	100.1
0920	Plaster & Gypsum Board	113.6	126.3	122.0	105.1	110.5	108.7	98.0	75.1	82.8	105.1	83.9	91.0	105.1	110.5	108.7	98.7	110.5	106.5
0950, 0980	Ceilings & Acoustic Treatment	100.8	126.3	117.8	87.2	110.5	102.7	79.8	75.1	76.7	88.1	83.9	85.3	87.2	110.5	102.7	96.8	110.5	105.9
0960	Flooring	93.8	153.3	111.1	93.0	110.0	97.9	93.9	70.4	87.1	93.0	74.3	87.6	92.5	104.4	96.0	97.9	104.4	99.8
0970, 0990	Wall Finishes & Painting/Coating	90.7	140.0	119.6	83.9	101.8	94.4	89.8	79.5	83.8	83.9	81.3	82.4	83.9	99.9	93.3	89.1	99.9	95.4
09	FINISHES	93.8	133.3	115.4	91.5	108.6	100.8	88.3	78.6	83.0	91.3	81.7	86.0	91.3	108.0	100.4	97.2	107.9	103.1
COVERS	DIVS. 10 - 14, 25, 28, 41, 43, 44, 46	100.0	108.7	102.0	100.0	103.0	100.7	100.0	95.3	98.9	100.0	89.1	97.5	100.0	103.8	100.9	100.0	103.6	100.8
21, 22, 23	FIRE SUPPRESSION, PLUMBING & HVAC	100.1	108.6	103.8	100.1	95.2	97.9	100.1	85.8	93.8	100.1	80.9	91.6	100.1	104.0	101.8	100.0	104.5	102.0
26, 27, 3370	ELECTRICAL, COMMUNICATIONS & UTIL.	99.6	105.2	102.5	97.5	103.5	100.7	94.9	82.2	88.1	96.6	92.4	94.4	97.5	97.7	97.6	98.8	97.6	98.2
MF2014	WEIGHTED AVERAGE	97.7	120.4	107.7	97.0	103.6	99.9	96.5	83.1	90.6	96.4	89.3	93.3	96.8	105.1	100.5	99.3	102.9	100.9

MICHIGAN

DIVISION		FLINT 484-485			GAYLORD 497			GRAND RAPIDS 493,495			IRON MOUNTAIN 498-499			JACKSON 492			KALAMAZOO 491		
		MAT.	INST.	TOTAL	MAT.	INST.	TOTAL	MAT.	INST.	TOTAL	MAT.	INST.	TOTAL	MAT.	INST.	TOTAL	MAT.	INST.	TOTAL
015433	CONTRACTOR EQUIPMENT		114.1	114.1		108.5	108.5		100.4	100.4		95.0	95.0		108.5	108.5		100.4	100.4
0241, 31-34	SITE & INFRASTRUCTURE, DEMOLITION	71.6	97.0	89.3	87.9	83.0	84.5	92.2	86.1	87.9	96.4	92.3	93.5	110.7	85.4	93.0	93.7	86.0	88.3
0310	Concrete Forming & Accessories	101.1	85.9	88.0	96.9	74.6	77.6	97.6	81.0	83.3	88.1	81.1	82.1	93.4	84.0	85.3	98.4	80.3	82.7
0320	Concrete Reinforcing	97.6	105.0	101.3	88.3	89.8	89.1	99.4	79.3	89.2	88.2	86.4	87.3	85.8	104.6	95.4	84.9	79.2	86.9
0330	Cast-in-Place Concrete	88.3	90.9	89.3	84.7	82.5	83.9	89.1	95.7	91.6	100.3	71.2	89.2	84.6	88.3	86.0	86.6	96.1	90.2
03	CONCRETE	91.1	92.4	91.7	84.9	81.9	83.5	92.2	85.4	89.1	93.5	79.2	86.9	80.0	90.4	84.8	91.4	85.2	88.6
04	MASONRY	99.4	91.1	94.3	110.1	77.4	89.9	92.0	83.1	86.5	95.0	82.0	87.0	89.2	84.1	86.0	97.7	81.6	87.8
05	METALS	99.4	115.5	104.3	105.1	112.3	107.3	100.5	81.6	94.7	104.5	91.1	100.4	105.3	112.9	107.6	103.5	81.6	96.8
06	WOOD, PLASTICS & COMPOSITES	94.8	84.8	89.3	82.9	74.1	78.1	92.4	79.9	85.5	78.5	81.7	80.3	81.7	82.6	82.2	89.4	79.2	83.8
07	THERMAL & MOISTURE PROTECTION	101.4	90.9	97.0	98.7	72.3	87.7	101.9	73.4	90.1	102.6	77.8	92.3	98.0	86.6	93.3	100.2	80.0	91.8
08	OPENINGS	96.8	88.2	94.8	92.2	81.8	89.9	99.1	78.9	94.5	99.2	72.6	93.2	91.3	86.5	90.2	91.9	74.2	87.9
0920	Plaster & Gypsum Board	107.1	84.0	91.7	97.8	72.3	80.9	97.9	75.7	83.2	52.7	81.8	72.0	96.2	81.0	86.1	98.0	75.1	82.8
0950, 0980	Ceilings & Acoustic Treatment	87.2	84.0	85.0	79.0	72.3	74.5	91.5	75.7	81.0	77.9	81.8	80.5	79.0	81.0	80.3	79.8	75.1	76.7
0960	Flooring	93.0	85.6	90.9	87.0	82.2	85.6	96.1	76.6	90.5	106.5	90.2	101.8	85.7	74.0	82.3	93.9	74.0	88.2
0970, 0990	Wall Finishes & Painting/Coating	83.9	80.0	81.6	86.1	82.5	84.0	91.1	79.2	84.1	104.1	69.2	83.6	86.1	99.9	94.2	89.8	79.5	83.8
09	FINISHES	91.0	84.7	87.5	87.7	76.6	81.7	92.3	79.8	85.5	88.1	81.7	84.6	88.7	83.2	85.7	88.3	78.6	83.0
COVERS	DIVS. 10-14, 25, 28, 41, 43, 44, 46	100.0	90.2	97.8	100.0	82.7	96.1	100.0	90.1	97.7	100.0	81.2	95.7	100.0	99.5	99.9	100.0	89.6	97.7
21, 22, 23	FIRE SUPPRESSION, PLUMBING & HVAC	100.1	86.7	94.2	96.8	73.9	86.7	100.1	82.4	92.3	96.7	80.5	89.6	96.8	86.7	92.3	100.1	77.7	90.2
26, 27, 3370	ELECTRICAL, COMMUNICATIONS & UTIL.	97.5	94.1	95.7	92.6	75.1	83.3	100.0	74.6	86.5	99.2	83.4	90.8	96.7	102.6	99.9	94.7	80.3	87.1
MF2014	WEIGHTED AVERAGE	96.7	92.4	94.8	95.7	80.7	89.1	97.8	81.5	90.6	97.7	82.6	91.0	95.0	91.4	93.4	96.8	80.9	89.8

MICHIGAN / MINNESOTA

DIVISION		LANSING 488-489			MUSKEGON 494			ROYAL OAK 480,483			SAGINAW 486			TRAVERSE CITY 496			BEMIDJI 566		
		MAT.	INST.	TOTAL	MAT.	INST.	TOTAL	MAT.	INST.	TOTAL	MAT.	INST.	TOTAL	MAT.	INST.	TOTAL	MAT.	INST.	TOTAL
015433	CONTRACTOR EQUIPMENT		114.1	114.1		100.4	100.4		93.2	93.2		114.1	114.1		95.0	95.0		101.8	101.8
0241, 31-34	SITE & INFRASTRUCTURE, DEMOLITION	92.5	97.1	95.7	91.3	86.0	87.6	86.4	96.9	93.7	74.7	96.8	90.1	82.0	91.7	88.8	95.9	100.6	99.2
0310	Concrete Forming & Accessories	96.3	85.3	86.7	98.7	78.8	81.4	93.5	108.8	106.7	98.3	84.2	86.1	88.1	74.8	76.6	86.7	84.8	85.1
0320	Concrete Reinforcing	99.4	104.6	102.1	95.4	79.0	87.1	88.4	90.7	89.6	97.6	104.6	101.1	89.5	78.5	84.0	97.4	95.8	96.6
0330	Cast-in-Place Concrete	93.6	90.1	92.3	84.6	90.6	86.9	76.8	103.4	86.9	86.7	87.1	86.8	78.2	78.9	78.5	101.5	101.4	101.5
03	CONCRETE	92.0	91.8	91.9	86.6	82.6	84.7	78.0	103.0	89.6	90.2	90.3	90.2	76.9	77.6	77.2	92.6	93.9	93.2
04	MASONRY	98.3	87.2	91.5	96.3	77.3	84.6	92.9	101.4	98.1	100.8	82.4	89.5	93.2	78.8	84.3	101.2	100.4	100.7
05	METALS	100.5	114.6	104.8	101.1	81.1	95.0	102.8	91.6	99.4	99.4	114.6	104.1	104.5	87.3	99.2	92.0	115.4	99.2
06	WOOD, PLASTICS & COMPOSITES	90.9	84.0	87.1	86.2	77.6	81.5	87.2	110.6	100.0	87.8	84.7	86.1	78.5	74.9	76.5	66.9	80.4	74.4
07	THERMAL & MOISTURE PROTECTION	98.9	84.0	92.7	99.1	73.5	88.5	99.7	104.3	101.6	102.3	87.1	96.0	101.7	70.4	88.7	107.0	95.0	102.0
08	OPENINGS	99.6	87.0	96.7	91.2	77.4	88.1	96.6	104.4	98.4	94.8	88.8	93.4	99.2	67.6	92.1	99.1	101.2	99.6
0920	Plaster & Gypsum Board	97.3	83.1	87.9	77.1	73.4	74.7	102.8	110.5	107.9	105.1	83.9	91.0	52.7	74.8	67.4	108.9	80.2	89.9
0950, 0980	Ceilings & Acoustic Treatment	89.0	83.1	85.1	80.7	73.4	75.8	86.4	110.5	102.4	87.2	83.9	85.0	77.9	74.8	75.9	119.6	80.2	93.4
0960	Flooring	97.5	76.6	91.4	92.6	76.6	88.0	89.9	101.8	93.4	93.0	74.3	87.6	106.5	88.3	101.2	95.1	110.6	99.6
0970, 0990	Wall Finishes & Painting/Coating	92.8	79.2	84.8	88.0	78.0	82.1	85.1	99.9	93.8	83.9	81.3	82.4	104.1	42.0	67.6	93.9	110.5	103.7
09	FINISHES	92.3	82.5	87.0	84.4	77.4	80.6	90.3	107.2	99.5	91.2	81.7	86.0	87.1	74.0	79.9	99.5	91.5	95.1
COVERS	DIVS. 10-14, 25, 28, 41, 43, 44, 46	100.0	98.7	99.7	100.0	89.4	97.6	100.0	100.1	100.0	100.0	89.1	97.5	100.0	79.7	95.4	100.0	97.2	99.4
21, 22, 23	FIRE SUPPRESSION, PLUMBING & HVAC	100.0	86.2	93.8	99.9	81.8	91.9	96.8	100.9	98.6	100.1	80.4	91.4	96.7	79.2	89.0	96.9	81.1	89.9
26, 27, 3370	ELECTRICAL, COMMUNICATIONS & UTIL.	100.3	88.0	93.8	95.1	76.9	85.5	99.6	100.0	99.8	95.6	89.8	92.5	94.3	75.1	84.1	104.8	104.7	104.8
MF2014	WEIGHTED AVERAGE	98.0	90.7	94.8	95.2	80.3	88.6	95.0	101.0	97.7	96.3	88.8	93.0	94.5	78.7	87.5	97.3	95.8	96.6

MINNESOTA

DIVISION		BRAINERD 564			DETROIT LAKES 565			DULUTH 556-558			MANKATO 560			MINNEAPOLIS 553-555			ROCHESTER 559		
		MAT.	INST.	TOTAL	MAT.	INST.	TOTAL	MAT.	INST.	TOTAL	MAT.	INST.	TOTAL	MAT.	INST.	TOTAL	MAT.	INST.	TOTAL
015433	CONTRACTOR EQUIPMENT		104.5	104.5		101.8	101.8		104.8	104.8		104.5	104.5		107.9	107.9		104.8	104.8
0241, 31-34	SITE & INFRASTRUCTURE, DEMOLITION	98.2	105.7	103.4	94.1	100.9	98.8	97.7	103.9	102.0	94.9	105.4	102.2	97.4	107.8	104.7	97.8	102.8	101.3
0310	Concrete Forming & Accessories	87.8	87.1	87.2	83.7	86.4	86.0	99.3	98.5	98.6	95.9	91.0	91.7	99.5	113.1	111.2	100.6	94.9	95.7
0320	Concrete Reinforcing	96.1	95.9	96.0	97.4	95.9	96.6	96.3	96.0	96.1	96.0	103.1	99.6	95.3	103.7	99.5	93.8	103.2	98.6
0330	Cast-in-Place Concrete	110.4	105.6	108.6	98.6	104.1	100.7	97.3	102.2	99.2	101.7	106.2	103.4	101.5	112.8	105.8	99.1	96.5	98.1
03	CONCRETE	96.6	96.4	96.5	90.3	95.5	92.7	95.7	100.4	97.9	92.1	99.6	95.6	98.9	112.0	105.0	94.1	98.2	96.0
04	MASONRY	126.1	108.0	115.0	125.7	105.3	113.1	100.7	108.1	105.2	114.0	101.6	106.4	106.4	117.5	113.2	100.6	104.1	102.7
05	METALS	93.2	115.2	99.9	92.0	115.1	99.0	99.7	117.3	105.1	93.0	118.8	100.9	99.1	122.4	106.2	99.3	120.7	105.9
06	WOOD, PLASTICS & COMPOSITES	83.8	80.2	81.8	64.2	80.4	73.1	88.8	96.5	93.0	92.6	87.8	90.0	93.6	110.6	103.0	94.6	93.0	93.7
07	THERMAL & MOISTURE PROTECTION	105.4	102.4	104.2	106.9	101.3	104.6	106.1	104.0	105.2	105.8	91.5	99.9	104.8	116.7	109.7	109.8	94.6	103.5
08	OPENINGS	86.0	101.1	89.4	99.1	101.2	99.6	107.3	104.2	106.6	90.5	107.8	94.4	100.7	120.3	105.1	101.2	110.6	103.4
0920	Plaster & Gypsum Board	94.8	80.2	85.1	107.9	80.2	89.5	96.2	96.9	96.6	99.4	88.0	91.9	99.0	111.2	107.1	103.3	93.2	96.6
0950, 0980	Ceilings & Acoustic Treatment	56.4	80.2	72.3	119.6	80.2	93.4	98.2	96.9	97.3	56.4	88.0	77.5	98.6	111.2	107.0	92.7	93.2	93.0
0960	Flooring	93.9	110.6	98.7	93.7	110.6	98.6	99.4	118.5	104.9	95.9	115.5	101.6	98.5	110.6	102.0	97.1	81.0	92.4
0970, 0990	Wall Finishes & Painting/Coating	88.2	110.5	101.3	93.9	88.8	90.9	88.6	104.5	98.0	99.5	102.0	101.0	104.8	125.5	117.0	89.5	103.1	97.5
09	FINISHES	83.7	93.0	88.7	98.8	90.3	94.2	94.0	102.7	98.8	85.5	96.2	91.4	98.4	114.0	106.9	92.7	93.4	93.1
COVERS	DIVS. 10-14, 25, 28, 41, 43, 44, 46	100.0	98.9	99.8	100.0	98.7	99.7	100.0	90.4	97.8	100.0	98.2	99.6	100.0	105.4	101.2	100.0	99.6	99.9
21, 22, 23	FIRE SUPPRESSION, PLUMBING & HVAC	95.9	84.4	90.8	96.9	83.5	90.9	99.9	96.4	98.3	95.9	85.4	91.3	100.0	108.0	103.5	100.0	92.9	96.8
26, 27, 3370	ELECTRICAL, COMMUNICATIONS & UTIL.	102.3	102.1	102.2	104.6	68.3	85.3	100.4	102.2	101.3	109.2	91.1	99.6	101.1	111.7	106.7	100.1	91.1	95.3
MF2014	WEIGHTED AVERAGE	96.1	98.1	97.0	98.0	92.1	95.4	99.8	102.6	101.1	96.3	97.3	96.7	100.1	112.8	105.7	98.9	98.9	98.9

City Cost Indexes

		MINNESOTA																MISSISSIPPI		
		SAINT PAUL			ST. CLOUD			THIEF RIVER FALLS			WILLMAR			WINDOM			BILOXI		
DIVISION		550 - 551			563			567			562			561			395		
		MAT.	INST.	TOTAL	MAT.	INST.	TOTAL	MAT.	INST.	TOTAL	MAT.	INST.	TOTAL	MAT.	INST.	TOTAL	MAT.	INST.	TOTAL
015433	CONTRACTOR EQUIPMENT		104.8	104.8		104.5	104.5		101.8	101.8		104.5	101.6		104.5	104.5		104.5	104.5
0241, 31 - 34	SITE & INFRASTRUCTURE, DEMOLITION	95.1	104.6	101.7	93.4	106.3	102.4	94.9	100.5	98.8	92.8	105.7	101.8	86.7	104.9	99.4	103.5	90.5	94.4
0310	Concrete Forming & Accessories	99.3	113.6	111.7	85.1	102.4	100.0	87.4	83.9	84.4	84.9	81.1	81.6	89.3	75.3	77.2	96.3	64.7	69.0
0320	Concrete Reinforcing	97.1	103.6	100.4	96.1	103.1	99.7	97.8	95.7	96.7	95.7	103.0	99.4	95.7	102.4	99.1	83.2	51.2	67.0
0330	Cast-in-Place Concrete	103.6	111.5	106.6	97.4	107.8	101.4	100.6	84.1	94.3	98.9	82.3	92.6	85.6	87.6	86.3	115.1	61.8	94.8
03	CONCRETE	99.0	111.8	104.9	88.1	105.3	96.1	91.3	87.4	89.5	88.1	86.9	87.5	79.1	86.1	82.3	101.5	63.1	83.7
04	MASONRY	99.7	117.4	110.6	110.1	104.3	106.5	101.1	100.4	100.7	114.2	104.4	108.2	125.3	86.4	101.3	99.4	62.2	76.5
05	METALS	99.7	122.3	106.6	93.8	119.5	101.7	92.1	114.4	98.9	93.0	118.5	100.8	92.9	117.2	100.3	93.1	87.1	91.3
06	WOOD, PLASTICS & COMPOSITES	94.7	111.4	103.9	81.3	99.9	91.5	67.9	80.4	74.8	81.0	72.2	76.2	85.0	69.9	76.7	102.9	69.7	84.7
07	THERMAL & MOISTURE PROTECTION	104.9	115.9	109.4	105.6	103.3	104.6	107.9	88.7	99.9	105.4	97.9	102.3	105.3	83.7	96.4	97.8	64.7	84.0
08	OPENINGS	99.8	120.7	104.5	91.0	114.5	96.3	99.1	101.2	99.6	88.0	99.2	90.6	91.6	98.0	93.1	101.0	59.1	91.5
0920	Plaster & Gypsum Board	97.1	112.2	107.1	94.8	100.5	98.6	108.6	80.2	89.7	94.8	72.0	79.6	94.8	69.6	78.1	97.0	69.3	78.6
0950, 0980	Ceilings & Acoustic Treatment	97.0	112.2	107.1	56.4	100.5	85.7	119.6	80.2	93.4	56.4	72.0	66.8	56.4	69.6	65.2	87.6	69.3	75.4
0960	Flooring	92.9	110.6	98.0	90.6	110.6	96.4	94.7	110.6	99.3	91.9	106.8	96.3	94.6	106.8	98.1	94.6	77.7	89.7
0970, 0990	Wall Finishes & Painting/Coating	91.3	125.5	111.4	99.5	125.5	114.8	93.9	88.8	90.9	93.9	88.8	90.9	93.9	102.0	98.6	84.9	49.9	64.4
09	FINISHES	91.7	114.4	104.1	83.1	106.1	95.7	99.3	89.1	93.7	83.1	85.2	84.3	83.4	82.9	83.1	88.4	66.3	76.3
COVERS	DIVS. 10 - 14, 25, 28, 41, 43, 44, 46	100.0	105.0	101.1	100.0	94.6	98.8	100.0	97.1	99.3	100.0	98.0	99.5	100.0	94.5	98.8	100.0	71.1	93.5
21, 22, 23	FIRE SUPPRESSION, PLUMBING & HVAC	99.9	109.6	104.3	99.5	104.8	101.8	96.9	80.9	89.8	95.9	102.0	98.6	95.9	81.9	89.7	99.9	51.3	78.4
26, 27, 3370	ELECTRICAL, COMMUNICATIONS & UTIL.	99.7	113.0	106.8	102.3	113.0	108.0	101.7	68.3	84.0	102.3	81.8	91.4	109.2	91.1	99.6	101.0	57.6	78.0
MF2014	WEIGHTED AVERAGE	99.0	113.2	105.3	95.5	107.6	100.9	96.8	89.3	93.5	94.5	96.4	95.3	94.9	90.4	92.9	98.2	64.7	83.4

		MISSISSIPPI																	
		CLARKSDALE			COLUMBUS			GREENVILLE			GREENWOOD			JACKSON			LAUREL		
DIVISION		386			397			387			389			390 - 392			394		
		MAT.	INST.	TOTAL	MAT.	INST.	TOTAL	MAT.	INST.	TOTAL	MAT.	INST.	TOTAL	MAT.	INST.	TOTAL	MAT.	INST.	TOTAL
015433	CONTRACTOR EQUIPMENT		104.5	104.5		104.5	104.5		104.5	104.5		104.5	104.5		104.5	104.5		104.5	104.5
0241, 31 - 34	SITE & INFRASTRUCTURE, DEMOLITION	96.6	89.9	91.9	102.2	90.7	94.1	102.1	91.0	94.4	99.3	89.6	92.5	98.4	91.1	93.3	107.4	89.9	95.2
0310	Concrete Forming & Accessories	86.5	47.0	52.3	84.7	48.9	53.7	83.1	66.2	68.5	95.9	46.9	53.5	94.6	66.7	70.4	84.8	63.5	66.3
0320	Concrete Reinforcing	96.9	65.4	80.9	89.1	36.3	62.3	97.4	52.1	74.4	96.9	44.5	70.3	92.4	51.3	71.5	89.7	33.2	61.1
0330	Cast-in-Place Concrete	101.4	51.7	82.5	117.4	57.0	94.4	104.5	58.0	86.8	109.1	51.3	87.1	100.3	66.7	87.5	114.8	53.0	91.3
03	CONCRETE	95.2	54.1	76.2	103.0	51.8	79.2	100.8	62.6	83.1	101.6	50.1	77.8	95.7	65.7	81.8	105.6	56.3	82.8
04	MASONRY	94.8	42.4	62.5	126.4	48.7	78.6	141.0	71.0	97.9	95.4	42.3	62.7	105.2	71.0	84.1	122.3	45.3	74.9
05	METALS	93.4	88.6	92.0	90.3	80.2	87.2	94.4	86.9	92.1	93.4	78.7	88.9	100.0	87.1	96.0	90.3	77.2	86.3
06	WOOD, PLASTICS & COMPOSITES	85.0	47.9	64.6	88.9	48.8	66.9	81.8	67.9	74.2	97.5	47.9	70.3	97.7	67.9	81.3	90.0	69.7	78.9
07	THERMAL & MOISTURE PROTECTION	96.6	52.1	78.1	97.7	52.1	78.8	97.1	66.6	84.4	97.0	54.4	79.3	96.1	67.9	84.4	97.9	54.2	79.8
08	OPENINGS	96.3	51.0	86.0	100.6	44.3	87.8	96.0	58.3	87.5	96.3	44.6	84.6	102.2	58.1	92.2	97.4	55.6	88.0
0920	Plaster & Gypsum Board	87.5	46.9	60.5	88.0	47.8	61.3	87.2	67.4	74.1	98.4	46.9	64.2	88.8	67.4	74.6	88.0	69.3	75.6
0950, 0980	Ceilings & Acoustic Treatment	82.1	46.9	58.7	82.3	47.8	59.4	85.0	67.4	73.3	82.1	46.9	58.7	90.9	67.4	75.3	82.3	69.3	73.7
0960	Flooring	100.1	47.7	84.9	88.5	53.5	78.4	98.3	47.7	83.7	106.0	47.7	89.1	91.8	77.7	87.7	87.1	47.7	75.7
0970, 0990	Wall Finishes & Painting/Coating	94.3	49.9	68.3	84.9	49.9	64.4	94.3	49.9	68.3	94.3	49.9	68.3	85.6	49.9	64.7	84.9	49.9	64.4
09	FINISHES	90.5	47.1	66.8	84.3	49.5	65.3	91.1	61.2	74.8	94.1	47.1	68.4	87.4	67.5	76.5	84.4	60.6	71.4
COVERS	DIVS. 10 - 14, 25, 28, 41, 43, 44, 46	100.0	51.3	89.0	100.0	52.4	89.2	100.0	73.8	94.1	100.0	51.3	89.0	100.0	73.8	94.1	100.0	36.5	85.6
21, 22, 23	FIRE SUPPRESSION, PLUMBING & HVAC	98.3	53.9	78.7	97.9	55.5	79.2	100.0	59.3	82.0	98.3	54.1	78.8	99.9	59.3	82.0	97.9	43.8	74.0
26, 27, 3370	ELECTRICAL, COMMUNICATIONS & UTIL.	96.4	45.1	69.2	98.2	47.8	71.5	96.4	57.3	75.7	96.4	42.3	67.7	102.4	57.3	78.5	99.9	57.3	77.3
MF2014	WEIGHTED AVERAGE	95.8	56.4	78.4	98.1	56.8	79.8	99.5	66.7	85.0	97.1	54.3	78.2	99.0	67.9	85.3	98.2	57.2	80.1

		MISSISSIPPI									MISSOURI								
		MCCOMB			MERIDIAN			TUPELO			BOWLING GREEN			CAPE GIRARDEAU			CHILLICOTHE		
DIVISION		396			393			388			633			637			646		
		MAT.	INST.	TOTAL	MAT.	INST.	TOTAL	MAT.	INST.	TOTAL	MAT.	INST.	TOTAL	MAT.	INST.	TOTAL	MAT.	INST.	TOTAL
015433	CONTRACTOR EQUIPMENT		104.5	104.5		104.5	104.5		104.5	104.5		112.3	112.3		112.3	112.3		106.4	106.4
0241, 31 - 34	SITE & INFRASTRUCTURE, DEMOLITION	95.1	89.7	91.4	99.2	90.8	93.4	94.0	89.8	91.1	88.4	95.3	93.2	90.0	95.2	93.6	108.5	94.2	98.5
0310	Concrete Forming & Accessories	84.7	48.4	53.3	81.9	65.5	67.7	83.6	48.7	53.5	95.1	91.8	92.3	87.6	79.7	80.8	84.7	98.5	96.7
0320	Concrete Reinforcing	90.2	34.9	62.2	89.1	51.3	69.9	94.8	44.5	69.3	106.5	93.0	99.7	107.8	79.0	93.2	104.0	94.9	99.4
0330	Cast-in-Place Concrete	101.9	51.2	82.6	109.1	65.0	92.3	101.4	72.3	90.3	91.8	99.6	94.8	90.9	88.9	90.1	98.5	90.4	95.4
03	CONCRETE	92.1	49.2	72.2	96.7	64.6	81.8	94.8	58.2	77.8	96.1	96.4	96.3	95.3	84.8	90.4	105.9	95.9	101.3
04	MASONRY	127.7	41.8	74.8	99.0	67.9	79.8	129.6	45.0	77.5	116.3	95.9	103.7	113.2	78.9	92.1	103.7	94.6	98.1
05	METALS	90.5	76.5	86.2	91.3	87.1	90.0	93.3	78.9	88.9	94.6	118.7	102.0	95.6	111.3	100.4	91.8	109.3	97.2
06	WOOD, PLASTICS & COMPOSITES	88.9	50.5	67.8	86.4	67.9	76.2	82.4	48.8	63.9	97.8	92.2	94.7	90.9	77.7	83.7	94.9	100.6	98.0
07	THERMAL & MOISTURE PROTECTION	97.2	54.5	79.5	97.4	66.4	84.6	96.6	55.8	79.6	100.8	99.4	100.2	100.2	84.3	93.6	93.1	96.6	94.5
08	OPENINGS	100.6	44.3	87.9	100.3	58.1	90.7	96.2	48.1	85.3	99.9	98.2	99.5	99.9	76.0	94.5	92.9	97.8	94.0
0920	Plaster & Gypsum Board	88.0	49.6	62.5	88.0	67.4	74.3	87.2	47.8	61.0	99.3	92.2	94.6	98.6	77.4	84.5	99.3	100.4	100.0
0950, 0980	Ceilings & Acoustic Treatment	82.3	49.6	60.5	84.2	67.4	73.0	82.1	47.8	59.3	91.6	92.2	92.0	91.6	77.4	82.2	90.2	100.4	97.0
0960	Flooring	88.5	47.7	76.7	87.1	77.7	84.4	98.6	47.7	83.8	99.4	97.8	98.9	95.9	82.9	92.1	95.9	104.9	98.5
0970, 0990	Wall Finishes & Painting/Coating	84.9	49.9	64.4	84.9	49.9	64.4	94.3	48.2	67.2	100.2	102.8	101.8	100.2	71.4	83.3	95.4	86.6	90.2
09	FINISHES	83.7	48.5	64.5	83.9	66.7	74.5	90.0	48.1	67.1	100.5	94.2	97.1	99.4	78.5	87.9	99.8	99.1	99.4
COVERS	DIVS. 10 - 14, 25, 28, 41, 43, 44, 46	100.0	54.4	89.7	100.0	72.8	93.8	100.0	52.4	89.2	100.0	84.7	96.5	100.0	91.8	98.1	100.0	86.0	96.8
21, 22, 23	FIRE SUPPRESSION, PLUMBING & HVAC	97.9	53.3	78.2	99.9	57.7	81.2	98.5	55.1	79.3	96.4	96.3	96.4	100.0	95.1	97.8	96.6	97.6	97.0
26, 27, 3370	ELECTRICAL, COMMUNICATIONS & UTIL.	96.7	48.1	70.9	99.9	58.0	77.7	96.1	47.9	70.6	103.2	81.7	91.8	103.2	91.0	96.7	95.9	79.2	87.0
MF2014	WEIGHTED AVERAGE	96.4	54.9	78.1	96.5	67.0	83.5	97.3	57.1	79.6	98.7	95.8	97.4	99.2	89.5	95.0	97.5	95.2	96.5

MISSOURI

DIVISION		COLUMBIA 652			FLAT RIVER 636			HANNIBAL 634			HARRISONVILLE 647			JEFFERSON CITY 650 - 651			JOPLIN 648		
		MAT.	INST.	TOTAL	MAT.	INST.	TOTAL	MAT.	INST.	TOTAL	MAT.	INST.	TOTAL	MAT.	INST.	TOTAL	MAT.	INST.	TOTAL
015433	CONTRACTOR EQUIPMENT		115.9	115.9		112.3	112.3		112.3	112.3		106.4	106.4		115.9	115.9		110.0	110.0
0241, 31 - 34	SITE & INFRASTRUCTURE, DEMOLITION	96.7	100.2	99.1	91.0	95.2	94.0	86.3	95.2	92.5	99.6	95.3	96.6	96.1	100.8	99.4	108.8	99.1	102.1
0310	Concrete Forming & Accessories	84.2	83.8	83.8	101.5	88.1	89.9	93.3	84.6	85.8	82.1	103.9	100.9	94.6	82.1	83.8	95.8	76.2	78.8
0320	Concrete Reinforcing	91.2	109.7	100.6	107.8	101.8	104.8	105.9	92.9	99.3	103.6	107.7	105.7	98.5	101.5	100.0	107.4	87.7	97.4
0330	Cast-in-Place Concrete	86.0	88.1	86.8	94.8	93.0	94.1	86.9	98.9	91.5	100.9	104.0	102.1	91.1	88.1	89.9	106.7	78.0	95.8
03	CONCRETE	84.8	91.8	88.1	99.2	94.0	96.8	92.4	92.9	92.6	101.6	105.2	103.3	91.8	89.6	90.8	104.5	80.1	93.2
04	MASONRY	147.1	75.9	103.2	113.5	78.6	92.0	107.7	94.9	99.8	98.1	102.5	100.8	104.1	75.9	86.7	96.9	82.4	88.0
05	METALS	102.4	124.2	109.0	94.5	121.1	102.6	94.6	118.3	101.9	92.3	115.1	99.2	102.0	121.0	107.8	94.8	102.1	97.0
06	WOOD, PLASTICS & COMPOSITES	85.9	81.6	83.6	105.8	87.9	96.0	96.1	83.3	89.1	91.7	104.8	98.9	94.6	79.4	86.2	105.5	75.3	88.9
07	THERMAL & MOISTURE PROTECTION	94.9	84.8	90.7	101.0	94.2	98.2	100.7	95.7	98.6	92.3	103.5	96.9	102.3	84.6	94.9	92.2	78.9	86.7
08	OPENINGS	99.7	89.2	97.4	99.9	98.4	99.6	99.9	87.1	97.0	92.9	106.3	96.0	96.5	85.8	94.0	94.0	79.7	90.8
0920	Plaster & Gypsum Board	93.1	81.2	85.2	105.2	87.8	93.7	98.9	83.1	88.4	94.9	104.7	101.5	97.4	78.8	85.1	105.7	74.4	84.9
0950, 0980	Ceilings & Acoustic Treatment	90.3	81.2	84.2	91.6	87.8	89.1	91.6	83.1	86.0	90.2	104.7	99.9	93.3	78.8	83.7	91.1	74.4	80.0
0960	Flooring	94.7	74.4	88.8	102.7	82.9	97.0	98.7	97.8	98.4	91.4	74.4	86.5	100.5	74.4	92.9	121.3	74.4	107.7
0970, 0990	Wall Finishes & Painting/Coating	95.7	80.1	86.5	100.2	76.4	86.3	100.2	100.2	100.2	99.8	105.9	103.4	89.1	80.1	83.8	94.9	80.8	86.6
09	FINISHES	88.6	81.2	84.6	102.5	85.0	93.0	100.1	87.8	93.4	97.4	98.5	98.0	92.0	79.8	85.4	106.5	76.7	90.2
COVERS	DIVS. 10 - 14, 25, 28, 41, 43, 44, 46	100.0	97.2	99.4	100.0	92.8	98.4	100.0	83.4	96.3	100.0	88.0	97.3	100.0	96.9	99.3	100.0	84.5	96.5
21, 22, 23	FIRE SUPPRESSION, PLUMBING & HVAC	99.9	96.9	98.6	96.4	95.8	96.1	96.4	95.8	96.1	96.5	101.1	98.5	99.9	97.5	98.8	100.1	70.8	87.2
26, 27, 3370	ELECTRICAL, COMMUNICATIONS & UTIL.	94.3	85.1	89.4	108.0	98.4	102.9	101.9	81.7	91.2	102.5	98.7	100.5	99.5	85.1	91.8	93.8	75.1	83.9
MF2014	WEIGHTED AVERAGE	99.0	92.5	96.1	99.7	95.0	97.6	97.6	93.5	95.8	96.9	101.9	99.1	98.3	91.7	95.4	98.8	80.8	90.9

MISSOURI

DIVISION		KANSAS CITY 640 - 641			KIRKSVILLE 635			POPLAR BLUFF 639			ROLLA 654 - 655			SEDALIA 653			SIKESTON 638		
		MAT.	INST.	TOTAL	MAT.	INST.	TOTAL	MAT.	INST.	TOTAL	MAT.	INST.	TOTAL	MAT.	INST.	TOTAL	MAT.	INST.	TOTAL
015433	CONTRACTOR EQUIPMENT		106.2	106.2		101.8	101.8		104.2	104.2		115.9	115.9		105.3	105.3		104.2	104.2
0241, 31 - 34	SITE & INFRASTRUCTURE, DEMOLITION	101.5	96.0	97.7	90.5	90.4	90.4	77.6	94.5	89.4	95.6	100.0	98.7	95.0	95.3	95.2	81.0	94.6	90.5
0310	Concrete Forming & Accessories	94.8	104.8	103.5	85.6	78.2	79.2	85.9	81.8	82.4	91.6	96.8	96.1	89.4	81.2	82.3	87.1	78.7	79.9
0320	Concrete Reinforcing	102.0	111.2	106.7	106.9	84.1	95.3	110.1	78.9	94.3	91.6	84.5	88.0	90.4	107.0	98.8	109.4	79.0	93.9
0330	Cast-in-Place Concrete	99.2	105.8	101.7	94.7	86.7	91.7	72.9	87.8	78.6	88.0	96.2	91.1	91.9	86.7	89.9	77.9	87.9	81.7
03	CONCRETE	100.7	106.9	103.6	111.9	83.5	98.8	86.0	84.6	85.3	86.6	96.0	90.0	100.9	88.9	95.3	89.8	83.3	86.8
04	MASONRY	100.2	104.6	102.9	120.2	85.5	98.8	111.5	76.1	89.7	119.7	87.9	100.1	126.2	83.9	100.1	111.1	76.1	89.5
05	METALS	102.3	117.0	106.8	94.3	103.0	97.0	94.9	100.1	96.5	101.8	114.4	105.7	100.7	113.1	104.5	95.3	100.8	97.0
06	WOOD, PLASTICS & COMPOSITES	104.7	104.7	104.7	83.7	75.8	79.4	82.9	82.4	82.6	93.2	99.1	96.4	86.2	79.4	82.5	84.4	77.7	80.7
07	THERMAL & MOISTURE PROTECTION	92.4	106.1	98.1	107.6	91.4	100.9	105.8	84.4	96.9	95.2	95.0	95.1	101.1	91.4	97.1	105.9	85.0	97.2
08	OPENINGS	100.0	107.1	101.6	105.4	80.3	99.7	106.4	78.6	100.1	99.7	89.0	97.3	104.7	89.5	101.3	106.4	76.1	99.5
0920	Plaster & Gypsum Board	103.3	104.7	104.3	94.3	75.4	81.7	94.6	82.2	86.4	95.1	99.1	97.7	88.8	78.8	82.2	96.3	77.4	83.7
0950, 0980	Ceilings & Acoustic Treatment	99.5	104.7	103.0	89.9	75.4	80.2	91.6	82.2	85.4	90.3	99.1	96.2	90.3	78.8	82.7	91.6	77.4	82.2
0960	Flooring	97.9	104.9	100.0	77.0	74.4	76.2	90.7	82.9	88.4	98.5	74.4	91.5	76.9	74.4	76.2	91.2	82.9	88.8
0970, 0990	Wall Finishes & Painting/Coating	99.8	109.5	105.5	95.9	80.1	86.6	95.0	71.4	81.2	95.7	98.2	97.2	95.7	104.2	100.7	95.0	71.4	81.2
09	FINISHES	102.4	105.3	104.0	99.5	77.2	87.3	99.1	80.7	89.0	90.2	93.6	92.0	87.4	81.6	84.3	99.8	78.3	88.0
COVERS	DIVS. 10 - 14, 25, 28, 41, 43, 44, 46	100.0	101.0	100.2	100.0	82.7	96.1	100.0	91.4	98.1	100.0	86.5	96.9	100.0	90.6	97.9	100.0	88.1	97.3
21, 22, 23	FIRE SUPPRESSION, PLUMBING & HVAC	100.0	101.7	100.7	96.4	94.6	95.6	96.4	93.6	95.2	96.3	97.1	96.7	96.3	93.6	95.1	96.4	93.7	95.2
26, 27, 3370	ELECTRICAL, COMMUNICATIONS & UTIL.	104.2	101.0	102.5	102.2	80.0	90.4	102.4	91.0	96.3	92.7	78.2	85.0	93.9	98.7	96.4	101.4	133.3	118.3
MF2014	WEIGHTED AVERAGE	100.9	104.4	102.5	101.4	87.1	95.1	97.5	88.2	93.4	97.0	94.1	95.7	99.4	92.7	96.4	98.1	93.5	96.1

DIVISION		MISSOURI SPRINGFIELD 656 - 658			ST. JOSEPH 644 - 645			ST. LOUIS 630 - 631			MONTANA BILLINGS 590 - 591			BUTTE 597			GREAT FALLS 594		
		MAT.	INST.	TOTAL	MAT.	INST.	TOTAL	MAT.	INST.	TOTAL	MAT.	INST.	TOTAL	MAT.	INST.	TOTAL	MAT.	INST.	TOTAL
015433	CONTRACTOR EQUIPMENT		107.8	107.8		106.4	106.4		112.1	112.1		102.0	102.0		101.8	101.8		101.8	101.8
0241, 31 - 34	SITE & INFRASTRUCTURE, DEMOLITION	97.7	97.4	97.5	103.2	93.2	96.2	90.3	98.0	95.6	94.2	98.7	97.3	99.9	97.4	98.2	103.6	98.4	100.0
0310	Concrete Forming & Accessories	97.9	78.5	81.1	94.6	92.4	92.7	101.6	104.2	103.9	96.6	67.4	71.4	84.1	65.7	68.2	96.5	65.7	69.9
0320	Concrete Reinforcing	87.9	110.0	99.1	100.8	107.4	104.1	98.6	103.0	100.8	102.3	81.7	91.8	110.9	81.6	96.1	102.3	81.6	91.8
0330	Cast-in-Place Concrete	93.4	77.4	87.3	99.1	101.3	100.0	90.9	101.7	95.0	118.5	70.9	100.3	130.4	69.4	107.2	137.8	69.4	111.7
03	CONCRETE	96.9	84.9	91.3	100.5	99.1	99.8	94.9	104.4	99.3	100.6	72.1	87.4	104.7	70.8	89.0	109.8	70.8	91.7
04	MASONRY	96.0	82.8	87.9	100.1	94.2	96.5	93.7	107.0	101.9	130.7	75.1	96.5	126.6	72.8	93.5	131.0	72.8	95.2
05	METALS	107.1	110.3	108.1	98.5	114.5	103.4	100.3	123.0	107.3	105.5	89.2	100.5	99.6	89.0	96.4	103.1	89.0	98.8
06	WOOD, PLASTICS & COMPOSITES	93.7	77.7	84.9	105.5	91.9	98.0	105.6	103.7	104.6	86.8	65.1	74.9	74.9	64.2	69.0	87.9	64.2	74.9
07	THERMAL & MOISTURE PROTECTION	99.3	79.4	91.0	92.7	93.6	93.1	100.8	101.5	101.1	110.3	71.3	94.1	110.1	69.6	93.3	110.7	65.0	91.8
08	OPENINGS	107.2	92.3	103.8	98.2	99.2	98.4	100.3	107.3	101.9	97.0	67.1	90.2	97.0	66.6	88.8	98.2	66.6	91.0
0920	Plaster & Gypsum Board	96.1	77.1	83.5	107.5	91.5	96.8	106.2	104.1	104.8	113.3	64.5	80.8	112.3	63.5	79.9	121.9	63.5	83.1
0950, 0980	Ceilings & Acoustic Treatment	90.3	77.1	81.6	98.7	91.5	93.9	97.5	104.1	101.9	89.2	64.5	72.7	95.1	63.5	74.1	96.8	63.5	74.6
0960	Flooring	97.5	74.4	90.8	101.0	104.9	102.2	102.4	97.8	101.1	99.4	81.1	94.1	96.6	81.8	92.3	103.9	81.1	97.3
0970, 0990	Wall Finishes & Painting/Coating	90.1	105.9	99.4	95.4	81.8	87.4	100.2	108.5	105.1	98.6	72.2	83.1	97.5	72.2	82.6	97.5	72.2	82.6
09	FINISHES	92.4	81.0	86.2	103.4	93.4	98.0	103.7	103.5	103.6	94.3	70.0	81.0	94.3	69.0	80.5	98.4	68.8	82.2
COVERS	DIVS. 10 - 14, 25, 28, 41, 43, 44, 46	100.0	94.2	98.7	100.0	97.9	99.5	100.0	101.8	100.4	100.0	93.9	98.6	100.0	93.0	98.4	100.0	93.0	98.4
21, 22, 23	FIRE SUPPRESSION, PLUMBING & HVAC	100.0	72.8	87.9	100.1	87.9	94.7	100.0	104.8	102.1	100.1	72.0	87.7	100.2	68.9	86.4	100.2	68.9	86.4
26, 27, 3370	ELECTRICAL, COMMUNICATIONS & UTIL.	98.2	72.4	84.5	102.5	98.5	100.4	105.8	91.1	98.0	99.4	73.9	85.9	107.0	70.1	87.4	98.8	71.3	84.2
MF2014	WEIGHTED AVERAGE	100.5	83.6	93.0	100.1	96.1	98.3	99.8	104.0	101.7	101.8	76.4	90.5	101.7	74.5	89.6	103.2	74.6	90.5

For customer support on your Electrical Costs with RSMeans Data, call 800.448.8182.

MONTANA

DIVISION		HAVRE 595 MAT.	INST.	TOTAL	HELENA 596 MAT.	INST.	TOTAL	KALISPELL 599 MAT.	INST.	TOTAL	MILES CITY 593 MAT.	INST.	TOTAL	MISSOULA 598 MAT.	INST.	TOTAL	WOLF POINT 592 MAT.	INST.	TOTAL
015433	CONTRACTOR EQUIPMENT		101.8	101.8		101.8	101.8		101.8	101.8		101.8	101.8		101.8	101.8		101.8	101.8
0241, 31 - 34	SITE & INFRASTRUCTURE, DEMOLITION	107.1	97.2	100.2	93.6	97.4	96.3	90.1	97.4	95.2	96.3	96.8	96.7	82.8	97.1	92.8	113.4	97.0	101.9
0310	Concrete Forming & Accessories	77.3	63.8	65.6	100.1	59.6	65.1	87.1	65.8	68.7	95.1	62.3	66.7	87.1	65.5	68.4	87.9	62.5	65.9
0320	Concrete Reinforcing	111.8	81.6	96.5	118.0	80.4	98.9	113.9	80.4	96.9	111.4	81.6	96.3	112.8	80.3	96.3	113.0	80.4	96.5
0330	Cast-in-Place Concrete	140.5	66.6	112.3	101.9	69.5	89.6	113.2	69.6	96.6	124.0	64.3	101.2	96.1	69.3	85.9	138.9	64.7	110.6
03	CONCRETE	112.8	69.0	92.5	96.9	67.9	83.5	94.3	70.7	83.4	101.5	67.6	85.8	82.9	70.5	77.1	116.0	67.6	93.5
04	MASONRY	127.7	67.9	90.9	118.2	73.2	90.5	125.4	73.6	93.5	132.9	63.9	90.4	152.5	73.3	103.7	134.2	64.5	91.3
05	METALS	96.0	89.0	93.8	101.8	88.5	97.7	95.8	88.6	93.6	95.2	89.0	93.3	96.3	88.4	93.9	95.3	88.5	93.2
06	WOOD, PLASTICS & COMPOSITES	67.4	64.2	65.6	90.3	55.9	71.4	77.8	64.2	70.3	85.3	64.2	73.7	77.8	64.2	70.3	77.6	64.2	70.2
07	THERMAL & MOISTURE PROTECTION	110.5	63.1	90.8	104.5	65.6	88.3	109.7	72.6	94.3	110.1	61.3	89.8	109.3	69.7	92.9	111.0	61.6	90.5
08	OPENINGS	95.8	66.6	89.2	99.0	61.8	90.6	95.8	66.3	89.1	95.3	66.6	88.8	95.3	66.3	88.7	95.3	66.3	88.7
0920	Plaster & Gypsum Board	108.0	63.5	78.4	108.2	55.0	72.8	112.3	63.5	79.9	121.1	63.5	82.8	112.3	63.5	79.9	115.9	63.5	81.1
0950, 0980	Ceilings & Acoustic Treatment	95.1	63.5	74.1	99.4	55.0	69.9	95.1	63.5	74.1	93.4	63.5	73.5	95.1	63.5	74.1	93.4	63.5	73.5
0960	Flooring	94.0	81.1	90.2	105.1	81.1	98.1	98.5	81.8	93.6	103.7	81.1	97.2	98.5	81.8	93.6	100.0	81.1	94.5
0970, 0990	Wall Finishes & Painting/Coating	97.5	72.2	82.6	97.8	72.2	82.7	97.5	72.2	82.6	97.5	72.2	82.6	97.5	57.1	73.8	97.5	72.2	82.6
09	FINISHES	93.5	67.6	79.4	98.3	64.1	79.6	94.3	69.1	80.5	97.1	66.6	80.4	93.7	67.3	79.3	96.6	66.8	80.3
COVERS	DIVS. 10 - 14, 25, 28, 41, 43, 44, 46	100.0	91.3	98.0	100.0	92.2	98.2	100.0	93.1	98.4	100.0	90.0	97.7	100.0	93.0	98.4	100.0	90.2	97.8
21, 22, 23	FIRE SUPPRESSION, PLUMBING & HVAC	96.6	66.4	83.3	100.0	69.1	86.3	96.6	64.5	82.4	96.6	64.9	82.6	100.2	64.2	84.3	96.6	65.2	82.7
26, 27, 3370	ELECTRICAL, COMMUNICATIONS & UTIL.	98.8	70.2	83.6	105.5	70.1	86.8	103.4	69.5	85.4	98.8	75.2	86.3	104.6	69.5	86.0	98.8	75.2	86.3
MF2014	WEIGHTED AVERAGE	100.7	72.7	88.3	101.1	73.0	88.7	98.4	73.5	87.4	99.5	72.3	87.5	99.0	73.1	87.5	101.7	72.4	88.8

NEBRASKA

DIVISION		ALLIANCE 693 MAT.	INST.	TOTAL	COLUMBUS 686 MAT.	INST.	TOTAL	GRAND ISLAND 688 MAT.	INST.	TOTAL	HASTINGS 689 MAT.	INST.	TOTAL	LINCOLN 683 - 685 MAT.	INST.	TOTAL	MCCOOK 690 MAT.	INST.	TOTAL
015433	CONTRACTOR EQUIPMENT		99.7	99.7		106.9	106.9		106.9	106.9		106.9	106.9		106.9	106.9		106.9	106.9
0241, 31 - 34	SITE & INFRASTRUCTURE, DEMOLITION	99.1	101.5	100.8	101.5	94.8	96.8	106.3	95.6	98.8	105.1	94.9	98.0	91.7	95.6	94.4	102.5	94.7	97.1
0310	Concrete Forming & Accessories	88.1	55.9	60.3	97.3	75.3	78.3	96.9	72.0	75.4	100.2	74.9	78.4	97.1	74.0	77.1	93.7	55.8	60.9
0320	Concrete Reinforcing	111.5	81.6	96.3	100.9	87.5	94.1	100.4	73.9	86.9	100.4	74.6	87.3	99.8	74.0	86.7	103.8	70.1	86.7
0330	Cast-in-Place Concrete	105.6	76.7	94.6	107.6	80.0	97.1	114.0	64.9	95.3	114.0	61.1	93.8	89.5	71.5	82.6	114.1	57.3	92.4
03	CONCRETE	118.6	68.5	95.4	102.5	80.2	92.2	107.4	71.2	90.6	107.6	71.3	90.7	90.7	74.4	83.2	107.4	60.6	85.7
04	MASONRY	112.3	71.1	86.9	118.3	74.5	91.3	110.8	72.1	86.9	120.4	83.1	97.4	98.5	72.0	82.2	107.5	70.9	84.9
05	METALS	103.2	82.1	96.8	94.9	97.7	95.7	96.5	93.7	95.7	97.5	93.3	96.2	98.5	93.9	97.1	97.8	89.9	95.4
06	WOOD, PLASTICS & COMPOSITES	86.6	51.7	67.4	99.5	76.4	86.8	98.8	71.6	83.9	102.3	76.4	88.1	99.2	74.2	85.5	95.2	51.7	71.3
07	THERMAL & MOISTURE PROTECTION	104.3	65.1	88.1	102.7	80.2	93.4	102.9	79.0	93.0	102.9	81.7	94.1	99.8	78.8	91.1	99.1	75.6	89.3
08	OPENINGS	94.3	59.2	86.4	94.0	75.9	89.9	94.0	70.5	88.7	94.0	72.5	89.1	103.1	68.2	95.2	94.8	56.4	86.1
0920	Plaster & Gypsum Board	82.7	50.4	61.2	94.6	75.8	82.1	93.9	70.9	78.6	95.6	75.8	82.4	103.6	73.5	83.6	94.7	50.4	65.3
0950, 0980	Ceilings & Acoustic Treatment	90.5	50.4	63.8	83.3	75.8	78.3	83.3	70.9	75.0	83.3	75.8	78.3	94.1	73.5	80.4	86.5	50.4	62.5
0960	Flooring	94.0	76.2	88.8	88.1	93.1	89.5	87.8	99.5	91.2	89.2	93.1	90.3	100.4	88.4	96.9	92.8	76.2	88.0
0970, 0990	Wall Finishes & Painting/Coating	154.6	53.9	95.5	75.9	62.7	68.2	75.9	66.6	70.4	75.9	62.7	68.2	94.7	81.3	86.8	87.5	47.0	63.7
09	FINISHES	93.5	58.4	74.3	86.2	77.1	81.2	86.3	75.4	80.4	87.0	76.4	81.2	94.7	77.6	85.4	91.3	57.2	72.6
COVERS	DIVS. 10 - 14, 25, 28, 41, 43, 44, 46	100.0	61.7	91.3	100.0	85.6	96.7	100.0	88.8	97.5	100.0	85.6	96.7	100.0	89.1	97.5	100.0	61.0	91.2
21, 22, 23	FIRE SUPPRESSION, PLUMBING & HVAC	96.6	72.5	85.9	96.5	75.6	87.3	100.1	78.7	90.6	96.5	75.2	87.1	99.9	78.7	90.5	96.4	75.3	87.1
26, 27, 3370	ELECTRICAL, COMMUNICATIONS & UTIL.	93.1	67.3	79.4	91.5	82.3	86.7	90.3	67.4	78.1	89.7	83.6	86.4	100.4	67.4	82.9	95.2	67.3	80.4
MF2014	WEIGHTED AVERAGE	100.9	71.1	87.7	97.1	81.3	90.1	98.4	77.6	89.2	98.3	80.4	90.4	98.2	78.3	89.4	98.4	70.8	86.2

NEBRASKA / NEVADA

DIVISION		NORFOLK 687 MAT.	INST.	TOTAL	NORTH PLATTE 691 MAT.	INST.	TOTAL	OMAHA 680 - 681 MAT.	INST.	TOTAL	VALENTINE 692 MAT.	INST.	TOTAL	CARSON CITY 897 MAT.	INST.	TOTAL	ELKO 898 MAT.	INST.	TOTAL
015433	CONTRACTOR EQUIPMENT		95.8	95.8		106.9	106.9		95.8	95.8		99.4	99.4		98.8	98.8		98.8	98.8
0241, 31 - 34	SITE & INFRASTRUCTURE, DEMOLITION	84.0	94.0	90.9	103.8	94.7	97.4	91.3	94.7	93.7	87.2	100.1	96.2	87.7	98.5	95.2	70.1	97.2	89.0
0310	Concrete Forming & Accessories	83.3	74.3	75.5	96.3	70.7	74.1	96.7	74.5	78.2	84.2	55.2	59.2	108.1	80.2	84.0	113.8	77.0	81.9
0320	Concrete Reinforcing	101.0	64.9	82.7	103.2	73.8	88.3	99.5	74.1	86.6	103.8	64.6	83.9	105.9	109.7	107.8	113.7	90.9	102.1
0330	Cast-in-Place Concrete	108.3	60.1	89.9	114.1	62.0	94.3	89.8	79.8	86.0	100.7	55.1	83.4	95.3	82.0	90.2	92.3	75.0	85.7
03	CONCRETE	101.1	68.3	85.9	107.5	69.5	89.9	90.8	77.3	84.5	105.0	58.0	83.2	97.2	86.1	92.1	95.0	78.9	87.5
04	MASONRY	125.1	74.5	93.9	95.3	70.9	80.3	99.5	75.6	84.8	107.4	70.9	84.9	117.1	70.7	88.5	123.8	69.5	90.4
05	METALS	98.4	78.6	92.3	96.9	91.4	95.2	98.5	83.8	94.0	109.5	78.3	99.9	108.2	92.7	103.5	111.8	83.1	103.0
06	WOOD, PLASTICS & COMPOSITES	82.7	75.9	79.0	97.1	71.6	83.1	94.5	75.9	84.3	81.0	51.2	64.7	91.2	80.3	85.2	102.0	77.1	88.3
07	THERMAL & MOISTURE PROTECTION	102.5	78.6	92.6	99.0	77.8	90.2	98.6	80.0	90.9	99.9	74.2	89.2	106.6	79.4	95.3	103.3	73.2	90.8
08	OPENINGS	95.6	69.9	89.8	94.1	69.9	88.6	100.9	75.4	95.1	96.5	56.4	87.5	98.1	80.8	94.2	101.7	72.7	95.1
0920	Plaster & Gypsum Board	94.7	75.8	82.1	94.7	70.9	78.9	101.4	75.8	84.4	96.1	50.4	65.7	98.3	79.7	86.0	101.3	76.4	84.8
0950, 0980	Ceilings & Acoustic Treatment	96.1	75.8	82.6	86.5	70.9	76.1	95.3	75.8	82.3	101.9	50.4	67.7	96.9	79.7	85.5	97.4	76.4	83.4
0960	Flooring	109.0	93.1	104.4	93.9	93.1	93.7	100.4	85.1	96.0	119.8	74.0	106.5	102.7	71.1	93.5	108.0	71.1	97.3
0970, 0990	Wall Finishes & Painting/Coating	132.2	62.7	91.4	87.5	62.7	73.0	105.0	66.1	82.2	154.2	65.0	101.8	97.3	78.1	86.0	96.8	75.7	84.4
09	FINISHES	102.8	76.4	88.4	91.6	73.6	81.7	97.9	76.2	86.0	111.9	58.4	82.6	95.7	78.2	86.1	95.8	75.7	84.8
COVERS	DIVS. 10 - 14, 25, 28, 41, 43, 44, 46	100.0	84.5	96.5	100.0	63.2	91.7	100.0	82.2	97.3	100.0	59.1	90.7	100.0	81.8	95.9	100.0	92.9	98.4
21, 22, 23	FIRE SUPPRESSION, PLUMBING & HVAC	96.2	75.3	86.9	100.0	74.8	88.9	99.9	76.0	89.3	96.0	74.7	86.6	100.0	70.1	86.8	98.4	75.5	88.3
26, 27, 3370	ELECTRICAL, COMMUNICATIONS & UTIL.	90.5	82.3	86.2	93.4	67.3	79.6	98.8	82.9	90.4	90.6	67.3	78.3	104.1	91.0	97.2	101.3	89.3	94.9
MF2014	WEIGHTED AVERAGE	98.6	77.3	89.2	98.2	75.1	88.0	98.0	79.8	90.0	100.9	69.7	87.1	101.6	81.8	92.8	101.5	80.1	92.0

527

For customer support on your Electrical Costs with RSMeans Data, call 800.448.8182.

NEVADA / NEW HAMPSHIRE

DIVISION		ELY 893 MAT.	INST.	TOTAL	LAS VEGAS 889-891 MAT.	INST.	TOTAL	RENO 894-895 MAT.	INST.	TOTAL	CHARLESTON 036 MAT.	INST.	TOTAL	CLAREMONT 037 MAT.	INST.	TOTAL	CONCORD 032-033 MAT.	INST.	TOTAL
015433	CONTRACTOR EQUIPMENT		98.8	98.8		98.8	98.8		98.8	98.8		99.8	99.8		99.8	99.8		99.8	99.8
0241, 31 - 34	SITE & INFRASTRUCTURE, DEMOLITION	76.1	98.6	91.8	79.5	101.0	94.5	75.8	98.5	91.6	85.6	97.9	94.2	79.4	97.9	92.3	91.5	102.0	98.9
0310	Concrete Forming & Accessories	106.6	102.5	103.1	107.6	105.7	106.0	102.7	80.3	83.4	87.9	81.3	82.2	93.9	81.0	82.8	99.7	93.4	94.3
0320	Concrete Reinforcing	112.4	92.9	102.5	103.5	118.3	111.0	106.2	117.2	111.8	86.6	84.0	85.3	86.6	83.9	85.3	101.2	84.0	92.5
0330	Cast-in-Place Concrete	99.1	98.6	98.9	96.0	106.5	100.0	104.8	82.0	96.1	88.2	89.5	88.7	81.0	103.1	89.4	104.0	114.3	107.9
03	CONCRETE	103.3	99.3	101.4	98.5	107.7	102.8	102.9	87.5	95.7	90.5	84.9	87.9	83.2	89.5	86.1	98.1	99.0	98.5
04	MASONRY	129.4	80.6	99.3	116.2	96.3	103.9	122.9	70.7	90.8	97.6	80.2	86.9	97.8	80.2	87.0	106.1	95.9	99.8
05	METALS	111.7	93.5	106.1	120.4	100.9	114.4	113.4	95.2	107.8	89.9	89.9	89.9	89.9	89.7	89.8	96.2	91.2	94.7
06	WOOD, PLASTICS & COMPOSITES	93.0	104.2	99.1	91.0	104.2	98.3	87.3	80.3	83.4	94.6	87.9	90.9	100.3	87.9	93.5	94.3	92.9	93.5
07	THERMAL & MOISTURE PROTECTION	103.8	97.7	101.3	117.1	97.9	109.1	103.3	79.4	93.4	101.3	75.6	90.6	101.1	75.6	90.5	105.5	94.5	100.9
08	OPENINGS	101.6	92.6	99.6	100.6	108.2	102.3	99.4	82.5	95.6	97.5	85.4	94.7	98.6	85.4	95.6	97.1	88.2	95.0
0920	Plaster & Gypsum Board	96.7	104.3	101.8	91.9	104.3	100.2	87.0	79.7	82.2	104.8	87.1	93.0	106.1	87.1	93.5	104.4	92.2	96.3
0950, 0980	Ceilings & Acoustic Treatment	97.4	104.3	102.0	105.0	104.3	104.6	102.5	79.7	87.3	95.8	87.1	90.0	95.8	87.1	90.0	102.3	92.2	95.6
0960	Flooring	105.3	71.1	95.4	96.4	99.4	97.3	101.7	71.1	92.8	88.8	100.0	92.1	91.4	100.0	93.9	97.9	102.5	99.2
0970, 0990	Wall Finishes & Painting/Coating	96.8	113.1	106.4	99.4	117.1	109.8	96.8	78.1	85.8	87.9	93.9	91.4	87.9	93.9	91.4	92.0	93.9	93.1
09	FINISHES	94.9	98.4	96.8	93.3	105.7	100.1	93.3	78.2	85.0	88.8	86.9	87.8	89.3	86.9	88.0	92.4	95.0	93.9
COVERS	DIVS. 10 - 14, 25, 28, 41, 43, 44, 46	100.0	75.0	94.3	100.0	102.1	100.5	100.0	81.8	95.9	100.0	88.3	97.3	100.0	88.3	97.3	100.0	107.5	101.7
21, 22, 23	FIRE SUPPRESSION, PLUMBING & HVAC	98.4	100.6	99.3	100.3	99.6	100.0	100.1	70.1	86.9	96.5	60.6	80.6	96.5	59.7	80.3	99.9	84.5	93.1
26, 27, 3370	ELECTRICAL, COMMUNICATIONS & UTIL.	101.5	100.8	101.1	105.9	112.4	109.3	102.0	91.0	96.2	95.9	50.4	71.8	95.9	50.4	71.8	96.8	81.1	88.5
MF2014	WEIGHTED AVERAGE	102.9	96.1	99.9	104.1	103.6	103.9	102.7	82.3	93.7	94.3	76.0	86.2	93.4	76.4	85.9	98.0	91.7	95.2

NEW HAMPSHIRE / NEW JERSEY

DIVISION		KEENE 034 MAT.	INST.	TOTAL	LITTLETON 035 MAT.	INST.	TOTAL	MANCHESTER 031 MAT.	INST.	TOTAL	NASHUA 030 MAT.	INST.	TOTAL	PORTSMOUTH 038 MAT.	INST.	TOTAL	ATLANTIC CITY 082,084 MAT.	INST.	TOTAL
015433	CONTRACTOR EQUIPMENT		99.8	99.8		99.8	99.8		99.8	99.8		99.8	99.8		99.8	99.8		97.2	97.2
0241, 31 - 34	SITE & INFRASTRUCTURE, DEMOLITION	92.9	98.2	96.6	79.6	98.2	92.6	92.3	102.0	99.1	94.3	102.0	99.7	87.8	102.1	97.8	91.5	105.8	101.5
0310	Concrete Forming & Accessories	92.5	83.0	84.2	105.2	83.0	86.0	99.7	93.6	94.4	100.9	93.6	94.6	89.4	93.5	93.0	112.0	145.5	140.9
0320	Concrete Reinforcing	86.6	84.0	85.3	87.4	84.0	85.7	101.2	84.1	92.5	108.3	84.1	96.0	86.6	84.1	85.3	76.8	136.5	107.1
0330	Cast-in-Place Concrete	88.6	105.3	95.0	79.5	104.6	89.1	104.0	114.4	107.9	83.9	114.4	95.5	79.5	114.4	92.8	82.0	141.0	104.5
03	CONCRETE	90.2	91.1	90.7	82.7	90.9	86.5	98.0	99.1	98.5	90.2	99.1	94.3	82.8	99.1	90.3	86.8	140.6	111.8
04	MASONRY	100.4	83.6	90.0	110.6	83.6	94.0	102.8	95.9	98.5	102.8	95.9	98.5	98.0	95.9	96.7	112.4	131.5	124.2
05	METALS	90.5	90.3	90.5	90.6	90.3	90.5	97.7	91.3	95.8	96.0	91.3	94.6	92.0	91.5	91.9	92.9	114.7	99.6
06	WOOD, PLASTICS & COMPOSITES	98.7	87.9	92.8	109.5	87.9	97.6	94.5	92.9	93.6	107.9	92.9	99.7	95.7	92.9	94.1	118.4	146.3	133.7
07	THERMAL & MOISTURE PROTECTION	101.8	77.2	91.6	101.2	77.2	91.2	104.9	94.5	100.6	102.2	94.5	99.0	101.8	104.0	102.7	100.6	136.8	115.6
08	OPENINGS	96.1	89.2	94.6	99.5	85.4	96.3	98.4	91.9	96.9	100.8	91.6	98.7	101.0	81.5	96.6	97.0	141.0	106.9
0920	Plaster & Gypsum Board	105.1	87.1	93.1	118.9	87.1	97.8	104.4	92.2	96.3	114.6	92.2	99.7	104.8	92.2	96.4	116.0	147.2	136.7
0950, 0980	Ceilings & Acoustic Treatment	95.8	87.1	90.0	95.8	87.1	90.0	102.3	92.2	95.6	107.8	92.2	97.4	96.8	92.2	93.7	88.7	147.2	127.6
0960	Flooring	91.0	100.0	93.6	102.4	100.0	101.7	95.1	102.5	97.2	95.0	102.5	97.2	89.0	102.5	92.9	98.6	163.0	117.3
0970, 0990	Wall Finishes & Painting/Coating	87.9	108.1	99.8	87.9	93.9	91.4	94.0	108.1	102.3	87.9	108.9	100.2	87.9	108.9	100.2	86.0	144.6	120.4
09	FINISHES	90.7	89.3	89.9	94.3	87.8	90.7	93.4	96.6	95.2	95.6	96.7	96.2	89.7	96.7	93.5	92.4	150.2	124.0
COVERS	DIVS. 10 - 14, 25, 28, 41, 43, 44, 46	100.0	89.5	97.6	100.0	96.1	99.1	100.0	107.5	101.7	100.0	107.5	101.7	100.0	107.5	101.7	100.0	119.8	104.5
21, 22, 23	FIRE SUPPRESSION, PLUMBING & HVAC	96.5	63.9	82.1	96.5	70.4	85.0	99.9	84.5	93.1	100.1	84.5	93.2	100.1	84.5	93.2	99.7	130.6	113.4
26, 27, 3370	ELECTRICAL, COMMUNICATIONS & UTIL.	95.9	60.2	77.0	97.0	53.3	73.8	96.9	81.1	88.5	98.3	81.1	89.2	96.4	81.1	88.3	90.1	144.7	119.0
MF2014	WEIGHTED AVERAGE	94.7	79.9	88.2	94.8	80.2	88.3	98.4	92.1	95.6	97.8	92.1	95.3	95.1	91.9	93.7	95.8	134.7	113.0

NEW JERSEY

DIVISION		CAMDEN 081 MAT.	INST.	TOTAL	DOVER 078 MAT.	INST.	TOTAL	ELIZABETH 072 MAT.	INST.	TOTAL	HACKENSACK 076 MAT.	INST.	TOTAL	JERSEY CITY 073 MAT.	INST.	TOTAL	LONG BRANCH 077 MAT.	INST.	TOTAL
015433	CONTRACTOR EQUIPMENT		97.2	97.2		99.8	99.8		99.8	99.8		99.8	99.8		97.2	97.2		96.8	96.8
0241, 31 - 34	SITE & INFRASTRUCTURE, DEMOLITION	92.7	105.8	101.8	96.5	106.3	103.3	100.4	106.3	104.5	97.4	107.1	104.1	88.7	107.0	101.4	92.7	106.9	102.6
0310	Concrete Forming & Accessories	102.7	145.4	139.7	101.4	146.3	140.2	114.3	146.3	142.0	101.4	146.3	140.3	105.9	146.4	141.0	106.4	146.0	140.7
0320	Concrete Reinforcing	100.8	133.8	117.5	84.6	151.9	118.8	84.6	151.9	118.8	84.6	151.9	118.8	109.8	151.9	131.2	84.6	151.8	118.7
0330	Cast-in-Place Concrete	79.5	141.3	103.1	87.8	136.3	106.3	75.4	136.3	98.6	85.8	136.3	105.0	68.5	136.4	94.3	76.1	141.2	100.9
03	CONCRETE	87.3	140.2	111.8	89.0	142.4	113.8	85.4	142.4	111.8	87.4	142.4	112.9	83.3	142.2	110.6	87.0	143.7	113.3
04	MASONRY	103.5	142.7	127.6	95.4	143.3	124.9	113.2	143.3	131.7	99.5	143.3	126.4	91.1	143.3	123.2	105.2	143.3	128.6
05	METALS	98.6	113.1	103.0	90.8	124.8	101.2	92.3	124.8	102.2	90.9	124.8	101.3	96.6	121.7	104.3	90.9	121.3	100.2
06	WOOD, PLASTICS & COMPOSITES	107.1	146.3	128.6	102.7	146.3	126.7	117.7	146.3	133.4	102.7	146.3	126.7	103.5	146.3	127.0	104.5	146.3	127.5
07	THERMAL & MOISTURE PROTECTION	100.5	137.9	116.0	102.9	139.9	118.2	103.1	139.9	118.4	102.6	135.9	116.5	102.4	139.9	117.9	102.5	132.8	115.1
08	OPENINGS	99.3	139.9	108.5	104.4	144.1	113.4	104.4	144.1	112.1	102.2	144.1	111.7	100.9	144.1	110.7	96.8	144.1	107.5
0920	Plaster & Gypsum Board	111.5	147.2	135.2	107.2	147.2	133.7	114.4	147.2	136.2	107.2	147.2	133.7	110.2	147.2	134.8	109.2	147.2	134.4
0950, 0980	Ceilings & Acoustic Treatment	98.2	147.2	130.8	85.2	147.2	126.4	87.0	147.2	127.0	85.2	147.2	126.4	94.7	147.2	129.6	85.2	147.2	126.4
0960	Flooring	94.5	163.0	114.3	86.7	189.9	116.7	92.1	189.9	120.5	86.7	189.9	116.7	87.9	189.9	117.5	88.1	187.5	116.9
0970, 0990	Wall Finishes & Painting/Coating	86.0	144.6	120.4	87.0	144.6	120.8	87.0	144.6	120.8	87.0	144.6	120.8	87.1	144.6	120.9	87.1	144.6	120.9
09	FINISHES	92.4	150.2	124.0	87.9	155.0	124.6	91.4	155.0	126.1	87.8	155.0	124.5	90.4	155.0	125.7	88.8	154.6	124.8
COVERS	DIVS. 10 - 14, 25, 28, 41, 43, 44, 46	100.0	119.8	104.5	100.0	131.6	107.1	100.0	131.6	107.1	100.0	131.6	107.1	100.0	131.6	107.1	100.0	119.9	104.5
21, 22, 23	FIRE SUPPRESSION, PLUMBING & HVAC	100.0	130.6	113.5	99.8	137.9	116.7	100.1	137.9	116.8	99.8	137.9	116.7	100.1	137.9	116.8	99.8	137.9	116.7
26, 27, 3370	ELECTRICAL, COMMUNICATIONS & UTIL.	94.6	139.8	118.6	90.5	143.6	118.7	91.1	143.6	119.0	90.5	144.6	119.2	95.0	144.6	121.3	90.2	137.5	115.3
MF2014	WEIGHTED AVERAGE	97.0	133.7	113.2	95.4	138.5	114.5	96.5	138.5	115.1	95.2	138.6	114.4	95.5	138.4	114.5	94.8	137.0	113.4

For customer support on your Electrical Costs with RSMeans Data, call 800.448.8182.

NEW JERSEY

DIVISION		NEW BRUNSWICK 088-089			NEWARK 070-071			PATERSON 074-075			POINT PLEASANT 087			SUMMIT 079			TRENTON 085-086		
		MAT.	INST.	TOTAL	MAT.	INST.	TOTAL	MAT.	INST.	TOTAL	MAT.	INST.	TOTAL	MAT.	INST.	TOTAL	MAT.	INST.	TOTAL
015433	CONTRACTOR EQUIPMENT		96.8	96.8		99.8	99.8		99.8	99.8		96.0	96.8		99.8	99.8		96.8	96.8
0241, 31 - 34	SITE & INFRASTRUCTURE, DEMOLITION	104.1	106.9	106.1	100.6	106.3	104.6	99.2	107.1	104.7	105.7	106.9	106.5	98.1	106.3	103.8	90.8	106.9	102.0
0310	Concrete Forming & Accessories	105.9	146.4	140.9	103.4	146.3	140.5	103.5	146.3	140.5	100.1	146.0	139.8	104.3	146.3	140.6	103.1	145.7	140.0
0320	Concrete Reinforcing	77.7	115.9	115.3	108.0	151.9	130.3	109.8	151.9	131.2	77.7	151.8	115.3	84.6	151.9	118.8	102.0	119.6	111.0
0330	Cast-in-Place Concrete	101.4	141.3	116.6	96.8	136.3	111.9	87.3	136.3	106.0	101.4	141.2	116.5	72.9	136.3	97.1	99.8	141.0	115.5
03	CONCRETE	103.2	143.9	122.1	96.8	142.4	117.9	92.2	142.4	115.5	102.9	143.7	121.8	82.7	142.4	110.3	97.4	137.9	116.2
04	MASONRY	112.0	143.3	131.2	98.5	143.3	126.1	95.9	143.3	125.1	100.1	143.3	126.7	98.5	143.3	126.1	104.0	143.3	128.2
05	METALS	93.0	121.6	101.8	98.3	124.8	106.4	92.1	124.8	102.1	93.0	121.3	101.7	90.8	124.8	101.2	98.3	109.4	101.7
06	WOOD, PLASTICS & COMPOSITES	111.9	146.3	130.8	96.0	146.3	123.7	105.3	146.3	127.9	104.5	146.3	127.4	106.5	146.3	128.4	98.3	146.3	124.7
07	THERMAL & MOISTURE PROTECTION	100.9	139.1	116.8	104.4	139.9	119.1	103.0	135.9	116.6	101.0	136.9	115.9	103.3	139.9	118.5	101.0	137.1	116.0
08	OPENINGS	92.1	144.1	103.9	102.7	144.1	112.1	107.5	144.1	115.8	93.9	145.2	105.5	108.5	144.1	116.6	100.5	136.2	108.6
0920	Plaster & Gypsum Board	113.4	147.2	135.8	103.7	147.2	132.6	110.2	147.2	134.8	108.4	147.2	134.2	109.2	147.2	134.4	105.3	147.2	133.1
0950, 0980	Ceilings & Acoustic Treatment	88.7	147.2	127.6	97.2	147.2	130.4	94.7	147.2	129.6	88.7	147.2	127.6	85.2	147.2	126.4	99.6	147.2	131.3
0960	Flooring	96.0	189.9	123.2	92.6	189.9	120.8	87.9	189.9	117.5	93.3	163.0	113.5	88.1	189.9	117.6	97.9	187.5	123.9
0970, 0990	Wall Finishes & Painting/Coating	86.0	144.6	120.4	88.4	144.6	121.4	87.0	144.6	120.8	86.0	144.6	120.4	87.0	144.6	120.8	89.7	144.6	121.9
09	FINISHES	92.4	155.0	126.6	90.3	155.0	125.7	90.5	155.0	125.8	90.9	150.3	123.4	88.9	155.0	125.0	93.0	154.6	126.6
COVERS	DIVS. 10 - 14, 25, 28, 41, 43, 44, 46	100.0	131.4	107.1	100.0	131.6	107.1	100.0	131.6	107.1	100.0	119.4	104.4	100.0	131.6	107.1	100.0	119.9	104.5
21, 22, 23	FIRE SUPPRESSION, PLUMBING & HVAC	99.7	137.9	116.6	100.1	137.9	116.8	100.1	137.9	116.8	99.7	137.9	116.6	99.8	137.9	116.7	100.0	137.6	116.6
26, 27, 3370	ELECTRICAL, COMMUNICATIONS & UTIL.	90.7	142.3	118.1	98.4	144.6	122.9	95.0	143.6	120.8	90.1	137.5	115.2	91.1	143.6	119.0	97.9	137.7	119.0
MF2014	WEIGHTED AVERAGE	97.6	138.3	115.6	98.7	138.7	116.4	97.2	138.5	115.5	96.9	136.6	114.4	95.5	138.5	114.5	98.6	134.8	114.6

DIVISION		NEW JERSEY VINELAND 080,083			NEW MEXICO ALBUQUERQUE 870 - 872			CARRIZOZO 883			CLOVIS 881			FARMINGTON 874			GALLUP 873		
		MAT.	INST.	TOTAL	MAT.	INST.	TOTAL	MAT.	INST.	TOTAL	MAT.	INST.	TOTAL	MAT.	INST.	TOTAL	MAT.	INST.	TOTAL
015433	CONTRACTOR EQUIPMENT		97.2	97.2		112.7	112.7		112.7	112.7		112.7	112.7		112.7	112.7		112.7	112.7
0241, 31 - 34	SITE & INFRASTRUCTURE, DEMOLITION	95.8	105.8	102.8	90.9	103.8	99.9	110.4	103.8	105.8	97.3	103.8	101.8	97.6	103.8	101.9	107.1	103.8	104.8
0310	Concrete Forming & Accessories	97.2	145.7	139.1	100.0	65.7	70.3	99.5	65.7	70.3	99.5	65.6	70.2	100.0	65.7	70.3	100.0	65.7	70.3
0320	Concrete Reinforcing	76.8	136.5	107.1	106.0	70.0	87.7	113.0	70.0	91.2	114.3	70.0	91.8	116.0	70.0	92.6	111.0	70.0	90.2
0330	Cast-in-Place Concrete	88.4	141.3	108.6	89.2	70.2	82.0	92.5	70.2	84.0	92.4	70.2	83.9	90.0	70.2	82.5	84.7	70.2	79.2
03	CONCRETE	91.3	140.8	114.3	95.2	69.4	83.3	118.1	69.4	95.5	105.8	69.4	88.9	98.9	69.4	85.2	105.5	69.4	88.8
04	MASONRY	100.7	143.3	126.9	108.9	60.8	79.2	109.3	60.8	79.4	109.3	60.8	79.4	118.6	60.8	83.0	103.0	60.8	77.0
05	METALS	92.9	114.7	99.6	106.6	91.2	101.9	104.4	91.2	100.4	104.1	91.0	100.1	104.2	91.2	100.2	102.1	91.2	99.6
06	WOOD, PLASTICS & COMPOSITES	101.3	146.3	126.0	95.0	66.6	79.4	93.0	66.6	78.5	93.0	66.6	78.5	95.1	66.6	79.5	95.1	66.6	79.5
07	THERMAL & MOISTURE PROTECTION	100.4	137.1	115.6	98.1	73.1	87.7	101.0	73.1	89.4	99.7	73.1	88.7	98.3	73.1	87.9	99.5	73.1	88.5
08	OPENINGS	93.5	141.0	104.2	98.7	66.8	91.4	96.9	66.8	90.1	97.1	66.8	90.2	101.0	66.8	93.3	101.1	66.8	93.3
0920	Plaster & Gypsum Board	106.8	147.2	133.6	100.6	65.4	77.2	77.5	65.4	69.5	77.5	65.4	69.5	92.7	65.4	74.6	92.7	65.4	74.6
0950, 0980	Ceilings & Acoustic Treatment	88.7	147.2	127.6	96.6	65.4	75.9	98.5	65.4	76.5	98.5	65.4	76.5	94.5	65.4	75.1	94.5	65.4	75.1
0960	Flooring	92.3	163.0	112.8	93.3	66.7	85.6	101.4	66.7	91.4	101.4	66.7	91.4	95.0	66.7	86.8	95.0	66.7	86.8
0970, 0990	Wall Finishes & Painting/Coating	86.0	144.6	120.4	98.7	54.3	72.6	96.0	54.3	71.5	96.0	54.3	71.5	93.2	54.3	70.3	93.2	54.3	70.3
09	FINISHES	89.6	150.4	122.8	91.9	64.5	76.9	95.5	64.5	78.6	94.2	64.5	78.0	90.8	64.5	76.4	92.1	64.5	77.0
COVERS	DIVS. 10 - 14, 25, 28, 41, 43, 44, 46	100.0	120.0	104.5	100.0	86.5	97.0	100.0	86.5	97.0	100.0	86.5	97.0	100.0	86.5	97.0	100.0	86.5	97.0
21, 22, 23	FIRE SUPPRESSION, PLUMBING & HVAC	99.7	130.9	113.5	100.1	69.0	86.4	97.8	69.0	85.1	97.8	68.7	85.0	100.0	69.0	86.3	97.8	69.0	85.1
26, 27, 3370	ELECTRICAL, COMMUNICATIONS & UTIL.	90.1	144.7	119.0	90.7	74.4	82.1	92.1	74.4	82.7	89.7	74.4	81.6	88.5	74.4	81.0	87.7	74.4	80.7
MF2014	WEIGHTED AVERAGE	95.1	134.8	112.6	98.9	73.7	87.8	101.7	73.7	89.4	99.5	73.7	88.1	99.6	73.7	88.2	99.3	73.7	88.0

NEW MEXICO

DIVISION		LAS CRUCES 880			LAS VEGAS 877			ROSWELL 882			SANTA FE 875			SOCORRO 878			TRUTH/CONSEQUENCES 879		
		MAT.	INST.	TOTAL	MAT.	INST.	TOTAL	MAT.	INST.	TOTAL	MAT.	INST.	TOTAL	MAT.	INST.	TOTAL	MAT.	INST.	TOTAL
015433	CONTRACTOR EQUIPMENT		86.8	86.8		112.7	112.7		112.7	112.7		112.7	112.7		112.7	112.7		86.8	86.8
0241, 31 - 34	SITE & INFRASTRUCTURE, DEMOLITION	97.4	81.9	86.6	96.9	103.8	101.7	99.5	103.8	102.5	100.6	103.8	102.8	93.2	103.8	100.6	113.1	81.9	91.3
0310	Concrete Forming & Accessories	96.0	64.6	68.8	100.0	65.7	70.3	99.5	65.7	70.3	99.6	65.7	70.3	100.0	65.7	70.3	97.7	64.6	69.0
0320	Concrete Reinforcing	110.0	69.8	89.6	112.9	70.0	91.1	114.3	70.0	91.8	105.5	70.0	87.5	115.1	70.0	92.2	108.3	69.8	88.8
0330	Cast-in-Place Concrete	87.3	62.6	77.9	87.5	70.2	81.0	92.4	70.2	84.0	92.9	70.2	84.3	85.8	70.2	79.9	94.0	62.6	82.0
03	CONCRETE	83.4	65.8	75.2	96.4	69.4	83.9	106.6	69.4	89.4	95.4	69.4	83.4	95.3	69.4	83.3	88.7	65.9	78.1
04	MASONRY	104.5	60.4	77.4	103.3	60.8	77.1	120.9	60.8	83.9	96.2	60.8	74.4	103.2	60.8	77.1	100.4	60.4	75.8
05	METALS	102.8	83.0	96.8	103.1	91.2	99.4	105.3	91.2	101.0	100.4	91.2	97.6	103.4	91.2	99.6	102.9	83.0	96.8
06	WOOD, PLASTICS & COMPOSITES	81.8	65.5	72.9	95.1	66.6	79.5	93.0	66.6	78.5	97.9	66.6	80.7	95.1	66.6	79.5	86.2	65.5	74.8
07	THERMAL & MOISTURE PROTECTION	87.0	68.1	79.2	97.9	73.1	87.6	99.9	73.1	88.8	100.0	73.1	88.8	97.9	73.1	87.6	86.6	68.1	78.9
08	OPENINGS	92.6	66.2	86.6	97.4	66.8	90.5	96.9	66.8	90.1	98.7	66.8	91.5	97.3	66.8	90.4	90.9	66.2	85.3
0920	Plaster & Gypsum Board	75.8	65.4	68.9	92.7	65.4	74.6	77.5	65.4	69.5	106.3	65.4	79.2	92.7	65.4	74.6	94.1	65.4	75.0
0950, 0980	Ceilings & Acoustic Treatment	85.3	65.4	72.1	94.5	65.4	75.1	98.5	65.4	76.5	95.7	65.4	75.6	94.5	65.4	75.1	83.3	65.4	71.4
0960	Flooring	133.1	66.7	113.9	95.0	66.7	86.8	101.4	66.7	91.4	103.3	66.7	92.7	95.0	66.7	86.8	125.6	66.7	108.5
0970, 0990	Wall Finishes & Painting/Coating	84.9	54.3	66.9	93.2	54.3	70.3	96.0	54.3	71.5	99.4	54.3	72.9	93.2	54.3	70.3	85.3	54.3	67.1
09	FINISHES	104.3	63.7	82.1	90.7	64.5	76.4	94.3	64.5	78.0	96.4	64.5	79.0	90.6	64.5	76.3	102.9	63.7	81.4
COVERS	DIVS. 10 - 14, 25, 28, 41, 43, 44, 46	100.0	83.9	96.4	100.0	86.5	97.0	100.0	86.5	97.0	100.0	86.5	97.0	100.0	86.5	97.0	100.0	83.9	96.4
21, 22, 23	FIRE SUPPRESSION, PLUMBING & HVAC	100.5	68.7	86.4	97.8	69.0	85.1	99.9	69.0	86.3	99.9	69.0	86.3	97.8	69.0	85.1	97.8	68.7	84.9
26, 27, 3370	ELECTRICAL, COMMUNICATIONS & UTIL.	91.5	74.2	82.3	90.3	74.4	81.9	91.1	74.4	82.3	102.1	74.4	87.4	88.2	74.4	80.9	92.0	74.4	82.7
MF2014	WEIGHTED AVERAGE	96.8	70.3	85.1	97.6	73.7	87.0	101.0	73.7	88.9	99.1	73.7	87.9	97.2	73.7	86.8	96.9	70.3	85.2

529

For customer support on your Electrical Costs with RSMeans Data, call 800.448.8182.

NEW MEXICO / NEW YORK

DIVISION		TUCUMCARI 884 MAT.	INST.	TOTAL	ALBANY 120-122 MAT.	INST.	TOTAL	BINGHAMTON 137-139 MAT.	INST.	TOTAL	BRONX 104 MAT.	INST.	TOTAL	BROOKLYN 112 MAT.	INST.	TOTAL	BUFFALO 140-142 MAT.	INST.	TOTAL
015433	CONTRACTOR EQUIPMENT		112.7	112.7		117.3	117.3		122.6	122.6		108.7	108.7		113.7	113.7		97.4	97.4
0241, 31 - 34	SITE & INFRASTRUCTURE, DEMOLITION	96.9	103.8	101.7	84.7	105.8	99.4	96.3	94.1	94.8	95.4	115.1	109.2	121.1	126.8	125.1	97.9	100.1	99.5
0310	Concrete Forming & Accessories	99.5	65.6	70.2	102.2	106.4	105.8	102.9	93.0	94.4	100.4	198.3	185.1	109.4	187.4	176.9	103.1	122.3	119.7
0320	Concrete Reinforcing	112.1	70.0	90.7	111.0	120.5	115.8	100.0	105.3	102.7	99.9	173.5	137.3	101.4	224.2	163.8	106.1	113.9	110.0
0330	Cast-in-Place Concrete	92.4	70.2	83.9	76.5	115.2	91.2	106.7	109.2	107.7	89.9	176.4	122.9	108.8	174.6	133.9	110.9	122.0	115.2
03	CONCRETE	105	69.4	88.5	86.2	113.1	98.7	96.2	103.2	99.5	93.1	185.3	135.8	107.7	187.6	144.7	105.3	120.0	112.1
04	MASONRY	120.8	60.8	83.8	91.9	116.4	107.0	108.2	107.6	107.8	91.5	177.7	144.6	118.9	177.6	155.1	106.2	124.7	117.6
05	METALS	104.1	91.0	100.1	97.7	129.9	107.5	91.7	135.8	105.2	87.1	171.8	113.0	99.4	168.7	120.6	99.2	106.2	101.3
06	WOOD, PLASTICS & COMPOSITES	93.0	66.6	78.5	96.9	103.3	100.4	106.1	89.3	96.8	100.1	204.1	157.3	107.5	189.2	152.4	104.9	122.8	114.7
07	THERMAL & MOISTURE PROTECTION	99.7	73.1	88.6	108.0	109.7	108.7	108.1	97.3	103.6	106.3	169.3	132.4	108.4	167.2	132.8	102.2	115.0	107.5
08	OPENINGS	96.8	66.8	90.0	97.2	105.6	99.1	92.4	94.0	92.8	94.2	205.2	119.4	100.0	194.8	113.8	101.4	114.9	104.5
0920	Plaster & Gypsum Board	77.5	65.4	69.5	103.4	103.2	103.3	107.4	88.7	94.9	96.2	206.7	169.6	103.6	191.7	162.1	106.9	123.4	117.8
0950, 0980	Ceilings & Acoustic Treatment	98.5	65.4	76.5	94.3	103.2	100.2	92.3	88.7	89.9	82.5	206.7	165.1	88.1	191.7	157.0	100.7	123.4	115.8
0960	Flooring	101.4	66.7	91.4	96.8	108.5	100.2	105.0	99.5	103.4	102.9	190.4	128.3	112.1	190.4	134.8	97.5	118.8	103.7
0970, 0990	Wall Finishes & Painting/Coating	96.0	54.3	71.5	97.1	100.6	99.2	89.3	101.5	96.5	108.8	162.9	140.6	116.9	162.9	143.9	98.8	118.0	110.0
09	FINISHES	94.1	64.5	77.9	92.4	105.6	99.6	93.6	94.3	94.0	95.7	194.8	149.9	106.8	186.0	150.1	101.4	122.1	112.7
COVERS	DIVS. 10 - 14, 25, 28, 41, 43, 44, 46	100.0	86.5	97.0	100.0	101.9	100.4	100.0	99.4	99.9	100.0	135.6	108.0	100.0	133.2	107.5	100.0	107.3	101.7
21, 22, 23	FIRE SUPPRESSION, PLUMBING & HVAC	97.8	68.7	85.0	100.0	107.2	103.2	100.6	98.0	99.5	100.2	170.9	131.5	99.7	170.7	131.1	100.0	101.8	100.8
26, 27, 3370	ELECTRICAL, COMMUNICATIONS & UTIL.	92.1	74.4	82.7	95.7	110.1	103.4	99.2	103.5	101.5	90.8	186.2	141.4	98.6	186.2	145.1	101.7	105.5	103.7
MF2014	WEIGHTED AVERAGE	100.1	73.6	88.4	96.0	110.9	102.6	97.4	103.0	99.9	94.8	175.1	130.3	101.9	174.2	133.8	101.3	111.3	105.7

NEW YORK

DIVISION		ELMIRA 148-149 MAT.	INST.	TOTAL	FAR ROCKAWAY 116 MAT.	INST.	TOTAL	FLUSHING 113 MAT.	INST.	TOTAL	GLENS FALLS 128 MAT.	INST.	TOTAL	HICKSVILLE 115,117,118 MAT.	INST.	TOTAL	JAMAICA 114 MAT.	INST.	TOTAL
015433	CONTRACTOR EQUIPMENT		125.3	125.3		113.7	113.7		113.7	113.7		117.3	117.3		113.7	113.7		113.7	113.7
0241, 31 - 34	SITE & INFRASTRUCTURE, DEMOLITION	100.8	94.3	96.3	124.4	126.8	126.1	124.5	126.8	126.1	74.7	105.4	96.1	113.9	125.9	122.3	118.6	126.8	124.3
0310	Concrete Forming & Accessories	84.5	98.7	96.8	95.2	198.2	184.3	99.3	198.2	184.9	87.6	98.9	97.3	91.6	166.6	156.5	99.3	198.2	184.9
0320	Concrete Reinforcing	106.4	107.2	106.8	101.4	224.2	163.8	103.2	224.2	164.6	106.6	112.4	109.6	101.4	224.1	163.7	101.4	224.2	163.8
0330	Cast-in-Place Concrete	99.6	108.6	103.0	117.7	174.6	139.4	117.7	174.6	139.4	73.8	112.4	88.5	100.0	171.1	127.1	108.8	174.6	133.9
03	CONCRETE	91.6	106.0	98.3	114.0	192.5	150.4	114.5	192.5	150.7	80.2	107.3	92.8	99.5	176.9	135.4	107.1	192.5	146.7
04	MASONRY	104.4	108.6	107.0	123.5	177.6	154.5	117.5	177.6	154.5	98.1	111.6	106.4	113.2	172.6	149.8	121.2	177.6	156.0
05	METALS	94.3	138.4	107.8	99.4	168.8	120.6	99.4	168.8	120.6	91.5	126.3	102.2	100.8	165.7	120.7	99.4	168.8	120.6
06	WOOD, PLASTICS & COMPOSITES	84.3	97.3	91.4	91.5	203.8	153.2	96.0	203.8	155.2	87.5	95.8	92.0	88.2	164.5	130.2	96.0	203.8	155.2
07	THERMAL & MOISTURE PROTECTION	104.3	98.0	101.7	108.3	168.8	133.4	108.4	168.8	133.5	101.4	106.6	103.6	108.0	162.3	130.5	108.2	168.8	133.3
08	OPENINGS	99.3	98.9	99.2	88.7	202.8	114.5	88.7	202.8	114.5	90.6	100.1	92.7	89.1	181.3	110.0	88.7	202.8	114.5
0920	Plaster & Gypsum Board	103.7	97.1	99.3	92.5	206.7	168.4	94.8	206.7	169.2	95.0	95.5	95.4	92.1	166.4	141.5	94.8	206.7	169.2
0950, 0980	Ceilings & Acoustic Treatment	95.8	97.1	96.7	77.1	206.7	163.4	77.1	206.7	163.4	83.1	95.5	91.4	76.2	166.4	136.2	77.1	206.7	163.4
0960	Flooring	90.9	102.6	94.3	106.7	190.4	131.0	108.4	190.4	132.1	87.9	108.5	93.9	105.6	176.8	126.3	108.4	190.4	132.1
0970, 0990	Wall Finishes & Painting/Coating	96.0	93.3	94.4	116.9	162.9	143.9	116.9	162.9	143.9	93.0	99.2	96.6	116.9	162.9	143.9	116.9	162.9	143.9
09	FINISHES	94.5	98.8	96.8	101.8	194.6	152.5	102.6	194.6	152.9	84.9	99.9	93.1	100.4	167.9	137.3	102.2	194.6	152.7
COVERS	DIVS. 10 - 14, 25, 28, 41, 43, 44, 46	100.0	100.9	100.2	100.0	134.7	107.9	100.0	134.7	107.9	100.0	98.6	99.7	100.0	128.7	106.5	100.0	134.7	107.9
21, 22, 23	FIRE SUPPRESSION, PLUMBING & HVAC	96.7	95.9	96.3	96.1	170.7	129.1	96.1	170.7	129.1	96.7	105.5	100.6	99.7	161.1	126.9	96.1	170.7	129.1
26, 27, 3370	ELECTRICAL, COMMUNICATIONS & UTIL.	98.3	106.6	102.7	105.9	186.2	148.5	105.9	186.2	148.5	90.8	110.1	101.0	98.0	146.2	123.6	97.0	186.2	144.3
MF2014	WEIGHTED AVERAGE	96.8	104.6	100.3	102.3	176.5	135.1	102.1	176.5	135.0	91.4	107.7	98.6	99.8	160.8	126.8	100.3	176.5	134.0

NEW YORK

DIVISION		JAMESTOWN 147 MAT.	INST.	TOTAL	KINGSTON 124 MAT.	INST.	TOTAL	LONG ISLAND CITY 111 MAT.	INST.	TOTAL	MONTICELLO 127 MAT.	INST.	TOTAL	MOUNT VERNON 105 MAT.	INST.	TOTAL	NEW ROCHELLE 108 MAT.	INST.	TOTAL
015433	CONTRACTOR EQUIPMENT		93.6	93.6		113.7	113.7		113.7	113.7		113.7	113.7		108.7	108.7		108.7	108.7
0241, 31 - 34	SITE & INFRASTRUCTURE, DEMOLITION	102.2	94.9	97.1	147.0	122.3	129.7	122.2	126.8	125.4	141.9	122.8	128.6	100.5	111.4	108.1	100.2	111.4	108.1
0310	Concrete Forming & Accessories	84.6	91.6	90.6	89.0	131.7	126.0	103.8	198.2	185.5	96.5	131.7	127.0	90.5	143.6	136.4	105.8	143.6	138.5
0320	Concrete Reinforcing	106.6	113.3	110.0	107.1	158.3	133.1	101.4	224.2	163.8	106.2	158.3	132.6	98.9	172.4	136.3	99.0	172.4	136.3
0330	Cast-in-Place Concrete	103.3	86.8	97.0	99.7	147.7	118.0	112.3	174.6	136.1	93.4	147.7	114.0	100.4	150.6	119.5	100.4	150.6	119.5
03	CONCRETE	94.6	93.8	94.2	100.4	141.5	119.4	110.3	192.5	148.4	95.6	141.5	116.9	102.8	150.3	124.8	102.1	150.3	124.4
04	MASONRY	113.8	104.8	108.3	112.9	155.7	139.3	115.7	177.6	153.8	105.7	155.7	136.5	97.4	157.3	134.2	97.4	157.3	134.2
05	METALS	91.7	103.3	95.2	99.4	136.0	110.6	99.4	168.8	120.6	99.4	136.0	110.6	86.9	142.3	103.8	87.1	142.2	104.0
06	WOOD, PLASTICS & COMPOSITES	82.9	88.8	86.2	88.7	125.9	109.1	101.8	203.8	157.9	95.5	125.9	112.2	91.0	139.2	117.5	107.4	139.2	124.9
07	THERMAL & MOISTURE PROTECTION	103.8	96.3	100.7	125.5	147.0	134.4	108.3	168.8	133.4	125.1	147.0	134.2	107.3	148.8	124.5	107.3	148.8	124.5
08	OPENINGS	99.1	96.3	98.5	92.8	143.9	104.4	88.7	202.8	114.5	88.4	143.9	101.0	94.2	154.7	107.9	94.3	154.7	108.0
0920	Plaster & Gypsum Board	88.6	88.4	88.4	97.2	126.7	116.8	99.4	206.7	170.7	97.9	126.7	117.0	91.6	139.9	123.7	104.1	139.9	127.9
0950, 0980	Ceilings & Acoustic Treatment	92.4	88.4	89.7	73.8	126.7	109.0	77.1	206.7	163.4	73.8	126.7	109.0	80.8	139.9	120.2	80.8	139.9	120.2
0960	Flooring	93.3	102.6	96.0	105.6	163.4	122.3	110.1	190.4	133.4	108.1	163.4	124.1	94.0	173.8	117.1	102.1	173.8	122.9
0970, 0990	Wall Finishes & Painting/Coating	96.8	96.9	96.8	123.0	127.5	125.6	116.9	162.9	143.9	123.0	127.5	125.6	107.1	162.9	139.9	107.1	162.9	139.9
09	FINISHES	92.5	93.5	93.0	99.1	136.7	119.6	103.5	194.6	153.3	99.5	136.7	119.8	92.6	150.9	124.4	96.6	150.9	126.3
COVERS	DIVS. 10 - 14, 25, 28, 41, 43, 44, 46	100.0	99.6	99.9	100.0	119.4	104.4	100.0	134.7	107.9	100.0	119.4	104.4	100.0	123.5	105.3	100.0	120.4	104.6
21, 22, 23	FIRE SUPPRESSION, PLUMBING & HVAC	96.5	89.9	93.6	96.6	126.9	110.0	99.7	170.7	131.1	96.6	123.1	108.3	96.8	141.6	116.6	96.8	141.6	116.6
26, 27, 3370	ELECTRICAL, COMMUNICATIONS & UTIL.	97.3	96.3	96.8	92.1	124.2	109.1	97.5	186.2	144.6	92.1	124.2	109.1	89.1	153.6	123.3	89.1	153.6	123.3
MF2014	WEIGHTED AVERAGE	96.9	95.7	96.4	100.1	134.2	115.2	101.5	176.5	134.6	98.6	133.4	114.0	95.1	145.1	117.2	95.5	145.0	117.4

City Cost Indexes

NEW YORK

DIVISION		NEW YORK 100 - 102			NIAGARA FALLS 143			PLATTSBURGH 129			POUGHKEEPSIE 125 - 126			QUEENS 110			RIVERHEAD 119		
		MAT.	INST.	TOTAL	MAT.	INST.	TOTAL	MAT.	INST.	TOTAL	MAT.	INST.	TOTAL	MAT.	INST.	TOTAL	MAT.	INST.	TOTAL
015433	CONTRACTOR EQUIPMENT		106.9	106.9		93.6	93.6		97.7	97.7		113.7	113.7		113.7	113.7		113.7	113.7
0241, 31 - 34	SITE & INFRASTRUCTURE, DEMOLITION	102.6	112.8	109.7	104.5	96.4	98.9	113.2	102.8	106.0	142.9	122.5	128.7	117.3	126.8	124.0	115.2	126.0	122.7
0310	Concrete Forming & Accessories	104.5	200.4	187.4	84.5	121.8	116.8	93.4	98.3	97.7	89.0	180.6	168.2	91.9	198.2	183.9	96.3	166.7	157.2
0320	Concrete Reinforcing	105.7	231.8	169.7	105.2	114.4	109.8	110.9	114.4	112.7	107.1	158.4	133.1	103.2	224.2	164.6	103.4	224.1	164.6
0330	Cast-in-Place Concrete	101.1	183.0	132.3	106.8	130.9	116.0	90.3	107.6	96.9	96.6	145.1	115.0	103.4	174.6	130.5	101.6	171.4	128.2
03	CONCRETE	103.1	197.6	146.9	96.8	122.8	108.9	92.9	104.0	98.0	97.8	162.5	127.8	102.8	192.5	144.4	100.1	177.0	135.8
04	MASONRY	100.6	182.2	150.8	120.9	134.8	129.5	92.1	104.9	100.0	105.3	150.4	133.0	109.7	177.6	151.5	119.1	173.0	152.3
05	METALS	98.1	171.8	120.6	94.3	104.9	97.6	95.5	101.4	97.3	99.4	136.7	110.8	99.4	168.8	120.6	101.3	165.9	121.1
06	WOOD, PLASTICS & COMPOSITES	104.1	204.1	159.0	82.9	117.0	101.6	93.9	95.3	94.7	88.7	194.0	146.6	88.4	203.8	151.8	93.1	164.5	132.4
07	THERMAL & MOISTURE PROTECTION	106.4	172.0	133.6	103.9	118.3	109.8	119.4	101.7	112.1	125.4	152.0	136.5	108.0	168.8	133.2	108.9	162.4	131.1
08	OPENINGS	100.8	204.7	124.3	99.1	111.9	102.0	98.3	100.5	98.8	92.8	181.2	112.8	88.7	202.8	114.5	89.1	181.3	110.0
0920	Plaster & Gypsum Board	102.2	206.7	171.7	88.6	117.4	107.7	114.8	94.6	101.4	97.2	196.7	163.3	92.1	206.7	168.3	93.3	166.4	141.9
0950, 0980	Ceilings & Acoustic Treatment	98.5	206.7	170.5	92.4	117.4	109.0	101.0	94.6	96.8	73.8	196.7	155.5	77.1	206.7	163.4	77.0	166.4	136.5
0960	Flooring	104.3	190.4	129.2	93.3	118.8	100.7	111.6	108.5	110.7	105.6	168.1	123.7	105.6	190.4	130.2	106.7	176.8	127.1
0970, 0990	Wall Finishes & Painting/Coating	108.8	159.1	138.3	96.8	118.7	109.7	118.5	97.9	106.4	123.0	127.5	125.6	116.9	162.9	143.9	116.9	162.9	143.9
09	FINISHES	100.7	195.5	152.5	92.7	121.3	108.3	97.4	99.5	98.6	98.9	176.1	141.1	100.8	194.6	152.0	101.0	167.6	137.4
COVERS	DIVS. 10 - 14, 25, 28, 41, 43, 44, 46	100.0	143.4	109.8	100.0	110.3	102.3	100.0	99.5	99.9	100.0	125.1	105.7	100.0	134.7	107.9	100.0	128.8	106.5
21, 22, 23	FIRE SUPPRESSION, PLUMBING & HVAC	100.1	173.2	132.4	96.5	107.0	101.2	96.6	105.6	100.6	96.6	126.6	109.9	99.7	170.7	131.1	99.9	161.3	127.1
26, 27, 3370	ELECTRICAL, COMMUNICATIONS & UTIL.	97.3	186.2	144.5	95.8	104.2	100.2	89.5	95.4	92.6	92.1	131.4	112.9	98.0	186.2	144.8	99.7	146.2	124.3
MF2014	WEIGHTED AVERAGE	100.3	177.9	134.6	97.9	113.1	104.6	96.7	101.9	99.3	99.3	145.2	119.6	99.9	176.5	133.7	100.6	160.9	127.3

NEW YORK

DIVISION		ROCHESTER 144 - 146			SCHENECTADY 123			STATEN ISLAND 103			SUFFERN 109			SYRACUSE 130 - 132			UTICA 133 - 135		
		MAT.	INST.	TOTAL	MAT.	INST.	TOTAL	MAT.	INST.	TOTAL	MAT.	INST.	TOTAL	MAT.	INST.	TOTAL	MAT.	INST.	TOTAL
015433	CONTRACTOR EQUIPMENT		122.0	122.0		117.3	117.3		108.7	108.7		108.7	108.7		117.3	117.3		117.3	117.3
0241, 31 - 34	SITE & INFRASTRUCTURE, DEMOLITION	92.0	110.6	104.9	85.1	105.8	99.5	104.6	115.1	111.9	97.4	110.8	106.8	94.9	105.0	101.9	73.4	104.2	94.9
0310	Concrete Forming & Accessories	102.1	104.3	104.0	104.7	106.4	106.2	89.9	187.8	174.6	99.0	151.8	144.7	102.0	97.5	98.1	103.2	93.0	94.4
0320	Concrete Reinforcing	109.8	107.1	108.4	105.5	120.5	113.1	99.9	224.3	163.0	99.0	158.5	129.2	101.1	105.2	103.2	101.1	113.0	107.1
0330	Cast-in-Place Concrete	98.9	109.6	103.0	89.1	115.2	99.0	100.4	176.5	129.4	97.4	149.1	117.1	99.1	111.8	103.9	90.7	108.0	97.3
03	CONCRETE	97.8	107.9	102.5	93.3	113.1	102.5	104.5	188.6	143.5	99.2	151.0	123.2	98.9	105.1	101.8	96.7	103.2	99.7
04	MASONRY	101.5	111.5	107.6	94.7	116.4	108.1	103.5	177.7	149.2	96.9	153.2	131.6	100.8	113.2	108.5	91.8	107.1	101.2
05	METALS	99.5	124.2	107.1	95.5	129.9	106.0	85.2	172.0	111.8	85.2	137.0	101.1	95.1	121.5	103.2	93.2	124.4	102.8
06	WOOD, PLASTICS & COMPOSITES	96.0	103.1	99.9	105.6	103.3	104.3	89.6	189.5	144.5	100.0	154.1	129.7	102.3	93.0	97.2	102.3	89.4	95.2
07	THERMAL & MOISTURE PROTECTION	103.3	105.5	104.2	102.9	109.7	105.7	106.7	167.7	132.0	107.2	148.6	124.4	102.7	102.4	102.6	91.1	100.5	95.0
08	OPENINGS	103.4	102.7	103.3	96.3	105.6	98.4	94.2	197.2	117.5	94.3	159.4	109.0	94.8	94.4	94.7	97.6	94.4	96.9
0920	Plaster & Gypsum Board	104.9	103.3	103.8	104.3	103.2	103.6	91.6	191.8	158.1	95.5	155.3	135.3	98.8	92.6	94.7	98.8	89.0	92.3
0950, 0980	Ceilings & Acoustic Treatment	99.0	103.3	101.8	89.7	103.2	98.7	82.5	191.7	155.2	80.8	155.3	130.4	92.3	92.6	92.5	92.3	89.0	90.1
0960	Flooring	95.8	111.3	100.3	95.6	108.5	99.3	97.9	190.4	124.7	97.8	181.8	122.1	93.5	97.8	94.8	91.3	97.9	93.2
0970, 0990	Wall Finishes & Painting/Coating	98.1	104.8	102.1	93.0	100.6	97.5	108.8	162.9	140.6	107.1	135.2	123.6	93.3	105.2	100.3	86.7	105.2	97.5
09	FINISHES	97.1	105.9	101.9	90.5	105.6	98.8	94.4	186.3	144.6	93.9	156.7	128.3	92.7	97.7	95.4	90.9	94.4	92.8
COVERS	DIVS. 10 - 14, 25, 28, 41, 43, 44, 46	100.0	102.8	100.6	100.0	101.9	100.4	100.0	134.0	107.7	100.0	123.2	105.2	100.0	101.1	100.3	100.0	96.3	99.2
21, 22, 23	FIRE SUPPRESSION, PLUMBING & HVAC	100.0	92.7	96.8	100.2	106.7	103.1	100.2	170.9	131.5	96.8	130.2	111.6	100.3	98.3	99.4	100.3	97.5	99.0
26, 27, 3370	ELECTRICAL, COMMUNICATIONS & UTIL.	101.3	97.4	99.2	95.2	110.1	103.1	90.8	186.2	141.4	95.5	124.2	110.7	99.2	105.9	102.7	97.4	105.9	101.9
MF2014	WEIGHTED AVERAGE	99.8	104.5	101.9	96.3	110.8	102.7	96.5	173.9	130.7	95.1	138.8	114.4	97.8	104.4	100.7	95.9	102.9	99.0

NEW YORK / NORTH CAROLINA

DIVISION		WATERTOWN 136			WHITE PLAINS 106			YONKERS 107			ASHEVILLE 287 - 288			CHARLOTTE 281 - 282			DURHAM 277		
		MAT.	INST.	TOTAL	MAT.	INST.	TOTAL	MAT.	INST.	TOTAL	MAT.	INST.	TOTAL	MAT.	INST.	TOTAL	MAT.	INST.	TOTAL
015433	CONTRACTOR EQUIPMENT		117.3	117.3		108.7	108.7		108.7	108.7		103.2	103.2		103.2	103.2		108.7	108.7
0241, 31 - 34	SITE & INFRASTRUCTURE, DEMOLITION	81.2	104.7	97.6	95.1	111.4	106.5	102.1	111.5	108.6	96.9	82.4	86.8	98.7	82.6	87.5	98.6	91.8	93.8
0310	Concrete Forming & Accessories	87.6	100.1	98.4	104.1	143.6	138.3	104.3	155.1	148.3	93.9	65.2	69.1	97.5	64.7	69.2	98.4	65.2	69.7
0320	Concrete Reinforcing	101.7	105.3	103.5	99.0	172.4	136.3	103.0	172.5	138.3	99.3	67.5	83.2	103.8	65.7	84.4	102.7	65.7	83.9
0330	Cast-in-Place Concrete	105.6	111.9	108.0	89.2	150.6	112.6	99.7	150.9	119.2	108.2	72.4	94.6	110.3	71.6	95.6	93.6	72.4	85.5
03	CONCRETE	109.5	106.3	108.0	92.7	150.3	119.4	102.2	155.6	126.9	102.6	69.8	87.4	102.2	69.0	86.8	95.5	69.5	83.4
04	MASONRY	93.0	112.9	105.3	96.3	157.3	133.8	100.2	157.3	135.3	91.9	74.4	81.1	95.8	73.0	81.7	88.0	74.4	79.7
05	METALS	93.3	121.5	101.9	86.7	142.3	103.7	94.7	142.8	109.4	95.5	92.7	94.6	96.2	92.1	95.0	111.6	92.1	105.6
06	WOOD, PLASTICS & COMPOSITES	84.9	97.2	91.7	105.2	139.2	123.9	105.1	154.1	132.0	91.0	63.8	76.1	91.9	63.8	76.4	95.2	63.8	77.9
07	THERMAL & MOISTURE PROTECTION	91.4	103.9	96.6	107.0	148.8	124.3	107.3	151.7	125.7	103.9	67.2	88.6	98.2	66.5	85.0	104.7	67.2	89.1
08	OPENINGS	97.6	98.9	97.9	94.3	154.7	108.0	98.1	162.4	112.7	93.9	63.4	87.0	96.2	63.0	88.7	101.0	63.0	92.4
0920	Plaster & Gypsum Board	89.9	97.0	94.6	98.5	139.9	126.0	101.9	155.3	137.4	106.6	62.6	77.4	104.9	62.6	76.8	98.7	62.6	74.7
0950, 0980	Ceilings & Acoustic Treatment	92.3	97.0	95.4	80.8	139.9	120.2	96.9	155.3	135.8	81.3	62.6	68.8	85.3	62.6	70.2	83.7	62.6	69.6
0960	Flooring	84.2	97.9	88.2	100.4	173.8	121.7	99.9	190.4	126.1	99.6	81.8	94.4	98.7	81.8	93.8	103.1	81.8	96.9
0970, 0990	Wall Finishes & Painting/Coating	86.7	99.1	93.9	107.1	162.9	139.9	107.1	162.9	139.9	108.2	60.9	80.4	100.5	60.9	77.2	102.4	60.9	78.0
09	FINISHES	88.2	99.3	94.2	94.8	150.9	125.4	98.9	162.9	133.9	92.8	67.9	79.2	91.0	67.5	78.2	92.2	67.9	78.9
COVERS	DIVS. 10 - 14, 25, 28, 41, 43, 44, 46	100.0	101.1	100.3	100.0	123.5	105.3	100.0	133.0	107.5	100.0	85.6	96.8	100.0	85.2	96.6	100.0	85.6	96.8
21, 22, 23	FIRE SUPPRESSION, PLUMBING & HVAC	100.0	90.7	96.0	100.4	141.6	118.6	100.4	141.8	118.7	100.5	62.1	83.5	99.9	62.1	83.2	100.5	62.1	83.5
26, 27, 3370	ELECTRICAL, COMMUNICATIONS & UTIL.	99.2	95.4	97.2	89.1	153.6	123.3	95.6	169.1	134.6	100.9	60.5	79.5	100.0	62.6	80.1	99.0	62.2	79.4
MF2014	WEIGHTED AVERAGE	97.5	101.9	99.5	94.8	145.1	117.0	99.0	150.4	121.7	98.0	70.3	85.8	98.1	70.2	85.8	100.3	71.1	87.4

For customer support on your Electrical Costs with RSMeans Data, call 800.448.8182.

531

NORTH CAROLINA

DIVISION		ELIZABETH CITY 279			FAYETTEVILLE 283			GASTONIA 280			GREENSBORO 270,272 - 274			HICKORY 286			KINSTON 285		
		MAT.	INST.	TOTAL	MAT.	INST.	TOTAL	MAT.	INST.	TOTAL	MAT.	INST.	TOTAL	MAT.	INST.	TOTAL	MAT.	INST.	TOTAL
015433	CONTRACTOR EQUIPMENT		113.0	113.0		108.7	108.7		103.2	103.2		108.7	108.7		108.7	108.7		108.7	108.7
0241, 31 - 34	SITE & INFRASTRUCTURE, DEMOLITION	102.6	93.6	96.3	96.3	91.7	93.1	96.8	82.7	87.0	98.5	91.9	93.9	95.9	90.4	92.1	94.9	90.3	91.7
0310	Concrete Forming & Accessories	84.0	65.2	67.7	93.5	64.7	68.6	100.3	65.3	70.0	98.2	65.2	69.7	90.2	65.0	68.4	86.4	64.3	67.3
0320	Concrete Reinforcing	100.4	73.1	86.6	103.2	65.7	84.2	99.7	65.7	82.4	101.4	65.6	83.2	99.3	65.6	82.2	98.8	65.6	81.9
0330	Cast-in-Place Concrete	93.8	74.1	86.3	113.5	71.6	97.5	105.8	72.4	93.1	92.9	72.4	85.1	108.1	72.4	94.5	104.4	71.5	91.9
03	CONCRETE	95.7	71.3	84.4	104.6	69.0	88.1	101.1	69.5	86.5	95.0	69.5	83.2	102.4	69.4	87.1	99.2	68.7	85.1
04	MASONRY	100.5	73.0	83.5	95.1	73.0	81.5	96.3	74.4	82.8	84.0	74.4	78.1	80.5	74.4	76.7	87.5	73.0	78.6
05	METALS	98.1	95.4	97.3	115.3	92.1	108.2	96.0	92.1	94.8	104.3	92.1	100.5	95.5	91.9	94.4	94.3	91.7	93.5
06	WOOD, PLASTICS & COMPOSITES	80.4	64.5	71.6	90.3	63.8	75.7	98.8	63.8	79.6	94.9	63.8	77.8	86.2	63.8	73.9	83.2	63.8	72.5
07	THERMAL & MOISTURE PROTECTION	103.9	66.4	88.3	103.3	66.5	88.1	104.1	67.2	88.8	104.5	67.2	89.0	104.2	67.2	88.9	104.1	66.5	88.5
08	OPENINGS	97.8	65.1	90.4	94.0	63.0	87.0	97.6	63.0	89.8	101.0	63.0	92.4	93.9	63.0	86.9	94.0	63.0	87.0
0920	Plaster & Gypsum Board	92.3	62.6	72.6	110.8	62.6	78.8	112.7	62.6	79.4	100.2	62.6	75.2	106.6	62.6	77.4	106.4	62.6	77.3
0950, 0980	Ceilings & Acoustic Treatment	83.7	62.6	69.6	83.0	62.6	69.4	84.7	62.6	70.0	83.7	62.6	69.6	81.3	62.6	68.8	84.7	62.6	70.0
0960	Flooring	94.9	81.8	91.1	99.8	81.8	94.6	103.1	81.8	96.9	103.1	81.8	96.9	99.5	81.8	94.4	96.6	81.8	92.3
0970, 0990	Wall Finishes & Painting/Coating	102.4	60.9	78.0	108.2	60.9	80.4	108.2	60.9	80.4	102.4	60.9	78.0	108.2	60.9	80.4	108.2	60.9	80.4
09	FINISHES	89.2	68.0	77.6	93.8	67.5	79.5	95.3	67.9	80.3	92.4	67.9	79.0	93.0	67.9	79.3	92.6	67.5	78.9
COVERS	DIVS. 10 - 14, 25, 28, 41, 43, 44, 46	100.0	89.7	97.7	100.0	85.2	96.6	100.0	85.7	96.8	100.0	84.9	96.6	100.0	85.6	96.7	100.0	85.1	96.6
21, 22, 23	FIRE SUPPRESSION, PLUMBING & HVAC	96.8	61.1	81.0	100.2	61.4	83.0	100.5	62.1	83.5	100.4	62.1	83.4	96.9	62.1	81.5	96.9	60.9	81.0
26, 27, 3370	ELECTRICAL, COMMUNICATIONS & UTIL.	98.7	34.2	64.5	100.2	62.2	80.0	100.4	62.6	80.3	98.0	60.5	78.1	98.5	62.6	79.4	98.3	60.5	78.2
MF2014	WEIGHTED AVERAGE	97.2	67.8	84.2	101.7	70.7	88.0	98.8	70.5	86.3	98.7	70.9	86.4	96.4	71.1	85.2	96.0	70.2	84.6

NORTH CAROLINA / NORTH DAKOTA

DIVISION		MURPHY 289			RALEIGH 275 - 276			ROCKY MOUNT 278			WILMINGTON 284			WINSTON-SALEM 271			BISMARCK 585		
		MAT.	INST.	TOTAL	MAT.	INST.	TOTAL	MAT.	INST.	TOTAL	MAT.	INST.	TOTAL	MAT.	INST.	TOTAL	MAT.	INST.	TOTAL
015433	CONTRACTOR EQUIPMENT		103.2	103.2		108.7	108.7		108.7	108.7		103.2	103.2		108.7	108.7		101.8	101.8
0241, 31 - 34	SITE & INFRASTRUCTURE, DEMOLITION	98.1	80.9	86.1	98.2	91.8	93.7	100.9	91.8	94.5	98.1	82.3	87.1	98.8	91.9	94.0	99.7	100.0	99.9
0310	Concrete Forming & Accessories	101.0	64.5	69.4	97.3	64.6	69.0	90.3	64.6	68.1	95.3	64.7	68.8	100.1	65.2	69.9	107.1	75.0	79.3
0320	Concrete Reinforcing	98.8	67.5	82.9	103.6	65.6	84.3	100.4	65.6	82.8	100.1	65.7	82.6	101.4	65.6	83.2	96.4	91.5	93.9
0330	Cast-in-Place Concrete	111.9	71.6	96.5	96.3	71.6	86.9	91.7	71.6	84.1	107.8	71.6	94.0	95.2	73.3	86.9	99.1	78.1	91.1
03	CONCRETE	105.7	69.2	88.8	93.6	68.9	82.2	92.6	68.9	83.7	102.6	69.0	87.0	96.2	69.8	84.0	103.9	79.7	87.4
04	MASONRY	83.6	73.0	77.1	82.3	73.0	76.6	77.4	73.0	74.7	81.1	73.0	76.1	84.2	74.4	78.2	105.2	80.2	89.8
05	METALS	93.4	92.5	93.1	96.8	92.0	95.3	97.3	92.0	95.7	95.0	92.1	94.1	101.5	92.1	98.6	101.3	92.9	98.7
06	WOOD, PLASTICS & COMPOSITES	99.4	63.8	79.8	92.0	63.8	76.5	86.9	63.8	74.2	92.8	63.8	76.9	94.9	63.8	77.8	97.4	70.7	82.8
07	THERMAL & MOISTURE PROTECTION	104.1	66.5	88.5	99.1	66.5	85.6	104.4	66.5	88.7	103.9	66.5	88.4	104.5	67.2	89.0	108.9	83.3	98.3
08	OPENINGS	93.8	63.4	87.0	99.3	63.0	91.1	97.0	63.0	89.3	94.0	63.0	87.0	101.0	63.0	92.4	106.4	80.7	100.6
0920	Plaster & Gypsum Board	111.9	62.6	79.1	91.8	62.6	72.4	94.2	62.6	73.2	108.7	62.6	78.0	100.2	62.6	75.2	97.7	70.3	79.5
0950, 0980	Ceilings & Acoustic Treatment	81.3	62.6	68.8	85.3	62.6	70.2	82.0	62.6	69.1	83.0	62.6	69.4	83.7	62.6	69.6	110.3	70.3	83.7
0960	Flooring	103.4	81.8	97.2	96.2	81.8	92.0	98.6	81.8	93.7	100.4	81.8	95.0	103.1	81.8	96.9	91.8	48.1	79.2
0970, 0990	Wall Finishes & Painting/Coating	108.2	60.9	80.4	97.1	60.9	75.8	102.4	60.9	78.0	108.2	60.9	80.4	102.4	54.2	74.1	94.5	60.0	74.3
09	FINISHES	94.9	67.5	79.9	89.1	67.5	77.3	90.3	67.5	77.9	93.7	67.5	79.4	92.4	67.2	78.6	95.6	68.9	81.0
COVERS	DIVS. 10 - 14, 25, 28, 41, 43, 44, 46	100.0	85.1	96.6	100.0	85.1	96.6	100.0	85.2	96.6	100.0	85.2	96.6	100.0	85.6	96.8	100.0	89.4	97.6
21, 22, 23	FIRE SUPPRESSION, PLUMBING & HVAC	96.9	61.4	81.2	99.9	61.3	82.9	96.8	61.2	81.1	100.5	61.4	83.2	100.4	62.1	83.4	100.0	77.4	90.0
26, 27, 3370	ELECTRICAL, COMMUNICATIONS & UTIL.	101.9	60.5	79.9	101.0	40.0	68.6	100.9	62.2	80.3	101.2	60.5	79.6	98.0	60.5	78.1	101.6	76.0	88.0
MF2014	WEIGHTED AVERAGE	97.2	69.7	85.1	96.7	67.6	83.9	96.3	70.6	85.0	97.6	69.7	85.3	98.4	70.8	86.2	100.5	80.5	91.7

NORTH DAKOTA

DIVISION		DEVILS LAKE 583			DICKINSON 586			FARGO 580 - 581			GRAND FORKS 582			JAMESTOWN 584			MINOT 587		
		MAT.	INST.	TOTAL	MAT.	INST.	TOTAL	MAT.	INST.	TOTAL	MAT.	INST.	TOTAL	MAT.	INST.	TOTAL	MAT.	INST.	TOTAL
015433	CONTRACTOR EQUIPMENT		101.8	101.8		101.8	101.8		101.8	101.8		101.8	101.8		101.8	101.8		101.8	101.8
0241, 31 - 34	SITE & INFRASTRUCTURE, DEMOLITION	105.6	99.9	101.7	113.4	99.9	104.0	97.7	99.1	98.7	109.3	99.9	102.8	104.7	99.9	101.4	106.9	100.0	102.0
0310	Concrete Forming & Accessories	102.5	74.5	78.2	91.8	74.4	76.8	100.7	70.4	74.5	95.7	74.4	77.3	93.5	74.7	77.3	91.6	75.0	77.2
0320	Concrete Reinforcing	97.6	91.7	94.6	98.5	91.4	94.9	97.4	92.2	94.8	96.1	91.7	93.9	98.2	92.2	95.1	99.5	91.7	95.5
0330	Cast-in-Place Concrete	118.9	77.9	103.3	107.6	77.9	96.3	97.8	78.9	90.6	107.6	77.9	96.3	117.4	78.0	102.4	107.6	86.0	99.3
03	CONCRETE	103.0	79.5	92.1	101.9	79.4	91.5	95.3	78.1	87.3	99.4	79.5	90.2	101.6	79.7	91.4	98.1	82.5	90.9
04	MASONRY	122.3	85.4	99.5	124.0	80.2	97.0	109.0	79.2	90.7	115.9	85.4	97.1	135.8	92.0	108.8	115.0	83.6	95.7
05	METALS	97.3	92.8	95.9	97.3	92.4	95.8	99.8	94.0	98.0	97.3	92.8	95.9	97.3	93.5	96.1	97.6	93.2	96.2
06	WOOD, PLASTICS & COMPOSITES	92.8	70.7	80.7	80.9	70.7	75.3	92.0	70.7	80.3	85.0	70.7	77.2	82.7	70.7	76.1	80.6	70.7	75.2
07	THERMAL & MOISTURE PROTECTION	108.5	83.5	98.1	109.1	82.4	98.1	107.0	80.9	96.2	108.8	83.5	98.3	108.4	85.8	99.0	108.5	84.3	98.5
08	OPENINGS	100.3	80.7	95.9	100.3	80.7	95.9	100.2	80.7	95.8	98.9	80.7	94.8	100.3	80.7	95.9	99.1	80.7	94.9
0920	Plaster & Gypsum Board	121.8	70.3	87.5	112.6	70.3	84.5	98.9	70.3	79.9	113.9	70.3	84.9	113.6	70.3	84.8	112.6	70.3	84.5
0950, 0980	Ceilings & Acoustic Treatment	104.7	70.3	81.8	104.7	70.3	81.8	102.7	70.3	81.1	104.7	70.3	81.8	104.7	70.3	81.8	104.7	70.3	81.8
0960	Flooring	99.1	48.1	84.3	92.1	48.1	79.4	103.0	48.1	87.1	94.1	48.1	80.8	92.9	48.1	79.9	91.9	48.1	79.2
0970, 0990	Wall Finishes & Painting/Coating	92.8	60.0	73.6	92.8	60.0	73.6	94.1	70.4	80.2	92.8	70.4	79.6	92.8	60.0	73.6	92.8	60.0	73.6
09	FINISHES	98.9	68.9	82.5	96.5	68.9	81.4	97.8	66.8	80.9	96.7	70.0	82.1	95.9	68.9	81.1	95.6	68.9	81.0
COVERS	DIVS. 10 - 14, 25, 28, 41, 43, 44, 46	100.0	56.5	90.2	100.0	56.6	90.2	100.0	85.1	96.6	100.0	56.6	90.2	100.0	86.8	97.0	100.0	89.4	97.6
21, 22, 23	FIRE SUPPRESSION, PLUMBING & HVAC	96.7	82.1	90.3	96.7	74.7	87.0	100.0	75.7	89.3	100.3	73.3	88.4	96.7	73.4	86.4	100.3	73.4	88.4
26, 27, 3370	ELECTRICAL, COMMUNICATIONS & UTIL.	97.5	49.3	71.9	106.5	73.5	89.0	101.4	66.8	83.0	101.1	64.6	81.8	97.5	49.3	71.9	104.5	77.0	89.9
MF2014	WEIGHTED AVERAGE	100.4	77.3	90.2	101.1	78.5	91.1	99.9	78.1	90.3	100.4	77.7	90.4	100.5	77.2	90.2	100.4	80.6	91.6

City Cost Indexes

NORTH DAKOTA / OHIO

DIVISION		WILLISTON 588 MAT.	INST.	TOTAL	AKRON 442-443 MAT.	INST.	TOTAL	ATHENS 457 MAT.	INST.	TOTAL	CANTON 446-447 MAT.	INST.	TOTAL	CHILLICOTHE 456 MAT.	INST.	TOTAL	CINCINNATI 451-452 MAT.	INST.	TOTAL
015433	CONTRACTOR EQUIPMENT		101.8	101.8		92.0	92.8		88.2	88.2		92.8	92.8		99.6	99.6		93.9	93.9
0241, 31 - 34	SITE & INFRASTRUCTURE, DEMOLITION	107.3	97.6	100.5	97.2	100.6	99.6	115.5	89.9	97.6	97.4	100.3	99.4	101.2	101.0	101.1	97.8	97.2	97.4
0310	Concrete Forming & Accessories	97.6	74.2	77.3	101.7	86.8	88.8	93.1	90.0	90.4	101.7	77.3	80.6	95.5	82.2	84.0	97.3	71.7	75.1
0320	Concrete Reinforcing	100.4	91.6	95.9	97.7	90.9	94.3	101.4	84.3	92.7	97.7	79.4	88.4	98.1	79.0	88.4	104.0	78.5	91.1
0330	Cast-in-Place Concrete	107.6	77.8	96.2	102.8	91.8	98.6	109.4	87.6	101.1	103.8	89.3	98.3	99.3	84.7	93.7	91.5	75.7	85.5
03	CONCRETE	99.4	79.3	90.1	100.1	88.7	94.8	106.0	87.6	97.5	100.6	81.6	91.8	100.3	82.9	92.2	94.6	74.7	85.3
04	MASONRY	109.1	83.6	93.4	94.8	90.5	92.1	84.2	83.9	84.0	95.5	80.7	86.4	90.9	94.2	92.9	90.4	78.8	83.3
05	METALS	97.4	92.4	95.9	98.5	80.6	93.0	103.6	78.2	95.8	98.5	75.7	91.5	95.5	86.5	92.7	97.9	81.1	92.7
06	WOOD, PLASTICS & COMPOSITES	86.4	70.7	77.8	108.0	85.7	95.8	85.2	93.5	89.7	108.4	75.8	90.5	98.3	79.4	87.9	100.7	69.7	83.7
07	THERMAL & MOISTURE PROTECTION	108.7	83.4	98.2	104.7	93.6	100.1	99.7	89.7	95.5	105.7	89.1	98.8	101.8	87.9	96.1	99.6	80.2	91.5
08	OPENINGS	100.4	80.7	95.9	109.9	86.1	104.6	98.6	86.4	95.9	103.6	73.8	96.9	89.8	75.8	86.6	97.9	71.2	91.5
0920	Plaster & Gypsum Board	113.9	70.3	84.9	103.0	85.1	91.1	95.1	93.1	93.8	104.0	75.0	84.7	97.8	79.2	85.4	99.7	69.3	79.5
0950, 0980	Ceilings & Acoustic Treatment	104.7	70.3	81.8	93.4	85.1	87.9	102.3	93.1	96.2	93.4	75.0	81.2	96.8	79.2	85.1	97.6	69.3	78.8
0960	Flooring	95.1	48.1	81.5	93.7	79.0	89.5	122.4	78.4	109.7	93.9	68.2	86.4	99.9	78.4	93.7	101.0	78.0	94.4
0970, 0990	Wall Finishes & Painting/Coating	92.8	60.0	73.6	93.4	92.4	92.8	106.8	90.5	97.2	93.4	73.6	81.8	104.0	80.0	89.9	104.0	72.3	85.4
09	FINISHES	96.9	68.9	81.6	96.7	85.6	90.6	101.6	88.4	94.4	96.9	74.4	84.6	98.6	80.9	88.9	99.1	72.3	84.5
COVERS	DIVS. 10 - 14, 25, 28, 41, 43, 44, 46	100.0	56.6	90.2	100.0	94.0	98.6	100.0	90.7	97.9	100.0	91.6	98.1	100.0	90.5	97.9	100.0	86.7	97.0
21, 22, 23	FIRE SUPPRESSION, PLUMBING & HVAC	96.7	74.7	87.0	100.0	89.9	95.5	96.5	76.8	87.8	100.0	78.3	90.4	97.1	89.5	93.7	100.0	75.6	89.2
26, 27, 3370	ELECTRICAL, COMMUNICATIONS & UTIL.	101.6	74.5	87.2	99.3	87.3	92.9	101.2	93.0	96.9	98.5	87.9	92.9	101.0	78.5	89.1	99.7	74.8	86.5
MF2014	WEIGHTED AVERAGE	99.5	78.8	90.4	100.4	88.8	95.3	100.2	85.2	93.6	99.8	81.8	91.8	97.1	86.4	92.4	98.1	77.7	89.1

OHIO

DIVISION		CLEVELAND 441 MAT.	INST.	TOTAL	COLUMBUS 430-432 MAT.	INST.	TOTAL	DAYTON 453-454 MAT.	INST.	TOTAL	HAMILTON 450 MAT.	INST.	TOTAL	LIMA 458 MAT.	INST.	TOTAL	LORAIN 440 MAT.	INST.	TOTAL
015433	CONTRACTOR EQUIPMENT		91.1	91.1		91.1	91.1		92.4	92.4		99.6	99.6		91.8	91.8		92.8	92.8
0241, 31 - 34	SITE & INFRASTRUCTURE, DEMOLITION	97.1	96.0	96.3	101.3	92.0	94.8	96.6	100.2	99.1	96.6	100.5	99.3	108.8	90.0	95.6	96.5	100.7	99.4
0310	Concrete Forming & Accessories	101.7	91.4	92.8	99.5	77.5	80.4	97.3	69.8	73.5	97.4	72.1	75.5	93.1	79.6	81.4	101.7	78.1	81.3
0320	Concrete Reinforcing	98.2	91.4	94.7	99.2	80.3	89.6	104.0	80.7	92.2	104.0	78.5	91.1	101.4	80.9	91.0	97.7	91.3	94.5
0330	Cast-in-Place Concrete	100.8	99.3	100.2	92.0	82.7	88.5	85.1	79.1	82.8	91.2	76.4	85.6	100.5	89.0	96.1	97.8	94.6	96.6
03	CONCRETE	99.2	93.5	96.6	94.3	79.8	87.6	91.5	75.1	83.9	94.4	75.4	85.6	98.7	83.1	91.4	97.7	85.9	92.2
04	MASONRY	99.4	101.1	100.5	93.6	87.2	89.7	89.9	77.2	82.1	90.3	79.7	83.7	114.5	80.5	93.5	91.3	95.7	94.0
05	METALS	100.0	83.7	95.0	98.0	80.2	92.5	97.1	77.9	91.2	97.1	85.9	93.7	103.6	80.9	96.7	99.1	81.9	93.8
06	WOOD, PLASTICS & COMPOSITES	107.0	89.0	97.1	98.2	76.4	86.2	102.0	67.3	83.0	100.7	69.8	83.7	85.1	79.2	81.9	108.0	74.0	89.4
07	THERMAL & MOISTURE PROTECTION	102.3	98.9	100.9	98.5	86.3	93.5	106.2	78.7	94.8	101.9	80.4	93.0	99.2	86.0	93.7	105.6	94.9	101.2
08	OPENINGS	99.8	87.9	97.1	98.5	74.4	93.0	97.3	70.4	91.2	94.9	71.2	89.6	98.7	73.5	93.0	103.6	79.7	98.2
0920	Plaster & Gypsum Board	102.3	88.4	93.1	97.9	75.7	83.1	99.7	66.8	77.8	99.7	69.3	79.5	95.1	78.5	84.0	103.0	73.2	83.2
0950, 0980	Ceilings & Acoustic Treatment	91.7	88.4	89.5	93.4	75.7	81.6	98.6	66.8	77.4	97.6	69.3	78.8	101.3	78.5	86.1	93.4	73.2	79.9
0960	Flooring	93.5	91.1	92.8	98.9	78.4	93.0	103.6	85.8	98.4	101.0	78.0	94.4	121.3	78.1	108.8	93.9	91.1	93.1
0970, 0990	Wall Finishes & Painting/Coating	93.4	94.7	94.1	100.1	80.0	88.3	104.0	72.9	85.7	104.0	72.3	85.4	106.9	73.2	87.1	93.4	94.7	94.1
09	FINISHES	96.3	91.5	93.7	96.5	77.5	86.1	100.0	72.5	84.9	99.0	72.6	84.6	100.6	78.5	88.5	96.8	81.4	88.4
COVERS	DIVS. 10 - 14, 25, 28, 41, 43, 44, 46	100.0	98.3	99.6	100.0	89.0	97.5	100.0	86.3	96.9	100.0	87.1	97.1	100.0	88.6	97.4	100.0	94.6	98.8
21, 22, 23	FIRE SUPPRESSION, PLUMBING & HVAC	100.0	92.3	96.6	100.0	86.0	93.8	100.9	75.0	89.4	100.6	75.9	89.7	96.5	83.5	90.7	100.0	86.5	94.0
26, 27, 3370	ELECTRICAL, COMMUNICATIONS & UTIL.	98.8	98.2	98.5	98.4	84.3	90.9	98.4	78.4	87.8	98.7	78.7	88.1	101.6	78.4	89.3	98.6	83.0	90.3
MF2014	WEIGHTED AVERAGE	99.5	93.7	96.9	98.0	83.4	91.5	97.8	77.8	89.0	97.7	79.2	89.5	100.6	81.8	92.3	99.3	86.9	93.8

OHIO

DIVISION		MANSFIELD 448-449 MAT.	INST.	TOTAL	MARION 433 MAT.	INST.	TOTAL	SPRINGFIELD 455 MAT.	INST.	TOTAL	STEUBENVILLE 439 MAT.	INST.	TOTAL	TOLEDO 434-436 MAT.	INST.	TOTAL	YOUNGSTOWN 444-445 MAT.	INST.	TOTAL
015433	CONTRACTOR EQUIPMENT		92.8	92.8		92.8	92.8		92.4	92.4		96.8	96.8		96.8	96.8		92.8	92.8
0241, 31 - 34	SITE & INFRASTRUCTURE, DEMOLITION	93.2	100.4	98.2	96.9	96.5	96.7	96.9	100.2	99.2	142.5	105.1	116.4	100.4	97.0	98.1	97.1	100.3	99.3
0310	Concrete Forming & Accessories	90.7	77.0	78.9	95.7	77.6	80.0	97.3	74.2	77.3	97.2	82.5	84.5	99.5	89.0	90.4	101.7	80.2	83.1
0320	Concrete Reinforcing	88.9	80.0	84.4	91.4	80.5	85.9	104.0	80.7	92.2	89.1	95.4	92.3	99.2	83.6	91.3	97.7	85.7	91.6
0330	Cast-in-Place Concrete	95.2	84.3	91.0	84.0	82.5	83.5	87.4	79.2	84.3	91.2	83.4	88.2	92.0	93.4	92.5	101.8	90.1	97.3
03	CONCRETE	92.3	79.8	86.5	86.5	79.8	83.4	92.6	77.1	85.4	90.5	84.6	87.7	94.3	89.5	92.1	99.6	84.2	92.5
04	MASONRY	93.9	93.2	93.5	95.3	90.7	92.4	90.1	77.2	82.2	82.9	91.7	88.3	101.6	93.7	96.7	95.1	86.9	90.1
05	METALS	99.3	76.6	92.4	97.0	79.7	91.7	97.0	78.1	91.2	93.5	82.1	90.0	97.7	86.5	94.3	98.5	78.5	92.4
06	WOOD, PLASTICS & COMPOSITES	96.0	74.0	83.9	94.4	76.4	84.5	103.6	73.0	86.8	90.0	80.9	85.0	98.2	88.7	93.0	108.0	78.9	92.0
07	THERMAL & MOISTURE PROTECTION	103.9	92.0	98.9	98.1	92.9	95.0	106.1	79.3	95.0	110.0	88.4	101.0	98.2	94.0	96.5	105.9	90.4	99.5
08	OPENINGS	104.2	70.7	96.6	93.1	71.7	88.3	95.4	73.5	90.4	93.4	82.0	90.8	95.8	85.5	93.5	103.6	78.7	98.0
0920	Plaster & Gypsum Board	96.6	73.2	81.0	95.9	75.7	82.5	99.7	72.6	81.7	95.0	79.9	84.9	97.9	88.4	91.6	103.0	78.1	86.5
0950, 0980	Ceilings & Acoustic Treatment	94.3	73.2	80.2	93.4	75.7	81.6	98.6	72.6	81.3	90.5	79.9	83.4	93.4	88.4	90.1	93.4	78.1	83.2
0960	Flooring	88.9	92.4	89.9	97.4	92.4	96.0	103.6	85.8	98.4	125.8	83.9	113.7	97.7	87.4	94.7	93.9	81.0	90.2
0970, 0990	Wall Finishes & Painting/Coating	93.4	77.9	84.3	100.1	77.9	87.1	104.0	72.9	85.7	112.5	88.3	98.3	100.2	88.9	93.6	93.4	81.6	86.5
09	FINISHES	94.3	79.4	86.2	95.4	80.1	87.0	100.0	75.8	86.8	112.9	82.9	96.5	96.1	88.5	92.0	96.8	79.9	87.6
COVERS	DIVS. 10 - 14, 25, 28, 41, 43, 44, 46	100.0	92.1	98.2	100.0	88.5	97.4	100.0	87.0	97.1	100.0	87.5	97.2	100.0	95.2	98.9	100.0	92.1	98.2
21, 22, 23	FIRE SUPPRESSION, PLUMBING & HVAC	96.4	85.9	91.8	96.4	86.5	92.1	100.0	81.3	92.2	96.9	88.9	93.4	100.0	94.1	97.5	100.0	82.2	92.1
26, 27, 3370	ELECTRICAL, COMMUNICATIONS & UTIL.	96.2	72.4	83.6	92.7	72.4	81.9	98.4	84.3	90.9	87.6	104.0	96.3	98.5	109.9	104.6	98.6	87.5	92.7
MF2014	WEIGHTED AVERAGE	97.4	83.0	91.0	94.8	82.7	89.4	97.7	80.9	90.3	96.7	90.3	93.8	98.0	94.1	96.3	99.6	84.8	93.1

For customer support on your Electrical Costs with RSMeans Data, call 800.448.8182.

533

OHIO / OKLAHOMA

		ZANESVILLE 437-438			ARDMORE 734			CLINTON 736			DURANT 747			ENID 737			GUYMON 739		
DIVISION		MAT.	INST.	TOTAL	MAT.	INST.	TOTAL	MAT.	INST.	TOTAL	MAT.	INST.	TOTAL	MAT.	INST.	TOTAL	MAT.	INST.	TOTAL
015433	CONTRACTOR EQUIPMENT		92.8	92.8		83.6	83.6		82.7	82.7		82.7	82.7		82.7	82.7		82.7	82.7
0241, 31 - 34	SITE & INFRASTRUCTURE, DEMOLITION	100.0	96.5	97.6	99.0	98.4	98.6	100.6	96.8	97.9	95.6	94.3	94.7	102.2	96.8	98.4	104.9	96.6	99.1
0310	Concrete Forming & Accessories	92.9	77.4	79.5	94.9	58.7	63.5	93.4	58.7	63.3	85.2	58.3	61.9	97.1	58.8	64.0	100.5	58.6	64.3
0320	Concrete Reinforcing	90.9	93.9	92.4	91.0	65.9	78.3	91.6	65.9	78.5	95.5	66.3	80.7	91.0	65.9	78.2	91.6	63.3	77.2
0330	Cast-in-Place Concrete	88.5	82.3	86.2	98.4	74.1	89.1	95.1	74.1	87.1	92.7	74.0	85.6	95.1	74.2	87.1	95.1	73.9	87.0
03	CONCRETE	90.2	81.9	86.4	91.5	65.1	79.3	90.9	65.1	78.9	89.1	65.0	77.9	91.3	65.2	79.2	94.0	64.5	80.3
04	MASONRY	92.6	80.3	85.0	97.3	57.0	72.5	121.6	57.0	81.8	90.8	65.3	75.1	103.1	57.0	74.7	99.6	56.9	73.3
05	METALS	98.4	84.0	94.0	107.2	61.2	93.1	107.3	61.2	93.2	92.3	61.4	82.9	108.7	61.3	94.2	107.8	59.7	93.1
06	WOOD, PLASTICS & COMPOSITES	90.3	76.4	82.7	104.4	58.8	79.3	103.5	58.8	78.9	92.5	58.8	74.0	106.8	58.8	80.4	110.3	58.8	82.0
07	THERMAL & MOISTURE PROTECTION	98.2	84.7	92.6	106.6	65.6	89.6	106.7	65.6	89.7	100.0	66.9	86.3	106.8	65.6	89.7	107.2	65.6	89.9
08	OPENINGS	93.1	77.9	89.7	103.4	58.0	93.1	103.4	58.0	93.1	97.5	58.0	88.5	104.6	58.0	94.0	100.5	57.4	93.1
0920	Plaster & Gypsum Board	92.6	75.7	81.4	88.9	58.2	68.5	88.5	58.2	68.4	77.9	58.2	64.8	89.2	58.2	68.6	89.2	58.2	68.6
0950, 0980	Ceilings & Acoustic Treatment	93.4	75.7	81.6	83.4	58.2	66.6	83.4	58.2	66.6	78.8	58.2	65.1	83.4	58.2	66.6	83.4	58.2	66.6
0960	Flooring	95.3	78.4	90.4	94.6	60.7	84.8	93.5	60.7	84.0	95.0	54.8	83.3	95.3	75.0	89.4	96.9	60.7	86.4
0970, 0990	Wall Finishes & Painting/Coating	100.1	80.0	88.3	87.0	45.0	62.3	87.0	45.0	62.3	94.9	45.0	65.6	87.0	45.0	62.3	87.0	45.0	62.3
09	FINISHES	94.6	77.3	85.1	84.1	56.7	69.1	83.9	56.7	69.1	84.2	55.5	68.5	84.7	59.7	71.0	85.5	58.1	70.5
COVERS	DIVS. 10 - 14, 25, 28, 41, 43, 44,.46	100.0	84.4	96.5	100.0	78.8	95.2	100.0	78.8	95.2	100.0	78.8	95.2	100.0	78.8	95.2	100.0	78.8	95.2
21, 22, 23	FIRE SUPPRESSION, PLUMBING & HVAC	96.4	87.7	92.6	96.8	66.8	83.5	96.8	66.8	83.5	96.8	66.8	83.5	100.3	66.8	85.5	96.8	65.5	82.9
26, 27, 3370	ELECTRICAL, COMMUNICATIONS & UTIL.	92.8	75.9	83.9	94.4	71.3	82.1	95.4	71.3	82.6	96.7	63.7	79.2	95.4	71.3	82.6	97.1	59.0	76.9
MF2014	WEIGHTED AVERAGE	95.3	82.8	89.8	98.1	66.7	84.2	99.4	66.6	84.4	94.1	66.1	81.7	99.8	67.0	85.3	99.2	64.5	83.9

OKLAHOMA

		LAWTON 735			MCALESTER 745			MIAMI 743			MUSKOGEE 744			OKLAHOMA CITY 730-731			PONCA CITY 746		
DIVISION		MAT.	INST.	TOTAL	MAT.	INST.	TOTAL	MAT.	INST.	TOTAL	MAT.	INST.	TOTAL	MAT.	INST.	TOTAL	MAT.	INST.	TOTAL
015433	CONTRACTOR EQUIPMENT		83.6	83.6		82.7	82.7		94.6	94.6		94.6	94.6		83.9	83.9		82.7	82.7
0241, 31 - 34	SITE & INFRASTRUCTURE, DEMOLITION	98.1	98.4	98.3	88.8	96.6	94.3	90.1	93.7	92.6	90.4	93.7	92.7	96.5	99.0	98.2	96.2	96.8	96.6
0310	Concrete Forming & Accessories	100.5	58.8	64.4	83.2	43.7	49.1	96.7	58.5	63.7	101.2	58.3	64.1	97.3	59.0	64.1	92.0	58.7	63.2
0320	Concrete Reinforcing	91.2	65.9	78.4	95.2	65.8	80.3	93.8	65.9	79.6	94.6	65.5	79.8	100.7	65.9	83.0	94.6	65.9	80.0
0330	Cast-in-Place Concrete	91.9	74.2	85.2	81.3	73.8	78.4	85.2	75.2	81.4	86.2	75.1	82.0	92.0	74.4	85.3	95.2	74.2	87.2
03	CONCRETE	87.7	65.2	77.3	79.9	58.3	69.9	84.4	66.5	76.1	86.1	66.3	76.9	90.8	65.4	79.0	91.3	65.1	79.2
04	MASONRY	99.5	57.0	73.3	109.0	56.9	76.9	93.8	57.1	71.2	111.1	51.4	74.3	101.9	57.4	74.5	86.5	57.0	68.3
05	METALS	112.8	61.3	97.1	92.3	60.4	82.5	92.2	76.9	87.6	93.7	76.1	88.3	105.1	61.3	91.7	92.2	61.2	82.7
06	WOOD, PLASTICS & COMPOSITES	109.4	58.8	81.6	90.2	39.0	62.1	104.7	58.9	79.5	108.9	58.9	81.4	97.7	58.8	76.3	100.4	58.8	77.5
07	THERMAL & MOISTURE PROTECTION	106.6	65.6	89.6	99.6	62.5	84.2	100.0	65.6	85.7	100.3	63.7	85.1	97.4	66.0	84.4	100.2	65.9	85.9
08	OPENINGS	106.4	58.0	95.4	97.4	47.1	86.1	97.4	58.1	88.5	98.7	58.1	89.5	103.1	58.0	92.9	97.4	58.0	88.5
0920	Plaster & Gypsum Board	90.8	58.2	69.1	76.9	37.9	51.0	83.8	58.2	66.8	85.8	58.2	67.4	95.4	58.2	70.7	82.8	58.2	66.4
0950, 0980	Ceilings & Acoustic Treatment	90.1	58.2	68.9	78.8	37.9	51.6	78.8	58.2	65.1	87.3	58.2	67.9	93.4	58.2	70.0	78.8	58.2	65.1
0960	Flooring	97.3	75.0	90.8	93.8	60.7	84.2	101.4	54.8	87.9	103.9	35.2	83.0	94.4	75.0	88.7	98.2	60.7	87.4
0970, 0990	Wall Finishes & Painting/Coating	87.0	45.0	62.3	94.9	45.0	65.6	94.9	45.0	65.6	94.9	45.0	65.6	90.3	45.0	63.7	94.9	45.0	65.6
09	FINISHES	86.3	59.7	71.8	83.1	45.1	62.4	86.2	55.6	69.5	89.1	52.0	68.8	88.2	59.8	72.7	85.9	57.7	70.5
COVERS	DIVS. 10 - 14, 25, 28, 41, 43, 44, 46	100.0	78.8	95.2	100.0	76.7	94.7	100.0	79.3	95.3	100.0	79.3	95.3	100.0	79.0	95.2	100.0	78.8	95.2
21, 22, 23	FIRE SUPPRESSION, PLUMBING & HVAC	100.3	66.8	85.5	96.8	62.2	81.5	96.8	62.3	81.5	100.3	62.3	83.5	100.1	67.0	85.5	96.8	62.3	81.5
26, 27, 3370	ELECTRICAL, COMMUNICATIONS & UTIL.	97.2	71.3	83.4	95.1	66.2	79.8	96.5	66.3	80.5	94.6	72.8	83.0	102.5	71.3	85.9	94.6	69.4	81.2
MF2014	WEIGHTED AVERAGE	100.2	67.1	85.6	93.4	61.6	79.3	93.8	66.2	81.6	96.1	66.0	82.8	99.3	67.3	85.1	94.2	65.5	81.5

OKLAHOMA / OREGON

		POTEAU 749			SHAWNEE 748			TULSA 740-741			WOODWARD 738			BEND 977			EUGENE 974		
DIVISION		MAT.	INST.	TOTAL	MAT.	INST.	TOTAL	MAT.	INST.	TOTAL	MAT.	INST.	TOTAL	MAT.	INST.	TOTAL	MAT.	INST.	TOTAL
015433	CONTRACTOR EQUIPMENT		93.3	93.3		82.7	82.7		94.6	94.6		82.7	82.7		100.3	100.3		100.3	100.3
0241, 31 - 34	SITE & INFRASTRUCTURE, DEMOLITION	77.1	89.0	85.4	99.3	96.8	97.6	96.7	92.7	93.9	100.9	96.8	98.0	107.9	103.4	104.7	97.8	103.4	101.7
0310	Concrete Forming & Accessories	89.9	58.2	62.5	85.1	58.6	62.2	101.3	58.4	64.2	93.5	46.0	52.4	110.8	94.9	97.0	107.1	95.0	96.6
0320	Concrete Reinforcing	95.7	65.8	80.5	94.6	63.3	78.7	94.9	65.9	80.1	91.0	65.8	78.2	94.8	103.7	99.3	93.0	103.7	101.4
0330	Cast-in-Place Concrete	85.2	75.1	81.3	98.3	74.1	89.1	93.9	75.1	86.7	95.1	74.1	87.1	105.7	99.5	103.3	102.3	99.5	101.1
03	CONCRETE	86.6	66.3	77.2	93.0	64.7	79.8	91.4	66.4	79.8	91.1	59.4	76.4	106.5	97.6	102.4	98.0	97.7	97.9
04	MASONRY	94.2	57.1	71.3	110.4	57.0	77.5	94.7	57.1	71.5	92.5	57.0	70.6	105.8	96.4	100.0	102.7	96.4	98.8
05	METALS	92.3	76.6	87.5	92.2	60.2	82.4	96.6	76.8	90.6	107.4	61.1	93.2	97.6	92.5	96.0	98.3	92.7	96.6
06	WOOD, PLASTICS & COMPOSITES	97.1	58.9	76.1	92.4	58.8	73.9	108.1	58.9	81.1	103.6	41.7	69.6	102.2	94.5	98.0	98.1	94.5	96.1
07	THERMAL & MOISTURE PROTECTION	100.1	65.6	85.8	100.2	65.4	85.7	100.3	65.7	86.0	106.8	64.0	89.0	110.5	95.6	104.3	109.6	99.3	105.3
08	OPENINGS	97.4	58.1	88.5	97.4	57.4	88.4	100.4	58.1	90.8	103.4	48.6	91.0	101.4	96.5	100.2	101.6	96.5	100.5
0920	Plaster & Gypsum Board	80.9	58.2	65.8	77.9	58.2	64.8	85.8	58.2	67.4	88.5	40.6	56.7	115.2	94.2	101.2	113.2	94.2	100.6
0950, 0980	Ceilings & Acoustic Treatment	78.8	58.2	65.1	78.8	58.2	65.1	87.3	58.2	67.9	83.4	40.6	54.9	88.1	94.2	92.2	89.1	94.2	92.5
0960	Flooring	97.5	54.8	85.1	95.0	60.7	85.1	102.8	51.2	87.8	93.5	57.9	83.2	104.2	99.3	102.8	102.4	99.3	101.5
0970, 0990	Wall Finishes & Painting/Coating	94.9	45.0	65.6	94.9	45.0	65.6	94.9	45.0	65.6	87.0	45.0	62.3	94.2	72.2	81.3	94.2	72.2	81.3
09	FINISHES	83.9	55.6	68.4	84.4	56.7	69.3	88.9	54.9	70.3	84.0	46.2	63.3	98.9	93.0	95.7	97.2	93.0	94.9
COVERS	DIVS. 10 - 14, 25, 28, 41, 43, 44, 46	100.0	79.1	95.3	100.0	78.8	95.2	100.0	79.2	95.3	100.0	77.0	94.8	100.0	98.9	99.7	100.0	98.9	99.7
21, 22, 23	FIRE SUPPRESSION, PLUMBING & HVAC	96.8	62.3	81.5	96.8	66.8	83.5	100.3	64.1	84.3	96.8	66.8	83.5	96.5	101.9	98.9	100.1	101.9	100.9
26, 27, 3370	ELECTRICAL, COMMUNICATIONS & UTIL.	94.7	66.3	79.7	96.7	71.3	83.2	96.7	66.3	80.6	97.0	71.3	83.3	100.6	95.0	97.6	99.2	95.0	97.0
MF2014	WEIGHTED AVERAGE	93.3	65.8	81.2	95.7	66.4	82.7	97.0	66.5	83.5	98.1	63.8	82.9	100.6	97.3	99.2	99.7	97.5	98.7

City Cost Indexes

OREGON

DIVISION		KLAMATH FALLS 976 MAT.	INST.	TOTAL	MEDFORD 975 MAT.	INST.	TOTAL	PENDLETON 978 MAT.	INST.	TOTAL	PORTLAND 970 - 972 MAT.	INST.	TOTAL	SALEM 973 MAT.	INST.	TOTAL	VALE 979 MAT.	INST.	TOTAL
015433	CONTRACTOR EQUIPMENT		100.3	100.3		100.3	100.3		97.7	97.7		100.3	100.3		100.3	100.3		97.7	97.7
0241, 31 - 34	SITE & INFRASTRUCTURE, DEMOLITION	112.0	103.3	106.0	105.6	103.3	104.0	104.5	96.2	98.7	100.3	103.4	102.4	92.1	103.4	99.9	91.6	96.1	94.7
0310	Concrete Forming & Accessories	103.4	94.6	95.8	102.4	94.6	95.6	103.9	95.1	96.4	108.3	94.9	96.7	107.0	94.9	96.5	110.8	93.9	96.1
0320	Concrete Reinforcing	94.8	103.6	99.3	96.4	103.6	100.1	93.9	103.7	98.9	99.7	103.7	101.7	107.2	103.7	105.4	91.6	103.5	97.7
0330	Cast-in-Place Concrete	105.7	101.9	104.2	105.7	99.4	103.3	106.5	100.3	104.1	105.2	99.5	102.9	96.6	99.5	97.7	83.8	102.9	91.1
03	CONCRETE	109.3	98.3	104.2	104.0	97.5	101.0	90.7	98.1	94.1	99.5	97.7	98.7	95.4	97.6	96.5	75.7	98.3	86.2
04	MASONRY	120.1	96.4	105.5	99.7	96.4	97.7	110.3	96.5	101.8	104.5	96.4	99.5	109.1	96.4	101.3	108.4	96.5	101.1
05	METALS	97.6	92.2	96.0	97.9	92.2	96.1	104.6	93.2	101.1	99.4	92.6	97.3	105.3	92.5	101.4	104.5	92.0	100.7
06	WOOD, PLASTICS & COMPOSITES	93.2	94.5	93.9	92.1	94.5	93.5	94.9	94.6	94.8	99.1	94.5	96.6	93.6	94.5	94.1	103.2	94.6	98.5
07	THERMAL & MOISTURE PROTECTION	110.7	91.8	102.9	110.3	91.8	102.7	103.2	95.3	99.9	109.5	95.6	103.8	106.0	95.6	101.7	102.5	92.4	98.3
08	OPENINGS	101.4	96.5	100.3	104.5	96.5	102.7	97.9	96.5	97.6	99.3	96.5	98.7	101.3	96.5	100.2	97.8	87.6	95.5
0920	Plaster & Gypsum Board	110.0	94.2	99.5	109.4	94.2	99.3	96.7	94.2	95.0	113.1	94.2	100.5	109.1	94.2	99.2	102.9	94.2	97.1
0950, 0980	Ceilings & Acoustic Treatment	95.7	94.2	94.7	102.4	94.2	96.9	63.5	94.2	83.9	91.0	94.2	93.1	96.1	94.2	94.8	63.5	94.2	83.9
0960	Flooring	100.9	99.3	100.4	100.2	99.3	100.0	70.1	99.3	78.6	100.1	99.3	99.9	103.8	99.3	102.5	72.4	99.3	80.2
0970, 0990	Wall Finishes & Painting/Coating	94.2	67.0	78.2	94.2	67.0	78.2	86.5	74.1	79.2	94.0	74.1	82.3	93.8	72.2	81.1	86.5	72.2	78.1
09	FINISHES	99.2	92.4	95.5	99.5	92.4	95.6	70.2	93.3	82.8	96.9	93.2	94.9	95.9	93.0	94.3	70.8	93.1	83.0
COVERS	DIVS. 10 - 14, 25, 28, 41, 43, 44, 46	100.0	98.8	99.7	100.0	98.8	99.7	100.0	101.4	100.3	100.0	98.9	99.8	100.0	98.9	99.7	100.0	99.1	99.8
21, 22, 23	FIRE SUPPRESSION, PLUMBING & HVAC	96.5	101.9	98.9	100.1	101.9	100.9	98.6	108.5	103.0	100.1	101.8	100.8	100.1	101.9	100.9	98.6	69.6	85.8
26, 27, 3370	ELECTRICAL, COMMUNICATIONS & UTIL.	99.2	78.0	87.9	102.8	78.0	89.6	91.5	96.2	94.0	99.3	106.2	103.0	106.5	95.0	100.4	91.5	68.7	79.4
MF2014	WEIGHTED AVERAGE	101.6	94.8	98.6	101.3	94.7	98.4	96.5	98.6	97.4	100.0	98.9	99.5	101.2	97.3	99.5	94.3	85.8	90.5

PENNSYLVANIA

DIVISION		ALLENTOWN 181 MAT.	INST.	TOTAL	ALTOONA 166 MAT.	INST.	TOTAL	BEDFORD 155 MAT.	INST.	TOTAL	BRADFORD 167 MAT.	INST.	TOTAL	BUTLER 160 MAT.	INST.	TOTAL	CHAMBERSBURG 172 MAT.	INST.	TOTAL
015433	CONTRACTOR EQUIPMENT		117.3	117.3		117.3	117.3		114.8	114.8		117.3	117.3		117.3	117.3		116.4	116.4
0241, 31 - 34	SITE & INFRASTRUCTURE, DEMOLITION	93.6	103.9	100.8	96.5	103.3	101.2	106.2	100.6	102.3	92.7	102.2	99.3	87.8	104.0	99.1	89.3	100.6	97.2
0310	Concrete Forming & Accessories	101.3	113.6	111.9	85.8	85.4	85.5	83.5	82.0	82.2	88.1	103.8	101.7	87.3	91.1	90.6	88.9	82.2	83.1
0320	Concrete Reinforcing	101.1	114.3	107.8	97.9	105.2	101.6	99.7	103.0	101.4	100.0	105.0	102.6	98.6	118.7	108.8	93.7	113.1	103.5
0330	Cast-in-Place Concrete	89.8	107.2	96.5	100.1	92.8	97.3	115.6	87.6	104.9	95.6	96.9	96.1	88.4	101.1	93.2	96.6	98.3	97.2
03	CONCRETE	93.4	112.4	102.2	89.4	92.9	91.1	106.4	89.2	98.4	95.4	102.6	98.8	81.3	100.8	90.3	99.4	94.8	97.3
04	MASONRY	95.7	101.6	99.3	99.2	89.9	93.5	110.5	86.5	95.7	96.5	84.8	89.3	101.3	98.2	99.4	102.4	85.0	91.7
05	METALS	95.4	124.0	104.1	89.6	117.0	98.0	98.3	115.0	103.4	93.3	116.9	100.5	89.3	123.5	99.8	91.7	119.3	100.1
06	WOOD, PLASTICS & COMPOSITES	101.7	115.1	109.1	81.0	83.8	82.5	86.3	81.6	83.7	87.3	109.5	99.5	82.3	88.3	85.6	88.5	81.7	84.8
07	THERMAL & MOISTURE PROTECTION	102.7	114.6	107.7	101.6	94.3	98.6	100.4	90.4	96.2	102.6	93.4	98.8	101.2	97.0	99.4	94.8	88.1	92.0
08	OPENINGS	94.8	111.4	98.6	88.5	87.1	88.2	96.5	85.8	94.1	94.8	101.1	96.2	88.5	97.1	90.4	91.6	86.6	90.5
0920	Plaster & Gypsum Board	96.8	115.4	109.2	88.7	83.2	85.1	96.9	81.1	86.4	89.8	109.6	103.0	88.7	87.9	88.2	104.3	81.1	88.8
0950, 0980	Ceilings & Acoustic Treatment	83.8	115.4	104.8	87.2	83.2	84.6	95.0	81.1	85.7	87.3	109.6	102.1	88.1	87.9	88.0	85.9	81.1	82.7
0960	Flooring	93.5	95.9	94.2	87.0	104.9	92.2	91.3	82.6	88.8	87.6	104.9	92.6	87.9	82.6	86.4	93.6	82.6	90.4
0970, 0990	Wall Finishes & Painting/Coating	93.3	108.5	102.2	88.8	110.5	101.5	96.8	113.1	106.4	93.3	107.3	101.5	88.8	113.1	103.1	91.8	107.3	100.9
09	FINISHES	90.6	110.4	101.4	88.5	91.0	89.9	97.1	85.2	90.6	88.7	105.3	97.7	88.5	91.2	90.0	89.2	84.6	86.7
COVERS	DIVS. 10 - 14, 25, 28, 41, 43, 44, 46	100.0	104.9	101.1	100.0	98.4	99.6	100.0	96.8	99.3	100.0	100.7	100.2	100.0	100.5	100.1	100.0	95.2	98.9
21, 22, 23	FIRE SUPPRESSION, PLUMBING & HVAC	100.3	114.8	106.7	99.7	85.8	93.5	96.4	82.4	90.2	96.7	95.4	96.1	96.2	98.0	97.0	96.7	89.0	93.3
26, 27, 3370	ELECTRICAL, COMMUNICATIONS & UTIL.	98.5	100.6	99.6	89.0	113.5	102.0	95.2	113.5	104.9	92.2	113.5	103.5	89.6	112.0	101.5	88.6	88.6	88.6
MF2014	WEIGHTED AVERAGE	96.7	110.2	102.6	93.3	96.6	94.8	99.2	93.7	96.8	94.9	102.1	98.1	91.4	102.2	96.2	94.5	92.5	93.6

PENNSYLVANIA

DIVISION		DOYLESTOWN 189 MAT.	INST.	TOTAL	DUBOIS 158 MAT.	INST.	TOTAL	ERIE 164 - 165 MAT.	INST.	TOTAL	GREENSBURG 156 MAT.	INST.	TOTAL	HARRISBURG 170 - 171 MAT.	INST.	TOTAL	HAZLETON 182 MAT.	INST.	TOTAL
015433	CONTRACTOR EQUIPMENT		94.5	94.5		114.8	114.8		117.3	117.3		114.8	114.8		116.4	116.4		117.3	117.3
0241, 31 - 34	SITE & INFRASTRUCTURE, DEMOLITION	107.3	89.9	95.1	111.0	100.7	103.8	93.4	103.2	100.3	122.2	102.6	102.5	89.4	101.8	98.1	87.0	102.7	98.0
0310	Concrete Forming & Accessories	84.9	129.8	123.7	83.0	82.9	82.9	100.7	89.3	90.8	89.9	95.2	94.5	89.9	89.9	91.2	82.3	89.1	88.2
0320	Concrete Reinforcing	97.8	145.9	122.2	99.1	105.1	102.1	100.0	106.3	103.2	99.1	118.5	108.9	102.7	114.2	108.5	98.1	114.1	106.2
0330	Cast-in-Place Concrete	84.8	133.5	103.4	111.5	96.1	105.6	98.4	94.5	96.9	107.3	100.6	104.7	95.1	101.8	97.6	84.8	100.8	90.9
03	CONCRETE	89.0	133.0	109.4	107.9	92.8	100.9	88.4	95.4	91.7	101.1	102.4	101.7	94.4	99.8	96.9	86.2	99.0	92.1
04	MASONRY	99.1	124.4	114.7	111.0	86.9	96.2	88.4	93.5	91.6	121.7	96.0	105.9	96.4	89.3	92.1	108.8	94.6	100.0
05	METALS	93.0	121.1	101.6	98.3	115.2	103.5	89.8	116.9	98.1	98.2	121.7	105.4	98.0	122.9	105.6	95.1	121.4	103.1
06	WOOD, PLASTICS & COMPOSITES	83.1	130.6	109.2	85.3	81.6	83.3	97.8	87.1	91.9	92.2	94.1	93.3	96.0	89.1	92.2	81.7	86.5	84.3
07	THERMAL & MOISTURE PROTECTION	100.1	129.2	112.2	100.7	92.3	97.2	102.1	94.0	98.8	100.3	97.0	98.9	97.2	106.0	100.9	102.1	103.2	102.6
08	OPENINGS	97.2	136.0	106.0	96.5	85.8	94.1	88.7	91.0	89.2	96.5	100.3	97.5	95.9	90.9	94.8	95.4	95.2	95.3
0920	Plaster & Gypsum Board	87.5	131.3	116.6	95.9	81.1	86.0	96.8	86.6	90.0	98.0	93.9	95.3	108.7	88.7	95.4	87.9	86.0	86.6
0950, 0980	Ceilings & Acoustic Treatment	83.1	131.3	115.2	95.0	81.1	85.7	83.8	86.6	85.7	94.2	93.9	94.0	95.4	88.7	90.9	84.8	86.0	85.6
0960	Flooring	77.7	136.6	94.7	91.1	104.9	95.1	93.9	104.9	97.1	95.1	82.6	91.5	96.2	90.7	94.6	84.8	94.7	87.6
0970, 0990	Wall Finishes & Painting/Coating	92.9	148.7	125.6	96.8	113.1	106.4	98.7	93.6	95.7	96.8	113.1	106.4	93.8	90.3	91.8	93.3	110.9	103.6
09	FINISHES	82.0	133.0	109.9	97.4	89.5	93.0	91.6	92.1	91.9	97.9	94.6	96.1	92.9	89.5	91.0	86.6	92.0	89.6
COVERS	DIVS. 10 - 14, 25, 28, 41, 43, 44, 46	100.0	116.4	103.7	100.0	97.3	99.4	100.0	100.1	100.0	100.0	101.0	100.2	100.0	97.4	99.4	100.0	99.7	99.9
21, 22, 23	FIRE SUPPRESSION, PLUMBING & HVAC	96.2	129.3	110.8	96.4	83.1	90.6	99.7	101.5	100.5	96.4	91.1	94.1	100.0	93.0	96.9	96.7	96.7	96.7
26, 27, 3370	ELECTRICAL, COMMUNICATIONS & UTIL.	91.7	130.3	112.2	95.8	113.5	105.2	90.7	94.8	92.9	95.8	113.5	105.2	95.5	91.1	93.2	93.1	94.1	93.6
MF2014	WEIGHTED AVERAGE	94.0	126.0	108.2	99.6	95.0	97.6	93.2	98.5	95.5	99.2	101.3	100.1	96.9	96.7	96.8	94.5	98.7	96.3

For customer support on your Electrical Costs with RSMeans Data, call 800.448.8182.

535

PENNSYLVANIA

DIVISION		INDIANA 157			JOHNSTOWN 159			KITTANNING 162			LANCASTER 175-176			LEHIGH VALLEY 180			MONTROSE 188		
		MAT.	INST.	TOTAL	MAT.	INST.	TOTAL	MAT.	INST.	TOTAL	MAT.	INST.	TOTAL	MAT.	INST.	TOTAL	MAT.	INST.	TOTAL
015433	CONTRACTOR EQUIPMENT		114.8	114.8		114.8	114.8		117.3	117.3		116.4	116.4		117.3	117.3		117.3	117.3
0241, 31 - 34	SITE & INFRASTRUCTURE, DEMOLITION	100.2	101.5	101.1	106.7	101.9	103.4	90.4	103.7	99.7	81.2	101.8	95.6	90.9	104.0	100.0	89.6	103.3	99.1
0310	Concrete Forming & Accessories	84.1	92.2	91.1	83.0	85.3	85.0	87.3	96.4	95.2	91.1	90.2	90.3	94.6	131.0	126.1	83.4	93.0	91.7
0320	Concrete Reinforcing	98.3	118.5	108.6	99.7	118.3	109.2	98.6	118.6	108.8	93.3	114.2	103.9	98.1	112.5	105.4	102.8	114.2	108.6
0330	Cast-in-Place Concrete	105.2	99.0	102.8	116.7	92.5	107.5	91.9	99.6	94.8	82.2	101.8	89.7	91.9	111.0	99.1	90.1	99.3	93.6
03	CONCRETE	98.5	100.4	99.4	107.3	95.0	101.6	83.9	102.6	92.6	87.3	99.9	93.1	92.6	121.0	105.8	91.2	100.2	95.4
04	MASONRY	107.0	95.5	99.9	107.9	90.2	97.0	104.0	95.4	98.7	108.5	89.8	97.0	95.7	113.5	106.7	95.7	98.6	97.5
05	METALS	98.3	120.8	105.2	98.3	119.9	104.9	89.4	122.9	99.6	91.7	123.0	101.3	95.0	121.7	103.2	93.4	121.7	102.0
06	WOOD, PLASTICS & COMPOSITES	87.0	91.5	89.5	85.3	83.7	84.4	82.3	96.6	90.1	91.2	89.1	90.1	93.6	134.4	116.0	82.5	90.1	86.7
07	THERMAL & MOISTURE PROTECTION	100.1	96.6	98.7	100.4	92.6	97.2	101.3	97.2	99.6	94.2	106.3	99.2	102.5	116.6	108.3	102.1	92.8	98.3
08	OPENINGS	96.5	94.4	96.0	96.5	90.2	95.1	88.5	101.6	91.5	91.6	90.9	91.4	91.2	126.1	101.3	92.0	94.8	92.6
0920	Plaster & Gypsum Board	97.2	91.3	93.3	95.7	83.2	87.4	88.7	96.3	93.8	106.3	88.7	94.6	90.6	135.2	120.2	88.5	89.7	89.3
0950, 0980	Ceilings & Acoustic Treatment	95.0	91.3	92.5	94.2	83.2	86.9	88.1	96.3	93.6	85.9	88.7	87.8	84.8	135.2	118.3	87.3	89.7	88.9
0960	Flooring	92.0	104.9	95.8	91.1	82.6	88.6	87.9	104.9	92.8	94.6	101.4	96.6	90.3	99.7	93.1	85.5	104.9	91.1
0970, 0990	Wall Finishes & Painting/Coating	96.8	113.1	106.4	96.8	110.5	104.9	88.8	113.1	103.1	91.8	90.3	90.9	93.3	63.7	75.9	93.3	110.9	103.6
09	FINISHES	96.9	96.4	96.7	96.7	87.1	91.5	88.6	99.4	94.5	89.2	91.5	90.4	88.9	119.5	105.6	87.6	96.4	92.4
COVERS	DIVS. 10 - 14, 25, 28, 41, 43, 44, 46	100.0	100.0	100.0	100.0	98.3	99.6	100.0	100.7	100.2	100.0	97.6	99.5	100.0	106.1	101.4	100.0	101.4	100.3
21, 22, 23	FIRE SUPPRESSION, PLUMBING & HVAC	96.4	83.0	90.5	96.4	81.8	89.9	96.2	94.2	95.3	96.7	93.2	95.2	96.7	114.2	104.4	96.7	99.6	98.0
26, 27, 3370	ELECTRICAL, COMMUNICATIONS & UTIL.	95.8	113.5	105.2	95.8	113.5	105.2	89.0	113.5	102.0	90.0	97.2	93.8	93.1	140.2	118.1	92.2	98.7	95.7
MF2014	WEIGHTED AVERAGE	98.0	99.0	98.4	99.2	95.8	97.7	91.9	102.9	96.8	92.7	97.9	95.3	95.0	119.6	105.9	93.8	101.0	97.0

PENNSYLVANIA

DIVISION		NEW CASTLE 161			NORRISTOWN 194			OIL CITY 163			PHILADELPHIA 190-191			PITTSBURGH 150-152			POTTSVILLE 179		
		MAT.	INST.	TOTAL	MAT.	INST.	TOTAL	MAT.	INST.	TOTAL	MAT.	INST.	TOTAL	MAT.	INST.	TOTAL	MAT.	INST.	TOTAL
015433	CONTRACTOR EQUIPMENT		117.3	117.3		100.8	100.8		117.3	117.3		96.8	96.8		106.0	106.0		116.4	116.4
0241, 31 - 34	SITE & INFRASTRUCTURE, DEMOLITION	88.2	104.2	99.3	97.3	100.8	99.8	86.8	102.4	97.7	103.0	97.9	99.4	105.8	100.1	101.8	84.2	101.7	96.4
0310	Concrete Forming & Accessories	87.3	99.2	97.6	86.1	130.2	124.2	87.3	95.9	94.8	103.2	138.9	134.1	97.4	99.6	99.3	82.3	91.3	90.1
0320	Concrete Reinforcing	97.4	101.1	99.3	96.8	145.9	121.7	98.6	98.7	98.6	105.3	146.4	126.2	100.3	118.8	109.7	92.6	113.2	103.1
0330	Cast-in-Place Concrete	89.2	101.1	93.7	83.7	133.7	102.8	86.7	99.2	91.5	93.5	137.2	110.1	111.5	101.2	107.6	87.6	102.8	93.4
03	CONCRETE	81.7	101.4	90.8	87.9	133.3	109.0	80.1	98.8	88.8	99.3	138.4	117.4	104.5	103.9	104.2	90.9	100.5	95.4
04	MASONRY	100.9	98.2	99.3	111.4	124.9	119.7	100.3	91.4	94.8	99.7	135.3	121.6	101.7	100.6	101.0	101.7	94.3	97.1
05	METALS	89.4	117.4	98.0	95.5	122.4	103.7	89.4	115.5	97.4	97.9	121.4	105.1	99.7	112.8	103.7	91.9	121.2	100.9
06	WOOD, PLASTICS & COMPOSITES	82.3	99.4	91.7	81.7	130.5	108.5	82.3	96.6	90.1	98.4	139.7	121.1	101.0	99.5	100.1	81.2	88.3	85.1
07	THERMAL & MOISTURE PROTECTION	101.2	108.1	104.0	105.8	129.5	115.6	101.1	95.1	98.6	102.5	137.3	116.9	100.5	99.2	100.0	94.4	105.6	99.0
08	OPENINGS	88.5	95.7	90.1	87.4	136.0	98.4	88.5	97.5	90.6	101.1	141.0	110.1	100.3	103.2	100.9	91.6	96.1	92.7
0920	Plaster & Gypsum Board	88.7	99.3	95.7	86.5	131.3	116.3	88.7	96.3	93.8	100.1	140.6	127.0	102.3	99.3	100.3	101.0	87.9	92.3
0950, 0980	Ceilings & Acoustic Treatment	88.1	99.3	95.6	87.4	131.3	116.6	88.1	96.3	93.6	99.8	140.6	126.9	95.0	99.3	97.9	85.9	87.9	87.2
0960	Flooring	87.9	82.6	86.4	87.0	136.6	101.4	87.9	106.4	93.3	101.6	147.6	115.0	99.0	106.4	101.1	90.4	101.4	93.6
0970, 0990	Wall Finishes & Painting/Coating	88.8	113.1	103.1	90.5	148.7	124.6	88.8	113.1	103.1	96.7	148.7	127.2	96.8	113.1	106.4	91.8	110.9	103.0
09	FINISHES	88.5	97.7	93.5	86.4	132.9	111.8	88.4	99.7	94.6	100.8	141.8	123.2	100.1	101.9	101.0	87.4	94.4	91.2
COVERS	DIVS. 10 - 14, 25, 28, 41, 43, 44, 46	100.0	101.7	100.4	100.0	116.6	103.7	100.0	100.7	100.2	100.0	119.5	104.4	100.0	101.8	100.4	100.0	98.1	99.6
21, 22, 23	FIRE SUPPRESSION, PLUMBING & HVAC	96.2	101.9	98.7	96.4	128.3	110.5	96.2	97.4	96.7	100.2	134.0	115.1	100.0	102.0	100.9	96.7	98.6	97.5
26, 27, 3370	ELECTRICAL, COMMUNICATIONS & UTIL.	89.6	103.4	96.9	93.2	153.9	125.4	91.4	112.0	102.3	97.2	153.9	127.3	98.3	113.5	106.4	88.2	93.4	91.0
MF2014	WEIGHTED AVERAGE	91.5	102.6	96.4	94.3	130.1	110.1	91.4	101.4	95.8	99.6	134.5	115.0	100.0	104.5	102.3	93.0	99.5	95.9

PENNSYLVANIA

DIVISION		READING 195-196			SCRANTON 184-185			STATE COLLEGE 168			STROUDSBURG 183			SUNBURY 178			UNIONTOWN 154		
		MAT.	INST.	TOTAL	MAT.	INST.	TOTAL	MAT.	INST.	TOTAL	MAT.	INST.	TOTAL	MAT.	INST.	TOTAL	MAT.	INST.	TOTAL
015433	CONTRACTOR EQUIPMENT		124.1	124.1		117.3	117.3		116.4	116.4		117.3	117.3		117.3	117.3		114.8	114.8
0241, 31 - 34	SITE & INFRASTRUCTURE, DEMOLITION	101.7	115.2	111.1	94.1	103.3	100.5	84.5	101.8	96.6	88.6	103.9	99.3	96.6	102.7	100.9	100.8	102.6	102.1
0310	Concrete Forming & Accessories	102.9	92.6	94.0	101.5	93.1	94.2	86.3	85.5	85.6	88.9	98.0	96.7	94.6	88.4	89.2	77.3	95.1	92.7
0320	Concrete Reinforcing	98.1	144.5	121.7	101.1	111.3	106.2	99.3	105.3	102.3	101.4	114.3	107.9	95.2	114.1	104.8	99.1	118.5	108.9
0330	Cast-in-Place Concrete	75.0	102.3	85.4	93.8	99.5	95.9	90.4	92.8	91.4	88.4	106.1	95.1	95.7	100.1	97.4	105.2	100.6	103.4
03	CONCRETE	86.9	106.5	96.0	95.4	100.0	97.5	95.5	93.0	94.3	89.9	104.8	96.8	94.7	98.5	96.4	98.2	102.3	100.1
04	MASONRY	100.6	96.1	97.8	96.1	98.9	97.8	101.6	90.4	94.7	93.7	113.2	105.7	102.2	87.2	93.0	123.1	96.0	106.4
05	METALS	95.8	134.8	107.8	97.3	122.7	105.1	93.1	117.1	100.4	95.1	121.9	103.3	91.7	121.9	100.9	98.1	121.6	105.3
06	WOOD, PLASTICS & COMPOSITES	99.2	89.1	93.6	101.7	90.1	95.3	89.1	83.8	86.2	88.2	90.1	89.2	89.2	88.3	88.7	79.9	94.1	87.7
07	THERMAL & MOISTURE PROTECTION	106.0	108.9	107.2	102.6	96.8	100.2	101.8	103.9	102.7	102.3	101.5	101.9	95.4	98.5	96.7	100.0	97.0	98.8
08	OPENINGS	91.8	104.4	94.7	94.8	95.6	95.0	91.8	87.1	90.7	95.4	97.7	95.9	91.7	93.9	92.2	96.4	100.2	97.3
0920	Plaster & Gypsum Board	96.7	88.7	91.4	98.8	89.7	92.7	90.4	83.2	85.6	89.2	89.7	89.5	100.2	87.9	92.0	94.1	93.9	93.9
0950, 0980	Ceilings & Acoustic Treatment	80.5	88.7	86.0	92.3	89.7	90.5	83.9	83.2	83.5	83.1	89.7	87.5	82.5	87.9	86.1	94.2	93.9	94.0
0960	Flooring	91.8	82.6	89.1	93.5	94.7	93.8	90.9	82.6	88.5	88.2	99.7	91.5	91.3	104.9	95.2	88.1	82.6	86.5
0970, 0990	Wall Finishes & Painting/Coating	89.2	108.5	100.5	93.3	110.9	103.6	93.3	110.5	103.4	93.3	110.9	103.6	91.8	110.9	103.0	96.8	111.0	105.1
09	FINISHES	88.1	91.3	89.8	92.6	94.7	93.7	88.0	87.1	87.5	87.6	98.7	93.6	88.3	93.3	91.0	95.2	94.3	94.7
COVERS	DIVS. 10 - 14, 25, 28, 41, 43, 44, 46	100.0	100.3	100.1	100.0	101.5	100.3	100.0	96.7	99.3	100.0	105.7	101.3	100.0	98.1	99.6	100.0	101.0	100.2
21, 22, 23	FIRE SUPPRESSION, PLUMBING & HVAC	100.1	111.0	105.0	100.3	99.8	100.1	96.7	92.6	94.9	96.7	105.8	100.8	96.7	90.5	93.9	96.4	85.7	91.7
26, 27, 3370	ELECTRICAL, COMMUNICATIONS & UTIL.	99.6	97.2	98.3	98.5	98.7	98.6	91.4	113.5	103.1	93.1	146.7	121.5	88.5	95.6	92.3	92.7	113.5	103.7
MF2014	WEIGHTED AVERAGE	96.0	106.1	100.5	97.4	101.0	99.0	94.5	97.8	95.9	94.4	111.9	102.1	94.0	96.8	95.2	98.2	100.1	99.0

For customer support on your Electrical Costs with RSMeans Data, call 800.448.8182.

DIVISION		PENNSYLVANIA																
		WASHINGTON 153			WELLSBORO 169			WESTCHESTER 193			WILKES-BARRE 186 - 187			WILLIAMSPORT 177			YORK 173 - 174		
		MAT.	INST.	TOTAL	MAT.	INST.	TOTAL	MAT.	INST.	TOTAL	MAT.	INST.	TOTAL	MAT.	INST.	TOTAL	MAT.	INST.	TOTAL
015433	CONTRACTOR EQUIPMENT		111.0	111.0		117.3	117.3		100.8	100.8		117.3	117.3		117.3	117.3		116.4	116.4
0241, 31 - 34	SITE & INFRASTRUCTURE, DEMOLITION	100.9	102.8	102.2	96.2	102.7	100.7	103.4	101.7	102.2	86.6	103.2	98.2	87.4	103.2	98.4	85.0	101.8	96.7
0310	Concrete Forming & Accessories	84.2	97.1	95.4	87.5	88.2	88.1	93.2	130.6	125.6	91.7	91.7	91.7	91.1	88.7	89.0	85.8	88.1	87.8
0320	Concrete Reinforcing	99.1	118.8	109.1	99.3	113.2	106.3	95.8	145.0	120.8	100.0	114.1	107.2	94.5	114.2	104.5	95.2	113.2	104.3
0330	Cast-in-Place Concrete	105.2	100.7	103.5	94.8	94.0	94.5	92.7	134.8	108.7	84.8	99.3	90.3	81.0	95.4	86.5	88.0	101.7	93.2
03	CONCRETE	98.6	103.3	100.8	97.8	96.1	97.0	95.7	133.7	113.3	87.0	99.7	92.9	82.4	97.0	89.2	92.0	98.8	95.2
04	MASONRY	107.4	100.6	103.3	102.9	87.7	93.5	106.1	127.1	119.0	109.1	98.6	102.6	93.6	91.0	92.0	103.3	89.8	95.0
05	METALS	98.0	122.2	105.4	93.2	121.6	101.9	95.5	121.7	103.5	93.3	122.7	102.3	91.7	122.6	101.1	93.3	122.9	102.3
06	WOOD, PLASTICS & COMPOSITES	87.0	96.5	92.2	86.8	88.3	87.6	88.4	130.5	111.6	90.5	88.3	89.3	85.8	88.3	87.2	84.6	86.5	85.6
07	THERMAL & MOISTURE PROTECTION	100.1	98.9	99.6	102.8	91.0	97.9	106.2	126.1	114.4	102.1	96.5	99.7	94.8	93.0	94.1	94.8	106.0	99.2
08	OPENINGS	96.4	101.6	97.6	94.8	93.9	94.6	87.4	135.8	98.3	92.0	94.7	92.6	91.7	93.9	92.2	91.6	89.4	91.1
0920	Plaster & Gypsum Board	97.0	96.3	96.6	89.0	87.9	88.3	87.5	131.3	116.6	90.1	87.9	88.6	101.0	87.9	92.3	101.3	86.0	91.1
0950, 0980	Ceilings & Acoustic Treatment	94.2	96.3	95.6	83.9	87.9	86.5	87.4	131.3	116.6	87.3	87.9	87.7	85.9	87.9	87.2	85.0	86.0	85.6
0960	Flooring	92.1	82.6	89.3	87.2	101.4	91.3	90.0	136.6	103.5	89.1	94.7	90.7	90.1	92.0	90.6	91.8	101.4	94.6
0970, 0990	Wall Finishes & Painting/Coating	96.8	111.0	105.1	93.3	110.9	103.6	90.5	144.8	122.4	93.3	108.5	102.2	91.8	108.5	101.6	91.8	90.3	90.9
09	FINISHES	96.8	95.7	96.2	88.1	93.1	90.8	87.9	133.4	112.7	88.7	93.3	91.2	88.0	90.5	89.3	87.7	89.9	88.9
COVERS	DIVS. 10 - 14, 25, 28, 41, 43, 44, 46	100.0	101.2	100.3	100.0	95.7	99.0	100.0	114.5	103.3	100.0	101.2	100.3	100.0	97.1	99.4	100.0	97.2	99.4
21, 22, 23	FIRE SUPPRESSION, PLUMBING & HVAC	96.4	98.0	97.1	96.7	89.8	93.7	96.4	129.4	111.0	96.7	99.6	98.0	96.7	92.4	94.8	100.2	93.2	97.1
26, 27, 3370	ELECTRICAL, COMMUNICATIONS & UTIL.	95.2	113.5	104.9	92.2	96.0	94.2	93.1	112.3	103.3	93.1	94.1	93.6	89.0	77.9	83.1	90.0	83.4	86.5
MF2014	WEIGHTED AVERAGE	97.9	103.8	100.5	95.6	96.1	95.8	95.3	124.7	108.3	94.1	100.0	96.7	91.8	94.5	93.0	94.5	95.6	94.9

DIVISION		PUERTO RICO			RHODE ISLAND						SOUTH CAROLINA								
		SAN JUAN 009			NEWPORT 028			PROVIDENCE 029			AIKEN 298			BEAUFORT 299			CHARLESTON 294		
		MAT.	INST.	TOTAL	MAT.	INST.	TOTAL	MAT.	INST.	TOTAL	MAT.	INST.	TOTAL	MAT.	INST.	TOTAL	MAT.	INST.	TOTAL
015433	CONTRACTOR EQUIPMENT		87.9	87.9		102.1	102.1		102.1	102.1		108.3	108.3		108.3	108.3		108.3	108.3
0241, 31 - 34	SITE & INFRASTRUCTURE, DEMOLITION	132.0	90.3	102.9	89.3	103.6	99.2	89.3	103.6	99.3	122.8	90.3	100.1	118.1	89.7	98.3	103.3	90.0	94.0
0310	Concrete Forming & Accessories	93.1	17.1	27.4	100.6	122.3	119.4	100.6	122.3	119.3	98.6	64.5	69.1	97.5	39.5	47.3	96.6	64.4	68.7
0320	Concrete Reinforcing	193.7	13.3	102.2	102.6	112.7	107.7	103.8	112.7	108.3	99.3	63.1	81.0	98.3	26.8	62.0	98.1	64.3	81.0
0330	Cast-in-Place Concrete	96.0	28.3	70.2	74.5	119.1	91.5	92.4	119.1	102.6	84.6	66.7	77.8	84.6	66.3	77.6	99.3	66.7	86.8
03	CONCRETE	99.7	21.5	63.4	86.8	119.0	101.7	92.8	119.0	105.0	105.8	66.8	87.7	102.9	49.2	78.8	97.6	66.9	83.3
04	MASONRY	89.9	15.9	44.4	97.0	117.9	109.9	101.0	117.9	111.4	79.2	65.8	70.9	93.6	65.8	76.4	94.9	65.8	76.9
05	METALS	112.9	35.9	89.4	93.1	110.9	98.5	97.6	110.9	101.7	97.3	91.2	95.4	97.3	81.3	92.4	99.1	91.5	96.8
06	WOOD, PLASTICS & COMPOSITES	103.3	16.8	55.7	103.7	122.8	114.2	98.5	122.8	111.9	95.3	67.6	80.1	94.0	35.0	61.5	92.9	67.6	79.0
07	THERMAL & MOISTURE PROTECTION	129.1	21.3	84.4	100.0	117.4	107.2	103.0	117.4	109.0	99.7	65.9	85.7	99.4	56.4	81.6	98.5	64.0	84.2
08	OPENINGS	154.4	14.8	122.8	99.6	120.8	104.4	100.8	120.8	105.4	95.5	63.9	88.4	95.5	40.0	83.0	99.4	64.5	91.5
0920	Plaster & Gypsum Board	168.8	14.5	66.3	90.9	123.0	112.2	96.6	123.0	114.1	99.3	66.5	77.5	102.6	33.0	56.3	104.1	66.5	79.1
0950, 0980	Ceilings & Acoustic Treatment	240.9	14.5	90.3	94.9	123.0	113.6	99.9	123.0	115.3	83.8	66.5	72.3	86.3	33.0	50.8	86.3	66.5	73.1
0960	Flooring	213.3	15.1	155.9	94.1	127.9	103.9	92.7	127.9	102.9	102.0	95.1	100.0	103.6	80.3	96.9	103.2	81.8	97.0
0970, 0990	Wall Finishes & Painting/Coating	194.9	16.4	90.1	93.9	118.5	108.3	90.2	118.5	106.8	98.3	63.6	77.9	98.3	35.2	61.2	98.3	63.6	77.9
09	FINISHES	201.0	16.8	100.3	92.1	123.7	109.4	90.3	123.7	108.6	94.0	70.4	81.1	95.0	45.6	68.0	93.2	68.1	79.5
COVERS	DIVS. 10 - 14, 25, 28, 41, 43, 44, 46	100.0	16.2	81.1	100.0	107.5	101.7	100.0	107.5	101.7	100.0	72.0	93.7	100.0	78.2	95.1	100.0	71.9	93.7
21, 22, 23	FIRE SUPPRESSION, PLUMBING & HVAC	104.2	13.5	64.1	100.3	108.6	104.0	100.1	108.6	103.9	97.0	56.1	78.9	97.0	55.9	78.8	100.5	56.8	81.2
26, 27, 3370	ELECTRICAL, COMMUNICATIONS & UTIL.	124.0	17.7	67.6	100.6	99.1	99.8	100.4	99.1	99.7	100.8	63.9	81.2	104.8	33.5	67.0	103.0	59.3	79.8
MF2014	WEIGHTED AVERAGE	121.1	24.3	78.3	96.2	112.3	103.3	97.9	112.3	104.2	98.2	68.6	85.1	98.9	56.4	80.1	99.1	67.8	85.2

DIVISION		SOUTH CAROLINA															SOUTH DAKOTA		
		COLUMBIA 290 - 292			FLORENCE 295			GREENVILLE 296			ROCK HILL 297			SPARTANBURG 293			ABERDEEN 574		
		MAT.	INST.	TOTAL	MAT.	INST.	TOTAL	MAT.	INST.	TOTAL	MAT.	INST.	TOTAL	MAT.	INST.	TOTAL	MAT.	INST.	TOTAL
015433	CONTRACTOR EQUIPMENT		108.3	108.3		108.3	108.3		108.3	108.3		108.3	108.3		108.3	108.3		101.8	101.8
0241, 31 - 34	SITE & INFRASTRUCTURE, DEMOLITION	102.1	90.0	93.6	112.4	89.8	96.7	107.6	89.4	94.9	105.3	89.2	94.1	107.4	89.4	94.8	102.7	95.1	97.4
0310	Concrete Forming & Accessories	95.6	64.4	68.6	84.2	64.4	67.0	96.1	64.3	68.6	94.2	64.0	68.0	99.0	64.3	69.0	96.9	37.2	45.2
0320	Concrete Reinforcing	103.6	64.3	83.6	97.7	64.3	80.8	97.7	64.3	80.7	98.5	64.2	81.1	97.7	63.9	80.5	101.9	41.2	71.1
0330	Cast-in-Place Concrete	100.4	66.7	87.5	84.6	66.6	77.7	84.5	66.6	77.7	84.5	66.5	77.7	84.5	66.6	77.7	108.7	65.6	92.3
03	CONCRETE	95.5	66.9	82.2	97.1	66.8	83.1	95.6	66.8	82.3	93.5	66.6	81.0	95.8	66.8	82.3	101.2	49.4	77.2
04	MASONRY	88.5	65.8	74.5	79.3	65.7	70.9	76.8	65.8	70.0	101.1	65.8	79.3	79.3	65.8	70.9	115.3	53.1	77.0
05	METALS	96.2	91.5	94.8	98.0	91.4	96.0	98.0	91.5	96.0	97.3	90.3	95.1	98.0	91.3	96.0	97.8	68.0	88.7
06	WOOD, PLASTICS & COMPOSITES	93.0	67.6	79.1	80.2	67.6	73.3	92.5	67.6	78.8	91.2	67.6	78.2	96.4	67.6	80.6	92.7	35.8	61.4
07	THERMAL & MOISTURE PROTECTION	94.6	64.0	81.9	98.8	64.0	84.4	98.7	64.0	84.3	98.6	59.6	82.4	98.8	64.0	84.4	102.7	51.1	81.2
08	OPENINGS	97.7	64.5	90.2	95.6	64.5	88.5	95.5	64.5	88.5	95.5	64.5	88.5	95.5	64.4	88.5	95.8	35.1	82.1
0920	Plaster & Gypsum Board	96.5	66.5	76.6	93.6	66.5	75.6	98.4	66.5	77.2	98.0	66.5	77.1	101.0	66.5	78.1	112.0	34.3	60.4
0950, 0980	Ceilings & Acoustic Treatment	88.8	66.5	74.0	84.7	66.5	72.6	83.8	66.5	72.3	83.8	66.5	72.3	83.8	66.5	72.3	91.5	34.3	53.5
0960	Flooring	92.7	80.4	89.2	94.1	80.3	90.1	100.8	80.3	94.8	99.6	80.3	94.0	102.2	80.3	95.9	98.3	46.4	83.3
0970, 0990	Wall Finishes & Painting/Coating	92.2	63.6	75.4	98.3	63.6	77.9	98.3	63.6	77.9	98.3	63.6	77.9	98.3	63.6	77.9	93.6	35.5	59.5
09	FINISHES	88.8	67.8	77.4	89.9	67.9	77.8	91.9	67.9	78.8	91.3	67.8	78.5	92.7	67.9	79.1	94.0	38.4	63.6
COVERS	DIVS. 10 - 14, 25, 28, 41, 43, 44, 46	100.0	72.0	93.7	100.0	72.0	93.7	100.0	71.9	93.7	100.0	71.9	93.7	100.0	71.9	93.7	100.0	38.7	86.1
21, 22, 23	FIRE SUPPRESSION, PLUMBING & HVAC	100.0	56.8	80.9	100.5	56.8	81.2	100.5	56.8	81.2	97.0	56.9	78.9	100.5	56.8	81.2	100.2	54.9	75.1
26, 27, 3370	ELECTRICAL, COMMUNICATIONS & UTIL.	102.8	64.7	82.6	100.7	64.7	81.6	103.1	62.0	81.3	103.1	62.0	81.3	103.1	62.0	81.3	104.3	73.8	88.1
MF2014	WEIGHTED AVERAGE	97.1	68.5	84.5	97.3	68.5	84.5	97.3	68.1	84.4	97.3	67.6	84.2	97.6	68.1	84.5	100.1	54.7	80.1

For customer support on your Electrical Costs with RSMeans Data, call 800.448.8182.

City Cost Indexes

SOUTH DAKOTA

DIVISION		MITCHELL 573			MOBRIDGE 576			PIERRE 575			RAPID CITY 577			SIOUX FALLS 570 - 571			WATERTOWN 572		
		MAT.	INST.	TOTAL	MAT.	INST.	TOTAL	MAT.	INST.	TOTAL	MAT.	INST.	TOTAL	MAT.	INST.	TOTAL	MAT.	INST.	TOTAL
015433	CONTRACTOR EQUIPMENT		101.8	101.8		101.8	101.8		101.8	101.8		101.8	101.8		102.8	102.8		101.8	101.8
0241, 31 - 34	SITE & INFRASTRUCTURE, DEMOLITION	99.4	95.1	96.4	99.4	95.1	96.4	102.6	95.4	97.6	101.0	95.3	97.0	92.5	97.1	95.7	99.3	95.1	96.3
0310	Concrete Forming & Accessories	96.1	36.8	44.8	86.7	37.3	43.9	99.2	39.9	47.9	104.7	50.2	57.5	102.9	56.1	62.4	83.4	36.4	42.8
0320	Concrete Reinforcing	101.3	50.0	75.3	103.9	41.2	72.1	102.9	95.7	99.3	95.3	95.9	95.6	102.9	96.0	99.4	98.5	41.2	69.5
0330	Cast-in-Place Concrete	105.6	40.8	80.9	105.6	43.4	81.9	103.5	48.5	82.5	104.8	47.7	83.0	86.6	49.4	72.4	105.6	44.4	82.3
03	CONCRETE	98.9	42.1	72.5	98.6	41.8	72.3	96.4	54.2	76.8	98.2	58.6	79.8	88.5	61.8	76.1	97.7	41.8	71.8
04	MASONRY	103.0	52.5	71.9	111.8	54.6	76.6	114.1	55.3	77.9	111.9	55.7	77.3	93.8	57.8	71.6	139.6	56.6	88.5
05	METALS	96.8	67.5	87.9	96.9	68.0	88.1	101.3	86.8	96.8	99.5	87.4	95.8	98.5	87.5	95.1	96.8	67.8	88.0
06	WOOD, PLASTICS & COMPOSITES	91.7	36.3	61.2	81.3	36.3	56.4	98.0	36.5	64.2	96.4	50.8	71.3	96.1	57.9	75.1	77.7	35.8	54.7
07	THERMAL & MOISTURE PROTECTION	102.4	49.4	80.4	102.5	51.5	81.3	103.6	51.1	81.8	103.1	53.0	82.3	102.0	55.3	82.6	102.3	51.9	81.4
08	OPENINGS	94.9	35.6	81.5	97.5	34.7	83.3	101.3	47.7	89.2	99.6	55.5	89.6	101.9	59.3	92.3	94.9	34.8	81.3
0920	Plaster & Gypsum Board	110.4	34.9	60.2	105.1	34.6	58.2	101.4	35.1	57.4	111.4	49.8	70.4	99.9	57.0	71.4	102.8	34.3	57.3
0950, 0980	Ceilings & Acoustic Treatment	87.3	34.9	52.4	91.5	34.6	53.6	96.1	35.1	55.5	93.2	49.8	64.3	87.2	57.0	67.1	87.3	34.3	52.0
0960	Flooring	97.9	46.4	82.9	93.1	49.2	80.4	100.0	33.1	80.6	97.6	72.8	90.4	101.5	73.3	93.3	91.7	46.4	78.6
0970, 0990	Wall Finishes & Painting/Coating	93.6	38.9	61.5	93.6	39.9	62.1	98.5	97.9	98.1	93.6	97.9	96.1	100.9	97.9	99.1	93.6	35.6	59.5
09	FINISHES	92.6	38.5	63.0	91.3	39.0	62.8	95.9	43.1	67.1	94.0	59.2	75.0	93.8	63.8	77.4	89.7	37.8	61.4
COVERS	DIVS. 10 - 14, 25, 28, 41, 43, 44, 46	100.0	35.8	85.5	100.0	43.1	87.1	100.0	75.3	94.4	100.0	76.3	94.6	100.0	77.8	95.0	100.0	38.6	86.1
21, 22, 23	FIRE SUPPRESSION, PLUMBING & HVAC	96.6	39.3	71.3	96.6	62.6	81.6	100.0	70.2	86.8	100.2	69.4	86.6	100.0	58.5	81.7	96.6	42.3	72.6
26, 27, 3370	ELECTRICAL, COMMUNICATIONS & UTIL.	102.5	42.2	70.5	104.3	43.0	71.8	108.4	49.7	77.3	100.4	49.7	73.5	103.0	72.6	86.9	101.5	47.3	72.8
MF2014	WEIGHTED AVERAGE	97.8	48.3	75.9	98.5	53.9	78.8	101.3	62.0	83.9	99.9	65.2	84.6	97.8	67.8	84.6	99.0	50.0	77.4

TENNESSEE

DIVISION		CHATTANOOGA 373 - 374			COLUMBIA 384			COOKEVILLE 385			JACKSON 383			JOHNSON CITY 376			KNOXVILLE 377 - 379		
		MAT.	INST.	TOTAL	MAT.	INST.	TOTAL	MAT.	INST.	TOTAL	MAT.	INST.	TOTAL	MAT.	INST.	TOTAL	MAT.	INST.	TOTAL
015433	CONTRACTOR EQUIPMENT		109.2	109.2		103.9	103.9		103.9	103.9		110.4	110.4		102.8	102.8		102.8	102.8
0241, 31 - 34	SITE & INFRASTRUCTURE, DEMOLITION	103.0	99.5	100.5	87.4	89.8	89.0	92.9	86.7	88.6	95.9	100.1	98.9	109.7	86.0	93.1	89.5	88.9	89.1
0310	Concrete Forming & Accessories	97.2	57.2	62.6	83.3	63.6	66.2	83.5	33.8	40.5	90.5	43.6	50.0	83.4	61.5	64.5	95.3	66.2	70.1
0320	Concrete Reinforcing	89.4	67.4	78.2	85.1	63.9	74.3	85.1	63.4	74.1	85.1	66.6	75.7	90.0	63.9	76.8	89.4	63.9	76.5
0330	Cast-in-Place Concrete	99.4	61.7	85.1	90.5	63.2	80.1	102.5	41.6	79.3	100.1	70.1	88.7	80.0	51.4	69.1	93.4	65.0	82.6
03	CONCRETE	96.7	62.4	80.8	93.8	65.2	80.6	104.1	44.3	76.4	94.7	59.1	78.2	106.6	60.2	85.1	94.1	67.0	81.6
04	MASONRY	104.1	49.3	70.4	119.2	58.2	81.6	113.6	40.6	68.7	119.4	44.1	73.0	118.4	42.0	71.3	81.6	52.8	63.9
05	METALS	98.9	88.9	95.8	94.5	89.6	93.0	94.6	88.4	92.7	96.8	89.7	94.7	96.0	87.4	93.4	99.3	87.9	95.8
06	WOOD, PLASTICS & COMPOSITES	104.2	58.9	79.3	72.2	64.8	68.1	72.4	31.7	50.0	88.3	42.8	63.3	77.5	67.7	72.1	90.1	67.7	77.8
07	THERMAL & MOISTURE PROTECTION	99.7	60.4	83.4	94.5	63.3	81.5	95.0	51.5	76.9	97.0	57.3	80.5	95.1	55.4	78.7	93.0	63.9	80.9
08	OPENINGS	98.6	53.7	88.5	92.0	54.4	83.5	92.0	37.2	79.6	99.1	46.8	87.3	94.9	63.9	87.9	92.5	58.5	84.8
0920	Plaster & Gypsum Board	79.7	58.3	65.5	85.4	64.2	71.3	85.4	30.3	48.8	87.4	41.7	57.0	101.8	67.2	78.8	108.6	67.2	81.1
0950, 0980	Ceilings & Acoustic Treatment	103.5	58.3	73.4	77.0	64.2	68.5	77.0	30.3	45.9	85.5	41.7	56.3	99.8	67.2	78.1	100.6	67.2	78.4
0960	Flooring	97.7	54.0	85.0	83.7	57.2	76.0	83.8	53.0	74.8	83.1	57.5	75.7	92.7	46.5	79.3	97.9	49.6	83.9
0970, 0990	Wall Finishes & Painting/Coating	98.2	60.1	75.8	84.9	60.1	70.4	84.9	60.1	70.4	86.6	60.1	71.1	95.3	62.6	76.1	95.3	60.1	74.7
09	FINISHES	96.1	56.8	74.6	86.3	62.0	73.0	86.8	38.8	60.6	86.5	46.6	64.7	100.3	59.4	77.9	93.6	62.5	76.6
COVERS	DIVS. 10 - 14, 25, 28, 41, 43, 44, 46	100.0	39.9	86.4	100.0	71.3	93.5	100.0	38.3	86.1	100.0	65.6	92.2	100.0	79.1	95.3	100.0	83.0	96.2
21, 22, 23	FIRE SUPPRESSION, PLUMBING & HVAC	100.2	57.1	81.1	97.7	75.1	87.7	97.7	66.7	84.0	100.1	60.1	82.4	99.9	57.5	81.1	99.9	62.0	83.1
26, 27, 3370	ELECTRICAL, COMMUNICATIONS & UTIL.	103.6	88.9	95.8	93.5	54.8	73.0	95.2	63.4	78.3	99.7	55.8	76.4	94.0	44.2	67.6	100.1	57.9	77.7
MF2014	WEIGHTED AVERAGE	99.6	67.1	85.3	95.4	68.7	83.6	96.8	57.7	79.5	98.3	61.3	81.9	99.8	60.7	82.5	96.3	66.4	83.1

TENNESSEE / TEXAS

DIVISION		MCKENZIE 382			MEMPHIS 375,380 - 381			NASHVILLE 370 - 372			ABILENE 795 - 796			AMARILLO 790 - 791			AUSTIN 786 - 787		
		MAT.	INST.	TOTAL	MAT.	INST.	TOTAL	MAT.	INST.	TOTAL	MAT.	INST.	TOTAL	MAT.	INST.	TOTAL	MAT.	INST.	TOTAL
015433	CONTRACTOR EQUIPMENT		103.9	103.9		104.1	104.1		103.4	103.4		94.6	94.6		94.6	94.6		93.7	93.7
0241, 31 - 34	SITE & INFRASTRUCTURE, DEMOLITION	92.5	86.8	88.5	91.3	97.5	95.6	98.9	95.6	96.6	98.1	93.5	94.9	95.7	92.8	93.7	97.9	92.9	94.1
0310	Concrete Forming & Accessories	91.5	36.2	43.6	96.1	66.5	70.5	96.9	66.5	70.6	99.3	63.8	68.6	96.1	54.8	60.4	95.3	54.9	60.4
0320	Concrete Reinforcing	85.2	66.7	75.8	96.0	68.6	82.1	95.6	64.6	79.9	98.3	51.6	74.6	106.7	51.6	78.7	96.4	49.0	72.4
0330	Cast-in-Place Concrete	100.3	54.8	83.0	90.0	78.3	85.5	91.0	66.6	81.7	87.7	69.9	80.9	79.0	69.8	75.5	92.7	69.5	83.8
03	CONCRETE	102.6	50.5	78.4	93.8	72.2	83.8	94.0	67.4	81.6	86.4	64.6	76.3	85.1	60.5	73.7	90.2	60.0	76.2
04	MASONRY	118.1	48.5	75.3	93.5	56.7	70.8	90.4	68.7	77.0	96.9	63.5	76.3	96.2	63.5	76.0	99.1	62.2	76.4
05	METALS	94.6	89.3	93.0	100.3	85.9	95.9	100.4	85.1	95.7	104.4	71.7	94.4	99.6	71.5	91.0	96.4	71.3	88.7
06	WOOD, PLASTICS & COMPOSITES	80.7	34.2	55.2	97.8	67.1	80.9	98.7	66.9	81.2	105.0	65.7	83.4	100.7	53.6	74.8	94.9	54.1	72.5
07	THERMAL & MOISTURE PROTECTION	95.0	48.1	75.5	97.0	67.1	84.6	94.1	68.3	83.4	99.6	67.1	86.1	95.7	65.4	83.1	97.4	66.4	84.5
08	OPENINGS	92.0	39.5	80.2	98.1	63.1	90.2	98.4	63.4	90.5	102.4	60.4	92.9	104.4	53.8	92.9	105.4	51.8	93.2
0920	Plaster & Gypsum Board	88.3	32.8	51.4	93.7	66.4	75.6	94.0	66.1	75.5	84.9	65.1	71.7	93.8	52.7	66.5	89.6	53.2	65.4
0950, 0980	Ceilings & Acoustic Treatment	77.0	32.8	47.6	97.8	66.4	76.9	98.7	66.1	77.0	89.1	65.1	73.1	95.9	52.7	67.2	92.4	53.2	66.3
0960	Flooring	86.7	57.2	78.1	98.5	78.0	92.6	93.8	76.5	88.8	99.3	71.7	91.3	100.7	67.6	91.1	94.0	67.6	86.4
0970, 0990	Wall Finishes & Painting/Coating	84.9	47.0	62.7	90.8	60.7	73.2	97.7	71.7	82.4	94.2	55.0	71.2	89.7	55.0	69.3	95.7	47.1	67.2
09	FINISHES	88.0	40.2	61.9	95.2	67.9	80.3	98.5	68.7	82.2	86.2	64.7	74.4	90.2	56.8	71.9	88.5	55.8	70.6
COVERS	DIVS. 10 - 14, 25, 28, 41, 43, 44, 46	100.0	25.5	83.2	100.0	83.0	96.2	100.0	83.3	96.2	100.0	81.2	95.7	100.0	77.7	95.0	100.0	79.1	95.3
21, 22, 23	FIRE SUPPRESSION, PLUMBING & HVAC	97.7	60.3	81.2	100.0	72.0	87.6	99.9	78.0	90.2	100.3	50.1	78.1	100.0	54.1	79.7	100.0	59.4	82.0
26, 27, 3370	ELECTRICAL, COMMUNICATIONS & UTIL.	95.0	60.0	76.4	101.6	65.7	82.6	100.6	63.4	80.9	99.7	57.6	77.4	101.9	63.8	81.7	99.0	61.0	78.8
MF2014	WEIGHTED AVERAGE	96.9	57.4	79.5	98.2	72.2	86.7	98.4	73.6	87.4	98.1	63.7	82.9	97.5	63.2	82.4	97.5	63.6	82.5

538

TEXAS

DIVISION		BEAUMONT 776 - 777			BROWNWOOD 768			BRYAN 778			CHILDRESS 792			CORPUS CHRISTI 783 - 784			DALLAS 752 - 753		
		MAT.	INST.	TOTAL	MAT.	INST.	TOTAL	MAT.	INST.	TOTAL	MAT.	INST.	TOTAL	MAT.	INST.	TOTAL	MAT.	INST.	TOTAL
015433	CONTRACTOR EQUIPMENT		99.0	99.0		94.6	94.6		99.0	99.0		94.6	94.6		105.2	105.2		105.1	105.1
0241, 31 - 34	SITE & INFRASTRUCTURE, DEMOLITION	87.9	97.4	94.5	106.5	93.4	97.4	79.1	98.1	92.4	109.3	91.8	97.1	144.2	88.7	105.5	107.3	95.3	98.9
0310	Concrete Forming & Accessories	104.5	57.4	63.8	101.0	63.4	68.4	82.6	61.9	64.7	97.6	63.3	67.9	100.2	54.7	60.9	95.6	64.5	68.7
0320	Concrete Reinforcing	92.3	62.9	77.4	93.8	51.0	72.0	94.9	52.0	73.1	98.4	51.0	74.3	85.3	47.6	66.2	94.2	51.7	72.6
0330	Cast-in-Place Concrete	92.8	62.8	81.4	108.3	63.0	91.1	74.3	62.8	69.9	89.9	63.0	79.7	113.6	70.0	97.0	118.8	72.0	100.9
03	CONCRETE	96.2	61.3	80.0	99.4	61.9	82.0	80.2	61.5	71.5	94.5	61.8	79.3	98.9	60.9	81.3	106.5	66.2	87.8
04	MASONRY	103.5	59.4	76.4	130.7	54.2	83.6	145.0	54.9	89.5	100.9	54.2	72.2	87.3	51.8	65.5	103.9	63.6	79.1
05	METALS	95.1	76.4	89.3	94.8	70.5	87.4	95.0	73.7	88.5	102.0	70.5	92.4	93.9	86.2	91.5	99.3	82.3	94.1
06	WOOD, PLASTICS & COMPOSITES	115.3	56.8	83.1	105.0	65.7	83.4	80.2	62.9	70.7	104.4	65.7	83.1	124.3	54.6	86.0	96.7	65.9	79.8
07	THERMAL & MOISTURE PROTECTION	103.5	65.4	87.7	96.9	63.2	82.9	95.3	64.7	82.6	100.2	61.8	84.3	103.5	64.3	87.3	93.2	69.3	83.3
08	OPENINGS	95.7	57.9	87.2	98.2	60.4	89.6	96.3	58.7	87.8	97.6	60.4	89.2	104.2	51.8	92.3	100.3	60.5	91.3
0920	Plaster & Gypsum Board	97.4	56.0	69.9	85.3	65.1	71.8	85.4	62.3	70.0	84.5	65.1	71.6	98.6	53.6	68.7	91.1	65.1	73.8
0950, 0980	Ceilings & Acoustic Treatment	96.6	56.0	69.6	76.1	65.1	68.8	88.6	62.3	71.1	87.4	65.1	72.5	91.1	53.6	66.1	93.2	65.1	74.5
0960	Flooring	119.3	65.9	103.8	83.3	57.9	76.0	89.2	59.8	80.7	97.6	57.9	86.1	109.2	57.9	94.3	96.0	67.6	87.8
0970, 0990	Wall Finishes & Painting/Coating	91.6	56.3	70.9	92.9	55.0	70.7	89.6	59.4	71.9	94.2	55.0	71.2	109.4	47.1	72.8	102.2	55.0	74.5
09	FINISHES	94.8	58.4	74.9	78.9	61.8	69.6	82.2	61.0	70.7	86.6	61.8	73.0	100.6	53.9	75.0	97.1	64.0	79.0
COVERS	DIVS. 10 - 14, 25, 28, 41, 43, 44, 46	100.0	83.5	96.3	100.0	79.0	95.2	100.0	80.6	95.6	100.0	79.0	95.2	100.0	82.7	96.1	100.0	81.9	95.9
21, 22, 23	FIRE SUPPRESSION, PLUMBING & HVAC	100.1	65.3	84.7	96.6	48.1	75.2	96.6	64.8	82.5	96.7	54.1	77.9	100.1	56.9	81.0	100.0	61.5	83.0
26, 27, 3370	ELECTRICAL, COMMUNICATIONS & UTIL.	96.9	68.0	81.6	94.7	50.0	71.0	94.9	68.8	81.1	99.7	60.4	78.9	95.1	57.1	74.9	96.5	63.6	79.0
MF2014	WEIGHTED AVERAGE	97.6	67.3	84.2	97.5	60.3	81.1	95.0	67.0	82.7	97.9	62.8	82.4	99.7	62.5	83.3	100.3	68.4	86.2

TEXAS

DIVISION		DEL RIO 788			DENTON 762			EASTLAND 764			EL PASO 798 - 799,885			FORT WORTH 760 - 761			GALVESTON 775		
		MAT.	INST.	TOTAL	MAT.	INST.	TOTAL	MAT.	INST.	TOTAL	MAT.	INST.	TOTAL	MAT.	INST.	TOTAL	MAT.	INST.	TOTAL
015433	CONTRACTOR EQUIPMENT		93.7	93.7		104.7	104.7		94.6	94.6		94.6	94.6		94.6	94.6		112.6	112.6
0241, 31 - 34	SITE & INFRASTRUCTURE, DEMOLITION	124.1	91.3	101.2	105.7	85.0	91.2	109.5	91.4	96.9	98.0	91.2	93.3	101.9	94.3	96.6	103.8	96.7	98.8
0310	Concrete Forming & Accessories	96.8	55.1	60.7	108.5	62.5	68.7	101.7	63.2	68.4	97.9	59.0	64.2	98.7	63.8	68.5	92.4	58.8	63.4
0320	Concrete Reinforcing	86.0	47.5	66.5	95.2	51.0	72.8	94.0	51.4	72.4	103.7	51.0	76.9	100.9	51.0	75.6	94.3	61.6	77.7
0330	Cast-in-Place Concrete	122.4	62.6	99.6	83.8	62.7	75.7	114.5	63.0	94.9	84.0	62.0	75.6	99.7	63.2	85.8	98.7	63.9	85.4
03	CONCRETE	119.7	57.3	90.8	78.3	62.5	71.0	104.2	61.9	84.6	87.2	59.4	74.3	94.5	62.2	79.5	97.6	63.3	81.7
04	MASONRY	102.8	54.0	72.8	140.1	51.7	85.6	98.8	62.3	76.3	87.6	53.9	66.8	98.0	54.2	71.0	100.0	55.0	72.3
05	METALS	93.8	67.7	85.8	94.5	86.6	92.1	94.7	71.0	87.4	99.6	69.2	90.3	96.4	71.0	88.6	96.7	94.3	95.9
06	WOOD, PLASTICS & COMPOSITES	102.3	54.4	76.0	116.5	65.8	88.6	112.2	65.7	86.6	90.3	60.3	73.8	99.1	65.7	80.7	97.8	58.5	76.2
07	THERMAL & MOISTURE PROTECTION	100.0	63.5	84.9	94.8	62.9	81.6	97.3	65.4	84.1	98.1	61.8	83.0	93.2	64.5	81.3	94.4	65.0	82.2
08	OPENINGS	99.4	51.0	88.5	115.8	60.0	103.2	70.6	60.4	68.3	97.9	53.5	87.8	101.4	60.4	92.1	100.5	58.6	91.0
0920	Plaster & Gypsum Board	94.9	53.6	67.4	89.9	65.1	73.4	85.3	65.1	71.8	93.8	59.6	71.1	88.8	65.1	73.0	92.0	57.6	69.2
0950, 0980	Ceilings & Acoustic Treatment	87.5	53.6	64.9	82.0	65.1	70.7	76.1	65.1	68.8	90.7	59.6	70.0	87.9	65.1	72.7	92.9	57.6	69.4
0960	Flooring	93.7	57.9	83.3	78.9	57.9	72.8	105.5	57.9	91.7	96.8	57.9	85.5	101.5	57.9	88.8	104.6	59.8	91.6
0970, 0990	Wall Finishes & Painting/Coating	96.6	45.3	66.5	103.3	52.1	73.2	94.3	55.0	71.3	98.9	49.8	70.1	95.3	55.2	71.7	100.4	57.2	75.0
09	FINISHES	92.8	54.2	71.7	78.0	60.9	68.7	85.9	61.8	72.7	88.7	57.9	71.9	88.4	61.8	73.9	91.9	58.3	73.5
COVERS	DIVS. 10 - 14, 25, 28, 41, 43, 44, 46	100.0	79.2	95.3	100.0	77.6	94.9	100.0	77.2	94.8	100.0	78.1	95.0	100.0	81.2	95.7	100.0	84.0	96.4
21, 22, 23	FIRE SUPPRESSION, PLUMBING & HVAC	96.5	62.2	81.3	96.6	57.7	79.4	96.6	48.1	75.1	99.9	64.7	84.3	99.9	58.6	81.6	96.5	64.9	82.5
26, 27, 3370	ELECTRICAL, COMMUNICATIONS & UTIL.	97.4	64.8	80.1	96.9	63.6	79.2	94.6	63.5	78.1	99.3	54.1	75.3	96.2	63.5	78.9	96.5	64.6	79.6
MF2014	WEIGHTED AVERAGE	100.5	62.8	83.9	97.5	64.8	83.0	94.1	62.9	80.3	96.3	62.8	81.5	97.3	64.7	82.9	97.3	68.3	84.5

TEXAS

DIVISION		GIDDINGS 789			GREENVILLE 754			HOUSTON 770 - 772			HUNTSVILLE 773			LAREDO 780			LONGVIEW 756		
		MAT.	INST.	TOTAL	MAT.	INST.	TOTAL	MAT.	INST.	TOTAL	MAT.	INST.	TOTAL	MAT.	INST.	TOTAL	MAT.	INST.	TOTAL
015433	CONTRACTOR EQUIPMENT		93.7	93.7		105.1	105.1		102.3	102.3		99.0	99.0		93.7	93.7		95.7	95.7
0241, 31 - 34	SITE & INFRASTRUCTURE, DEMOLITION	108.9	91.9	97.1	100.3	88.1	91.8	102.5	96.9	98.6	94.6	98.1	97.1	102.3	92.6	95.5	99.4	94.9	96.2
0310	Concrete Forming & Accessories	94.1	54.4	59.7	87.1	61.6	65.0	94.5	59.0	63.8	90.0	58.5	62.8	96.9	55.7	61.3	83.5	63.4	66.1
0320	Concrete Reinforcing	86.6	48.5	67.3	94.7	51.0	72.6	94.1	52.3	72.9	95.1	52.0	73.3	86.0	48.2	66.8	93.6	51.0	72.0
0330	Cast-in-Place Concrete	103.6	62.0	87.7	108.1	64.1	91.4	95.7	64.9	84.0	102.3	63.1	87.3	87.5	70.2	80.9	125.8	63.0	101.8
03	CONCRETE	96.0	57.1	78.0	98.0	62.4	81.5	95.2	61.2	79.4	104.3	60.1	83.8	90.4	60.5	76.5	115.9	61.8	90.8
04	MASONRY	110.6	52.4	74.8	161.3	54.2	95.4	99.7	58.9	74.6	142.9	55.0	88.8	96.0	63.6	76.0	157.2	54.8	94.2
05	METALS	93.3	70.3	86.3	96.9	84.9	93.2	99.3	78.1	92.8	95.0	74.1	88.6	96.2	71.0	88.5	89.7	69.4	83.5
06	WOOD, PLASTICS & COMPOSITES	101.3	54.4	75.6	87.9	63.1	74.3	100.1	58.6	77.3	88.8	58.4	72.1	102.3	54.4	76.0	82.7	65.7	73.4
07	THERMAL & MOISTURE PROTECTION	100.6	62.6	84.8	93.2	63.1	80.7	93.9	66.3	82.6	96.4	64.2	83.0	99.3	67.1	85.9	94.8	62.8	81.5
08	OPENINGS	98.5	51.9	88.0	98.5	59.0	89.5	103.1	56.3	92.5	96.3	56.2	87.2	99.5	51.7	88.7	88.9	60.0	82.4
0920	Plaster & Gypsum Board	93.9	53.6	67.1	85.2	62.3	70.0	94.1	57.6	69.9	89.4	57.6	68.3	95.7	53.6	67.7	84.2	65.1	71.5
0950, 0980	Ceilings & Acoustic Treatment	87.5	53.6	64.9	89.0	62.3	71.2	97.9	57.6	71.1	88.6	57.6	68.0	90.9	53.6	66.0	84.8	65.1	71.7
0960	Flooring	93.3	57.9	83.0	91.0	57.9	81.4	106.1	59.8	92.7	93.8	57.9	83.4	93.5	67.6	86.0	96.4	57.9	85.2
0970, 0990	Wall Finishes & Painting/Coating	96.6	47.1	67.5	102.2	55.0	74.5	100.4	59.4	76.3	89.6	59.4	71.9	96.6	47.1	67.5	92.4	52.1	68.7
09	FINISHES	91.4	53.7	70.8	93.4	60.4	75.4	99.6	58.6	77.2	85.0	58.0	70.3	91.9	56.3	72.5	99.0	61.5	78.5
COVERS	DIVS. 10 - 14, 25, 28, 41, 43, 44, 46	100.0	74.8	94.3	100.0	79.2	95.3	100.0	84.2	96.4	100.0	75.1	94.4	100.0	79.3	95.3	100.0	79.1	95.3
21, 22, 23	FIRE SUPPRESSION, PLUMBING & HVAC	96.6	62.3	81.4	96.5	59.9	80.3	100.0	64.8	84.4	96.6	64.7	82.5	100.1	62.3	83.4	96.4	59.1	79.6
26, 27, 3370	ELECTRICAL, COMMUNICATIONS & UTIL.	94.2	60.3	76.2	93.3	63.6	77.5	98.5	68.8	82.8	94.9	64.1	78.5	97.5	61.9	78.6	93.8	54.2	72.8
MF2014	WEIGHTED AVERAGE	97.0	62.1	81.6	99.9	65.5	84.7	99.3	67.5	85.2	98.6	65.5	84.0	97.1	64.7	82.8	100.1	63.1	83.7

For customer support on your Electrical Costs with RSMeans Data, call 800.448.8182.

539

City Cost Indexes

TEXAS

DIVISION		LUBBOCK 793-794 MAT.	INST.	TOTAL	LUFKIN 759 MAT.	INST.	TOTAL	MCALLEN 785 MAT.	INST.	TOTAL	MCKINNEY 750 MAT.	INST.	TOTAL	MIDLAND 797 MAT.	INST.	TOTAL	ODESSA 797 MAT.	INST.	TOTAL
015433	CONTRACTOR EQUIPMENT		107.6	107.6		95.7	95.7		105.3	105.3		105.1	105.1		107.6	107.6		94.6	94.6
0241, 31 - 34	SITE & INFRASTRUCTURE, DEMOLITION	123.2	92.5	101.8	94.1	96.2	95.6	149.1	88.9	107.1	96.6	88.1	90.7	126.4	90.5	101.4	98.3	94.3	95.5
0310	Concrete Forming & Accessories	98.2	55.0	60.9	86.4	58.4	62.2	101.3	55.3	61.5	86.2	61.6	64.9	102.3	63.7	68.9	99.3	64.0	68.8
0320	Concrete Reinforcing	99.5	51.6	75.2	95.3	61.4	78.1	85.5	47.6	66.3	94.7	51.0	72.6	100.6	51.6	75.7	98.3	51.6	74.6
0330	Cast-in-Place Concrete	87.8	71.0	81.4	112.5	62.6	93.5	123.5	64.5	101.0	101.4	64.1	87.2	93.4	70.9	84.8	87.7	70.0	80.9
03	CONCRETE	85.2	62.1	74.5	106.9	61.2	85.7	106.8	59.3	84.8	92.8	62.4	78.7	89.4	65.9	78.5	86.4	64.7	76.3
04	MASONRY	96.2	63.6	76.1	120.7	54.7	80.1	102.5	54.1	72.7	173.3	54.2	100.0	113.1	63.6	82.6	96.9	63.5	76.3
05	METALS	108.3	87.6	102.0	97.0	72.0	89.4	93.7	85.8	91.3	96.8	84.9	93.2	106.7	87.5	100.8	103.8	71.8	94.0
06	WOOD, PLASTICS & COMPOSITES	104.2	53.8	76.5	90.3	58.5	72.8	123.1	54.6	85.4	87.0	63.1	73.9	108.9	65.8	85.2	105.0	65.7	83.4
07	THERMAL & MOISTURE PROTECTION	88.9	66.4	79.6	94.6	61.5	80.9	103.3	64.4	87.2	93.0	63.1	80.6	89.2	67.7	80.3	99.6	66.7	86.0
08	OPENINGS	110.0	53.9	97.3	67.6	59.0	65.6	103.4	51.0	91.5	98.4	59.0	89.5	111.5	60.5	100.0	102.4	60.4	92.9
0920	Plaster & Gypsum Board	85.1	52.7	63.6	83.3	57.6	66.2	99.3	53.6	68.9	85.2	62.3	70.0	87.0	65.1	72.4	84.9	65.1	71.7
0950, 0980	Ceilings & Acoustic Treatment	89.9	52.7	65.2	80.5	57.6	65.3	90.9	53.6	66.0	89.0	62.3	71.2	88.2	65.1	72.8	89.1	65.1	73.1
0960	Flooring	92.6	67.6	85.4	128.5	57.9	108.0	108.6	56.3	93.4	90.5	57.9	81.1	93.9	67.6	86.3	99.3	67.6	90.1
0970, 0990	Wall Finishes & Painting/Coating	105.1	55.0	75.7	92.4	55.0	70.5	109.4	45.3	71.8	102.2	55.0	74.5	105.1	55.0	75.7	94.2	55.0	71.2
09	FINISHES	88.5	56.9	71.2	107.3	58.0	80.4	100.9	53.9	75.2	93.1	60.4	75.2	89.3	63.6	75.3	86.2	63.8	74.0
COVERS	DIVS. 10 - 14, 25, 28, 41, 43, 44, 46	100.0	80.2	95.5	100.0	75.4	94.4	100.0	79.5	95.4	100.0	79.2	95.3	100.0	79.3	95.3	100.0	79.0	95.3
21, 22, 23	FIRE SUPPRESSION, PLUMBING & HVAC	99.7	50.0	77.7	96.4	61.4	80.9	96.6	58.1	79.5	96.5	59.9	80.3	96.1	50.2	75.8	100.3	56.2	80.8
26, 27, 3370	ELECTRICAL, COMMUNICATIONS & UTIL.	98.4	63.2	79.8	95.1	66.5	79.9	94.9	34.3	62.7	93.3	63.6	77.5	98.4	63.2	79.8	99.8	63.2	80.4
MF2014	WEIGHTED AVERAGE	99.7	64.1	84.0	96.7	65.0	82.7	100.7	59.5	82.5	99.7	65.5	84.6	100.4	65.8	85.1	98.0	65.7	83.7

TEXAS

DIVISION		PALESTINE 758 MAT.	INST.	TOTAL	SAN ANGELO 769 MAT.	INST.	TOTAL	SAN ANTONIO 781-782 MAT.	INST.	TOTAL	TEMPLE 765 MAT.	INST.	TOTAL	TEXARKANA 755 MAT.	INST.	TOTAL	TYLER 757 MAT.	INST.	TOTAL
015433	CONTRACTOR EQUIPMENT		95.7	95.7		94.6	94.6		98.1	98.1		94.6	94.6		95.7	95.7		95.7	95.7
0241, 31 - 34	SITE & INFRASTRUCTURE, DEMOLITION	99.6	95.2	96.5	102.6	93.9	96.5	102.8	96.0	98.1	90.5	94.0	92.9	88.4	97.7	94.9	98.7	95.0	96.1
0310	Concrete Forming & Accessories	78.0	63.5	65.4	101.3	55.4	61.6	96.6	56.0	61.5	104.9	54.8	61.6	93.4	64.2	68.1	88.2	63.6	66.9
0320	Concrete Reinforcing	92.9	51.0	71.6	93.6	51.0	72.0	92.2	48.2	69.9	93.8	48.5	70.8	92.7	51.6	71.9	93.6	51.0	72.0
0330	Cast-in-Place Concrete	102.8	63.0	87.6	102.2	64.9	89.9	88.0	71.6	81.7	83.7	62.5	75.6	103.6	70.0	90.8	123.5	63.1	100.5
03	CONCRETE	108.1	61.8	86.6	94.8	60.6	79.0	91.3	61.2	77.3	80.9	57.5	70.0	98.9	64.7	83.0	115.2	61.9	90.5
04	MASONRY	114.8	54.8	77.9	127.1	54.9	82.6	91.6	63.7	74.4	139.2	53.6	86.5	177.7	63.5	107.4	167.5	54.9	98.2
05	METALS	96.8	69.5	88.4	95.0	70.8	87.6	99.3	72.9	91.2	94.7	70.5	87.3	89.6	70.8	83.9	96.7	69.6	88.4
06	WOOD, PLASTICS & COMPOSITES	82.2	65.7	73.1	105.3	54.5	77.3	100.1	54.6	75.1	114.9	54.5	81.7	92.9	65.7	78.0	91.7	65.7	77.4
07	THERMAL & MOISTURE PROTECTION	95.1	63.9	82.2	96.7	64.3	83.3	97.3	68.1	85.2	96.4	62.7	82.4	94.4	67.6	83.3	94.9	63.9	82.1
08	OPENINGS	67.5	60.4	65.9	98.2	54.2	88.3	98.4	51.8	87.9	67.3	53.6	64.2	88.9	60.4	82.4	67.4	60.4	65.9
0920	Plaster & Gypsum Board	81.0	65.1	70.4	85.3	53.6	64.2	95.0	53.6	67.5	85.3	53.6	64.2	87.9	65.1	72.7	83.3	65.1	71.2
0950, 0980	Ceilings & Acoustic Treatment	80.5	65.1	70.2	76.1	53.6	61.1	96.9	53.6	68.1	76.1	53.6	61.1	84.8	65.1	71.7	80.5	65.1	70.2
0960	Flooring	118.8	57.9	101.1	83.5	57.9	76.0	102.5	67.6	92.4	107.2	57.9	92.9	105.3	67.6	94.4	130.9	57.9	109.7
0970, 0990	Wall Finishes & Painting/Coating	92.4	55.0	70.5	92.9	55.0	70.7	99.4	47.1	68.7	94.3	47.1	66.6	92.4	55.0	70.5	92.4	55.0	70.5
09	FINISHES	104.6	61.9	81.3	78.7	55.3	65.9	100.4	56.5	76.4	85.1	54.0	68.1	101.6	63.9	81.0	108.3	61.9	82.9
COVERS	DIVS. 10 - 14, 25, 28, 41, 43, 44, 46	100.0	79.1	95.3	100.0	79.7	95.4	100.0	79.7	95.4	100.0	77.3	94.9	100.0	81.4	95.8	100.0	81.3	95.8
21, 22, 23	FIRE SUPPRESSION, PLUMBING & HVAC	96.4	58.6	79.7	96.6	50.0	76.0	100.0	65.0	84.5	96.6	53.9	77.7	96.4	57.6	79.3	96.4	61.5	81.0
26, 27, 3370	ELECTRICAL, COMMUNICATIONS & UTIL.	91.3	52.4	70.7	98.8	59.2	77.8	99.0	61.9	79.3	95.8	56.4	74.9	95.0	59.1	76.0	93.8	58.2	74.9
MF2014	WEIGHTED AVERAGE	96.0	63.0	81.4	97.1	60.8	81.0	98.1	65.8	83.9	92.4	60.3	78.2	99.1	65.7	84.4	100.1	64.5	84.4

TEXAS / UTAH

DIVISION		VICTORIA 779 MAT.	INST.	TOTAL	WACO 766-767 MAT.	INST.	TOTAL	WAXAHACHIE 751 MAT.	INST.	TOTAL	WHARTON 774 MAT.	INST.	TOTAL	WICHITA FALLS 763 MAT.	INST.	TOTAL	LOGAN 843 MAT.	INST.	TOTAL
015433	CONTRACTOR EQUIPMENT		111.2	111.2		94.6	94.6		105.1	105.1		112.6	112.6		94.6	94.6		98.0	98.0
0241, 31 - 34	SITE & INFRASTRUCTURE, DEMOLITION	108.7	93.9	98.4	99.3	94.5	95.9	98.4	88.1	91.2	113.8	95.9	101.3	100.1	94.0	96.1	99.8	95.2	96.6
0310	Concrete Forming & Accessories	91.9	55.5	60.4	103.3	64.2	69.4	86.2	63.5	66.5	86.9	57.2	61.2	103.3	63.8	69.1	104.9	59.1	65.3
0320	Concrete Reinforcing	90.5	47.2	68.6	93.5	49.1	70.9	94.7	51.0	72.5	94.2	52.0	72.8	93.5	51.4	72.1	105.2	86.8	95.9
0330	Cast-in-Place Concrete	110.9	63.9	93.0	90.6	70.2	82.8	107.0	64.1	90.7	113.9	63.7	94.8	96.8	63.2	84.0	84.3	70.2	78.9
03	CONCRETE	105.5	59.3	84.1	87.5	64.4	76.8	96.9	63.2	81.3	109.8	60.8	87.0	90.5	62.2	77.4	106.7	68.6	89.0
04	MASONRY	118.3	55.0	79.3	96.9	63.6	76.4	161.9	54.2	95.6	101.2	54.8	72.6	97.4	60.5	74.7	110.9	58.4	78.5
05	METALS	95.1	89.2	93.3	96.9	71.7	89.2	96.9	84.8	93.2	96.7	89.1	94.3	96.9	71.4	89.1	107.1	84.3	100.1
06	WOOD, PLASTICS & COMPOSITES	101.3	54.5	75.6	113.1	65.7	87.0	87.0	65.9	75.4	91.4	56.9	72.5	113.1	65.7	87.0	84.7	56.7	69.3
07	THERMAL & MOISTURE PROTECTION	98.2	64.6	84.3	97.2	67.9	85.1	93.2	63.3	80.8	94.8	64.9	82.4	97.2	64.9	83.8	97.9	64.8	84.2
08	OPENINGS	100.3	53.0	89.6	78.8	59.8	74.5	98.5	60.5	89.9	100.5	55.4	90.3	78.8	60.4	74.7	92.7	61.4	85.6
0920	Plaster & Gypsum Board	88.9	53.6	65.4	85.9	65.1	72.0	85.6	65.1	72.0	87.7	56.0	66.6	85.9	65.1	72.0	77.7	55.5	62.9
0950, 0980	Ceilings & Acoustic Treatment	93.7	53.6	67.0	78.6	65.1	69.6	90.7	65.1	73.6	92.9	56.0	68.3	78.6	65.1	69.6	99.4	55.5	70.2
0960	Flooring	103.0	57.9	89.9	106.4	67.6	95.2	90.5	57.9	81.1	101.6	70.6	92.6	107.3	67.5	95.8	101.4	61.0	89.7
0970, 0990	Wall Finishes & Painting/Coating	100.6	59.4	76.4	94.3	55.0	71.3	102.2	55.0	74.5	100.4	59.4	76.3	96.8	55.0	72.3	96.0	57.8	73.6
09	FINISHES	89.5	55.8	71.1	86.0	63.8	73.9	93.7	62.0	76.4	91.1	59.4	73.8	86.4	63.8	74.1	95.0	58.3	74.9
COVERS	DIVS. 10 - 14, 25, 28, 41, 43, 44, 46	100.0	74.9	94.3	100.0	81.2	95.7	100.0	79.5	95.4	100.0	75.2	94.4	100.0	79.0	95.3	100.0	83.5	96.3
21, 22, 23	FIRE SUPPRESSION, PLUMBING & HVAC	96.6	64.6	82.5	100.2	60.1	82.5	96.5	53.4	77.4	96.5	62.0	81.3	100.3	53.5	79.6	99.9	66.1	84.9
26, 27, 3370	ELECTRICAL, COMMUNICATIONS & UTIL.	101.3	54.6	76.6	98.9	57.1	76.7	93.3	63.6	77.5	100.3	64.1	81.1	100.6	57.0	77.5	96.7	71.0	83.1
MF2014	WEIGHTED AVERAGE	99.5	64.7	84.1	94.2	65.7	81.6	99.7	64.5	84.2	99.4	66.4	84.8	94.8	63.6	81.0	100.8	69.5	87.0

City Cost Indexes

UTAH / VERMONT

DIVISION		OGDEN 842,844 MAT.	INST.	TOTAL	PRICE 845 MAT.	INST.	TOTAL	PROVO 846 - 847 MAT.	INST.	TOTAL	SALT LAKE CITY 840 - 841 MAT.	INST.	TOTAL	BELLOWS FALLS 051 MAT.	INST.	TOTAL	BENNINGTON 052 MAT.	INST.	TOTAL
015433	CONTRACTOR EQUIPMENT		98.0	98.0		97.0	97.0		97.0	97.0		97.9	97.9		99.8	99.8		99.8	99.8
0241, 31 - 34	SITE & INFRASTRUCTURE, DEMOLITION	87.4	95.2	92.8	97.2	93.1	94.3	96.0	93.5	94.3	87.0	95.1	92.7	90.4	102.1	98.6	89.8	102.1	98.4
0310	Concrete Forming & Accessories	105.0	59.1	65.3	107.5	46.5	54.7	106.7	59.1	65.5	107.4	59.1	65.6	96.9	107.0	105.7	94.5	106.8	105.1
0320	Concrete Reinforcing	104.9	86.8	95.7	112.8	86.7	99.5	113.8	86.8	100.1	107.2	86.8	96.9	86.1	81.9	83.9	86.1	81.8	83.9
0330	Cast-in-Place Concrete	85.6	70.2	79.7	84.4	58.5	74.5	84.4	70.2	79.0	93.5	70.2	84.6	87.6	113.6	97.5	87.6	113.5	97.5
03	CONCRETE	95.6	68.6	83.1	107.9	58.9	85.2	106.2	68.6	88.8	115.7	68.7	93.9	87.2	104.4	95.2	87.0	104.2	95.0
04	MASONRY	105.0	58.4	76.3	116.6	56.5	79.6	116.7	58.4	80.8	119.5	58.4	81.8	106.0	87.9	94.9	117.6	87.9	99.3
05	METALS	107.6	84.3	100.5	104.3	82.9	97.8	105.2	84.3	98.8	111.0	84.3	102.9	90.1	88.4	89.6	90.1	88.1	89.5
06	WOOD, PLASTICS & COMPOSITES	84.7	56.7	69.3	87.7	41.7	62.4	86.0	56.7	69.9	86.4	56.7	70.1	108.7	113.0	111.1	105.9	113.0	109.8
07	THERMAL & MOISTURE PROTECTION	96.8	64.8	83.5	99.7	60.0	83.2	99.8	64.8	85.2	104.3	64.8	87.9	97.3	89.5	94.1	97.3	85.5	92.4
08	OPENINGS	92.7	61.4	85.6	96.6	49.4	86.0	96.7	61.4	88.7	94.6	61.4	87.1	100.6	101.3	100.7	100.6	101.3	100.7
0920	Plaster & Gypsum Board	77.7	55.5	62.9	80.3	40.1	53.6	78.0	55.5	63.1	90.7	55.5	67.3	105.6	112.9	110.4	103.9	112.9	109.9
0950, 0980	Ceilings & Acoustic Treatment	99.4	55.5	70.2	99.4	40.1	59.9	99.4	55.5	70.2	92.8	55.5	68.0	91.2	112.9	105.6	91.2	112.9	105.6
0960	Flooring	99.3	61.0	88.2	102.6	45.6	86.1	102.3	61.0	90.3	103.5	61.0	91.2	96.5	96.5	96.5	95.7	96.5	95.9
0970, 0990	Wall Finishes & Painting/Coating	96.0	57.8	73.6	96.0	57.8	73.6	96.0	57.8	73.6	99.2	66.3	79.9	89.3	106.1	99.2	89.3	106.1	99.2
09	FINISHES	93.1	58.3	74.1	96.2	45.9	68.7	95.7	58.3	75.2	95.5	59.2	75.7	90.6	106.1	99.0	90.1	106.1	98.8
COVERS	DIVS. 10 - 14, 25, 28, 41, 43, 44, 46	100.0	83.5	96.3	100.0	56.0	90.0	100.0	83.5	96.3	100.0	83.5	96.3	100.0	96.3	99.2	100.0	96.2	99.1
21, 22, 23	FIRE SUPPRESSION, PLUMBING & HVAC	99.9	66.1	84.9	98.1	65.0	83.4	99.9	66.1	84.9	100.1	66.1	85.0	96.7	91.9	94.6	96.7	91.9	94.6
26, 27, 3370	ELECTRICAL, COMMUNICATIONS & UTIL.	97.0	71.0	83.2	102.3	71.0	85.7	97.4	71.0	83.4	99.6	71.0	84.4	102.8	86.2	94.0	102.8	59.0	79.6
MF2014	WEIGHTED AVERAGE	98.7	69.5	85.8	101.5	64.2	85.0	101.3	69.4	87.2	103.4	69.6	88.5	95.6	95.4	95.5	96.1	91.4	94.0

VERMONT

DIVISION		BRATTLEBORO 053 MAT.	INST.	TOTAL	BURLINGTON 054 MAT.	INST.	TOTAL	GUILDHALL 059 MAT.	INST.	TOTAL	MONTPELIER 056 MAT.	INST.	TOTAL	RUTLAND 057 MAT.	INST.	TOTAL	ST. JOHNSBURY 058 MAT.	INST.	TOTAL
015433	CONTRACTOR EQUIPMENT		99.8	99.8		99.8	99.8		99.8	99.8		99.8	99.8		99.8	99.8		99.8	99.8
0241, 31 - 34	SITE & INFRASTRUCTURE, DEMOLITION	91.4	102.1	98.9	95.0	102.0	99.9	89.4	97.4	95.0	93.6	102.0	99.4	93.9	102.0	99.5	89.5	101.0	97.5
0310	Concrete Forming & Accessories	97.1	106.9	105.6	98.9	84.3	86.2	95.0	99.8	99.2	98.9	105.7	104.8	97.4	84.3	86.0	93.6	100.3	99.4
0320	Concrete Reinforcing	85.2	81.8	83.5	105.8	81.7	93.5	86.9	81.6	84.2	105.8	81.7	93.6	107.6	81.7	94.5	85.2	81.7	83.4
0330	Cast-in-Place Concrete	90.4	113.6	99.2	104.6	112.5	107.6	84.9	104.2	92.3	104.5	112.6	107.5	85.8	112.5	96.0	84.9	104.4	92.3
03	CONCRETE	89.2	104.3	96.2	98.9	93.7	96.5	84.8	97.8	90.8	98.8	103.4	100.9	89.9	93.7	91.7	84.5	98.1	90.8
04	MASONRY	117.2	87.9	99.2	115.6	86.6	97.8	117.5	72.1	89.6	111.9	86.6	96.3	96.5	86.6	90.4	147.0	72.1	100.9
05	METALS	90.1	88.3	89.5	97.6	87.4	94.5	90.1	87.1	89.2	95.7	87.6	93.2	95.8	87.4	93.2	90.1	87.5	89.3
06	WOOD, PLASTICS & COMPOSITES	109.0	113.0	111.2	101.1	84.0	91.7	105.5	113.0	109.6	95.4	113.0	105.1	109.1	84.0	95.3	100.9	113.0	107.5
07	THERMAL & MOISTURE PROTECTION	97.4	85.5	92.5	103.8	83.9	95.6	97.2	78.3	89.3	104.6	87.1	97.3	97.5	83.9	91.9	97.1	78.3	89.3
08	OPENINGS	100.6	101.3	100.7	105.4	81.6	100.0	100.6	97.5	99.9	106.0	97.5	104.1	103.8	81.6	98.8	100.6	97.5	99.9
0920	Plaster & Gypsum Board	105.6	112.9	110.4	104.9	83.1	90.4	111.5	112.9	112.4	104.5	112.9	110.1	106.0	83.1	90.8	112.8	112.9	112.9
0950, 0980	Ceilings & Acoustic Treatment	91.2	112.9	105.6	97.1	83.1	87.8	91.2	112.9	105.6	97.3	112.9	107.7	95.7	83.1	87.3	91.2	112.9	105.6
0960	Flooring	96.6	96.5	96.6	102.9	96.5	101.0	99.5	96.5	98.6	104.4	96.5	102.1	96.5	96.5	96.5	102.9	96.5	101.0
0970, 0990	Wall Finishes & Painting/Coating	89.3	106.1	99.2	99.2	92.1	95.1	89.3	92.1	91.0	95.6	92.1	93.6	89.3	92.1	91.0	89.3	92.1	91.0
09	FINISHES	90.7	106.1	99.1	94.6	87.2	90.6	92.2	100.6	96.8	94.8	104.2	99.9	91.7	87.2	89.2	93.4	100.6	97.3
COVERS	DIVS. 10 - 14, 25, 28, 41, 43, 44, 46	100.0	96.3	99.2	100.0	92.6	98.3	100.0	90.8	97.9	100.0	95.8	99.0	100.0	92.6	98.3	100.0	90.9	97.9
21, 22, 23	FIRE SUPPRESSION, PLUMBING & HVAC	96.7	91.9	94.6	100.0	68.8	86.2	96.7	61.4	81.1	96.4	68.8	84.2	100.3	68.8	86.4	96.7	61.4	81.1
26, 27, 3370	ELECTRICAL, COMMUNICATIONS & UTIL.	102.8	86.2	94.0	102.7	57.0	78.5	102.8	59.0	79.6	101.9	57.0	78.1	102.8	57.0	78.5	102.8	59.0	79.6
MF2014	WEIGHTED AVERAGE	96.5	95.2	95.9	100.7	80.8	91.9	96.0	80.7	89.3	99.3	85.5	93.2	97.8	80.8	90.3	97.5	81.1	90.3

VERMONT / VIRGINIA

DIVISION		WHITE RIVER JCT. 050 MAT.	INST.	TOTAL	ALEXANDRIA 223 MAT.	INST.	TOTAL	ARLINGTON 222 MAT.	INST.	TOTAL	BRISTOL 242 MAT.	INST.	TOTAL	CHARLOTTESVILLE 229 MAT.	INST.	TOTAL	CULPEPER 227 MAT.	INST.	TOTAL
015433	CONTRACTOR EQUIPMENT		99.8	99.8		110.1	110.1		108.7	108.7		108.7	108.7		113.1	113.1		108.7	108.7
0241, 31 - 34	SITE & INFRASTRUCTURE, DEMOLITION	94.0	101.1	99.0	114.7	94.0	100.2	124.8	92.0	101.9	109.0	90.6	96.1	113.3	93.1	99.2	112.4	91.5	97.8
0310	Concrete Forming & Accessories	91.7	100.3	99.6	92.9	71.7	74.5	91.9	71.9	74.6	88.0	40.2	46.6	86.4	47.2	52.5	83.4	71.2	72.9
0320	Concrete Reinforcing	86.1	81.7	83.9	85.6	83.6	84.6	96.6	83.6	90.0	96.5	64.5	80.3	95.9	69.8	82.7	96.6	83.5	90.0
0330	Cast-in-Place Concrete	90.4	105.2	96.0	105.4	79.0	95.4	102.6	81.1	94.4	102.2	46.4	80.9	106.2	76.3	94.8	105.0	80.5	95.7
03	CONCRETE	90.8	98.6	94.4	101.8	77.9	90.7	106.4	78.8	93.6	102.6	49.1	77.8	103.2	63.6	84.8	100.2	78.1	90.0
04	MASONRY	131.9	73.6	96.0	93.3	74.2	81.6	108.9	74.3	87.6	97.6	48.8	67.5	123.0	52.4	79.6	109.7	74.1	87.8
05	METALS	90.1	87.5	89.3	100.8	101.5	101.0	99.4	102.9	100.5	98.3	91.0	96.0	98.5	96.1	97.8	98.6	100.7	99.2
06	WOOD, PLASTICS & COMPOSITES	103.0	113.0	108.5	93.8	70.0	80.7	90.5	70.0	79.3	83.8	37.5	58.4	82.4	42.8	60.7	81.2	70.0	75.1
07	THERMAL & MOISTURE PROTECTION	97.5	79.0	89.8	103.2	82.2	94.5	105.3	82.0	95.6	104.6	57.6	85.1	104.2	65.3	88.1	104.4	81.6	95.0
08	OPENINGS	100.6	97.5	99.9	97.8	74.2	92.5	95.9	74.2	91.0	98.9	43.8	86.4	97.1	52.2	86.9	97.4	73.9	92.1
0920	Plaster & Gypsum Board	102.6	112.9	109.5	103.9	69.0	80.7	100.6	69.0	79.6	97.1	35.6	56.2	97.1	40.4	59.4	97.3	69.0	78.5
0950, 0980	Ceilings & Acoustic Treatment	91.2	112.9	105.6	90.9	69.0	76.3	89.2	69.0	75.8	88.3	35.6	53.3	88.3	40.4	56.4	89.2	69.0	75.8
0960	Flooring	94.5	96.5	95.1	100.6	76.7	93.7	99.0	76.7	92.5	95.3	59.0	84.8	93.9	59.0	83.8	93.9	76.7	88.9
0970, 0990	Wall Finishes & Painting/Coating	89.3	92.1	91.0	118.5	76.4	93.8	118.5	76.4	93.8	104.9	51.5	73.5	104.9	60.9	79.1	118.5	60.7	84.5
09	FINISHES	89.9	100.9	95.9	96.2	72.3	83.1	96.1	72.3	83.1	92.7	43.9	66.0	92.3	49.1	68.7	93.0	70.5	80.7
COVERS	DIVS. 10 - 14, 25, 28, 41, 43, 44, 46	100.0	91.4	98.1	100.0	89.2	97.6	100.0	88.8	97.5	100.0	64.5	92.0	100.0	83.6	96.3	100.0	88.8	97.5
21, 22, 23	FIRE SUPPRESSION, PLUMBING & HVAC	96.7	62.2	81.4	100.4	85.7	93.9	100.4	85.7	93.9	96.9	67.5	83.9	96.9	67.5	83.9	96.9	70.8	85.3
26, 27, 3370	ELECTRICAL, COMMUNICATIONS & UTIL.	102.8	57.0	78.5	98.0	99.5	98.8	95.6	99.5	97.7	97.7	39.4	66.7	97.6	72.4	84.2	100.2	99.5	99.8
MF2014	WEIGHTED AVERAGE	97.4	81.3	90.3	99.8	85.2	93.3	100.7	85.3	93.9	98.5	54.4	79.0	99.8	68.0	85.7	99.0	81.5	91.3

For customer support on your Electrical Costs with RSMeans Data, call 800.448.8182.

541

City Cost Indexes

VIRGINIA

DIVISION		FAIRFAX 220-221 MAT.	INST.	TOTAL	FARMVILLE 239 MAT.	INST.	TOTAL	FREDERICKSBURG 224-225 MAT.	INST.	TOTAL	GRUNDY 246 MAT.	INST.	TOTAL	HARRISONBURG 228 MAT.	INST.	TOTAL	LYNCHBURG 245 MAT.	INST.	TOTAL
015433	CONTRACTOR EQUIPMENT		108.7	108.7		113.1	113.1		108.7	108.7		108.7	108.7		108.7	108.7		108.7	108.7
0241, 31 - 34	SITE & INFRASTRUCTURE, DEMOLITION	123.5	91.9	101.4	108.0	92.4	97.1	111.9	91.5	97.7	106.8	89.4	94.7	120.5	90.0	99.3	107.6	90.8	95.9
0310	Concrete Forming & Accessories	86.3	71.7	73.7	98.4	45.6	52.7	86.3	70.4	72.6	91.2	34.4	42.1	82.3	40.2	45.9	88.0	57.8	61.9
0320	Concrete Reinforcing	96.6	83.6	90.0	93.0	45.4	68.8	97.3	83.6	90.3	95.2	45.8	70.1	96.6	58.8	77.5	95.9	64.6	80.0
0330	Cast-in-Place Concrete	102.6	92.3	98.6	104.6	57.8	86.8	104.1	79.3	94.7	102.1	45.4	80.5	102.6	55.7	84.7	102.1	59.3	85.8
03	CONCRETE	106.1	82.5	95.2	99.1	52.0	77.3	99.9	77.4	89.5	101.2	42.6	74.0	103.8	51.3	79.4	101.1	61.5	82.7
04	MASONRY	108.8	74.1	87.5	106.1	53.8	73.9	108.8	71.9	86.1	98.3	44.9	65.4	106.8	47.7	70.4	114.3	52.4	76.2
05	METALS	98.7	102.6	99.9	94.1	82.7	90.6	98.6	101.6	99.5	98.3	76.4	91.6	98.5	88.5	95.5	98.4	91.7	96.4
06	WOOD, PLASTICS & COMPOSITES	83.8	70.0	76.2	94.1	41.4	65.2	83.8	69.8	76.1	86.4	32.9	57.0	80.3	36.6	56.3	83.8	58.8	70.1
07	THERMAL & MOISTURE PROTECTION	105.0	77.3	93.5	105.1	52.8	83.4	104.4	80.6	94.5	104.6	43.7	79.3	104.8	61.7	86.9	104.4	64.2	87.7
08	OPENINGS	95.9	73.9	90.9	97.8	40.2	84.7	97.1	73.6	91.8	98.9	32.3	83.8	97.4	46.3	85.8	97.4	55.5	87.9
0920	Plaster & Gypsum Board	97.3	69.0	78.5	106.4	38.9	61.6	97.3	68.8	78.4	97.1	30.9	53.1	97.1	34.7	55.6	97.1	57.5	70.8
0950, 0980	Ceilings & Acoustic Treatment	89.2	69.0	75.8	85.0	38.9	54.3	89.2	68.8	75.6	88.3	30.9	50.1	88.3	34.7	52.6	88.3	57.5	67.8
0960	Flooring	95.7	76.7	90.2	98.3	53.5	85.3	95.7	76.7	90.2	96.7	29.9	77.3	93.6	65.7	85.5	95.3	59.0	84.8
0970, 0990	Wall Finishes & Painting/Coating	118.5	76.4	93.8	103.3	60.9	78.4	118.5	60.7	84.5	104.9	33.3	62.8	118.5	51.5	79.1	104.9	51.5	73.5
09	FINISHES	94.6	72.2	82.4	93.2	48.3	68.7	93.5	69.8	80.6	92.9	32.7	60.0	93.4	44.5	66.7	92.5	56.5	72.8
COVERS	DIVS. 10 - 14, 25, 28, 41, 43, 44, 46	100.0	88.8	97.5	100.0	47.2	88.1	100.0	84.0	96.4	100.0	41.4	86.7	100.0	64.3	91.9	100.0	68.1	92.8
21, 22, 23	FIRE SUPPRESSION, PLUMBING & HVAC	96.9	85.6	91.9	97.0	47.0	74.9	96.9	84.1	91.2	96.9	61.1	81.0	96.9	68.8	84.4	96.9	67.2	83.7
26, 27, 3370	ELECTRICAL, COMMUNICATIONS & UTIL.	98.8	99.5	99.2	93.9	46.3	69.7	95.8	99.5	97.7	97.7	42.8	68.6	97.8	93.6	95.6	98.7	50.5	73.2
MF2014	WEIGHTED AVERAGE	99.9	85.5	93.6	97.5	55.1	78.8	98.6	83.8	92.0	98.4	51.8	77.8	99.4	66.5	84.8	99.1	64.8	83.9

VIRGINIA

DIVISION		NEWPORT NEWS 236 MAT.	INST.	TOTAL	NORFOLK 233-235 MAT.	INST.	TOTAL	PETERSBURG 238 MAT.	INST.	TOTAL	PORTSMOUTH 237 MAT.	INST.	TOTAL	PULASKI 243 MAT.	INST.	TOTAL	RICHMOND 230-232 MAT.	INST.	TOTAL
015433	CONTRACTOR EQUIPMENT		113.1	113.1		113.7	113.7		113.1	113.1		113.0	113.0		108.7	108.7		113.1	113.1
0241, 31 - 34	SITE & INFRASTRUCTURE, DEMOLITION	106.8	93.5	97.5	105.8	94.5	98.0	110.5	93.4	98.6	105.4	92.8	96.6	106.1	89.7	94.7	101.4	93.4	95.8
0310	Concrete Forming & Accessories	97.7	63.0	67.7	100.2	63.0	68.0	91.3	65.0	68.6	87.3	50.3	55.3	91.2	36.5	43.9	96.2	65.0	69.2
0320	Concrete Reinforcing	92.8	66.2	79.3	101.7	66.2	83.7	92.4	70.0	81.0	92.4	66.2	79.1	95.2	58.6	76.6	101.7	70.0	85.6
0330	Cast-in-Place Concrete	101.7	79.0	93.0	102.3	79.0	93.4	100.8	79.2	97.0	100.7	63.5	86.5	102.1	46.2	80.8	100.0	79.2	92.0
03	CONCRETE	96.3	71.0	84.6	96.6	71.0	84.7	101.6	72.6	88.2	95.2	59.9	78.8	101.2	46.3	75.7	95.3	72.6	84.8
04	MASONRY	100.3	55.9	73.0	98.1	55.9	72.1	114.8	60.3	81.2	106.4	51.1	72.4	93.1	45.8	64.0	99.4	60.3	75.3
05	METALS	96.4	94.5	95.8	98.0	94.5	96.9	94.2	96.5	94.9	95.4	94.2	95.0	98.3	87.2	94.9	98.0	96.5	97.6
06	WOOD, PLASTICS & COMPOSITES	93.1	62.1	76.1	91.7	62.1	75.5	85.4	64.3	73.8	82.3	48.4	63.6	86.4	34.5	57.9	92.7	64.3	77.1
07	THERMAL & MOISTURE PROTECTION	105.0	68.0	89.7	102.9	68.0	88.4	105.0	70.2	90.8	105.1	63.6	87.9	104.6	49.4	81.7	102.1	70.7	89.1
08	OPENINGS	98.1	58.2	89.1	96.1	58.2	87.6	97.5	64.0	89.9	98.2	50.7	87.5	98.9	39.1	85.4	98.5	64.0	90.7
0920	Plaster & Gypsum Board	107.4	60.2	76.0	99.9	60.2	73.5	100.7	62.4	75.3	101.2	46.0	64.5	97.1	32.5	54.2	102.7	62.4	75.9
0950, 0980	Ceilings & Acoustic Treatment	89.2	60.2	69.9	93.5	60.2	71.3	85.8	62.4	70.3	89.2	46.0	60.5	88.3	32.5	51.2	88.8	62.4	71.3
0960	Flooring	98.3	59.0	86.9	93.3	59.0	83.4	94.0	63.2	85.1	90.8	59.0	81.6	96.7	59.0	85.8	93.4	63.2	84.6
0970, 0990	Wall Finishes & Painting/Coating	103.3	60.9	78.4	100.9	60.9	77.4	103.3	60.9	78.4	103.3	60.9	78.4	104.9	51.5	73.5	96.0	60.9	75.4
09	FINISHES	94.0	61.6	76.3	91.2	61.6	75.0	91.5	63.7	76.3	91.0	51.6	69.5	92.9	40.7	64.4	91.3	63.7	76.2
COVERS	DIVS. 10 - 14, 25, 28, 41, 43, 44, 46	100.0	87.4	97.1	100.0	87.3	97.1	100.0	87.6	97.2	100.0	68.5	92.9	100.0	41.6	86.8	100.0	87.6	97.2
21, 22, 23	FIRE SUPPRESSION, PLUMBING & HVAC	100.5	64.6	84.6	100.1	65.7	84.9	97.0	70.1	85.1	100.5	62.8	83.9	96.9	60.0	80.5	100.0	70.1	86.7
26, 27, 3370	ELECTRICAL, COMMUNICATIONS & UTIL.	96.8	65.4	80.1	99.2	61.6	79.3	96.9	72.4	83.9	95.0	61.6	77.3	97.7	58.1	76.7	101.0	72.4	85.8
MF2014	WEIGHTED AVERAGE	98.3	69.7	85.8	98.1	69.7	85.5	98.3	73.5	87.4	97.8	64.5	83.1	98.1	56.8	79.9	98.3	73.5	87.3

VIRGINIA / WASHINGTON

DIVISION		ROANOKE 240-241 MAT.	INST.	TOTAL	STAUNTON 244 MAT.	INST.	TOTAL	WINCHESTER 226 MAT.	INST.	TOTAL	CLARKSTON 994 MAT.	INST.	TOTAL	EVERETT 982 MAT.	INST.	TOTAL	OLYMPIA 985 MAT.	INST.	TOTAL
015433	CONTRACTOR EQUIPMENT		108.7	108.7		113.1	113.1		108.7	108.7		92.7	92.7		103.5	103.5		103.5	103.5
0241, 31 - 34	SITE & INFRASTRUCTURE, DEMOLITION	106.7	90.8	95.6	109.9	91.8	97.3	119.1	91.6	99.9	105.4	90.4	94.9	93.1	111.8	106.1	91.3	111.9	105.7
0310	Concrete Forming & Accessories	97.6	58.1	63.4	90.9	47.2	53.1	84.7	71.4	73.2	114.2	68.6	74.7	117.1	102.1	104.1	106.6	102.7	103.2
0320	Concrete Reinforcing	96.3	64.8	80.3	95.9	44.5	69.8	96.0	83.6	89.7	110.9	91.7	101.1	110.8	109.3	110.0	115.9	109.4	112.6
0330	Cast-in-Place Concrete	116.0	59.5	94.5	106.2	49.3	84.5	102.6	68.2	89.5	89.5	89.4	89.5	98.2	107.3	101.7	84.5	108.1	93.5
03	CONCRETE	105.5	61.7	85.2	102.5	49.8	78.1	103.3	74.0	89.7	99.2	80.2	90.4	93.4	104.6	98.6	86.6	105.2	95.2
04	MASONRY	99.6	55.0	72.1	109.4	48.7	72.0	104.1	74.5	85.9	102.3	84.0	91.0	114.0	99.5	105.1	108.3	102.3	104.6
05	METALS	100.5	92.1	98.0	98.5	85.6	94.5	98.6	101.3	99.4	93.9	85.0	91.2	104.7	95.5	101.9	104.7	95.7	102.0
06	WOOD, PLASTICS & COMPOSITES	94.6	58.8	75.0	86.4	46.9	64.7	82.4	70.0	75.6	107.8	63.2	83.3	111.9	102.1	106.5	96.5	102.1	99.6
07	THERMAL & MOISTURE PROTECTION	104.4	68.0	89.3	104.2	50.2	81.8	104.9	80.0	94.6	159.1	83.7	127.8	111.9	104.0	108.7	110.6	104.3	108.0
08	OPENINGS	97.8	55.5	88.2	97.4	44.9	85.5	99.0	73.4	93.2	118.4	68.2	107.0	106.7	103.5	106.0	110.4	104.1	109.0
0920	Plaster & Gypsum Board	103.9	57.5	73.1	97.1	44.5	62.2	97.3	69.0	78.5	149.2	62.0	91.2	112.3	102.2	105.6	101.6	102.2	102.0
0950, 0980	Ceilings & Acoustic Treatment	90.9	57.5	68.7	88.3	44.5	59.2	89.2	69.0	75.8	105.1	62.0	76.4	104.8	102.2	103.1	104.6	102.2	103.0
0960	Flooring	100.6	59.0	88.6	96.2	35.0	78.5	95.1	76.7	89.8	91.4	73.4	86.2	109.4	104.4	107.9	98.9	109.2	101.9
0970, 0990	Wall Finishes & Painting/Coating	104.9	51.5	73.5	104.9	32.7	62.5	118.5	82.6	97.4	81.4	76.9	78.7	92.9	95.2	94.2	90.2	96.8	94.1
09	FINISHES	95.1	57.3	74.4	92.7	43.3	65.7	94.0	72.8	82.4	108.6	68.8	86.8	105.2	101.7	103.3	96.5	103.2	100.2
COVERS	DIVS. 10 - 14, 25, 28, 41, 43, 44, 46	100.0	68.1	92.8	100.0	67.5	92.6	100.0	88.8	97.5	100.0	95.7	99.0	100.0	101.9	100.4	100.0	102.5	100.6
21, 22, 23	FIRE SUPPRESSION, PLUMBING & HVAC	100.4	64.8	84.7	96.9	56.0	78.8	96.9	85.6	91.9	97.2	83.0	90.9	100.2	97.0	98.8	99.9	97.8	99.0
26, 27, 3370	ELECTRICAL, COMMUNICATIONS & UTIL.	97.7	58.2	76.7	96.5	74.1	84.6	96.2	99.5	97.9	87.5	95.0	91.5	104.2	95.9	99.8	102.2	98.4	100.2
MF2014	WEIGHTED AVERAGE	100.2	65.8	85.0	98.9	60.5	81.9	99.2	84.4	92.7	102.0	82.9	93.5	102.6	100.4	101.6	100.7	101.5	101.1

City Cost Indexes

WASHINGTON

DIVISION		RICHLAND 993			SEATTLE 980-981,987			SPOKANE 990-992			TACOMA 983-984			VANCOUVER 986			WENATCHEE 988		
		MAT.	INST.	TOTAL	MAT.	INST.	TOTAL	MAT.	INST.	TOTAL	MAT.	INST.	TOTAL	MAT.	INST.	TOTAL	MAT.	INST.	TOTAL
015433	CONTRACTOR EQUIPMENT		92.7	92.7		104.2	104.2		92.7	92.7		103.5	103.5		99.7	99.7		103.5	103.5
0241, 31 - 34	SITE & INFRASTRUCTURE, DEMOLITION	107.4	91.2	96.1	98.4	111.6	107.6	106.8	91.2	95.9	96.3	111.9	107.2	106.4	98.7	101.0	105.8	110.4	109.0
0310	Concrete Forming & Accessories	114.3	79.9	84.5	107.8	103.0	103.6	119.9	79.3	84.8	107.2	102.7	103.3	107.8	93.5	95.5	109.1	77.4	81.7
0320	Concrete Reinforcing	106.3	91.8	99.0	115.9	109.5	112.7	107.0	91.7	99.3	109.4	109.4	109.4	110.3	109.0	109.7	110.3	92.1	101.1
0330	Cast-in-Place Concrete	89.7	85.0	87.9	102.8	107.9	104.7	93.3	84.8	90.0	100.9	108.1	103.7	112.7	98.9	107.5	103.0	76.8	93.0
03	CONCRETE	98.8	83.9	91.9	99.8	105.4	102.4	101.0	83.5	92.9	95.1	105.2	99.8	104.9	98.0	101.7	102.6	80.0	92.1
04	MASONRY	103.4	84.5	91.7	117.6	103.4	108.9	103.9	84.5	92.0	113.8	102.3	106.7	113.0	94.6	101.7	117.2	90.3	100.6
05	METALS	94.2	87.8	92.3	105.0	97.6	102.7	96.6	87.3	93.7	106.5	95.7	103.2	104.1	96.5	101.8	104.0	88.0	99.1
06	WOOD, PLASTICS & COMPOSITES	107.9	77.3	91.1	101.9	102.0	102.0	116.5	77.3	95.0	101.5	102.1	101.8	92.9	93.4	93.1	103.1	75.0	87.7
07	THERMAL & MOISTURE PROTECTION	160.2	83.8	128.5	109.2	105.1	107.5	156.4	85.2	126.9	111.7	104.3	108.6	111.8	96.5	105.5	111.1	90.1	102.4
08	OPENINGS	116.3	74.7	106.9	102.9	104.1	103.2	117.0	72.6	106.9	104.4	104.1	104.3	103.7	96.4	102.0	107.0	74.4	99.6
0920	Plaster & Gypsum Board	149.2	76.5	100.9	106.7	102.2	103.7	139.6	76.5	97.7	110.5	102.2	105.0	108.6	93.5	98.6	113.4	74.3	87.4
0950, 0980	Ceilings & Acoustic Treatment	111.7	76.5	88.3	114.6	102.2	106.3	107.0	76.5	86.7	108.2	102.2	104.2	105.2	93.5	97.4	100.3	74.3	83.0
0960	Flooring	91.7	80.7	88.5	102.9	99.8	102.0	90.7	90.3	90.6	101.6	106.9	103.2	107.7	97.3	104.7	104.8	57.4	91.1
0970, 0990	Wall Finishes & Painting/Coating	81.4	76.9	78.8	102.0	96.8	99.0	81.5	73.7	76.9	92.9	96.8	95.2	95.7	74.6	83.3	92.9	75.5	82.7
09	FINISHES	110.2	78.6	93.0	106.4	101.2	103.6	107.7	80.3	92.7	103.4	102.7	103.1	101.7	92.1	96.4	104.2	72.1	86.6
COVERS	DIVS. 10 - 14, 25, 28, 41, 43, 44, 46	100.0	97.3	99.4	100.0	102.4	100.6	100.0	97.3	99.4	100.0	102.5	100.6	100.0	95.9	99.1	100.0	96.4	99.2
21, 22, 23	FIRE SUPPRESSION, PLUMBING & HVAC	100.9	110.3	105.0	100.1	115.4	106.8	100.8	83.0	92.9	100.2	97.8	99.1	100.3	91.2	96.3	96.7	84.9	91.5
26, 27, 3370	ELECTRICAL, COMMUNICATIONS & UTIL.	85.4	95.0	90.5	103.9	110.6	107.5	83.6	78.7	81.0	104.0	98.4	101.0	109.5	98.4	103.6	104.9	95.9	100.1
MF2014	WEIGHTED AVERAGE	102.6	91.4	97.6	103.2	107.1	104.9	102.9	83.3	94.3	103.0	101.5	102.4	104.0	95.2	100.1	103.3	86.9	96.0

WASHINGTON / WEST VIRGINIA

DIVISION		YAKIMA 989			BECKLEY 258-259			BLUEFIELD 247-248			BUCKHANNON 262			CHARLESTON 250-253			CLARKSBURG 263-264		
		MAT.	INST.	TOTAL	MAT.	INST.	TOTAL	MAT.	INST.	TOTAL	MAT.	INST.	TOTAL	MAT.	INST.	TOTAL	MAT.	INST.	TOTAL
015433	CONTRACTOR EQUIPMENT		103.5	103.5		108.7	108.7		108.7	108.7		108.7	108.7		108.7	108.7		108.7	108.7
0241, 31 - 34	SITE & INFRASTRUCTURE, DEMOLITION	98.8	111.2	107.4	100.8	92.9	95.3	100.7	92.9	95.2	106.9	92.8	97.1	100.2	93.9	95.8	107.6	92.8	97.3
0310	Concrete Forming & Accessories	107.7	98.0	99.3	89.7	88.1	88.3	87.9	88.2	88.1	87.3	88.6	88.4	103.2	89.3	91.2	84.7	88.6	88.0
0320	Concrete Reinforcing	109.9	91.9	100.7	93.4	85.8	89.6	94.9	95.2	95.1	95.5	95.3	95.4	101.1	85.8	93.3	95.5	96.1	95.8
0330	Cast-in-Place Concrete	107.8	84.7	99.0	102.3	95.4	99.7	99.9	95.4	98.2	99.6	94.9	97.8	99.0	114.8	105.0	109.2	93.1	103.0
03	CONCRETE	99.7	92.0	96.1	98.1	91.3	95.0	96.9	93.0	95.1	100.0	93.0	96.8	96.9	98.6	97.7	104.1	92.5	98.7
04	MASONRY	106.6	83.2	92.2	94.7	91.7	92.9	94.9	91.7	92.9	107.1	90.5	96.9	90.3	93.0	92.0	111.1	90.5	98.4
05	METALS	104.6	88.5	99.7	103.3	103.9	103.5	98.5	107.2	101.2	98.7	107.5	101.4	101.8	104.2	102.6	98.7	107.7	101.4
06	WOOD, PLASTICS & COMPOSITES	101.9	102.1	102.0	85.4	87.4	86.5	85.6	87.4	86.6	84.9	88.3	86.8	97.1	87.4	91.8	81.6	88.3	85.2
07	THERMAL & MOISTURE PROTECTION	111.8	86.5	101.3	108.4	89.0	100.4	104.3	89.0	98.0	104.6	90.0	98.6	105.5	89.5	98.9	104.5	89.7	98.4
08	OPENINGS	107.0	100.4	105.5	96.5	83.1	93.4	99.3	85.3	96.2	99.4	85.8	96.3	96.6	83.1	93.6	99.4	86.0	96.3
0920	Plaster & Gypsum Board	110.1	102.2	104.8	98.9	86.8	90.9	96.4	86.8	90.0	96.8	87.7	90.8	101.0	86.8	91.6	94.1	87.7	89.9
0950, 0980	Ceilings & Acoustic Treatment	102.2	102.2	102.2	81.6	86.8	85.1	86.6	86.8	86.8	88.3	87.7	87.9	90.8	86.8	88.2	88.3	87.7	87.9
0960	Flooring	102.6	52.9	90.0	98.2	96.9	97.8	93.0	96.9	94.1	92.7	98.7	94.5	100.5	96.9	99.5	91.7	98.7	93.7
0970, 0990	Wall Finishes & Painting/Coating	92.9	73.7	81.6	95.9	86.3	90.3	104.9	86.3	93.3	104.9	89.2	95.7	91.4	91.9	91.7	104.9	89.2	95.2
09	FINISHES	102.7	87.9	94.6	90.9	89.6	90.2	90.9	89.6	90.2	91.8	90.5	91.1	93.5	90.8	92.0	91.0	90.5	90.7
COVERS	DIVS. 10 - 14, 25, 28, 41, 43, 44, 46	100.0	99.3	99.8	100.0	93.7	98.6	100.0	93.7	98.6	100.0	92.9	98.4	100.0	94.0	98.7	100.0	92.9	98.4
21, 22, 23	FIRE SUPPRESSION, PLUMBING & HVAC	100.2	109.9	104.5	97.0	89.3	93.6	96.9	88.1	93.0	96.9	92.1	94.8	100.2	90.8	96.1	96.9	92.1	94.7
26, 27, 3370	ELECTRICAL, COMMUNICATIONS & UTIL.	107.0	95.0	100.7	94.0	89.3	91.5	96.6	89.3	92.7	98.0	94.3	96.0	99.1	89.3	93.9	98.0	94.3	96.0
MF2014	WEIGHTED AVERAGE	103.2	96.6	100.2	97.8	91.4	95.0	97.3	91.7	94.8	98.7	93.3	96.3	98.6	93.1	96.2	99.3	93.3	96.7

WEST VIRGINIA

DIVISION		GASSAWAY 266			HUNTINGTON 255-257			LEWISBURG 249			MARTINSBURG 254			MORGANTOWN 265			PARKERSBURG 261		
		MAT.	INST.	TOTAL	MAT.	INST.	TOTAL	MAT.	INST.	TOTAL	MAT.	INST.	TOTAL	MAT.	INST.	TOTAL	MAT.	INST.	TOTAL
015433	CONTRACTOR EQUIPMENT		108.7	108.7		108.7	108.7		108.7	108.7		108.7	108.7		108.7	108.7		108.7	108.7
0241, 31 - 34	SITE & INFRASTRUCTURE, DEMOLITION	104.3	92.8	96.3	105.5	93.9	97.4	116.4	92.8	100.0	104.7	93.6	97.0	101.7	93.7	96.1	109.9	93.8	98.7
0310	Concrete Forming & Accessories	86.7	94.1	93.1	102.0	89.3	91.0	85.0	87.8	87.4	89.7	79.9	81.2	85.0	88.7	88.2	89.6	85.5	86.1
0320	Concrete Reinforcing	95.5	95.1	95.3	94.8	94.1	94.5	95.5	95.0	95.3	93.4	95.1	94.3	95.5	96.1	95.8	94.9	95.0	94.9
0330	Cast-in-Place Concrete	104.3	112.8	107.5	111.6	90.4	103.5	100.0	95.3	98.2	107.2	82.3	97.7	99.6	94.9	97.8	101.8	91.2	97.8
03	CONCRETE	100.4	101.7	101.0	103.5	91.6	98.0	106.9	92.7	100.3	101.9	84.4	93.8	96.7	93.2	95.1	102.2	90.3	96.7
04	MASONRY	112.1	87.6	97.0	93.5	94.5	94.1	97.7	88.8	92.2	96.2	90.5	92.7	129.7	90.5	105.5	84.0	87.4	86.1
05	METALS	98.6	107.3	101.3	105.7	107.1	106.1	98.6	106.6	101.0	103.7	100.7	102.8	98.7	107.9	101.5	99.3	107.0	101.7
06	WOOD, PLASTICS & COMPOSITES	84.1	95.7	90.5	96.2	87.6	91.5	81.9	87.4	84.9	85.4	77.6	81.1	81.9	88.3	85.4	85.0	83.3	84.0
07	THERMAL & MOISTURE PROTECTION	104.3	89.7	98.3	108.5	89.8	100.8	105.2	88.2	98.2	108.7	86.0	99.3	104.4	90.0	98.4	104.5	89.0	98.0
08	OPENINGS	97.5	89.9	95.7	95.8	85.2	93.4	99.3	85.3	96.2	98.3	70.4	92.0	100.6	86.0	97.3	98.3	83.1	94.8
0920	Plaster & Gypsum Board	96.1	95.4	95.6	106.2	87.1	93.5	94.1	86.8	89.3	99.3	76.8	84.3	94.1	87.7	89.9	97.1	82.6	87.5
0950, 0980	Ceilings & Acoustic Treatment	88.3	95.4	93.0	83.3	87.1	85.8	88.3	86.8	87.3	83.3	76.8	79.0	88.3	87.7	87.9	88.3	82.6	84.5
0960	Flooring	92.5	96.9	93.8	105.9	100.0	104.2	91.8	96.9	93.3	98.2	96.9	97.8	91.8	98.7	93.8	95.8	96.9	96.1
0970, 0990	Wall Finishes & Painting/Coating	104.9	91.9	97.2	95.9	86.3	90.3	104.9	68.7	83.6	95.9	89.2	92.0	104.9	89.2	95.7	104.9	86.3	93.9
09	FINISHES	91.3	94.8	93.2	94.5	90.9	92.5	92.1	87.7	89.7	91.5	83.5	87.1	90.6	90.5	90.6	92.8	87.4	89.9
COVERS	DIVS. 10 - 14, 25, 28, 41, 43, 44, 46	100.0	98.3	98.6	100.0	94.0	98.6	100.0	69.1	93.0	100.0	86.5	96.9	100.0	89.2	97.6	100.0	93.0	98.4
21, 22, 23	FIRE SUPPRESSION, PLUMBING & HVAC	96.9	87.7	92.8	100.6	90.7	96.2	96.9	89.3	93.5	97.0	84.9	91.7	96.9	92.1	94.8	100.3	91.5	95.8
26, 27, 3370	ELECTRICAL, COMMUNICATIONS & UTIL.	98.0	89.3	93.4	97.8	93.4	95.5	93.9	89.3	91.5	100.0	78.0	88.3	98.2	94.3	96.1	98.1	80.4	88.7
MF2014	WEIGHTED AVERAGE	98.7	93.4	96.3	100.4	93.2	97.2	98.9	90.6	95.3	99.4	85.8	93.4	99.3	93.4	96.7	98.7	89.7	94.7

For customer support on your Electrical Costs with RSMeans Data, call 800.448.8182.

543

DIVISION		WEST VIRGINIA									WISCONSIN								
		PETERSBURG			ROMNEY			WHEELING			BELOIT			EAU CLAIRE			GREEN BAY		
		268			267			260			535			547			541 - 543		
		MAT.	INST.	TOTAL	MAT.	INST.	TOTAL	MAT.	INST.	TOTAL	MAT.	INST.	TOTAL	MAT.	INST.	TOTAL	MAT.	INST.	TOTAL
015433	CONTRACTOR EQUIPMENT		108.7	108.7		108.7	108.7		108.7	108.7		103.4	103.4		104.1	104.1		101.8	101.8
0241, 31 - 34	SITE & INFRASTRUCTURE, DEMOLITION	100.9	93.6	95.8	103.8	93.7	96.7	110.6	93.7	98.8	96.7	108.2	104.7	96.8	105.5	102.9	100.1	101.2	100.8
0310	Concrete Forming & Accessories	88.3	80.0	81.2	84.3	80.4	80.9	91.2	88.6	88.9	98.1	94.8	95.3	97.4	108.7	107.2	106.2	108.2	108.0
0320	Concrete Reinforcing	94.9	95.2	95.0	95.5	95.2	95.4	94.3	95.8	95.0	97.3	133.0	115.4	94.2	111.7	103.1	92.2	107.2	99.8
0330	Cast-in-Place Concrete	99.6	82.4	93.0	104.3	82.5	96.0	101.8	84.0	95.0	105.3	100.7	103.6	99.6	101.3	100.3	103.0	105.5	103.9
03	CONCRETE	96.8	84.8	91.3	100.3	85.1	93.2	102.2	89.3	96.2	98.5	103.7	101.0	94.6	106.6	100.2	97.6	107.1	102.0
04	MASONRY	101.9	90.5	94.9	98.0	90.5	93.4	110.2	85.8	95.2	98.7	105.7	103.0	93.1	101.9	98.5	124.6	101.3	110.3
05	METALS	98.8	106.7	101.2	98.8	107.1	101.3	99.5	107.2	101.8	95.9	112.2	100.9	94.8	105.8	98.2	97.3	104.9	99.6
06	WOOD, PLASTICS & COMPOSITES	85.8	77.6	81.3	81.1	77.6	79.2	86.4	88.3	87.4	94.5	91.6	92.9	98.4	111.2	105.5	103.0	111.2	107.5
07	THERMAL & MOISTURE PROTECTION	104.4	86.2	96.8	104.5	86.9	97.2	104.8	88.0	97.8	100.1	96.3	98.5	104.5	100.1	102.6	106.7	88.6	99.2
08	OPENINGS	100.6	80.0	96.0	100.6	80.0	95.9	99.1	86.0	96.1	96.6	107.4	99.1	102.1	109.6	103.8	98.5	109.4	101.0
0920	Plaster & Gypsum Board	96.8	76.8	83.5	93.8	76.8	82.5	97.1	87.7	90.9	96.7	91.8	93.4	110.1	111.9	111.3	106.5	111.9	110.1
0950, 0980	Ceilings & Acoustic Treatment	88.3	76.8	80.7	88.3	76.8	80.7	88.3	87.7	87.9	83.7	91.8	89.1	86.7	111.9	103.5	81.1	111.9	101.6
0960	Flooring	93.6	98.7	95.1	91.6	98.7	93.6	96.7	98.7	97.3	93.1	125.5	102.5	84.8	112.9	92.9	101.2	126.0	108.4
0970, 0990	Wall Finishes & Painting/Coating	104.9	89.2	95.7	104.9	89.2	95.7	104.9	89.2	95.7	98.0	106.5	103.0	87.7	81.4	84.0	97.2	85.2	90.2
09	FINISHES	91.5	84.3	87.6	90.7	84.3	87.2	93.1	90.7	91.8	92.7	101.3	97.4	89.2	107.4	99.2	93.7	110.2	102.7
COVERS	DIVS. 10 - 14, 25, 28, 41, 43, 44, 46	100.0	56.8	90.2	100.0	91.7	98.1	100.0	84.4	96.5	100.0	96.9	99.3	100.0	99.2	99.8	100.0	99.2	99.8
21, 22, 23	FIRE SUPPRESSION, PLUMBING & HVAC	96.9	87.6	92.8	96.9	87.4	92.7	100.4	92.3	96.8	100.1	96.7	98.6	100.1	88.2	94.8	100.4	86.5	94.2
26, 27, 3370	ELECTRICAL, COMMUNICATIONS & UTIL.	101.4	78.0	89.0	100.6	78.0	88.6	95.3	94.3	94.8	99.8	87.4	93.2	104.6	87.1	95.3	98.7	83.4	90.6
MF2014	WEIGHTED AVERAGE	98.4	86.6	93.2	98.5	87.7	93.7	100.0	92.2	96.5	97.9	100.6	99.1	98.0	99.2	98.5	100.0	97.9	99.1

DIVISION		WISCONSIN																	
		KENOSHA			LA CROSSE			LANCASTER			MADISON			MILWAUKEE			NEW RICHMOND		
		531			546			538			537			530,532			540		
		MAT.	INST.	TOTAL	MAT.	INST.	TOTAL	MAT.	INST.	TOTAL	MAT.	INST.	TOTAL	MAT.	INST.	TOTAL	MAT.	INST.	TOTAL
015433	CONTRACTOR EQUIPMENT		101.3	101.3		104.1	104.1		103.4	103.4		103.4	103.4		90.4	90.4		104.5	104.5
0241, 31 - 34	SITE & INFRASTRUCTURE, DEMOLITION	102.3	105.5	104.5	90.6	105.6	101.1	95.8	108.0	104.3	93.9	108.9	104.3	94.1	98.5	97.2	95.6	105.9	102.8
0310	Concrete Forming & Accessories	106.2	111.4	110.7	84.3	108.5	105.3	97.4	99.0	98.8	103.3	98.2	98.9	98.7	115.3	113.1	92.7	95.8	95.3
0320	Concrete Reinforcing	97.1	111.9	104.6	93.9	104.1	99.1	98.8	103.8	101.3	100.3	104.2	102.3	102.1	112.0	107.2	91.2	111.3	101.4
0330	Cast-in-Place Concrete	114.6	109.3	112.6	89.6	101.5	94.1	104.7	100.3	103.0	95.3	100.7	97.3	100.2	112.7	104.9	103.7	81.1	95.1
03	CONCRETE	103.5	110.5	106.7	86.0	105.3	94.9	98.2	100.4	99.2	93.8	100.2	96.8	99.0	118.1	107.8	92.5	93.8	93.1
04	MASONRY	96.2	113.2	106.7	92.2	101.9	98.2	98.8	99.0	98.9	96.7	102.9	100.5	100.8	118.1	111.5	119.5	98.9	106.8
05	METALS	96.8	105.4	99.4	94.7	103.8	97.5	93.5	100.7	95.7	99.0	102.0	99.9	95.7	95.8	95.8	95.1	104.9	98.1
06	WOOD, PLASTICS & COMPOSITES	98.1	111.2	105.3	84.5	111.2	99.2	93.8	98.7	96.5	94.7	96.3	95.6	98.5	114.4	107.2	88.0	94.6	91.6
07	THERMAL & MOISTURE PROTECTION	100.3	108.9	103.9	103.9	99.8	102.2	99.9	95.5	98.1	98.5	102.5	100.1	99.4	112.8	104.9	105.6	90.5	99.3
08	OPENINGS	91.3	110.4	95.6	102.1	102.4	102.2	92.6	95.6	93.2	102.6	100.5	102.1	96.8	112.1	100.2	88.2	93.8	89.4
0920	Plaster & Gypsum Board	86.6	111.9	103.4	105.0	111.9	109.6	95.9	99.1	98.0	106.1	96.6	99.8	97.0	114.8	108.8	95.6	95.0	95.2
0950, 0980	Ceilings & Acoustic Treatment	83.7	111.9	102.5	85.9	111.9	103.2	80.3	99.1	92.8	91.3	96.6	94.8	91.8	114.8	107.1	55.6	95.0	81.8
0960	Flooring	110.2	118.3	112.6	78.5	118.3	90.0	92.6	105.5	96.4	95.8	114.0	101.1	94.2	117.6	101.0	94.0	110.0	98.7
0970, 0990	Wall Finishes & Painting/Coating	108.7	121.1	116.0	87.7	82.8	84.8	98.0	104.1	101.6	93.4	106.5	101.1	102.7	123.3	114.8	99.5	87.0	92.2
09	FINISHES	97.3	114.2	106.5	86.0	108.7	98.4	91.7	101.3	96.9	92.7	101.9	97.7	98.6	117.0	108.6	84.3	98.0	91.8
COVERS	DIVS. 10 - 14, 25, 28, 41, 43, 44, 46	100.0	101.4	100.3	100.0	99.2	99.8	100.0	89.3	97.6	100.0	100.2	100.1	100.0	103.6	100.8	100.0	91.6	98.1
21, 22, 23	FIRE SUPPRESSION, PLUMBING & HVAC	100.3	97.4	99.0	100.1	88.1	94.8	96.5	88.0	92.8	100.0	97.7	98.9	99.9	106.2	102.7	95.9	88.3	92.6
26, 27, 3370	ELECTRICAL, COMMUNICATIONS & UTIL.	100.2	99.9	100.0	104.9	87.1	95.4	99.5	87.1	92.9	99.6	96.6	98.0	100.7	101.9	101.3	102.5	87.1	94.3
MF2014	WEIGHTED AVERAGE	98.6	105.8	101.8	96.3	98.7	97.4	96.1	95.8	96.0	98.3	100.5	99.3	98.6	107.9	102.7	95.9	94.6	95.3

DIVISION		WISCONSIN																	
		OSHKOSH			PORTAGE			RACINE			RHINELANDER			SUPERIOR			WAUSAU		
		549			539			534			545			548			544		
		MAT.	INST.	TOTAL	MAT.	INST.	TOTAL	MAT.	INST.	TOTAL	MAT.	INST.	TOTAL	MAT.	INST.	TOTAL	MAT.	INST.	TOTAL
015433	CONTRACTOR EQUIPMENT		101.8	101.8		103.4	103.4		103.4	103.4		101.8	101.8		104.5	104.5		101.8	101.8
0241, 31 - 34	SITE & INFRASTRUCTURE, DEMOLITION	91.9	100.8	98.1	86.7	107.8	101.4	96.4	109.5	105.5	104.0	108.3	107.0	92.3	105.6	101.6	87.7	102.1	97.7
0310	Concrete Forming & Accessories	88.9	92.1	91.6	89.4	94.1	93.5	98.4	111.5	109.7	86.6	92.8	92.0	90.7	91.9	91.7	88.4	107.9	105.3
0320	Concrete Reinforcing	92.4	99.4	95.9	98.9	104.0	101.4	97.3	111.9	104.7	92.5	97.8	95.2	91.2	103.9	97.7	92.5	103.8	98.3
0330	Cast-in-Place Concrete	95.5	95.7	95.6	89.9	101.0	94.1	103.3	109.1	105.5	108.3	98.5	104.6	97.7	103.5	99.9	89.0	97.4	92.2
03	CONCRETE	87.6	95.0	91.1	85.9	98.4	91.7	97.6	110.4	103.5	99.5	96.1	97.9	87.2	98.5	92.4	82.8	103.5	92.4
04	MASONRY	106.6	98.8	101.8	97.6	100.3	99.2	98.7	113.2	107.6	125.0	97.9	108.3	118.7	104.2	109.8	106.1	98.0	101.1
05	METALS	95.3	100.6	96.9	94.1	101.1	96.2	97.5	105.5	99.9	95.2	100.5	96.8	96.0	103.6	98.3	95.0	103.2	97.5
06	WOOD, PLASTICS & COMPOSITES	84.0	91.7	88.2	84.8	91.6	88.5	94.8	111.2	103.8	81.7	91.7	87.2	86.4	90.2	88.5	83.5	111.2	98.8
07	THERMAL & MOISTURE PROTECTION	105.7	83.7	96.6	99.3	91.1	95.9	100.2	108.5	103.6	106.6	84.8	97.5	105.2	91.4	99.5	105.6	86.3	97.6
08	OPENINGS	94.9	91.4	94.1	92.7	97.5	93.8	96.6	110.4	99.7	94.9	90.2	93.8	87.7	91.7	88.6	95.1	102.8	96.9
0920	Plaster & Gypsum Board	94.4	91.8	92.6	89.2	91.8	90.9	96.7	111.9	106.8	94.4	91.8	92.6	95.4	90.5	92.1	94.4	111.9	106.0
0950, 0980	Ceilings & Acoustic Treatment	81.1	91.8	88.2	82.9	91.8	88.8	83.7	111.9	102.5	81.1	91.8	88.2	56.4	90.5	79.1	81.1	111.9	101.6
0960	Flooring	91.9	118.3	99.6	88.8	115.1	96.5	93.1	118.3	100.4	91.3	111.9	97.3	95.1	127.5	104.5	91.8	111.9	97.7
0970, 0990	Wall Finishes & Painting/Coating	93.9	85.2	88.8	98.0	104.1	101.6	98.0	121.1	111.5	93.9	85.2	88.8	88.2	104.8	98.0	93.9	85.2	88.8
09	FINISHES	88.4	96.7	92.9	89.6	98.9	94.7	92.7	114.2	104.4	89.2	94.8	92.3	83.7	100.0	92.6	88.1	107.5	98.7
COVERS	DIVS. 10 - 14, 25, 28, 41, 43, 44, 46	100.0	89.1	97.5	100.0	90.0	97.7	100.0	101.4	100.3	100.0	90.2	97.8	100.0	89.8	97.7	100.0	99.2	99.8
21, 22, 23	FIRE SUPPRESSION, PLUMBING & HVAC	96.9	81.8	90.2	96.5	97.5	97.0	100.1	97.5	98.9	96.9	87.3	92.6	95.9	92.3	94.3	96.9	87.7	92.8
26, 27, 3370	ELECTRICAL, COMMUNICATIONS & UTIL.	103.1	78.3	90.0	103.4	96.6	99.8	99.6	103.5	101.7	102.4	79.7	90.4	107.7	101.3	104.3	104.3	82.4	92.7
MF2014	WEIGHTED AVERAGE	95.9	90.7	93.6	94.6	98.6	96.3	98.1	106.6	101.8	98.6	91.9	95.7	95.7	98.5	96.9	95.3	96.4	95.8

		WYOMING																
	DIVISION	CASPER			CHEYENNE			NEWCASTLE			RAWLINS			RIVERTON			ROCK SPRINGS		
		826			820			827			823			825			829 - 831		
		MAT.	INST.	TOTAL	MAT.	INST.	TOTAL	MAT.	INST.	TOTAL	MAT.	INST.	TOTAL	MAT.	INST.	TOTAL	MAT.	INST.	TOTAL
015433	CONTRACTOR EQUIPMENT		98.8	98.8		98.8	98.8		98.8	98.8		98.8	98.8		98.8	98.8		98.8	98.8
0241, 31 - 34	SITE & INFRASTRUCTURE, DEMOLITION	97.3	95.7	96.2	93.2	95.7	95.0	85.4	95.4	92.4	99.6	95.4	96.7	92.9	95.3	94.6	89.6	95.4	93.6
0310	Concrete Forming & Accessories	102.8	53.4	60.1	103.9	68.5	73.3	94.6	75.8	78.4	98.8	75.9	79.0	93.6	64.4	68.4	101.0	65.4	70.2
0320	Concrete Reinforcing	111.9	83.0	97.6	107.4	83.8	95.4	115.3	84.3	99.6	115.0	84.3	99.4	116.0	84.2	99.9	116.0	84.0	99.8
0330	Cast-in-Place Concrete	97.1	75.8	89.0	91.7	75.8	85.7	92.6	75.8	86.2	92.7	70.4	84.2	92.7	65.0	82.1	92.6	65.0	82.1
03	CONCRETE	100.2	67.4	85.0	97.8	74.2	86.9	98.1	77.5	88.6	111.7	75.7	95.0	106.3	68.7	88.9	98.6	69.1	84.9
04	MASONRY	105.2	55.1	74.4	108.7	55.1	75.7	105.2	63.8	79.7	105.2	63.8	79.7	105.2	63.8	79.8	170.3	59.4	102.0
05	METALS	103.0	80.9	96.2	105.5	81.0	98.0	101.8	81.6	95.6	101.8	81.6	95.6	101.9	81.3	95.6	102.6	81.0	96.0
06	WOOD, PLASTICS & COMPOSITES	93.5	48.1	68.5	91.3	68.5	78.8	82.5	78.6	80.3	86.1	78.6	81.9	81.5	63.4	71.6	90.8	64.8	76.5
07	THERMAL & MOISTURE PROTECTION	106.0	64.2	88.6	100.6	66.4	86.4	102.3	67.7	87.9	103.8	77.9	93.1	103.2	65.3	87.5	102.4	68.5	88.3
08	OPENINGS	103.3	60.1	93.5	104.2	71.3	96.7	108.3	76.8	101.1	107.9	76.8	100.9	108.1	68.5	99.2	108.7	69.2	99.7
0920	Plaster & Gypsum Board	102.5	46.7	65.4	91.7	67.6	75.7	88.5	78.0	81.5	88.9	78.0	81.6	88.5	62.4	71.2	100.1	63.8	76.0
0950, 0980	Ceilings & Acoustic Treatment	103.2	46.7	65.6	95.1	67.6	76.8	97.0	78.0	84.3	97.0	78.0	84.3	97.0	62.4	74.0	97.0	63.8	74.9
0960	Flooring	112.6	73.8	101.4	111.7	73.8	100.8	105.1	47.2	88.3	108.1	47.2	90.5	104.6	63.9	92.8	110.6	47.2	92.2
0970, 0990	Wall Finishes & Painting/Coating	94.8	58.7	73.6	100.9	58.7	76.1	97.5	58.7	74.7	97.5	58.7	74.7	97.5	58.7	74.7	97.5	58.7	74.7
09	FINISHES	101.2	56.4	76.7	98.2	68.3	81.9	93.4	68.7	79.9	95.7	68.7	81.0	94.1	63.3	77.3	96.6	60.7	77.0
COVERS	DIVS. 10 - 14, 25, 28, 41, 43, 44, 46	100.0	86.2	96.9	100.0	88.4	97.4	100.0	90.6	97.9	100.0	90.6	97.9	100.0	83.0	96.1	100.0	81.2	95.8
21, 22, 23	FIRE SUPPRESSION, PLUMBING & HVAC	100.0	71.5	87.4	100.0	71.5	87.4	98.1	71.5	86.3	98.1	71.5	86.3	98.1	71.5	86.3	99.9	71.5	87.3
26, 27, 3370	ELECTRICAL, COMMUNICATIONS & UTIL.	101.2	62.0	80.4	103.5	65.0	83.0	102.2	83.1	92.1	102.2	69.3	84.8	102.2	64.1	82.0	100.3	83.1	91.2
MF2014	WEIGHTED AVERAGE	101.4	68.3	86.8	101.5	72.0	88.5	100.1	76.4	89.6	102.3	74.5	90.0	101.3	71.0	87.9	104.2	73.0	90.4

		WYOMING												CANADA					
	DIVISION	SHERIDAN			WHEATLAND			WORLAND			YELLOWSTONE NAT'L PA			BARRIE, ONTARIO			BATHURST, NEW BRUNSWICK		
		828			822			824			821								
		MAT.	INST.	TOTAL	MAT.	INST.	TOTAL	MAT.	INST.	TOTAL	MAT.	INST.	TOTAL	MAT.	INST.	TOTAL	MAT.	INST.	TOTAL
015433	CONTRACTOR EQUIPMENT		98.8	98.8		98.8	98.8		98.8	98.8		98.8	98.8		104.3	104.3		103.8	103.8
0241, 31 - 34	SITE & INFRASTRUCTURE, DEMOLITION	93.3	95.7	95.0	90.3	95.4	93.9	87.5	95.4	93.0	87.7	95.4	93.0	118.8	101.1	106.5	105.3	96.6	99.2
0310	Concrete Forming & Accessories	101.7	64.8	69.8	96.5	51.6	57.6	96.6	65.4	69.6	96.6	65.4	69.6	126.3	88.5	93.6	104.8	62.2	67.9
0320	Concrete Reinforcing	116.0	84.3	99.9	115.3	83.7	99.3	116.0	84.2	99.9	118.0	84.2	100.9	177.8	90.4	133.5	147.5	59.9	103.0
0330	Cast-in-Place Concrete	95.8	75.8	88.2	96.7	62.7	83.8	92.6	65.0	82.1	92.6	65.0	82.1	159.5	87.7	132.2	118.0	59.8	95.8
03	CONCRETE	106.3	72.6	90.7	103.0	62.0	84.0	98.3	69.1	84.8	98.6	69.1	84.9	144.2	89.0	118.6	116.8	61.9	91.4
04	MASONRY	105.5	63.8	79.9	105.6	55.1	74.5	105.2	63.8	79.8	105.3	63.8	79.8	169.6	96.0	124.4	161.6	61.8	100.1
05	METALS	105.3	81.6	98.0	101.7	80.3	95.2	101.9	81.3	95.6	102.5	80.7	95.8	108.3	94.6	104.1	103.7	75.6	95.1
06	WOOD, PLASTICS & COMPOSITES	92.5	63.4	76.6	84.1	46.4	63.4	84.2	64.8	73.5	84.2	64.8	73.5	118.3	87.2	101.2	98.7	62.4	78.7
07	THERMAL & MOISTURE PROTECTION	103.5	68.3	88.9	102.5	59.5	84.7	102.3	66.9	87.6	101.7	65.6	86.8	114.2	92.4	105.2	109.9	62.6	90.3
08	OPENINGS	108.9	68.5	99.7	106.8	59.2	96.0	108.5	69.2	99.6	101.5	68.9	94.1	92.6	86.8	91.3	86.4	54.8	79.3
0920	Plaster & Gypsum Board	112.5	62.4	79.2	88.5	44.9	59.5	88.5	63.8	72.1	88.7	63.8	72.2	151.5	86.8	108.5	126.6	61.2	83.2
0950, 0980	Ceilings & Acoustic Treatment	99.8	62.4	74.9	97.0	44.9	62.3	97.0	63.8	74.9	97.8	63.8	75.2	92.7	86.8	88.7	108.8	61.2	77.1
0960	Flooring	109.1	63.9	96.0	106.7	46.4	89.3	106.7	47.2	89.5	106.7	47.2	89.5	123.9	92.3	114.8	105.2	43.9	87.4
0970, 0990	Wall Finishes & Painting/Coating	99.7	58.7	75.7	97.5	58.7	74.7	97.5	58.7	74.7	97.5	58.7	74.7	107.7	89.1	96.8	113.9	51.0	76.9
09	FINISHES	101.1	63.6	80.6	94.2	49.8	69.9	93.9	60.7	75.7	94.1	60.8	75.9	112.3	89.5	99.9	107.6	57.6	80.3
COVERS	DIVS. 10 - 14, 25, 28, 41, 43, 44, 46	100.0	87.8	97.3	100.0	80.0	95.5	100.0	81.7	95.9	100.0	81.8	95.9	139.2	69.5	123.5	131.1	61.8	115.5
21, 22, 23	FIRE SUPPRESSION, PLUMBING & HVAC	98.1	71.5	86.3	98.1	71.5	86.3	98.1	71.5	86.3	98.1	71.5	86.3	103.1	98.3	101.0	103.2	68.0	87.6
26, 27, 3370	ELECTRICAL, COMMUNICATIONS & UTIL.	104.8	64.1	83.2	102.2	83.1	92.1	102.2	83.1	92.1	101.1	93.3	97.0	115.9	89.7	102.0	112.4	60.4	84.9
MF2014	WEIGHTED AVERAGE	103.0	71.9	89.2	100.7	69.2	86.8	100.2	73.4	88.4	99.5	74.8	88.6	117.1	92.7	106.3	109.8	66.2	90.5

		CANADA																	
	DIVISION	BRANDON, MANITOBA			BRANTFORD, ONTARIO			BRIDGEWATER, NOVA SCOTIA			CALGARY, ALBERTA			CAP-DE-LA-MADELEINE, QUEBEC			CHARLESBOURG, QUEBEC		
		MAT.	INST.	TOTAL	MAT.	INST.	TOTAL	MAT.	INST.	TOTAL	MAT.	INST.	TOTAL	MAT.	INST.	TOTAL	MAT.	INST.	TOTAL
015433	CONTRACTOR EQUIPMENT		106.6	106.6		104.3	104.3		103.6	103.6		123.7	123.7		104.4	104.4		104.4	104.4
0241, 31 - 34	SITE & INFRASTRUCTURE, DEMOLITION	135.8	99.7	110.6	118.8	101.4	106.7	103.1	98.5	99.9	123.5	117.3	119.2	98.6	100.0	99.6	98.6	100.0	99.6
0310	Concrete Forming & Accessories	148.3	71.1	81.5	125.6	95.9	100.0	97.4	73.0	76.3	123.6	100.6	103.7	131.6	85.2	91.5	131.6	85.2	91.5
0320	Concrete Reinforcing	195.9	56.7	125.3	171.4	89.1	129.6	145.8	49.6	97.0	138.1	79.0	108.1	145.8	75.4	110.1	145.8	75.4	110.1
0330	Cast-in-Place Concrete	124.8	75.1	105.9	139.8	109.1	128.1	143.6	71.3	116.1	155.3	107.9	137.2	112.8	93.6	105.5	112.8	93.6	105.5
03	CONCRETE	136.0	70.9	105.8	131.7	99.4	116.8	130.0	69.2	101.8	137.5	99.9	120.0	115.7	86.8	102.3	115.7	86.8	102.3
04	MASONRY	227.8	65.3	127.7	168.3	100.4	126.5	163.8	70.5	106.4	197.8	91.5	132.3	164.4	82.1	113.7	164.4	82.1	113.7
05	METALS	117.3	81.0	106.2	102.5	95.3	100.3	101.8	78.3	94.6	123.6	100.0	116.3	100.9	87.7	96.9	100.9	87.7	96.9
06	WOOD, PLASTICS & COMPOSITES	151.4	72.1	107.8	120.2	94.7	106.2	91.0	72.7	80.9	96.7	100.6	98.9	130.9	85.2	105.8	130.9	85.2	105.8
07	THERMAL & MOISTURE PROTECTION	136.9	73.7	110.7	118.3	98.1	109.9	112.9	72.5	96.1	122.4	98.3	112.4	111.6	90.3	102.8	111.6	90.3	102.8
08	OPENINGS	102.5	64.2	93.8	90.4	92.9	90.9	84.5	65.7	80.3	84.3	86.9	84.9	91.7	77.5	88.5	91.7	77.5	88.5
0920	Plaster & Gypsum Board	113.1	70.9	85.0	116.6	94.5	101.9	122.4	71.9	88.8	115.2	99.8	105.0	144.8	84.7	104.8	144.8	84.7	104.8
0950, 0980	Ceilings & Acoustic Treatment	114.4	70.9	85.4	99.5	94.5	96.1	99.5	71.9	81.1	142.4	99.8	114.0	99.5	84.7	89.6	99.5	84.7	89.6
0960	Flooring	138.8	65.5	117.5	119.2	92.3	111.4	100.7	62.3	89.5	124.7	88.7	114.3	119.2	90.9	111.0	119.2	90.9	111.0
0970, 0990	Wall Finishes & Painting/Coating	121.2	57.5	83.8	112.9	97.8	104.0	112.9	63.1	83.6	121.3	112.0	115.8	112.9	88.9	98.8	112.9	88.9	98.8
09	FINISHES	121.7	69.0	92.9	109.1	95.8	101.9	103.8	70.3	85.5	124.6	100.2	111.3	112.4	87.0	98.5	112.4	87.0	98.5
COVERS	DIVS. 10 - 14, 25, 28, 41, 43, 44, 46	131.1	64.4	116.0	131.1	71.6	117.7	131.1	65.0	116.2	131.1	97.5	123.5	131.1	81.0	119.8	131.1	81.0	119.8
21, 22, 23	FIRE SUPPRESSION, PLUMBING & HVAC	103.3	82.9	94.2	103.2	101.2	102.3	103.2	83.6	94.5	105.2	93.1	99.9	103.5	88.5	96.9	103.5	88.5	96.9
26, 27, 3370	ELECTRICAL, COMMUNICATIONS & UTIL.	117.7	68.3	91.5	111.1	89.2	99.5	116.2	63.5	88.2	109.7	101.8	105.5	110.5	70.6	89.3	110.5	70.6	89.3
MF2014	WEIGHTED AVERAGE	123.4	75.1	102.0	113.0	96.6	105.8	111.0	74.7	95.0	119.8	98.6	110.4	110.4	85.1	99.2	110.4	85.1	99.2

City Cost Indexes

CANADA

DIVISION		CHARLOTTETOWN, PRINCE EDWARD ISLAND			CHICOUTIMI, QUEBEC			CORNER BROOK, NEWFOUNDLAND			CORNWALL, ONTARIO			DALHOUSIE, NEW BRUNSWICK			DARTMOUTH, NOVA SCOTIA		
		MAT.	INST.	TOTAL	MAT.	INST.	TOTAL	MAT.	INST.	TOTAL	MAT.	INST.	TOTAL	MAT.	INST.	TOTAL	MAT.	INST.	TOTAL
015433	CONTRACTOR EQUIPMENT		117.9	117.9		104.4	104.4		104.6	104.6		104.3	104.3		103.8	103.8		103.6	103.6
0241, 31 - 34	SITE & INFRASTRUCTURE, DEMOLITION	128.4	106.2	112.9	102.2	99.5	100.3	140.2	96.7	109.9	116.8	100.9	105.7	101.6	96.6	98.1	126.4	98.5	106.9
0310	Concrete Forming & Accessories	119.5	56.7	65.2	134.6	92.0	97.7	124.4	58.8	67.6	123.3	88.7	93.4	103.3	62.4	67.9	113.7	73.0	78.5
0320	Concrete Reinforcing	156.7	48.4	101.7	111.3	93.4	102.2	179.7	49.5	113.6	171.4	88.8	129.4	149.2	59.9	103.9	187.8	49.6	117.6
0330	Cast-in-Place Concrete	149.5	59.0	115.0	111.1	97.2	105.8	145.3	67.6	115.7	125.7	99.4	115.7	121.0	59.9	97.7	140.2	71.3	114.0
03	CONCRETE	137.6	57.8	100.6	107.4	94.1	101.3	170.7	61.5	120.1	124.8	92.7	109.9	123.0	62.0	94.8	151.8	69.2	113.5
04	MASONRY	182.9	59.0	106.6	163.9	91.7	119.4	223.6	60.2	123.0	167.2	92.1	120.9	163.1	61.8	100.7	238.4	70.5	135.0
05	METALS	125.8	80.8	112.0	103.5	92.5	100.1	117.7	75.6	104.9	102.4	93.9	99.8	97.1	75.8	90.6	118.1	78.3	105.9
06	WOOD, PLASTICS & COMPOSITES	98.0	56.2	75.0	131.6	92.6	110.2	129.7	57.8	90.2	118.5	88.0	101.7	97.9	62.4	78.4	117.9	72.7	93.0
07	THERMAL & MOISTURE PROTECTION	130.7	59.9	101.3	110.3	98.8	105.5	141.8	62.0	108.7	118.1	92.5	107.5	114.4	62.6	92.9	138.8	72.5	111.3
08	OPENINGS	82.8	48.9	75.1	90.5	78.1	87.7	109.0	54.9	96.8	91.7	86.4	90.5	87.3	54.8	79.9	92.8	65.7	86.7
0920	Plaster & Gypsum Board	116.2	54.6	75.2	144.8	92.2	109.8	147.0	56.5	86.9	173.1	87.6	116.4	130.5	61.2	84.5	142.6	71.9	95.6
0950, 0980	Ceilings & Acoustic Treatment	126.5	54.6	78.7	107.9	92.2	97.5	115.3	56.5	76.2	102.0	87.6	92.5	102.8	61.2	75.1	122.1	71.9	88.7
0960	Flooring	113.7	58.5	97.7	121.9	90.9	112.9	119.6	52.4	100.1	119.2	91.0	111.0	106.7	67.1	95.2	114.2	62.3	99.2
0970, 0990	Wall Finishes & Painting/Coating	121.7	42.4	75.1	113.9	105.2	108.8	121.1	60.0	85.2	112.9	91.1	100.1	116.6	51.0	78.0	121.1	63.1	87.0
09	FINISHES	117.5	55.8	84.4	114.6	94.1	103.4	121.4	57.7	86.5	117.5	89.6	102.3	108.7	62.4	83.4	119.1	70.3	92.4
COVERS	DIVS. 10 - 14, 25, 28, 41, 43, 44, 46	131.1	61.7	115.4	131.1	84.5	120.6	131.1	61.5	115.4	131.1	69.1	117.1	131.1	61.8	115.5	131.1	65.0	116.2
21, 22, 23	FIRE SUPPRESSION, PLUMBING & HVAC	103.6	61.9	85.2	103.2	80.8	93.3	103.3	68.8	88.0	103.5	99.1	101.5	103.2	68.1	87.7	103.3	83.6	94.5
26, 27, 3370	ELECTRICAL, COMMUNICATIONS & UTIL.	111.5	51.4	79.6	109.3	86.2	97.0	115.3	55.7	83.7	111.7	90.2	100.3	113.1	57.1	83.4	120.0	63.5	90.0
MF2014	WEIGHTED AVERAGE	119.0	63.4	94.4	109.7	89.3	100.7	128.1	65.4	100.4	113.0	93.0	104.1	109.8	66.4	90.6	124.5	74.7	102.5

CANADA

DIVISION		EDMONTON, ALBERTA			FORT MCMURRAY, ALBERTA			FREDERICTON, NEW BRUNSWICK			GATINEAU, QUEBEC			GRANBY, QUEBEC			HALIFAX, NOVA SCOTIA		
		MAT.	INST.	TOTAL	MAT.	INST.	TOTAL	MAT.	INST.	TOTAL	MAT.	INST.	TOTAL	MAT.	INST.	TOTAL	MAT.	INST.	TOTAL
015433	CONTRACTOR EQUIPMENT		123.8	123.8		106.8	106.8		118.7	118.7		104.4	104.4		104.4	104.4		117.3	117.3
0241, 31 - 34	SITE & INFRASTRUCTURE, DEMOLITION	134.4	117.4	122.5	123.9	102.2	108.7	110.0	107.5	108.3	98.4	100.0	99.5	98.9	100.0	99.7	106.8	109.0	108.3
0310	Concrete Forming & Accessories	122.2	100.6	103.5	123.4	93.9	97.9	124.9	63.0	71.4	131.6	85.1	91.4	131.6	85.0	91.3	118.4	83.6	88.3
0320	Concrete Reinforcing	139.1	79.0	108.6	158.6	78.9	118.1	146.9	60.1	102.8	154.2	75.4	114.2	154.2	75.4	114.2	156.7	66.7	111.0
0330	Cast-in-Place Concrete	160.6	107.9	140.5	185.6	104.4	154.6	124.6	60.7	100.3	111.3	93.5	104.5	115.0	93.5	106.8	112.5	83.9	101.6
03	CONCRETE	140.1	99.9	121.4	152.1	95.1	125.7	124.6	63.3	96.2	116.0	86.7	102.4	117.8	86.7	103.4	119.0	81.8	101.7
04	MASONRY	197.6	91.5	132.3	208.7	88.5	134.7	178.1	63.2	107.3	164.3	82.1	113.7	164.6	82.1	113.8	181.8	85.9	122.7
05	METALS	123.6	100.0	116.4	127.3	90.6	116.1	122.6	86.0	111.4	100.9	87.6	96.9	101.1	87.5	97.0	124.1	92.5	114.4
06	WOOD, PLASTICS & COMPOSITES	100.1	100.6	100.4	114.6	93.6	103.0	111.8	62.7	84.8	130.9	85.2	105.8	130.9	85.2	105.8	99.8	82.9	90.5
07	THERMAL & MOISTURE PROTECTION	126.1	98.3	114.5	126.8	95.4	113.8	125.2	62.9	99.3	111.6	90.3	102.8	111.6	88.7	102.1	125.2	84.4	108.3
08	OPENINGS	82.3	87.0	83.4	91.7	83.1	89.7	85.9	53.9	78.7	91.7	72.9	87.4	91.7	72.9	87.4	90.4	73.4	86.5
0920	Plaster & Gypsum Board	112.9	99.8	104.2	117.4	93.0	101.2	121.0	61.2	81.3	114.5	84.7	94.7	114.5	84.7	94.7	113.7	82.1	92.7
0950, 0980	Ceilings & Acoustic Treatment	137.5	99.8	112.4	107.1	93.0	97.7	128.2	61.2	83.6	99.5	84.7	89.6	99.5	84.7	89.6	120.4	82.1	94.9
0960	Flooring	120.7	88.7	111.4	119.2	88.7	110.3	115.9	70.0	102.6	119.2	90.9	111.0	119.2	90.9	111.0	106.7	83.9	100.1
0970, 0990	Wall Finishes & Painting/Coating	112.2	112.0	112.1	113.0	93.9	101.8	118.9	64.9	87.2	112.9	88.9	98.8	112.9	88.9	98.8	116.9	89.4	100.8
09	FINISHES	118.6	100.2	108.5	112.1	93.3	101.8	119.3	64.7	89.5	108.1	87.0	96.6	108.1	87.0	96.6	112.5	84.8	97.3
COVERS	DIVS. 10 - 14, 25, 28, 41, 43, 44, 46	131.1	97.5	123.5	131.1	94.9	122.9	131.1	62.6	115.6	131.1	81.0	119.8	131.1	81.0	119.8	131.1	69.7	117.2
21, 22, 23	FIRE SUPPRESSION, PLUMBING & HVAC	105.2	93.1	99.9	103.7	97.8	101.1	103.4	77.4	91.9	103.5	88.5	96.8	103.2	88.5	96.7	104.8	79.7	93.7
26, 27, 3370	ELECTRICAL, COMMUNICATIONS & UTIL.	109.8	101.8	105.6	105.5	83.8	94.0	111.7	75.4	92.4	110.5	70.5	89.3	111.1	70.5	89.6	110.3	85.0	96.9
MF2014	WEIGHTED AVERAGE	119.8	98.6	110.4	122.1	92.8	109.2	116.4	73.3	97.4	110.1	84.9	98.9	110.3	84.8	99.0	116.1	85.0	102.4

CANADA

DIVISION		HAMILTON, ONTARIO			HULL, QUEBEC			JOLIETTE, QUEBEC			KAMLOOPS, BRITISH COLUMBIA			KINGSTON, ONTARIO			KITCHENER, ONTARIO		
		MAT.	INST.	TOTAL	MAT.	INST.	TOTAL	MAT.	INST.	TOTAL	MAT.	INST.	TOTAL	MAT.	INST.	TOTAL	MAT.	INST.	TOTAL
015433	CONTRACTOR EQUIPMENT		120.6	120.6		104.4	104.4		104.4	104.4		107.8	107.8		106.6	106.6		106.5	106.5
0241, 31 - 34	SITE & INFRASTRUCTURE, DEMOLITION	110.0	115.8	114.1	98.4	100.0	99.5	99.0	100.0	99.7	121.3	103.8	109.1	116.8	104.9	108.5	98.0	106.3	103.8
0310	Concrete Forming & Accessories	122.0	94.3	98.0	131.6	85.1	91.4	131.6	85.2	91.5	123.3	88.5	93.2	123.4	88.8	93.4	114.2	91.1	94.2
0320	Concrete Reinforcing	137.6	99.4	118.2	154.2	75.4	114.2	145.8	75.4	110.1	114.3	78.9	96.4	171.4	88.8	129.4	97.8	99.6	98.7
0330	Cast-in-Place Concrete	119.2	101.0	112.3	111.3	93.5	104.5	115.9	93.6	107.4	100.3	98.2	99.5	125.7	99.4	115.7	116.2	101.1	110.4
03	CONCRETE	116.8	98.3	108.2	116.0	86.7	102.4	117.2	86.8	103.1	124.9	90.5	108.9	126.7	92.8	110.9	102.7	96.3	99.7
04	MASONRY	171.5	99.1	126.9	164.3	82.1	113.7	164.7	82.1	113.8	171.6	90.3	121.5	174.1	92.1	123.7	145.3	102.3	118.8
05	METALS	120.2	107.7	116.3	101.1	87.6	97.0	101.1	87.7	97.0	103.1	90.1	99.1	103.8	93.9	100.8	111.7	98.6	107.7
06	WOOD, PLASTICS & COMPOSITES	99.5	93.2	96.0	130.9	85.2	105.8	130.9	85.2	105.8	102.9	87.0	94.1	118.5	88.1	101.8	107.9	89.1	97.6
07	THERMAL & MOISTURE PROTECTION	124.0	101.7	114.8	111.6	90.3	102.8	111.6	90.3	102.8	127.9	87.7	111.2	118.1	93.7	108.0	115.2	101.4	109.4
08	OPENINGS	86.7	93.3	88.2	91.7	72.9	87.4	91.7	77.5	88.5	88.4	84.2	87.5	91.7	86.1	90.4	83.2	85.9	84.5
0920	Plaster & Gypsum Board	123.7	92.6	103.1	114.5	84.7	94.7	144.8	84.7	104.8	102.2	86.2	91.6	176.2	87.8	117.4	105.6	88.7	94.4
0950, 0980	Ceilings & Acoustic Treatment	126.1	92.6	103.8	99.5	84.7	89.6	99.5	84.7	89.6	99.5	86.2	90.6	114.7	87.8	96.8	101.4	88.7	93.0
0960	Flooring	116.1	97.8	110.8	119.2	90.9	111.0	119.2	90.9	111.0	117.8	52.0	98.8	119.2	91.0	111.0	106.4	97.8	103.9
0970, 0990	Wall Finishes & Painting/Coating	106.6	101.8	103.7	112.9	88.9	98.8	112.9	88.9	98.8	112.9	81.3	94.3	112.9	84.2	96.0	106.8	96.9	101.0
09	FINISHES	116.2	95.6	105.0	108.1	87.0	96.6	114.4	87.0	98.5	108.6	81.2	93.6	120.6	88.9	103.3	101.7	92.5	96.7
COVERS	DIVS. 10 - 14, 25, 28, 41, 43, 44, 46	131.1	94.6	122.9	131.1	81.0	119.8	131.1	81.0	119.8	131.1	90.4	121.9	131.1	69.1	117.1	131.1	93.3	122.6
21, 22, 23	FIRE SUPPRESSION, PLUMBING & HVAC	105.4	88.4	97.9	103.2	88.5	96.7	103.2	88.5	96.7	103.2	90.0	98.2	103.5	99.2	101.6	104.4	91.9	98.9
26, 27, 3370	ELECTRICAL, COMMUNICATIONS & UTIL.	105.8	99.7	102.5	112.3	70.5	90.2	111.1	70.6	89.6	114.4	80.2	96.3	111.8	88.9	99.6	109.6	102.7	106.0
MF2014	WEIGHTED AVERAGE	114.3	98.1	107.1	110.2	84.9	99.0	110.6	85.1	99.3	112.7	88.8	102.2	114.1	93.1	104.8	107.8	97.0	103.0

CANADA

DIVISION		LAVAL, QUEBEC MAT.	INST.	TOTAL	LETHBRIDGE, ALBERTA MAT.	INST.	TOTAL	LLOYDMINSTER, ALBERTA MAT.	INST.	TOTAL	LONDON, ONTARIO MAT.	INST.	TOTAL	MEDICINE HAT, ALBERTA MAT.	INST.	TOTAL	MONCTON, NEW BRUNSWICK MAT.	INST.	TOTAL
015433	CONTRACTOR EQUIPMENT		104.4	104.4		106.8	106.8		106.8	106.8		118.6	118.6		106.8	106.8		103.8	103.8
0241, 31 - 34	SITE & INFRASTRUCTURE, DEMOLITION	98.9	100.0	99.6	116.2	102.8	106.8	116.1	102.1	106.4	107.6	112.7	111.1	114.8	102.2	106.0	104.7	97.0	99.3
0310	Concrete Forming & Accessories	131.9	85.1	91.4	124.8	94.0	98.1	122.9	83.9	89.2	121.8	92.3	96.3	124.8	83.9	89.4	104.8	64.8	70.2
0320	Concrete Reinforcing	154.2	75.4	114.2	158.6	78.9	118.1	158.6	78.9	118.1	138.0	99.6	118.5	158.6	78.9	118.1	147.5	65.3	105.8
0330	Cast-in-Place Concrete	115.0	93.5	106.8	139.2	104.4	125.9	129.1	100.6	118.3	124.3	103.4	116.3	129.1	100.6	118.3	113.6	77.8	100.0
03	CONCRETE	117.9	86.7	103.4	129.7	95.1	113.7	124.7	89.3	108.3	119.3	98.1	109.5	124.9	89.3	108.4	114.7	70.7	94.3
04	MASONRY	164.6	82.1	113.8	182.3	88.5	124.6	163.7	81.9	113.3	175.7	103.3	131.1	163.7	81.9	113.3	161.3	63.4	101.0
05	METALS	101.0	87.6	96.9	121.8	90.7	112.3	103.1	90.5	99.2	120.2	105.9	115.8	103.2	90.5	99.3	103.7	86.0	98.3
06	WOOD, PLASTICS & COMPOSITES	131.0	85.2	105.9	118.0	93.6	104.6	114.6	83.6	97.5	106.2	90.3	97.5	118.0	83.6	96.1	98.7	64.4	79.8
07	THERMAL & MOISTURE PROTECTION	112.2	90.3	103.1	124.0	95.4	112.1	120.5	90.7	108.1	125.4	101.4	115.4	127.2	90.7	112.0	114.3	67.0	94.7
08	OPENINGS	91.7	72.9	87.4	91.7	83.1	89.7	91.7	77.6	88.5	81.0	89.7	83.0	91.7	77.6	88.5	86.4	62.2	80.9
0920	Plaster & Gypsum Board	114.8	84.7	94.8	106.7	93.0	97.6	102.7	82.7	89.4	131.6	89.7	103.7	105.0	82.7	90.2	126.6	63.3	84.5
0950, 0980	Ceilings & Acoustic Treatment	99.5	84.7	89.6	107.1	93.0	97.7	99.5	82.7	88.3	132.0	89.7	103.8	99.5	82.7	88.3	108.8	63.3	78.5
0960	Flooring	119.2	90.9	111.0	119.2	88.7	110.3	119.2	88.7	110.3	113.3	97.8	108.8	119.2	88.7	110.3	105.2	68.7	94.6
0970, 0990	Wall Finishes & Painting/Coating	112.9	88.9	98.8	112.8	102.5	106.8	113.0	79.9	93.5	113.2	103.9	107.8	112.8	79.9	93.5	113.9	52.2	77.7
09	FINISHES	108.2	87.0	96.6	109.7	94.2	101.2	107.7	84.2	94.8	119.0	94.3	105.5	107.8	84.2	94.9	107.6	64.2	83.9
COVERS	DIVS. 10 - 14, 25, 28, 41, 43, 44, 46	131.1	81.0	119.8	131.1	94.9	122.9	131.1	91.5	122.2	131.1	94.4	122.8	131.1	91.5	122.2	131.1	63.5	115.9
21, 22, 23	FIRE SUPPRESSION, PLUMBING & HVAC	104.5	88.5	97.4	103.5	94.5	99.5	103.5	94.4	99.5	105.4	90.3	98.7	103.2	91.1	97.8	103.2	70.4	88.7
26, 27, 3370	ELECTRICAL, COMMUNICATIONS & UTIL.	109.6	70.5	88.9	106.9	83.8	94.6	104.7	83.8	93.6	104.9	102.7	103.7	104.7	83.8	93.6	116.5	62.3	87.8
MF2014	WEIGHTED AVERAGE	110.5	84.9	99.2	116.7	92.3	105.9	111.5	88.9	101.5	114.3	98.5	107.3	111.7	88.2	101.3	110.1	70.6	92.6

CANADA

DIVISION		MONTREAL, QUEBEC MAT.	INST.	TOTAL	MOOSE JAW, SASKATCHEWAN MAT.	INST.	TOTAL	NEW GLASGOW, NOVA SCOTIA MAT.	INST.	TOTAL	NEWCASTLE, NEW BRUNSWICK MAT.	INST.	TOTAL	NORTH BAY, ONTARIO MAT.	INST.	TOTAL	OSHAWA, ONTARIO MAT.	INST.	TOTAL
015433	CONTRACTOR EQUIPMENT		120.1	120.1		102.8	102.8		103.6	103.6		103.8	103.8		104.3	104.3		106.5	106.5
0241, 31 - 34	SITE & INFRASTRUCTURE, DEMOLITION	112.3	110.7	111.2	116.3	96.2	102.2	120.4	98.5	105.1	105.3	96.6	99.2	136.3	100.5	111.3	109.1	105.1	106.3
0310	Concrete Forming & Accessories	121.4	92.4	96.3	107.5	58.7	65.3	113.6	73.0	78.5	104.8	62.4	68.1	149.2	86.1	94.7	119.8	91.0	94.9
0320	Concrete Reinforcing	141.2	93.5	117.0	111.9	63.9	87.5	179.7	49.6	113.7	147.5	59.9	103.1	212.2	88.3	149.3	155.0	94.4	124.2
0330	Cast-in-Place Concrete	131.7	98.5	119.0	125.3	67.9	103.4	140.2	71.3	114.0	118.0	59.9	95.9	135.1	85.8	116.3	134.4	88.5	116.9
03	CONCRETE	123.2	95.4	110.3	109.8	63.8	88.5	150.7	69.2	112.9	116.8	62.1	91.4	152.5	86.8	122.1	125.1	91.0	109.3
04	MASONRY	171.6	91.7	122.4	162.4	60.7	99.7	223.2	70.5	129.2	161.6	61.8	100.1	229.5	88.1	142.4	148.3	94.7	115.3
05	METALS	124.5	102.4	117.8	99.9	77.4	93.0	115.7	78.3	104.3	103.7	75.8	95.2	116.5	93.6	109.5	103.1	97.2	101.3
06	WOOD, PLASTICS & COMPOSITES	104.2	93.0	98.0	100.4	57.3	76.7	117.9	72.7	93.0	98.7	62.4	78.7	154.4	86.6	117.1	114.5	90.0	101.0
07	THERMAL & MOISTURE PROTECTION	118.4	98.5	110.1	111.0	64.4	91.7	138.8	72.5	111.3	114.3	62.6	92.9	145.6	88.7	122.0	116.1	93.2	106.6
08	OPENINGS	86.3	80.3	84.9	87.6	55.1	80.2	92.8	65.7	86.7	86.4	54.8	79.3	100.8	83.9	97.0	88.5	90.7	89.0
0920	Plaster & Gypsum Board	121.2	92.2	101.9	99.6	56.1	70.7	140.9	71.9	95.0	126.6	61.2	83.2	134.7	86.2	102.4	108.8	89.7	96.1
0950, 0980	Ceilings & Acoustic Treatment	133.8	92.2	106.1	99.5	56.1	70.6	114.4	71.9	86.1	108.8	61.2	77.1	114.4	86.2	95.6	98.0	89.7	92.5
0960	Flooring	117.1	93.1	110.1	108.9	56.7	93.8	114.2	62.3	99.2	105.2	67.1	94.1	138.8	91.0	124.9	109.4	100.4	106.8
0970, 0990	Wall Finishes & Painting/Coating	108.2	105.2	106.4	112.9	64.9	84.7	121.1	63.1	87.0	113.9	51.0	76.9	121.1	90.4	103.1	106.8	111.6	109.6
09	FINISHES	116.8	94.8	104.8	104.0	58.7	79.2	117.3	70.3	91.6	107.6	62.4	82.9	124.5	87.9	104.5	103.0	94.8	98.5
COVERS	DIVS. 10 - 14, 25, 28, 41, 43, 44, 46	131.1	85.4	120.8	131.1	61.5	115.4	131.1	65.0	116.2	131.1	63.6	115.5	131.1	67.9	116.8	131.1	93.0	122.5
21, 22, 23	FIRE SUPPRESSION, PLUMBING & HVAC	105.2	80.9	94.5	103.5	73.9	90.4	103.3	83.6	94.5	103.2	68.1	87.6	103.3	97.1	100.5	104.4	102.7	103.7
26, 27, 3370	ELECTRICAL, COMMUNICATIONS & UTIL.	106.4	86.2	95.7	113.3	60.9	85.5	115.6	63.5	87.9	111.8	60.4	84.5	115.8	90.1	102.2	110.7	92.5	101.1
MF2014	WEIGHTED AVERAGE	115.7	91.5	105.0	108.7	67.9	90.7	122.4	74.7	101.4	109.9	66.8	90.9	125.5	90.8	110.2	110.5	96.4	104.2

CANADA

DIVISION		OTTAWA, ONTARIO MAT.	INST.	TOTAL	OWEN SOUND, ONTARIO MAT.	INST.	TOTAL	PETERBOROUGH, ONTARIO MAT.	INST.	TOTAL	PORTAGE LA PRAIRIE, MANITOBA MAT.	INST.	TOTAL	PRINCE ALBERT, SASKATCHEWAN MAT.	INST.	TOTAL	PRINCE GEORGE, BRITISH COLUMBIA MAT.	INST.	TOTAL
015433	CONTRACTOR EQUIPMENT		119.1	119.1		104.3	104.3		104.3	104.3		106.6	106.6		102.8	102.8		107.8	107.8
0241, 31 - 34	SITE & INFRASTRUCTURE, DEMOLITION	107.1	113.2	111.3	118.8	100.9	106.3	118.8	100.8	106.2	117.4	99.6	105.0	111.7	96.3	101.0	124.8	103.8	110.2
0310	Concrete Forming & Accessories	123.1	92.4	96.5	126.3	84.7	90.3	125.6	87.2	92.4	125.0	70.1	78.0	107.5	58.5	65.1	113.0	83.4	87.4
0320	Concrete Reinforcing	130.1	99.6	114.6	177.8	90.4	133.5	171.4	88.8	129.5	158.6	56.7	106.9	116.9	63.9	90.0	114.3	78.9	96.4
0330	Cast-in-Place Concrete	132.3	105.4	122.0	159.5	81.8	129.9	139.8	87.4	119.8	129.1	74.5	108.3	113.6	67.9	96.1	125.7	98.2	115.3
03	CONCRETE	122.2	98.9	111.4	144.2	85.2	116.8	131.7	88.0	111.4	118.6	70.5	96.3	104.7	63.7	85.7	136.5	88.2	114.1
04	MASONRY	170.3	105.9	130.6	169.9	93.6	122.9	168.3	94.7	123.0	166.9	64.2	103.7	161.5	60.7	99.4	173.7	90.3	122.3
05	METALS	122.9	106.6	117.9	108.3	94.4	104.0	102.5	94.1	100.0	103.2	80.9	96.4	100.0	77.2	93.0	103.1	90.1	99.1
06	WOOD, PLASTICS & COMPOSITES	105.7	89.1	96.6	118.3	83.3	99.1	120.2	85.3	101.0	117.9	72.1	92.7	100.4	57.3	76.7	102.9	79.9	90.3
07	THERMAL & MOISTURE PROTECTION	128.0	102.6	117.5	114.2	89.6	104.0	118.3	94.5	108.4	111.5	73.2	95.6	110.9	63.3	91.1	121.9	86.9	107.4
08	OPENINGS	90.9	89.0	90.4	92.6	83.3	90.5	90.4	85.7	89.3	91.7	64.2	85.4	86.5	55.1	79.4	88.4	80.3	86.6
0920	Plaster & Gypsum Board	136.2	88.5	104.5	151.5	82.8	105.9	116.6	84.8	95.5	104.6	70.9	82.2	99.6	56.1	70.7	102.2	78.9	86.7
0950, 0980	Ceilings & Acoustic Treatment	131.1	88.5	102.7	92.7	82.8	86.1	99.5	84.8	89.7	99.5	70.9	80.4	99.5	56.1	70.6	99.5	78.9	85.8
0960	Flooring	107.9	93.2	103.7	123.9	92.3	114.8	119.2	91.0	111.0	119.2	65.5	103.6	108.9	56.7	93.8	114.5	71.3	102.0
0970, 0990	Wall Finishes & Painting/Coating	114.0	98.5	104.9	107.7	89.1	96.8	112.9	92.7	101.0	113.0	57.5	80.4	112.9	55.3	79.1	112.9	81.3	94.3
09	FINISHES	119.1	92.8	104.7	112.3	86.7	98.3	109.1	88.5	97.9	107.8	68.7	86.4	104.0	57.6	78.7	107.6	80.4	92.7
COVERS	DIVS. 10 - 14, 25, 28, 41, 43, 44, 46	131.1	93.0	122.5	139.2	68.3	123.2	131.1	69.3	117.2	131.1	64.0	116.0	131.1	61.5	115.4	131.1	89.6	121.8
21, 22, 23	FIRE SUPPRESSION, PLUMBING & HVAC	105.5	92.0	99.5	103.1	97.0	100.4	103.2	100.6	102.1	103.2	82.4	94.0	103.5	66.6	87.2	103.2	92.0	98.2
26, 27, 3370	ELECTRICAL, COMMUNICATIONS & UTIL.	107.8	103.5	105.5	117.3	88.9	102.2	111.1	89.7	99.8	113.0	58.9	84.3	113.3	60.9	85.5	111.3	80.2	94.8
MF2014	WEIGHTED AVERAGE	116.3	99.2	108.8	117.3	90.9	105.6	113.0	92.7	104.1	111.4	73.4	94.6	107.8	66.1	89.4	113.8	88.1	102.4

City Cost Indexes

CANADA

DIVISION		QUEBEC CITY, QUEBEC MAT.	INST.	TOTAL	RED DEER, ALBERTA MAT.	INST.	TOTAL	REGINA, SASKATCHEWAN MAT.	INST.	TOTAL	RIMOUSKI, QUEBEC MAT.	INST.	TOTAL	ROUYN-NORANDA, QUEBEC MAT.	INST.	TOTAL	SAINT HYACINTHE, QUEBEC MAT.	INST.	TOTAL
015433	CONTRACTOR EQUIPMENT		120.7	120.7		106.8	106.8		121.5	121.5		104.4	104.4		104.4	104.4		104.4	104.4
0241, 31 - 34	SITE & INFRASTRUCTURE, DEMOLITION	113.9	110.1	111.2	114.8	102.2	106.0	120.9	112.3	114.9	98.8	99.5	99.3	98.4	100.0	99.5	98.9	100.0	99.6
0310	Concrete Forming & Accessories	123.7	92.6	96.8	139.6	83.9	91.4	120.9	89.1	93.4	131.6	92.0	97.3	131.6	85.1	91.4	131.6	85.1	91.4
0320	Concrete Reinforcing	145.8	93.5	119.3	158.6	78.9	118.1	144.5	87.8	115.7	110.0	93.4	101.6	154.2	75.4	114.2	154.2	75.4	114.2
0330	Cast-in-Place Concrete	127.6	98.7	116.6	129.1	100.6	118.3	142.6	93.8	124.0	117.0	97.2	109.5	111.3	93.5	104.5	115.0	93.5	106.8
03	CONCRETE	122.0	95.7	109.8	125.7	89.3	108.8	130.3	91.3	112.2	113.0	94.1	104.3	116.0	86.7	102.4	117.8	86.7	103.4
04	MASONRY	166.1	91.7	120.3	163.7	81.9	113.5	188.8	91.2	128.7	164.1	91.7	119.5	164.3	82.1	113.7	164.6	82.1	113.8
05	METALS	124.5	103.8	118.2	103.2	90.5	99.3	126.5	100.6	118.6	100.7	92.5	98.2	101.1	87.6	97.0	101.1	87.6	97.0
06	WOOD, PLASTICS & COMPOSITES	112.2	93.0	101.6	118.0	83.6	99.1	105.6	89.7	96.8	130.9	92.6	109.8	130.9	85.2	105.8	130.9	85.2	105.8
07	THERMAL & MOISTURE PROTECTION	118.7	98.6	110.4	137.2	90.7	117.9	127.1	87.3	110.6	111.6	98.8	106.3	111.6	90.3	102.8	111.9	90.3	102.9
08	OPENINGS	89.2	88.0	89.0	91.7	77.6	88.5	87.8	78.9	85.8	91.2	78.1	88.3	91.7	72.9	87.4	91.7	72.9	87.4
0920	Plaster & Gypsum Board	123.6	92.2	102.7	105.0	82.7	90.2	125.8	88.9	101.3	144.6	92.2	109.8	114.3	84.7	94.6	114.3	84.7	94.6
0950, 0980	Ceilings & Acoustic Treatment	132.9	92.2	105.8	99.5	82.7	88.3	139.1	88.9	105.7	98.6	92.2	94.4	98.6	84.7	89.3	98.6	84.7	89.3
0960	Flooring	117.5	93.1	110.4	121.5	88.7	112.0	120.1	97.8	113.7	120.6	90.9	112.0	119.2	90.9	111.0	119.2	90.9	111.0
0970, 0990	Wall Finishes & Painting/Coating	126.4	105.2	114.0	112.8	79.9	93.5	119.2	72.2	91.6	116.2	105.2	109.7	112.9	88.9	98.8	112.9	88.9	98.8
09	FINISHES	118.7	94.8	105.6	108.5	84.2	95.2	126.0	89.8	106.2	112.9	94.1	102.6	107.9	87.0	96.5	107.9	87.0	96.5
COVERS	DIVS. 10 - 14, 25, 28, 41, 43, 44, 46	131.1	85.4	120.8	131.1	91.5	122.2	131.1	71.2	117.6	131.1	84.5	120.6	131.1	81.0	119.8	131.1	81.0	119.8
21, 22, 23	FIRE SUPPRESSION, PLUMBING & HVAC	105.2	81.0	94.5	103.2	91.1	97.8	104.9	82.5	95.0	103.2	80.8	93.3	103.2	88.5	96.7	100.3	88.5	95.1
26, 27, 3370	ELECTRICAL, COMMUNICATIONS & UTIL.	109.7	86.2	97.2	104.7	83.8	93.6	112.9	89.7	100.6	111.1	86.2	97.9	111.1	70.5	89.6	111.8	70.5	89.9
MF2014	WEIGHTED AVERAGE	116.2	92.0	105.5	112.1	88.2	101.6	119.8	90.2	106.7	110.0	89.3	100.9	110.1	84.9	98.9	109.8	84.9	98.8

CANADA

DIVISION		SAINT JOHN, NEW BRUNSWICK MAT.	INST.	TOTAL	SARNIA, ONTARIO MAT.	INST.	TOTAL	SASKATOON, SASKATCHEWAN MAT.	INST.	TOTAL	SAULT STE MARIE, ONTARIO MAT.	INST.	TOTAL	SHERBROOKE, QUEBEC MAT.	INST.	TOTAL	SOREL, QUEBEC MAT.	INST.	TOTAL
015433	CONTRACTOR EQUIPMENT		103.8	103.8		104.3	104.3		102.8	102.8		104.3	104.3		104.4	104.4		104.4	104.4
0241, 31 - 34	SITE & INFRASTRUCTURE, DEMOLITION	105.4	98.4	100.5	117.3	100.9	105.9	112.5	98.4	102.7	107.1	100.5	102.5	98.9	100.0	99.7	99.0	100.0	99.7
0310	Concrete Forming & Accessories	125.7	68.1	75.9	124.3	94.3	98.4	107.1	88.7	91.2	113.3	90.3	93.4	131.6	85.1	91.4	131.6	85.2	91.5
0320	Concrete Reinforcing	147.5	65.8	106.0	122.0	90.2	105.9	119.6	87.7	103.4	110.0	88.9	99.3	154.2	75.4	114.2	145.8	75.4	110.1
0330	Cast-in-Place Concrete	116.3	79.6	102.3	129.0	100.9	118.2	124.3	91.9	111.9	115.9	86.0	104.5	115.0	93.5	106.8	115.9	93.6	107.4
03	CONCRETE	117.4	72.8	96.7	119.9	96.0	108.8	111.1	89.8	101.2	105.3	88.9	97.7	117.8	86.7	103.4	117.2	86.8	103.1
04	MASONRY	183.0	72.8	115.1	179.9	97.4	129.1	172.1	91.1	122.3	165.1	96.9	123.1	164.6	82.1	113.8	164.7	82.1	113.8
05	METALS	103.6	87.4	98.6	102.5	94.5	100.0	97.8	89.6	95.3	101.7	94.8	99.6	100.9	87.6	96.9	101.1	87.7	97.0
06	WOOD, PLASTICS & COMPOSITES	120.8	66.3	90.9	119.1	93.6	105.1	97.9	89.3	93.2	107.0	91.5	98.5	130.9	85.2	105.8	130.9	85.2	105.8
07	THERMAL & MOISTURE PROTECTION	114.6	73.7	97.6	118.4	98.2	110.0	110.6	86.7	100.7	117.1	93.4	107.3	111.6	90.3	102.8	111.6	90.3	102.8
08	OPENINGS	86.3	62.2	80.9	92.9	89.6	92.1	87.1	78.7	85.2	84.7	87.9	85.4	91.7	72.9	87.4	91.7	77.5	88.5
0920	Plaster & Gypsum Board	139.3	65.3	90.1	139.9	93.4	109.0	115.6	88.9	97.9	107.8	91.2	96.8	114.3	84.7	94.6	144.6	84.7	104.8
0950, 0980	Ceilings & Acoustic Treatment	113.8	65.3	81.5	103.7	93.4	96.8	119.7	88.9	99.2	99.5	91.2	94.0	98.6	84.7	89.3	98.6	84.7	89.3
0960	Flooring	117.4	68.7	103.3	119.2	99.5	113.5	111.4	97.8	107.5	111.8	96.4	107.4	119.2	90.9	111.0	119.2	90.9	111.0
0970, 0990	Wall Finishes & Painting/Coating	113.9	83.0	95.7	112.9	104.8	108.1	116.6	90.2	101.1	112.9	97.0	103.6	112.9	88.9	98.8	112.9	88.9	98.8
09	FINISHES	114.1	69.4	89.6	113.3	96.8	104.3	112.2	91.5	100.9	105.0	92.5	98.2	107.9	87.0	96.5	112.2	87.0	98.4
COVERS	DIVS. 10 - 14, 25, 28, 41, 43, 44, 46	131.1	64.8	116.1	131.1	70.8	117.5	131.1	70.7	117.5	131.1	92.0	122.3	131.1	81.0	119.8	131.1	81.0	119.8
21, 22, 23	FIRE SUPPRESSION, PLUMBING & HVAC	103.2	80.5	93.1	103.2	106.7	104.7	104.6	82.4	94.8	103.2	94.8	99.5	103.5	88.5	96.8	103.2	88.5	96.7
26, 27, 3370	ELECTRICAL, COMMUNICATIONS & UTIL.	119.2	88.9	103.1	113.9	91.9	102.2	112.0	89.7	100.2	112.7	90.1	100.7	111.1	70.5	89.6	111.1	70.6	89.6
MF2014	WEIGHTED AVERAGE	112.5	78.8	97.6	113.0	97.2	106.0	109.6	88.0	100.1	108.2	93.3	101.6	110.4	84.9	99.1	110.6	85.1	99.3

CANADA

DIVISION		ST CATHARINES, ONTARIO MAT.	INST.	TOTAL	ST JEROME, QUEBEC MAT.	INST.	TOTAL	ST JOHNS, NEWFOUNDLAND MAT.	INST.	TOTAL	SUDBURY, ONTARIO MAT.	INST.	TOTAL	SUMMERSIDE, PRINCE EDWARD ISLAND MAT.	INST.	TOTAL	SYDNEY, NOVA SCOTIA MAT.	INST.	TOTAL
015433	CONTRACTOR EQUIPMENT		104.3	104.3		104.4	104.4		117.3	117.3		104.3	104.3		103.6	103.6		103.6	103.6
0241, 31 - 34	SITE & INFRASTRUCTURE, DEMOLITION	98.2	102.6	101.3	98.4	100.0	99.5	121.2	108.1	112.0	98.4	102.2	101.0	130.9	95.8	106.4	116.0	98.5	103.8
0310	Concrete Forming & Accessories	112.1	97.6	99.5	131.6	85.1	91.4	124.9	90.2	94.9	107.9	92.4	94.5	113.9	56.4	64.2	113.6	73.0	78.5
0320	Concrete Reinforcing	98.7	99.6	99.2	154.2	75.4	114.2	173.2	77.5	124.6	99.5	98.9	99.2	177.3	48.4	111.8	179.7	49.6	113.7
0330	Cast-in-Place Concrete	111.0	103.0	108.0	111.3	93.5	104.5	140.8	101.8	125.9	111.9	99.5	107.2	133.1	58.3	104.6	108.2	71.3	94.1
03	CONCRETE	100.1	99.9	100.0	116.0	86.7	102.4	136.5	92.9	116.3	100.4	96.1	98.4	159.3	56.8	111.8	135.2	69.2	104.6
04	MASONRY	144.9	104.7	120.1	164.3	82.1	113.7	182.3	96.8	129.6	144.9	100.9	117.8	222.4	59.0	121.8	220.5	70.5	128.2
05	METALS	103.0	98.6	101.7	101.1	87.6	97.0	129.9	98.7	120.4	102.5	96.5	100.7	115.7	71.4	102.2	115.7	78.3	104.3
06	WOOD, PLASTICS & COMPOSITES	105.7	97.1	101.0	130.9	85.2	105.8	105.0	88.3	95.9	101.9	91.5	96.2	118.3	55.9	84.0	117.9	72.7	93.0
07	THERMAL & MOISTURE PROTECTION	115.1	106.7	111.6	111.6	90.3	102.8	140.3	99.9	123.5	114.5	100.0	108.5	138.0	61.4	106.2	138.8	72.5	111.3
08	OPENINGS	82.7	94.1	85.3	91.7	72.9	87.4	87.3	78.1	85.2	83.3	88.4	84.5	104.9	48.7	92.1	92.8	65.7	86.7
0920	Plaster & Gypsum Board	97.0	97.0	97.0	114.3	84.7	94.6	136.8	87.5	104.1	98.8	91.2	93.8	141.5	54.6	83.8	140.9	71.9	95.0
0950, 0980	Ceilings & Acoustic Treatment	98.0	97.0	97.4	98.6	84.7	89.3	124.7	87.5	100.0	93.0	91.2	91.8	114.4	54.6	74.6	114.4	71.9	86.1
0960	Flooring	105.1	94.6	102.0	119.2	90.9	111.0	118.0	54.2	99.5	103.2	96.4	101.2	114.3	58.5	98.1	114.2	62.3	99.2
0970, 0990	Wall Finishes & Painting/Coating	106.8	115.0	111.6	112.9	88.9	98.8	116.6	105.0	109.8	106.8	97.9	101.6	121.1	42.4	74.9	121.1	63.1	87.0
09	FINISHES	99.5	99.0	99.2	107.9	87.0	96.5	121.6	85.0	101.6	98.1	93.6	95.6	118.4	55.6	84.1	117.3	70.3	91.6
COVERS	DIVS. 10 - 14, 25, 28, 41, 43, 44, 46	131.1	72.5	117.9	131.1	81.0	119.8	131.1	71.3	117.6	131.1	93.4	122.6	131.1	61.0	115.3	131.1	65.0	116.2
21, 22, 23	FIRE SUPPRESSION, PLUMBING & HVAC	104.4	91.7	98.8	103.2	88.5	96.7	105.0	87.2	97.1	103.1	91.1	97.8	103.3	61.8	84.9	103.3	83.6	94.5
26, 27, 3370	ELECTRICAL, COMMUNICATIONS & UTIL.	111.1	103.5	107.1	111.7	70.5	89.9	115.5	88.2	101.0	111.1	104.0	107.3	114.7	51.3	81.1	115.6	63.5	87.9
MF2014	WEIGHTED AVERAGE	105.9	98.2	102.5	110.1	84.9	99.0	121.1	91.0	107.8	105.5	96.4	101.5	125.1	61.5	97.0	120.3	74.7	100.2

City Cost Indexes

CANADA

DIVISION		THUNDER BAY, ONTARIO			TIMMINS, ONTARIO			TORONTO, ONTARIO			TROIS RIVIERES, QUEBEC			TRURO, NOVA SCOTIA			VANCOUVER, BRITISH COLUMBIA		
		MAT.	INST.	TOTAL	MAT.	INST.	TOTAL	MAT.	INST.	TOTAL	MAT.	INST.	TOTAL	MAT.	INST.	TOTAL	MAT.	INST.	TOTAL
015433	CONTRACTOR EQUIPMENT		104.3	104.3		104.3	104.3		118.6	118.6		104.4	104.4		103.6	103.6		134.3	134.3
0241, 31 - 34	SITE & INFRASTRUCTURE, DEMOLITION	103.1	102.4	102.6	118.8	100.5	106.0	123.7	113.4	116.5	116.3	100.0	104.9	103.3	98.5	100.0	113.0	122.7	119.8
0310	Concrete Forming & Accessories	119.8	95.8	99.0	125.6	86.1	91.5	120.9	103.7	106.0	157.2	85.2	94.9	97.4	73.1	76.3	123.8	93.9	98.0
0320	Concrete Reinforcing	88.2	98.4	93.4	171.4	88.3	129.2	137.8	102.8	120.1	179.7	75.4	126.8	145.8	49.6	97.0	128.1	84.4	105.9
0330	Cast-in-Place Concrete	122.2	102.2	114.6	139.8	85.8	119.2	115.7	114.8	115.3	112.0	93.6	105.0	145.1	71.3	117.0	126.4	101.9	117.0
03	CONCRETE	107.7	98.5	103.4	131.7	86.8	110.9	115.0	107.8	111.7	137.6	86.8	114.0	130.7	69.2	102.2	121.6	96.2	109.8
04	MASONRY	145.5	104.9	120.5	168.3	88.1	118.9	171.3	111.0	134.2	224.8	82.1	136.9	163.9	70.5	106.4	166.2	96.1	123.0
05	METALS	103.0	96.7	101.1	102.5	93.6	99.8	122.1	108.2	117.8	114.9	87.7	106.6	101.8	78.3	94.6	124.5	107.1	119.2
06	WOOD, PLASTICS & COMPOSITES	114.5	94.4	103.5	120.2	86.6	101.7	103.6	101.5	102.4	168.7	85.2	122.8	91.0	72.7	80.9	105.0	91.5	97.6
07	THERMAL & MOISTURE PROTECTION	115.4	102.6	110.1	118.3	88.7	106.0	133.5	110.4	123.9	137.1	90.3	117.7	112.9	72.5	96.1	131.8	92.1	115.3
08	OPENINGS	81.9	91.4	84.1	90.4	83.9	88.9	85.2	99.9	88.6	102.5	77.5	96.8	84.5	65.7	80.3	84.2	87.7	85.0
0920	Plaster & Gypsum Board	124.9	94.2	104.5	116.6	86.2	96.4	119.1	101.2	107.2	169.3	84.7	113.1	122.4	71.9	88.8	108.9	90.3	96.5
0950, 0980	Ceilings & Acoustic Treatment	93.0	94.2	93.8	99.5	86.2	90.6	120.8	101.2	107.8	113.6	84.7	94.3	99.5	71.9	81.1	129.9	90.3	103.5
0960	Flooring	109.4	101.3	107.0	119.2	91.0	111.0	111.6	103.7	109.3	138.8	90.9	124.9	100.7	62.3	89.5	127.5	91.9	117.2
0970, 0990	Wall Finishes & Painting/Coating	106.8	99.0	102.2	112.9	90.4	99.7	104.5	111.6	108.7	121.1	88.9	102.2	112.9	63.1	83.6	114.8	94.9	103.1
09	FINISHES	103.9	97.2	100.2	109.1	87.9	97.5	112.7	104.9	108.2	128.3	87.0	105.7	103.8	70.3	85.5	120.1	93.7	105.7
COVERS	DIVS. 10 - 14, 25, 28, 41, 43, 44, 46	131.1	72.7	117.9	131.1	67.9	116.8	131.1	97.9	123.6	131.1	81.0	119.8	131.1	65.0	116.2	131.1	95.6	123.1
21, 22, 23	FIRE SUPPRESSION, PLUMBING & HVAC	104.4	92.0	98.9	103.2	97.1	100.5	105.1	100.0	102.8	103.3	88.5	96.7	103.2	83.6	94.5	105.3	84.6	96.1
26, 27, 3370	ELECTRICAL, COMMUNICATIONS & UTIL.	109.6	102.1	105.7	112.7	90.1	100.7	105.6	105.8	105.7	115.9	70.6	91.8	110.8	63.5	85.7	104.5	81.6	92.3
MF2014	WEIGHTED AVERAGE	107.2	97.2	102.8	113.2	90.8	103.3	114.5	105.6	110.6	123.0	85.1	106.3	110.6	74.7	94.8	115.6	93.9	106.0

CANADA

DIVISION		VICTORIA, BRITISH COLUMBIA			WHITEHORSE, YUKON			WINDSOR, ONTARIO			WINNIPEG, MANITOBA			YARMOUTH, NOVA SCOTIA			YELLOWKNIFE, NWT		
		MAT.	INST.	TOTAL	MAT.	INST.	TOTAL	MAT.	INST.	TOTAL	MAT.	INST.	TOTAL	MAT.	INST.	TOTAL	MAT.	INST.	TOTAL
015433	CONTRACTOR EQUIPMENT		111.1	111.1		126.7	126.7		104.3	104.3		121.4	121.4		103.6	103.6		124.9	124.9
0241, 31 - 34	SITE & INFRASTRUCTURE, DEMOLITION	123.5	108.5	113.0	144.9	113.4	122.9	94.6	102.4	100.0	113.4	109.4	110.6	120.2	98.5	105.1	157.1	117.7	129.7
0310	Concrete Forming & Accessories	112.2	92.8	95.4	135.0	60.6	70.7	119.8	93.6	97.2	127.9	68.3	76.4	113.6	73.0	78.5	135.5	81.2	88.5
0320	Concrete Reinforcing	117.0	84.2	100.4	163.4	65.8	113.9	96.7	99.5	98.1	151.1	61.8	105.8	179.7	49.6	113.7	159.7	68.4	113.4
0330	Cast-in-Place Concrete	128.8	99.8	117.7	187.5	73.3	144.0	113.7	103.2	109.7	148.6	74.0	120.2	138.8	71.3	113.1	186.9	91.0	150.4
03	CONCRETE	140.0	93.8	118.6	165.9	67.7	120.4	101.6	98.1	100.0	134.5	70.6	104.9	150.0	69.2	112.6	165.2	83.5	127.3
04	MASONRY	175.1	96.1	126.5	255.8	62.3	136.6	145.0	102.9	119.1	185.5	68.3	113.3	223.1	70.5	129.1	251.4	74.0	142.1
05	METALS	99.2	89.9	96.3	131.7	91.1	119.3	103.0	96.6	101.1	128.5	88.6	116.3	115.7	78.3	104.3	129.1	94.1	118.4
06	WOOD, PLASTICS & COMPOSITES	101.7	91.0	95.8	124.1	59.3	88.5	114.5	92.6	102.5	113.0	69.1	88.9	117.9	72.7	93.0	126.2	82.8	102.3
07	THERMAL & MOISTURE PROTECTION	120.4	92.0	108.6	145.5	65.9	112.5	115.2	101.8	109.6	125.6	72.8	103.7	138.8	72.5	111.3	149.5	82.6	121.7
08	OPENINGS	88.6	83.1	87.4	106.2	56.6	95.0	81.7	90.5	83.7	82.1	62.1	77.6	92.8	65.7	86.7	99.0	70.1	92.4
0920	Plaster & Gypsum Board	108.9	90.3	96.5	154.1	57.3	89.8	109.8	92.4	98.2	117.1	67.4	84.1	140.9	71.9	95.0	158.8	81.5	107.4
0950, 0980	Ceilings & Acoustic Treatment	101.9	90.3	94.2	155.4	57.3	90.1	93.0	92.4	92.6	140.6	67.4	91.9	114.4	71.9	86.1	149.2	81.5	104.2
0960	Flooring	117.2	71.3	103.9	133.4	58.3	111.6	109.4	98.6	106.2	115.5	70.4	102.4	114.2	62.3	99.2	131.4	87.6	118.7
0970, 0990	Wall Finishes & Painting/Coating	116.6	92.5	102.4	124.0	56.5	84.4	106.8	99.9	102.8	111.6	55.3	78.5	121.1	63.1	87.0	123.2	80.7	98.2
09	FINISHES	110.8	89.4	99.1	142.4	59.5	97.1	101.5	95.2	98.1	121.1	67.7	91.9	117.3	70.3	91.6	139.0	81.8	107.8
COVERS	DIVS. 10 - 14, 25, 28, 41, 43, 44, 46	131.1	70.5	117.4	131.1	64.0	116.0	131.1	71.7	117.7	131.1	66.2	116.4	131.1	65.0	116.2	131.1	67.5	116.7
21, 22, 23	FIRE SUPPRESSION, PLUMBING & HVAC	103.2	82.6	94.1	104.0	75.2	91.2	104.4	91.3	98.6	105.2	66.0	87.9	103.3	83.6	94.5	103.9	92.0	99.0
26, 27, 3370	ELECTRICAL, COMMUNICATIONS & UTIL.	111.9	81.0	95.5	127.0	61.8	92.4	114.2	105.5	109.6	111.8	66.7	87.9	115.6	63.5	87.9	129.1	83.8	105.0
MF2014	WEIGHTED AVERAGE	113.9	88.8	102.8	134.4	71.9	106.8	106.4	96.9	102.2	119.2	72.7	98.7	122.3	74.7	101.3	133.2	86.9	112.8

Location Factors - Commercial

Costs shown in RSMeans cost data publications are based on national averages for materials and installation. To adjust these costs to a specific location, simply multiply the base cost by the factor and divide by 100 for that city. The data is arranged alphabetically by state and postal zip code numbers. For a city not listed, use the factor for a nearby city with similar economic characteristics.

STATE/ZIP	CITY	MAT.	INST.	TOTAL
ALABAMA				
350-352	Birmingham	97.5	71.7	86.1
354	Tuscaloosa	97.5	72.5	86.4
355	Jasper	97.9	72.1	86.5
356	Decatur	97.5	72.3	86.3
357-358	Huntsville	97.4	71.5	86.0
359	Gadsden	97.5	71.9	86.2
360-361	Montgomery	95.8	73.6	86.0
362	Anniston	95.7	70.0	84.3
363	Dothan	96.1	75.7	87.1
364	Evergreen	95.7	74.3	86.2
365-366	Mobile	96.6	71.2	85.4
367	Selma	95.8	75.2	86.7
368	Phenix City	96.6	74.0	86.6
369	Butler	96.0	74.3	86.4
ALASKA				
995-996	Anchorage	119.7	115.0	117.6
997	Fairbanks	122.3	115.9	119.4
998	Juneau	121.5	115.0	118.6
999	Ketchikan	133.4	115.0	125.3
ARIZONA				
850,853	Phoenix	98.8	72.7	87.3
851,852	Mesa/Tempe	98.4	73.0	87.2
855	Globe	99.3	73.3	87.8
856-857	Tucson	97.2	71.0	85.6
859	Show Low	99.5	73.2	87.9
860	Flagstaff	102.3	72.3	89.1
863	Prescott	99.8	72.8	87.9
864	Kingman	98.3	72.9	87.1
865	Chambers	98.3	76.2	88.6
ARKANSAS				
716	Pine Bluff	98.4	62.9	82.7
717	Camden	96.3	60.9	80.7
718	Texarkana	97.0	61.4	81.3
719	Hot Springs	95.6	61.8	80.7
720-722	Little Rock	96.4	65.7	82.8
723	West Memphis	95.2	66.8	82.6
724	Jonesboro	95.6	63.7	81.5
725	Batesville	93.6	60.9	79.1
726	Harrison	94.9	59.6	79.3
727	Fayetteville	92.4	62.3	79.1
728	Russellville	93.6	59.8	78.7
729	Fort Smith	96.1	60.2	80.2
CALIFORNIA				
900-902	Los Angeles	101.6	128.2	113.4
903-905	Inglewood	97.3	126.7	110.3
906-908	Long Beach	99.0	127.3	111.5
910-912	Pasadena	97.7	126.5	110.4
913-916	Van Nuys	100.9	126.5	112.2
917-918	Alhambra	99.8	127.1	111.8
919-921	San Diego	102.0	118.1	109.1
922	Palm Springs	98.2	125.1	110.1
923-924	San Bernardino	95.8	124.5	108.5
925	Riverside	100.2	125.2	111.2
926-927	Santa Ana	97.9	124.1	109.5
928	Anaheim	100.3	125.5	111.4
930	Oxnard	98.9	125.1	110.4
931	Santa Barbara	98.2	125.2	110.1
932-933	Bakersfield	99.4	122.6	109.6
934	San Luis Obispo	99.3	124.7	110.5
935	Mojave	96.5	122.7	108.1
936-938	Fresno	99.5	126.1	111.3
939	Salinas	100.2	133.2	114.8
940-941	San Francisco	105.6	157.7	128.6
942,956-958	Sacramento	101.0	129.1	113.4
943	Palo Alto	99.4	148.3	121.0
944	San Mateo	101.8	147.3	121.9
945	Vallejo	100.5	139.9	117.9
946	Oakland	103.5	147.7	123.1
947	Berkeley	103.3	147.7	123.0
948	Richmond	102.7	143.7	120.8
949	San Rafael	104.9	148.2	124.0
950	Santa Cruz	105.6	133.6	118.0

STATE/ZIP	CITY	MAT.	INST.	TOTAL
CALIFORNIA (CONT'D)				
951	San Jose	103.6	148.6	123.5
952	Stockton	101.7	128.2	113.4
953	Modesto	101.6	126.6	112.6
954	Santa Rosa	102.3	147.1	122.1
955	Eureka	103.6	130.6	115.5
959	Marysville	102.8	129.2	114.5
960	Redding	109.8	129.2	118.4
961	Susanville	109.5	128.3	117.8
COLORADO				
800-802	Denver	102.2	74.2	89.8
803	Boulder	99.7	76.0	89.2
804	Golden	102.1	73.0	89.2
805	Fort Collins	103.2	74.8	90.7
806	Greeley	100.2	75.7	89.4
807	Fort Morgan	100.3	70.9	87.3
808-809	Colorado Springs	102.1	71.8	88.7
810	Pueblo	101.9	67.4	86.7
811	Alamosa	103.9	67.3	87.8
812	Salida	103.6	66.2	87.0
813	Durango	104.3	68.2	88.3
814	Montrose	103.0	67.7	87.4
815	Grand Junction	106.2	73.2	91.6
816	Glenwood Springs	104.2	67.8	88.1
CONNECTICUT				
060	New Britain	97.1	117.7	106.2
061	Hartford	97.9	117.9	106.8
062	Willimantic	97.7	118.2	106.8
063	New London	94.4	118.1	104.9
064	Meriden	96.3	117.8	105.8
065	New Haven	98.7	117.8	107.1
066	Bridgeport	98.3	118.0	107.0
067	Waterbury	97.8	118.6	107.0
068	Norwalk	97.8	125.2	109.9
069	Stamford	97.9	125.6	110.2
D.C.				
200-205	Washington	100.2	86.1	94.0
DELAWARE				
197	Newark	97.9	111.9	104.1
198	Wilmington	97.0	112.0	103.6
199	Dover	97.6	112.1	104.0
FLORIDA				
320,322	Jacksonville	96.2	67.3	83.4
321	Daytona Beach	96.4	71.8	85.6
323	Tallahassee	97.2	68.2	84.4
324	Panama City	97.7	60.7	81.4
325	Pensacola	100.4	67.1	85.7
326,344	Gainesville	98.0	66.7	84.2
327-328,347	Orlando	98.1	69.1	85.3
329	Melbourne	99.3	72.7	87.5
330-332,340	Miami	97.1	66.9	83.8
333	Fort Lauderdale	96.6	66.4	83.2
334,349	West Palm Beach	95.6	66.2	82.6
335-336,346	Tampa	98.1	69.7	85.5
337	St. Petersburg	100.6	67.5	86.0
338	Lakeland	97.6	68.8	84.9
339,341	Fort Myers	96.9	65.9	83.2
342	Sarasota	99.4	68.5	85.8
GEORGIA				
300-303,399	Atlanta	98.5	75.9	88.5
304	Statesboro	98.9	66.9	84.7
305	Gainesville	97.4	68.3	84.5
306	Athens	96.8	70.0	84.9
307	Dalton	98.5	69.5	85.7
308-309	Augusta	97.1	76.1	87.8
310-312	Macon	94.9	71.8	84.7
313-314	Savannah	96.2	76.8	87.6
315	Waycross	96.3	70.4	84.9
316	Valdosta	96.2	68.0	83.8
317,398	Albany	96.1	73.8	86.3
318-319	Columbus	96.0	76.5	87.4

Location Factors - Commercial

STATE/ZIP	CITY	MAT.	INST.	TOTAL
HAWAII				
967	Hilo	117.7	113.9	116.0
968	Honolulu	122.0	113.9	118.5
STATES & POSS.				
969	Guam	140.4	54.4	102.4
IDAHO				
832	Pocatello	102.1	79.0	91.9
833	Twin Falls	103.5	70.8	89.1
834	Idaho Falls	100.7	78.3	90.8
835	Lewiston	109.1	84.1	98.1
836-837	Boise	101.1	79.7	91.6
838	Coeur d'Alene	109.0	83.7	97.8
ILLINOIS				
600-603	North Suburban	99.0	143.5	118.7
604	Joliet	99.0	143.9	118.8
605	South Suburban	99.0	143.5	118.6
606-608	Chicago	99.5	146.0	120.0
609	Kankakee	95.6	136.3	113.6
610-611	Rockford	98.6	128.9	112.0
612	Rock Island	96.8	102.4	99.2
613	La Salle	98.0	129.1	111.7
614	Galesburg	97.8	109.4	102.9
615-616	Peoria	99.7	113.4	105.8
617	Bloomington	97.1	113.1	104.2
618-619	Champaign	100.8	110.2	104.9
620-622	East St. Louis	94.9	111.5	102.3
623	Quincy	97.3	103.9	100.2
624	Effingham	96.4	109.5	102.2
625	Decatur	97.9	108.6	102.6
626-627	Springfield	98.4	110.4	103.7
628	Centralia	93.9	110.4	101.2
629	Carbondale	93.7	111.0	101.3
INDIANA				
460	Anderson	96.2	83.3	90.5
461-462	Indianapolis	98.2	83.3	91.6
463-464	Gary	97.5	111.8	103.8
465-466	South Bend	96.9	84.6	91.5
467-468	Fort Wayne	96.7	78.4	88.7
469	Kokomo	94.4	82.2	89.0
470	Lawrenceburg	93.5	79.5	87.3
471	New Albany	94.8	77.8	87.3
472	Columbus	97.1	80.8	89.9
473	Muncie	97.2	81.7	90.4
474	Bloomington	98.8	81.6	91.2
475	Washington	95.5	87.0	91.7
476-477	Evansville	96.4	87.1	92.3
478	Terre Haute	97.2	86.2	92.4
479	Lafayette	96.8	80.3	89.5
IOWA				
500-503,509	Des Moines	97.3	88.4	93.3
504	Mason City	96.1	76.9	87.6
505	Fort Dodge	96.2	73.9	86.4
506-507	Waterloo	97.5	75.5	87.8
508	Creston	96.5	82.9	90.5
510-511	Sioux City	98.3	78.6	89.6
512	Sibley	97.4	61.8	81.7
513	Spencer	99.1	62.9	83.1
514	Carroll	96.0	80.6	89.2
515	Council Bluffs	99.4	80.4	91.0
516	Shenandoah	96.6	77.7	88.3
520	Dubuque	97.7	81.5	90.5
521	Decorah	97.1	75.5	87.6
522-524	Cedar Rapids	98.6	85.6	92.8
525	Ottumwa	96.9	77.1	88.2
526	Burlington	96.2	82.7	90.3
527-528	Davenport	97.6	94.7	96.3
KANSAS				
660-662	Kansas City	99.0	98.8	98.9
664-666	Topeka	99.4	77.0	89.5
667	Fort Scott	97.7	79.3	89.6
668	Emporia	97.7	77.1	88.6
669	Belleville	99.5	71.1	86.9
670-672	Wichita	99.7	77.2	89.8
673	Independence	100.0	76.9	89.8
674	Salina	100.2	71.4	87.5
675	Hutchinson	95.5	71.0	84.7
676	Hays	99.7	70.3	86.7
677	Colby	100.2	73.3	88.3

STATE/ZIP	CITY	MAT.	INST.	TOTAL
KANSAS (CONT'D)				
678	Dodge City	101.4	72.6	88.7
679	Liberal	99.6	68.8	86.0
KENTUCKY				
400-402	Louisville	95.5	79.9	88.6
403-405	Lexington	95.7	80.0	88.8
406	Frankfort	96.4	77.7	88.1
407-409	Corbin	93.5	77.3	86.3
410	Covington	95.5	81.1	89.2
411-412	Ashland	94.3	93.7	94.0
413-414	Campton	95.5	78.3	87.9
415-416	Pikeville	96.8	83.3	90.8
417-418	Hazard	94.9	76.9	87.0
420	Paducah	93.4	83.8	89.1
421-422	Bowling Green	95.5	80.7	88.9
423	Owensboro	95.5	84.6	90.7
424	Henderson	93.2	83.3	88.8
425-426	Somerset	92.7	78.9	86.6
427	Elizabethtown	92.2	78.0	85.9
LOUISIANA				
700-701	New Orleans	99.1	69.3	86.0
703	Thibodaux	96.8	66.5	83.4
704	Hammond	94.2	65.4	81.5
705	Lafayette	96.0	67.8	83.6
706	Lake Charles	96.3	69.6	84.5
707-708	Baton Rouge	97.7	70.0	85.5
710-711	Shreveport	99.4	60.2	82.1
712	Monroe	98.2	64.3	83.2
713-714	Alexandria	98.3	68.3	85.1
MAINE				
039	Kittery	93.0	80.6	87.5
040-041	Portland	99.0	83.1	92.0
042	Lewiston	96.6	83.1	90.6
043	Augusta	98.6	75.3	88.3
044	Bangor	96.1	82.5	90.1
045	Bath	95.0	77.8	87.4
046	Machias	94.4	78.9	87.6
047	Houlton	94.6	78.9	87.7
048	Rockland	93.7	78.9	87.1
049	Waterville	94.9	75.3	86.3
MARYLAND				
206	Waldorf	96.7	84.2	91.2
207-208	College Park	96.8	86.0	92.0
209	Silver Spring	96.0	85.6	91.4
210-212	Baltimore	100.7	85.5	94.0
214	Annapolis	99.2	85.6	93.2
215	Cumberland	96.3	86.6	92.0
216	Easton	98.0	74.2	87.5
217	Hagerstown	96.6	88.3	92.9
218	Salisbury	98.4	68.8	85.4
219	Elkton	95.2	86.8	91.5
MASSACHUSETTS				
010-011	Springfield	97.7	109.1	102.7
012	Pittsfield	97.2	107.1	101.6
013	Greenfield	95.5	109.1	101.5
014	Fitchburg	94.2	120.0	105.6
015-016	Worcester	97.7	120.4	107.7
017	Framingham	93.5	126.5	108.1
018	Lowell	97.0	126.1	109.9
019	Lawrence	97.9	127.6	111.1
020-022, 024	Boston	99.9	133.4	114.7
023	Brockton	97.8	120.3	107.7
025	Buzzards Bay	92.6	119.2	104.3
026	Hyannis	94.9	119.2	105.6
027	New Bedford	96.9	119.3	106.8
MICHIGAN				
480,483	Royal Oak	95.0	101.0	97.7
481	Ann Arbor	97.0	103.6	99.9
482	Detroit	99.3	102.9	100.9
484-485	Flint	96.7	92.4	94.8
486	Saginaw	96.3	88.8	93.0
487	Bay City	96.4	89.3	93.3
488-489	Lansing	98.0	90.7	94.8
490	Battle Creek	96.5	83.1	90.6
491	Kalamazoo	96.8	80.9	89.8
492	Jackson	95.0	91.4	93.4
493,495	Grand Rapids	97.8	81.5	90.6
494	Muskegon	95.2	80.3	88.6

551

Location Factors - Commercial

STATE/ZIP	CITY	MAT.	INST.	TOTAL
MICHIGAN (CONT'D)				
496	Traverse City	94.5	78.7	87.5
497	Gaylord	95.7	80.7	89.1
498-499	Iron Mountain	97.7	82.6	91.0
MINNESOTA				
550-551	Saint Paul	99.0	113.2	105.3
553-555	Minneapolis	100.1	112.8	105.7
556-558	Duluth	99.8	102.6	101.1
559	Rochester	98.9	98.9	98.9
560	Mankato	96.3	97.3	96.7
561	Windom	94.9	90.4	92.9
562	Willmar	94.5	96.4	95.3
563	St. Cloud	95.5	107.6	100.9
564	Brainerd	96.1	98.1	97.0
565	Detroit Lakes	98.0	92.1	95.4
566	Bemidji	97.3	95.8	96.6
567	Thief River Falls	96.8	89.3	93.5
MISSISSIPPI				
386	Clarksdale	95.8	56.4	78.4
387	Greenville	99.5	66.7	85.0
388	Tupelo	97.3	57.1	79.6
389	Greenwood	97.1	54.3	78.2
390-392	Jackson	99.0	67.9	85.3
393	Meridian	96.5	67.0	83.5
394	Laurel	98.2	57.2	80.1
395	Biloxi	98.2	64.7	83.4
396	McComb	96.4	54.9	78.1
397	Columbus	98.1	56.8	79.8
MISSOURI				
630-631	St. Louis	99.8	104.0	101.7
633	Bowling Green	98.7	95.8	97.4
634	Hannibal	97.6	93.5	95.8
635	Kirksville	101.4	87.1	95.1
636	Flat River	99.7	95.0	97.6
637	Cape Girardeau	99.2	89.5	95.0
638	Sikeston	98.1	93.5	96.1
639	Poplar Bluff	97.5	88.2	93.4
640-641	Kansas City	100.9	104.4	102.5
644-645	St. Joseph	100.1	96.1	98.3
646	Chillicothe	97.5	95.2	96.5
647	Harrisonville	96.9	101.9	99.1
648	Joplin	98.8	80.8	90.9
650-651	Jefferson City	98.3	91.7	95.4
652	Columbia	99.0	92.5	96.1
653	Sedalia	99.4	92.7	96.4
654-655	Rolla	97.0	94.1	95.7
656-658	Springfield	100.5	83.6	93.0
MONTANA				
590-591	Billings	101.8	76.4	90.5
592	Wolf Point	101.7	72.4	88.8
593	Miles City	99.5	72.3	87.5
594	Great Falls	103.2	74.6	90.5
595	Havre	100.7	72.7	88.3
596	Helena	101.0	73.0	88.7
597	Butte	101.7	74.5	89.6
598	Missoula	99.0	73.1	87.5
599	Kalispell	98.4	73.5	87.4
NEBRASKA				
680-681	Omaha	98.0	79.8	90.0
683-685	Lincoln	98.2	78.3	89.4
686	Columbus	97.1	81.3	90.1
687	Norfolk	98.6	77.3	89.2
688	Grand Island	98.4	77.6	89.2
689	Hastings	98.3	80.4	90.4
690	McCook	98.4	70.8	86.2
691	North Platte	98.2	75.1	88.0
692	Valentine	100.9	69.7	87.1
693	Alliance	100.9	71.1	87.7
NEVADA				
889-891	Las Vegas	104.1	103.6	103.9
893	Ely	102.9	96.1	99.9
894-895	Reno	102.7	82.3	93.7
897	Carson City	101.6	81.8	92.8
898	Elko	101.5	80.1	92.0
NEW HAMPSHIRE				
030	Nashua	97.8	92.1	95.3
031	Manchester	98.4	92.1	95.6

STATE/ZIP	CITY	MAT.	INST.	TOTAL
NEW HAMPSHIRE (CONT'D)				
032-033	Concord	98.0	91.7	95.2
034	Keene	94.7	79.9	88.2
035	Littleton	94.8	80.2	88.3
036	Charleston	94.3	76.0	86.2
037	Claremont	93.4	76.4	85.9
038	Portsmouth	95.1	91.9	93.7
NEW JERSEY				
070-071	Newark	98.7	138.7	116.4
072	Elizabeth	96.5	138.5	115.1
073	Jersey City	95.5	138.4	114.5
074-075	Paterson	97.2	138.5	115.5
076	Hackensack	95.2	138.6	114.4
077	Long Branch	94.8	137.0	113.4
078	Dover	95.4	138.5	114.5
079	Summit	95.5	138.5	114.5
080,083	Vineland	95.1	134.8	112.6
081	Camden	97.0	133.7	113.2
082,084	Atlantic City	95.8	134.7	113.0
085-086	Trenton	98.6	134.8	114.6
087	Point Pleasant	96.9	136.6	114.4
088-089	New Brunswick	97.6	138.3	115.6
NEW MEXICO				
870-872	Albuquerque	98.9	73.7	87.8
873	Gallup	99.3	73.7	88.0
874	Farmington	99.6	73.7	88.2
875	Santa Fe	99.1	73.7	87.9
877	Las Vegas	97.6	73.7	87.0
878	Socorro	97.2	73.7	86.8
879	Truth/Consequences	96.9	70.3	85.2
880	Las Cruces	96.8	70.3	85.1
881	Clovis	99.5	73.6	88.1
882	Roswell	101.0	73.7	88.9
883	Carrizozo	101.7	73.7	89.4
884	Tucumcari	100.1	73.6	88.4
NEW YORK				
100-102	New York	100.3	177.9	134.6
103	Staten Island	96.5	173.9	130.7
104	Bronx	94.8	175.1	130.3
105	Mount Vernon	95.1	145.1	117.2
106	White Plains	94.8	145.1	117.0
107	Yonkers	99.0	150.4	121.7
108	New Rochelle	95.5	145.0	117.4
109	Suffern	95.1	138.8	114.4
110	Queens	99.9	176.5	133.7
111	Long Island City	101.5	176.5	134.6
112	Brooklyn	101.9	174.2	133.8
113	Flushing	102.1	176.5	135.0
114	Jamaica	100.3	176.5	134.0
115,117,118	Hicksville	99.8	160.8	126.8
116	Far Rockaway	102.3	176.5	135.1
119	Riverhead	100.6	160.9	127.3
120-122	Albany	96.0	110.9	102.6
123	Schenectady	96.3	110.8	102.7
124	Kingston	100.1	134.2	115.2
125-126	Poughkeepsie	99.3	145.2	119.6
127	Monticello	98.6	133.4	114.0
128	Glens Falls	91.4	107.7	98.6
129	Plattsburgh	96.7	101.9	99.0
130-132	Syracuse	97.8	104.4	100.7
133-135	Utica	95.9	102.9	99.0
136	Watertown	97.5	101.9	99.5
137-139	Binghamton	97.4	103.0	99.9
140-142	Buffalo	101.3	111.3	105.7
143	Niagara Falls	97.9	113.1	104.6
144-146	Rochester	99.8	104.5	101.9
147	Jamestown	96.9	95.7	96.4
148-149	Elmira	96.8	104.6	100.3
NORTH CAROLINA				
270,272-274	Greensboro	98.7	70.9	86.4
271	Winston-Salem	98.4	70.8	86.2
275-276	Raleigh	96.7	67.6	83.9
277	Durham	100.3	71.1	87.4
278	Rocky Mount	96.3	70.6	85.0
279	Elizabeth City	97.2	67.8	84.2
280	Gastonia	98.8	70.5	86.3
281-282	Charlotte	98.1	70.2	85.8
283	Fayetteville	101.7	70.7	88.0
284	Wilmington	97.6	69.7	85.3
285	Kinston	96.0	70.2	84.6

Location Factors - Commercial

STATE/ZIP	CITY	MAT.	INST.	TOTAL
NORTH CAROLINA (CONT'D)				
286	Hickory	96.4	71.1	85.2
287-288	Asheville	98.0	70.3	85.8
289	Murphy	97.2	69.7	85.1
NORTH DAKOTA				
580-581	Fargo	99.9	78.1	90.3
582	Grand Forks	100.4	77.7	90.4
583	Devils Lake	100.4	77.3	90.2
584	Jamestown	100.5	77.2	90.2
585	Bismarck	100.5	80.5	91.7
586	Dickinson	101.1	78.5	91.1
587	Minot	100.4	80.6	91.6
588	Williston	99.5	78.8	90.4
OHIO				
430-432	Columbus	98.0	83.4	91.5
433	Marion	94.8	82.7	89.4
434-436	Toledo	98.0	94.1	96.3
437-438	Zanesville	95.3	82.8	89.8
439	Steubenville	96.7	90.3	93.8
440	Lorain	99.3	86.9	93.8
441	Cleveland	99.5	93.7	96.9
442-443	Akron	100.4	88.8	95.3
444-445	Youngstown	99.6	84.8	93.1
446-447	Canton	99.8	81.8	91.8
448-449	Mansfield	97.4	83.0	91.0
450	Hamilton	97.7	79.2	89.5
451-452	Cincinnati	98.1	77.7	89.1
453-454	Dayton	97.8	77.8	89.0
455	Springfield	97.7	80.9	90.3
456	Chillicothe	97.1	86.4	92.4
457	Athens	100.2	85.2	93.6
458	Lima	100.6	81.8	92.3
OKLAHOMA				
730-731	Oklahoma City	99.3	67.3	85.1
734	Ardmore	98.1	66.7	84.2
735	Lawton	100.2	67.1	85.6
736	Clinton	99.4	66.6	84.9
737	Enid	99.8	67.0	85.3
738	Woodward	98.1	63.8	82.9
739	Guymon	99.2	64.5	83.9
740-741	Tulsa	97.0	66.5	83.5
743	Miami	93.8	66.2	81.6
744	Muskogee	96.1	66.0	82.8
745	McAlester	93.4	61.6	79.3
746	Ponca City	94.2	65.5	81.5
747	Durant	94.1	66.1	81.7
748	Shawnee	95.7	66.4	82.7
749	Poteau	93.3	65.8	81.2
OREGON				
970-972	Portland	100.0	98.9	99.5
973	Salem	101.2	97.3	99.5
974	Eugene	99.7	97.5	98.7
975	Medford	101.3	94.7	98.4
976	Klamath Falls	101.6	94.8	98.6
977	Bend	100.6	97.3	99.2
978	Pendleton	96.5	98.6	97.4
979	Vale	94.3	85.8	90.5
PENNSYLVANIA				
150-152	Pittsburgh	100.6	104.5	102.3
153	Washington	97.9	103.8	100.5
154	Uniontown	98.2	100.1	99.0
155	Bedford	99.2	93.7	96.8
156	Greensburg	99.2	101.3	100.1
157	Indiana	98.0	99.0	98.4
158	Dubois	99.6	95.0	97.6
159	Johnstown	99.2	95.8	97.7
160	Butler	91.4	102.2	96.2
161	New Castle	91.5	102.6	96.4
162	Kittanning	91.9	102.9	96.8
163	Oil City	91.4	101.4	95.8
164-165	Erie	93.2	98.5	95.5
166	Altoona	93.3	96.6	94.8
167	Bradford	94.9	102.1	98.1
168	State College	94.5	97.8	95.9
169	Wellsboro	95.6	96.1	95.8
170-171	Harrisburg	96.9	96.7	96.8
172	Chambersburg	94.5	92.5	93.6
173-174	York	94.5	95.6	94.9
175-176	Lancaster	93.2	97.9	95.3

STATE/ZIP	CITY	MAT.	INST.	TOTAL
PENNSYLVANIA (CONT'D)				
177	Williamsport	91.8	94.5	93.0
178	Sunbury	94.0	96.8	95.2
179	Pottsville	93.0	99.5	95.9
180	Lehigh Valley	95.0	119.6	105.9
181	Allentown	96.7	110.2	102.6
182	Hazleton	94.5	98.7	96.3
183	Stroudsburg	94.4	111.9	102.1
184-185	Scranton	97.4	101.0	99.0
186-187	Wilkes-Barre	94.1	100.0	96.7
188	Montrose	93.8	101.0	97.0
189	Doylestown	94.0	126.0	108.2
190-191	Philadelphia	99.6	134.5	115.0
193	Westchester	95.3	124.7	108.3
194	Norristown	94.3	130.1	110.1
195-196	Reading	96.0	106.1	100.5
PUERTO RICO				
009	San Juan	121.1	24.3	78.3
RHODE ISLAND				
028	Newport	96.2	112.3	103.3
029	Providence	97.9	112.3	104.2
SOUTH CAROLINA				
290-292	Columbia	97.1	68.5	84.5
293	Spartanburg	97.6	68.1	84.5
294	Charleston	99.1	67.8	85.2
295	Florence	97.3	68.5	84.5
296	Greenville	97.3	68.1	84.4
297	Rock Hill	97.3	67.6	84.2
298	Aiken	98.2	68.6	85.1
299	Beaufort	98.9	56.4	80.1
SOUTH DAKOTA				
570-571	Sioux Falls	97.8	67.8	84.6
572	Watertown	99.0	50.0	77.4
573	Mitchell	97.8	48.3	75.9
574	Aberdeen	100.1	54.7	80.1
575	Pierre	101.3	62.0	83.9
576	Mobridge	98.5	53.9	78.8
577	Rapid City	99.9	65.2	84.6
TENNESSEE				
370-372	Nashville	98.4	73.6	87.4
373-374	Chattanooga	99.6	67.1	85.3
375,380-381	Memphis	98.2	72.2	86.7
376	Johnson City	99.8	60.7	82.5
377-379	Knoxville	96.3	66.4	83.1
382	McKenzie	96.9	57.4	79.5
383	Jackson	98.3	61.3	81.9
384	Columbia	95.4	68.7	83.6
385	Cookeville	96.8	57.7	79.5
TEXAS				
750	McKinney	99.7	65.5	84.6
751	Waxahachie	99.7	64.5	84.2
752-753	Dallas	100.3	68.4	86.2
754	Greenville	99.9	65.5	84.7
755	Texarkana	99.1	65.7	84.4
756	Longview	100.1	63.1	83.7
757	Tyler	100.1	64.5	84.4
758	Palestine	96.0	63.0	81.4
759	Lufkin	96.7	65.0	82.7
760-761	Fort Worth	97.3	64.7	82.9
762	Denton	97.5	64.8	83.0
763	Wichita Falls	94.8	63.6	81.0
764	Eastland	94.1	62.9	80.3
765	Temple	92.4	60.3	78.2
766-767	Waco	94.2	65.7	81.6
768	Brownwood	97.5	60.3	81.1
769	San Angelo	97.1	60.8	81.0
770-772	Houston	99.3	67.5	85.2
773	Huntsville	98.6	65.5	84.0
774	Wharton	99.4	66.4	84.8
775	Galveston	97.3	68.3	84.5
776-777	Beaumont	97.6	67.3	84.2
778	Bryan	95.0	67.0	82.7
779	Victoria	99.5	64.7	84.1
780	Laredo	97.1	64.7	82.8
781-782	San Antonio	98.1	65.8	83.9
783-784	Corpus Christi	99.7	62.5	83.3
785	McAllen	100.7	59.5	82.5
786-787	Austin	97.5	63.6	82.5

Location Factors - Commercial

STATE/ZIP	CITY	MAT.	INST.	TOTAL
TEXAS (CONT'D)				
788	Del Rio	100.5	62.8	83.9
789	Giddings	97.0	62.1	81.6
790-791	Amarillo	97.5	63.2	82.4
792	Childress	97.9	62.8	82.4
793-794	Lubbock	99.7	64.1	84.0
795-796	Abilene	98.1	63.7	82.9
797	Midland	100.4	65.8	85.1
798-799,885	El Paso	96.3	62.8	81.5
UTAH				
840-841	Salt Lake City	103.4	69.6	88.5
842,844	Ogden	98.7	69.5	85.8
843	Logan	100.8	69.5	87.0
845	Price	101.5	64.2	85.0
846-847	Provo	101.3	69.4	87.2
VERMONT				
050	White River Jct.	97.4	81.3	90.3
051	Bellows Falls	95.6	95.4	95.5
052	Bennington	96.1	91.4	94.0
053	Brattleboro	96.5	95.2	95.9
054	Burlington	100.7	80.8	91.9
056	Montpelier	99.3	85.5	93.2
057	Rutland	97.8	80.8	90.3
058	St. Johnsbury	97.5	81.1	90.3
059	Guildhall	96.0	80.7	89.3
VIRGINIA				
220-221	Fairfax	99.9	85.5	93.6
222	Arlington	100.7	85.3	93.9
223	Alexandria	99.8	85.2	93.3
224-225	Fredericksburg	98.6	83.8	92.0
226	Winchester	99.2	84.4	92.7
227	Culpeper	99.0	81.5	91.3
228	Harrisonburg	99.4	66.5	84.8
229	Charlottesville	99.8	68.0	85.7
230-232	Richmond	98.3	73.5	87.3
233-235	Norfolk	98.1	69.7	85.5
236	Newport News	98.3	69.9	85.8
237	Portsmouth	97.8	64.5	83.1
238	Petersburg	98.3	73.5	87.4
239	Farmville	97.5	55.1	78.8
240-241	Roanoke	100.2	65.8	85.0
242	Bristol	98.5	54.4	79.0
243	Pulaski	98.1	56.8	79.9
244	Staunton	98.9	60.5	81.9
245	Lynchburg	99.1	64.8	83.9
246	Grundy	98.4	51.8	77.8
WASHINGTON				
980-981,987	Seattle	103.2	107.1	104.9
982	Everett	102.6	100.4	101.6
983-984	Tacoma	103.0	101.5	102.4
985	Olympia	100.7	101.5	101.1
986	Vancouver	104.0	95.2	100.1
988	Wenatchee	103.3	86.9	96.0
989	Yakima	103.2	96.6	100.2
990-992	Spokane	102.9	83.3	94.3
993	Richland	102.6	91.4	97.6
994	Clarkston	102.0	82.9	93.5
WEST VIRGINIA				
247-248	Bluefield	97.3	91.7	94.8
249	Lewisburg	98.9	90.6	95.3
250-253	Charleston	98.6	93.1	96.2
254	Martinsburg	99.4	85.8	93.4
255-257	Huntington	100.4	93.2	97.2
258-259	Beckley	97.8	91.4	95.0
260	Wheeling	100.0	92.2	96.5
261	Parkersburg	98.7	89.7	94.7
262	Buckhannon	98.7	93.3	96.3
263-264	Clarksburg	99.3	93.3	96.7
265	Morgantown	99.3	93.4	96.7
266	Gassaway	98.7	93.4	96.3
267	Romney	98.5	87.7	93.7
268	Petersburg	98.4	86.6	93.2
WISCONSIN				
530,532	Milwaukee	98.6	107.9	102.7
531	Kenosha	98.6	105.8	101.8
534	Racine	98.1	106.6	101.8
535	Beloit	97.9	100.6	99.1
537	Madison	98.3	100.5	99.3

STATE/ZIP	CITY	MAT.	INST.	TOTAL
WISCONSIN (CONT'D)				
538	Lancaster	96.1	95.8	96.0
539	Portage	94.6	98.6	96.3
540	New Richmond	95.9	94.6	95.3
541-543	Green Bay	100.0	97.9	99.1
544	Wausau	95.3	96.4	95.8
545	Rhinelander	98.6	91.9	95.7
546	La Crosse	96.3	98.7	97.4
547	Eau Claire	98.0	99.2	98.5
548	Superior	95.7	98.5	96.9
549	Oshkosh	95.9	90.7	93.6
WYOMING				
820	Cheyenne	101.5	72.0	88.5
821	Yellowstone Nat'l Park	99.5	74.8	88.6
822	Wheatland	100.7	69.2	86.8
823	Rawlins	102.3	74.5	90.0
824	Worland	100.2	73.4	88.4
825	Riverton	101.3	71.0	87.9
826	Casper	101.4	68.3	86.8
827	Newcastle	100.1	76.4	89.6
828	Sheridan	103.0	71.9	89.2
829-831	Rock Springs	104.2	73.0	90.4
CANADIAN FACTORS (reflect Canadian currency)				
ALBERTA				
	Calgary	119.8	98.6	110.4
	Edmonton	119.8	98.6	110.4
	Fort McMurray	122.1	92.8	109.2
	Lethbridge	116.7	92.3	105.9
	Lloydminster	111.5	88.9	101.5
	Medicine Hat	111.7	88.2	101.3
	Red Deer	112.1	88.2	101.6
BRITISH COLUMBIA				
	Kamloops	112.7	88.8	102.2
	Prince George	113.8	88.1	102.4
	Vancouver	115.6	93.9	106.0
	Victoria	113.9	88.8	102.8
MANITOBA				
	Brandon	123.4	75.1	102.0
	Portage la Prairie	111.4	73.4	94.6
	Winnipeg	119.2	72.7	98.7
NEW BRUNSWICK				
	Bathurst	109.8	66.2	90.5
	Dalhousie	109.8	66.4	90.6
	Fredericton	116.4	73.3	97.4
	Moncton	110.1	70.6	92.6
	Newcastle	109.9	66.8	90.9
	St. John	112.5	78.8	97.6
NEWFOUNDLAND				
	Corner Brook	128.1	65.4	100.4
	St. Johns	121.1	91.0	107.8
NORTHWEST TERRITORIES				
	Yellowknife	133.2	86.9	112.8
NOVA SCOTIA				
	Bridgewater	111.0	74.7	95.0
	Dartmouth	124.5	74.7	102.5
	Halifax	116.1	85.0	102.4
	New Glasgow	122.4	74.7	101.4
	Sydney	120.3	74.7	100.2
	Truro	110.6	74.7	94.8
	Yarmouth	122.3	74.7	101.3
ONTARIO				
	Barrie	117.1	92.7	106.3
	Brantford	113.0	96.6	105.8
	Cornwall	113.0	93.0	104.1
	Hamilton	114.3	98.1	107.1
	Kingston	114.1	93.1	104.8
	Kitchener	107.8	97.0	103.0
	London	114.3	98.5	107.3
	North Bay	125.5	90.8	110.2
	Oshawa	110.5	96.4	104.2
	Ottawa	116.3	99.2	108.8
	Owen Sound	117.3	90.9	105.6
	Peterborough	113.0	92.7	104.1
	Sarnia	113.0	97.2	106.0
	Sault Ste. Marie	108.2	93.3	101.6

Location Factors - Commercial

STATE/ZIP	CITY	MAT.	INST.	TOTAL
	St. Catharines	105.9	98.2	102.5
	Sudbury	105.5	96.4	101.5
	Thunder Bay	107.2	97.2	102.8
	Timmins	110.2	90.0	102.7
	Toronto	114.5	105.6	110.6
	Windsor	106.4	96.9	102.2
PRINCE EDWARD ISLAND				
	Charlottetown	119.0	63.4	94.4
	Summerside	125.1	61.5	97.0
QUEBEC				
	Cap-de-la-Madeleine	110.4	85.1	99.2
	Charlesbourg	110.4	85.1	99.2
	Chicoutimi	109.7	89.3	100.7
	Gatineau	110.1	84.9	98.9
	Granby	110.3	84.8	99.0
	Hull	110.2	84.9	99.0
	Joliette	110.6	85.1	99.3
	Laval	110.5	84.9	99.2
	Montreal	115.7	91.5	105.0
	Quebec City	116.2	92.0	105.5
	Rimouski	110.0	89.3	100.9
	Rouyn-Noranda	110.1	84.9	98.9
	Saint-Hyacinthe	109.8	84.9	98.8
	Sherbrooke	110.4	84.9	99.1
	Sorel	110.6	85.1	99.3
	Saint-Jerome	110.1	84.9	99.0
	Trois-Rivieres	123.0	85.1	106.3
SASKATCHEWAN				
	Moose Jaw	108.7	67.9	90.7
	Prince Albert	107.8	66.1	89.4
	Regina	119.8	90.2	106.7
	Saskatoon	109.6	88.0	100.1
YUKON				
	Whitehorse	134.4	71.9	106.8

Reference Tables

R011105-05 Tips for Accurate Estimating

1. Use pre-printed or columnar forms for orderly sequence of dimensions and locations and for recording telephone quotations.

2. Use only the front side of each paper or form except for certain pre-printed summary forms.

3. Be consistent in listing dimensions: For example, length x width x height. This helps in rechecking to ensure that the total length of partitions is appropriate for the building area.

4. Use printed (rather than measured) dimensions where given.

5. Add up multiple printed dimensions for a single entry where possible.

6. Measure all other dimensions carefully.

7. Use each set of dimensions to calculate multiple related quantities.

8. Convert foot and inch measurements to decimal feet when listing. Memorize decimal equivalents to .01 parts of a foot (1/8″ equals approximately .01′).

9. Do not "round off" quantities until the final summary.

10. Mark drawings with different colors as items are taken off.

11. Keep similar items together, different items separate.

12. Identify location and drawing numbers to aid in future checking for completeness.

13. Measure or list everything on the drawings or mentioned in the specifications.

14. It may be necessary to list items not called for to make the job complete.

15. Be alert for: Notes on plans such as N.T.S. (not to scale); changes in scale throughout the drawings; reduced size drawings; discrepancies between the specifications and the drawings.

16. Develop a consistent pattern of performing an estimate. For example:
    a. Start the quantity takeoff at the lower floor and move to the next higher floor.
    b. Proceed from the main section of the building to the wings.
    c. Proceed from south to north or vice versa, clockwise or counterclockwise.
    d. Take off floor plan quantities first, elevations next, then detail drawings.

17. List all gross dimensions that can be either used again for different quantities, or used as a rough check of other quantities for verification (exterior perimeter, gross floor area, individual floor areas, etc.).

18. Utilize design symmetry or repetition (repetitive floors, repetitive wings, symmetrical design around a center line, similar room layouts, etc.). Note: Extreme caution is needed here so as not to omit or duplicate an area.

19. Do not convert units until the final total is obtained. For instance, when estimating concrete work, keep all units to the nearest cubic foot, then summarize and convert to cubic yards.

20. When figuring alternatives, it is best to total all items involved in the basic system, then total all items involved in the alternates. Therefore, you work with positive numbers in all cases. When adds and deducts are used, it is often confusing whether to add or subtract a portion of an item; especially on a complicated or involved alternate.

R011105-10 Unit Gross Area Requirements

The figures in the table below indicate typical ranges in square feet as a function of the "occupant" unit. This table is best used in the preliminary design stages to help determine the probable size requirement for the total project.

Building Type	Unit	Gross Area in S.F.		
		1/4	Median	3/4
Apartments	Unit	660	860	1,100
Auditorium & Play Theaters	Seat	18	25	38
Bowling Alleys	Lane		940	
Churches & Synagogues	Seat	20	28	39
Dormitories	Bed	200	230	275
Fraternity & Sorority Houses	Bed	220	315	370
Garages, Parking	Car	325	355	385
Hospitals	Bed	685	850	1,075
Hotels	Rental Unit	475	600	710
Housing for the elderly	Unit	515	635	755
Housing, Public	Unit	700	875	1,030
Ice Skating Rinks	Total	27,000	30,000	36,000
Motels	Rental Unit	360	465	620
Nursing Homes	Bed	290	350	450
Restaurants	Seat	23	29	39
Schools, Elementary	Pupil	65	77	90
Junior High & Middle		85	110	129
Senior High		102	130	145
Vocational		110	135	195
Shooting Ranges	Point		450	
Theaters & Movies	Seat		15	

R011105-50   Metric Conversion Factors

Description: This table is primarily for converting customary U.S. units in the left hand column to SI metric units in the right hand column. In addition, conversion factors for some commonly encountered Canadian and non-SI metric units are included.

	If You Know		Multiply By		To Find
Length	Inches	x	25.4[a]	=	Millimeters
	Feet	x	0.3048[a]	=	Meters
	Yards	x	0.9144[a]	=	Meters
	Miles (statute)	x	1.609	=	Kilometers
Area	Square inches	x	645.2	=	Square millimeters
	Square feet	x	0.0929	=	Square meters
	Square yards	x	0.8361	=	Square meters
Volume (Capacity)	Cubic inches	x	16,387	=	Cubic millimeters
	Cubic feet	x	0.02832	=	Cubic meters
	Cubic yards	x	0.7646	=	Cubic meters
	Gallons (U.S. liquids)[b]	x	0.003785	=	Cubic meters[c]
	Gallons (Canadian liquid)[b]	x	0.004546	=	Cubic meters[c]
	Ounces (U.S. liquid)[b]	x	29.57	=	Milliliters[c, d]
	Quarts (U.S. liquid)[b]	x	0.9464	=	Liters[c, d]
	Gallons (U.S. liquid)[b]	x	3.785	=	Liters[c, d]
Force	Kilograms force[d]	x	9.807	=	Newtons
	Pounds force	x	4.448	=	Newtons
	Pounds force	x	0.4536	=	Kilograms force[d]
	Kips	x	4448	=	Newtons
	Kips	x	453.6	=	Kilograms force[d]
Pressure, Stress, Strength (Force per unit area)	Kilograms force per square centimeter[d]	x	0.09807	=	Megapascals
	Pounds force per square inch (psi)	x	0.006895	=	Megapascals
	Kips per square inch	x	6.895	=	Megapascals
	Pounds force per square inch (psi)	x	0.07031	=	Kilograms force per square centimeter[d]
	Pounds force per square foot	x	47.88	=	Pascals
	Pounds force per square foot	x	4.882	=	Kilograms force per square meter[d]
Flow	Cubic feet per minute	x	0.4719	=	Liters per second
	Gallons per minute	x	0.0631	=	Liters per second
	Gallons per hour	x	1.05	=	Milliliters per second
Bending Moment Or Torque	Inch-pounds force	x	0.01152	=	Meter-kilograms force[d]
	Inch-pounds force	x	0.1130	=	Newton-meters
	Foot-pounds force	x	0.1383	=	Meter-kilograms force[d]
	Foot-pounds force	x	1.356	=	Newton-meters
	Meter-kilograms force[d]	x	9.807	=	Newton-meters
Mass	Ounces (avoirdupois)	x	28.35	=	Grams
	Pounds (avoirdupois)	x	0.4536	=	Kilograms
	Tons (metric)	x	1000	=	Kilograms
	Tons, short (2000 pounds)	x	907.2	=	Kilograms
	Tons, short (2000 pounds)	x	0.9072	=	Megagrams[e]
Mass per Unit Volume	Pounds mass per cubic foot	x	16.02	=	Kilograms per cubic meter
	Pounds mass per cubic yard	x	0.5933	=	Kilograms per cubic meter
	Pounds mass per gallon (U.S. liquid)[b]	x	119.8	=	Kilograms per cubic meter
	Pounds mass per gallon (Canadian liquid)[b]	x	99.78	=	Kilograms per cubic meter
Temperature	Degrees Fahrenheit	(F-32)/1.8		=	Degrees Celsius
	Degrees Fahrenheit	(F+459.67)/1.8		=	Degrees Kelvin
	Degrees Celsius	C+273.15		=	Degrees Kelvin

[a]The factor given is exact
[b]One U.S. gallon = 0.8327 Canadian gallon
[c]1 liter = 1000 milliliters = 1000 cubic centimeters
  1 cubic decimeter = 0.001 cubic meter
[d]Metric but not SI unit
[e]Called "tonne" in England and "metric ton" in other metric countries

557

R011105-60   Weights and Measures

Measures of Length
1 Mile = 1760 Yards = 5280 Feet
1 Yard = 3 Feet = 36 inches
1 Foot = 12 Inches
1 Mil = 0.001 Inch
1 Fathom = 2 Yards = 6 Feet
1 Rod = 5.5 Yards = 16.5 Feet
1 Hand = 4 Inches
1 Span = 9 Inches
1 Micro-inch = One Millionth Inch or 0.000001 Inch
1 Micron = One Millionth Meter + 0.00003937 Inch

Surveyor's Measure
1 Mile = 8 Furlongs = 80 Chains
1 Furlong = 10 Chains = 220 Yards
1 Chain = 4 Rods = 22 Yards = 66 Feet = 100 Links
1 Link = 7.92 Inches

Square Measure
1 Square Mile = 640 Acres = 6400 Square Chains
1 Acre = 10 Square Chains = 4840 Square Yards = 43,560 Sq. Ft.
1 Square Chain = 16 Square Rods = 484 Square Yards = 4356 Sq. Ft.
1 Square Rod = 30.25 Square Yards = 272.25 Square Feet = 625 Square Lines
1 Square Yard = 9 Square Feet
1 Square Foot = 144 Square Inches
An Acre equals a Square 208.7 Feet per Side

Cubic Measure
1 Cubic Yard = 27 Cubic Feet
1 Cubic Foot = 1728 Cubic Inches
1 Cord of Wood = 4 x 4 x 8 Feet = 128 Cubic Feet
1 Perch of Masonry = 16½ x 1½ x 1 Foot = 24.75 Cubic Feet

Avoirdupois or Commercial Weight
1 Gross or Long Ton = 2240 Pounds
1 Net or Short Ton = 2000 Pounds
1 Pound = 16 Ounces = 7000 Grains
1 Ounce = 16 Drachms = 437.5 Grains
1 Stone = 14 Pounds

Power
1 British Thermal Unit per Hour = 0.2931 Watts
1 Ton (Refrigeration) = 3.517 Kilowatts
1 Horsepower (Boiler) = 9.81 Kilowatts
1 Horsepower (550 ft-lb/s) = 0.746 Kilowatts

Shipping Measure
For Measuring Internal Capacity of a Vessel:
    1 Register Ton = 100 Cubic Feet

For Measurement of Cargo:
    Approximately 40 Cubic Feet of Merchandise is considered a Shipping Ton, unless that bulk would weigh more than 2000 Pounds, in which case Freight Charge may be based upon weight.

40 Cubic Feet = 32.143 U.S. Bushels = 31.16 Imp. Bushels

Liquid Measure
1 Imperial Gallon = 1.2009 U.S. Gallon = 277.42 Cu. In.
1 Cubic Foot = 7.48 U.S. Gallons

Reference Tables

R011110-30   Engineering Fees

Typical **Structural Engineering Fees** based on type of construction and total project size. These fees are included in Architectural Fees.

Type of Construction	Total Project Size (in thousands of dollars)			
	$500	$500-$1,000	$1,000-$5,000	Over $5000
Industrial buildings, factories & warehouses	Technical payroll times 2.0 to 2.5	1.60%	1.25%	1.00%
Hotels, apartments, offices, dormitories, hospitals, public buildings, food stores		2.00%	1.70%	1.20%
Museums, banks, churches and cathedrals		2.00%	1.75%	1.25%
Thin shells, prestressed concrete, earthquake resistive		2.00%	1.75%	1.50%
Parking ramps, auditoriums, stadiums, convention halls, hangars & boiler houses		2.50%	2.00%	1.75%
Special buildings, major alterations, underpinning & future expansion		Add to above 0.5%	Add to above 0.5%	Add to above 0.5%

For complex reinforced concrete or unusually complicated structures, add 20% to 50%.

Typical **Mechanical and Electrical Engineering Fees** are based on the size of the subcontract. The fee structure for both is shown below. These fees are included in Architectural Fees.

Type of Construction	Subcontract Size							
	$25,000	$50,000	$100,000	$225,000	$350,000	$500,000	$750,000	$1,000,000
Simple structures	6.4%	5.7%	4.8%	4.5%	4.4%	4.3%	4.2%	4.1%
Intermediate structures	8.0	7.3	6.5	5.6	5.1	5.0	4.9	4.8
Complex structures	10.1	9.0	9.0	8.0	7.5	7.5	7.0	7.0

For renovations, add 15% to 25% to applicable fee.

R012153-10   Repair and Remodeling

Cost figures are based on new construction utilizing the most cost-effective combination of labor, equipment and material with the work scheduled in proper sequence to allow the various trades to accomplish their work in an efficient manner.

The costs for repair and remodeling work must be modified due to the following factors that may be present in any given repair and remodeling project.

1. Equipment usage curtailment due to the physical limitations of the project, with only hand-operated equipment being used.

2. Increased requirement for shoring and bracing to hold up the building while structural changes are being made and to allow for temporary storage of construction materials on above-grade floors.

3. Material handling becomes more costly due to having to move within the confines of an enclosed building. For multi-story construction, low capacity elevators and stairwells may be the only access to the upper floors.

4. Large amounts of cutting and patching and attempting to match the existing construction is required. It is often more economical to remove entire walls rather than create many new door and window openings. This sort of trade-off has to be carefully analyzed.

5. Cost of protection of completed work is increased since the usual sequence of construction usually cannot be accomplished.

6. Economies of scale usually associated with new construction may not be present. If small quantities of components must be custom fabricated due to job requirements, unit costs will naturally increase. Also, if only small work areas are available at a given time, job scheduling between trades becomes difficult and subcontractor quotations may reflect the excessive start-up and shut-down phases of the job.

7. Work may have to be done on other than normal shifts and may have to be done around an existing production facility which has to stay in production during the course of the repair and remodeling.

8. Dust and noise protection of adjoining non-construction areas can involve substantial special protection and alter usual construction methods.

9. Job may be delayed due to unexpected conditions discovered during demolition or removal. These delays ultimately increase construction costs.

10. Piping and ductwork runs may not be as simple as for new construction. Wiring may have to be snaked through walls and floors.

11. Matching "existing construction" may be impossible because materials may no longer be manufactured. Substitutions may be expensive.

12. Weather protection of existing structure requires additional temporary structures to protect building at openings.

13. On small projects, because of local conditions, it may be necessary to pay a tradesman for a minimum of four hours for a task that is completed in one hour.

All of the above areas can contribute to increased costs for a repair and remodeling project. Each of the above factors should be considered in the planning, bidding and construction stage in order to minimize the increased costs associated with repair and remodeling jobs.

General Requirements — R0121 Allowances

R012153-60 Security Factors

Contractors entering, working in, and exiting secure facilities often lose productive time during a normal workday. The recommended allowances in this section are intended to provide for the loss of productivity by increasing labor costs. Note that different costs are associated with searches upon entry only and searches upon entry and exit. Time spent in a queue is unpredictable and not part of these allowances. Contractors should plan ahead for this situation.

Security checkpoints are designed to reflect the level of security required to gain access or egress. An extreme example is when contractors, along with any materials, tools, equipment, and vehicles, must be physically searched and have all materials, tools, equipment, and vehicles inventoried and documented prior to both entry and exit.

Physical searches without going through the documentation process represent the next level and take up less time.

Electronic searches—passing through a detector or x-ray machine with no documentation of materials, tools, equipment, and vehicles—take less time than physical searches.

Visual searches of materials, tools, equipment, and vehicles represent the next level of security.

Finally, access by means of an ID card or displayed sticker takes the least amount of time.

Another consideration is if the searches described above are performed each and every day, or if they are performed only on the first day with access granted by ID card or displayed sticker for the remainder of the project. The figures for this situation have been calculated to represent the initial check-in as described and subsequent entry by ID card or displayed sticker for up to 20 days on site. For the situation described above, where the time period is beyond 20 days, the impact on labor cost is negligible.

There are situations where tradespeople must be accompanied by an escort and observed during the work day. The loss of freedom of movement will slow down productivity for the tradesperson. Costs for the observer have not been included. Those costs are normally born by the owner.

General Requirements — R0129 Payment Procedures

R012909-80 Sales Tax by State

State sales tax on materials is tabulated below (5 states have no sales tax). Many states allow local jurisdictions, such as a county or city, to levy additional sales tax.

Some projects may be sales tax exempt, particularly those constructed with public funds.

State	Tax (%)	State	Tax (%)	State	Tax (%)	State	Tax (%)
Alabama	4	Illinois	6.25	Montana	0	Rhode Island	7
Alaska	0	Indiana	7	Nebraska	5.5	South Carolina	6
Arizona	5.6	Iowa	6	Nevada	6.85	South Dakota	4
Arkansas	6.5	Kansas	6.5	New Hampshire	0	Tennessee	7
California	7.5	Kentucky	6	New Jersey	7	Texas	6.25
Colorado	2.9	Louisiana	4	New Mexico	5.125	Utah	5.95
Connecticut	6.35	Maine	5.5	New York	4	Vermont	6
Delaware	0	Maryland	6	North Carolina	4.75	Virginia	5.3
District of Columbia	5.75	Massachusetts	6.25	North Dakota	5	Washington	6.5
Florida	6	Michigan	6	Ohio	5.75	West Virginia	6
Georgia	4	Minnesota	6.875	Oklahoma	4.5	Wisconsin	5
Hawaii	4	Mississippi	7	Oregon	0	Wyoming	4
Idaho	6	Missouri	4.225	Pennsylvania	6	Average	5.09 %

Sales Tax by Province (Canada)

GST - a value-added tax, which the government imposes on most goods and services provided in or imported into Canada. PST - a retail sales tax, which five of the provinces impose on the prices of most goods and some services. QST - a value-added tax, similar to the federal GST, which Quebec imposes. HST - Three provinces have combined their retail sales taxes with the federal GST into one harmonized tax.

Province	PST (%)	QST (%)	GST (%)	HST (%)
Alberta	0	0	5	0
British Columbia	7	0	5	0
Manitoba	8	0	5	0
New Brunswick	0	0	0	13
Newfoundland	0	0	0	13
Northwest Territories	0	0	5	0
Nova Scotia	0	0	0	15
Ontario	0	0	0	13
Prince Edward Island	0	0	0	14
Quebec	0	9.975	5	0
Saskatchewan	5	0	5	0
Yukon	0	0	5	0

R012909-85   Unemployment Taxes and Social Security Taxes

State unemployment tax rates vary not only from state to state, but also with the experience rating of the contractor. The federal unemployment tax rate is 6.0% of the first $7,000 of wages. This is reduced by a credit of up to 5.4% for timely payment to the state. The minimum federal unemployment tax is 0.6% after all credits.

Social security (FICA) for 2017 is estimated at time of publication to be 7.65% of wages up to $118,500.

R012909-86   Unemployment Tax by State

Information is from the U.S. Department of Labor, state unemployment tax rates.

State	Tax (%)	State	Tax (%)	State	Tax (%)	State	Tax (%)
Alabama	7.1	Illinois	8.15	Montana	6.12	Rhode Island	9.79
Alaska	5.4	Indiana	7.5	Nebraska	5.4	South Carolina	6.03
Arizona	7.79	Iowa	7.5	Nevada	5.4	South Dakota	9.5
Arkansas	6.8	Kansas	7.4	New Hampshire	6	Tennessee	10
California	6.2	Kentucky	10	New Jersey	7	Texas	7.49
Colorado	8.2	Louisiana	6.2	New Mexico	6.4	Utah	7.3
Connecticut	6.8	Maine	6.86	New York	8.9	Vermont	8.4
Delaware	8.2	Maryland	9	North Carolina	5.76	Virginia	6.54
District of Columbia	7.2	Massachusetts	11.13	North Dakota	9.7	Washington	5.84
Florida	5.4	Michigan	10.3	Ohio	8.6	West Virginia	7.5
Georgia	5.4	Minnesota	9.1	Oklahoma	5.5	Wisconsin	12
Hawaii	5.8	Mississippi	5.6	Oregon	5.4	Wyoming	10
Idaho	5.4	Missouri	9.75	Pennsylvania	10.89	Median	7.3 %

R012909-90   Overtime

One way to improve the completion date of a project or eliminate negative float from a schedule is to compress activity duration times. This can be achieved by increasing the crew size or working overtime with the proposed crew.

To determine the costs of working overtime to compress activity duration times, consider the following examples. Below is an overtime efficiency and cost chart based on a five, six, or seven day week with an eight through twelve hour day. Payroll percentage increases for time and one half and double times are shown for the various working days.

Days per Week	Hours per Day	Production Efficiency					Payroll Cost Factors	
		1st Week	2nd Week	3rd Week	4th Week	Average 4 Weeks	@ 1-1/2 Times	@ 2 Times
	8	100%	100%	100%	100%	100%	1.000	1.000
	9	100	100	95	90	96	1.056	1.111
5	10	100	95	90	85	93	1.100	1.200
	11	95	90	75	65	81	1.136	1.273
	12	90	85	70	60	76	1.167	1.333
	8	100	100	95	90	96	1.083	1.167
	9	100	95	90	85	93	1.130	1.259
6	10	95	90	85	80	88	1.167	1.333
	11	95	85	70	65	79	1.197	1.394
	12	90	80	65	60	74	1.222	1.444
	8	100	95	85	75	89	1.143	1.286
	9	95	90	80	70	84	1.183	1.365
7	10	90	85	75	65	79	1.214	1.429
	11	85	80	65	60	73	1.240	1.481
	12	85	75	60	55	69	1.262	1.524

R013113-40   Builder's Risk Insurance

Builder's risk insurance is insurance on a building during construction. Premiums are paid by the owner or the contractor. Blasting, collapse and underground insurance would raise total insurance costs.

R013113-50   General Contractor's Overhead

There are two distinct types of overhead on a construction project: Project overhead and main office overhead. Project overhead includes those costs at a construction site not directly associated with the installation of construction materials. Examples of project overhead costs include the following:

1. Superintendent
2. Construction office and storage trailers
3. Temporary sanitary facilities
4. Temporary utilities
5. Security fencing
6. Photographs
7. Cleanup
8. Performance and payment bonds

The above project overhead items are also referred to as general requirements and therefore are estimated in Division 1. Division 1 is the first division listed in the CSI MasterFormat but it is usually the last division estimated. The sum of the costs in Divisions 1 through 49 is referred to as the sum of the direct costs.

All construction projects also include indirect costs. The primary components of indirect costs are the contractor's main office overhead and profit. The amount of the main office overhead expense varies depending on the following:

1. Owner's compensation
2. Project managers' and estimators' wages
3. Clerical support wages
4. Office rent and utilities
5. Corporate legal and accounting costs
6. Advertising
7. Automobile expenses
8. Association dues
9. Travel and entertainment expenses

These costs are usually calculated as a percentage of annual sales volume. This percentage can range from 35% for a small contractor doing less than $500,000 to 5% for a large contractor with sales in excess of $100 million.

R013113-55   Installing Contractor's Overhead

Installing contractors (subcontractors) also incur costs for general requirements and main office overhead.

Included within the total incl. overhead and profit costs is a percent mark-up for overhead that includes:

1. Compensation and benefits for office staff and project managers
2. Office rent, utilities, business equipment, and maintenance
3. Corporate legal and accounting costs

4. Advertising
5. Vehicle expenses (for office staff and project managers)
6. Association dues
7. Travel, entertainment
8. Insurance
9. Small tools and equipment

R013113-60 Workers' Compensation Insurance Rates by Trade

The table below tabulates the national averages for workers' compensation insurance rates by trade and type of building. The average "Insurance Rate" is multiplied by the "% of Building Cost" for each trade. This produces the "Workers' Compensation" cost by % of total labor cost, to be added for each trade by building type to determine the weighted average workers' compensation rate for the building types analyzed.

Trade	Insurance Rate (% Labor Cost) Range		Average	% of Building Cost Office Bldgs.	Schools & Apts.	Mfg.	Workers' Compensation Office Bldgs.	Schools & Apts.	Mfg.
Excavation, Grading, etc.	3.3 % to	20.7%	9.0%	4.8%	4.9%	4.5%	0.43%	0.44%	0.41%
Piles & Foundations	6.3 to	34.3	14.5	7.1	5.2	8.7	1.03	0.75	1.26
Concrete	4.5 to	32.5	12.4	5.0	14.8	3.7	0.62	1.84	0.46
Masonry	4.4 to	43.4	14.5	6.9	7.5	1.9	1.00	1.09	0.28
Structural Steel	6.3 to	71.0	24.4	10.7	3.9	17.6	2.61	0.95	4.29
Miscellaneous & Ornamental Metals	4.4 to	28.9	11.3	2.8	4.0	3.6	0.32	0.45	0.41
Carpentry & Millwork	4.7 to	39.7	13.9	3.7	4.0	0.5	0.51	0.56	0.07
Metal or Composition Siding	6.3 to	92.8	19.1	2.3	0.3	4.3	0.44	0.06	0.82
Roofing	6.3 to	108.8	30.7	2.3	2.6	3.1	0.71	0.80	0.95
Doors & Hardware	3.9 to	39.7	11.6	0.9	1.4	0.4	0.10	0.16	0.05
Sash & Glazing	4.5 to	29.4	12.9	3.5	4.0	1.0	0.45	0.52	0.13
Lath & Plaster	3.2 to	42.3	10.7	3.3	6.9	0.8	0.35	0.74	0.09
Tile, Marble & Floors	2.9 to	22.4	9.1	2.6	3.0	0.5	0.24	0.27	0.05
Acoustical Ceilings	2.6 to	43.8	8.7	2.4	0.2	0.3	0.21	0.02	0.03
Painting	4.6 to	35.9	11.7	1.5	1.6	1.6	0.18	0.19	0.19
Interior Partitions	4.7 to	39.7	13.9	3.9	4.3	4.4	0.54	0.60	0.61
Miscellaneous Items	2.1 to	97.7	11.9	5.2	3.7	9.7	0.62	0.44	1.16
Elevators	1.4 to	14.4	5.0	2.1	1.1	2.2	0.11	0.06	0.11
Sprinklers	2.3 to	23.4	7.1	0.5	—	2.0	0.04	—	0.14
Plumbing	1.8 to	17.8	6.6	4.9	7.2	5.2	0.32	0.48	0.34
Heat., Vent., Air Conditioning	3.3 to	19.2	8.8	13.5	11.0	12.9	1.19	0.97	1.14
Electrical	2.2 to	14.4	5.5	10.1	8.4	11.1	0.56	0.46	0.61
Total	1.4 % to	108.8%	—	100.0%	100.0%	100.0%	12.58%	11.85%	13.60%

Overall Weighted Average 12.68%

Workers' Compensation Insurance Rates by States

The table below lists the weighted average Workers' Compensation base rate for each state with a factor comparing this with the national average of 12.6%.

State	Weighted Average	Factor	State	Weighted Average	Factor	State	Weighted Average	Factor
Alabama	17.8%	141	Kentucky	10.5%	83	North Dakota	7.2%	57
Alaska	10.6	84	Louisiana	19.2	152	Ohio	7.7	61
Arizona	11.2	89	Maine	11.3	90	Oklahoma	11.1	88
Arkansas	7.0	56	Maryland	12.3	98	Oregon	10.0	79
California	29.4	233	Massachusetts	11.4	90	Pennsylvania	19.5	155
Colorado	7.8	62	Michigan	9.2	73	Rhode Island	13.8	110
Connecticut	20.9	166	Minnesota	19.7	156	South Carolina	15.6	124
Delaware	14.1	112	Mississippi	11.9	94	South Dakota	12.5	99
District of Columbia	10.2	81	Missouri	13.5	107	Tennessee	10.2	81
Florida	9.6	76	Montana	8.2	65	Texas	7.3	58
Georgia	31.3	248	Nebraska	14.1	112	Utah	8.3	66
Hawaii	8.6	68	Nevada	8.4	67	Vermont	12.0	95
Idaho	9.7	77	New Hampshire	13.8	110	Virginia	7.9	63
Illinois	23.7	188	New Jersey	15.3	121	Washington	9.8	78
Indiana	4.8	38	New Mexico	14.7	117	West Virginia	5.7	45
Iowa	15.2	121	New York	18.4	146	Wisconsin	14.1	112
Kansas	7.2	57	North Carolina	16.5	131	Wyoming	6.4	51

Weighted Average for U.S. is 12.7% of payroll = 100%

The weighted average skilled worker rate for 35 trades is 12.6%. For bidding purposes, apply the full value of Workers' Compensation directly to total labor costs, or if labor is 38%, materials 42% and overhead and profit 20% of total cost, carry 38/80 x 12.6% = 6.0% of cost (before overhead and profit)

into overhead. Rates vary not only from state to state but also with the experience rating of the contractor.

Rates are the most current available at the time of publication.

563

R013113-80 Performance Bond

This table shows the cost of a Performance Bond for a construction job scheduled to be completed in 12 months. Add 1% of the premium cost per month for jobs requiring more than 12 months to complete. The rates are "standard" rates offered to contractors that the bonding company considers financially sound and capable of doing the work. Preferred rates are offered by some bonding companies based upon financial strength of the contractor. Actual rates vary from contractor to contractor and from bonding company to bonding company. Contractors should prequalify through a bonding agency before submitting a bid on a contract that requires a bond.

Contract Amount	Building Construction Class B Projects			Highways & Bridges					
				Class A New Construction			Class A-1 Highway Resurfacing		
First $ 100,000 bid	$25.00 per M			$15.00 per M			$9.40 per M		
Next 400,000 bid	$ 2,500	plus	$15.00 per M	$ 1,500	plus	$10.00 per M	$ 940	plus	$7.20 per M
Next 2,000,000 bid	8,500	plus	10.00 per M	5,500	plus	7.00 per M	3,820	plus	5.00 per M
Next 2,500,000 bid	28,500	plus	7.50 per M	19,500	plus	5.50 per M	15,820	plus	4.50 per M
Next 2,500,000 bid	47,250	plus	7.00 per M	33,250	plus	5.00 per M	28,320	plus	4.50 per M
Over 7,500,000 bid	64,750	plus	6.00 per M	45,750	plus	4.50 per M	39,570	plus	4.00 per M

R015113-65 Temporary Power Equipment

Cost data for the temporary equipment was developed utilizing the following information.

1) Re-usable material-services, transformers, equipment and cords are based on new purchase and prorated to three projects.
2) PVC feeder includes trench and backfill.
3) Connections include disconnects and fuses.
4) Labor units include an allowance for removal.
5) No utility company charges or fees are included.
6) Concrete pads or vaults are not included.
7) Utility company conduits not included.

R015423-10   Steel Tubular Scaffolding

On new construction, tubular scaffolding is efficient up to 60' high or five stories. Above this it is usually better to use hung scaffolding if construction permits. Swing scaffolding operations may interfere with tenants. In this case, the tubular is more practical at all heights.

In repairing or cleaning the front of an existing building the cost of tubular scaffolding per S.F. of building front goes up as the height increases above the first tier. The first tier cost is relatively high due to leveling and alignment.

The minimum efficient crew for erecting and dismantling is three workers. They can set up and remove 18 frame sections per day up to 5 stories high. For 6 to 12 stories high, a crew of four is most efficient. Use two or more on top and two on the bottom for handing up or hoisting. They can

also set up and remove 18 frame sections per day. At 7' horizontal spacing, this will run about 800 S.F. per day of erecting and dismantling. Time for placing and removing planks must be added to the above. A crew of three can place and remove 72 planks per day up to 5 stories. For over 5 stories, a crew of four can place and remove 80 planks per day.

The table below shows the number of pieces required to erect tubular steel scaffolding for 1000 S.F. of building frontage. This area is made up of a scaffolding system that is 12 frames (11 bays) long by 2 frames high.

For jobs under twenty-five frames, add 50% to the rental cost. Rental rates will be lower for jobs over three months duration. Large quantities for long periods can reduce rental rates by 20%.

Description of Component	Number of Pieces for 1000 S.F. of Building Front	Unit
5' Wide Standard Frame, 6'-4" High	24	Ea.
Leveling Jack & Plate	24	
Cross Brace	44	
Side Arm Bracket, 21"	12	
Guardrail Post	12	
Guardrail, 7' section	22	
Stairway Section	2	
Stairway Starter Bar	1	
Stairway Inside Handrail	2	
Stairway Outside Handrail	2	
Walk-Through Frame Guardrail	2	

Scaffolding is often used as falsework over 15' high during construction of cast-in-place concrete beams and slabs. Two foot wide scaffolding is generally used for heavy beam construction. The span between frames depends upon the load to be carried with a maximum span of 5'.

Heavy duty shoring frames with a capacity of 10,000#/leg can be spaced up to 10' O.C. depending upon form support design and loading.

Scaffolding used as horizontal shoring requires less than half the material required with conventional shoring.

On new construction, erection is done by carpenters.

Rolling towers supporting horizontal shores can reduce labor and speed the job. For maintenance work, catwalks with spans up to 70' can be supported by the rolling towers.

R015433-10 Contractor Equipment

Rental Rates shown elsewhere in the data set pertain to late model high quality machines in excellent working condition, rented from equipment dealers. Rental rates from contractors may be substantially lower than the rental rates from equipment dealers depending upon economic conditions; for older, less productive machines, reduce rates by a maximum of 15%. Any overtime must be added to the base rates. For shift work, rates are lower. Usual rule of thumb is 150% of one shift rate for two shifts; 200% for three shifts.

For periods of less than one week, operated equipment is usually more economical to rent than renting bare equipment and hiring an operator.

Costs to move equipment to a job site (mobilization) or from a job site (demobilization) are not included in rental rates, nor in any Equipment costs on any Unit Price line items or crew listings. These costs can be found elsewhere. If a piece of equipment is already at a job site, it is not appropriate to utilize mob/demob costs in an estimate again.

Rental rates vary throughout the country with larger cities generally having lower rates. Lease plans for new equipment are available for periods in excess of six months with a percentage of payments applying toward purchase.

Rental rates can also be treated as reimbursement costs for contractor-owned equipment. Owned equipment costs include depreciation, loan payments, interest, taxes, insurance, storage, and major repairs.

Monthly rental rates vary from 2% to 5% of the cost of the equipment depending on the anticipated life of the equipment and its wearing parts. Weekly rates are about 1/3 the monthly rates and daily rental rates are about 1/3 the weekly rates.

The hourly operating costs for each piece of equipment include costs to the user such as fuel, oil, lubrication, normal expendables for the equipment, and a percentage of the mechanic's wages chargeable to maintenance. The hourly operating costs listed do not include the operator's wages.

The daily cost for equipment used in the standard crews is figured by dividing the weekly rate by five, then adding eight times the hourly operating cost to give the total daily equipment cost, not including the operator. This figure is in the right hand column of the Equipment listings under Equipment Cost/Day.

Pile Driving rates shown for the pile hammer and extractor do not include leads, cranes, boilers or compressors. Vibratory pile driving requires an added field specialist during set-up and pile driving operation for the electric model. The hydraulic model requires a field specialist for set-up only. Up to 125 reuses of sheet piling are possible using vibratory drivers. For normal conditions, crane capacity for hammer type and size is as follows.

Crane Capacity	Hammer Type and Size		
	Air or Steam	Diesel	Vibratory
25 ton	to 8,750 ft.-lb.		70 H.P.
40 ton	15,000 ft.-lb.	to 32,000 ft.-lb.	170 H.P.
60 ton	25,000 ft.-lb.		300 H.P.
100 ton		112,000 ft.-lb.	

Cranes should be specified for the job by size, building and site characteristics, availability, performance characteristics, and duration of time required.

Backhoes & Shovels rent for about the same as equivalent size cranes but maintenance and operating expenses are higher. The crane operator's rate must be adjusted for high boom heights. Average adjustments: for 150' boom add 2% per hour; over 185', add 4% per hour; over 210', add 6% per hour; over 250', add 8% per hour and over 295', add 12% per hour.

Tower Cranes of the climbing or static type have jibs from 50' to 200' and capacities at maximum reach range from 4,000 to 14,000 pounds. Lifting capacities increase up to maximum load as the hook radius decreases.

Typical rental rates, based on purchase price, are about 2% to 3% per month.

Erection and dismantling run between 500 and 2000 labor hours. Climbing operation takes 10 labor hours per 20' climb. Crane dead time is about 5 hours per 40' climb. If crane is bolted to side of the building add cost of ties and extra mast sections. Climbing cranes have from 80' to 180' of mast while static cranes have 80' to 800' of mast.

Truck Cranes can be converted to tower cranes by using tower attachments. Mast heights over 400' have been used.

A single 100' high material **Hoist and Tower** can be erected and dismantled in about 400 labor hours; a double 100' high hoist and tower in about 600 labor hours. Erection times for additional heights are 3 and 4 labor hours

per vertical foot respectively up to 150', and 4 to 5 labor hours per vertical foot over 150' high. A 40' high portable Buck hoist takes about 160 labor hours to erect and dismantle. Additional heights take 2 labor hours per vertical foot to 80' and 3 labor hours per vertical foot for the next 100'. Most material hoists do not meet local code requirements for carrying personnel.

A 150' high **Personnel Hoist** requires about 500 to 800 labor hours to erect and dismantle. Budget erection time at 5 labor hours per vertical foot for all trades. Local code requirements or labor scarcity requiring overtime can add up to 50% to any of the above erection costs.

Earthmoving Equipment: The selection of earthmoving equipment depends upon the type and quantity of material, moisture content, haul distance, haul road, time available, and equipment available. Short haul cut and fill operations may require dozers only, while another operation may require excavators, a fleet of trucks, and spreading and compaction equipment. Stockpiled material and granular material are easily excavated with front end loaders. Scrapers are most economically used with hauls between 300' and 1-1/2 miles if adequate haul roads can be maintained. Shovels are often used for blasted rock and any material where a vertical face of 8' or more can be excavated. Special conditions may dictate the use of draglines, clamshells, or backhoes. Spreading and compaction equipment must be matched to the soil characteristics, the compaction required and the rate the fill is being supplied.

R015433-15 Heavy Lifting

Hydraulic Climbing Jacks

The use of hydraulic heavy lift systems is an alternative to conventional type crane equipment. The lifting, lowering, pushing, or pulling mechanism is a hydraulic climbing jack moving on a square steel jackrod from 1-5/8" to 4" square, or a steel cable. The jackrod or cable can be vertical or horizontal, stationary or movable, depending on the individual application. When the jackrod is stationary, the climbing jack will climb the rod and push or pull the load along with itself. When the climbing jack is stationary, the jackrod is movable with the load attached to the end and the climbing jack will lift or lower the jackrod with the attached load. The heavy lift system is normally operated by a single control lever located at the hydraulic pump.

The system is flexible in that one or more climbing jacks can be applied wherever a load support point is required, and the rate of lift synchronized.

Economic benefits have been demonstrated on projects such as: erection of ground assembled roofs and floors, complete bridge spans, girders and trusses, towers, chimney liners and steel vessels, storage tanks, and heavy machinery. Other uses are raising and lowering offshore work platforms, caissons, tunnel sections and pipelines.

R015436-50 Mobilization

Costs to move rented construction equipment to a job site from an equipment dealer's or contractor's yard (mobilization) or off the job site (demobilization) are not included in the rental or operating rates, nor in the equipment cost on a unit price line or in a crew listing. These costs can be found consolidated in the Mobilization section of the data and elsewhere in particular site work sections. If a piece of

equipment is already on the job site, it is not appropriate to include mob/demob costs in a new estimate that requires use of that equipment. The following table identifies approximate sizes of rented construction equipment that would be hauled on a towed trailer. Because this listing is not all-encompassing, the user can infer as to what size trailer might be required for a piece of equipment not listed.

3-ton Trailer	20-ton Trailer	40-ton Trailer	50-ton Trailer
20 H.P. Excavator	110 H.P. Excavator	200 H.P. Excavator	270 H.P. Excavator
50 H.P. Skid Steer	165 H.P. Dozer	300 H.P. Dozer	Small Crawler Crane
35 H.P. Roller	150 H.P. Roller	400 H.P. Scraper	500 H.P. Scraper
40 H.P. Trencher	Backhoe	450 H.P. Art. Dump Truck	500 H.P. Art. Dump Truck

R024119-10 Demolition Defined

Whole Building Demolition - Demolition of the whole building with no concern for any particular building element, component, or material type being demolished. This type of demolition is accomplished with large pieces of construction equipment that break up the structure, load it into trucks and haul it to a disposal site, but disposal or dump fees are not included. Demolition of below-grade foundation elements, such as footings, foundation walls, grade beams, slabs on grade, etc., is not included. Certain mechanical equipment containing flammable liquids or ozone-depleting refrigerants, electric lighting elements, communication equipment components, and other building elements may contain hazardous waste, and must be removed, either selectively or carefully, as hazardous waste before the building can be demolished.

Foundation Demolition - Demolition of below-grade foundation footings, foundation walls, grade beams, and slabs on grade. This type of demolition is accomplished by hand or pneumatic hand tools, and does not include saw cutting, or handling, loading, hauling, or disposal of the debris.

Gutting - Removal of building interior finishes and electrical/mechanical systems down to the load-bearing and sub-floor elements of the rough building frame, with no concern for any particular building element, component, or material type being demolished. This type of demolition is accomplished by hand or pneumatic hand tools, and includes loading into trucks, but not hauling, disposal or dump fees, scaffolding, or shoring. Certain mechanical equipment containing flammable liquids or ozone-depleting refrigerants, electric lighting elements, communication equipment components, and other building elements may contain hazardous waste, and must be removed, either selectively or carefully, as hazardous waste, before the building is gutted.

Selective Demolition - Demolition of a selected building element, component, or finish, with some concern for surrounding or adjacent elements, components, or finishes (see the first Subdivision (s) at the beginning of appropriate Divisions). This type of demolition is accomplished by hand or pneumatic hand tools, and does not include handling, loading,

storing, hauling, or disposal of the debris, scaffolding, or shoring. "Gutting" methods may be used in order to save time, but damage that is caused to surrounding or adjacent elements, components, or finishes may have to be repaired at a later time.

Careful Removal - Removal of a piece of service equipment, building element or component, or material type, with great concern for both the removed item and surrounding or adjacent elements, components or finishes. The purpose of careful removal may be to protect the removed item for later re-use, preserve a higher salvage value of the removed item, or replace an item while taking care to protect surrounding or adjacent elements, components, connections, or finishes from cosmetic and/or structural damage. An approximation of the time required to perform this type of removal is 1/3 to 1/2 the time it would take to install a new item of like kind (see Reference Number R260105-30). This type of removal is accomplished by hand or pneumatic hand tools, and does not include loading, hauling, or storing the removed item, scaffolding, shoring, or lifting equipment.

Cutout Demolition - Demolition of a small quantity of floor, wall, roof, or other assembly, with concern for the appearance and structural integrity of the surrounding materials. This type of demolition is accomplished by hand or pneumatic hand tools, and does not include saw cutting, handling, loading, hauling, or disposal of debris, scaffolding, or shoring.

Rubbish Handling - Work activities that involve handling, loading or hauling of debris. Generally, the cost of rubbish handling must be added to the cost of all types of demolition, with the exception of whole building demolition.

Minor Site Demolition - Demolition of site elements outside the footprint of a building. This type of demolition is accomplished by hand or pneumatic hand tools, or with larger pieces of construction equipment, and may include loading a removed item onto a truck (check the Crew for equipment used). It does not include saw cutting, hauling or disposal of debris, and, sometimes, handling or loading.

R024119-20 Dumpsters

Dumpster rental costs on construction sites are presented in two ways.

The cost per week rental includes the delivery of the dumpster; its pulling or emptying once per week, and its final removal. The assumption is made that the dumpster contractor could choose to empty a dumpster by simply bringing in an empty unit and removing the full one. These costs also include the disposal of the materials in the dumpster.

The Alternate Pricing can be used when actual planned conditions are not approximated by the weekly numbers. For example, these lines can be used when a dumpster is needed for 4 weeks and will need to be emptied 2 or 3 times per week. Conversely the Alternate Pricing lines can be used when a dumpster will be rented for several weeks or months but needs to be emptied only a few times over this period.

R053100-10   Decking Descriptions

General - All Deck Products

A steel deck is made by cold forming structural grade sheet steel into a repeating pattern of parallel ribs. The strength and stiffness of the panels are the result of the ribs and the material properties of the steel. Deck lengths can be varied to suit job conditions, but because of shipping considerations, are usually less than 40 feet. Standard deck width varies with the product used but full sheets are usually 12", 18", 24", 30", or 36". The deck is typically furnished in a standard width with the ends cut square. Any cutting for width, such as at openings or for angular fit, is done at the job site.

The deck is typically attached to the building frame with arc puddle welds, self-drilling screws, or powder or pneumatically driven pins. Sheet to sheet fastening is done with screws, button punching (crimping), or welds.

Composite Floor Deck

After installation and adequate fastening, a floor deck serves several purposes. It (a) acts as a working platform, (b) stabilizes the frame, (c) serves as a concrete form for the slab, and (d) reinforces the slab to carry the design loads applied during the life of the building. Composite decks are distinguished by the presence of shear connector devices as part of the deck. These devices are designed to mechanically lock the concrete and deck together so that the concrete and the deck work together to carry subsequent floor loads. These shear connector devices can be rolled-in embossments, lugs, holes, or wires welded to the panels. The deck profile can also be used to interlock concrete and steel.

Composite deck finishes are either galvanized (zinc coated) or phosphatized/painted. Galvanized deck has a zinc coating on both the top and bottom surfaces. The phosphatized/painted deck has a bare (phosphatized) top surface that will come into contact with the concrete. This bare top surface can be expected to develop rust before the concrete is placed. The bottom side of the deck has a primer coat of paint.

A composite floor deck is normally installed so the panel ends do not overlap on the supporting beams. Shear lugs or panel profile shapes often prevent a tight metal to metal fit if the panel ends overlap; the air gap caused by overlapping will prevent proper fusion with the structural steel supports when the panel end laps are shear stud welded.

Adequate end bearing of the deck must be obtained as shown on the drawings. If bearing is actually less in the field than shown on the drawings, further investigation is required.

Roof Deck

A roof deck is not designed to act compositely with other materials. A roof deck acts alone in transferring horizontal and vertical loads into the building frame. Roof deck rib openings are usually narrower than floor deck rib openings. This provides adequate support of the rigid thermal insulation board.

A roof deck is typically installed to endlap approximately 2" over supports. However, it can be butted (or lapped more than 2") to solve field fit problems. Since designers frequently use the installed deck system as part of the horizontal bracing system (the deck as a diaphragm), any fastening substitution or change should be approved by the designer. Continuous perimeter support of the deck is necessary to limit edge deflection in the finished roof and may be required for diaphragm shear transfer.

Standard roof deck finishes are galvanized or primer painted. The standard factory applied paint for roof decks is a primer paint and is not intended to weather for extended periods of time. Field painting or touching up of abrasions and deterioration of the primer coat or other protective finishes is the responsibility of the contractor.

Cellular Deck

A cellular deck is made by attaching a bottom steel sheet to a roof deck or composite floor deck panel. A cellular deck can be used in the same manner as a floor deck. Electrical, telephone, and data wires are easily run through the chase created between the deck panel and the bottom sheet.

When used as part of the electrical distribution system, the cellular deck must be installed so that the ribs line up and create a smooth cell transition at abutting ends. The joint that occurs at butting cell ends must be taped or otherwise sealed to prevent wet concrete from seeping into the cell. Cell interiors must be free of welding burrs, or other sharp intrusions, to prevent damage to wires.

When used as a roof deck, the bottom flat plate is usually left exposed to view. Care must be maintained during erection to keep good alignment and prevent damage.

A cellular deck is sometimes used with the flat plate on the top side to provide a flat working surface. Installation of the deck for this purpose requires special methods for attachment to the frame because the flat plate, now on the top, can prevent direct access to the deck material that is bearing on the structural steel. It may be advisable to treat the flat top surface to prevent slipping.

A cellular deck is always furnished galvanized or painted over galvanized.

Form Deck

A form deck can be any floor or roof deck product used as a concrete form. Connections to the frame are by the same methods used to anchor floor and roof decks. Welding washers are recommended when welding a deck that is less than 20 gauge thickness.

A form deck is furnished galvanized, prime painted, or uncoated. A galvanized deck must be used for those roof deck systems where a form deck is used to carry a lightweight insulating concrete fill.

R078413-30   Firestopping

Firestopping is the sealing of structural, mechanical, electrical and other penetrations through fire-rated assemblies. The basic components of firestop systems are safing insulation and firestop sealant on both sides of wall penetrations and the top side of floor penetrations.

Pipe penetrations are assumed to be through concrete, grout, or joint compound and can be sleeved or unsleeved. Costs for the penetrations and sleeves are not included. An annular space of 1" is assumed. Escutcheons are not included.

A metallic pipe is assumed to be copper, aluminum, cast iron or similar metallic material. An insulated metallic pipe is assumed to be covered with a thermal insulating jacket of varying thickness and materials.

A non-metallic pipe is assumed to be PVC, CPVC, FR Polypropylene or similar plastic piping material. Intumescent firestop sealant or wrap strips are included. Collars on both sides of wall penetrations and a sheet metal plate on the underside of floor penetrations are included.

Ductwork is assumed to be sheet metal, stainless steel or similar metallic material. Duct penetrations are assumed to be through concrete, grout or joint compound. Costs for penetrations and sleeves are not included. An annular space of 1/2" is assumed.

Multi-trade openings include costs for sheet metal forms, firestop mortar, wrap strips, collars and sealants as necessary.

Structural penetrations joints are assumed to be 1/2" or less. CMU walls are assumed to be within 1-1/2" of the metal deck. Drywall walls are assumed to be tight to the underside of metal decking.

Metal panel, glass or curtain wall systems include a spandrel area of 5' filled with mineral wool foil-faced insulation. Fasteners and stiffeners are included.

R224000-10 Water Consumption Rates

Fixture Type	Water Supply Fixture Unit Value		
	Hot Water	Cold Water	Combined
Bathtub	1.0	1.0	1.4
Clothes Washer	1.0	1.0	1.4
Dishwasher	1.4	0.0	1.4
Kitchen Sink	1.0	1.0	1.4
Laundry Tub	1.0	1.0	1.4
Lavatory	0.5	0.5	0.7
Shower Stall	1.0	1.0	1.4
Water Closet (tank type)	0.0	2.2	2.2
Full Bath Group			
w/bathtub or shower stall	1.5	2.7	3.6
Half Bath Group			
w/W.C. and Lavatory	0.5	2.5	2.6
Kitchen Group			
w/Dishwasher and Sink	1.9	1.0	2.5
Laundry Group			
w/Clothes Washer and			
Laundry Tub	1.8	1.8	2.5
Hose bibb (sillcock)	0.0	2.5	2.5

Notes:
Typically, WSFU = 1GPM

Supply loads in the building water-distribution system shall be determined by total load on the pipe being sized, in terms of water supply fixture units (WSFU) and gallons per minute (GPM) flow rates. For fixtures not listed, choose a WSFU value of a fixture with similar flow characteristics. Water Fixture Supply Units determined the required water supply to fixtures and their service systems. Fixture units are equal to one (1) cubic foot of water drained in a 1-1/4″ pipe per minute. It is not a flow rate unit but a design factor.

Excerpted from the 2012 *International Plumbing Code*, Copyright 2011.
Washington, D.C.: International Code Council. Reproduced with permission.
All rights reserved. www.ICCSAFE.org

R224000-20   Fixture Demands in Gallons per Fixture per Hour

The table below is based on a 140°F final temperature except for dishwashers in public places where 180°F water is mandatory.

Supply Systems for Flush Tanks			Supply Systems for Flushometer Valves		
Load	Demand		Load	Demand	
WSFU	GPM	CU. FT.	WSFU	GPM	CU. FT.
1.0	3.0	0.041040	–	–	–
2.0	5.0	0.068400	–	–	–
3.0	6.5	0.868920	–	–	–
4.0	8.0	1.069440	–	–	–
5.0	9.4	1.256592	5.0	15	2.0052
6.0	10.7	1.430376	6.0	17.4	2.326032
7.0	11.8	1.577424	7.0	19.8	2.646364
8.0	12.8	1.711104	8.0	22.2	2.967696
9.0	13.7	1.831416	9.0	24.6	3.288528
10.0	14.6	1.951728	10.0	27	3.60936
11.0	15.4	2.058672	11.0	27.8	3.716304
12.0	16.0	2.138880	12.0	28.6	3.823248
13.0	16.5	2.205720	13.0	29.4	3.930192
14.0	17.0	2.272560	14.0	30.2	4.037136
15.0	17.5	2.339400	15.0	31	4.14408
16.0	18.0	2.906240	16.0	31.8	4.241024
17.0	18.4	2.459712	17.0	32.6	4.357968
18.0	18.8	2.513184	18.0	33.4	4.464912
19.0	19.2	2.566656	19.0	34.2	4.571856
20.0	19.6	2.620218	20.0	35.0	4.678800
25.0	21.5	2.874120	25.0	38.0	5.079840
30.0	23.3	3.114744	30.0	42.0	5.611356
35.0	24.9	3.328632	35.0	44.0	5.881920
40.0	26.3	3.515784	40.0	46.0	6.149280
45.0	27.7	3.702936	45.0	48.0	6.416640
50.0	29.1	3.890088	50.0	50.0	6.684000

Notes:

When designing a plumbing system that utilizes fixtures other than, or in addition to, water closets, use the data provided in the Supply Systems for Flush Tanks section of the above table.

To obtain the probable maximum demand, multiply the total demands for the fixtures (gal./fixture/hour) by the demand factor. The heater should have a heating capacity in gallons per hour equal to this maximum. The storage tank should have a capacity in gallons equal to the probable maximum demand multiplied by the storage capacity factor.

Reference Tables

Fig. R238313-11

R238313-10   Heat Trace Systems

Before you can determine the cost of a HEAT TRACE installation, the method of attachment must be established. There are four (4) common methods:

1. Cable is simply attached to the pipe with polyester tape every 12'.
2. Cable is attached with a continuous cover of 2" wide aluminum tape.
3. Cable is attached with factory extruded heat transfer cement and covered with metallic raceway with clips every 10'.
4. Cable is attached between layers of pipe insulation using either clips or polyester tape.

Example: Components for method 3 must include:
- A. Heat trace cable by voltage and watts per linear foot.
- B. Heat transfer cement, 1 gallon per 60 linear feet of cover.
- C. Metallic raceway by size and type.
- D. Raceway clips by size of pipe.

When taking off linear foot lengths of cable add the following for each valve in the system. (E)

In all of the above methods each component of the system must be priced individually.

SCREWED OR WELDED VALVE:			FLANGED VALVE:			BUTTERFLY VALVES:		
1/2"	=	6"	1/2"	=	1' -0"	1/2"	=	0'
3/4"	=	9"	3/4"	=	1' -6"	3/4"	=	0'
1"	=	1' -0"	1"	=	2' -0"	1"	=	1' -0"
1-1/2"	=	1' -6"	1-1/2"	=	2' -6"	1-1/2"	=	1' -6"
2"	=	2'	2"	=	2' -6"	2"	=	2' -0"
2-1/2"	=	2' -6"	2-1/2"	=	3' -0"	2-1/2"	=	2' -6"
3"	=	2' -6"	3"	=	3' -6"	3"	=	2' -6"
4"	=	4' -0"	4"	=	4' -0"	4"	=	3' -0"
6"	=	7' -0"	6"	=	8' -0"	6"	=	3' -6"
8"	=	9' -6"	8"	=	11' -0"	8"	=	4' -0"
10"	=	12' -6"	10"	=	14' -0"	10"	=	4' -0"
12"	=	15' -0"	12"	=	16' -6"	12"	=	5' -0"
14"	=	18' -0"	14"	=	19' -6"	14"	=	5' -6"
16"	=	21' -6"	16"	=	23' -0"	16"	=	6' -0"
18"	=	25' -6"	18"	=	27' -0"	18"	=	6' -6"
20"	=	28' -6"	20"	=	30' -0"	20"	=	7' -0"
24"	=	34' -0"	24"	=	36' -0"	24"	=	8' -0"
30"	=	40' -0"	30"	=	42' -0"	30"	=	10' -0"

572

For customer support on your Electrical Costs with RSMeans Data, call 800.448.8182.

R238313-10 Heat Trace Systems (cont.)

Add the following quantities of heat transfer cement to linear foot totals for each valve:

Nominal Valve Size	Gallons of Cement per Valve
1/2"	0.14
3/4"	0.21
1"	0.29
1-1/2"	0.36
2"	0.43
2-1/2"	0.70
3"	0.71
4"	1.00
6"	1.43
8"	1.48
10"	1.50
12"	1.60
14"	1.75
16"	2.00
18"	2.25
20"	2.50
24"	3.00
30"	3.75

The following must be added to the list of components to accurately price HEAT TRACE systems:

1. Expediter fitting and clamp fasteners (F)
2. Junction box and nipple connected to expediter fitting (G)
3. Field installed terminal blocks within junction box
4. Ground lugs
5. Piping from power source to expediter fitting
6. Controls
7. Thermostats
8. Branch wiring
9. Cable splices
10. End of cable terminations
11. Branch piping fittings and boxes

Deduct the following percentages from labor if cable lengths in the same area exceed:

150' to 250'	10%	351' to 500'	20%
251' to 350'	15%	Over 500'	25%

Add the following percentages to labor for elevated installations:

15' to 20' high	10%	31' to 35' high	40%
21' to 25' high	20%	36' to 40' high	50%
26' to 30' high	30%	Over 40' high	60%

R238313-20 Spiral-Wrapped Heat Trace Cable (Pitch Table)

In order to increase the amount of heat, occasionally heat trace cable is wrapped in a spiral fashion around a pipe, increasing the number of feet of heater cable per linear foot of pipe.

Engineers first determine the heat loss per foot of pipe (based on the insulating material, its thickness, and the temperature differential across it). A ratio is then calculated by the formula:

$$\text{Feet of Heat Trace per Foot of Pipe} = \frac{\text{Watts/Foot of Heat Loss}}{\text{Watts/Foot of the Cable}}$$

The linear distance between wraps (pitch) is then taken from a chart or table. Generally, the pitch is listed on a drawing leaving the estimator to calculate the total length of heat tape required. An approximation may be taken from this table.

Feet of Heat Trace Per Foot of Pipe

Pitch In Inches	1	1¼	1½	2	2½	3	4	6	8	10	12	14	16	18	20	24
3.5	1.80															
4	1.65															
5	1.46	1.60	1.80													
6	1.34	1.45	1.55	1.75												
7	1.25	1.35	1.43	1.57	1.75											
8	1.20	1.28	1.34	1.45	1.60	1.80										
9	1.16	1.23	1.28	1.37	1.51	1.68										
10	1.13	1.19	1.24	1.32	1.44	1.57	1.82									
15	1.06	1.08	1.10	1.15	1.21	1.29	1.42	1.78								
20	1.04	1.05	1.06	1.08	1.13	1.17	1.25	1.49	1.73							
25		1.04	1.04	1.06	1.08	1.11	1.17	1.33	1.51	1.72						
30				1.04	1.05	1.07	1.12	1.24	1.37	1.54	1.70	1.80				
35					1.06	1.06	1.09	1.17	1.28	1.42	1.54	1.64	1.78			
40						1.05	1.07	1.14	1.22	1.33	1.44	1.52	1.64	1.75		
50							1.05	1.09	1.15	1.22	1.29	1.35	1.44	1.53	1.64	1.83
60								1.06	1.11	1.16	1.21	1.25	1.31	1.39	1.46	1.62
70								1.05	1.08	1.12	1.17	1.19	1.24	1.30	1.35	1.47
80									1.06	1.09	1.13	1.15	1.19	1.24	1.28	1.38
90									1.04	1.06	1.10	1.13	1.16	1.19	1.23	1.32
100										1.05	1.08	1.10	1.13	1.15	1.19	1.23

Note: Common practice would normally limit the lower end of the table to 5% of additional heat. Above 80% an engineer would likely opt for two (2) parallel cables.

R260102-20 Labor Adjustment Factors

Labor Adjustment Factors are provided for Divisions 26, 27, and 28 to assist the mechanical estimator account for the various complexities and special conditions of any particular project. While a single percentage has been entered on each line of Division 26 01 02.20, it should be understood that these are just suggested midpoints of ranges of values commonly used by mechanical estimators. They may be increased or decreased depending on the severity of the special conditions.

The group for "existing occupied buildings" has been the subject of requests for explanation. Actually there are two stages to this group: buildings that arc existing and "finished" but unoccupied, and those that also are occupied. Buildings that are "finished" may result in higher labor costs due to the

workers having to be more careful not to damage finished walls, ceilings, floors, etc. and may necessitate special protective coverings and barriers. Also corridor bends and doorways may not accommodate long pieces of pipe or larger pieces of equipment. Work above an already hung ceiling can be very time consuming. The addition of occupants may force the work to be done on premium time (nights and/or weekends), eliminate the possible use of some preferred tools such as pneumatic drivers, powder charged drivers, etc. The estimator should evaluate the access to the work area and just how the work is going to be accomplished to arrive at an increase in labor costs over "normal" new construction productivity.

R260105-30 Electrical Demolition (Removal for Replacement)

The purpose of this reference number is to provide a guide to users for electrical "removal for replacement" by applying the rule of thumb: 1/3 of new installation time (typical range from 20% to 50%) for removal. Remember to use reasonable judgment when applying the suggested percentage factor. For example:

Contractors have been requested to remove an existing fluorescent lighting fixture and replace with a new fixture utilizing energy saver lamps and electronic ballast:

In order to fully understand the extent of the project, contractors should visit the job site and estimate the time to perform the renovation work in accordance with applicable national, state and local regulation and codes.

The contractor may need to add extra labor hours to his estimate if he discovers unknown concealed conditions such as: contaminated asbestos ceiling, broken acoustical ceiling tile and need to repair, patch and touch-up paint all the damaged or disturbed areas, tasks normally assigned to general contractors. In addition, the owner could request that the contractors salvage the materials removed and turn over the materials to the owner or dispose of the materials to a reclamation station. The normal removal item is 0.5 labor-hour for a lighting fixture and 1.5 labor-hours for new installation time. Revise the estimate times from 2 labor-hours work up to a minimum 4 labor-hours work for just a fluorescent lighting fixture.

For removal of large concentrations of lighting fixtures in the same area, apply an "economy of scale" to reduce estimating labor hours.

Figure R260110-10　Typical Overhead Service Entrance

Utility Pole

Service Entrance Cap 3"

Building Wall

Galvanized Conduit 3"

Two Hole Pipe Clip 3"

Coupling

Grade Line

3" Locknut

3" Locknut & Bushing Insulated In Pullbox

Pullbox

3" Galv. Conduit

Elbow

3" PVC Conduit

3" PVC To Galv. Adapter

Adapter

For 600 AMP Service, Wiring 2 Parallel Runs of 3" Galv. Conduit to 600 AMP. Circuit Breaker Below

4 - 350 kcmil XHHW In Above Conduit

3" Galv. Conduit Used For Safety On Pole And Through Foundation

2 Locknuts And 1 Insulating Bushing Required Where #4 Or Larger Wire Used

Figure R260110-11　Typical Commercial Electric System

Panel First Floor 100 AMP.

Floor Box In Slab

Plate for Concrete Ring　Concrete Ring

Meter

600 AMP. Circuit Breaker

C

F

F

To Pull Box

B

B

D

200A CB

CT Cabinet

E

Cutaway Box Showing Wire Room

A

Ground Rod

Panel Basement 600 AMP.

D NEMA-3R 200 AMP.

100 AMP.

Ground Clamp

A = 1" Conduit w/1-#1/0 Wire XHHW
B = 2-3" Conduits w/4-350 kcmil XHHW in Each
C = 1¼" Conduit w/4 #3 THHN
D = 1¼" Conduit w/3 #1 XHHW
E = 1" Conduit w/4 #6 THHN
F = ½" Conduit w/2 #12 THHN

D Condenser Unit

E Elevator Controller

F

575

Figure R260110-12 Preliminary Procedure

1. Determine building size and use.
2. Develop total load in watts.
   a. Lighting
   b. Receptacle
   c. Air Conditioning
   d. Elevator
   e. Other power requirements
3. Determine best voltage available from utility company.
4. Determine cost from tables for loads (a) through (e) above.
5. Determine size of service from formulas (R260110-17).
6. Determine costs for service, panels, and feeders from tables.

Figure R260110-13 Office Building 90' x 210', 3 story, w/garage

Garage Area = 18,900 S.F.
Office Area = 56,700 S.F.
Elevator = 2 @ 125 FPM

Tables	Power Required	Watts
D5010-1151	Garage Lighting .5 Watt/S.F.	9,450
	Office Lighting 3 Watts/S.F.	170,100
D5010-1151	Office Receptacles 2 Watts/S.F.	113,400
D5010-1151, R262213-27	Low Rise Office A.C. 4.3 Watts/S.F.	243,810
D5010-1152, 1153	Elevators - 2 @ 20 HP = 2 @ 17,404 Watts/Ea.	34,808
D5010-1151	Misc. Motors + Power 1.2 Watts/S.F.	68,040
	Total	639,608 Watts

Voltage Available

277/480V, 3 Phase, 4 Wire

Formula

D5010-116
$$\text{Amperes} = \frac{\text{Watts}}{\text{Volts x Power Factor x 1.73}} = \frac{639,608}{480V \text{ x } .8 \text{ x } 1.73} = 963 \text{ Amps}$$

Use 1200 Amp Service

System	Description	Unit Cost	Unit	Total
D5020 210 0200	Garage Lighting (Interpolated)	$2.72	S.F.	$ 51,408
D5020 210 0540	Office Lighting (Using 32 W lamps)	8.24	S.F.	467,208
D5020 115 0880	Receptacle-Undercarpet	3.92	S.F.	222,264
D5020 140 0280	Air Conditioning	0.65	S.F.	36,855
D5020 135 0320	Misc. Pwr.	0.35	S.F.	19,845
D5020 145 2120	Elevators - 2 @ 20HP	2,775.00	Ea.	5,550
D5010 130 1250	Underground Electric Service - 1200 Amp	60,100.00	Ea.	60,100
D5010 230 0480	Feeder - Assume 200 feet	313.00	L.F.	62,600
D5010 240 0580	Panels - 277/480V, 1200 Amp	35,275.00	Ea.	35,275
D5030 910 0400	Fire Detection	35,400.00	Ea.	35,400
		Total		$996,505
		or		$996,500

Table R260110-14 Nominal Watts Per S.F. for Electric Systems for Various Building Types

Type Construction	1. Lighting	2. Devices	3. HVAC	4. Misc.	5. Elevator	Total Watts
Apartment, luxury high rise	2	2.2	3	1		
Apartment, low rise	2	2	3	1		
Auditorium	2.5	1	3.3	.8		
Bank, branch office	3	2.1	5.7	1.4		
Bank, main office	2.5	1.5	5.7	1.4		
Church	1.8	.8	3.3	.8		
College, science building	3	3	5.3	1.3		
College, library	2.5	.8	5.7	1.4		
College, physical education center	2	1	4.5	1.1		
Department store	2.5	.9	4	1		
Dormitory, college	1.5	1.2	4	1		
Drive-in doughnut shop	3	4	6.8	1.7		
Garage, commercial	.5	.5	0	.5		
Hospital, general	2	4.5	5	1.3		
Hospital, pediatric	3	3.8	5	1.3		
Hotel, airport	2	1	5	1.3		
Housing for the elderly	2	1.2	4	1		
Manufacturing, food processing	3	1	4.5	1.1		
Manufacturing, apparel	2	1	4.5	1.1		
Manufacturing, tools	4	1	4.5	1.1		
Medical clinic	2.5	1.5	3.2	1		
Nursing home	2	1.6	4	1		
Office building, high rise	3	2	4.7	1.2		
Office building, low rise	3	2	4.3	1.2		
Radio-TV studio	3.8	2.2	7.6	1.9		
Restaurant	2.5	2	6.8	1.7		
Retail store	2.5	.9	5.5	1.4		
School, elementary	3	1.9	5.3	1.3		
School, junior high	3	1.5	5.3	1.3		
School, senior high	2.3	1.7	5.3	1.3		
Supermarket	3	1	4	1		
Telephone exchange	1	.6	4.5	1.1		
Theater	2.5	1	3.3	.8		
Town Hall	2	1.9	5.3	1.3		
U.S. Post Office	3	2	5	1.3		
Warehouse, grocery	1	.6	0	.5		

Rule of Thumb: 1 KVA = 1 HP (Single Phase)

Three Phase:

Watts = 1.73 x Volts x Current x Power Factor x Efficiency

$$\text{Horsepower} = \frac{\text{Volts x Current x 1.73 x Power Factor}}{746 \text{ Watts}}$$

See R260120 for an additional reference

Table R260110-15 Horsepower Requirements for Elevators with 3 Phase Motors

Type	Maximum Travel Height in Ft.	Travel Speeds in FPM	Capacity of Cars in Lbs.		
			1200	1500	1800
Hydraulic	70	70	10	15	15
		85	15	15	15
		100	15	15	20
		110	20	20	20
		125	20	20	20
		150	25	25	25
		175	25	30	30
		200	30	30	40
Geared Traction	300	200			
		350			
			2000	2500	3000
Hydraulic	70	70	15	20	20
		85	20	20	25
		100	20	25	30
		110	20	25	30
		125	25	30	40
		150	30	40	50
		175	40	50	50
		200	40	50	60
Geared Traction	300	200	10	10	15
		350	15	15	23
			3500	4000	4500
Hydraulic	70	70	20	25	30
		85	25	30	30
		100	30	40	40
		110	40	40	50
		125	40	50	50
		150	50	50	60
		175	60		
		200	60		
Geared Traction	300	200	15		23
		350	23		35

The power factor of electric motors varies from 80% to 90% in larger size motors. The efficiency likewise varies from 80% on a small motor to 90% on a large motor.

Table R260110-16 Watts per Motor

90% Power Factor & Efficiency @ 200 or 460V			
HP	Watts	HP	Watts
10	9024	30	25784
15	13537	40	33519
20	17404	50	41899
25	21916	60	49634

577

For customer support on your Electrical Costs with RSMeans Data, call 800.448.8182.

Table R260110-17 Electrical Formulas

Ohm's Law

Ohm's Law is a method of explaining the relation between voltage, current, and resistance in an electrical circuit. It is practically the basis of all electrical calculations. The term "electromotive force" is often used to designate pressure in volts. This formula can be expressed in various forms.

To find the current in amperes:

$$\text{Current} = \frac{\text{Voltage}}{\text{Resistance}} \quad \text{or} \quad \text{Amperes} = \frac{\text{Volts}}{\text{Ohms}} \quad \text{or} \quad I = \frac{E}{R}$$

The flow of current in amperes through any circuit is equal to the voltage or electromotive force divided by the resistance of that circuit.

To find the pressure or voltage:

Voltage = Current x Resistance   or   Volts = Amperes x Ohms
or   E = I x R

The voltage required to force a current through a circuit is equal to the resistance of the circuit multiplied by the current.

To find the resistance:

$$\text{Resistance} = \frac{\text{Voltage}}{\text{Current}} \quad \text{or} \quad \text{Ohms} = \frac{\text{Volts}}{\text{Amperes}} \quad \text{or} \quad R = \frac{E}{I}$$

The resistance of a circuit is equal to the voltage divided by the current flowing through that circuit.

Power Formulas

One horsepower = 746 watts   One kilowatt = 1000 watts

The power factor of electric motors varies from 80% to 90% in the larger size motors.

Single-Phase Alternating Current Circuits

Power in Watts = Volts x Amperes x Power Factor

To find current in amperes:

$$\text{Current} = \frac{\text{Watts}}{\text{Volts x Power Factor}} \quad \text{or}$$

$$\text{Amperes} = \frac{\text{Watts}}{\text{Volts x Power Factor}} \quad \text{or} \quad I = \frac{W}{E \times PF}$$

To find current of a motor, single phase:

$$\text{Current} = \frac{\text{Horsepower x 746}}{\text{Volts x Power Factor x Efficiency}} \quad \text{or}$$

$$I = \frac{HP \times 746}{E \times PF \times Eff.}$$

To find horsepower of a motor, single phase:

$$\text{Horsepower} = \frac{\text{Volts x Current x Power Factor x Efficiency}}{746 \text{ Watts}}$$

$$HP = \frac{E \times I \times PF \times Eff.}{746}$$

To find power in watts of a motor, single phase:

Watts = Volts x Current x Power Factor x Efficiency   or
Watts = E x I x PF x Eff.

To find single phase kVA:

$$1 \text{ Phase kVA} = \frac{\text{Volts x Amps}}{1000}$$

Three-Phase Alternating Current Circuits

Power in Watts = Volts x Amperes x Power Factor x 1.73

To find current in amperes in each wire:

$$\text{Current} = \frac{\text{Watts}}{\text{Voltage x Power Factor x 1.73}} \quad \text{or}$$

$$\text{Amperes} = \frac{\text{Watts}}{\text{Volts x Power Factor x 1.73}} \quad \text{or} \quad I = \frac{W}{E \times PF \times 1.73}$$

To find current of a motor, 3 phase:

$$\text{Current} = \frac{\text{Horsepower x 746}}{\text{Volts x Power Factor x Efficiency x 1.73}} \quad \text{or}$$

$$I = \frac{HP \times 746}{E \times PF \times Eff. \times 1.73}$$

To find horsepower of a motor, 3 phase:

$$\text{Horsepower} = \frac{\text{Volts x Current x 1.73 x Power Factor}}{746 \text{ Watts}}$$

$$HP = \frac{E \times I \times 1.73 \times PF}{746}$$

To find power in watts of a motor, 3 phase:

Watts = Volts x Current x 1.73 x Power Factor x Efficiency   or
Watts = E x I x 1.73 x PF x Eff.

To find 3 phase kVA:

$$3 \text{ phase kVA} = \frac{\text{Volts x Amps x 1.73}}{1000} \quad \text{or}$$

$$kVA = \frac{V \times A \times 1.73}{1000}$$

Power Factor (PF) is the percentage ratio of the measured watts (effective power) to the volt-amperes (apparent watts)

$$\text{Power Factor} = \frac{\text{Watts}}{\text{Volts x Amperes}} \times 100\%$$

Table R260120-10 ASHRAE Climate Zone Map

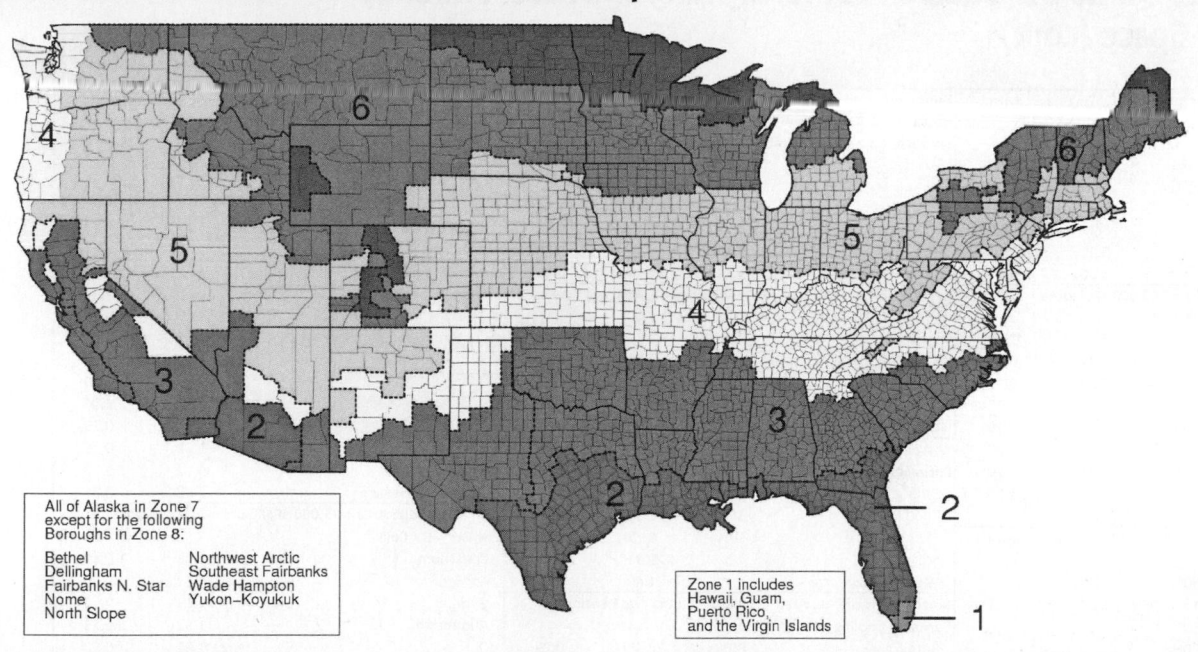

All of Alaska in Zone 7
except for the following
Boroughs in Zone 8:

Bethel
Dellingham
Fairbanks N. Star
Nome
North Slope

Northwest Arctic
Southeast Fairbanks
Wade Hampton
Yukon–Koyukuk

Zone 1 includes
Hawaii, Guam,
Puerto Rico,
and the Virgin Islands

Table R260120-20 Watts per Square Foot for Lighting and Misc. Power by Building Type & Space

Building / Space	Percent	Lighting	Misc
Apartment, Low: Area = 20,000 SF; Floors = 2; Heating = DX Coils; Cooling = DX Coils			
Room	85%	0.50	0.10
Storage	8%	1.19	0.00
Laundry	7%	1.28	0.15
Weighted Average		**0.61**	**0.10**
Apartment, Mid: Area = 40,000 SF; Floors = 5; Heating = DX Coils; Cooling = DX Coils			
Room	71%	0.50	0.30
Corridor	16%	0.57	0.00
Storage	7%	1.19	0.00
Laundry	6%	1.28	0.15
Average		**0.61**	**0.22**
Apartment, High: Area = 72,000 SF; Floors = 8; Heating = DX Coils; Cooling = DX Coils			
Room	71%	0.50	0.30
Corridor	16%	0.57	0.00
Storage	7%	1.19	0.00
Laundry	6%	1.28	0.15
Weighted Average		**0.61**	**0.22**
Assisted Living: Area = 10,000 SF; Floors = 1; Heating = Furnace; Cooling = DX Coils			
Room	70%	1.46	0.25
Dining	15%	1.85	0.10
Food Prep	10%	1.19	1.00
Care	5%	1.34	1.00
Weighted Average		**1.49**	**0.34**

Building / Space	Percent	Lighting	Misc
Auditorium: Area = 70,000 SF; Floors = 1; Heating = Hot Water Coils; Cooling = Chilled Water Coils			
Theater	70%	0.90	
Lobby	15%	1.50	
Office	5%	1.30	
Corridor	5%	0.60	
MEP	5%	0.70	
Weighted Average		**0.99**	
Bank: Area = 25,000 SF; Floors = 2; Heating = Furnace; Cooling = DX Coils			
Bank	60%	2.33	0.45
Corridor	10%	0.57	0.00
Office	10%	1.49	0.75
Lobby	5%	1.52	0.25
Restrooms	5%	0.77	0.10
Conference	4%	0.92	0.10
MEP	4%	0.81	0.10
Production	2%	1.64	0.70
Weighted Average		**1.82**	**0.38**
Community Center: Area = 35,000 SF; Floors = 1; Heating = Furnace; Cooling = DX Coils			
Convention	50%	1.27	
Dining	15%	1.85	
Food Prep	15%	1.19	
Storage	10%	1.19	
Corridor	5%	0.57	
Restrooms	5%	0.77	
Weighted Average		**1.28**	
Convention Center: Area = 150,000 SF; Floors = 2; Heating = Hot Water Coils; Cooling = Chilled Water Coils			
Convention	65%	1.27	0.25
Conference	20%	0.92	0.10
Dining	5%	1.85	0.10
Corridor	4%	0.57	0.00
Food Prep	3%	1.19	1.00
Restrooms	3%	0.77	0.10
Weighted Average		**1.18**	**0.22**

Building / Space	Percent	Lighting	Misc
Day Care: Area = 2,500 SF; Floors = 1; Heating = Furnace; Cooling = DX Coils			
Classroom	45%	1.45	
Corridor	15%	0.57	
Library	15%	1.67	
Food Prep	10%	1.19	
Restrooms	7%	0.77	
Office	5%	1.49	
Storage	3%	1.19	
Weighted Average		**1.27**	
Fitness Center: Area = 20,000 SF; Floors = 1; Heating = Furnace; Cooling = DX Coils			
Exercise	80%	1.13	0.10
Corridor	5%	0.57	0.00
MEP	5%	0.81	0.10
Office	5%	1.24	0.75
Restrooms	7%	0.77	0.10
Weighted Average		**1.07**	**0.13**
Hospital: Area = 250,000 SF; Floors = 4; Heating = Hot Water Coils; Cooling = Chilled Water Coils			
Medical	60%	1.34	1.00
Laboratory	15%	3.19	1.00
Corridor	10%	0.57	0.00
Laundry	5%	1.28	0.15
MEP	5%	0.81	0.10
Restrooms	5%	0.77	0.10
Weighted Average		**1.48**	**0.77**
Hotel: Area = 180,000 SF; Floors = 10; Heating = Furnace; Cooling = DX Coils			
Room	75%	1.46	
Meeting Center	15%	1.27	
Corridor	8%	0.57	
MEP	2%	0.81	
Weighted Average		**1.35**	

Steps:
1. Determine climate zone using R260120-10
2. Use R260120-20 to determine lighting and miscellaneous power for appropriate building type
3. Use corresponding building type and climate zone in R260120-30 to determine other systems

*Values for R260120-20 & -30 were derived by performing an energy analysis using the eQUEST® software from James J. Hirsch & Associates. eQUEST is a trademark of James J. Hirsch
**Additional systems may be necessary

Table R260120-20 Watts per Square Foot for Lighting and Misc. Power by Building Type & Space (cont)

Manufacturing, General: Area = 100,000 SF; Floors = 10; Heating = Furnace; Cooling = DX Coils

Building / Space	Percent	Lighting	Misc
Work	60%	2.66	1.00
Storage	25%	1.19	0.00
Office	10%	1.24	0.75
Restrooms	3%	0.77	0.10
MEP	2%	0.81	0.10
Weighted Average		**2.06**	**0.68**

Manufacturing, High Tech: Area = 200,000 SF; Floors = 1; Heating = Furnace; Cooling = DX Coils

Building / Space	Percent	Lighting	Misc
Work	45%	3.19	1.00
Office	27%	1.24	0.75
Corridor	18%	0.57	0.00
Dining	3%	1.85	0.10
Conference	2%	0.92	0.10
Server	2%	1.24	5.00
MEP	2%	0.81	0.10
Food Prep	1%	1.19	1.00
Weighted Average		**2.00**	**0.77**

Medical Clinic: Area = 20,000 SF; Floors = 1; Heating = Furnace; Cooling = DX Coils

Building / Space	Percent	Lighting	Misc
Clinic	50%	1.40	
General Office	15%	1.30	
Private Office	10%	1.30	
Laboratory	10%	1.30	
Storage	5%	0.60	
Restrooms	5%	0.60	
MEP	5%	0.70	
Weighted Average		**1.25**	

Motel: Area = 10,000 SF; Floors = 1; Heating = DX Coils; Cooling = DX Coils

Building / Space	Percent	Lighting	Misc
Room	95%	1.46	0.25
Office	3%	1.24	0.75
MEP	2%	0.81	0.10
Weighted Average		**1.44**	**0.26**

Museum: Area = 20,000 SF; Floors = 1; Heating = Hot Water Coils; Cooling = Chilled Water Coils

Building / Space	Percent	Lighting	Misc
Exhibit Area	65%	1.03	0.25
Theater	15%	1.02	0.25
Lobby	5%	1.77	0.25
MEP	5%	0.81	0.10
Office	5%	1.49	0.75
Restrooms	5%	0.77	0.10
Weighted Average		**1.06**	**0.26**

Office, Low: Area = 25,000 SF; Floors = 2; Heating = Furnace; Cooling = DX Coils

Building / Space	Percent	Lighting	Misc
Office	70%	1.30	0.75
Corridor	10%	0.60	0.00
Lobby	5%	1.10	0.25
Restrooms	5%	0.60	0.10
Conference	4%	1.60	0.10
MEP	4%	0.70	0.10
Production	2%	1.50	0.70
Weighted Average		**1.18**	**0.56**

Office, Mid: Area = 125,000 SF; Floors = 4; Heating = Hot Water Coils; Cooling = Chilled Water Coils

Building / Space	Percent	Lighting	Misc
Office Open	40%	1.24	0.75
Office Private	30%	1.49	0.75
Corridor	10%	0.57	0.00
Lobby	5%	1.52	0.25
Restrooms	5%	0.77	0.10
Conference	4%	0.92	0.10
MEP	4%	0.81	0.10
Production	2%	1.64	0.70
Weighted Average		**1.22**	**0.56**

Office, High: Area = 250,000 SF; Floors = 8; Heating = Hot Water Coils; Cooling = Chilled Water Coils

Building / Space	Percent	Lighting	Misc
Office Open	45%	1.24	0.75
Office Private	25%	1.49	0.75
Corridor	10%	0.57	0.00
Lobby	5%	1.52	0.25
Conference	4%	0.92	0.10
Production	2%	1.64	0.70
Restrooms	5%	0.77	0.10
MEP	4%	0.81	0.10
Weighted Average		**1.20**	**0.56**

Restaurant, Bar/Lounge: Area = 4,000 SF; Floors = 1; Heating = Furnace; Cooling = DX Coils

Building / Space	Percent	Lighting	Misc
Lounge	35%	1.85	0.10
Dining	30%	1.85	0.10
Food Prep	25%	1.19	1.00
MEP	5%	0.81	0.10
Restrooms	5%	0.77	0.10
Weighted Average		**1.58**	**0.33**

Restaurant, Full: Area = 5,000 SF; Floors = 1; Heating = Furnace; Cooling = DX Coils

Building / Space	Percent	Lighting	Misc
Dining	60%	1.85	0.10
Food Prep	30%	1.19	1.00
Restrooms	5%	0.77	0.10
MEP	5%	0.81	0.10
Weighted Average		**1.55**	**0.37**

Restaurant, Quick: Area = 2,500 SF; Floors = 1; Heating = Furnace; Cooling = DX Coils

Building / Space	Percent	Lighting	Misc
Dining	50%	1.85	0.10
Food Prep	35%	1.19	1.00
Restrooms	10%	0.77	0.10
MEP	5%	0.81	0.10
Weighted Average		**1.46**	**0.42**

Store, Convenience: Area = 3,000 SF; Floors = 1; Heating = Furnace; Cooling = DX Coils

Building / Space	Percent	Lighting	Misc
Retail	80%	2.38	0.25
Office	10%	1.49	0.75
Restrooms	10%	0.77	0.10
Weighted Average		**2.13**	**0.29**

Store, Department: Area = 120,000 SF; Floors = 2; Heating = Hot Water Coils; Cooling = Chilled Water Coils

Building / Space	Percent	Lighting	Misc
Retail	55%	2.38	0.25
Exhibit Area	15%	1.03	0.25
Storage	16%	1.19	0.00
Office	5%	1.24	0.75
Smoking Lounge	2%	1.85	0.10
Restrooms	2%	0.77	0.10
MEP	5%	0.81	0.10
Weighted Average		**1.81**	**0.22**

Store, Large: Area = 70,000 SF; Floors = 1; Heating = Furnace; Cooling = DX Coils

Building / Space	Percent	Lighting	Misc
Retail	65%	2.38	0.25
Storage	20%	1.19	0.00
Office	5%	1.24	0.75
Dining	3%	1.85	0.10
Food Prep	1%	1.19	1.00
Lounge	2%	1.85	0.10
Restrooms	2%	0.77	0.10
MEP	2%	0.81	0.10
Weighted Average		**1.98**	**0.22**

Store, Small: Area = 5,000 SF; Floors = 1; Heating = Furnace; Cooling = DX Coils

Building / Space	Percent	Lighting	Misc
Retail	58%	2.38	0.25
Exhibit Area	15%	1.03	0.25
Storage	15%	1.19	0.00
Office	5%	1.24	0.75
Restrooms	5%	0.77	0.10
MEP	2%	0.81	0.10
Weighted Average		**1.83**	**0.23**

Store, Strip Mall: Area = 15,000 SF; Floors = 1; Heating = Furnace; Cooling = DX Coils

Building / Space	Percent	Lighting	Misc
Retail	38%	2.38	0.25
Atrium	20%	1.55	0.13
Exhibit Area	15%	1.03	0.25
Storage	15%	1.19	0.00
Office	5%	1.24	0.75
Restrooms	5%	0.77	0.10
MEP	2%	0.81	0.10
Weighted Average		**1.66**	**0.20**

Store, Warehouse: Area = 150,000 SF; Floors = 1; Heating = Furnace; Cooling = DX Coils

Building / Space	Percent	Lighting	Misc
Retail	75%	2.38	0.25
Storage	20%	1.19	0.00
Office	4%	1.24	0.75
Restrooms	1%	0.77	0.10
Weighted Average		**2.08**	**0.22**

School, Elementary: Area = 35,000 SF; Floors = 1; Heating = Furnace; Cooling = DX Coils

Building / Space	Percent	Lighting	Misc
Classroom	50%	1.45	0.50
Corridor	15%	0.57	0.00
Gym	10%	1.13	0.10
Dining	5%	1.85	0.10
Food Prep	5%	1.19	1.00
Library	5%	1.78	0.25
Auditorium	5%	1.62	0.25
Restrooms	5%	0.77	0.10
Weighted Average		**1.28**	**0.35**

School, Middle: Area = 75,000 SF; Floors = 1; Heating = Furnace; Cooling = DX Coils

Building / Space	Percent	Lighting	Misc
Classroom	50%	1.45	0.50
Corridor	14%	0.57	0.00
Gym	9%	1.13	0.10
Auditorium	7%	1.62	0.25
Dining	6%	1.85	0.10
Food Prep	5%	1.19	1.00
Library	5%	1.78	0.25
Restrooms	4%	0.77	0.10
Weighted Average		**1.31**	**0.35**

School, High: Area = 150,000 SF; Floors = 2; Heating = Furnace; Cooling = DX Coils

Building / Space	Percent	Lighting	Misc
Classroom	45%	1.45	0.50
Corridor	10%	0.57	0.00
Gym	10%	1.13	0.10
Dining	10%	1.85	0.10
Food Prep	5%	1.19	1.00
Library	5%	1.78	0.25
Auditorium	10%	1.62	0.25
Restrooms	5%	0.77	0.10
Weighted Average		**1.36**	**0.34**

School, College: Area = 250,000 SF; Floors = 4; Heating = Furnace; Cooling = DX Coils

Building / Space	Percent	Lighting	Misc
Classroom	50%	1.45	0.50
Office	15%	1.49	0.75
Corridor	12%	0.57	0.00
Gym	10%	1.13	0.10
Library	5%	1.78	0.25
Dining	3%	1.85	0.10
Restrooms	3%	0.77	0.10
Food Prep	2%	1.19	1.00
Weighted Average		**1.32**	**0.41**

Service Station: Area = 2,000 SF; Floors = 1; Heating = Furnace; Cooling = DX Coils

Building / Space	Percent	Lighting	Misc
Workshop	70%	1.31	0.50
Office	10%	1.49	0.75
Restrooms	10%	0.77	0.10
Retail	10%	2.38	0.25
Weighted Average		**1.38**	**0.46**

Storage, High Bay: Area = 200,000 SF; Floors = 1; Heating = Furnace; Cooling = DX Coils

Building / Space	Percent	Lighting	Misc
Storage	85%	1.19	0.00
Office	10%	1.24	0.75
Restrooms	3%	0.77	0.10
MEP	2%	0.81	0.10
Weighted Average		**1.17**	**0.08**

Storage, Low Bay: Area = 70,000 SF; Floors = 1; Heating = Furnace; Cooling = DX Coils

Building / Space	Percent	Lighting	Misc
Storage	85%	1.19	0.00
Office	10%	1.24	0.75
Restrooms	3%	0.77	0.10
MEP	2%	0.81	0.10
Weighted Average		**1.17**	**0.08**

Table R260120-30 Watts per S.F. for Various Systems by Building Type & Climate Zone

Building / Zone	Heating	Cooling	Heat rejection	Auxiliary (pumps)	Vent fan	Suppl heat pump
Apartment, Low						
Zone 1	0.42	3.65	0.00	0.00	0.12	1.47
Zone 2	0.63	3.53	0.00	0.00	0.12	4.01
Zone 3	0.64	3.45	0.00	0.00	0.13	4.63
Zone 4	0.65	3.09	0.00	0.00	0.13	7.41
Zone 5	0.67	2.88	0.00	0.00	0.12	10.30
Zone 6	0.69	2.66	0.00	0.00	0.13	10.68
Zone 7	0.85	2.11	0.00	0.00	0.12	11.76
Average	**0.65**	**3.05**	**0.00**	**0.00**	**0.13**	**7.18**
Apartment, Mid						
Zone 1	0.00	1.90	0.00	0.00	0.11	0.00
Zone 2	0.43	1.82	0.00	0.00	0.11	2.12
Zone 3	0.48	1.69	0.00	0.00	0.11	2.32
Zone 4	0.67	1.67	0.00	0.00	0.12	4.25
Zone 5	0.70	1.54	0.00	0.00	0.12	4.79
Zone 6	0.72	1.45	0.00	0.00	0.12	5.07
Zone 7	0.93	1.39	0.00	0.00	0.12	5.11
Average	**0.56**	**1.63**	**0.00**	**0.00**	**0.12**	**3.38**
Apartment, High						
Zone 1	0.00	2.11	0.00	0.00	0.14	0.00
Zone 2	0.00	2.03	0.00	0.00	0.13	0.00
Zone 3	0.48	1.88	0.00	0.00	0.14	1.75
Zone 4	0.57	1.77	0.00	0.00	0.14	4.22
Zone 5	0.66	1.64	0.00	0.00	0.14	5.40
Zone 6	0.71	1.63	0.00	0.00	0.15	5.64
Zone 7	0.91	1.18	0.00	0.00	0.14	5.75
Average	**0.48**	**1.75**	**0.00**	**0.00**	**0.14**	**3.25**
Assisted Living						
Zone 1	0.00	2.65	0.00	0.04	0.31	0.00
Zone 2	0.00	2.63	0.00	0.04	0.31	0.00
Zone 3	0.00	2.57	0.00	0.04	0.31	0.00
Zone 4	0.00	2.50	0.00	0.04	0.31	0.00
Zone 5	0.00	2.42	0.00	0.04	0.30	0.00
Zone 6	0.00	1.99	0.00	0.04	0.32	0.00
Zone 7	0.00	1.90	0.00	0.04	0.30	0.00
Average	**0.00**	**2.38**	**0.00**	**0.04**	**0.31**	**0.00**
Auditorium						
Zone 1	0.00	2.32	0.34	0.37	1.03	0.00
Zone 2	0.00	2.32	0.34	0.38	1.03	0.00
Zone 3	0.00	2.29	0.33	0.38	1.04	0.00
Zone 4	0.00	2.26	0.29	0.35	1.05	0.00
Zone 5	0.00	2.20	0.34	0.39	1.04	0.00
Zone 6	0.00	1.71	0.14	0.34	1.05	0.00
Zone 7	0.00	1.38	0.23	0.36	1.04	0.00
Average	**0.00**	**2.07**	**0.29**	**0.37**	**1.04**	**0.00**
Bank						
Zone 1	0.00	3.32	0.00	0.00	0.60	0.00
Zone 2	0.00	3.28	0.00	0.00	0.61	0.00
Zone 3	0.00	3.28	0.00	0.00	0.61	0.00
Zone 4	0.00	3.21	0.00	0.00	0.60	0.00
Zone 5	0.00	3.06	0.00	0.00	0.59	0.00
Zone 6	0.00	2.82	0.00	0.00	0.61	0.00
Zone 7	0.00	2.66	0.00	0.00	0.60	0.00
Average	**0.00**	**3.09**	**0.00**	**0.00**	**0.60**	**0.00**

Building / Zone	Heating	Cooling	Heat rejection	Auxiliary (pumps)	Vent fan	Suppl heat pump
Community Center						
Zone 1	0.00	2.70	0.00	0.00	0.44	0.00
Zone 2	0.00	2.66	0.00	0.00	0.44	0.00
Zone 3	0.00	2.66	0.00	0.00	0.45	0.00
Zone 4	0.00	2.44	0.00	0.00	0.45	0.00
Zone 5	0.00	2.42	0.00	0.00	0.44	0.00
Zone 6	0.00	2.16	0.00	0.00	0.44	0.00
Zone 7	0.00	1.91	0.00	0.00	0.44	0.00
Average	**0.00**	**2.42**	**0.00**	**0.00**	**0.45**	**0.00**
Convention Center						
Zone 1	0.00	1.46	0.25	0.27	0.31	0.00
Zone 2	0.00	1.44	0.25	0.27	0.29	0.00
Zone 3	0.00	1.43	0.24	0.26	0.30	0.00
Zone 4	0.00	1.42	0.23	0.26	0.28	0.00
Zone 5	0.00	1.30	0.29	0.31	0.22	0.00
Zone 6	0.00	1.17	0.12	0.29	0.16	0.00
Zone 7	0.00	0.90	0.20	0.31	0.16	0.00
Average	**0.00**	**1.30**	**0.22**	**0.28**	**0.25**	**0.00**
Day Care						
Zone 1	0.00	3.47	0.00	0.02	0.29	0.00
Zone 2	0.00	3.42	0.00	0.02	0.28	0.00
Zone 3	0.00	3.40	0.00	0.02	0.29	0.00
Zone 4	0.00	3.29	0.00	0.02	0.29	0.00
Zone 5	0.00	3.08	0.00	0.02	0.29	0.00
Zone 6	0.00	2.29	0.00	0.02	0.29	0.00
Zone 7	0.00	2.12	0.00	0.02	0.24	0.00
Average	**0.05**	**3.01**	**0.05**	**0.07**	**0.29**	**0.05**
Fitness Center						
Zone 1	0.00	4.97	0.00	0.00	0.59	0.00
Zone 2	0.00	4.94	0.00	0.00	0.59	0.00
Zone 3	0.00	4.80	0.00	0.00	0.60	0.00
Zone 4	0.00	4.76	0.00	0.00	0.60	0.00
Zone 5	0.00	4.75	0.00	0.00	0.59	0.00
Zone 6	0.00	4.13	0.00	0.00	0.60	0.00
Zone 7	0.00	3.27	0.00	0.00	0.60	0.00
Average	**0.00**	**4.52**	**0.00**	**0.00**	**0.59**	**0.00**
Hospital						
Zone 1	0.00	1.54	0.23	0.26	0.80	0.00
Zone 2	0.00	1.47	0.22	0.25	0.80	0.00
Zone 3	0.00	1.44	0.22	0.25	0.81	0.00
Zone 4	0.00	1.42	0.22	0.25	0.81	0.00
Zone 5	0.00	1.37	0.23	0.27	0.81	0.00
Zone 6	0.00	1.26	0.15	0.25	0.82	0.00
Zone 7	0.00	1.07	0.19	0.26	0.82	0.00
Average	**0.00**	**1.36**	**0.21**	**0.26**	**0.81**	**0.00**
Hotel						
Zone 1	0.00	1.77	0.00	0.01	0.26	0.00
Zone 2	0.00	1.64	0.00	0.01	0.26	0.00
Zone 3	0.00	1.62	0.00	0.01	0.27	0.00
Zone 4	0.00	1.62	0.00	0.01	0.27	0.00
Zone 5	0.00	1.51	0.00	0.01	0.27	0.00
Zone 6	0.00	1.25	0.00	0.01	0.28	0.00
Zone 7	0.00	1.23	0.00	0.01	0.28	0.00
Average	**0.00**	**1.52**	**0.00**	**0.01**	**0.27**	**0.00**

581

For customer support on your Electrical Costs with RSMeans Data, call 800.448.8182.

Table R260120-30 Watts per S.F. for Various Systems by Building Type & Climate Zone (cont.)

Building / Zone	Heating	Cooling	Heat rejection	Auxiliary (pumps)	Vent fan	Supp heat pump
Manufacturing, General						
Zone 1	0.00	1.46		0.00	0.13	0.00
Zone 2	0.00	1.45		0.00	0.13	0.00
Zone 3	0.00	1.43		0.00	0.13	0.00
Zone 4	0.00	1.39		0.00	0.13	0.00
Zone 5	0.00	1.39		0.00	0.13	0.00
Zone 6	0.00	1.21		0.00	0.13	0.00
Zone 7	0.00	1.00		0.00	0.13	0.00
Average	0.00	1.33	0.00	0.00	0.13	0.00
Manufacturing, High Tech						
Zone 1	0.00	2.15		0.00	0.17	0.00
Zone 2	0.00	2.12		0.00	0.17	0.00
Zone 3	0.00	2.04		0.00	0.17	0.00
Zone 4	0.00	2.01		0.00	0.17	0.00
Zone 5	0.00	1.88		0.00	0.17	0.00
Zone 6	0.00	1.63		0.00	0.17	0.00
Zone 7	0.00	1.50		0.00	0.17	0.00
Average	0.00	1.90	0.00	0.00	0.17	0.00
Medical Clinic						
Zone 1	0.00	3.15	0.00	0.00	0.54	0.00
Zone 2	0.00	3.09	0.00	0.00	0.53	0.00
Zone 3	0.00	3.07	0.00	0.00	0.54	0.00
Zone 4	0.00	3.02	0.00	0.00	0.54	0.00
Zone 5	0.00	2.99	0.00	0.00	0.54	0.00
Zone 6	0.00	2.58	0.00	0.00	0.55	0.00
Zone 7	0.00	2.45	0.00	0.00	0.52	0.00
Average	0.00	2.91	0.00	0.00	0.54	0.00
Motel						
Zone 1	0.97	2.68	0.00	0.00	0.19	2.15
Zone 2	1.19	2.52	0.00	0.00	0.18	4.43
Zone 3	1.19	2.52	0.00	0.00	0.19	4.81
Zone 4	1.19	2.42	0.00	0.00	0.21	7.39
Zone 5	1.28	2.26	0.00	0.00	0.21	7.82
Zone 6	1.29	2.07	0.00	0.00	0.23	8.89
Zone 7	1.39	1.97	0.00	0.00	0.23	9.51
Average	1.21	2.35	0.00	0.00	0.21	6.43
Museum						
Zone 1	0.00	3.77	0.00	0.11	0.67	0.00
Zone 2	0.00	3.71	0.00	0.12	0.77	0.00
Zone 3	0.00	3.59	0.00	0.12	0.72	0.00
Zone 4	0.00	3.47	0.00	0.14	0.74	0.00
Zone 5	0.00	3.42	0.00	0.16	0.51	0.00
Zone 6	0.00	2.39	0.00	0.15	0.23	0.00
Zone 7	0.00	1.69	0.00	0.17	0.24	0.00
Average	0.00	3.15	0.00	0.14	0.55	0.00
Office, Low						
Zone 1	0.00	2.90	0.00	0.02	0.29	0.00
Zone 2	0.00	2.90	0.00	0.02	0.30	0.00
Zone 3	0.00	2.81	0.00	0.02	0.30	0.00
Zone 4	0.00	2.70	0.00	0.02	0.29	0.00
Zone 5	0.00	2.66	0.00	0.02	0.29	0.00
Zone 6	0.00	2.04	0.00	0.02	0.30	0.00
Zone 7	0.00	1.82	0.00	0.02	0.29	0.00
Average	0.00	2.55	0.00	0.02	0.29	0.00

Building / Zone	Heating	Cooling	Heat rejection	Auxiliary (pumps)	Vent fan	Supp heat pump
Office, Mid						
Zone 1	0.00	1.61	0.31	0.33	0.45	0.00
Zone 2	0.00	1.60	0.29	0.32	0.46	0.00
Zone 3	0.00	1.59	0.28	0.34	0.42	0.00
Zone 4	0.00	1.56	0.27	0.33	0.43	0.00
Zone 5	0.00	1.55	0.34	0.36	0.37	0.00
Zone 6	0.00	1.29	0.16	0.34	0.31	0.00
Zone 7	0.00	1.10	0.22	0.35	0.32	0.00
Average	0.00	1.47	0.27	0.34	0.40	0.00
Office, High						
Zone 1	0.00	1.70	0.30	0.33	0.44	0.00
Zone 2	0.00	1.59	0.29	0.32	0.41	0.00
Zone 3	0.00	1.59	0.32	0.34	0.42	0.00
Zone 4	0.00	1.58	0.28	0.35	0.42	0.00
Zone 5	0.00	1.58	0.32	0.36	0.41	0.00
Zone 6	0.00	1.11	0.16	0.29	0.33	0.00
Zone 7	0.00	0.86	0.23	0.31	0.37	0.00
Average	0.00	1.43	0.27	0.33	0.40	0.00
Restaurant, Bar/Lounge						
Zone 1	0.00	3.07	0.00	0.06	0.24	0.00
Zone 2	0.00	2.87	0.00	0.06	0.25	0.00
Zone 3	0.00	2.85	0.00	0.06	0.24	0.00
Zone 4	0.00	2.83	0.00	0.06	0.24	0.00
Zone 5	0.00	2.80	0.00	0.06	0.24	0.00
Zone 6	0.00	1.88	0.00	0.06	0.24	0.00
Zone 7	0.00	1.87	0.00	0.06	0.23	0.00
Average	0.00	2.59	0.00	0.06	0.24	0.00
Restaurant, Full						
Zone 1	0.00	3.37	0.00	0.05	0.38	0.00
Zone 2	0.00	3.30	0.00	0.05	0.39	0.00
Zone 3	0.00	3.25	0.00	0.05	0.39	0.00
Zone 4	0.00	3.20	0.00	0.05	0.39	0.00
Zone 5	0.00	3.03	0.00	0.05	0.38	0.00
Zone 6	0.00	2.35	0.00	0.05	0.39	0.00
Zone 7	0.00	2.33	0.00	0.05	0.38	0.00
Average	0.00	2.98	0.00	0.05	0.38	0.00
Restaurant, Quick						
Zone 1	0.00	3.78	0.00	0.08	0.48	0.00
Zone 2	0.00	3.72	0.00	0.08	0.50	0.00
Zone 3	0.00	3.64	0.00	0.08	0.50	0.00
Zone 4	0.00	3.60	0.00	0.08	0.50	0.00
Zone 5	0.00	3.42	0.00	0.08	0.49	0.00
Zone 6	0.00	2.74	0.00	0.08	0.51	0.00
Zone 7	0.00	2.69	0.00	0.08	0.49	0.00
Average	0.00	3.37	0.00	0.08	0.50	0.00
Store, Convenience						
Zone 1	0.00	4.08	0.00	0.02	0.29	0.00
Zone 2	0.00	3.66	0.00	0.02	0.30	0.00
Zone 3	0.00	3.60	0.00	0.02	0.30	0.00
Zone 4	0.00	3.46	0.00	0.02	0.29	0.00
Zone 5	0.00	3.28	0.00	0.02	0.29	0.00
Zone 6	0.00	2.66	0.00	0.02	0.27	0.00
Zone 7	0.00	2.50	0.00	0.02	0.24	0.00
Average	0.00	3.32	0.00	0.02	0.28	0.00

For customer support on your Electrical Costs with RSMeans Data, call 800.448.8182.

Table R260120-30 Watts per S.F. for Various Systems by Building Type & Climate Zone (cont.)

Building / Zone	Heating	Cooling	Heat rejection	Auxiliary (pumps)	Vent fan	Supp heat pump	Building / Zone	Heating	Cooling	Heat rejection	Auxiliary (pumps)	Vent fan	Supp heat pump
Store, Department							**School, Middle**						
Zone 1	0.00	1.65	0.20	0.23	0.63	0.00	Zone 1	0.00	2.48	0.00	0.00	0.17	0.00
Zone 2	0.00	1.61	0.20	0.23	0.63	0.00	Zone 2	0.00	2.45	0.00	0.00	0.17	0.00
Zone 3	0.00	1.59	0.19	0.22	0.64	0.00	Zone 3	0.00	2.41	0.00	0.00	0.18	0.00
Zone 4	0.00	1.52	0.19	0.23	0.64	0.00	Zone 4	0.00	2.35	0.00	0.00	0.17	0.00
Zone 5	0.00	1.51	0.21	0.24	0.63	0.00	Zone 5	0.00	2.26	0.00	0.00	0.17	0.00
Zone 6	0.00	1.32	0.13	0.21	0.63	0.00	Zone 6	0.00	1.61	0.00	0.00	0.17	0.00
Zone 7	0.00	0.98	0.17	0.23	0.63	0.00	Zone 7	0.00	1.49	0.00	0.00	0.17	0.00
Average	**0.00**	**1.45**	**0.18**	**0.23**	**0.63**	**0.00**	**Average**	**0.00**	**2.15**	**0.00**	**0.00**	**0.17**	**0.00**
Store, Large							**School, High**						
Zone 1	0.00	2.68	0.00	0.00	0.16	0.00	Zone 1	0.00	3.24	0.00	0.01	0.22	0.00
Zone 2	0.00	2.61	0.00	0.00	0.17	0.00	Zone 2	0.00	3.08	0.00	0.01	0.22	0.00
Zone 3	0.00	2.61	0.00	0.00	0.17	0.00	Zone 3	0.00	3.05	0.00	0.01	0.23	0.00
Zone 4	0.00	2.56	0.00	0.00	0.16	0.00	Zone 4	0.00	3.00	0.00	0.01	0.23	0.00
Zone 5	0.00	2.53	0.00	0.00	0.16	0.00	Zone 5	0.00	2.94	0.00	0.01	0.23	0.00
Zone 6	0.00	1.84	0.00	0.00	0.16	0.00	Zone 6	0.00	1.98	0.00	0.01	0.23	0.00
Zone 7	0.00	1.50	0.00	0.00	0.16	0.00	Zone 7	0.00	1.81	0.00	0.01	0.23	0.00
Average	**0.00**	**2.33**	**0.00**	**0.00**	**0.16**	**0.00**	**Average**	**0.00**	**2.73**	**0.00**	**0.01**	**0.23**	**0.00**
Store, Small							**School, College**						
Zone 1	0.00	3.60	0.00	0.01	0.25	0.00	Zone 1	0.00	2.92	0.00	0.00	0.20	0.00
Zone 2	0.00	3.51	0.00	0.01	0.26	0.00	Zone 2	0.00	2.91	0.00	0.00	0.20	0.00
Zone 3	0.00	3.38	0.00	0.01	0.25	0.00	Zone 3	0.00	2.78	0.00	0.00	0.20	0.00
Zone 4	0.00	3.32	0.00	0.01	0.25	0.00	Zone 4	0.00	2.72	0.00	0.00	0.20	0.00
Zone 5	0.00	3.23	0.00	0.01	0.24	0.00	Zone 5	0.00	2.43	0.00	0.00	0.20	0.00
Zone 6	0.00	2.49	0.00	0.01	0.23	0.00	Zone 6	0.00	1.77	0.00	0.00	0.20	0.00
Zone 7	0.00	2.17	0.00	0.01	0.21	0.00	Zone 7	0.00	1.51	0.00	0.00	0.19	0.00
Average	**0.00**	**3.10**	**0.00**	**0.01**	**0.24**	**0.00**	**Average**	**0.00**	**2.43**	**0.00**	**0.00**	**0.20**	**0.00**
Store, Strip Mall							**Service Station**						
Zone 1	0.00	3.36	0.00	0.02	0.25	0.00	Zone 1	0.00	10.42	0.00	0.03	0.47	0.00
Zone 2	0.00	3.30	0.00	0.02	0.25	0.00	Zone 2	0.00	9.01	0.00	0.03	0.46	0.00
Zone 3	0.00	3.14	0.00	0.02	0.25	0.00	Zone 3	0.00	7.82	0.00	0.03	0.49	0.00
Zone 4	0.00	3.14	0.00	0.02	0.25	0.00	Zone 4	0.00	7.02	0.00	0.03	0.47	0.00
Zone 5	0.00	2.24	0.00	0.02	0.24	0.00	Zone 5	0.00	6.13	0.00	0.03	0.46	0.00
Zone 6	0.00	1.96	0.00	0.02	0.25	0.00	Zone 6	0.00	4.32	0.00	0.03	0.45	0.00
Zone 7	0.00	1.64	0.00	0.02	0.24	0.00	Zone 7	0.00	4.18	0.00	0.03	0.40	0.00
Average	**0.00**	**2.52**	**0.00**	**0.02**	**0.25**	**0.00**	**Average**	**0.00**	**6.99**	**0.00**	**0.03**	**0.46**	**0.00**
Store, Warehouse							**Storage, High Bay**						
Zone 1	0.00	2.99	0.00	0.00	0.21	0.00	Zone 1	0.00	1.98	0.00	0.00	0.17	0.00
Zone 2	0.00	2.97	0.00	0.00	0.21	0.00	Zone 2	0.00	1.97	0.00	0.00	0.18	0.00
Zone 3	0.00	2.94	0.00	0.00	0.21	0.00	Zone 3	0.00	1.90	0.00	0.00	0.18	0.00
Zone 4	0.00	2.83	0.00	0.00	0.21	0.00	Zone 4	0.00	1.89	0.00	0.00	0.18	0.00
Zone 5	0.00	2.70	0.00	0.00	0.21	0.00	Zone 5	0.00	1.85	0.00	0.00	0.17	0.00
Zone 6	0.00	2.10	0.00	0.00	0.21	0.00	Zone 6	0.00	1.29	0.00	0.00	0.17	0.00
Zone 7	0.00	1.78	0.00	0.00	0.21	0.00	Zone 7	0.00	1.10	0.00	0.00	0.17	0.00
Average	**0.00**	**2.61**	**0.00**	**0.00**	**0.21**	**0.00**	**Average**	**0.00**	**1.71**	**0.00**	**0.00**	**0.17**	**0.00**
School, Elementary							**Storage, Low Bay**						
Zone 1	0.00	2.73	0.00	0.01	0.21	0.00	Zone 1	0.00	1.87	0.00	0.00	0.16	0.00
Zone 2	0.00	2.69	0.00	0.01	0.21	0.00	Zone 2	0.00	1.85	0.00	0.00	0.16	0.00
Zone 3	0.00	2.63	0.00	0.01	0.21	0.00	Zone 3	0.00	1.82	0.00	0.00	0.16	0.00
Zone 4	0.00	2.61	0.00	0.01	0.20	0.00	Zone 4	0.00	1.77	0.00	0.00	0.16	0.00
Zone 5	0.00	2.51	0.00	0.01	0.20	0.00	Zone 5	0.00	1.76	0.00	0.00	0.16	0.00
Zone 6	0.00	1.71	0.00	0.01	0.20	0.00	Zone 6	0.00	1.20	0.00	0.00	0.16	0.00
Zone 7	0.00	1.64	0.00	0.01	0.20	0.00	Zone 7	0.00	1.00	0.00	0.00	0.16	0.00
Average	**0.00**	**2.36**	**0.00**	**0.01**	**0.20**	**0.00**	**Average**	**0.00**	**1.61**	**0.00**	**0.00**	**0.16**	**0.00**

R260519-20 Armored Cable

Armored Cable – Quantities are taken off in the same manner as wire.

Bx Type Cable – Productivities are based on an average run of 50' before terminating at a box fixture, etc. Each 50' section includes field preparation of (2) ends with hacksaw, identification and tagging of wire. Set up is open coil type without reels attaching cable to snake and pulling across a suspended ceiling or open face wood or steel studding, price does not include drilling of studs.

Cable in Tray – Productivities are based on an average run of 100 L.F. with set up of pulling equipment for (2) 90° bends, attaching cable to pull-in means, identification and tagging of wires, set up of reels. Wire termination to breakers equipment, etc., are not included.

Job Conditions – Productivities are based on new construction to a height of 15' using rolling staging in an unobstructed area. Material staging is assumed to be within 100' of work being performed.

R260519-80 Undercarpet Systems

Takeoff Procedure for Power Systems: List components for each fitting type, tap, splice, and bend on your quantity takeoff sheet. Each component must be priced separately. Start at the power supply transition fittings and survey each circuit for the components needed. List the quantities of each component under a specific circuit number. Use the floor plan layout scale to get cable footage.

Reading across the list, combine the totals of each component in each circuit and list the total quantity in the last column. Calculate approximately 5% for scrap for items such as cable, top shield, tape, and spray adhesive. Also provide for final variations that may occur on-site.

Suggested guidelines are:
1. Equal amounts of cable and top shield should be priced.
2. For each roll of cable, price a set of cable splices.
3. For every 1 ft. of cable, price 2-1/2 ft. of hold-down tape.
4. For every 3 rolls of hold-down tape, price 1 can of spray adhesive.

Adjust final figures wherever possible to accommodate standard packaging of the product. This information is available from the distributor.

Each transition fitting requires:
1. 1 base
2. 1 cover
3. 1 transition block

Each floor fitting requires:
1. 1 frame/base kit
2. 1 transition block
3. 2 covers (duplex/blank)

Each tap requires:
1. 1 tap connector for each conductor
2. 1 pair insulating patches
3. 2 top shield connectors

Each splice requires:
1. 1 splice connector for each conductor
2. 1 pair insulating patches
3. 3 top shield connectors

Each cable bend requires:
1. 2 top shield connectors

Each cable dead end (outside of transition block) requires:
1. 1 pair insulating patches

Labor does not include:
1. Patching or leveling uneven floors.
2. Filling in holes or removing projections from concrete slabs.
3. Sealing porous floors.
4. Sweeping and vacuuming floors.
5. Removal of existing carpeting.
6. Carpet square cut-outs.
7. Installation of carpet squares.

Takeoff Procedures for Telephone Systems: After reviewing floor plans identify each transition. Number or letter each cable run from that fitting.

Start at the transition fitting and survey each circuit for the components needed. List the cable type, terminations, cable length, and floor fitting type under the specific circuit number. Use the floor plan layout scale to get the cable footage. Add some extra length (next higher increment of 5 feet) to preconnectorized cable.

Transition fittings require:
1. 1 base plate
2. 1 cover
3. 1 transition block

Floor fittings require:
1. 1 frame/base kit
2. 2 covers
3. Modular jacks

Reading across the list, combine the list of components in each circuit and list the total quantity in the last column. Calculate the necessary scrap factors for such items as tape, bottom shield and spray adhesive. Also provide for final variations that may occur on-site.

Adjust final figures whenever possible to accommodate standard packaging. Check that items such as transition fittings, floor boxes, and floor fittings that are to utilize both power and telephone have been priced as combination fittings, so as to avoid duplication.

Make sure to include marking of floors and drilling of fasteners if fittings specified are not the adhesive type.

Labor does not include:
1. Conduit or raceways before transition of floor boxes
2. Telephone cable before transition boxes
3. Terminations before transition boxes
4. Floor preparation as described in power section

Be sure to include all cable folds when pricing labor.

Takeoff Procedure for Data Systems: Start at the transition fittings and take off quantities in the same manner as the telephone system, keeping in mind that data cable does not require top or bottom shields.

The data cable is simply cross-taped on the cable run to the floor fitting.

Data cable can be purchased in either bulk form in which case coaxial connector material and labor must be priced, or in preconnectorized cut lengths.

Data cable cannot be folded and must be notched at 1 inch intervals. A count of all turns must be added to the labor portion of the estimate. (Note: Some manufacturers have prenotched cable.)

Notching required:
1. 90 degree turn requires 8 notches per side.
2. 180 degree turn requires 16 notches per side.

Floor boxes, transition boxes, and fittings are the same as described in the power and telephone procedures.

Since undercarpet systems require special hand tools, be sure to include this cost in proportion to number of crews involved in the installation.

Job Conditions: Productivity is based on new construction in an unobstructed area. Staging area is assumed to be within 200' of work being performed.

R260519-90 Wire

Wire quantities are taken off by either measuring each cable run or by extending the conduit and raceway quantities times the number of conductors in the raceway. Ten percent should be added for waste and tic-ins. Keep in mind that the unit of measure of wire is C.L.F. not L.F. as in raceways so the formula would read:

$$\frac{\text{(L.F. Raceway x No. of Conductors) x 1.10}}{100} = \text{C.L.F.}$$

Price per C.L.F. of wire includes:
1. Setting up wire coils or spools on racks
2. Attaching wire to pull in means
3. Measuring and cutting wire
4. Pulling wire into a raceway
5. Identifying and tagging

Price does not include:
1. Connections to breakers, panelboards, or equipment
2. Splices

Job Conditions: Productivity is based on new construction to a height of 15′ using rolling staging in an unobstructed area. Material staging is assumed to be within 100′ of work being performed.

Economy of Scale: If more than three wires at a time are being pulled, deduct the following percentages from the labor of that grouping:

4-5 wires	25%
6-10 wires	30%
11-15 wires	35%
over 15	40%

If a wire pull is less than 100′ in length and is interrupted several times by boxes, lighting outlets, etc., it may be necessary to add the following lengths to each wire being pulled:

Junction box to junction box	2 L.F.
Lighting panel to junction box	6 L.F.
Distribution panel to sub panel	8 L.F.
Switchboard to distribution panel	12 L.F.
Switchboard to motor control center	20 L.F.
Switchboard to cable tray	40 L.F.

Measure of Drops and Riser: It is important when taking off wire quantities to include the wire for drops to electrical equipment. If heights of electrical equipment are not clearly stated, use the following guide:

	Bottom A.F.F.	Top A.F.F.	Inside Cabinet
Safety switch to 100A	5′	6′	2′
Safety switch 400 to 600A	4′	6′	3′
100A panel 12 to 30 circuit	4′	6′	3′
42 circuit panel	3′	6′	4′
Switch box	3′	3′6″	1′
Switchgear	0′	8′	8′
Motor control centers	0′	8′	8′
Transformers - wall mount	4′	8′	2′
Transformers - floor mount	0′	12′	4′

R260519-92 Minimum Copper and Aluminum Wire Size Allowed for Various Types of Insulation

Minimum Wire Sizes

Amperes	Copper		Aluminum		Amperes	Copper		Aluminum	
	THW THWN or XHHW	THHN XHHW *	THW XHHW	THHN XHHW *		THW THWN or XHHW	THHN XHHW *	THW XHHW	THHN XHHW *
15A	#14	#14	#12	#12	195	3/0	2/0	250kcmil	4/0
20	#12	#12	#10	#10	200	3/0	3/0	250kcmil	4/0
25	#10	#10	#10	#10	205	4/0	3/0	250kcmil	4/0
30	#10	#10	#8	#8	225	4/0	3/0	300kcmil	250kcmil
40	#8	#8	#8	#8	230	4/0	4/0	300kcmil	250kcmil
45	#8	#8	#6	#8	250	250kcmil	4/0	350kcmil	300kcmil
50	#8	#8	#6	#6	255	250kcmil	4/0	400kcmil	300kcmil
55	#6	#8	#4	#6	260	300kcmil	4/0	400kcmil	350kcmil
60	#6	#6	#4	#6	270	300kcmil	250kcmil	400kcmil	350kcmil
65	#6	#6	#4	#4	280	300kcmil	250kcmil	500kcmil	350kcmil
75	#4	#6	#3	#4	285	300kcmil	250kcmil	500kcmil	400kcmil
85	#4	#4	#2	#3	290	350kcmil	250kcmil	500kcmil	400kcmil
90	#3	#4	#2	#2	305	350kcmil	300kcmil	500kcmil	400kcmil
95	#3	#4	#1	#2	310	350kcmil	300kcmil	500kcmil	500kcmil
100	#3	#3	#1	#2	320	400kcmil	300kcmil	600kcmil	500kcmil
110	#2	#3	1/0	#1	335	400kcmil	350kcmil	600kcmil	500kcmil
115	#2	#2	1/0	#1	340	500kcmil	350kcmil	600kcmil	500kcmil
120	#1	#2	1/0	1/0	350	500kcmil	350kcmil	700kcmil	500kcmil
130	#1	#2	2/0	1/0	375	500kcmil	400kcmil	700kcmil	600kcmil
135	1/0	#1	2/0	1/0	380	500kcmil	400kcmil	750kcmil	600kcmil
150	1/0	#1	3/0	2/0	385	600kcmil	500kcmil	750kcmil	600kcmil
155	2/0	1/0	3/0	3/0	420	600kcmil	500kcmil		700kcmil
170	2/0	1/0	4/0	3/0	430		500kcmil		750kcmil
175	2/0	2/0	4/0	3/0	435		600kcmil		750kcmil
180	3/0	2/0	4/0	4/0	475		600kcmil		

*Dry Locations Only

Notes:

1. Size #14 to 4/0 is in AWG units (American Wire Gauge).
2. Size 250 to 750 is in kcmil units (Thousand Circular Mils).
3. Use next higher ampere value if exact value is not listed in table.
4. For loads that operate continuously increase ampere value by 25% to obtain proper wire size.
5. Table R260519-92 has been written for estimating only. It is based on an ambient temperature of 30°C (86° F). For an ambient temperature other than 30°C (86° F), ampacity correction factors will be applied.

Reference Tables

R260519-93 Metric Equivalent, Wire

United States		European	
Size AWG or kcmil	Area Cir. Mils. (cmil) mm²	Size mm²	Area Cir. Mils.
18	1620/.82	.75	1480
16	2580/1.30	1.0	1974
14	4110/2.08	1.5	2961
12	6530/3.30	2.5	4935
10	10,380/5.25	4	7896
8	16,510/8.36	6	11,844
6	26,240/13.29	10	19,740
4	41,740/21.14	16	31,584
3	52,620/26.65	25	49,350
2	66,360/33.61	–	–
1	83,690/42.39	35	69,090
1/0	105,600/53.49	50	98,700
2/0	133,100/67.42	–	–
3/0	167,800/85.00	70	138,180
4/0	211,600/107.19	95	187,530
250	250,000/126.64	120	236,880
300	300,000/151.97	150	296,100
350	350,000/177.30	–	–
400	400,000/202.63	185	365,190
500	500,000/253.29	240	473,760
600	600,000/303.95	300	592,200
700	700,000/354.60	–	–
750	750,000/379.93	–	–

R260519-94 Size Required and Weight (Lbs./1000 L.F.) of Aluminum and Copper THW Wire by Ampere Load

Amperes	Copper Size	Aluminum Size	Copper Weight	Aluminum Weight
15	14	12	24	11
20	12	10	33	17
30	10	8	48	39
45	8	6	77	52
65	6	4	112	72
85	4	2	167	101
100	3	1	205	136
115	2	1/0	252	162
130	1	2/0	324	194
150	1/0	3/0	397	233
175	2/0	4/0	491	282
200	3/0	250	608	347
230	4/0	300	753	403
255	250	400	899	512
285	300	500	1068	620
310	350	500	1233	620
335	400	600	1396	772
380	500	750	1732	951

Reference Tables

R260533-20 Grounding

Grounding When taking off grounding systems, identify separately the type and size of wire.

Example:

Bare copper & size

Bare aluminum & size

Insulated copper & size

Insulated aluminum & size

Count the number of ground rods and their size.

Example:

1. 8' grounding rod – 5/8" dia. 20 Ea.
2. 10' grounding rod – 5/8" dia. 12 Ea.
3. 15' grounding rod – 3/4" dia. 4 Ea.

Count the number of connections; the size of the largest wire will determine the productivity.

Example:

Braze a #2 wire to a #4/0 cable

The 4/0 cable will determine the L.H. and cost to be used.

Include individual connections to:

1. Ground rods
2. Building steel
3. Equipment
4. Raceways

Price does not include:

1. Excavation
2. Backfill
3. Sleeves or raceways used to protect grounding wires
4. Wall penetrations
5. Floor cutting
6. Core drilling

Job Conditions: Productivity is based on a ground floor area, using cable reels in an unobstructed area. The material staging area is assumed to be within 100' of work being performed.

R260533-20 Conduit To 10' High

List conduit by quantity, size, and type. Do not deduct for lengths occupied by fittings, since this will be allowance for scrap. Example:

A. Aluminum — size
B. Rigid galvanized — size
C. Steel intermediate (IMC) — size
D. Rigid steel, plastic-coated 20 Mil. — size
E. Rigid steel, plastic-coated 40 Mil. — size
F. Electric metallic tubing (EMT) — size
G. PVC Schedule 40 — size

Types (A) through (E) listed above contain the following per 100 L.F.:

1. (11) Threaded couplings
2. (11) Beam-type hangers
3. (2) Factory sweeps
4. (2) Fiber bushings
5. (4) Locknuts
6. (2) Field threaded pipe terminations
7. (2) Removal of concentric knockouts

Type (F) contains per 100 L.F.:

1. (11) Set screw couplings
2. (11) Beam clamps
3. (2) Field bends on 1/2" and 3/4" diameter
4. (2) Factory sweeps for 1" and above
5. (2) Set screw steel connectors
6. (2) Removal of concentric knockouts

Type (G) contains per 100 L.F.:

1. (11) Field cemented couplings
2. (34) Beam clamps

3. (2) Factory sweeps
4. (2) Adapters
5. (2) Locknuts
6. (2) Removal of concentric knockouts

Labor-hours for all conduit to 10' include:

1. Unloading by hand
2. Hauling by hand to an area up to 200' from loading dock
3. Setup of rolling staging
4. Installation of conduit and fittings as described in Conduit models (A) through (G)

Not included in the material and labor are:

1. Staging rental or purchase
2. Structural modifications
3. Wire
4. Junction boxes
5. Fittings in excess of those described in conduit models (A) through (G)
6. Painting of conduit

Fittings

Only those fittings listed above are included in the linear foot totals, although they should be listed separately from conduit lengths, without prices, to ensure proper quantities for material procurement.

If the fittings required exceed the quantities included in the model conduit runs, then material and labor costs must be added to the difference. If actual needs per 100 L.F. of conduit are: (2) sweeps, (4) LBs and (1) field bend, then, (4) LBs and (1) field bend must be priced additionally.

R260533-21 Hangers

It is sometimes desirable to substitute an alternate style of hanger if the support being used is not the type described in the conduit models.

One approach is the substitution method:
1. Find the cost of the type hanger described in the conduit model.
2. Calculate the cost of the desired type hanger (it may be necessary to calculate individual components such as drilling, expansion shields, etc.).
3. Calculate the cost difference (delta) between the two types of hangers.
4. Multiply the cost delta by the number of hangers in the model.
5. Divide the total delta cost for hangers in the model by the length of the model to find the delta cost per L.F. for that model.
6. Modify the given unit costs per L.F. for the model by the delta cost per L.F.

Another approach to hanger configurations would be to start with the conduit only and add all the supports and any other items as separate lines. This procedure is most useful if the project involves racking many runs of conduit on a single hanger; for instance, a trapeze type hanger.

Example: Five (5) 2″ RGS conduits, 50 L.F. each, are to be run on trapeze hangers from one pull box to another. The run includes one 90° bend.

1. List the hangers' components to create an assembly cost for each 2′-wide trapeze.
2. List the components for the 50′ conduit run, noting that 6 trapeze supports will be required

Job Conditions: Productivities are based on new construction to 10′ high, using scaffolding, scissor lift, bucket lift in an unobstructed area. Material storage is assumed to be within 100′ of work being performed.

Add to labor for elevated installations:

10′ to 14.5′ High–10%	30′ to 35′ High–40%
15′ to 20′ High–20%	35′ to 40′ High–50%
20′ to 25′ High–25%	Over 40′ High–55%
25′ to 30′ High–35%	

Add these percentages to the L.F. labor cost, but not to fittings. Add these percentages only to quantities exceeding the different height levels, rather than the total conduit quantities.

Linear foot price for labor does not include penetrations in walls or floors and must be added to the estimate.

R260533-22   Conductors in Conduit

The table below lists the maximum number of conductors for various sized conduit using THW, TW or THWN insulations.

Copper Wire Size	1/2″ TW	1/2″ THW	1/2″ THWN	3/4″ TW	3/4″ THW	3/4″ THWN	1″ TW	1″ THW	1″ THWN	1-1/4″ TW	1-1/4″ THW	1-1/4″ THWN	1-1/2″ TW	1-1/2″ THW	1-1/2″ THWN	2″ TW	2″ THW	2″ THWN	2-1/2″ TW	2-1/2″ THW	2-1/2″ THWN	3″ THW	3″ THWN	3-1/2″ THW	3-1/2″ THWN	4″ THW	4″ THWN
#14	9	6	13	15	10	24	25	16	39	44	29	69	60	40	94	99	65	154	142	93		143		192			
#12	7	4	10	12	8	18	19	13	29	35	24	51	47	32	70	78	53	114	111	76	164	117		157			
#10	5	4	6	9	6	11	15	11	18	26	19	32	36	26	44	60	43	73	85	61	104	95	160	127		163	
#8	2	1	3	4	3	5	7	5	9	12	10	16	17	13	22	28	22	36	40	32	51	49	79	66	106	85	136
#6		1	1		2	4		4	6		7	11		10	15		16	26		23	37	36	57	48	76	62	98
#4		1	1		1	2		3	4		5	7		7	9		12	16		17	22	27	35	36	47	47	60
#3		1	1		1	1		2	3		4	6		6	8		10	13		15	19	23	29	31	39	40	51
#2		1	1		1	1		2	3		4	5		5	7		9	11		13	16	20	25	27	33	34	43
#1					1	1		1	1		3	3		4	5		6	8		9	12	14	18	19	25	25	32
1/0					1	1		1	1		2	3		3	4		5	7		8	10	12	15	16	21	21	27
2/0					1	1		1	1		1	2		3	3		5	6		7	8	10	13	14	17	18	22
3/0					1	1		1	1		1	1		2	3		4	5		6	7	9	11	12	14	15	18
4/0						1		1	1		1	1		1	2		3	4		5	6	7	9	10	12	13	15
250 kcmil								1	1		1	1		1	1		2	3		4	4	6	7	8	10	10	12
300								1	1		1	1		1	1		2	3		3	4	5	6	7	8	9	11
350									1		1	1		1	1		1	2		3	3	4	5	6	7	8	9
400											1	1		1	1		1	1		2	3	4	5	5	6	7	8
500											1	1		1	1		1	1		1	2	3	4	4	5	6	7
600												1		1	1		1	1		1	1	3	3	4	4	5	5
700														1	1		1	1		1	1	2	3	3	4	4	5
750														1	1		1	1		1	1	2	2	3	3	4	4

Reprinted with permission from NFPA 70-2014, *National Electrical Code®*, Copyright © 2013, National Fire Protection Association, Quincy, MA. This reprinted material is not the complete and official position of the NFPA on the referenced subject, which is represented solely by the standard in its entirety.

589

R260533-25   Conduit Weight Comparisons (Lbs. per 100 ft.) with Maximum Cable Fill*

Type	1/2″	3/4″	1″	1-1/4″	1-1/2″	2″	2-1/2″	3″	3-1/2″	4″	5″	6″
Rigid Galvanized Steel (RGS)	104	140	235	358	455	721	1022	1451	1749	2148	3083	4343
Intermediate Steel (IMC)	84	113	186	293	379	611	883	1263	1501	1830		
Electrical Metallic Tubing (EMT)	54	116	183	296	368	445	641	930	1215	1540		

*Conduit & Heaviest Conductor Combination

R260533-30   Labor for Couplings and Fittings

The labor included in the unit price lines for couplings is for their installation separate from a fitting. However, the labor included in the unit price lines for fittings covers their complete installation, which may include the labor installation of the coupling(s). If coupling(s) are required to complete a fitting installation, only the material for the required number of couplings needs to be added to the appropriate unit price lines.

R260533-60   Wireway

When "taking off" Wireway, list by size and type.

Example:
1. Screw cover, unflanged + size
2. Screw cover, flanged + size
3. Hinged cover, flanged + size
4. Hinged cover, unflanged + size

Each 10' length on Wireway contains:
1. 10' of cover either screw or hinged type
2. (1) Coupling or flange gasket
3. (1) Wall type mount

All fittings must be priced separately.

Substitution of hanger types is done the same as described in R260533-21, "HANGERS," keeping in mind that the wireway model is based on 10' sections instead of a 100' conduit run.

Labor-hours for wireway include:
1. Unloading by hand
2. Hauling by hand up to 100' from loading dock
3. Measuring and marking
4. Mounting wall bracket using two (2) anchor type lead fasteners
5. Installing wireway on brackets, to 10' high (for higher elevations use factors in R260533-20)

Job Conditions: Productivity is based on new construction, to a height of 10' using rolling staging, scissor lift, bucket lift in an unobstructed area.

Material staging area is assumed to be within 100' of work being performed.

R260533-65   Outlet Boxes

Outlet boxes should be included on the same takeoff sheet as branch piping or devices to better explain what is included in each circuit.

Each unit price in this section is a stand alone item and contains no other component unless specified. For example, to estimate a duplex outlet, components that must be added are:
1. 4" square box
2. 4" plaster ring
3. Duplex receptacle
4. Device cover

The method of mounting outlet boxes is two (2) plastic shield fasteners.

Outlet boxes plastic, labor-hours include:
1. Marking box location on wood studding
2. Mounting box

Economy of Scale – For large concentrations of plastic boxes in the same area deduct the following percentages from labor-hour totals:

1	to	10	0%
11	to	25	20%
26	to	50	25%
51	to	100	30%
	over	100	35%

Note: It is important to understand that these percentages are not used on the total job quantities, but only areas where concentrations exceed the levels specified.

R260533-70   Pull Boxes and Cabinets

List cabinets and pull boxes by NEMA type and size.

Example:	**TYPE**	**SIZE**
	NEMA 1	6"W x 6"H x 4"D
	NEMA 3R	6"W x 6"H x 4"D

Labor-hours for wall mount (indoor or outdoor) installations include:
1. Unloading and uncrating
2. Handling of enclosures up to 200' from loading dock using a dolly or pipe rollers
3. Measuring and marking
4. Drilling four (4) anchor type lead fasteners using a hammer drill
5. Mounting and leveling boxes

Note: A plywood backboard is not included.

Labor-hours for ceiling mounting include:
1. Unloading and uncrating
2. Handling boxes up to 100' from loading dock

3. Measuring and marking
4. Drilling four (4) anchor type lead fasteners using a hammer drill
5. Installing and leveling boxes to a height of 10' using rolling staging

Labor-hours for free standing cabinets include:
1. Unloading and uncrating
2. Handling of cabinets up to 200' from loading dock using a dolly or pipe rollers
3. Marking of floor
4. Drilling four (4) anchor type lead fasteners using a hammer drill
5. Leveling and shimming

Labor-hours for telephone cabinets include:
1. Unloading and uncrating
2. Handling cabinets up to 200' using a dolly or pipe rollers
3. Measuring and marking
4. Mounting and leveling, using four (4) lead anchor type fasteners

Fig. R260536-11

R260536-10　Cable Tray

Cable Tray - When taking off cable tray it is important to identify separately the different types and sizes involved in the system being estimated. (Fig. R260536-11)

   A. – Ladder Type, galvanized or aluminum
   B. – Trough Type, galvanized or aluminum
   C. – Solid Bottom, galvanized or aluminum

The unit of measure is calculated in linear feet. Do not deduct from this footage any length occupied by fittings. This will be the only allowance for scrap. Be sure to include all vertical drops to panels, switch gear, etc.

Hangers – Included in the linear footage of cable tray is

   D. – 1 – Pair of connector plates per 12 L.F.

   E. – 1 – Pair clamp type hangers and 4' of 3/8" threaded rod per 12 L.F.

Not included are structural supports, which must be priced in addition to the hangers.

Fittings – Identify separately the different types of fittings

   A. – Ladder Type, galvanized or aluminum
   B. – Trough Type, galvanized or aluminum
   C. – Solid Bottom Type, galvanized or aluminum

The configuration, radius and rung spacing must also be listed. The unit of measure is "Ea."

   D. – Elbow, vertical Ea.
   E. – Elbow, horizontal Ea.
   F. – Tee, vertical Ea.
   G. – Cross, horizontal Ea.
   H. – Wye, horizontal Ea.
   I. – Tee, horizontal Ea.
   J. – Reducing fitting Ea.

Depending on the use of the system other examples of units which must be included are:

   K. – Divider strip L.F.
   L. – Drop-outs Ea.

   M. – End caps Ea.
   N. – Panel connectors Ea.

Wire and cable are not included and should be taken off separately. See Unit Price sections.

Job Conditions – Unit prices are based on a new installation to a work plane of 15' using rolling staging.

Add to labor for elevated installations:

10' to 14.5' High	10%
15' to 20' High	20%
20' to 25' High	25%
25' to 30' High	35%
30' to 35' High	40%
35' to 40' High	50%
Over 40' High	55%

Add these percentages for L.F. totals but not to fittings. Add percentages to only those quantities that fall in the different elevations. In other words, if the total quantity of cable tray is 200' but only 75' is above 15' then the 10% is added to the 75' only.

Linear foot costs do not include penetrations through walls and floors which must be added to the estimate.

Cable Tray Covers

Covers – Cable tray covers are taken off in the same manner as the tray itself, making distinctions as to the type of cover. (Fig. R260536-11)

   O. – Vented, galvanized or aluminum
   P. – Solid, galvanized or aluminum

Cover configurations are taken off separately noting type, specific radius and widths.

Note: Care should be taken to identify from plans and specifications exactly what is being covered. In many systems only vertical fittings are covered to retain wire and cable.

R260539-30   Conduit In Concrete Slab

List conduit by quantity, size and type.

Example:

  A. Rigid galvanized steel + size
  B. P.V.C. + size

Rigid galvanized steel (A) contains per 100 L.F.:

  1. (20) Ties to slab reinforcing
  2. (11) Threaded steel couplings
  3. (2) Factory sweeps
  4. (2) Field threaded conduit terminations

  5. (2) Fiber bushings + locknuts
  6. (2) Removal of concentric knockouts

P.V.C. (B) contains per 100 L.F.:

  1. (20) Ties to slab reinforcing
  2. (11) Field cemented couplings
  3. (2) Factory sweeps
  4. (2) Adapters
  5. (2) Removal of concentric knockouts

R260539-40   Conduit In Trench

Conduit in trench is galvanized steel and contains per 100 L.F.:

  1. (11) Threaded couplings
  2. (2) Factory sweeps
  3. (2) Fiber bushings + (4) locknuts
  4. (2) Field threaded conduit terminations
  5. (2) Removal of concentric knockouts

Note:

Conduit in Unit Price sections do not include:

  1. Floor cutting
  2. Excavation or backfill
  3. Grouting or patching

Conduit fittings in excess of those listed in the above Conduit model must be added. (Refer to R260533-20 for Procedure example.)

For customer support on your Electrical Costs with RSMeans Data, call 800.448.8182.

Reference Tables

Fig. R260543-51

R260543-50 Underfloor Duct

When pricing Underfloor Duct it is important to identify and list each component, since costs vary significantly from one type of fitting to another. Do not deduct boxes or fittings from linear foot totals; this will be your allowance for scrap.

The first step is to identify the system as either:

FIG. R260543-51 Single Level
FIG. R260543-52 Dual Level

Single Level System

Include on your "takeoff sheet" the following unit price items, making sure to distinquish between Standard and Super duct:

A. Feeder duct (blank) in L.F.
B. Distribution duct (Inserts 2′ on center) in L.F.
C. Elbows (Vertical) Ea.
D. Elbows (Horizontal) Ea.
E. Cabinet connector Ea.
F. Single duct junction box Ea.
G. Double duct junction box Ea.
H. Triple duct junction box Ea.
I. Support, single cell Ea.
J. Support, double cell Ea.
K. Support, triple cell Ea.
L. Carpet pan Ea.
M. Terrazzo pan Ea.
N. Insert to conduit adapter Ea.
O. Conduit adapter Ea.
P. Low tension outlet Ea.
Q. High tension outlet Ea.
R. Galvanized nipple Ea.
S. Wire per C.L.F.
T. Offset (Duct type) Ea.

Fig. R260543-52

R260543-50 Underfloor Duct (cont.)

Dual Level System + Labor

Dual Level

Include the following when "taking off" Dual Level systems:

Distinguish between Standard and Super duct.

- A. Feeder duct (blank) in L.F.
- B. Distribution duct (Inserts 2' on center) in L.F.
- C. Elbows (Vertical), Ea.
- D. Elbows (Horizontal), Ea.
- E. Cabinet connector, Ea.
- F. Single duct, 2 level, junction box, Ea.
- G. Double duct, 2 level, junction box, Ea.
- H. Support, single cell, Ea.
- I. Support, double cell, Ea.
- J. Support, triple cell, Ea.
- K. Carpet pan, Ea.
- L. Terrazzo pan, Ea.
- M. Insert to conduit adapter, Ea.
- N. Conduit adapter, Ea.
- O. Low tension outlet, Ea.
- P. High tension outlet, Ea.
- Q. Wire per C.L.F.

Note: Make sure to include risers in linear foot totals. High tension outlets include box, receptacle, covers and related mounting hardware.

Labor-hours for both Single and Dual Level systems include:

1. Unloading and uncrating
2. Hauling up to 200' from loading dock
3. Measuring and marking
4. Setting raceway and fittings in slab or on grade
5. Leveling raceway and fittings

Labor-hours do not include:

1. Floor cutting
2. Excavation or backfill
3. Concrete pour
4. Grouting or patching
5. Wire or wire pulls
6. Additional outlets after concrete is poured
7. Piping to or from Underfloor Duct

Note: Installation is based on installing up to 150' of duct. If quantities exceed this, deduct the following percentages:

1. 150' to 250' - 10%
2. 250' to 350' - 15%
3. 350' to 500' - 20%
4. over 500' - 25%

Deduct these percentages from labor only.

Deduct these percentages from straight sections only.

Do not deduct from fittings or junction boxes.

Job Conditions: Productivity is based on new construction.

Underfloor duct to be installed on first three floors.

The material staging area is within 100' of work being performed.

The area unobstructed and duct are not subject to physical damage.

R260580-75   Motor Connections

Motor connections should be listed by size and type of motor.
Included in the material and labor cost are:

1. (2) Flex connectors
2. 18″ of flexible metallic wireway
3. Wire identification and termination
4. Test for rotation
5. (2) or (3) Conductors

Price does not include:

1. Mounting of motor
2. Disconnect switch
3. Motor starter
4. Controls
5. Conduit or wire ahead of flex

Note: When "taking off" motor connections, it is advisable to list connections on the same quantity sheet as motors, motor starters and controls.

Electrical   R2609 Instrumen. & Cont. of Elect. Systems

R260913-80   Switchboard Instruments

Switchboard instruments are added to the price of switchboards according to job specifications. This equipment is usually included when ordering "gear" from the manufacturer and will arrive factory installed.

Included in the labor cost are:

1. Internal wiring connections
2. Wire identification
3. Wire tagging

Transition sections include:

1. Uncrating
2. Hauling sections up to 100′ from loading dock
3. Positioning sections
4. Leveling sections

5. Bolting enclosures
6. Bolting vertical bus bars

Price does not include:

1. Equipment pads
2. Steel channels embedded or grouted in concrete
3. Special knockouts
4. Rigging

Job Conditions: Productivity is based on new construction and equipment to be installed on the first floor within 200′ of the loading dock.

R262213-10 Electric Circuit Voltages

General: The following method provides the user with a simple non-technical means of obtaining comparative costs of wiring circuits. The circuits considered serve the electrical loads of motors, electric heating, lighting and transformers, for example, that require low voltage 60 Hertz alternating current.

The method used here is suitable only for obtaining estimated costs. It is **not** intended to be used as a substitute for electrical engineering design applications.

Conduit and wire circuits can represent from twenty to thirty percent of the total building electrical cost. By following the described steps and using the tables the user can translate the various types of electric circuits into estimated costs.

Wire Size: Wire size is a function of the electric load which is usually listed in one of the following units:

1. Amperes (A)
2. Watts (W)
3. Kilowatts (kW)
4. Volt amperes (VA)
5. Kilovolt amperes (kVA)
6. Horsepower (HP)

These units of electric load must be converted to amperes in order to obtain the size of wire necessary to carry the load. To convert electric load units to amperes one must have an understanding of the voltage classification of the power source and the voltage characteristics of the electrical equipment or load to be energized. The seven A.C. circuits commonly used are illustrated in Figures R262213-11 through R262213-17 showing the transformer load voltage and the point of use voltage at the point on the circuit where the load is connected. The difference between the source and point of use voltage is attributed to the circuit voltage drop and is considered to be approximately 4%.

Motor Voltages: Motor voltages are listed by their point of use voltage and not the power source voltage.

For example: 460 volts instead of 480 volts
200 instead of 208 volts
115 volts instead of 120 volts

Lighting and Heating Voltages: Lighting and heating equipment voltages are listed by the power source voltage and not the point of wire voltage.

For example: 480, 277, 120 volt lighting
480 volt heating or air conditioning unit
208 volt heating unit

Transformer Voltages: Transformer primary (input) and secondary (output) voltages are listed by the power source voltage.

For example: Single phase 10 kVA
Primary 240/480 volts
Secondary 120/240 volts

In this case, the primary voltage may be 240 volts with a 120 volts secondary or may be 480 volts with either a 120V or a 240V secondary.

For example: Three phase 10 kVA
Primary 480 volts
Secondary 208Y/120 volts

In this case the transformer is suitable for connection to a circuit with a 3 phase, 3 wire or a 3 phase, 4 wire circuit with a 480 voltage. This application will provide a secondary circuit of 3 phase, 4 wire with 208 volts between phase wires and 120 volts between any phase wire and the neutral (white) wire.

R262213-11

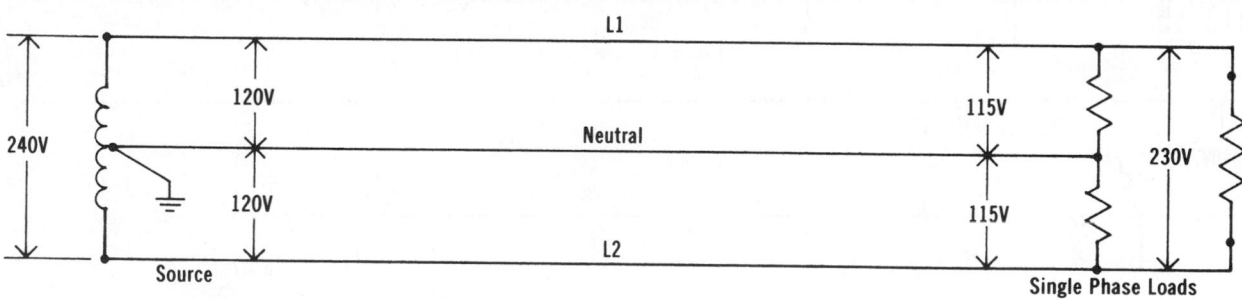

3 Wire, 1 Phase, 120/240 Volt System

R262213-12

4 Wire, 3 Phase, 208Y/120 Volt System

R262213-13   Electric Circuit Voltages (cont.)

3 Wire, 3 Phase 240 Volt System

R262213-14

4 Wire, 3 Phase, 240/120 Volt System

R262213-15

3 Wire, 3 Phase 480 Volt System

R262213-16

4 Wire, 3 Phase, 480Y/277 Volt System

R262213-17   Electric Circuit Voltages (cont.)

3 Wire, 3 Phase, 600 Volt System

R262213-20   kW Value/Cost Determination

General: Lighting and electric heating loads are expressed in watts and kilowatts.

Cost Determination:

The proper ampere values can be obtained as follows:
1. Convert watts to kilowatts
   (watts 1000 ÷ kilowatts)
2. Determine voltage rating of equipment.
3. Determine whether equipment is single phase or three phase.
4. Refer to Table R262213-21 to find ampere value from kW, Ton and BTU/hr. values.
5. Determine type of wire insulation – TW, THW, THWN.
6. Determine if wire is copper or aluminum.
7. Refer to Table R260519-92 to obtain copper or aluminum wire size from ampere values.
8. Next refer to Table R260533-22 for the proper conduit size to accommodate the number and size of wires in each particular case.
9. Next refer to unit cost data for the per linear foot cost of the conduit.
10. Next refer to unit cost data for the per linear foot cost of the wire. Multiply cost of wire per L.F. x number of wires in the circuits to obtain total wire cost per L.F.

11. Add values obtained in Step 9 and 10 for total cost per linear foot for conduit and wire x length of circuit = Total Cost.

Notes:
1. 1 Phase refers to single phase, 2 wire circuits.
2. 3 Phase refers to three phase, 3 wire circuits.
3. For circuits which operate continuously for 3 hours or more, multiply the ampere values by 1.25 for a given kW requirement.
4. For kW ratings not listed, add ampere values.

   For example: Find the ampere value of
   9 kW at 208 volt, single phase.

$$\begin{array}{r} 4 \text{ kW} = 19.2\text{A} \\ 5 \text{ kW} = 24.0\text{A} \\ \hline 9 \text{ kW} = 43.2\text{A} \end{array}$$

5. "Length of Circuit" refers to the one way distance of the run, not to the total sum of wire lengths.

R262213-21 Ampere Values as Determined by kW Requirements, BTU/HR or Ton, Voltage and Phase Values

			120V	208V		240V		277V	480V
kW	Ton	BTU/HR	1 Phase	1 Phase	3 Phase	1 Phase	3 Phase	1 Phase	3 Phase
0.5	.1422	1,707	4.2A	2.4A	1.4A	2.1A	1.2A	1.8A	0.6A
0.75	.2133	2,560	6.2	3.6	2.1	3.1	1.9	2.7	.9
1.0	.2844	3,413	8.3	4.9	2.8	4.2	2.4	3.6	1.2
1.25	.3555	4,266	10.4	6.0	3.5	5.2	3.0	4.5	1.5
1.5	.4266	5,120	12.5	7.2	4.2	6.3	3.1	5.4	1.8
2.0	.5688	6,826	16.6	9.7	5.6	8.3	4.8	7.2	2.4
2.5	.7110	8,533	20.8	12.0	7.0	10.4	6.1	9.1	3.1
3.0	.8532	10,239	25.0	14.4	8.4	12.5	7.2	10.8	3.6
4.0	1.1376	13,652	33.4	19.2	11.1	16.7	9.6	14.4	4.8
5.0	1.4220	17,065	41.6	24.0	13.9	20.8	12.1	18.1	6.1
7.5	2.1331	25,598	62.4	36.0	20.8	31.2	18.8	27.0	9.0
10.0	2.8441	34,130	83.2	48.0	27.7	41.6	24.0	36.5	12.0
12.5	3.5552	42,663	104.2	60.1	35.0	52.1	30.0	45.1	15.0
15.0	4.2662	51,195	124.8	72.0	41.6	62.4	37.6	54.0	18.0
20.0	5.6883	68,260	166.4	96.0	55.4	83.2	48.0	73.0	24.0
25.0	7.1104	85,325	208.4	120.2	70.0	104.2	60.0	90.2	30.0
30.0	8.5325	102,390		144.0	83.2	124.8	75.2	108.0	36.0
35.0	9.9545	119,455		168.0	97.1	145.6	87.3	126.0	42.1
40.0	11.3766	136,520		192.0	110.8	166.4	96.0	146.0	48.0
45.0	12.7987	153,585			124.8	187.5	112.8	162.0	54.0
50.0	14.2208	170,650			140.0	208.4	120.0	180.4	60.0
60.0	17.0650	204,780			166.4		150.4	216.0	72.0
70.0	19.9091	238,910			194.2		174.6		84.2
80.0	22.7533	273,040			221.6		192.0		96.0
90.0	25.5975	307,170					225.6		108.0
100.0	28.4416	341,300							120.0

R262213-25 kVA Value/Cost Determination

General: Control transformers are listed in VA. Step-down and power transformers are listed in kVA.

Cost Determination:

1. Convert VA to kVA. Volt amperes (VA) ÷ 1000 = Kilovolt amperes (kVA).
2. Determine voltage rating of equipment.
3. Determine whether equipment is single phase or three phase.
4. Refer to Table R262213-26 to find ampere value from kVA value.
5. Determine type of wire insulation – TW, THW, THWN.
6. Determine if wire is copper or aluminum.
7. Refer to Table R260519-92 to obtain copper or aluminum wire size from ampere values.

8. Next refer to Table R260533-22 for the proper conduit size to accommodate the number and size of wires in each particular case.
9. Next refer to unit price data for the per linear foot cost of the conduit.
10. Next refer to unit price data for the per linear foot cost of the wire. Multiply cost of wire per L.F. x number of wires in the circuits to obtain total wire cost.
11. Add values obtained in Step 9 and 10 for total cost per linear foot for conduit and wire x length of circuit = Total Cost.

Example: A transformer rated 10 kVA 480 volts primary, 240 volts secondary, 3 phase has the capacity to furnish the following:

1. Primary amperes = 10 kVA x 1.20 = 12 amperes (from Table R262213-26)
2. Secondary amperes = 10 kVA x 2.40 = 24 amperes (from Table R262213-26)

Note: Transformers can deliver generally 125% of their rated kVA. For instance, a 10 kVA rated transformer can safely deliver 12.5 kVA.

R262213-26 Multiplier Values for kVA to Amperes Determined by Voltage and Phase Values

Volts	Multiplier for Circuits	
	2 Wire, 1 Phase	3 Wire, 3 Phase
115	8.70	
120	8.30	
230	4.30	2.51
240	4.16	2.40
200	5.00	2.89
208	4.80	2.77
265	3.77	2.18
277	3.60	2.08
460	2.17	1.26
480	2.08	1.20
575	1.74	1.00
600	1.66	0.96

R262213-60   Oil Filled Transformers

Transformers in this section include:

1. Rigging (as required)
2. Rental of crane and operator
3. Setting of oil filled transformer
4. (4) Anchor bolts, nuts and washers in concrete pad

Price does not include:

1. Primary and secondary terminations
2. Transformer pad
3. Equipment grounding
4. Cable
5. Conduit locknuts or bushings

Transformers in Unit Price sections for dry type, back-boost and isolating transformers include:

1. Unloading and uncrating
2. Hauling transformer to within 200' of loading dock

3. Setting in place
4. Wall mounting hardware
5. Testing

Price does not include:

1. Structural supports
2. Suspension systems
3. Welding or fabrication
4. Primary & secondary terminations

Add the following percentages to the labor for ceiling mounted transformers:

10' to 15'	= + 15%
15' to 25'	= + 30%
Over 25'	= + 35%

Job Conditions: Productivities are based on new construction. Installation is assumed to be on the first floor, in an obstructed area to a height of 10'. Material staging area is within 100' of final transformer location.

R262416-50 Load Centers and Panelboards

When pricing load centers list panels by size and type. List breakers in a separate column of the "quantity sheet," and define by phase and ampere rating.

Material and labor prices include breakers; for example: a 100A, 3-Wire, 102/240V, 18 circuit panel w/ main breaker, as described in the unit cost section, contains 18 single pole 20A breakers.

If you do not choose to include a full panel of single pole breakers, use the following method to adjust material and labor costs.

Example: In an 18 circuit panel only 16 single pole breakers are desired, requiring that the cost of 2 breakers be subtracted from the panel cost.

1. Go to the appropriate unit cost section of the data set to find the unit prices of the given circuit breaker type.
2. Modify those costs as follows:
   Bare material price x 0.50
   Bare labor cost x 0.60.
3. Multiply those modified bare costs by 2 (breakers in this example).
4. Subtract the modified costs for the 2 breakers from the given cost of the panel.

Labor-hours for load center installation includes:
1. Unloading, uncrating, and handling enclosures 200' from unloading area

2. Measuring and marking
3. Drilling (4) lead anchor type fasteners using a hammer drill
4. Mounting and leveling panel to a height of 6'
5. Preparation and termination of feeder cable to lugs or main breaker
6. Branch circuit identification
7. Lacing using tie wraps
8. Testing and load balancing
9. Marking panel directory

Not included in the material and labor are:
1. Modifications to enclosure
2. Structural supports
3. Additional lugs
4. Plywood backboards
5. Painting or lettering

Note: Knockouts are included in the price of terminating pipe runs and need not be added to the load center costs.

Job Conditions: Productivity is based on new construction to a height of 6', in an unobstructed area. Material staging area is assumed to be within 100' of work being performed.

Fig. R262419-61

R262419-60   Motor Control Centers

When taking off motor control centers, list the size, type and height of structures.

Example:
1. 600A, 22,000 RMS, 72″ high
2. 600A, back to back, 72″ high

Next take off individual starters; the number of structures can also be determined by adding the height in inches of starters divided by the height of the structure, and list on the same quantity sheet as the structures. Identify starters by type, horsepower rating, size and height in inches.

Example:
A. Class 1, Type B, FVNR starter, 25 H.P., 18″ high.
    Add to the list with starters, factory installed controls.

Example:

B. Pilot lights

C. Push buttons

D. Auxiliary contacts

Identify starters and structures as either copper or aluminum and by the NEMA type of enclosure.

When pricing starters and structures, be sure to add or deduct adjustments, using lines in the unit price section.

Included in the cost of motor control structures are:
1. Uncrating
2. Hauling to location within 100′ of loading dock
3. Setting structures
4. Leveling
5. Aligning
6. Bolting together structure frames
7. Bolting horizontal bus bars

Labor-hours do not include:
1. Equipment pad
2. Steel channels embedded or grouted in concrete
3. Pull boxes
4. Special knockouts
5. Main switchboard section
6. Transition section
7. Instrumentation
8. External control wiring
9. Conduit or wire

Material for starters include:
1. Circuit breaker or fused disconnect
2. Magnetic motor starter
3. Control transformer
4. Control fuse and fuse block

Labor-hours for starters include:
1. Handling
2. Installing starter within structure
3. Internal wiring connections
4. Lacing within enclosure
5. Testing
6. Phasing

Job Conditions: Productivity is based on new construction. The motor control location is assumed to be on first floor in an unobstructed area. The material staging area is within 100′ of the final location.

Note: Additional labor-hours must be added if M.C.C. is to be installed on floors other than the first, or if rigging is required.

R262419-65   Motor Starters and Controls

Motor starters should be listed on the same "quantity sheet" as motors and motor connections. Identify each starter by:

1. Size
2. Voltage
3. Type

Example:

A. FVNR, 480V, 2HP, size 00
B. FVNR, 480V, 5HP, size 0, combination type
C. FVR, 480V, size 2

The NEMA type of enclosure should also be identified.

Included in the labor-hours are:

1. Unloading, uncrating and handling of starters up to 200' from loading area
2. Measuring and marking
3. Drilling (4) anchor type lead fasteners using a hammer drill
4. Mounting and leveling starter
5. Connecting wire or cable to line and load sides of starter (when already lugged)
6. Installation of (3) thermal type heaters
7. Testing

The following are not included unless specified in the unit price description.

1. Control transformer
2. Controls, either factory or field installed
3. Conduit and wire to or from starter
4. Plywood backboard
5. Cable terminations

The following material and labor were included for combination type starters:

1. Unloading, uncrating and handling of starter up to 200' of loading dock
2. Measuring and marking
3. Drilling (4) anchor type lead fasteners using a hammer drill
4. Mounting and leveling
5. Connecting prepared cable conductors
6. Installation of (3) dual element cartridge type fuses
7. Installation of (3) thermal type heaters
8. Test for rotation

MOTOR CONTROLS

When pricing motor controls make sure you consider the type of control system being utilized. If the controls are factory installed and located in the enclosure itself, then you would add to your starter price the items 5200 through 5800 in the Unit Price section. If control voltage is different from line voltage, add the material and labor cost of a control transformer.

For external control of starters include the following items:

1. Raceways
2. Wire & terminations
3. Control enclosures
4. Fittings
5. Push button stations
6. Indicators

Job Conditions: Productivity is based on new construction to a height of 10'.

Material staging area is assumed to be within 100' of work being performed.

605

Fig. R262419-81

R262419-80 Distribution Section

After "taking off" the switchboard section, include on the same "quantity sheet" the distribution section; identify by:
1. Voltage
2. Ampere rating
3. Type

Example:

(Fig. R262419-81) (B) Distribution Section

Included in the labor costs of the distribution section are:
1. Uncrating
2. Hauling to 200' of loading dock
3. Setting of distribution panel
4. Leveling & shimming

5. Anchoring of equipment to pad or floor
6. Bolting of horizontal bus bars between
7. Testing of equipment

Not included in the Distribution section are:
1. Breakers (C)
2. Equipment pads
3. Steel channels embedded or grouted in concrete
4. Pull boxes
5. Special knockouts
6. Transition section
7. Conduit or wire

R262419-82 Feeder Section

List quantities on the same sheet as the distribution section. Identify breakers by: (Fig. R262419-81)
1. Frame type
2. Number of poles
3. Ampere rating

Installation includes:
1. Handling

2. Placing breakers in distribution panel
3. Preparing wire or cable
4. Lacing wire
5. Marking each phase with colored tape
6. Marking panel legend
7. Testing
8. Balancing

R262419-84 Switchgear

It is recommended that "switchgear" or those items contained in the following sections be quoted from equipment manufacturers as a package price.

Switchboard instruments

Switchboard distribution sections

Switchboard feeder sections

Switchboard Service Disc.

Switchboard In-plant Dist.

Included in these sections are the most common types and sizes of factory assembled equipment.

The recommended procedure for low voltage switchgear would be to price (Fig. R262419-81) (A) Main Switchboard

Identify by:

1. Voltage
2. Amperage
3. Type

Example:

1. 120/208V, 4-wire, 600A, nonfused
2. 277/480V, 4-wire, 600A, nonfused
3. 120/208V, 4-wire, 400A w/fused switch & CT compartment
4. 277/480V, 4-wire, 400A, w/fused switch & CT compartment

5. 120/208V, 4-wire, 800A, w/pressure switch & CT compartment
6. 277/480V, 4-wire, 800A, w/molded CB & CT compartment

Included in the labor costs for switchboards are:

1. Uncrating
2. Hauling to 200' of loading dock
3. Setting equipment
4. Leveling and shimming
5. Anchoring
6. Cable identification
7. Testing of equipment

Not included in the switchboard price are:

1. Rigging
2. Equipment pads
3. Steel channels embedded or grouted in concrete
4. Special knockouts
5. Transition or Auxiliary sections
6. Instrumentation
7. External control
8. Conduit and wire
9. Conductor terminations

Fig. R16450-101

R262513-10   Aluminum Bus Duct

When taking off bus duct identify the system as either:
1. Aluminum
2. Copper

List straight lengths by type and size
- A. Feeder — 800 A
- B. Plug in — 800 A

Do not measure through fittings as you would on conduit, since there is no allowance for scrap in bus duct systems.

If upon taking off linear foot quantities of bus duct you find your quantities are not divisible evenly by 10 ft., then the remainder must be priced as a special item and quoted from the manufacturer. Do not use the bare material cost per L.F. for these special items. You can, however, safely use the bare labor cost per L.F. for the entire length.

Identify fittings by type and ampere rating.

Example:

C. Switchboard stub, 800 A

D. Elbows, 800 A

E. End box, 800 A

F. Cable tap box, 800 A

G. Tee Fittings, 800 A

H. Hangers

Plug-in Units – List separately plug-in units and identify by type and ampere rating

I. Plug-in switches 600 Volt 3 phase 60 A

J. Plug-in molded case C.B. 60 A

K. Combination starter FVNR NEMA 1

L. Combination contactor & fused switch NEMA 1

M. Combination fusible switch & lighting control 60 A

Labor-hours for feeder and plug-in sections include:
1. Unloading and uncrating
2. Hauling up to 200 ft. from loading dock
3. Measuring and marking
4. Setup of rolling staging
5. Installing hangers
6. Hanging and bolting sections
7. Aligning and leveling
8. Testing

Labor-hours do not include:
1. Modifications to existing structure for hanger supports
2. Threaded rod in excess of 2 ft.
3. Welding
4. Penetrations through walls
5. Staging rental

Deduct the following percentages from labor only:

$$\begin{aligned}
150 \text{ ft. to } 250 \text{ ft.} &- 10\% \\
251 \text{ ft. to } 350 \text{ ft.} &- 15\% \\
351 \text{ ft. to } 500 \text{ ft.} &- 20\% \\
\text{Over } 500 \text{ ft.} &- 25\%
\end{aligned}$$

Deduct percentage only if runs are contained in the same area.

Example: If the job entails running 100 ft. in 5 different locations do not deduct 20%, but if the duct is being run in 1 area and the quantity is 500 ft. then you would deduct 20%.

Deduct only from straight lengths, not fittings or plug-in units.

R262513-10 Aluminum Bus Duct (cont.)

Add to labor for elevated installations:

10 ft. to 14.5 ft. high	10%
15 ft. to 20 ft. high	20%
21 ft. to 25 ft. high	25%
26 ft. to 30 ft. high	35%
31 ft. to 35 ft. high	40%
36 ft. to 40 ft. high	50%
Over 40 ft. high	55%

Bus Duct Fittings:

Labor-hours for fittings include:
1. Unloading and uncrating
2. Hauling up to 200 ft. from loading dock
3. Installing, fitting, and bolting all ends to in-place sections

Plug-in units include:
1. Unloading and uncrating
2. Hauling up to 200 ft. from loading dock
3. Installing plug-in into in-place duct
4. Setup of rolling staging
5. Connecting load wire to lugs
6. Marking wire
7. Checking phase rotation

Labor-hours for plug-ins do not include:
1. Conduit runs from plug-in
2. Wire from plug-in
3. Conduit termination

Economy of Scale – For large concentrations of plug-in units in the same area deduct the following percentages:

11	to	25	15%
26	to	50	20%
51	to	75	25%
76	to	100	30%
100	and	over	35%

Job Conditions: Productivities are based on new construction in an unobstructed first floor area to a height of 15 ft. using rolling staging.

Material staging area is within 100 ft. of work being performed.
Add to the duct fittings and hangers:
    Plug-in switches (fused)
    Plug-in breakers
    Combination starters
    Combination contactors
    Combination fusible switch and lighting control

Labor-hours for duct and fittings include:
1. Unloading and uncrating
2. Hauling up to 200 ft. from loading dock
3. Measuring and marking
4. Installing duct runs
5. Leveling
6. Sound testing

Labor-hours for plug-ins include:
1. Unloading and uncrating
2. Hauling up to 200 ft. from loading dock
3. Installing plug-ins
4. Preparing wire
5. Wire connections and marking

R262716-40   Standard Electrical Enclosure Types

NEMA Enclosures

Electrical enclosures serve two basic purposes: they protect people from accidental contact with enclosed electrical devices and connections, and they protect the enclosed devices and connections from specified external conditions. The National Electrical Manufacturers Association (NEMA) has established the following standards. Because these descriptions are not intended to be complete representations of NEMA listings, consultation of NEMA literature is advised for detailed information.

The following definitions and descriptions pertain to NONHAZARDOUS locations.

NEMA   Type 1: General purpose enclosures intended for use indoors, primarily to prevent accidental contact of personnel with the enclosed equipment in areas that do not involve unusual conditions.

NEMA   Type 2: Dripproof indoor enclosures intended to protect the enclosed equipment against dripping noncorrosive liquids and falling dirt.

NEMA   Type 3: Dustproof, raintight and sleet-resistant (ice-resistant) enclosures intended for use outdoors to protect the enclosed equipment against wind-blown dust, rain, sleet, and external ice formation.

NEMA   Type 3R: Rainproof and sleet-resistant (ice-resistant) enclosures intended for use outdoors to protect the enclosed equipment against rain. These enclosures are constructed so that the accumulation and melting of sleet (ice) will not damage the enclosure and its internal mechanisms.

NEMA   Type 3S: Enclosures intended for outdoor use to provide limited protection against wind-blown dust, rain, and sleet (ice) and to allow operation of external mechanisms when ice-laden.

NEMA   Type 4: Watertight and dust-tight enclosures intended for use indoors and out – to protect the enclosed equipment against splashing water, seepage of water, falling or hose-directed water, and severe external condensation.

NEMA   Type 4X: Watertight, dust-tight, and corrosion-resistant indoor and outdoor enclosures featuring the same provisions as Type 4 enclosures, plus corrosion resistance.

NEMA   Type 5: Indoor enclosures intended primarily to provide limited protection against dust and falling dirt.

NEMA   Type 6: Enclosures intended for indoor and outdoor use – primarily to provide limited protection against the entry of water during occasional temporary submersion at a limited depth.

NEMA   Type 6R: Enclosures intended for indoor and outdoor use – primarily to provide limited protection against the entry of water during prolonged submersion at a limited depth.

NEMA   Type 11: Enclosures intended for indoor use – primarily to provide, by means of oil immersion, limited protection to enclosed equipment against the corrosive effects of liquids and gases.

NEMA   Type 12: Dust-tight and driptight indoor enclosures intended for use indoors in industrial locations to protect the enclosed equipment against fibers, flyings, lint, dust, and dirt, as well as light splashing, seepage, dripping, and external condensation of noncorrosive liquids.

NEMA   Type 13: Oil-tight and dust-tight indoor enclosures intended primarily to house pilot devices, such as limit switches, foot switches, push buttons, selector switches, and pilot lights, and to protect these devices against lint and dust, seepage, external condensation, and sprayed water, oil, and noncorrosive coolant.

The following definitions and descriptions pertain to HAZARDOUS, or CLASSIFIED, locations:

NEMA   Type 7: Enclosures intended to use in indoor locations classified as Class 1, Groups A, B, C, or D, as defined in the National Electrical Code.

NEMA   Type 9: Enclosures intended for use in indoor locations classified as Class 2, Groups E, F, or G, as defined in the National Electrical Code.

R262726-90   Wiring Devices

Wiring devices should be priced on a separate takeoff form which includes boxes, covers, conduit and wire.

Labor-hours for devices include:
1. Stripping of wire
2. Attaching wire to device using terminators on the device itself, lugs, set screws etc.
3. Mounting of device in box

Labor-hours do not include:
1. Conduit
2. Wire
3. Boxes
4. Plates

Economy of Scale – for large concentrations of devices in the same area deduct the following percentages from labor-hours:

1	to	10	0%
11	to	25	20%
26	to	50	25%
51	to	100	30%
	over	100	35%

R262726-90 Wiring Devices (cont.)

NEMA No.	15 R	20 R	30 R	50 R	60 R
1 125V 2 Pole, 2 Wire					
2 250V 2 Pole, 2 Wire					
5 125V 2 Pole, 3 Wire					
6 250V 2 Pole, 3 Wire					
7 277V, AC 2 Pole, 3 Wire					
10 125/250V 3 Pole, 3 Wire					
11 3 Phase 250V 3 Pole, 3 Wire					
14 125/250V 3 Pole, 4 Wire					
15 3 Phase 250V 3 Pole, 4 Wire					
18 3 Phase 208Y/120V 4 Pole, 4 Wire					

R262726-90   Wiring Devices (cont.)

NEMA No.	15 R	20 R	30 R	NEMA No.	15 R	20 R	30 R
L 1 125V 2 Pole, 2 Wire				**L 13** 3 Phase 600V 3 Pole, 3 Wire			
L 2 250V 2 Pole, 2 Wire		15A		**L 14** 125/250V 3 Pole, 4 Wire			
L 5 125 V 2 Pole, 3 Wire				**L 15** 3 Phase 250 V 3 Pole, 4 Wire			
L 6 250 V 2 Pole, 3 Wire				**L 16** 3 Phase 480V 3 Pole, 4 Wire			
L 7 227 V, AC 2 Pole, 3 Wire				**L 17** 3 Phase 600 V 3 Pole, 4 Wire			
L 8 480 V 2 Pole, 3 Wire				**L 18** 3 Phase 208Y/120V 4 Pole, 4 Wire			
L 9 600 V 2 Pole, 3 Wire				**L 19** 3 Phase 480Y/277V 4 Pole, 4 Wire			
L 10 125/250V 3 Pole, 3 Wire				**L 20** 3 Phase 600Y/347V 4 Pole, 4 Wire			
L 11 3 Phase 250 V 3 Pole, 3 Wire				**L 21** 3 Phase 208Y/120V 4 Pole, 5 Wire			
L 12 3 Phase 480 V 3 Pole, 3 Wire				**L 22** 3 Phase 480Y/277V 4 Pole, 5 Wire			
				L 23 3 Phase 600Y/347V 4 Pole, 5 Wire			

R262816-80 Safety Switches

List each safety switch by type, ampere rating, voltage, single or three phase, fused or nonfused.

Example:

A. General duty, 240V, 3-pole, fused
B. Heavy Duty, 600V, 3-pole, nonfused
C. Heavy Duty, 240V, 2-pole, fused
D. Heavy Duty, 600V, 3-pole, fused

Also include NEMA enclosure type and identify as:

1. Indoor
2. Weatherproof
3. Explosionproof

Installation of safety switches includes:

1. Unloading and uncrating
2. Handling disconnects up to 200′ from loading dock
3. Measuring and marking location
4. Drilling (4) anchor type lead fasteners using a hammer drill
5. Mounting and leveling safety switch
6. Installing (3) fuses
7. Phasing and tagging line and load wires

Price does not include:

1. Modifications to enclosure
2. Plywood backboard
3. Conduit or wire
4. Fuses
5. Termination of wires

Job Conditions: Productivities are based on new construction to an installed height of 6′ above finished floor.

Material staging area is assumed to be within 100′ of work in progress.

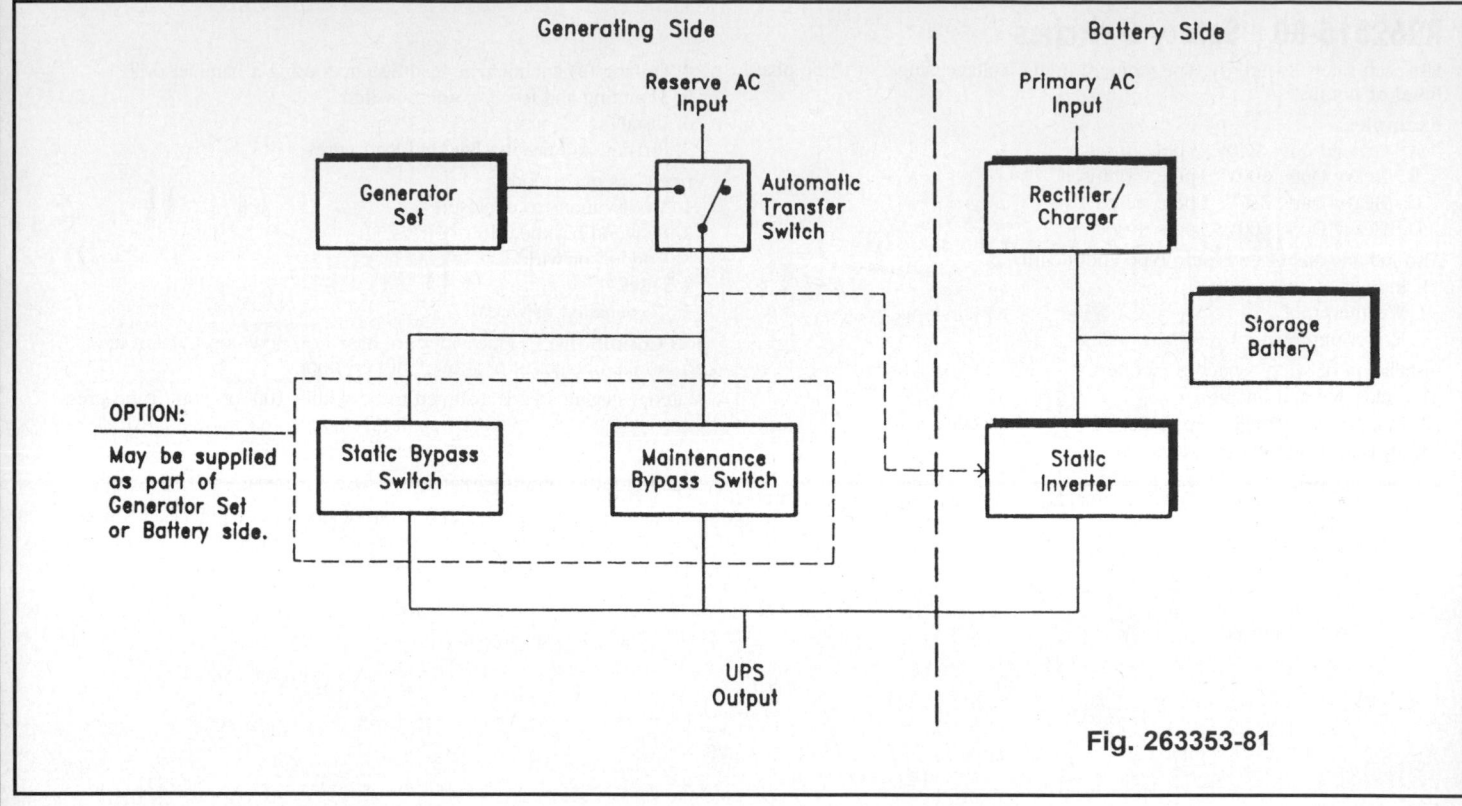

Fig. 263353-81

R263353-80 Uninterruptible Power Supply Systems

General: Uninterruptible Power Supply (UPS) Systems are used to provide power for legally required standby systems. They are also designed to protect computers and provide optional additional coverage for any or all loads in a facility. Figure R263353-81 shows a typical configuration for a UPS System with a generator set.

Cost Determination:

It is recommended that UPS System material costs be obtained from equipment manufacturers as a package. Installation costs should be obtained from a vendor or contractor.

The recommended procedure for pricing UPS Systems would be to identify:

1. Frequency – by Hertz (Hz.)
   For example: 50, 60, and 400/415 Hz.
2. Apparent power and real power
   For example: 200 kVA/170 kW
3. Input/Output voltage
   For example: 120V, 208V or 240V

4. Phase – either single or three-phase
5. Options and accessories – For extended run time more batteries would be required. Other accessories include battery cabinets, battery racks, remote control panel, power distribution unit (PDU), and warranty enhancement plans.

Note:

1. Larger systems can be configured by paralleling two or more standard small size single modules.
   For example: two 15 kVA modules combined together and configured to 30 kVA.
2. Maximum input current during battery recharge is typically 15% higher than normal current.
3. UPS Systems weights vary depending on options purchased and power rating in kVA.

614

For customer support on your Electrical Costs with RSMeans Data, call 800.448.8182.

R263413-30   HP Value/Cost Determination

General: Motors can be powered by any of the seven systems shown in Figure R262213-11 through Figure R262213-17 provided the motor voltage characteristics are compatible with the power system characteristics.

Cost Determination:

Motor Amperes for the various size H.P. and voltage are listed in Table R263413-31. To find the amperes, locate the required H.P. rating and locate the amperes under the appropriate circuit characteristics.

For example:

A. 100 H.P., 3 phase, 460 volt motor = 124 amperes (Table R263413-31)

B. 10 H.P., 3 phase, 200 volt motor = 32.2 amperes (Table R263413-31)

Motor Wire Size: After the amperes are found in Table R263413-31 the amperes must be increased 25% to compensate for power losses. Next refer to Table R260519-92. Find the appropriate insulation column for copper or aluminum wire to determine the proper wire size.

For example:

A. 100 H.P., 3 phase, 460 volt motor has an ampere value of 124 amperes from Table R263413-31

B. 124A x 1.25 = 155 amperes

C. Refer to Table R260519-92 for THW or THWN wire insulations to find the proper wire size. For a 155 ampere load using copper wire a size 2/0 wire is needed.

D. For the 3 phase motor three wires of 2/0 size are required.

Conduit Size: To obtain the proper conduit size for the wires and type of insulation used, refer to Table R260533-22.

For example: For the 100 H.P., 460V, 3 phase motor, it was determined that three 2/0 wires are required. Assuming THWN insulated copper wire, use Table R260533-22 to determine that three 2/0 wires require 1-1/2" conduit.

Material Cost of the conduit and wire system depends on:
1. Wire size required
2. Copper or aluminum wire
3. Wire insulation type selected
4. Steel or plastic conduit
5. Type of conduit raceway selected.

Labor Cost of the conduit and wire system depends on:
1. Type and size of conduit
2. Type and size of wires installed
3. Location and height of installation in building or depth of trench
4. Support system for conduit.

Magnetic starters, switches, and motor connection:

To complete the cost picture from H.P. to Costs additional items must be added to the cost of the conduit and wire system to arrive at a total cost.
1. Assembly Table D5020-160 Magnetic Starters Installed Cost lists the various size starters for single phase and three phase motors.
2. Assembly Table D5020-165 Heavy Duty Safety Switches Installed Cost lists safety switches required at the beginning of a motor circuit and also one required in the vicinity of the motor location.
3. Assembly Table D5020-170 Motor Connection lists the various costs for single and three phase motors.

Worksheet to obtain total motor wiring costs:

It is assumed that the motors or motor driven equipment are furnished and installed under other sections for this estimate and the following work is done under this section:
1. Conduit
2. Wire (add 10% for additional wire beyond conduit ends for connections to switches, boxes, starters, etc.)
3. Starters
4. Safety switches
5. Motor connections

R263413-31   Ampere Values Determined by Horsepower, Voltage and Phase Values

H.P.	Amperes							
	Single Phase			Three Phase				
	115V	208V	230V	200V	208V	230V	460V	575V
1/6	4.4A	2.4A	2.2A					
1/4	5.8	3.2	2.9					
1/3	7.2	4.0	3.6					
1/2	9.8	5.4	4.9	2.5A	2.4A	2.2A	1.1A	0.9A
3/4	13.8	7.6	6.9	3.7	3.5	3.2	1.6	1.3
1	16	8.8	8	4.8	4.6	4.2	2.1	1.7
1-1/2	20	11	10	6.9	6.6	6.0	3.0	2.4
2	24	13.2	12	7.8	7.5	6.8	3.4	2.7
3	34	18.7	17	11.0	10.6	9.6	4.8	3.9
5	56	30.8	28	17.5	16.7	15.2	7.6	6.1
7-1/2	80	44	40	25.3	24.2	22	11	9
10	100	55	50	32.2	30.8	28	14	11
15				48.3	46.2	42	21	17
20				62.1	59.4	54	27	22
25				78.2	74.8	68	34	27
30				92	88	80	40	32
40				120	114	104	52	41
50				150	143	130	65	52
60				177	169	154	77	62
75				221	211	192	96	77
100				285	273	248	124	99
125				359	343	312	156	125
150				414	396	360	180	144
200				552	528	480	240	192
250							302	242
300							361	289
350							414	336
400							477	382

For customer support on your Electrical Costs with RSMeans Data, call 800.448.8182.

Figure   R263413-32

header: Worksheet for Motor Circuits					

Item	Type	Size	Quantity	Cost Unit	Cost Total
Wire					
Conduit					
Switch					
Starter					
Switch					
Motor Connection					
Other					
Total Cost					

R263413-33   Maximum Horsepower for Starter Size by Voltage

Starter Size	Maximum HP (3φ)			
	208V	240V	480V	600V
00	1½	1½	2	2
0	3	3	5	5
1	7½	7½	10	10
2	10	15	25	25
3	25	30	50	50
4	40	50	100	100
5		100	200	200
6		200	300	300
7		300	600	600
8		450	900	900
8L		700	1500	1500

Electrical | R2636 Transfer Switches

R263623-60 Automatic Transfer Switches

When taking off automatic transfer switches identify by voltage, amperage and number of poles.

Example: Automatic transfer switch, 480V, 3 phase, 30A, NEMA 1 enclosure

Labor-hours for transfer switches include:
1. Unloading, uncrating and handling switches up to 200' from loading dock
2. Measuring and marking
3. Drilling (4) lead type anchors using a hammer drill
4. Mounting and leveling
5. Circuit identification
6. Testing and load balancing

Labor-hours do not include:
1. Modifications in enclosure
2. Structural supports
3. Additional lugs
4. Plywood backboard
5. Painting or lettering
6. Conduit runs to or from transfer switch
7. Wire
8. Termination of wires

Electrical | R2651 Interior Lighting

R265113-40 Interior Lighting Fixtures

When taking off interior lighting fixtures, it is advisable to set up your quantity worksheet to conform to the lighting schedule as it appears on the print. Include the alpha-numeric code plus the symbol on your worksheet.

Take off a particular section or floor of the building and count each type of fixture before going on to another type. It would also be advantageous to include on the same worksheet the pipe, wire, fittings and circuit number associated with each type of lighting fixture. This will help you identify the costs associated with any particular lighting system and in turn make material purchases more specific as to when and how much to order under the classification of lighting.

By taking off lighting first you can get a complete "walk through" of the job. This will become helpful when doing other phases of the project.

Materials for a recessed fixture include:
1. Fixture
2. Lamps
3. 6' of jack chain
4. (2) S hooks
5. (2) Wire nuts

Labor for interior recessed fixtures include:
1. Unloading by hand
2. Hauling by hand to an area up to 200' from loading dock
3. Uncrating
4. Layout
5. Installing fixture
6. Attaching jack chain & S hooks
7. Connecting circuit power
8. Reassembling fixture
9. Installing lamps
10. Testing

Material for surface mounted fixtures include:
1. Fixture
2. Lamps
3. Either (4) lead type anchors, (4) toggle bolts, or (4) ceiling grid clips
4. (2) Wire nuts

Material for pendent mounted fixtures include:
1. Fixture
2. Lamps
3. (2) Wire nuts
4. Rigid pendents as required by type of fixtures

5. Canopies as required by type of fixture

Labor hours include the following for both surface and pendent fixtures:
1. Unloading by hand
2. Hauling by hand to an area up to 200' from loading dock
3. Uncrating
4. Layout and marking
5. Drilling (4) holes for either lead anchors or toggle bolts using a hammer drill
6. Installing fixture
7. Leveling fixture
8. Connecting circuit power
9. Installing lamps
10. Testing

Labor for surface or pendent fixtures does not include:
1. Conduit
2. Boxes or covers
3. Connectors
4. Fixture whips
5. Special support
6. Switching
7. Wire

Economy of Scale: For large concentrations of lighting fixtures in the same area deduct the following percentages from labor:

25 to	50	fixtures	15%
51 to	75	fixtures	20%
76 to	100	fixtures	25%
101 and over			30%

Job Conditions: Productivity is based on new construction in an unobstructed first floor location, using rolling staging to 15' high.

Material staging is assumed to be within 100' of work being performed.

Add the following percentages to labor for elevated installations:

10' to	14.5'	high	10%
15' to	20'	high	20%
21' to	25'	high	25%
26' to	30'	high	35%
31' to	35'	high	40%
36' to	40'	high	50%
41' and over			55%

R265723-10   For Other than Regular Cool White (CW) Lamps

	Multiply Material Costs as Follows:					
Regular Lamps	Cool white deluxe (CWX)	x 1.35	Energy Saving Lamps	Cool white (CW/ES)	x 1.35
	Warm white deluxe (WWX)	x 1.35		Cool white deluxe (CWX/ES)	x 1.65
	Warm white (WW)	x 1.30		Warm white (WW/ES)	x 1.55
	Natural (N)	x 2.05		Warm white deluxe (WWX/ES)	x 1.65

R271323-40 Fiber Optics

Fiber optic systems use optical fiber such as plastic, glass, or fused silica, a transparent material, to transmit radiant power (i.e., light) for control, communication, and signaling applications. The types of fiber optic cables can be nonconductive, conductive, or composite. The composite cables contain fiber optics and current-carrying electrical conductors. The configuration for one of the fiber optic systems is as follows:

The transceiver module acts as transmitting and receiving equipment in a common house, which converts electrical energy to light energy or vice versa.

Pricing the fiber optic system is not an easy task. The performance of the whole system will affect the cost significantly. New specialized tools and techniques decrease the installing cost tremendously. In the fiber optic section of Means Electrical Cost Data, a benchmark for labor-hours and material costs is set up so that users can adjust their costs according to unique project conditions.

Units for Measure: Fiber optic cable is measured in hundred linear feet (C.L.F.) or industry units of measure - meter (m) or kilometer (km). The connectors are counted as units (EA.)

Material Units: Generally, the material costs include only the cable. All the accessories shall be priced separately.

Labor Units: The following procedures are generally included for the installation of fiber optic cables:

- Receiving
- Material handling
- Setting up pulling equipment
- Measuring and cutting cable
- Pulling cable

These additional items are listed and extended: Terminations

Takeoff Procedure: Cable should be taken off by type, size, number of fibers, and number of terminations required. List the lengths of each type of cable on the takeoff sheets. Total and add 10% for waste. Transfer the figures to a cost analysis sheet and extend.

Communications | R2715 Communications Horizontal Cabling

R271513-75 High Performance Cable

There are several categories used to describe high performance cable. The following information includes a description of categories CAT 3, 5, 5e, 6, and 7, and details classifications of frequency and specific standards. The category standards have evolved under the sponsorship of organizations such as the Telecommunication Industry Association (TIA), the Electronic Industries Alliance (EIA), the American National Standards Institute (ANSI), the International Organization for Standardization (ISO), and the International Electrotechnical Commission (IEC), all of which have catered to the increasing complexities of modern network technology. For network cabling, users must comply with national or international standards. A breakdown of these categories is as follows:

Category 3: Designed to handle frequencies up to 16 MHz.

Category 5: (TIA/EIA 568A) Designed to handle frequencies up to 100 MHz.

Category 5e: Additional transmission performance to exceed Category 5.

Category 6: Development by TIA and other international groups to handle frequencies of 250 MHz.

Category 7: Development to handle a frequency range up to 600 MHz.

R337116-60   Average Transmission Line Material Requirements (Per Mile)

		Flat				Rolling				Mountain			
Terrain:													
Item		69kV	161kV	161kV	500kV	69kV	101kV	101kV	500kV	69kV	161kV	161kV	500kV
Pole Type	**Unit**	Wood	Wood	Steel	Steel	Wood	Wood	Steel	Steel	Wood	Wood	Steel	Steel
Conductor: 397,500 – Cir. Mil., 26/7–ACSR													
Structures	Ea.	12[1]				9[2]				7[2]			
Poles	Ea.	12				18				14			
Crossarms	Ea.	24[3]				9[4]				7[4]			
Conductor	Ft.	15,990				15,990				15,990			
Insulators[5]	Ea.	180				135				105			
Ground Wire	Ft.	5,330				10,660				10,660			
Conductor: 636,000 – Cir. Mil., 26/7–ACSR													
Structures	Ea.	13[1]	11[6]			10[2]	9[2]	6[9]		8[2]	8[2]	6[9]	
Excavation	C.Y.	–	–			–	–	120		–	–	120	
Concrete	C.Y.	–	–			–	–	10		–	–	10	
Steel Towers	Tons	–	–			–	–	32		–	–	32	
Poles	Ea.	13	11			20	18	–		16	16	–	
Crossarms	Ea.	26[3]	33[7]			10[4]	9[8]	–		8[4]	8[8]	–	
Conductor	Ft.	15,990	15,990			15,990	15,990	15,990		15,990	15,990	15,990	
Insulators[5]	Ea.	195	165			150	297	297		120	264	297	
Ground Wire	Ft.	5330	5330			10,660	10,660	10,660		10,660	10,660	10,660	
Conductor: 954,000 – Cir. Mil., 45/7–ACSR													
Structures	Ea.	14[1]	12[6]		4[11]	10[2]	9[2]	6[9]	4[11]	8[2]	8[2]	6[9]	4[13]
Excavation	C.Y.	–	–		200	–	–	125	214	–	–	125	233
Concrete	C.Y.	–	–		20	–	–	10	21	–	–	10	21
Steel Towers	Tons	–	–		57	–	–	33	57	–	–	33	63
Poles	Ea.	14	12		–	20	18	–	–	16	16	–	–
Crossarms	Ea.	28[10]	36[7]		–	10[4]	9[8]	–	–	8[4]	8[8]	–	–
Conductor	Ft.	15,990	15,990		47,970[12]	15,990	15,990	15,990	47,970[12]	15,990	15,990	15,990	47,970[12]
Insulators[5]	Ea.	210	180		288	150	297	297	288	120	264	297	576
Ground Wire	Ft.	5330	5330		10,660	10,660	10,660	10,660	10,660	10,660	10,660	10,660	10,660
Conductor: 1,351,500 – Cir. Mil., 45/7–ACSR													
Structures	Ea.		8[14]				8[14]						
Excavation	C.Y.		220				220						
Concrete	C.Y.		28				28						
Steel Towers	Ton		46				46						
Conductor	Ft.		31,680[15]				31,680[15]						
Insulators	Ea.		528				528						
Ground Wire	Ft.		10,660				10,660						

1. Single pole two-arm suspension type construction
2. Two-pole wood H-frame construction
3. 4¾″ x 5¾″ x 8′ and 4¾″ x 5¾″ x 10′ wood crossarms
4. 6″ x 8″ x 26′-0″ wood crossarm
5. 5¾″ x 10″ disc insulator
6. Single pole construction with 3 fiberglass crossarms (5 fog-type insulators per phase)
7. 7′-0″ fiberglass crossarms
8. 6″ x 10″ x 35′-0″ wood crossarm

9. Laced steel tower, single circuit construction
10. 5″ x 7″ x 8′ and 5″ x 7″ x 10′ wood crossarms
11. Laced steel tower, single circuit 500-kV construction
12. Bundled conductor (3 sub-conductors per phase)
13. Laced steel tower, single circuit restrained phases (500-kV)
14. Laced steel tower, double circuit construction
15. Both sides of double circuit strung

Note: To allow for sagging, a mile (5280 Ft.) of transmission line uses 5330 Ft. of conductor per wire (called a wire mile).

621

For customer support on your Electrical Costs with RSMeans Data, call 800.448.8182.

R337119-30 Concrete for Conduit Encasement

The table below lists C.Y. of concrete for 100 L.F. of trench. Conduits separation center to center should meet 7.5″ (N.E.C.).

Number of Conduits	1	2	3	4	6	8	9	Number of Conduits
Trench Dimension	11.5″ x 11.5″	11.5″ x 19″	11.5″ x 27″	19″ x 19″	19″ x 27″	19″ x 38″	27″ x 27″	Trench Dimension
Conduit Diameter 2.0″	3.29	5.39	7.64	8.83	12.51	17.66	17.72	Conduit Diameter 2.0″
2.5″	3.23	5.29	7.49	8.62	12.19	17.23	17.25	2.5″
3.0″	3.15	5.13	7.24	8.29	11.71	16.59	16.52	3.0″
3.5″	3.08	4.97	7.02	7.99	11.26	15.98	15.84	3.5″
4.0″	2.99	4.80	6.76	7.65	10.74	15.30	15.07	4.0″
5.0″	2.78	4.37	6.11	6.78	9.44	13.57	13.12	5.0″
6.0″	2.52	3.84	5.33	5.74	7.87	11.48	10.77	6.0″

Change Orders

Change Order Considerations

A change order is a written document usually prepared by the design professional and signed by the owner, the architect/engineer, and the contractor. A change order states the agreement of the parties to: an addition, deletion, or revision in the work; an adjustment in the contract sum, if any; or an adjustment in the contract time, if any. Change orders, or "extras", in the construction process occur after execution of the construction contract and impact architects/ engineers, contractors, and owners.

Change orders that are properly recognized and managed can ensure orderly, professional, and profitable progress for everyone involved in the project. There are many causes for change orders and change order requests. In all cases, change orders or change order requests should be addressed promptly and in a precise and prescribed manner. The following paragraphs include information regarding change order pricing and procedures.

The Causes of Change Orders

Reasons for issuing change orders include:

- Unforeseen field conditions that require a change in the work
- Correction of design discrepancies, errors, or omissions in the contract documents
- Owner-requested changes, either by design criteria, scope of work, or project objectives
- Completion date changes for reasons unrelated to the construction process
- Changes in building code interpretations, or other public authority requirements that require a change in the work
- Changes in availability of existing or new materials and products

Procedures

Properly written contract documents must include the correct change order procedures for all parties—owners, design professionals, and contractors—to follow in order to avoid costly delays and litigation.

Being "in the right" is not always a sufficient or acceptable defense. The contract provisions requiring notification and documentation must be adhered to within a defined or reasonable time frame.

The appropriate method of handling change orders is by a written proposal and acceptance by all parties involved. Prior to starting work on a project, all parties should identify their

authorized agents who may sign and accept change orders, as well as any limits placed on their authority.

Time may be a critical factor when the need for a change arises. For such cases, the contractor might be directed to proceed on a "time and materials" basis, rather than wait for all paperwork to be processed—a delay that could impede progress. In this situation, the contractor must still follow the prescribed change order procedures including, but not limited to, notification and documentation.

Lack of documentation can be very costly, especially if legal judgments are to be made, and if certain field personnel are no longer available. For time and material change orders, the contractor should keep accurate daily records of all labor and material allocated to the change.

Owners or awarding authorities who do considerable and continual building construction (such as the federal government) realize the inevitability of change orders for numerous reasons, both predictable and unpredictable. As a result, the federal government, the American Institute of Architects (AIA), the Engineers Joint Contract Documents Committee (EJCDC), and other contractor, legal, and technical organizations have developed standards and procedures to be followed by all parties to achieve contract continuance and timely completion, while being financially fair to all concerned.

Pricing Change Orders

When pricing change orders, regardless of their cause, the most significant factor is when the change occurs. The need for a change may be perceived in the field or requested by the architect/engineer *before* any of the actual installation has begun, or may evolve or appear *during* construction when the item of work in question is partially installed. In the latter cases, the original sequence of construction is disrupted, along with all contiguous and supporting systems. Change orders cause the greatest impact when they occur *after* the installation has been completed and must be uncovered, or even replaced. Post-completion changes may be caused by necessary design changes, product failure, or changes in the owner's requirements that are not discovered until the building or the systems begin to function.

Specified procedures of notification and record keeping must be adhered to and enforced regardless of the stage of construction: *before, during,* or *after* installation. Some bidding documents anticipate change orders by requiring that unit prices including overhead and profit percentages—for additional as well as deductible changes—be listed. Generally these unit prices do not fully take into account the ripple effect, or impact on other trades, and should be used for general guidance only.

When pricing change orders, it is important to classify the time frame in which the change occurs. There are two basic time frames for change orders: *pre-installation change orders*, which occur before the start of construction, and *post-installation change orders*, which involve reworking after the original installation. Change orders that occur between these stages may be priced according to the extent of work completed using a combination of techniques developed for pricing *pre-* and *post-installation* changes.

Factors To Consider When Pricing Change Orders

As an estimator begins to prepare a change order, the following questions should be reviewed to determine their impact on the final price.

General

- *Is the change order work* pre-installation *or* post-installation?

  Change order work costs vary according to how much of the installation has been completed. Once workers have the project scoped in their minds, even though they have not started, it can be difficult to refocus. Consequently they may spend more than the normal amount of time understanding the change. Also, modifications to work in place, such as trimming or refitting, usually take more time than was initially estimated. The greater the amount of work in place, the more reluctant workers are to change it. Psychologically they may resent the change and as a result the rework takes longer than normal. Post-installation change order estimates must include demolition of existing work as required to accomplish the change. If the work is performed at a later time, additional obstacles, such as building finishes, may be present which must be protected. Regardless of whether the change occurs

For customer support on your Electrical Costs with RSMeans Data, call 800.448.8182.

623

pre-installation or post-installation, attempt to isolate the identifiable factors and price them separately. For example, add shipping costs that may be required pre-installation or any demolition required post-installation. Then analyze the potential impact on productivity of psychological and/or learning curve factors and adjust the output rates accordingly. One approach is to break down the typical workday into segments and quantify the impact on each segment.

Change Order Installation Efficiency

The labor-hours expressed (for new construction) are based on average installation time, using an efficiency level. For change order situations, adjustments to this efficiency level should reflect the daily labor-hour allocation for that particular occurrence.

- *Will the change substantially delay the original completion date?*

A significant change in the project may cause the original completion date to be extended. The extended schedule may subject the contractor to new wage rates dictated by relevant labor contracts. Project supervision and other project overhead must also be extended beyond the original completion date. The schedule extension may also put installation into a new weather season. For example, underground piping scheduled for October installation was delayed until January. As a result, frost penetrated the trench area, thereby changing the degree of difficulty of the task. Changes and delays may have a ripple effect throughout the project. This effect must be analyzed and negotiated with the owner.

- *What is the net effect of a deduct change order?*

In most cases, change orders resulting in a deduction or credit reflect only bare costs. The contractor may retain the overhead and profit based on the original bid.

Materials

- *Will you have to pay more or less for the new material, required by the change order, than you paid for the original purchase?*

The same material prices or discounts will usually apply to materials purchased for change orders as new construction. In some instances, however, the contractor may forfeit the advantages of competitive pricing for change orders. Consider the following example:

A contractor purchased over $20,000 worth of fan coil units for an installation and obtained the maximum discount. Some time later it was determined the project required an additional matching unit. The contractor has to purchase this unit from the original supplier to ensure a match. The supplier at this time may not discount the unit because of the small quantity, and he is no longer in a competitive situation. The impact of quantity on purchase can add between 0% and 25% to material prices and/or subcontractor quotes.

- *If materials have been ordered or delivered to the job site, will they be subject to a cancellation charge or restocking fee?*

Check with the supplier to determine if ordered materials are subject to a cancellation charge. Delivered materials not used as a result of a change order may be subject to a restocking fee if returned to the supplier. Common restocking charges run between 20% and 40%. Also, delivery charges to return the goods to the supplier must be added.

Labor

- *How efficient is the existing crew at the actual installation?*

Is the same crew that performed the initial work going to do the change order? Possibly the change consists of the installation of a unit identical to one already installed; therefore, the change should take less time. Be sure to consider this potential productivity increase and modify the productivity rates accordingly.

- *If the crew size is increased, what impact will that have on supervision requirements?*

Under most bargaining agreements or management practices, there is a point at which a working foreman is replaced by a nonworking foreman. This replacement increases project overhead by adding a nonproductive worker. If additional workers are added to accelerate the project or to perform changes while maintaining the schedule, be sure to add additional supervision time if warranted. Calculate the hours involved and the additional cost directly if possible.

- *What are the other impacts of increased crew size?*

The larger the crew, the greater the potential for productivity to decrease. Some of the factors that cause this productivity loss are: overcrowding (producing restrictive conditions in the working space) and possibly a shortage of any special tools and equipment required. Such factors affect not only the crew working on the elements directly involved in the change order, but other crews whose movements may also be hampered. As the crew increases, check its basic composition for changes by the addition or deletion of apprentices or nonworking foreman, and quantify the potential effects of equipment shortages or other logistical factors.

- *As new crews, unfamiliar with the project, are brought onto the site, how long will it take them to become oriented to the project requirements?*

The orientation time for a new crew to become 100% effective varies with the site and type of project. Orientation is easiest at a new construction site and most difficult at existing, very restrictive renovation sites. The type of work also affects orientation time. When all elements of the work are exposed, such as concrete or masonry work, orientation is decreased. When the work is concealed or less visible, such as existing electrical systems, orientation takes longer. Usually orientation can be accomplished in one day or less. Costs for added orientation should be itemized and added to the total estimated cost.

- *How much actual production can be gained by working overtime?*

Short term overtime can be used effectively to accomplish more work in a day. However, as overtime is scheduled to run beyond several weeks, studies have shown marked decreases in output. The following chart shows the effect of long term overtime on worker efficiency. If the anticipated change requires extended overtime to keep the job on schedule, these factors can be used as a guide to predict the impact on time and cost. Add project overhead, particularly supervision, that may also be incurred.

Days per Week	Hours per Day	Production Efficiency					Payroll Cost Factors	
		1st Week	2nd Week	3rd Week	4th Week	Average 4 Weeks	@ 1-1/2 Times	@ 2 Times
5	8	100%	100%	100%	100%	100%	100%	100%
	9	100	100	95	90	96.25	105.6	111.1
	10	100	95	90	85	92.50	110.0	120.0
	11	95	90	75	65	81.25	113.6	127.3
	12	90	85	70	60	76.25	116.7	133.3
6	8	100	100	95	90	96.25	108.3	116.7
	9	100	95	90	85	92.50	113.0	125.9
	10	95	90	85	80	87.50	116.7	133.3
	11	95	85	70	65	78.75	119.7	139.4
	12	90	80	65	60	73.75	122.2	144.4
7	8	100	95	85	75	88.75	114.3	128.6
	9	95	90	80	70	83.75	118.3	136.5
	10	90	85	75	65	78.75	121.4	142.9
	11	85	80	65	60	72.50	124.0	148.1
	12	85	75	60	55	68.75	126.2	152.4

Effects of Overtime

Caution: Under many labor agreements, Sundays and holidays are paid at a higher premium than the normal overtime rate.

The use of long-term overtime is counterproductive on almost any construction job; that is, the longer the period of overtime, the lower the actual production rate. Numerous studies have been conducted, and while they have resulted in slightly different numbers, all reach the same conclusion. The figure above tabulates the effects of overtime work on efficiency.

As illustrated, there can be a difference between the *actual* payroll cost per hour and the *effective* cost per hour for overtime work. This is due to the reduced production efficiency with the increase in weekly hours beyond 40. This difference between actual and effective cost results from overtime work over a prolonged period. Short-term overtime work does not result in as great a reduction in efficiency and, in such cases, effective cost may not vary significantly from the actual payroll cost. As the total hours per week are increased on a regular basis, more time is lost due to fatigue, lowered morale, and an increased accident rate.

As an example, assume a project where workers are working 6 days a week, 10 hours per day. From the figure above (based on productivity studies), the average effective productive hours over a 4-week period are:

$$0.875 \times 60 = 52.5$$

Depending upon the locale and day of week, overtime hours may be paid at time and a half or double time. For time and a half, the overall (average) *actual* payroll cost (including regular and overtime hours) is determined as follows:

$$\frac{40 \text{ reg. hrs.} + (20 \text{ overtime hrs.} \times 1.5)}{60 \text{ hrs.}} = 1.167$$

Based on 60 hours, the payroll cost per hour will be 116.7% of the normal rate at 40 hours per week. However, because the effective production (efficiency) for 60 hours is reduced to the equivalent of 52.5 hours, the effective cost of overtime is calculated as follows:

For time and a half:

$$\frac{40 \text{ reg. hrs.} + (20 \text{ overtime hrs.} \times 1.5)}{52.5 \text{ hrs.}} = 1.33$$

The installed cost will be 133% of the normal rate (for labor).

Thus, when figuring overtime, the actual cost per unit of work will be higher than the apparent overtime payroll dollar increase, due to the reduced productivity of the longer work week. These efficiency calculations are true only for those cost factors determined by hours worked. Costs that are applied weekly or monthly, such as equipment rentals, will not be similarly affected.

Equipment

- *What equipment is required to complete the change order?*

Change orders may require extending the rental period of equipment already on the job site, or the addition of special equipment brought in to accomplish the change work. In either case, the additional rental charges and operator labor charges must be added.

Summary

The preceding considerations and others you deem appropriate should be analyzed and applied to a change order estimate. The impact of each should be quantified and listed on the estimate to form an audit trail.

Change orders that are properly identified, documented, and managed help to ensure the orderly, professional, and profitable progress of the work. They also minimize potential claims or disputes at the end of the project.

Square Foot Costs

Back by customer demand!

You asked and we listened. For customer convenience and estimating ease, we have made the 2017 Square Foot Costs available for download at **http://info.thegordiangroup.com/2017-Cost-Data-Companion.html**. You will also find sample estimates, an RSMeans data overview video and book registration form to receive quarterly data updates throughout 2017.

Estimating Tips

- The cost figures available in the download were derived from hundreds of projects contained in the RSMeans database of completed construction projects. They include the contractor's overhead and profit. The figures have been adjusted to January of the current year.

- These projects were located throughout the U.S. and reflect a tremendous variation in square foot (S.F.) costs. This is due to differences, not only in labor and material costs, but also in individual owners' requirements. For instance, a bank in a large city would have different features than one in a rural area. This is true of all the different types of buildings analyzed. Therefore, caution should be exercised when using these square foot costs. For example, for courthouses, costs in the database are local courthouse costs and will not apply to the larger, more elaborate federal courthouses.

- None of the figures "go with" any others. All individual cost items were computed and tabulated separately. Thus, the sum of the median figures for plumbing, HVAC, and electrical will not normally total up to the total mechanical and electrical costs arrived at by separate analysis and tabulation of the projects.

- Each building was analyzed as to total and component costs and percentages. The figures were arranged in ascending order with the results tabulated as shown. The 1/4 column shows that 25% of the projects had lower costs and 75% had higher. The 3/4 column shows that 75% of the projects had lower costs and 25% had higher. The median column shows that 50% of the projects had lower costs and 50% had higher.

- Square foot costs are useful in the conceptual stage when no details are available. As soon as details become available in the project design, the square foot approach should be discontinued and the project priced as to its particular components. When more precision is required, or for estimating the replacement cost of specific buildings, the current edition of *RSMeans Square Foot Costs* should be used.

- In using the figures in this section, it is recommended that the median column be used for preliminary figures if no additional information is available. The median figures, when multiplied by the total city construction cost index figures (see City Cost Indexes) and then multiplied by the project size modifier at the end of this section, should present a fairly accurate base figure, which would then have to be adjusted in view of the estimator's experience, local economic conditions, code requirements, and the owner's particular requirements. There is no need to factor the percentage figures, as these should remain constant from city to city.

- The editors of this data would greatly appreciate receiving cost figures on one or more of your recent projects, which would then be included in the averages for next year. All cost figures received will be kept confidential, except that they will be averaged with other similar projects to arrive at square foot cost figures for next year.

See the website above for details and the discount available for submitting one or more of your projects.

Abbreviation	Definition
A	Area Square Feet; Ampere
AAFES	Army and Air Force Exchange Service
ABS	Acrylonitrile Butadiene Stryrene; Asbestos Bonded Steel
A.C., AC	Alternating Current; Air-Conditioning; Asbestos Cement; Plywood Grade A & C
ACI	American Concrete Institute
ACR	Air Conditioning Refrigeration
ADA	Americans with Disabilities Act
AD	Plywood, Grade A & D
Addit.	Additional
Adj.	Adjustable
af	Audio-frequency
AFFF	Aqueous Film Forming Foam
AFUE	Annual Fuel Utilization Efficiency
AGA	American Gas Association
Agg.	Aggregate
A.H., Ah	Ampere Hours
A hr.	Ampere-hour
A.H.U., AHU	Air Handling Unit
A.I.A.	American Institute of Architects
AIC	Ampere Interrupting Capacity
Allow.	Allowance
alt., alt	Alternate
Alum.	Aluminum
a.m.	Ante Meridiem
Amp.	Ampere
Anod.	Anodized
ANSI	American National Standards Institute
APA	American Plywood Association
Approx.	Approximate
Apt.	Apartment
Asb.	Asbestos
A.S.B.C.	American Standard Building Code
Asbe.	Asbestos Worker
ASCE	American Society of Civil Engineers
A.S.H.R.A.E.	American Society of Heating, Refrig. & AC Engineers
ASME	American Society of Mechanical Engineers
ASTM	American Society for Testing and Materials
Attchmt.	Attachment
Avg., Ave.	Average
AWG	American Wire Gauge
AWWA	American Water Works Assoc.
Bbl.	Barrel
B&B, BB	Grade B and Better; Balled & Burlapped
B&S	Bell and Spigot
B.&W.	Black and White
b.c.c.	Body-centered Cubic
B.C.Y.	Bank Cubic Yards
BE	Bevel End
B.F.	Board Feet
Bg. cem.	Bag of Cement
BHP	Boiler Horsepower; Brake Horsepower
B.I.	Black Iron
bidir.	bidirectional
Bit., Bitum.	Bituminous
Bit., Conc.	Bituminous Concrete
Bk.	Backed
Bkrs.	Breakers
Bldg., bldg	Building
Blk.	Block
Bm.	Beam
Boil.	Boilermaker
bpm	Blows per Minute
BR	Bedroom
Brg., brng.	Bearing
Brhe.	Bricklayer Helper
Bric.	Bricklayer
Brk., brk	Brick
brkt	Bracket
Brs.	Brass
Brz.	Bronze
Bsn.	Basin
Bu.	Butter
BTU	British Thermal Unit
BTUH	BTU per Hour
Bu.	Bushels
BUR	Built-up Roofing
BX	Interlocked Armored Cable
°C	Degree Centigrade
c	Conductivity, Copper Sweat
C	Hundred; Centigrade
C/C	Center to Center, Cedar on Cedar
C-C	Center to Center
Cab	Cabinet
Cair.	Air Tool Laborer
Cal.	Caliper
Calc	Calculated
Cap.	Capacity
Carp.	Carpenter
C.B.	Circuit Breaker
C.C.A.	Chromate Copper Arsenate
C.C.F.	Hundred Cubic Feet
cd	Candela
cd/sf	Candela per Square Foot
CD	Grade of Plywood Face & Back
CDX	Plywood, Grade C & D, exterior glue
Cefi.	Cement Finisher
Cem.	Cement
CF	Hundred Feet
C.F.	Cubic Feet
CFM	Cubic Feet per Minute
CFRP	Carbon Fiber Reinforced Plastic
c.g.	Center of Gravity
CHW	Chilled Water; Commercial Hot Water
C.I., CI	Cast Iron
C.I.P., CIP	Cast in Place
Circ.	Circuit
C.L.	Carload Lot
CL	Chain Link
Clab.	Common Laborer
Clam	Common Maintenance Laborer
C.L.F.	Hundred Linear Feet
CLF	Current Limiting Fuse
CLP	Cross Linked Polyethylene
cm	Centimeter
CMP	Corr. Metal Pipe
CMU	Concrete Masonry Unit
CN	Change Notice
Col.	Column
CO_2	Carbon Dioxide
Comb.	Combination
comm.	Commercial, Communication
Compr.	Compressor
Conc.	Concrete
Cont., cont	Continuous; Continued, Container
Corr.	Corrugated
Cos	Cosine
Cot	Cotangent
Cov.	Cover
C/P	Cedar on Paneling
CPA	Control Point Adjustment
Cplg.	Coupling
CPM	Critical Path Method
CPVC	Chlorinated Polyvinyl Chloride
C.Pr.	Hundred Pair
CRC	Cold Rolled Channel
Creos.	Creosote
Crpt.	Carpet & Linoleum Layer
CRT	Cathode-ray Tube
CS	Carbon Steel, Constant Shear Bar Joist
Csc	Cosecant
C.S.F.	Hundred Square Feet
CSI	Construction Specifications Institute
CT	Current Transformer
CTS	Copper Tube Size
Cu	Copper, Cubic
Cu. Ft.	Cubic Foot
cw	Continuous Wave
C.W.	Cool White; Cold Water
Cwt.	100 Pounds
C.W.X.	Cool White Deluxe
C.Y.	Cubic Yard (27 cubic feet)
C.Y./Hr.	Cubic Yard per Hour
Cyl.	Cylinder
d	Penny (nail size)
D	Deep; Depth; Discharge
Dis., Disch.	Discharge
Db	Decibel
Dbl.	Double
DC	Direct Current
DDC	Direct Digital Control
Demob.	Demobilization
d.f.t.	Dry Film Thickness
d.f.u.	Drainage Fixture Units
D.H.	Double Hung
DHW	Domestic Hot Water
DI	Ductile Iron
Diag.	Diagonal
Diam., Dia	Diameter
Distrib.	Distribution
Div.	Division
Dk.	Deck
D.L.	Dead Load; Diesel
DLH	Deep Long Span Bar Joist
dlx	Deluxe
Do.	Ditto
DOP	Dioctyl Phthalate Penetration Test (Air Filters)
Dp., dp	Depth
D.P.S.T.	Double Pole, Single Throw
Dr.	Drive
DR	Dimension Ratio
Drink.	Drinking
D.S.	Double Strength
D.S.A.	Double Strength A Grade
D.S.B.	Double Strength B Grade
Dty.	Duty
DWV	Drain Waste Vent
DX	Deluxe White, Direct Expansion
dyn	Dyne
e	Eccentricity
E	Equipment Only; East; Emissivity
Ea.	Each
EB	Encased Burial
Econ.	Economy
E.C.Y	Embankment Cubic Yards
EDP	Electronic Data Processing
EIFS	Exterior Insulation Finish System
E.D.R.	Equiv. Direct Radiation
Eq.	Equation
EL	Elevation
Elec.	Electrician; Electrical
Elev.	Elevator; Elevating
EMT	Electrical Metallic Conduit; Thin Wall Conduit
Eng.	Engine, Engineered
EPDM	Ethylene Propylene Diene Monomer
EPS	Expanded Polystyrene
Eqhv.	Equip. Oper., Heavy
Eqlt.	Equip. Oper., Light
Eqmd.	Equip. Oper., Medium
Eqmm.	Equip. Oper., Master Mechanic
Eqol.	Equip. Oper., Oilers
Equip.	Equipment
ERW	Electric Resistance Welded

E.S.	Energy Saver	H	High Henry	Lath.	Lather
Est.	Estimated	HC	High Capacity	Lav.	Lavatory
esu	Electrostatic Units	H.D., HD	Heavy Duty; High Density	lb.; #	Pound
E.W.	Each Way	H.D.O.	High Density Overlaid	L.B., LB	Load Bearing; L Conduit Body
EWT	Entering Water Temperature	HDPE	High Density Polyethylene Plastic	L. & E.	Labor & Equipment
Excav.	Excavation	Hdr.	Header	lb./hr.	Pounds per Hour
excl	Excluding	Hdwe.	Hardware	lb./L.F.	Pounds per Linear Foot
Exp., exp	Expansion, Exposure	H.I.D., HID	High Intensity Discharge	lbf/sq.in.	Pound-force per Square Inch
Ext., ext	Exterior; Extension	Help.	Helper Average	L.C.L.	Less than Carload Lot
Extru.	Extrusion	HEPA	High Efficiency Particulate Air	L.C.Y.	Loose Cubic Yard
f.	Fiber Stress		Filter	Ld.	Load
F	Fahrenheit; Female; Fill	Hg	Mercury	LE	Lead Equivalent
Fab., fab	Fabricated; Fabric	HIC	High Interrupting Capacity	LED	Light Emitting Diode
FBGS	Fiberglass	HM	Hollow Metal	L.F.	Linear Foot
F.C.	Footcandles	HMWPE	High Molecular Weight	L.F. Nose	Linear Foot of Stair Nosing
f.c.c.	Face-centered Cubic		Polyethylene	L.F. Rsr	Linear Foot of Stair Riser
f'c.	Compressive Stress in Concrete;	HO	High Output	Lg.	Long; Length; Large
	Extreme Compressive Stress	Horiz.	Horizontal	L & H	Light and Heat
F.E.	Front End	H.P., HP	Horsepower; High Pressure	LH	Long Span Bar Joist
FEP	Fluorinated Ethylene Propylene	H.P.F.	High Power Factor	L.H.	Labor Hours
	(Teflon)	Hr.	Hour	L.L., LL	Live Load
F.G.	Flat Grain	Hrs./Day	Hours per Day	L.L.D.	Lamp Lumen Depreciation
F.H.A.	Federal Housing Administration	HSC	High Short Circuit	lm	Lumen
Fig.	Figure	Ht.	Height	lm/sf	Lumen per Square Foot
Fin.	Finished	Htg.	Heating	lm/W	Lumen per Watt
FIPS	Female Iron Pipe Size	Htrs.	Heaters	LOA	Length Over All
Fixt.	Fixture	HVAC	Heating, Ventilation & Air-	log	Logarithm
FJP	Finger jointed and primed		Conditioning	L-O-L	Lateralolet
Fl. Oz.	Fluid Ounces	Hvy.	Heavy	long.	Longitude
Flr.	Floor	HW	Hot Water	L.P., LP	Liquefied Petroleum; Low Pressure
FM	Frequency Modulation;	Hyd.; Hydr.	Hydraulic	L.P.F.	Low Power Factor
	Factory Mutual	Hz	Hertz (cycles)	LR	Long Radius
Fmg.	Framing	I.	Moment of Inertia	L.S.	Lump Sum
FM/UL	Factory Mutual/Underwriters Labs	IBC	International Building Code	Lt.	Light
Fdn.	Foundation	I.C.	Interrupting Capacity	Lt. Ga.	Light Gauge
FNPT	Female National Pipe Thread	ID	Inside Diameter	L.T.L.	Less than Truckload Lot
Fori.	Foreman, Inside	I.D.	Inside Dimension; Identification	Lt. Wt.	Lightweight
Foro.	Foreman, Outside	I.F.	Inside Frosted	L.V.	Low Voltage
Fount.	Fountain	I.M.C.	Intermediate Metal Conduit	M	Thousand; Material; Male;
fpm	Feet per Minute	In.	Inch		Light Wall Copper Tubing
FPT	Female Pipe Thread	Incan.	Incandescent	M²CA	Meters Squared Contact Area
Fr	Frame	Incl.	Included; Including	m/hr.; M.H.	Man-hour
F.R.	Fire Rating	Int.	Interior	mA	Milliampere
FRK	Foil Reinforced Kraft	Inst.	Installation	Mach.	Machine
FSK	Foil/Scrim/Kraft	Insul., insul	Insulation/Insulated	Mag. Str.	Magnetic Starter
FRP	Fiberglass Reinforced Plastic	I.P.	Iron Pipe	Maint.	Maintenance
FS	Forged Steel	I.P.S., IPS	Iron Pipe Size	Marb.	Marble Setter
FSC	Cast Body; Cast Switch Box	IPT	Iron Pipe Threaded	Mat; Mat'l.	Material
Ft., ft	Foot; Feet	I.W.	Indirect Waste	Max.	Maximum
Ftng.	Fitting	J	Joule	MBF	Thousand Board Feet
Ftg.	Footing	J.I.C.	Joint Industrial Council	MBH	Thousand BTU's per hr.
Ft lb.	Foot Pound	K	Thousand; Thousand Pounds;	MC	Metal Clad Cable
Furn.	Furniture		Heavy Wall Copper Tubing, Kelvin	MCC	Motor Control Center
FVNR	Full Voltage Non-Reversing	K.A.H.	Thousand Amp. Hours	M.C.F.	Thousand Cubic Feet
FVR	Full Voltage Reversing	kcmil	Thousand Circular Mils	MCFM	Thousand Cubic Feet per Minute
FXM	Female by Male	KD	Knock Down	M.C.M.	Thousand Circular Mils
Fy.	Minimum Yield Stress of Steel	K.D.A.T.	Kiln Dried After Treatment	MCP	Motor Circuit Protector
g	Gram	kg	Kilogram	MD	Medium Duty
G	Gauss	kG	Kilogauss	MDF	Medium-density fibreboard
Ga.	Gauge	kgf	Kilogram Force	M.D.O.	Medium Density Overlaid
Gal., gal.	Gallon	kHz	Kilohertz	Med.	Medium
Galv., galv	Galvanized	Kip	1000 Pounds	MF	Thousand Feet
GC/MS	Gas Chromatograph/Mass	KJ	Kilojoule	M.F.B.M.	Thousand Feet Board Measure
	Spectrometer	K.L.	Effective Length Factor	Mfg.	Manufacturing
Gen.	General	K.L.F.	Kips per Linear Foot	Mfrs.	Manufacturers
GFI	Ground Fault Interrupter	Km	Kilometer	mg	Milligram
GFRC	Glass Fiber Reinforced Concrete	KO	Knock Out	MGD	Million Gallons per Day
Glaz.	Glazier	K.S.F.	Kips per Square Foot	MGPH	Million Gallons per Hour
GPD	Gallons per Day	K.S.I.	Kips per Square Inch	MH, M.H.	Manhole; Metal Halide; Man-Hour
gpf	Gallon per Flush	kV	Kilovolt	MHz	Megahertz
GPH	Gallons per Hour	kVA	Kilovolt Ampere	Mi.	Mile
gpm, GPM	Gallons per Minute	kVAR	Kilovar (Reactance)	MI	Malleable Iron; Mineral Insulated
GR	Grade	KW	Kilowatt	MIPS	Male Iron Pipe Size
Gran.	Granular	KWh	Kilowatt-hour	mj	Mechanical Joint
Grnd.	Ground	L	Labor Only; Length; Long;	m	Meter
GVW	Gross Vehicle Weight		Medium Wall Copper Tubing	mm	Millimeter
GWB	Gypsum Wall Board	Lab.	Labor	Mill.	Millwright
		lat	Latitude	Min., min.	Minimum, Minute

Misc.	Miscellaneous	PCM	Phase Contrast Microscopy	SBS	Styrene Butadiere Styrene
ml	Milliliter, Mainline	PDCA	Painting and Decorating	SC	Screw Cover
M.L.F.	Thousand Linear Feet		Contractors of America	SCFM	Standard Cubic Feet per Minute
Mo.	Month	P.E., PE	Professional Engineer;	Scaf.	Scaffold
Mobil.	Mobilization		Porcelain Enamel;	Sch., Sched.	Schedule
Mog.	Mogul Base		Polyethylene; Plain End	S.C.R.	Modular Brick
MPH	Miles per Hour	P.E.C.I.	Porcelain Enamel on Cast Iron	S.D.	Sound Deadening
MPT	Male Pipe Thread	Perf.	Perforated	SDR	Standard Dimension Ratio
MRGWB	Moisture Resistant Gypsum	PEX	Cross Linked Polyethylene	S.E.	Surfaced Edge
	Wallboard	Ph.	Phase	Sel.	Select
MRT	Mile Round Trip	P.I.	Pressure Injected	SER, SEU	Service Entrance Cable
ms	Millisecond	Pile.	Pile Driver	S.F.	Square Foot
M.S.F.	Thousand Square Feet	Pkg.	Package	S.F.C.A.	Square Foot Contact Area
Mstz.	Mosaic & Terrazzo Worker	Pl.	Plate	S.F. Flr.	Square Foot of Floor
M.S.Y.	Thousand Square Yards	Plah.	Plasterer Helper	S.F.G.	Square Foot of Ground
Mtd., mtd., mtd	Mounted	Plas.	Plasterer	S.F. Hor.	Square Foot Horizontal
Mthe.	Mosaic & Terrazzo Helper	plf	Pounds Per Linear Foot	SFR	Square Feet of Radiation
Mtng.	Mounting	Pluh.	Plumber Helper	S.F. Shlf.	Square Foot of Shelf
Mult.	Multi; Multiply	Plum.	Plumber	S4S	Surface 4 Sides
MUTCD	Manual on Uniform Traffic Control	Ply.	Plywood	Shee.	Sheet Metal Worker
	Devices	p.m.	Post Meridiem	Sin.	Sine
M.V.A.	Million Volt Amperes	Pntd.	Painted	Skwk.	Skilled Worker
M.V.A.R.	Million Volt Amperes Reactance	Pord.	Painter, Ordinary	SL	Saran Lined
MV	Megavolt	pp	Pages	S.L.	Slimline
MW	Megawatt	PP, PPL	Polypropylene	Sldr.	Solder
MXM	Male by Male	P.P.M.	Parts per Million	SLH	Super Long Span Bar Joist
MYD	Thousand Yards	Pr.	Pair	S.N.	Solid Neutral
N	Natural; North	P.E.S.B.	Pre-engineered Steel Building	SO	Stranded with oil resistant inside
nA	Nanoampere	Prefab.	Prefabricated		insulation
NA	Not Available; Not Applicable	Prefin.	Prefinished	S-O-L	Socketolet
N.B.C.	National Building Code	Prop.	Propelled	sp	Standpipe
NC	Normally Closed	PSF, psf	Pounds per Square Foot	S.P.	Static Pressure; Single Pole; Self-
NEMA	National Electrical Manufacturers	PSI, psi	Pounds per Square Inch		Propelled
	Assoc.	PSIG	Pounds per Square Inch Gauge	Spri.	Sprinkler Installer
NEHB	Bolted Circuit Breaker to 600V.	PSP	Plastic Sewer Pipe	spwg	Static Pressure Water Gauge
NFPA	National Fire Protection Association	Pspr.	Painter, Spray	S.P.D.T.	Single Pole, Double Throw
NLB	Non-Load-Bearing	Psst.	Painter, Structural Steel	SPF	Spruce Pine Fir; Sprayed
NM	Non-Metallic Cable	P.T.	Potential Transformer		Polyurethane Foam
nm	Nanometer	P. & T.	Pressure & Temperature	S.P.S.T.	Single Pole, Single Throw
No.	Number	Ptd.	Painted	SPT	Standard Pipe Thread
NO	Normally Open	Ptns.	Partitions	Sq.	Square; 100 Square Feet
N.O.C.	Not Otherwise Classified	Pu	Ultimate Load	Sq. Hd.	Square Head
Nose.	Nosing	PVC	Polyvinyl Chloride	Sq. In.	Square Inch
NPT	National Pipe Thread	Pvmt.	Pavement	S.S.	Single Strength; Stainless Steel
NQOD	Combination Plug-on/Bolt on	PRV	Pressure Relief Valve	S.S.B.	Single Strength B Grade
	Circuit Breaker to 240V.	Pwr.	Power	sst, ss	Stainless Steel
N.R.C., NRC	Noise Reduction Coefficient/	Q	Quantity Heat Flow	Sswk.	Structural Steel Worker
	Nuclear Regulator Commission	Qt.	Quart	Sswl.	Structural Steel Welder
N.R.S.	Non Rising Stem	Quan., Qty.	Quantity	St.; Stl.	Steel
ns	Nanosecond	Q.C.	Quick Coupling	STC	Sound Transmission Coefficient
NTP	Notice to Proceed	r	Radius of Gyration	Std.	Standard
nW	Nanowatt	R	Resistance	Stg.	Staging
OB	Opposing Blade	R.C.P.	Reinforced Concrete Pipe	STK	Select Tight Knot
OC	On Center	Rect.	Rectangle	STP	Standard Temperature & Pressure
OD	Outside Diameter	recpt.	Receptacle	Stpi.	Steamfitter, Pipefitter
O.D.	Outside Dimension	Reg.	Regular	Str.	Strength; Starter; Straight
ODS	Overhead Distribution System	Reinf.	Reinforced	Strd.	Stranded
O.G.	Ogee	Req'd.	Required	Struct.	Structural
O.H.	Overhead	Res.	Resistant	Sty.	Story
O&P	Overhead and Profit	Resi.	Residential	Subj.	Subject
Oper.	Operator	RF	Radio Frequency	Subs.	Subcontractors
Opng.	Opening	RFID	Radio-frequency Identification	Surf.	Surface
Orna.	Ornamental	Rgh.	Rough	Sw.	Switch
OSB	Oriented Strand Board	RGS	Rigid Galvanized Steel	Swbd.	Switchboard
OS&Y	Outside Screw and Yoke	RHW	Rubber, Heat & Water Resistant;	S.Y.	Square Yard
OSHA	Occupational Safety and Health		Residential Hot Water	Syn.	Synthetic
	Act	rms	Root Mean Square	S.Y.P.	Southern Yellow Pine
Ovhd.	Overhead	Rnd.	Round	Sys.	System
OWG	Oil, Water or Gas	Rodm.	Rodman	t.	Thickness
Oz.	Ounce	Rofc.	Roofer, Composition	T	Temperature; Ton
P.	Pole; Applied Load; Projection	Rofp.	Roofer, Precast	Tan	Tangent
p.	Page	Rohe.	Roofer Helpers (Composition)	T.C.	Terra Cotta
Pape.	Paperhanger	Rots.	Roofer, Tile & Slate	T & C	Threaded and Coupled
P.A.P.R.	Powered Air Purifying Respirator	R.O.W.	Right of Way	T.D.	Temperature Difference
PAR	Parabolic Reflector	RPM	Revolutions per Minute	TDD	Telecommunications Device for
P.B., PB	Push Button	R.S.	Rapid Start		the Deaf
Pc., Pcs.	Piece, Pieces	Rsr	Riser	T.E.M.	Transmission Electron Microscopy
P.C.	Portland Cement; Power Connector	RT	Round Trip	temp	Temperature, Tempered, Temporary
P.C.F.	Pounds per Cubic Foot	S.	Suction; Single Entrance; South	TFFN	Nylon Jacketed Wire

Abbreviations

TFE	Tetrafluoroethylene (Teflon)	U.L., UL	Underwriters Laboratory	w/	With
T. & G.	Tongue & Groove;	Uld.	Unloading	W.C., WC	Water Column; Water Closet
	Tar & Gravel	Unfin.	Unfinished	W.F.	Wide Flange
Th., Thk.	Thick	UPS	Uninterruptible Power Supply	W.G.	Water Gauge
Thn.	Thin	URD	Underground Residential	Wldg.	Welding
Thrded	Threaded		Distribution	W. Mile	Wire Mile
Tilf.	Tile Layer, Floor	US	United States	W-O-L	Weldolet
Tilh.	Tile Layer, Helper	USGBC	U.S. Green Building Council	W.R.	Water Resistant
THHN	Nylon Jacketed Wire	USP	United States Primed	Wrck.	Wrecker
THW.	Insulated Strand Wire	UTMCD	Uniform Traffic Manual For Control	WSFU	Water Supply Fixture Unit
THWN	Nylon Jacketed Wire		Devices	W.S.P.	Water, Steam, Petroleum
T.L., TL	Truckload	UTP	Unshielded Twisted Pair	WT., Wt.	Weight
T.M.	Track Mounted	V	Volt	WWF	Welded Wire Fabric
Tot.	Total	VA	Volt Amperes	XFER	Transfer
T-O-L	Threadolet	VAT	Vinyl Asbestos Tile	XFMR	Transformer
tmpd	Tempered	V.C.T.	Vinyl Composition Tile	XHD	Extra Heavy Duty
TPO	Thermoplastic Polyolefin	VAV	Variable Air Volume	XHHW	Cross-Linked Polyethylene Wire
T.S.	Trigger Start	VC	Veneer Core	XLPE	Insulation
Tr.	Trade	VDC	Volts Direct Current	XLP	Cross-linked Polyethylene
Transf.	Transformer	Vent.	Ventilation	Xport	Transport
Trhv.	Truck Driver, Heavy	Vert.	Vertical	Y	Wye
Trlr	Trailer	V.F.	Vinyl Faced	yd	Yard
Trlt.	Truck Driver, Light	V.G.	Vertical Grain	yr	Year
TTY	Teletypewriter	VHF	Very High Frequency	Δ	Delta
TV	Television	VHO	Very High Output	%	Percent
T.W.	Thermoplastic Water Resistant	Vib.	Vibrating	~	Approximately
	Wire	VLF	Vertical Linear Foot	Ø	Phase; diameter
UCI	Uniform Construction Index	VOC	Volatile Organic Compound	@	At
UF	Underground Feeder	Vol.	Volume	#	Pound; Number
UGND	Underground Feeder	VRP	Vinyl Reinforced Polyester	<	Less Than
UHF	Ultra High Frequency	W	Wire; Watt; Wide; West	>	Greater Than
U.I.	United Inch			Z	Zone

Index

Notes

Notes

Notes

Notes

Division Notes

		CREW	DAILY OUTPUT	LABOR-HOURS	UNIT	BARE COSTS				TOTAL INCL O&P
						MAT.	LABOR	EQUIP.	TOTAL	

Division Notes

		CREW	DAILY OUTPUT	LABOR-HOURS	UNIT	BARE COSTS				TOTAL INCL O&P
						MAT.	LABOR	EQUIP.	TOTAL	

Division Notes

		CREW	DAILY OUTPUT	LABOR-HOURS	UNIT	BARE COSTS				TOTAL INCL O&P
						MAT.	LABOR	EQUIP.	TOTAL	

Division Notes

	CREW	DAILY OUTPUT	LABOR-HOURS	UNIT	BARE COSTS				TOTAL INCL O&P
					MAT.	LABOR	EQUIP.	TOTAL	

Division Notes

		CREW	DAILY OUTPUT	LABOR-HOURS	UNIT	BARE COSTS				TOTAL INCL O&P
						MAT.	LABOR	EQUIP.	TOTAL	

Other Data & Services

A tradition of excellence in construction cost information and services since 1942

For more information visit our website at www.RSMeans.com

Unit prices according to the latest MasterFormat

Cost Data Selection Guide

The following table provides definitive information on the content of each cost data publication. The number of lines of data provided in each unit price or assemblies division, as well as the number of crews, is listed for each data set. The presence of other elements such as reference tables, square foot models, equipment rental costs, historical cost indexes, and city cost indexes, is also indicated. You can use the table to help select the RSMeans data set that has the quantity and type of information you most need in your work.

Unit Cost Divisions	Building Construction	Mechanical	Electrical	Commercial Renovation	Square Foot	Site Work Landsc.	Green Building	Interior	Concrete Masonry	Open Shop	Heavy Construction	Light Commercial	Facilities Construction	Plumbing	Residential
1	595	414	431	535	0	527	207	334	476	594	527	278	1071	424	180
2	777	280	86	733	0	992	207	399	214	776	734	481	1221	287	274
3	1691	340	230	1084	0	1483	986	354	2037	1691	1693	482	1791	316	389
4	960	21	0	920	0	725	180	615	1158	928	615	533	1175	0	447
5	1901	158	155	1093	0	852	1799	1106	729	1901	1037	979	1918	204	746
6	2453	18	18	2111	0	110	589	1528	281	2449	123	2141	2125	22	2662
7	1596	215	128	1634	0	580	763	532	523	1593	26	1329	1697	227	1049
8	2131	80	44	2711	0	255	1140	1793	105	2119	0	2301	2954	0	1540
9	2006	86	45	1830	0	309	452	2092	394	1948	15	1671	2255	54	1440
10	1063	17	10	657	0	217	27	873	138	1063	30	554	1154	234	224
11	1096	201	166	540	0	135	56	924	29	1063	0	231	1116	164	110
12	548	0	2	299	0	219	147	1551	14	515	0	273	1574	23	217
13	744	149	158	253	0	369	122	254	78	720	267	109	760	115	104
14	273	36	0	223	0	0	0	257	0	273	0	12	293	16	6
21	130	0	41	37	0	0	0	296	0	130	0	121	669	689	259
22	1168	7559	160	1227	0	1572	1066	849	20	1157	1681	875	7507	9411	719
23	1179	6972	579	930	0	157	900	779	38	1173	110	880	5211	1920	469
26	1505	490	10389	1160	0	812	639	1158	55	1437	596	1360	10301	399	636
27	94	0	419	83	0	0	0	71	0	94	39	67	378	0	56
28	125	79	193	107	0	0	27	90	0	110	0	56	182	57	41
31	1510	733	610	806	0	3262	288	7	1217	1455	3276	604	1569	660	613
32	814	49	8	882	0	4410	353	405	292	785	1827	421	1688	142	468
33	529	1076	538	252	0	2173	41	0	236	522	2157	128	1697	1283	154
34	107	0	47	4	0	190	0	0	31	62	212	0	136	0	0
35	18	0	0	0	0	327	0	0	0	18	442	0	84	0	0
41	60	0	0	33	0	8	0	22	0	61	31	0	68	14	0
44	75	79	0	0	0	0	0	0	0	0	0	0	75	75	0
46	23	16	0	0	0	274	261	0	0	23	264	0	33	33	0
48	12	0	25	0	0	0	25	0	0	12	17	12	12	0	12
Totals	25183	19068	14482	20144	0	19958	10275	16289	8065	24672	15719	15898	50714	16769	12815

Assem Div	Building Construction	Mechanical	Electrical	Commercial Renovation	Square Foot	Site Work Landscape	Assemblies	Green Building	Interior	Concrete Masonry	Heavy Construction	Light Commercial	Facilities Construction	Plumbing	Asm Div	Residential
A		15	0	188	150	577	598	0	0	536	571	154	24	0	1	378
B		0	0	848	2503	0	5662	56	329	1976	368	2095	174	0	2	211
C		0	0	647	929	0	1310	0	1632	146	0	818	251	0	3	588
D		1069	941	712	1861	72	2540	330	827	0	0	1348	1107	1088	4	850
E		0	0	86	261	0	301	0	5	0	0	258	5	0	5	391
F		0	0	0	114	0	143	0	0	0	0	114	0	0	6	357
G		527	447	318	311	3363	791	0	0	534	1349	205	293	677	7	307
															8	760
															9	80
															10	0
															11	0
															12	0
Totals		1611	1388	2799	6129	4012	11345	386	2793	3192	2288	4992	1854	1765		3922

Reference Section	Building Construction Costs	Mechanical	Electrical	Commercial Renovation	Square Foot	Site Work Landscape	Assem.	Green Building	Interior	Concrete Masonry	Open Shop	Heavy Construction	Light Commercial	Facilities Construction	Plumbing	Resi.
Reference Tables	yes	yes	yes	yes	no	yes	yes	yes	yes	yes	yes	yes	yes	yes	yes	yes
Models					111			25					50			28
Crews	578	578	578	556		578		578	578	578	555	578	555	556	578	555
Equipment Rental Costs	yes	yes	yes	yes		yes		yes	yes	yes	yes	yes	yes	yes	yes	yes
Historical Cost Indexes	yes	yes	yes	yes	yes	yes	yes	yes	yes	yes	yes	yes	yes	yes	yes	no
City Cost Indexes	yes	yes	yes	yes	yes	yes	yes	yes	yes	yes	yes	yes	yes	yes	yes	yes

Online Book CD eBook Online add-on available
for additional fee

Unit prices according to the latest MasterFormat

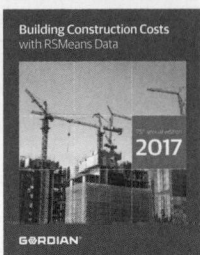

Building Construction Costs with RSMeans Data 2017

Offers you unchallenged unit price reliability in an easy-to-use format. Whether used for verifying complete, finished estimates or for periodic checks, it supplies more cost facts better and faster than any comparable source. The City Cost Indexes and Location Factors cover more than 930 areas for indexing to any project location in North America. Order and get RSMeans Quarterly Update Service FREE.

Green Building Costs with RSMeans Data 2017

Estimate, plan, and budget the costs of green building for both new commercial construction and renovation work with this seventh edition of *Green Building Costs with RSMeans Data*. More than 10,000 unit costs for a wide array of green building products plus assemblies costs. Easily identified cross references to LEED and Green Globes building rating systems criteria.

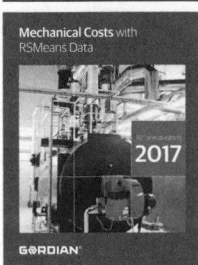

Mechanical Costs with RSMeans Data 2017

Total unit and systems price guidance for mechanical construction—materials, parts, fittings, and complete labor cost information. Includes prices for piping, heating, air conditioning, ventilation, and all related construction.

Plus new 2017 unit costs for:

- Thousands of installed HVAC/controls, sub-assemblies and assemblies
- "On-site" Location Factors for more than 930 cities and towns in the U.S. and Canada
- Crews, labor, and equipment

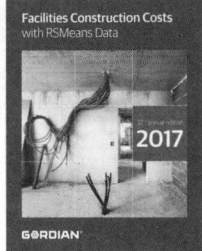

Facilities Construction Costs with RSMeans Data 2017

For the maintenance and construction of commercial, industrial, municipal, and institutional properties. Costs are shown for new and remodeling construction and are broken down into materials, labor, equipment, and overhead and profit. Special emphasis is given to sections on mechanical, electrical, furnishings, site work, building maintenance, finish work, and demolition.

More than 49,800 unit costs, plus assemblies costs and a comprehensive Reference Section are included.

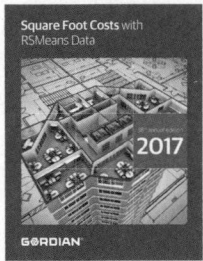

Square Foot Costs with RSMeans Data 2017
Accurate and Easy-to-Use

- Updated price information based on nationwide figures from suppliers, estimators, labor experts, and contractors.
- Green building models
- Realistic graphics, offering true-to-life illustrations of building projects
- Extensive information on using square foot cost data, including sample estimates and alternate pricing methods

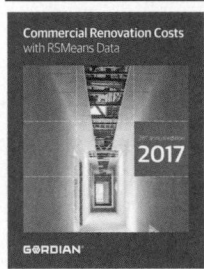

Commercial Renovation Costs with RSMeans Data 2017
Commercial/Multi-family Residential

Use this valuable tool to estimate commercial and multi-family residential renovation and remodeling.

Includes: Updated costs for hundreds of unique methods, materials, and conditions that only come up in repair and remodeling, PLUS:

- Unit costs for more than 19,600 construction components
- Installed costs for more than 2,700 assemblies
- More than 930 "on-site" localization factors for the U.S. and Canada

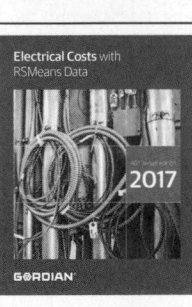

Electrical Costs with RSMeans Data 2017

Pricing information for every part of electrical cost planning. More than 13,800 unit and systems costs with design tables; clear specifications and drawings; engineering guides; illustrated estimating procedures; complete labor-hour and materials costs for better scheduling and procurement; and the latest electrical products and construction methods.

- A variety of special electrical systems, including cathodic protection
- Costs for maintenance, demolition, HVAC/mechanical, specialties, equipment, and more

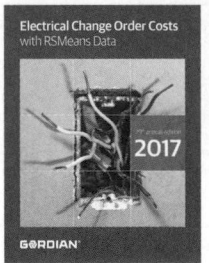

Electrical Change Order Costs with RSMeans Data 2017

Electrical Change Order Costs with RSMeans Data provides you with electrical unit prices exclusively for pricing change orders. Analyze and check your own change order estimates against those prepared when using RSMeans cost data. It also covers productivity analysis and change order cost justifications. With useful information for calculating the effects of change orders and dealing with their administration.

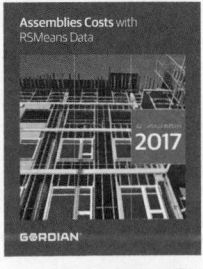

Assemblies Costs with RSMeans Data 2017

Assemblies Costs with RSMeans Data takes the guesswork out of preliminary or conceptual estimates. Now you don't have to try to calculate the assembled cost by working up individual component costs. We've done all the work for you.

Presents detailed illustrations, descriptions, specifications, and costs for every conceivable building assembly—over 350 types in all—arranged in the easy-to-use UNIFORMAT II system. Each illustrated "assembled" cost includes a complete grouping of materials and associated installation costs, including the installing contractor's overhead and profit.

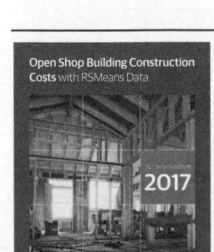

Open Shop Building Construction Costs with RSMeans Data 2017

The latest costs for accurate budgeting and estimating of new commercial and residential construction, renovation work, change orders, and cost engineering.

Open Shop "BCCD" with RSMeans Data will assist you to:

- Develop benchmark prices for change orders.
- Plug gaps in preliminary estimates and budgets.
- Estimate complex projects.
- Substantiate invoices on contracts.
- Price ADA-related renovations.

Annual Cost Guides

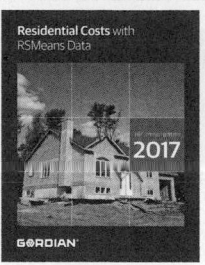

Residential Costs with RSMeans Data 2017

Contains square foot costs for 28 basic home models with the look of today, plus hundreds of custom additions and modifications you can quote right off the page. Includes more than 3,900 costs for 80 residential systems. Complete with blank estimating forms, sample estimates, and step-by-step instructions.

Contains line items for cultured stone and brick, PVC trim, lumber, and TPO roofing.

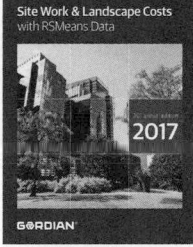

Site Work & Landscape Costs with RSMeans Data 2017

Includes unit and assemblies costs for earthwork, sewerage, piped utilities, site improvements, drainage, paving, trees and shrubs, street openings/repairs, underground tanks, and more. Contains more than 60 types of assemblies costs for accurate conceptual estimates.

Includes:

- Estimating for infrastructure improvements
- Environmentally-oriented construction
- ADA-mandated handicapped access
- Hazardous waste line items

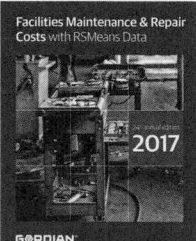

Facilities Maintenance & Repair Costs with RSMeans Data 2017

Facilities Maintenance & Repair Costs with RSMeans Data gives you a complete system to manage and plan your facility repair and maintenance costs and budget efficiently. Guidelines for auditing a facility and developing an annual maintenance plan. Budgeting is included, along with reference tables on cost and management, and information on frequency and productivity of maintenance operations.

The only nationally recognized source of maintenance and repair costs. Developed in cooperation with the Civil Engineering Research Laboratory (CERL) of the Army Corps of Engineers.

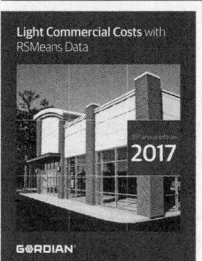

Light Commercial Costs with RSMeans Data 2017

Specifically addresses the light commercial market, which is a specialized niche in the construction industry. Aids you, the owner/designer/contractor, in preparing all types of estimates—from budgets to detailed bids. Includes new advances in methods and materials.

The Assemblies section allows you to evaluate alternatives in the early stages of design/planning.

More than 15,500 unit costs ensure that you have the prices you need, when you need them.

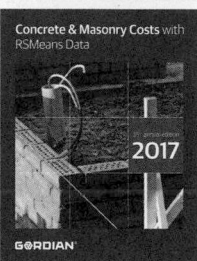

Concrete & Masonry Costs with RSMeans Data 2017

Provides you with cost facts for virtually all concrete/masonry estimating needs, from complicated formwork to various sizes and face finishes of brick and block—all in great detail. The comprehensive Unit Price Section contains more than 8,000 selected entries. Also contains an Assemblies [Cost] Section, and a detailed Reference Section that supplements the cost data.

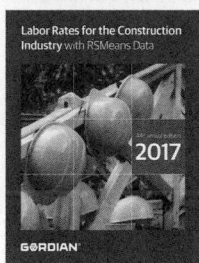

Labor Rates for the Construction Industry with RSMeans Data 2017

Complete information for estimating labor costs, making comparisons, and negotiating wage rates by trade for more than 300 U.S. and Canadian cities. With 46 construction trades in each city and historical wage rates included for comparison. Each city chart lists the county and is alphabetically arranged with handy visual flip tabs for quick reference.

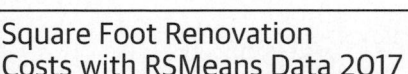

Square Foot Renovation Costs with RSMeans Data 2017

For conceptual estimating of renovation projects, *Square Foot Renovation Costs with RSMeans Data* provides whole building and assembly level renovation costs at varying levels for 44 building models. Renovation costs are unique to each model and adjust with the intensity of renovation work being represented. Levels of renovation are:

Level 1 – Cosmetics
Level 2 – Plus Non-Masonry Partitions
Level 3 – Plus Masonry Partitions
Level 4 – Plus Bathrooms, Kitchens
Level 5 – Plus Equip, Ext Doors & Windows

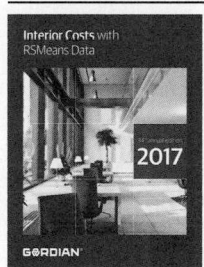

Interior Costs with RSMeans Data 2017

Provides you with prices and guidance needed to make accurate interior work estimates. Contains costs on materials, equipment, hardware, custom installations, furnishings, and labor for new and remodel commercial and industrial interior construction, including updated information on office furnishings, as well as reference information.

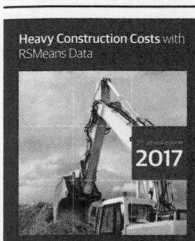

Heavy Construction Costs with RSMeans Data 2017

A comprehensive guide to heavy construction costs. Includes costs for highly specialized projects such as tunnels, dams, highways, airports, and waterways. Information on labor rates, equipment, and materials costs is included. Features unit price costs, systems costs, and numerous reference tables for costs and design.

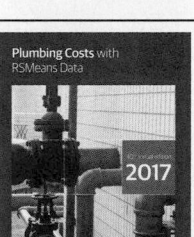

Plumbing Costs with RSMeans Data 2017

Comprehensive unit prices and assemblies for plumbing, irrigation systems, commercial and residential fire protection, point-of-use water heaters, and the latest approved materials. This publication and its companion, *Mechanical Costs with RSMeans Data*, provide full-range cost estimating coverage for all the mechanical trades.

Contains updated costs for potable water, radiant heat systems, and high efficiency fixtures.

Annual Cost Guides

Unit prices according to the latest MasterFormat

For more information visit our website at www.RSMeans.com

Annual Cost Guides (Continued)
Construction Cost Indexes with RSMeans Data 2017

What materials and labor costs will change unexpectedly this year? By how much?
- Breakdowns for 318 major cities
- National averages for 30 key cities
- Expanded five major city indexes

Our Online Estimating Solution

Competitive Cost Estimates Made Easy

Our online estimating solution is a web-based service that provides accurate and up-to-date cost information to help you build competitive estimates or budgets in less time.

Quick, intuitive, easy to use and automatically updated, you'll gain instant access to hundreds of thousands of material, labor, and equipment costs from RSMeans' comprehensive database, delivering the information you need to build budgets and competitive estimates every time.

With our online estimating solutions, you can perform quick searches to locate specific costs and adjust costs to reflect prices in your geographic area. Tag and store your favorites for fast access to your frequently used line items and assemblies and clone estimates to save time. System notifications will alert you as updated data becomes available. This data is automatically updated throughout the year.

Our visual, interactive estimating features help you create, manage, save and share estimates with ease! You'll enjoy increased flexibility with customizable advanced reports. Easily edit custom report templates and import your company logo onto your estimates.

	Core	Advanced	Complete
Unit Prices	✓	✓	✓
Assemblies	X	✓	✓
Sq Ft Models	X	X	✓
Editable Sq Foot Models	X	X	✓
Editable Assembly Components	X	✓	✓
Custom Cost Data	X	✓	✓
User Defined Components	X	✓	✓
Advanced Reporting & Customization	X	✓	✓
Union Labor Type	✓	✓	✓
Open Shop*	Available for add-on at $249.99	Available for add-on at $249.99	✓
History (3-year lookback)**	Available for add-on at $249.99	Available for add-on at $249.99	Available for add-on at $249.99
Full History (2007)	Available for add-on at $499.99	Available for add-on at $499.99	Available for add-on at $499.99
Life Cycle Costing***	X	Available for add-on at $999.99	Available for add-on at $999.99
Alerts	Available for add-on at $299.99	Available for add-on at $299.99	Available for add-on at $299.99

*Open shop included in Complete Library & Bundles   **3-year history look back included with complete library
***Not available as add-on with Residential data set

Continue to check our website at www.RSMeans.com for more product offerings.

Online Estimating Solution   Unit prices according to the latest MasterFormat

Estimate with Precision

Find everything you need to develop complete, accurate estimates.

- Verified costs for construction materials
- Equipment rental costs
- Crew sizing, labor hours and labor rates
- Localized costs for U.S. and Canada

Save Time & Increase Efficiency

Make cost estimating and calculating faster and easier than ever with secure, online estimating tools.

- Quickly locate costs in the searchable database
- Create estimates in minutes with RSMeans cost lines
- Tag and store favorites for fast access to frequently used items

Improve Planning & Decision-Making

Back your estimates with complete, accurate and up-to-date cost data for informed business decisions.

- Verify construction costs from third parties
- Check validity of subcontractor proposals
- Evaluate material and assembly alternatives

Increase Profits

Use our online estimating solution to estimate projects quickly and accurately, so you can gain an edge over your competition.

- Create accurate and competitive bids
- Minimize the risk of cost overruns
- Reduce variability

30 Day Free Trial

Register for a free trial at www.RSMeans.com/Trial

- Access to unit prices, building assemblies and facilities repair and remodeling items covering every category of construction
- Powerful tools to customize, save and share cost lists, estimates and reports with ease
- Access to square foot models for quick conceptual estimates
- Allows up to 10 users to evaluate the full range of collaborative functionality.

2017 Seminar Schedule

Note: call for exact dates and details.

Location	Dates	Location	Dates
Seattle, WA	January and August	San Francisco, CA	June
Dallas/Ft. Worth, TX	January	Bethesda, MD	June
Austin, TX	February	El Segundo, CA	August
Anchorage, AK	March and September	Dallas, TX	September
Las Vegas, NV	March	Raleigh, NC	October
New Orleans, LA	March	Salt Lake City, UT	October
Washington, DC	April and September	Baltimore, MD	November
Phoenix, AZ	April	Orlando, FL	November
Toronto	May	San Diego, CA	December
Denver, CO	May	San Antonio, TX	December

📞 877-620-6245

Gordian also offers a suite of online RSMeans data self-paced offerings. Check our website www.RSMeans.com for more information.

Professional Development

eLearning Training Sessions

Learn how to use our RSMeans online estimating solution from the convenience of your home or office. Our eLearning training sessions let you join a training conference call and share the instructors' desktops, so you can view the presentation and step-by-step instructions on your own computer screen. The live webinars are held from 9 a.m. to 5 p.m. or 11 a.m. to 7 p.m. eastern standard time, with a one-hour break for lunch.

For these sessions, you must have a computer with high speed Internet access and a compatible Web browser. Learn more at www.RSMeansOnline.com or call for a schedule: 781-422-5115. Webinars are generally held on selected Wednesdays each month.

Seminar Schedule and Professional Development

Training for our Online Estimating Solution

Construction estimating is vital to the decision-making process at each state of every project. Our online solution works the way you do. It's systematic, flexible and intuitive. In this one-day class you will see how you can estimate any phase of any project faster and better.

Some of what you'll learn:
- Customizing our online estimating solution
- Making the most of RSMeans "Circle Reference" numbers
- How to integrate your cost data
- Generating reports, exporting estimates to MS Excel, sharing, collaborating and more

Also available: Online estimating solution training webinar or a self-paced training program.

Facilities Construction Estimating

In this two-day course, professionals working in facilities management can get help with their daily challenges to establish budgets for all phases of a project.

Some of what you'll learn:
- Determining the full scope of a project
- Identifying the scope of risks and opportunities
- Creative solutions to estimating issues
- Organizing estimates for presentation and discussion
- Special techniques for repair/remodel and maintenance projects
- Negotiating project change orders

Who should attend: facility managers, engineers, contractors, facility tradespeople, planners, and project managers.

Construction Cost Estimating: Concepts and Practice

This one-day introductory course to improve estimating skills and effectiveness starts with the details of interpreting bid documents and ends with the summary of the estimate and bid submission.

Some of what you'll learn:
- Using the plans and specifications to create estimates
- The takeoff process—deriving all tasks with correct quantities
- Developing pricing using various sources; how subcontractor pricing fits in
- Summarizing the estimate to arrive at the final number
- Formulas for area and cubic measure, adding waste and adjusting productivity to specific projects
- Evaluating subcontractors' proposals and prices
- Adding insurance and bonds
- Understanding how labor costs are calculated
- Submitting bids and proposals

Who should attend: project managers, architects, engineers, owners' representatives, contractors, and anyone who's responsible for budgeting or estimating construction projects.

Maintenance & Repair Estimating for Facilities

This two-day course teaches attendees how to plan, budget, and estimate the cost of ongoing and preventive maintenance and repair for existing buildings and grounds.

Some of what you'll learn:
- The most financially favorable maintenance, repair, and replacement scheduling and estimating
- Auditing and value engineering facilities
- Preventive planning and facilities upgrading
- Determining both in-house and contract-out service costs
- Annual, asset-protecting M&R plan

Who should attend: facility managers, maintenance supervisors, buildings and grounds superintendents, plant managers, planners, estimators, and others involved in facilities planning and budgeting.

Practical Project Management for Construction Professionals

In this two-day course, acquire the essential knowledge and develop the skills to effectively and efficiently execute the day-to-day responsibilities of the construction project manager.

Some of what you'll learn:
- General conditions of the construction contract
- Contract modifications: change orders and construction change directives
- Negotiations with subcontractors and vendors
- Effective writing: notification and communications
- Dispute resolution: claims and liens

Who should attend: architects, engineers, owners' representatives, and project managers.

Mechanical & Electrical Estimating

This two-day course teaches attendees how to prepare more accurate and complete mechanical/electrical estimates, avoid the pitfalls of omission and double-counting, and understand the composition and rationale within the RSMeans mechanical/electrical database.

Some of what you'll learn:
- The unique way mechanical and electrical systems are interrelated
- M&E estimates—conceptual, planning, budgeting, and bidding stages
- Order of magnitude, square foot, assemblies, and unit price estimating
- Comparative cost analysis of equipment and design alternatives

Who should attend: architects, engineers, facilities managers, mechanical and electrical contractors, and others who need a highly reliable method for developing, understanding, and evaluating mechanical and electrical contracts.

Professional Development

Visit RSMeans.com/Online for more details on data titles in online format.

For more information visit our website at www.RSMeans.com

Unit Price Estimating

This interactive two-day seminar teaches attendees how to interpret project information and process it into final, detailed estimates with the greatest accuracy level.

The most important credential an estimator can take to the job is the ability to visualize construction and estimate accurately.

Some of what you'll learn:
- Interpreting the design in terms of cost
- The most detailed, time-tested methodology for accurate pricing
- Key cost drivers—material, labor, equipment, staging, and subcontracts
- Understanding direct and indirect costs for accurate job cost accounting and change order management

Who should attend: corporate and government estimators and purchasers, architects, engineers, and others who need to produce accurate project estimates.

Conceptual Estimating Using the CD

This two-day class uses the leading industry data and a powerful software package to develop highly accurate conceptual estimates for your construction projects. All attendees must bring a laptop computer loaded with the current year Square Foot Costs with RSMeans Data and Assemblies Costs with RSMeans Data.

Some of what you'll learn:
- Introduction to conceptual estimating
- Types of conceptual estimates
- Helpful hints
- Order of magnitude estimating
- Square foot estimating
- Assemblies estimating

Who should attend: architects, engineers, contractors, construction estimators, owners' representatives, and anyone looking for an electronic method for performing square foot estimating.

Training for our CD Estimating Solution

This one-day course helps users become more familiar with the functionality of the CD. Each menu, icon, screen, and function found in the program is explained in depth. Time is devoted to hands-on estimating exercises.

Some of what you'll learn:
- Searching the database using all navigation methods
- Exporting RSMeans data to your preferred spreadsheet format
- Viewing crews, assembly components, and much more
- Automatically regionalizing the database

This training session requires you to bring a laptop computer to class.

When you register for this course you will receive an outline for your laptop requirements.

Also offered as a self-paced training program!

Assessing Scope of Work for Facility Construction Estimating

This two-day practical training program addresses the vital importance of understanding the scope of projects in order to produce accurate cost estimates for facility repair and remodeling.

Some of what you'll learn:
- Discussions of site visits, plans/specs, record drawings of facilities, and site-specific lists
- Review of CSI divisions, including means, methods, materials, and the challenges of scoping each topic
- Exercises in scope identification and scope writing for accurate estimating of projects
- Hands-on exercises that require scope, take-off, and pricing

Who should attend: corporate and government estimators, planners, facility managers, and others who need to produce accurate project estimates.

Facilities Estimating Using the CD

Combines hands-on skill building with best estimating practices and real-life problems. Brings you up-to-date with key concepts and provides tips, pointers, and guidelines to save time and avoid cost oversights and errors in this two-day class.

Some of what you'll learn:
- Estimating process concepts
- Customizing and adapting RSMeans cost data
- Establishing scope of work to account for all known variables
- Budget estimating: when, why, and how
- Site visits: what to look for—what you can't afford to overlook
- How to estimate repair and remodeling variables

This training session requires you to bring a laptop computer to class.

Who should attend: facility managers, architects, engineers, contractors, facility tradespeople, planners, project managers, and anyone involved with JOC, SABRE, or IDIQ.

Building Systems and the Construction Process

This one-day course was written to assist novices and those outside the industry in obtaining a solid understanding of the construction process - from both a building systems and construction administration approach.

Some of what you'll learn:
- Various systems used and how components come together to create a building
- Start with foundation and end with the physical systems of the structure such as HVAC and Electrical
- Focus on the process from start of design through project closeout

This training session requires you to bring a laptop computer to class.

Who should attend: building professionals or novices to help make the crossover to the construction industry; suited for anyone responsible for providing high level oversight on construction projects.

Professional Development

Visit RSMeans.com/Online for more details on data titles in online format.

For more information visit our website at www.RSMeans.com

Self-Paced Professional Development Courses

Training and professional development courses on RSMeans data are now offered in a convenient self-paced format allowing more flexibility to learn around your busy schedule.

These self-paced training courses can be completed over the course of 45 days and most are comprised of 10 lessons complete with documentation, video presentation, assessment quizzes and certificate of completion.

To view and register for the currently offered self-paced course, visit https://rsmeans.myabsorb.com.

Registration Information

Register early and save up to $100!
Register 30 days before the start date of a seminar and save $100 off your total fee. Note: This discount can be applied only once per order. It cannot be applied to team discount registrations or any other special offer.

How to register
By Phone
Register by phone at 877-620-6245

Online
Register online at www.RSMeans.com/products/seminars.aspx
Note: Purchase Orders or Credits Cards are required to register.

Two-day seminar registration fee - $995. One-day CD or online training registration fee - $395.

One-Day Construction Cost Estimating or Building Systems and the Construction Process - $600.

Government pricing
All federal government employees save off the regular seminar price. Other promotional discounts cannot be combined with the government discount.

Team discount program
For over five attendee registrations. Call for pricing: 781-422-5115

Refund policy
Cancellations will be accepted up to ten business days prior to the seminar start. There are no refunds for cancellations received later than ten working days prior to the first day of the seminar. A $150 processing fee will be applied for all cancellations. Written notice of the cancellation is required. Substitutions can be made at any time before the session starts. No-shows are subject to the full seminar fee.

Note: Pricing subject to change.

AACE approved courses
Many seminars described and offered here have been approved for 14 hours (1.4 recertification credits) of credit by the AACE International Certification Board toward meeting the continuing education requirements for recertification as a Certified Cost Engineer/Certified Cost Consultant.

AIA Continuing Education
We are registered with the AIA Continuing Education System (AIA/CES) and are committed to developing quality learning activities in accordance with the CES criteria. Many seminars meet the AIA/CES criteria for Quality Level 2. AIA members may receive 14 learning units (LUs) for each two-day RSMeans course.

Daily course schedule
The first day of each seminar session begins at 8:30 a.m. and ends at 4:30 p.m. The second day begins at 8:00 a.m. and ends at 4:00 p.m. Participants are urged to bring a hand-held calculator since many actual problems will be worked out in each session.

Continental breakfast
Your registration includes the cost of a continental breakfast and a morning and afternoon refreshment break. These informal segments allow you to discuss topics of mutual interest with other seminar attendees. (You are free to make your own lunch and dinner arrangements.)

Hotel/transportation arrangements
We arrange to hold a block of rooms at most host hotels. To take advantage of special group rates when making your reservation, be sure to mention that you are attending the RSMeans Institute data seminar. You are, of course, free to stay at the lodging place of your choice. (Hotel reservations and transportation arrangements should be made directly by seminar attendees.)

Important
Class sizes are limited, so please register as soon as possible.

Professional Development